D1597531

PRINCIPLES OF PSYCHOPHARMACOLOGY

A Textbook for
Physicians, Medical Students,
and Behavioral Scientists

CONTRIBUTORS

G. K. AGHAJANIAN
FRANK N. ALLAN
T. A. BAN
F. M. BERGER
J. L. BERMAN
JOHN H. BIEL
EDWARD R. BLOOMQUIST
EUGENE M. CAFFEY, JR.
ANNE E. CALDWELL
WILLIAM G. CLARK
SIDNEY COHEN
GEORGE E. CRANE
THEODORE J. CURPHEY
JOHN M. DAVIS
JOSEPH DEL GIUDICE
W. G. DEWHURST
H. H. EVELOFF
NORMAN L. FARBEROW
VIVIAN FISHMAN
ROBERT M. FLEMING
CHARLES E. FROHMAN
JOHN L. FULLER
KJELL FUXE
S. GARATTINI
EDWARD F. GOCKA
JAMES L. GODDARD
SOLOMON C. GOLDBERG
HARRY GOLDENBERG
HARRY M. GRAYSON
MAX HAYMAN
JAMES N. HAYWARD
TOMAS HÖKFELT
LEO E. HOLLISTER
A. HORITA
OLEH HORNYKIEWICZ
JEROME H. JAFFE
SAMUEL C. KAIM
ALEXANDER G. KARCZMAR
GERALD L. KLERMAN
C. JAMES KLETT
M. KLETZKIN
NATHAN S. KLINE
T. KOBAYASHI
HENRI-MARIE LABORIT
H. E. LEHMANN
KENNETH LIFSHITZ
ALFRED R. LINDESMITH
S. MARGOLIN
CHARLES H. MARKHAM
JACK H. MENDELSON
RONALD OKUN
MARVIN K. OPLER
EUGENE S. PAYKEL
F. J. PETRACEK
J. H. QUASTEL
ALAIN J. SANSEIGNE
CARL L. SCHECKEL
MOGENS SCHOU
EDWIN S. SHNEIDMAN
JAY T. SHURLEY
SOLOMON H. SNYDER
RANDALL B. SPENCER
LARRY STEIN
JOHN M. SUAREZ
URBAN UNGERSTEDT
EARL USDIN
L. VALZELLI
H. WEIL-MALHERBE
JACK WERBOFF
C. DAVID WISE
D. YI-YUNG HSIA

Principles of Psychopharmacology

A TEXTBOOK FOR PHYSICIANS, MEDICAL STUDENTS, AND BEHAVIORAL SCIENTISTS

W. G. Clark, Ph.D., EDITOR IN CHIEF
PSYCHOPHARMACOLOGY RESEARCH LABORATORY
VETERANS ADMINISTRATION HOSPITAL
SEPULVEDA, CALIFORNIA

DEPARTMENT OF BIOLOGICAL CHEMISTRY
CENTER FOR THE HEALTH SCIENCES
UNIVERSITY OF CALIFORNIA
LOS ANGELES, CALIFORNIA

J. del Giudice, M.D., COEDITOR
VETERANS ADMINISTRATION HOSPITAL
SEPULVEDA, CALIFORNIA

SCHOOL OF MEDICINE
DEPARTMENT OF PSYCHIATRY
CENTER FOR THE HEALTH SCIENCES
UNIVERSITY OF CALIFORNIA
LOS ANGELES, CALIFORNIA

EDITORIAL ADVISORS

K. S. Ditman, M.D. UNIVERSITY OF CALIFORNIA, LOS ANGELES, CALIFORNIA
and
C. D. Leake, Ph.D. UNIVERSITY OF CALIFORNIA, SAN FRANCISCO, CALIFORNIA

ACADEMIC PRESS New York and London 1970

COPYRIGHT © 1970, BY ACADEMIC PRESS, INC.
ALL RIGHTS RESERVED
NO PART OF THIS BOOK MAY BE REPRODUCED IN ANY FORM, BY PHOTOSTAT, MICROFILM, RETRIEVAL SYSTEM, OR ANY OTHER MEANS, WITHOUT WRITTEN PERMISSION FROM THE PUBLISHERS.

ACADEMIC PRESS, INC.
111 Fifth Avenue, New York, New York 10003

United Kingdom Edition published by
ACADEMIC PRESS, INC. (LONDON) LTD.
Berkeley Square House, London WIX 6BA

LIBRARY OF CONGRESS CATALOG CARD NUMBER: 70-84253

PRINTED IN THE UNITED STATES OF AMERICA

LIST OF CONTRIBUTORS

Numbers in parentheses indicate the pages on which the authors' contributions begin.

G. K. AGHAJANIAN, M.D. (97), Yale University, New Haven, Connecticut

FRANK N. ALLAN, M.D. (451), Food and Drug Administration and Georgetown University, Washington, D.C.; Lahey Clinic and Boston University, Boston, Massachusetts

T. A. BAN, M.D. (621), McGill University, Montreal; and Douglas Hospital, Verdun, Quebec, Canada

F. M. BERGER, M.D. (3), Wallace Laboratories, Cranbury, New Jersey

J. L. BERMAN, M.D. (355), Chicago Medical School and Cook County Hospital, Chicago, Illinois

JOHN H. BIEL, Ph.D. (269, 289, 327), Abbott Laboratories, North Chicago, Illinois; and Marquette University, Milwaukee, Wisconsin

EDWARD R. BLOOMQUIST, M.D. (477), University of Southern California and California State College, Los Angeles, California

EUGENE M. CAFFEY, JR., M.D. (429), Veterans Administration Central Office, Washington, D.C.

ANNE E. CALDWELL, M.D. (9), National Library of Medicine, Bethesda, Maryland

WILLIAM G. CLARK, Ph.D. (585, 719), Veterans Administration Hospital, Sepulveda, and University of California, Los Angeles, California

SIDNEY COHEN, M.D. (489), National Institute of Mental Health, Chevy Chase, Maryland

GEORGE E. CRANE, M.D. (643), National Institute of Mental Health, Chevy Chase, Maryland

THEODORE J. CURPHEY, M.D. (523), University of California, Loma Linda University, and University of Southern California, Los Angeles, California

JOHN M. DAVIS, M.D. (597), National Institute of Mental Health, Bethesda, Maryland

JOSEPH DEL GIUDICE, M.D. (425, 457, 517, 667), Veterans Administration Hospital, Sepulveda, and University of California, Los Angeles, California*

W. G. DEWHURST, M.D. (105), University of Alberta, Edmonton, Alberta, Canada

H. H. EVELOFF, M.D. (683), University of California, Los Angeles, California

NORMAN L. FARBEROW, Ph.D. (523), Suicide Prevention Center, Veterans Administration Center, and University of Southern California, Los Angeles, California

VIVIAN FISHMAN, Ph.D. (179), Bio-Science Laboratories, Van Nuys, California

ROBERT M. FLEMING, B.S. (585), Veterans Administration Hospital, Sepulveda, California

CHARLES E. FROHMAN, Ph.D. (133), Lafayette Clinic and Wayne State University, Detroit, Michigan

JOHN L. FULLER, Ph.D. (337), The Jackson Laboratory, Bar Harbor, Maine

KJELL FUXE, M.D. (87), Karolinska Institute, Stockholm, Sweden

S. GARATTINI, M.D. (255), Istituto di Ricerche Farmacologiche, "Mario Negri," Milano, Italy

EDWARD F. GOCKA, Ph.D. (391), Veterans Administration Hospital, Sepulveda, California

JAMES L. GODDARD, M.D. (451), Food and Drug Administration, Washington, D.C.

SOLOMON C. GOLDBERG, Ph.D. (443), National Institute of Mental Health, Chevy Chase, Maryland

HARRY GOLDENBERG, Ph.D. (179), Bio-Science Laboratories, Van Nuys, California

HARRY M. GRAYSON, Ph.D. (405), Veterans Administration Center and University of California, Los Angeles, California

MAX HAYMAN, M.D. (517), Compton Foundation Hospital and University of California, Los Angeles, California

* Present affiliations: L. A. County Department of Mental Health, and University of California, Los Angeles, California

JAMES N. HAYWARD, M.D. (51), University of California, Los Angeles, California

TOMAS HÖKFELT, M.B. (87), Karolinska Institute, Stockholm, Sweden

LEO E. HOLLISTER, M.D. (429, 537), Veterans Administration Hospital and Stanford University, Palo Alto, California

A. HORITA, Ph.D. (279), University of Washington, Seattle, Washington

OLEH HORNYKIEWICZ, M.D. (585), University of Toronto and Clarke Institute of Psychiatry, Toronto, Ontario, Canada

JEROME H. JAFFE, M.D. (547), University of Chicago and Department of Psychiatry, Chicago, Illinois

SAMUEL C. KAIM, M.D. (429), Veterans Administration Central Office, Washington, D.C.

ALEXANDER G. KARCZMAR, Ph.D. (57), Loyola University, Hines, Illinois

GERALD L. KLERMAN, M.D. (627), Yale University and Connecticut Mental Health Center, New Haven, Connecticut

C. JAMES KLETT, Ph.D. (429), Veterans Administration Hospital, Perry Point, Maryland

M. KLETZKIN, Ph.D. (303), Wallace Laboratories, Cranbury, New Jersey

NATHAN S. KLINE, M.D. (673, 695), Rockland State Hospital, Orangeburg, New York

T. KOBAYASHI, M.D. (719), Neuropsychiatric Research Unit, Tokyo, Japan

HENRI-MARIE LABORIT, M.D. (259), Laboratoire d'Eutonologie, Hôpital Boucicaut, Paris, France

H. E. LEHMANN, M.D. (621), McGill University, Montreal, and Douglas Hospital, Verdun, Quebec, Canada

KENNETH LIFSHITZ, M.D. (695), Rockland State Hospital, Orangeburg, New York

ALFRED R. LINDESMITH, Ph.D. (471), Indiana University, Bloomington, Indiana

S. MARGOLIN, Ph.D. (303), A. M. E. Associates, Princeton, New Jersey

CHARLES H. MARKHAM, M.D. (585), University of California, Los Angeles, California

JACK H. MENDELSON, M.D. (505), National Institute of Mental Health, Chevy Chase, Maryland

RONALD OKUN, M.D. (381), Cedars-Sinai Medical Center, University of California, Los Angeles, and Veterans Administration Hospital, Sepulveda, California

MARVIN K. OPLER, Ph.D. (31), State University of New York at Buffalo, Buffalo, New York

EUGENE S. PAYKEL, M.B., M.R.C.P., D.P.M. (627), Yale University, New Haven, Connecticut

F. J. PETRACEK, Ph.D. (159), Riker Laboratories, Northridge, California

J. H. QUASTEL, Ph.D., F.R.S. (141), University of British Columbia and Kinsman Laboratory of Neurological Research, Vancouver, B.C., Canada

ALAIN J. SANSEIGNE, M.D. (259), E. R. Squibb and Sons, New York, New York

CARL L. SCHECKEL, Ph.D. (235), Hoffman-La Roche, Incorporated, Nutley, New Jersey

MOGENS SCHOU, M.D. (653), Aarhus University, Risskov, Denmark

EDWIN S. SHNEIDMAN, Ph.D. (523), The Center for Advanced Study in Behavioral Science, Stanford, California; The Johns Hopkins University and Georgetown University, Washington, D.C.

JAY T. SHURLEY, M.D. (373), Veterans Administration Hospital and University of Oklahoma, Oklahoma City, Oklahoma

SOLOMON H. SNYDER, M.D. (115), The Johns Hopkins University, Baltimore, Maryland

RANDALL B. SPENCER, M.D. (571), University of California, Los Angeles, California

LARRY STEIN, Ph.D. (313), Wyeth Laboratories, Incorporated, Philadelphia, Pennsylvania

JOHN M. SUAREZ, M.D. (571), University of California, Los Angeles, California

URBAN UNGERSTEDT, M.B. (87), Karolinska Institute, Stockholm, Sweden

EARL USDIN, Ph.D. (193), National Institute of Mental Health, Chevy Chase, Maryland

L. VALZELLI, M.D. (255), Istituto di Ricerche Farmacologiche, "Mario Negri," Milano, Italy

H. WEIL-MALHERBE, M.D., D.Sc. (127), National Institute of Mental Health, George Washington University and Saint Elizabeths Hospital, Washington, D.C.

JACK WERBOFF, Ph.D. (343), University of Connecticut Mental Health Center, Hartford, Connecticut

C. DAVID WISE, Ph.D. (313), Wyeth Laboratories, Incorporated, Philadelphia, Pennsylvania

D. YI-YUNG HSIA, M.D. (355), Northwestern University and Childrens Memorial Hospital, Chicago, Illinois

PREFACE

This book was the outgrowth of a series of lectures to residents in psychiatry which were formalized somewhat later in a manual entitled *Lectures in Psychopharmacology,* edited by William G. Clark and Keith S. Ditman in 1964. It is the natural development of this lecture series, and was conceived in order to fulfill a need in the rapidly advancing field of psychopharmacology. It was designed with an audience of relatively naive and unspecialized readers in mind, students and practitioners of a diverse group of disciplines.

Because of closely related material, overlap between chapters was a considerable problem. That remaining was necessary to the development of a particular chapter to allow it to stand alone as much as possible. For readability, references within chapters were kept to a minimum, and a bibliographic appendix included for those interested. The style of each chapter reflects essentially that author's own communicative approach, and, interestingly, to a large extent also reflects his field of specialization.

Author bias, where contrary evidence was not present, was allowed to some extent, and there was no effort to make contributors conform to a particular point of view, so that some material may be controversial among the authors, even as among the readers. For this, there is no apology forthcoming.

Most of the chapters were revised at least once, even though the initial manuscripts were satisfactory relative to scholarship and scientific worthiness. In this effort to simplify highly technical material we are grateful for the patience and cooperation of the contributors, who had many other simultaneous commitments.

A truly satisfactory classification for psychotropic drugs has not yet been devised. In keeping with the recommendation of the American Medical Association Council on Drugs, the use of the term "tranquilizer" has been avoided throughout this book. Instead, the psychotropic agents have been classified as antipsychotic, antianxiety, antidepressant, stimulant, and hallucinogenic drugs. These designations do not imply that the drugs placed in these categories have no other pharmacologic activities or combinations of activities, or that this classification is superior to other attempts to clarify the issue.

We sincerely hope that this attempt to present a comprehensive and understandable view of this important area of the behavioral sciences is worthy of its outstanding contributors.

William G. Clark
Joseph del Giudice

ACKNOWLEDGMENTS

Financial support for editorial expenses was generously forthcoming from many sources, and was charitably administered by P.A.N.A. Foundation, Santa Monica, California. We gratefully acknowledge to the following that without their support the text could not have been completed:

ASTRA PHARMACEUTICAL PRODUCTS, INCORPORATED
CIBA PHARMACEUTICAL COMPANY
ELI LILLY AND COMPANY
HOFFMAN-LA ROCHE, INCORPORATED
KNOLL PHARMACEUTICAL COMPANY
LEDERLE LABORATORIES
MEAD JOHNSON RESEARCH CENTER
MERCK SHARP & DOHME INTERNATIONAL
WILLIAM S. MERRELL COMPANY
RIKER LABORATORIES
A. H. ROBINS COMPANY
ROCHE LABORATORIES
SANDOZ PHARMACEUTICALS
SCHERING CORPORATION
SMITH KLINE & FRENCH LABORATORIES
IVAN SORVALL COMPANY, INCORPORATED
SQUIBB INTERNATIONAL
STERLING-WINTHROP RESEARCH INSTITUTE
THE STUART COMPANY
WALLACE LABORATORIES

Many other individuals participated unstintingly as referees, assistant editors, constructive critics, and as sources of encouragement and ideas. In this respect we thank *all of the authors* and the following individuals: Anthony Adinolfi, Nils-Erik Andén, Frank Ayd, Jr., André Barbeau, Claude Baxter, W. E. Brown, Jr.,

William J. Dixon, Daniel Efron, Samuel Eiduson, Guy Everett, Irene S. Forrest, Daniel X. Freedman, T. A. Geisman, Maxwell Gordon, Bo Holmstedt, L. M. Hussey, David Masuoka, Sidney Merlis, Orville Miller, Robert McCornack, Charles McKean, William Oldendorf, Irene Paulson, J. P. Rosenblum, Richard Schultes, Theodore Sourkes, Dermott Taylor, Milton Tobias, Glen E. Ullyot, A. Van Harraveld, Father Joseph Wadowicz, Harry Waisman, and Amanda Weikum.

For help with the references and section on reviews, our bibliographers, Mrs. Margorie Boche and Mrs. Theo Crednick, were efficient and invaluable. Our secretarial staff, Mrs. Ellen Bernier, Mrs. Julia Gibson, Mrs. Wanda Garrison, Mrs. Joanne Poole, Mrs. Beatrice Williams, and Mrs. Jean Stodder, also contributed, to a large extent, over and above their routine duties. Thanks too are due the librarians Mrs. Betty Connolly, Mrs. Ruth Maxwell, and Miss Frieda Dreyer. A source of continued support and aid, sometimes at odd hours, was supplied by Jerold Franks, our assistant.

We also wish to thank the Research and Education Service of the Veterans Administration for encouragement and real support.

Finally, we especially wish to thank the staff of Academic Press for their patience and helpful cooperation.

CONTENTS

Part I INTRODUCTION

1 Introduction

F. M. BERGER

2 History of Psychopharmacology

ANNE E. CALDWELL

3 Cross-Cultural Uses of Psychoactive Drugs (Ethnopsychopharmacology)

MARVIN K. OPLER

Part II SOME BASIC ANATOMICAL AND PHYSIOLOGICAL CONSIDERATIONS

4 Functional Neuroanatomy of the Hypothalamus

JAMES N. HAYWARD

5 Central Cholinergic Pathways and Their Behavioral Implications

ALEXANDER G. KARCZMAR

6 Central Monoaminergic Tracts

KJELL FUXE, TOMAS HÖKFELT, AND URBAN UNGERSTEDT

7 Electron Microscopic Aspects of Neural Function

G. K. AGHAJANIAN

8 The Blood-Brain Barrier and Other Membrane Phenomena in Psychopharmacology

W. G. DEWHURST

Part III THE BIOCHEMISTRY OF MENTAL DISEASE AND SOME EFFECTS OF PSYCHOTROPIC DRUGS

9 Catecholamines, Brain Function, and How Psychotropic Drugs Act

SOLOMON H. SNYDER

10 The Biochemistry of Affective Disorders

H. WEIL-MALHERBE

11 Possible Biochemical Mechanisms of Schizophrenia

Charles E. Frohman

12 Metabolic Effects of Some Psychopharmacological Agents in Brain *In Vitro*

J. H. Quastel

Part IV STRUCTURE AND METABOLISM OF PSYCHOTROPIC DRUGS

13 Chemistry of Psychopharmacological Agents

F. J. Petracek

14 Metabolism of Psychotropic Agents

Harry Goldenberg and Vivian Fishman

15 Classification of Psychopharmaca

EARL USDIN

Part V THE PHARMACOLOGIC BASIS OF PSYCHOPHARMACOTHERAPY

16 Preclinical Psychopharmacology

CARL L. SCHECKEL

17 Pharmacology of Phenothiazines

L. VALZELLI AND S. GARATTINI

18 Pharmacology of Other Antipsychotic Drugs

HENRI-MARIE LABORIT AND ALAIN SANSEIGNE

19 Non-Monamine Oxidase Inhibitor Antidepressants: Structure–Activity Relationships

JOHN H. BIEL

Part VI GENETIC AND ENVIRONMENTAL ASPECTS OF DRUGS AND BEHAVIOR

Part VII PSYCHOPHARMACOLOGIC DRUG STUDY DESIGN AND RESEARCH PROBLEMS WITH HUMANS

38 The Use and Abuse of Stimulants

Edward R. Bloomquist

39 The Hallucinogens

Sidney Cohen

40 Alcohol

Jack H. Mendelson

41 Psychotropic Drugs in Alcoholism

Max Hayman and Joseph del Giudice

42 Drugs, Deaths, and Suicides—Problems of the Coroner

Theodore J. Curphey, Edwin S. Shneidman, and
Norman L. Farberow

52 Antianxiety Drugs

JOSEPH DEL GIUDICE

53 Improved Clinical Practice and Research in the Treatment of Private Ambulatory Patients, Including the Use of the Computer with Precoded Data Forms

NATHAN S. KLINE

54 Pediatric Psychopharmacology

H. H. EVELOFF

55 Psychopharmacology in Geriatrics

KENNETH LIFSHITZ AND NATHAN S. KLINE

APPENDICES

WILLIAM G. CLARK AND T. KOBAYASHI

Appendix 2 Key Reviews, Monographs, Texts, Etc.

PART I

INTRODUCTION

1

INTRODUCTION

F. M. Berger

I. Introduction

Since 1952, new psychoactive substances have been introduced which have greatly influenced the treatment of mental disorders and substantially improved our understanding of mental disease. Each new discovery has been not only an addition to our knowledge but a challenge to our established beliefs as well. With the wide use of the new psychopharmacologic agents psychiatry, until recently a humanistic discipline, has become more of an empirical science seeking dependence on the laws of chemistry and physics. Some time has passed since these discoveries were first made. It now seems appropriate to review the advances that have been made and to speculate about future developments in this field.

A. *Substances Affecting the Mind*

Psychopharmacological or psychoactive agents, in the broadest sense of the word, are substances capable of modifying perception, sensation, mood, and mental as well as physical activity. Substances capable of producing these effects, such as alcohol, caffeine, nicotine, opium, cocaine, peyote, marihuana, hashish, and many others, have been used in many societies since time immemorial.

These substances have been used for many purposes, but rarely if ever with the aim of affecting or curing a disease. In our own culture some of these agents were used to facilitate social intercourse, to produce a sense of exhilaration, and to ease the pain of living. In other cultures various psychoactive substances are used to produce detachment or withdrawal or for religious or orgiastic purposes.

It is important to make a distinction between the use of the traditional psychoactive substances and the use of modern psychopharmacological drugs. The traditional agents were principally used to produce abnormal mental states in normal people. The modern drugs, however, are primarily used to treat mentally disturbed patients with the purpose of favorably influencing their abnormal behavior and restoring their mental and emotional balance.

B. Therapeutic Applications of Psychoactive Agents

The successful use of chemical agents for the specific purpose of influencing mental disease is of recent date. The highlights of this undertaking were the discovery of the usefulness of barbiturates for narcoanalysis (1), the insulin treatment of schizophrenia (2), and the convulsive treatment of depressive states (3). Yet, it was not until the middle 1950's that psychoactive agents were used to specifically treat mental disorders. The introduction of chlorpromazine (4), meprobamate (5), and imipramine (6) and many other drugs with similar actions evoked new interest in psychiatric treatment and accelerated the pace of research in an unprecedented manner. For more historical information, see Caldwell, Chapter 2. The clinical usefulness of these drugs made it possible to accept the idea that mental disturbances were related to changes in the biochemistry of the brain and that these disorders could be influenced by chemical substances just like other somatic diseases.

C. The Nature of Mental Disease

Establishing a clinical entity entails isolating and defining its specific anatomic or physiologic features. In most mental diseases there are no known pathological or biochemical lesions which might be of etiological significance. Mental disease also differs from other diseases in several other respects. Mental disturbances are not associated with any easily elicited and objectively measurable physical signs. These disorders are primarily disturbances of behavior, mood, and thought, manifesting themselves merely as exaggerations of these personality attributes. Thus, a normal person may at times display socially unacceptable behavior, become unduly depressed, or suffer disturbances of his thinking. In this sense, symptoms of mental disease represent subjective evaluations of the behavior of some individuals relative to the behavior of other individuals.

Mental disease has to be diagnosed on the basis of altered mental processes and changes in behavior. Outlines between the different disease entities are blurred, and it is often difficult to differentiate one disease from another. For example, it is not known whether the disturbances that we call schizophrenia or depression are unitary entities or a number of different disease states. This lack of knowledge makes the evaluation of psychoactive agents difficult.

II. The Psychopharmacological Agents

Perhaps the most significant aspect of recent psychopharmacological research is our new understanding of the site and mode of action of psychoactive drugs. Yet, there is not yet sufficient knowledge in terms of any one science such as anatomy, biochemistry, or psychology or in terms of the emerging science of psychiatry to permit us to make the fundamental generalizations which are the objects of our research. At the present time, the best understanding of the problems can be achieved by utilizing the distinctive methods and points of view of all these disciplines.

Tranquilizers have been classified according to their chemical structure, pharmacological effects, the mode of action, their clinical application, and a combination of these factors. At the present time psychopharmacological agents perhaps are best classified according to clinical usefulness. They can be broadly divided into five groups: the antipsychotic agents, the antianxiety agents, the sedative-hypnotics, the antidepressants, and the hallucinogenic substances. Each of these groups comprises substances of entirely unrelated chemical structure which nevertheless produce similar clinical effects.

The antipsychotic agents, also called thymoleptics, neuroleptics, or "major tranquilizers," are used in the treatment of psychoses. Phenothiazines, reserpine alkaloids, and the butyrophenones are representatives of this group. These agents act by counteracting hallucinations and delusional thinking, by alleviating psychomotor excitement and assaultiveness, by counteracting withdrawal, and by facilitating social adjustment. Neurophysiologically, these agents increase the excitability of the hypothalamic centers. On the biochemical level, they inhibit central adrenergic mechanisms.

The antianxiety agents, also called "minor tranquilizers," relaxants, antineurotic agents, anxiolytics, tranquillo-sedatives, or just tranquilizers are primarily of value in the treatment of anxiety and other psychoneurotic and psychosomatic symptoms. Meprobamate and the benzodiazepines are the most important members of this group. On the neurophysiological level, these agents act by depressing the hyperexcitability of the hippocampus and limbic system and by inhibiting the spread of impulses along the interneuronal circuits. While little is known about the biochemical effects of these compounds, they appear to be effective in suppressing the autonomic concomitants of conditioned reflexes.

The sedative-hypnotics, of which the barbiturates and the substituted amides (glutethimide, methyprylon) are typical, are most useful in reducing the awareness of the environment and in producing sleep. When given intravenously they increase the ability to communicate, give a feeling of well being, and release the thought content of previously resistive and seclusive patients. They act by decreasing the excitability of the cortex and by depressing the brain-stem reticular formation and by releasing inhibitions.

The antidepressant agents include the tricyclic amines, the monoamine oxidase inhibitors (also sometimes called psychic energizers), and certain CNS stimulants. All of these drugs act by increasing the availability of catecholamines at critical sites of the brain either by preventing their inactivation, as is the case with MAO inhibitors, or by making the synapses more sensitive to the effects of catecholamines, as is the case with tricyclic antidepressants.

The hallucinogenic substances, also called psychosomimetic, psychodysleptic, psychotogenic agents, or phantastica, of which lysergic acid diethylamide (LSD) and psilocybin are typical representatives, produce hallucinations and distortion of perception. Their action may be related to the effect of the hallucinogens on transmitter substances in the brain. The therapeutic usefulness of hallucinogens has not been proven, but they are of interest because they may produce conditions similar to the psychoses.

There are a few other psychopharmacological agents that do not fit easily into any of these groups. Their clinical value has not yet been clearly established. Among these are substances with anticholinergic and antihistaminic properties, such as benactyzine and hydroxyzine, that have been used in the treatment of phobias and anxiety states, or lithium, used for the prevention of manic episodes.

Psychoactive drugs are not entirely specific in their clinical actions. Sometimes an antianxiety agent can be effective in the treatment of psychoses or an antipsychotic drug effective in the treatment of depression or psychoneuroses. This lack of specificity may be more apparent than real. It may be due to our inability to diagnose mental disturbances. A number of different mental diseases may all have an important symptom in common. To give a specific example, anxiety may occur as a symptom of psychoneuroses, psychoses, hyperthyroidism, hypoglycemia, angina pectoris, or Cushing's disease.

A. *What Has Been Achieved*

The psychoactive agents available at the present time are primarily effective in counteracting many of the cardinal symptoms of psychiatric disease. They are of value in controlling disturbed behavior and agitation, in counteracting hallucinations and delusions, in facilitating social adjustment, and in ameliorating anxiety and depression. There is, however, not yet enough available evidence indicating that these drugs would affect the underlying process that leads to the appearance of the psychiatric symptoms.

As long as the physical basis of mental disease is not known, it will be difficult to find a cure, that is, to remove or rectify the cause of the disturbance. The word "cure," however, also implies the restoration of the preexisting state of mental health. In this sense modern psychopharmacological agents have helped many disturbed patients. However, most patients suffering from mental disease have not enjoyed optimal mental health before seeking psychiatric help. None of the drugs available at the present time can rectify the underlying hereditary and environmental influences that were responsible for the shaping of their personalities.

B. *Medical, Social, and Economic Consequences*

The introduction of the psychopharmacological agents has had important medical, social, and economic consequences. More patients have become amenable to treatment without the need for hospitalization or their hospital stay has been shortened. Many patients have been able to continue their occupations and social life while under treatment. As a result of treatment with psychoactive agents, many previously hospitalized patients have returned to their families and to society. The use of psychotherapeutic agents in hospitals has had important economic consequences. According to Brill and Patton (7), the savings in patient care and hospital construction was $2 billion on the basis of the predicted increase in hospitalized patients in the state of New York from 1955 to 1962. The use of antipsychotic agents in hospitals made possible the discharge of many patients who previously required institutional care for life. The striking improvements produced by pharmacotherapy were particularly impressive when evaluated by mean duration of hospital stay and the condition of the patient on discharge. The drugs had much less effect on longer term prognosis when measured by readmission rates.

Psychotherapeutic agents may also play an important part in making psychotherapy acceptable to the patient. They may do so by alleviating distressing symptoms, by making the patient more suggestible, and by impressing upon the patient that he is not suffering from "madness," which he considers a cursed and shameful condition, but from a bodily disease which can be treated like other somatic diseases. Psychoactive substances may also be a valuable adjunct to psychotherapy, inducing sleep and providing rest for the patient and facilitating the expression of repressed conflicts. Drugs may alleviate anxiety and tension and raise the threshold to irritating emotional outburst-producing stimuli.

C. *The Fear of Taking Drugs That Affect the Mind*

Drugs affecting the mind such as alcohol or opium are widely used all over the world because of their euphoriant action. The function and actions of these psychoactive substances differ entirely from those of the psychotherapeutic agents which are used to alleviate disease. In most people, psychopharmacologic drugs do not produce subjectively pleasurable experiences which would prompt continuous use and abuse. This is particularly true when these drugs are taken by normal individuals. In this respect, the psychotherapeutic drugs differ from agents such as alcohol and opium, which produce a state of well-being and subjective exhilaration in most normal people.

In usual doses the antianxiety agents do not produce subjectively noticeable effects in normal persons. In excessive doses, these substances produce sleepiness. Antipsychotic and antidepressant agents elicit in apparently healthy individuals a feeling of indisposition and unpleasant autonomic symptoms such as dryness of the mouth. In excessive doses they produce symptoms of Parkinsonism. There is little incentive for normal people to take these drugs. Psychotherapeutic agents do not make healthy people feel "happy," nor improve their disposition or performance.

There is a widespread and unfounded fear that psychotherapeutic drugs induce a state of mind that leads to socially and morally unacceptable acts. There is no evidence that any drug available at present could be used for such purposes against the will of the individual. There are no known methods of research that could be used to develop such a mind-control drug. It is, of course, true that brainwashing and mind control can be induced by psychological means, primarily by inducing a state of anxiety in the subject (8). In this respect, as well as in some others, the word still has unique powers. There is no evidence that psychopharmacological agents could change the basic underlying personality. At best, drugs can subdue excitement and normalize behavior. At worst, psychopharmacologic agents bring out latent emotional states such as anxiety or hallucinations, but they cannot change our basic attitudes, desires, and moral standards.

The psychoactive drugs may not be the final answer to the treatment of mental disease. There probably are no final answers. Before further progress can be made we must accumulate new fundamental knowledge of the nature of mental diseases and improve our ability to identify, classify, and diagnose them. Yet drugs can be no substitute for insight, understanding, and human kindness, and all of these are and always will be needed.

2

HISTORY OF PSYCHOPHARMACOLOGY

Anne E. Caldwell

I. Introduction

Ever since psychotropic plants existed, nature provided drugs in as colorful a variety as today's drug industry does. Blue morning glories covered the entrance to caveman's abode and a bowl with green seeds of ololiuqui might have stood inside. *Amanita muscaria,* the brilliant red mushroom with dots of white, grew in shady groves. Yellow-orange fruits of cactus studded arid plains. Red poppies bent their heads when it rained in the spring. Rauwolfia blossomed pink on tropical Himalaya mountains and so did cannabis nearly all over the world. Fresh or dried, leaves, fruits, roots, bark, stems, or seeds, whole or ground, were chewed or brewed and sipped or somehow ingested to alter mood or state of mind—and this is psychopharmacology, in its literal sense.

What drug started it? Mandrake, morphine, mescaline, or mushrooms? Maybe rauwolfia in India if not in Nigeria, teonanacatl in Mexico or the American

For references not cited in the Master Bibliography, see Caldwell, 1958 and 1970, Appendices 1 and 2.

Indians' peyote? Perhaps alcohol, ibogaine, cannabis, cocaine, ololiuqui, or yohimbine? Opinions vary as to drug, time, and place. But if one defines psychopharmacology precisely as the utilization of drugs in restoring or maintaining mental health and for exploring the mind, then everyone is agreed: The drug is chlorpromazine (CPZ), the time: 1952, and the place: Val-de-Grâce, the famed military hospital in Paris.

From there CPZ started its trek around the globe. Sweeping through mental hospitals, transforming disturbed wards, reforming therapy, and remodeling research, it created psychopharmacology. This very term was used before and so were many of the psychotropic drugs, like LSD, rauwolfia, lithium, even promethazine. And yet it was CPZ that pulled these older drugs from the psychiatric horizon, or even from oblivion, to the zenith of psychiatric interest; and it was CPZ that stimulated the syntheses of new drugs or the use of old ones that existed without ever being used in therapy, like meprobamate, promazine, and others. Above all, CPZ gave the old term psychopharmacology its true meaning and this put psychiatry into the very center of medicine—where it belongs!

Was all this due to some whim of fashion or because time's pendulum had swung drugward? Emphatically no! That pedulum's position was right quite often, but the drug was always wrong—until 1952. The rise of modern psychopharmacology was not a phenomenon of time, but was due to the development of a phenomenal drug: CPZ was the first reliably effective antipsychotic drug, the first ataraxic, in its literal sense "undisturber," or the first nonhypnotic CNS depressant.

II. Terminology

A. *Psychopharmacology*

The American pharmacologist David I. Macht coined the term psychopharmacology for "the domain" he described as "virgin soil, full of promise" in 1920—and he invented a laboratory test in 1943 that happened to become helpful in bringing about in 1952 what he had envisioned in 1920: psychopharmacology (9). The term was first used in psychiatry by Thorner in "The Psycho-pharmacology of Sodium Amytal," published in the *Journal of Nervous and Mental Disease* (February, 1935).

B. *Antipsychotic and Antianxiety Drugs*

The French surgeon Laborit (see Chapter 18) at first used the term "lytics," short for "central autonomolytics" for promethazine, diethazine, and other drugs with a somewhat CPZ-like action (hence the term "lytic" cocktail). In 1952 he replaced the term "lytics" with "neuroplegics" derived from "neuroplegia," a term coined by Durel. In February, 1955, the French psychiatrist Delay suggested the term "neuroleptics" (derived from "psycholepsis," the term Janet coined for his concept of reduced psychologic tension) because the suffix "plegic" in "neuro*plegic*" implies paralysis, whereas CPZ and CPZ-like drugs reduce rather than paralyze nervous tension.

In the French psychopharmacologic literature the term "neuroplegic" was used from 1952 until February 1955 exclusively and through 1957 frequently. The drug house Specia (Laboratoires Rhône-Poulenc) advertised Largactil (CPZ) as a "neuroplégique" through 1957. From 1956 on, the term "neuroleptic" appeared with increasing frequency and eventually replaced the term "neuroplegic" in most of the French literature, though one occasionally encounters even the term "neurolytic," as in the charming article "The Psychiatry that Heals" by Rondepierre (1965).

The word "ataraxy" (imperturbability) became a medical term in 1955 when the neurologist Howard Fabing, together with Alister Cameron, a professor of classics at the University of Cincinnati, named CPZ-like psychotropic drugs "ataraxics" and their action "ataractic"—from the Greek "ataraktos" meaning undisturbed. The Greek noun "ataraxia" and adjective "ataraktos" are derived from the verb "ataraktein" (to keep calm).

The term "ataraxic" is euphoneous and has additional advantages: It implies a desirable state of mind, like mental equilibrium; it remains appropriate for a stimulative drug too, if it corrects a disturbed state; and it means practically the same as stabilizer—the first article on CPZ is entitled: "A New Autonomic Stabilizer."

The term tranquilizer became a psychiatric term in 1810 when Benjamin Rush designed a wooden chair equipped with restraining straps and named it "tranquilizer." Somewhat later in the 19th century, and likewise without adding charm to the term, another tranquilizer appeared and disappeared quickly: the juice of ground ivy (10). An additional disadvantage of this term is that it suggests a picture of overdosage rather than a desirable state of mind.

Term coining developed with and in proportion to the drugs themselves. Terminology was discussed at meetings in great length and at one such occasion, the Second International Congress of Psychiatry in Zürich (1957), terms were even voted on: "Neuroleptics" won. "Tranquilizers" came in second, with three times as many votes as "ataraxics." An important American study of 1964 concluded that tranquilizer was not a suitable term (National Institute of Mental Health Psychopharmacology Service Center Collaborative Study Group, 1964).

C. *Antidepressants and Stimulants*

In 1955 Delay suggested the term "psychotonics." In 1957 he suggested "analeptics," and Kline, "psychoenergizers." Variations of these terms are "psychostimulants," "psychoanaleptics," "psychic energizers," etc.

D. *Hallucinogens*

"Phantastica" is the name Louis Lewin gave these drugs in 1924, when his famous book was published. The titles of its first translation into English (1931) and into French (1967) are: "Phantastica, Narcotic and Stimulating Drugs" and "Phantastica, Drogues Psychédéliques."

The term "hallucinogens" was first used in 1954 by Osmond. In 1955 Gerard suggested the term "psychosomimetics" (usual form: "psychotomimetics") because hallucinations were rarely observed in hallucinogen-induced states or "model psychoses." When it turned out that drug-induced states did not really mimic psychoses, the term "psychotomimetics" became inappropriate too. In 1956, at a meeting in New York, Osmond suggested several terms, among them "psychedelics" as the best suited.

In 1957, at a meeting in Zurich, Delay suggested the term "dysleptics." In 1958 appeared the term "psychotaraxics" meaning "mind-disturbers." (It is like "taraxein" derived from the Greek verb "tarassein," "to disturb.")

III. From Sorcery to Psychopharmacology

In antiquity and earlier, psychotropic substances came chiefly from plants—though some animal secretions are psychotropic, e.g., bufotenine is secreted by the skin of toads—and many if not most of them were hallucinogens. They could have opened "the doors of perception" (Huxley, 1954), but usually they opened doors of delusion. Perhaps cosmology was not yet "joyous" (Watts, 1962), or difficulties in dosing might have played a role, but frequently delusions were produced on purpose. The Viking Berserkers are said to have ingested *Amanita muscaria* to live up to their name. Circe produced different delusions: With a drug *and* a wand she transformed Odysseus' crew into swine, then back into men again with her wand and an ointment—to remove the bristles.

According to Homer, Circe was "polypharmakos," meaning "one who knows how to use drugs"—a compliment that he bestowed only rarely on "iatroi," meaning "physicians and surgeons." This suggests that not all "iatroi" were equally skillful in using drugs. Sorcerers had to "know their business." Pharmacognosy was essential and compounding necessary, but wand swinging was an absolute must in the sorcerer's armamentarium. On rare occasions, as in the case of Odysseus, the gods would intervene and prevent Circe's polypharmacologic stunt by pre-medicating the would-be transformee with another drug: "The root was black but the flower was like milk. Moly, the gods call it. For mortal men it is difficult to pull from the ground but gods can do everything," says Homer, who reported this early use of a drug as an antidote for a hallucinogenic drug (Homer, *Odyssey* **10,** 302–306).

Credit for another constructive use of a psychotropic drug goes to Pythia, the priestess of the Delphian oracle. She used a drug to facilitate oracling. In fact, she inhaled—probably carbon dioxide, or perhaps the drug was cannabis: the Scythians took vapor baths that were medicated with burnt hemp seeds, and the inhaled vapor fulfilled their deepest desires. Pythia's deepest desire was future-proof oracling. And so she sat on her golden tripod and oracled, blue streaks of vapor rising about her. It was impressive. And effective. Above all, it was an important advance in psychopharmacology—the first use of a drug to intensify perception in its practical application: prediction.

It is not surprising that psychopharmacotherapy too arose in ancient Greece, though only for a fleeting span of time, when drugs were studied by Helen of Troy and drug reports sung by Homer. That was the "golden age of psychopharmacology." Surprisingly, the Greeks had no word for it, neither the term "psychopharmacology" nor its correct version, "thymopharmacology," but they had the essential: the drug—and no name for it either, in rather un-Greek fashion. Homer leaves this drug nameless. He reports only its properties and gives examples for its efficacy: It is a "nepenthic" (against sorrow) and "acholic" (against anger) drug "to suppress despair." Whoever takes this drug "will not shed a tear all day long." Not even if he saw his loved ones dead, would he feel sorrow, and if they were murdered before his own eyes while he looked on, he would not get angry.

Environmental factors are important in the use of psychotropic drugs—perhaps they played a role when a psychotropic drug was used for the first time in therapy. The setting was elegant: Sparta's royal palace. The atmosphere was congenial: a party at the Menelaoses and the hostess was Helen. The conversation drifted to the Trojan war, to friends who had come home from Troy and to those who had not. Odysseus was still missing, some 10 years after the war—what if he had met his fate? Clouds of gloom descended on the scene and, gripped by compassion, everyone told a story in his honor.

Helen too had a story to tell, but she could not get a word in edgewise. The more they talked, the sadder they got. Eventually, all were in tears. Even Helen, who was all but immune to compassion, whipped up a tear or two. Suppertime came. Should one eat or weep? The two don't mix, said Nestor's son, who was also there. Weeping was indicated—couldn't one postpone storytelling until weeping would be more convenient?

Suddenly the men decide: "Let's eat—stories can wait until the morrow!" This threatened to spoil the evening for Helen who is not famous for her cooking but for having her cake and eating it too. And sure enough, she does it again: "a different idea has Helen," says Homer; and as usual, her idea is brilliant: "Quickly she puts in the wine they are drinking a drug against sorrow and anger" and serves this "lytic cocktail" to her guests.

It brings instant relief. The evening is saved. It is a tremendous success for Helen. For the drug too. All are free of compassion with Odysseus and yet alert enough to enjoy the conversation. Helen tells her story—how she bathed Odysseus and so on—it would infuriate any husband. But Menelaos, under the influence of this drug, its antianger radical, remains every inch the charming host: He even tells the famous story of the Trojan horse!

The correlation of Homeric drugs with modern ones is intriguing if one is not too serious about it and yet exact in analyzing the original text and context. One must take into consideration that, in his other "drug reports" Homer names the drugs and describes the plants, e.g., moly. Here, he does neither, and what he says about this nameless drug does not reveal but hides its identity: The drug was *one* among many drugs that Polydamna gave to Helen. But those who tried to interpret this drug considered solely an effect that, depending largely on dosage, is not characteristic of any particular psychotropic drug: It made the unbearable bearable. In all societies, primitive or civilized, drugs (like alcohol, cannabis, opium) and mushrooms are used for that very purpose. Homer's mysterious drug accomplished this feat without clouding consciousness, that is, in highly effective doses the drug had no undesirable effects. The ideal efficacy of this drug made it interesting, and this might explain why this drug was interpreted always as the very drug that interested a particular interpreter, or scientists in general, at a particular time. Thus, the most frequent interpretation in the 18th and 19th centuries was cannabis [Virey, 1803, cited by Moreau de Tours (1845)] and after interest in cannabis faded, in the 20th century, it was opium (Lewin, 1924).

Luckily, all attempts to interpret Homer's mystery drug have been futile. They might have been prevented if important clues in Homer's story had not been overlooked.

Who was Polydamna? Menelaos and Helen on their way home from Troy stopped over in Egypt, a country then known for its miracle drugs. Waiting for favorable winds, they made friends with the natives, "who all were physicians"—and one of them was Polydamna. At last the winds came, and when the royal couple was ready to sail, there arrived on the boat a basket full of miracle drugs—and one of them was this mysterious drug. From the handle of the basket hung a small papyrus that read in hieroglyphics: "Bon Voyage! from Polydamna." This name means "Super-tamer" or "Tranquilisateur par excellence"—it seems too fitting a name to be coincidental.

Only Homer mentions Polydamna, and he does so only in this one scene. This is widely known—and yet, none of those who tried so hard to interpret the drug, has ever translated the name "Polydamna."

Did Polydamna really exist? And the drug? Of course, Homer's audience knew instantly what the name "Polydamna" meant, and seeing Homer smile, they understood: The mysterious drug was, of course, just as Homer said—"a drug against sorrow and anger, a drug to survive despair."

IV. Psychiatric Drug Therapy, 1845–1952

The date 1845 is arbitrary—drugs were widely used by then and much earlier too (10). Many of these drugs were cathartics, diaphoretics, or emetics; they were not psychoactive and were not even expected to be so: One tried to treat the total patient and, hopefully, his mental illness too. Quite a few drugs, or specifics for the treatment of mental disease, were specific only for a particular physician and disappeared quickly or at the same time as their promoter. Here are a few examples: In the 17th century Thomas Willis recommended a "decoction of pimpernel with the purple flower" for the treatment of "madness." The plant belongs to the genus *Anagallis* and contains an alkaloid with diaphoretic and diuretic properties. Its flowers close at the approach of rainy or cloudy weather and this might have enhanced its appeal. The "juice of ground ivy" tranquilized mental patients according to Edward Sutliffe, who wrote about it in 1819. John Ford reported in 1803 that he used granulated preparations of tin with success in the treatment of hypomanic patients.

Other drugs, many of them for valid reasons, were generally popular throughout the ages with all physicians who treated mental patients. Among them are the mandrake, and it was used externally too, as an oily extract to anoint quite appropriately an important target structure, the head; hellebore, in white, green or black, each with its own properties and indications; and such perennial favorites as alcohol and opium.

Billod reported successful drug therapy with *Datura stramonium* against hallucinations and quinine sulfate against melancholy in 1844 from the psychiatric service of Moreau de Tours. Yet the year 1845 has a particular significance here. Moreau de Tours is known as the first true psychopharmocologist because he used a drug to induce and study mental symptoms and also to treat mental disease. The drug was cannabis. Moreau described his experience in a book "Du Hachisch et de l'Aliénation Mentale," and it was published in 1845.

1845. Cannabis introduced into psychiatry by Jacques-Joseph Moreau de Tours (1804–1884). He used it as a "dawamesc," a flavored paste of hashish, occasionally as a pure extract of hashish, and in either case always together with black coffee, to enhance (potentiate) and accelerate the effects of the drug and to mask its taste. (For chemistry, uses, etc., see Cohen, Chapter 39; Opler, Chapter 3.)

1847–1848. Chloroform and ether inhalations were tried in therapy of psychoses and neuroses. Effects were occasionally beneficial but always transient.

1869. Chloral hydrate is exceptional in that its first clinical use was in psychiatry, and it remained a valued depressant in that field. Liebig discovered chloral hydrate in 1830, but it took 39 years until its first use in therapy by Liebreich (1869), who used it the same year in treatment of insanity too. The following year the American psychiatrist Elstun reported its beneficial effects in 5 patients, 3 acutely manic, 2 melancholic with delusions, from the Indiana Hospital for the Insane. Chloral hydrate was more reliable in cases of wakefulness than any other agent known, "but when the medicine is suspended, the mania is as violent as before" (Elstun, 1871).

1875. Hyoscyamine entered psychiatry at the West Riding Pauper Lunatic Asylum in London. Lawson, who introduced it, gave hyoscyamine in doses of 1–1½ grains in alcohol per os. In support of his therapeutic concept he cited "the statement which Shakespere [sic] puts in the mouth of the Ghost of Hamlet's father when he refers to 'the juice of cursed hebenon,' as—

> 'The leperous distilment, whose effect
> Holds such an enmity with blood of man
> That *swift as quicksilver* it courses through
> The natural gates and alleys of the body.' "

(Lawson, 1876)

Savage disagreed—not with Shakespeare but with Lawson's concept of psychiatric therapy, and said: "I do not believe whipping a tired nervous system with strychnine is good, nor deranging an already deranged brain by belladonna, opium, chloral, or hyoscyamine will lead to happy results. We may make a desert and call it peace." (Savage, 1879).

1880. Cocaine therapy of morphine and alcohol addiction started in the United States and was even advertised by Parke-Davis in the *Quarterly Journal of Inebriety* (Hartford, Connecticut) for 1883 and 1884, and became quite popular. Few saw the danger of such therapy, many endorsed it, and one of them was Freud (1884). He was interested in cocaine because sedatives were plentiful but stimulants rare, and he treated chiefly neurasthenia and morphinism with this drug. His psychopharmacologic failure had a late result—psychoanalysis. Of ancillary but psychopharmacologic interest is that, in 1885, when Freud recommended subcutaneous injections of 0.03–0.05 mg cocaine for morphine withdrawal symptoms, to be repeated without restriction, he insisted that cocaine was not habit-forming. Lewin, the famed author of "Phantastica," disagreed immediately and emphatically: he explained why cocaine therapy of morphine addicts would lead to double addiction, and he emphasized the role of personality in the development of addiction (11).

1897. Sleep therapy started in Shanghai with sodium bromide by mouth or by nose through 6–7 days. First, it cured "a long standing morphine habit." Two years later it was used for several more conditions, including the cocaine habit and acute mania. By the turn of the century, it was used only in manias and quite far from Shanghai: in Kingston, Jamaica (Macleod, 1897, 1899, 1900; Ragg, 1900).

1899. The first phenothiazine derivative made its psychiatric debut: methylene blue. Though Ehrlich's hypothesis on its therapeutic effect in psychoses was invalidated by then, methylene blue worked anyway—as did all the other drugs then in use (Bodoni, 1899).

1920. Again, sleep therapy: Kläsi introduced his method in Switzerland. He used a premedication, morphine plus scopolamine, and then "Somnifen," a mixture of diethyl- and dipropenyl barbituric acid, intravenously or subcutaneously, for 6–7 days or longer. His first report concerns 30 patients: 12 improved—8 immediately and 4 within two months, 11 did not improve, and 7 died. This method, with Somnifen or various other short- and long-acting barbiturates, remained popular throughout Europe, particularly in Switzerland, France, and Russia, and in Canada.

1929. Sodium amytal, and in 1930 sodium amytal narcosis, was introduced by Bleckwenn.

Carbon dioxide inhalation was shown to have transient beneficial effects on psychotic patients by Loevenhart *et al.* This was confirmed in 1930 by Solomon *et al.* But carbon dioxide inhalation became an effective treatment only in neurotic patients, as introduced by Meduna in 1947.

1931. First use of rauwolfia alkaloids in modern Indian psychiatry by Sen and Bose.

1933. Insulin introduced into psychiatry by Sakel. Modern physical treatment of psychoses has its origin in this event. First, Sakel used subcomatose doses of insulin in morphine withdrawals. This treatment decreased the distressing symptoms of newly abstinent morphine addicts. He then decided to try it in other forms of excitation. When he attempted to determine optimal dosage, some of the schizophrenic patients being treated happened to fall into coma—and this proved beneficial for their psychotic symptoms too.

1935. Insulin coma became the preferred method of therapy in schizophrenias.

1935–1936. Amphetamines arrived in neuropsychiatry: first in narcolepsy and the following year in depressive states.

Metrazol, intravenously, as shock therapy in schizophrenias was introduced by Meduna. At first he used camphor, in oily solution, intramuscularly to produce convulsions. But many patients were highly resistant to this drug, and even the same patient required at different times different doses of camphor in order to react. Looking for a more suitable drug, Meduna tried metrazol. It has the additional advantage that convulsions occur immediately after injection, whereas with camphor they appear an hour or two after it has been injected. Camphor, incidentally, happens to be an old psychiatric "specific": As early as 1776, Auenbrugger "wrote about it and stressed that it [camphor] be given in repeated doses until convulsions occurred. . . ." (10).

1938. Histamine, in gradually increasing doses, as a "nonspecific desensitization" procedure (based on Marshall's hypothesis of pseudoallergy) was effectively used in therapy of psychotic patients by Marshall and Tarwater in the United States.

Histamine with insulin was successfully used in therapy of schizophrenia and other mental diseases by Hill in England. The literature on psychiatric histamine therapy includes a few more reports by these authors, (1939–1944) and another by Robb *et al.* (1940), in an article on nonconvulsive histamine therapy of psychoses by Sackler *et al.* in 1949.

1943. Phenbenzamine, the first antihistamine to enter psychiatry, was used in various mental disorders and with varying success. Most of these patients had asthma that disappeared when their mental symptoms appeared. When the treatment was effective and the mental symptoms disappeared, the asthma reappeared. The rationale of this treatment was based on the observation that manic-depressive psychoses and asthma are connected. These observations were made as early as 1851, but the mechanisms of that connection was explained only much later, by Tinel (1920). (Daumezon and Cassan, 1943; Montassut, 1943. See Caldwell, Appendix 5.)

1947. LSD, synthesized in 1943, made its clinical debut: as a therapeutic drug in mental disorders (Stoll, 1947).

Carbon dioxide inhalation in therapy of neuroses was introduced by Meduna.

1949. Lithium was introduced into psychiatry by Cade in Australia (see Schou, Chapter 51).

1950. Promethazine arrived in psychiatry.

In July, 1950, Guiraud reported his experience with promethazine in 24 regressed schizophrenic patients. He had chosen this drug "equally" for its antihistaminic as for its "hypnotic" activity. To be sure, he said, many hypnotics are available to psychiatrists, and he named barbiturates, opium derivatives, and scopolamine, "but since the chemical structure of these new antihistamines (meaning aminophenothiazines) is different, their hypnotic activity might present utilizable peculiarities." He was pleased with promethazine: "(It) acts as well and even better than ordinary sedatives do. . . . The patients become calm or even somnolent, just like after injection of gardénal . . ." (12).

For Guiraud, promethazine was but another, perhaps a better, sedative and this first use of an aminophenothiazine in psychoses remained without consequence. It did not revolutionize psychiatry—in fact, promethazine disappeared from the psychiatric scene for two full years.

For more than a century psychiatrists attempted psychopharmacologic therapy. Most any drug was tried—swallowed, injected or inhaled—and "effective": at first or to some extent, in some patients or at too great a risk. No drug was satisfactory. With the number of drugs increasing over the years, drug therapy became more frequent and eventually all inclusive in that antagonistic drugs, histamine and antihistamines were used to treat the very same mental illness. Shock therapies, with insulin or metrazol, were introduced, and physical treatment methods gained considerable popularity within that period of time: electroshock, convulsive or nonconvulsive, and psychosurgery. It is interesting that the development was similar in India, where standardized alkaloids of rauwolfia were available and frequently used since 1931.

Psychiatrists were certainly not nihilists in matters therapeutic: Everything was tried—drugs, shocks, and surgery. Nevertheless, disturbed wards remained distressing and chronic wards crowded: CPZ did not yet exist.

V. The Creation of Chlorpromazine

A. Forerunners

1. Drugs

Paul Charpentier, who is famous for his synthesis of phenothiazines, prepared the first amino derivative in 1944 at the Rhône-Poulenc Laboratories of Specia, the Paris drug house. Three aminophenothiazines were parent analogs of CPZ: compound R.P. 3276, that was not developed into a therapeutic drug because its antihistaminic activity was very poor; promethazine, the isopropyl derivative of "3276," that became quickly known as an excellent antihistamine and was widely used by 1947; diethazine, that was used in Parkinson's disease from 1946 on.

2. Investigations

The French surgeon Laborit (see his Chapter 18) decided in 1945 to investigate what with advancing surgical technique became an ever greater obstacle to surgical progress: shock. By 1947 Laborit obtained evidence to support the concept that shock resulted from exaggerated organic defense reactions to stress. He postulated that to control such reactions, the entire autonomic nervous system, the sympathetic and the parasympathetic, had to be inhibited peripherally and centrally.

In 1952, Leriche, in turn, was pleased to see the old tricky problem of shock clarified and found "Laborit's idea" to prevent shock by inhibiting autonomic reactivity revolutionary, fascinating, and extremely promising.

B. A Glimpse of Ataraxy

Early in 1949 Laborit began to use promethazine for its antihistaminic action. Surprisingly, his patients were calm and relaxed even after major operations. They appeared to really suffer less. Laborit attributed this to the central action of promethazine and saw immediately that it differed significantly from that of morphine. Ataraxy was but glimpsed, yet seen—and thus discovered, though it was too faint even to give it a name. Nonetheless, postoperative morphine became unnecessary, and this was most advantageous (13).

In using promethazine first solely for its antihistaminic action, while simultaneously looking for an autonomic drug with central action to prevent shock, Laborit discovered ataraxy by serendipity. But of course he did not discover the central effects of promethazine: They were all too well known—and deplored, ever since 1947, when this drug came into clinical use as an antihistamine.

Antihistamines are effective in relieving allergic symptoms like urticaria, asthma, hay fever, etc. These drugs were highly valued and widely used for their antihistaminic effects. But their central effects were just as widely known because they made many allergic patients drowsy, sleepy, or dizzy. Since these "sedative" effects were undesirable, and not due to the antihistaminic activity for which these drugs were given, one called them "side effects." For this reason the central effects of antihistamines became known as "sedative side effects." Somnolence, drowsiness, or dizziness were often so severe that they impaired work performance, or became a safety hazard that precluded the daytime use of these drugs. Many allergic patients preferred hay fever to antihistamines. All were agreed that antihistamines should not be sedative and manufacturers tried to produce antihistamines without sedative effects, but making one was difficult. First of all, a convenient animal test was necessary. But there was none because sedation, all too obvious in man, was not demonstrable in small laboratory animals. In fact, after injection of antihistamines they often became excited and practically never sedated. Early in 1948, investigators working for an American drug house (Merck) demonstrated sedative effects of antihistamines in mice by showing that these drugs, including promethazine provided by Specia, potentiate the effects of barbiturates. However, their ingenious method was not suitable as a routine test (Winter, 1948). The same authors first reported in March 1949 a satisfactory test, using a method described by Macht in 1943, with rats trained to climb a vertical rope (Winter and Flataker, 1949, 1951). There was hope for allergic patients! Perhaps it would become possible to make antihistamines without sedative side effects: antihistamines without central activity! But a test was not enough: Sedative effects, previously only seen in man, became demonstrable in rats—but not eradicable from antihistamines.

One made the best of it and gave antihistamines at night to make their sedative effects less troublesome. But no one recognized the true nature of these "sedative side effects" or utilized them for an important clinical purpose until Laborit did both in 1949: He saw that the "sedative side effects" of promethazine are neither "sedative" nor "side effects" but central autonomic, nonhypnotic "ataractic" effects due to an intrinsic property of this drug that made it clinically valuable (13,14).

In promethazine this ataractic property was not well enough developed to be satisfactory for Laborit's purpose. He tried another phenothiazine derivative, diethazine, and found it to reduce preoperative anxiety. A small quantity of a weak general anesthetic, nitrous oxide, became enough to obtain adequate anesthesia for major operations. Reflexes returned within minutes after discontinuation of nitrous oxide, but the patients appeared to remain calmly asleep. Says Laborit: "A little tap on the cheek is enough to attract their attention: they lift their eyelids, they answer questions and then they relapse into painless somnolence" (15). Only the *word* ataraxy is missing—it was not yet a medical term in 1950—but it could not say more, nor could it say better that this was not just ordinary cortical sedation.

C. The Synthesis of Chlorpromazine

Nonetheless, diethazine was not the answer: Some of its properties were undesirable, and it was too toxic for its efficacy. Laborit with the Paris anesthesiologist Huguenard tried many other drugs, chiefly phenothiazines, and urged the development of new ones. Diethazine was still the best, and promethazine was retained for its antihistaminic action. "Anesthesia without anesthetics" was successful, but its technique cumbersome with this "lytic cocktail"—the "ideal lytic drug" did not yet exist. Whereas neurologists who used diethazine and a psychiatrist who used promethazine were satisfied but not enthusiastic, Laborit and Huguenard were enthusiastic but not satisfied. More important, they used these inadequate drugs with amazing skill and in *surgery* for *shock prevention*. Most important, by midyear 1950 (16), the new method was clinically very successful—and immensely promising *if* a more effective autonomic stabilizer could be found and suddenly Specia decided to develop such a drug. In the fall of 1950 (Koetschet, 1955) they initiated a systematic study to produce a drug of extraordinarily great central activity—antihistaminic or not!

This was a complete reversal of Specia's earlier policy: weakly antihistaminic compounds were not developed into therapeutic drugs because only antihistaminic action was clinically important. Consequently, no data were available on the central activity of earlier prepared compounds. Was there among them perhaps some with satisfactory central activity, or one promising enough to become so if its structural formula was altered? No satisfactory compound was found. One seemed promising: compound R.P. 3276. Charpentier attributed this to its lateral side chain and branched it on a chlorophenothiazine he had just then prepared–and there it was: a "well crystallized salt"! (17). On December 11, 1950, he sent samples of it under the code number R.P. 4560 to Simone Courvoisier for pharmacologic testing. It passed with flying colors: The drug, hardly at all antihistaminic, was adrenolytic and parasympatholytic. On May

2, 1951, chlorpromazine was released for extramural investigation, and now for the first time Laborit saw ataraxy fully developed—he describes it: "*The Action of the Drug Used Alone.* With doses of 50–100 mg intravenously there is not any loss in consciousness, not any change in the patient's mentality but a slight tendency to sleep and above all 'disinterest' for all that goes on around him" (18).

VI. From Surgery to Psychiatry

A. Rationale of Psychiatric CPZ Therapy

Drugs, being chemicals, act biochemically on target structures or through biochemical mediators and affect target symptoms, such as anxiety and depression. Drugs cannot tell if a patient is scheduled for appendectomy or for psychotherapy. It was logical to assume that a drug abolishing anxiety and excitement in surgical patients might likewise abolish or mitigate these emotional reactions in psychiatric patients.

"Laborit's idea" that fascinated Leriche was actually more revolutionary in surgery than in psychiatry. "Anesthesia without anesthetics" had much impact on surgery and drug research in foreign countries too. Thus, in 1950, the Swiss drug house Geigy tried to find a drug that would facilitate these techniques and asked the psychiatrist Kuhn to find out if the antihistaminic dibenzazepine, G 22150, had sedative-hypnotic effects on his patients. "It had none, in most instances," said Kuhn, "it had however 'a peculiar sedating effect' on schizophrenic patients who were excited, manic or hallucinating. But we looked at this effect much too much solely from a 'limited viewpoint of sedation' and for this reason we overlooked the particular interest of such substances."

Since it is not customary to report futile attempts at the time they occur, Kuhn reported this seven years later, in 1957, together with his discovery of imipramine. His article begins with a fascinating discussion on "problems in psychopharmacology" that includes the section "pharmaco-psychopathologic research," where he explains what he means by limited viewpoint: The evaluation of substances by their inhibiting and stimulating effects is certainly practical but fraught with danger in that it "directs research along predetermined channels, binds the attention and makes one overlook what might be perhaps particularly important in order to find special psychic effects of drugs" (6).

The qualitics that differentiate CPZ from drugs previously used in psychiatry are:

1. In doses large enough to be effective, CPZ leaves consciousness unclouded. This is important in psychiatry because only conscious patients are responsive to psychotherapy—and for other obvious reasons too.

2. By inducing lack of interest in the environment, CPZ counteracts anxiety, excitement and other reactions to stress.

B. Attempts at Introducing CPZ into Psychiatry

Drugs usually drift from one field to another, by chance, depending on many specialists and what they consider necessary in their field. With CPZ it was different: Nothing was left to chance, everything to one individual, Laborit, and he jet-propelled CPZ into every field apt to benefit by an autonomic stabilizer. By November 1951 all such fields had adopted CPZ. Only one was strangely CPZ resistant—and this was psychiatry!

Psychiatrists remained adamant, even though Laborit gave valid reasons for suggesting CPZ in addition to describing its ataractic action: among other things, CPZ acted on the diencephalon and on synaptic transfer between it and cortex. He was much impressed with its deconditioning effect—it reminded him of Pavlovian deconditioning techniques. The validity of these reasons became more obvious after CPZ itself had advanced brain physiology and became known as a drug about which Pavlov might have dreamed (19)—Paris psychiatrists did not! All of Paris knew that CPZ permitted major operations with little and weak anesthetics or without any. No psychiatrist wanted to be the first to use such a drug with his patients. Their experience with drugs that were ineffective and yet quite toxic had been disappointing, dismal, or both—and by 1951 many psychiatrists were somewhat pharmacophobic. Their attitude caused a certain delay, a nuisance but historically unimportant because within a few months CPZ arrived in psychiatry.

VII. Psychopharmacology, 1952——

A. *1952*

The first psychiatrists Laborit could persuade to give the new drug a try were his own colleagues at Val-de-Grâce, Hamon, Paraire, and Velluz. They initially used CPZ in therapy of psychoses on Saturday, January 19, 1952. The first patient was Jacques Lh., 24 years old, who suffered his third severe manic attack. At both earlier occasions, in 1949 and 1951, he had been hospitalized for several months while he received shock treatments and was then discharged as moderately improved. This time it was different: After 20 days and a total of 855 mg CPZ, Jacques Lh. left the hospital to resume life outside. Colonel Paraire reported this event on February 25 at a meeting of the Société Médico-Psychologique in Paris (20)—and once more, Paris psychiatrists who long ago unchained the chained, became pioneers in liberating their patients, this time from inner torments and with a drug.

Four weeks later CPZ arrived at the psychiatric hospital St. Anne's, just a stone's throw from Val-de-Grâce. There, Delay and his group began using CPZ on March 24 (21). The experience with CPZ at St. Anne's and another from Montauban, near Toulouse, where CPZ had made an aggressive paranoic patient "charming and docile" within 3 days, were both reported on May 26 at the Centennial of the Société Médico-Psychologique in Paris (4). The occasion was glamorous and internationally important. Everybody was there and this perhaps contributed to the rapid spread of psychiatric CPZ therapy throughout Europe. No other psychiatrist accepted the new drug with quite the same enthusiasm as did Delay who, correctly evaluating the psychiatric importance of CPZ, propagated it, developed schedules for its administration and, I dare say, practically adopted it as his own. Indubitably, Delay was the most important force in assuring and hastening acceptance of CPZ.

1. Midyear

The first drug that CPZ pulled from the horizon of psychiatric interest was its clinical ancestor promethazine; and every few years, from then until now, promethazine is reintroduced into psychiatry.

Next, sleep therapy underwent a drastic change: Patients remain awake at daytime and ambulatory. The potentiating action of CPZ permits a substantial reduction in the dosage of barbiturates and this made "sleep therapy" safer and more efficient.

In the course of the single year 1952, CPZ raced through the mental hospitals of France and entered Italy. A study from Padua on 20 patients became the first Italian, the first non-French, and the only foreign publication on psychiatric CPZ therapy for 1952.

B. 1953

The atmosphere in the disturbed wards of mental hospitals in Paris was transformed! Physical restraints were a thing of the past!

Swiss psychiatrists introduced CPZ in January and the first meeting devoted entirely to psychiatric CPZ therapy was held in their country—in Basle on November 28. The great interest in CPZ stems chiefly from the fact that it was exactly the drug Staehelin had wished for since 1946. Nevertheless, it is remarkable that Swiss psychiatrists were not at all interested in reserpine, even though they had ample opportunity to be so because the most important work on reserpine had been done by Swiss workers in Basle and was already published at that time. In 1952, Swiss chemists isolated this alkaloid as the "sedative principle" of *Rauwolfia serpentina* Benth. and noted immediately that animals were easily aroused even after high doses (Müller *et al.*, 1952, September 15).

An extensive pharmacologic study by Bein was published in March, 1953. Another pharmacologic study by Bein *et al.* and the first clinical cardiologic study of reserpine, by Löffler *et al.*, both appeared on October 17, 1953—six weeks before the CPZ meeting of November 28.

It is perhaps of ancillary interest here that in Switzerland rauwolfia alkaloids entered cardiology in 1953 and psychiatry in 1954. The sequence was similar in the United States: cardiology in 1952 and psychiatry in 1954. In India, however, the sequence of events was reversed: rauwolfia was widely used in psychiatry before entering Indian cardiology.

The Basle CPZ meeting ("Largactil-Symposion") of November 28 was attended by more than fifty Swiss psychiatrists, for the most part delegates from mental hospitals. One of them was Kuhn, and his presence had an important late result.

By midyear the psychiatric revolution was well underway throughout continental Europe. News of this event stimulated psychiatric clinical studies on CPZ north of the English Channel and west of the Atlantic Ocean.

C. 1954

The resulting publications appeared now in the British Isles, North and South America. Interest was particularly keen in Canada and in the United States.

In the spring, interest in CPZ pulled yet another drug to the zenith of psychiatric interest from farther away and longer ago than promethazine—*Rauwolfia serpentina* from India's bazaars.

1. *Rauwolfia serpentina**

Rauwolfia serpentina is a glabrous shrub. It grows wild, about 3 feet tall, and has snakelike roots that are brown and about half an inch thick. The pink or white blossoms of rauwolfia beautify the Asian landscape from high up in the tropical mountains, where the shrub climbs to an altitude of 4000 feet, southeastward over the Malay peninsula down to the island of Java.

As if predestined to become a modern psychotropic drug, rauwolfia "thrives in a rich soil" and has many names: "Pagla-ka-dawa" is its popular name—it means "insanity herb" and indicates the most important use of this drug in India. In Sanskrit it is called "sarpagandha" and, varying with the regional languages, "Patala-garuda" or "Atalagandhi" in Telugu, "Karavi" in Bombay, "Chuvana-avilpori" in Malay, etc. (Chopra *et al.*, 1933).

In India, *Rauwolfia serpentina* is for sale in the baazars. The brown root, available in chunk style, about $2 \times \frac{1}{2}$ inches, or powdered is used for snakebites, stings of poisonous insects, intestinal diseases, and many other disorders. It is popular as a mild sedative for children and has been so ever since antiquity, when it was used as an ecbolic in childbirth too.

In antiquity, Ayurvedic physicians "cured" with this root insanity, epilepsy, and practically everything that ailed ancient Indians—from corneal opacities to cholera. To clear opacities of the cornea the juice of rauwolfia leaves was instilled into the afflicted eye. Cholera patients were given 3–4 tolas of rauwolfia root daily mixed with the root of *Aristolochia indica.*

Rauwolfia retained the esteem of Ayurvedic physicians and gained the appreciation of medically trained Indian psychiatrists and cardiologists. Standardized solutions of rauwolfia alkaloids, available since 1931, stimulated psychiatric research on this drug, increased the frequency of its use in mental illness (Chopra *et al.*, 1933, and many others), and initiated rauwolfia therapy of hypertensive disease (Bathia, 1942).

The Indian psychiatric literature from 1943 through 1952 is interesting in many respects. Here are but a few highlights:

The "new treatment methods" in India were shock therapies and psychosurgery. De (1950) found them far from satisfactory and thought that within the next ten years they would be replaced by still newer methods. Nonetheless, their popularity increased while, among the various indigenous Indian drugs, *Rauwolfia serpentina* was the most frequently used in mental illness. Rauwolfia-induced Parkinsonism was first observed by De in 1944, and was treated by

* See Laborit and Sanseigne, Chapter 18.

withholding the drug. Likewise disadvantageous in mental patients was the hypotensive action of this drug.

Rauwolfia therapy was frequently ineffective and only rarely successful. One decade before CPZ revolutionized psychiatry, Gupta made a controlled study on rauwolfia in 15 mental patients. He noted that in spite of the great advances in psychotherapy, psychoanalysis and hypnosis, sedatives and hypnotics occupy an important place in psychiatry and remarked on the paucity of publications on rauwolfia therapy compared to the frequency of its use. Indian psychiatrists are by far less print-prone than their Western colleagues, but their few publications show that Indian psychiatrists understood psychoses as diseases of "inner stress," that they recognized the peculiarities of the effect that rauwolfia has on psychotic patients and above all that they were fully aware of the limitations of rauwolfia compounds, alkaloids as well as powdered root (Gupta *et al.*, 1943; De, 1950; Roy, 1950, 1952). The opinion of Indian psychiatrists was eventually confirmed by American psychiatrists after intensive use of various rauwolfia compounds, including reserpine, for about five years (Lasky *et al.*, 1962).

Throughout the years 1943–1952, the decade preceding psychiatric CPZ therapy, Indian psychiatrists used rauwolfia "faute de mieux" and frequently but without enthusiasm. All were agreed that "the ideal sedative has not yet been found" (Gupta *et al.*, 1943). As mentioned earlier, the hypotensive action of rauwolfia was particularly inconvenient because "most mental patients are not hypertensive." In 1947 Gupta isolated the "hypnotic principle" from the root, a purely sedative nonhypotensive alcoholic extract of the resins. His report includes a brief account of psychiatric therapy with rauwolfia and is published in an American journal (Gupta *et al.*, 1947). It attracted no more attention than did the report of Guiraud and David on promethazine in 1950 (12). Occidental medicine acquired rauwolfia by accidental reading. Two such accidents happened, both in the United States, unrelated to each other, about 300 miles and three years apart. The first occurred in Boston when the cardiologist Wilkins happened to read an issue of the *British Heart Journal* for 1949 with an article by the Indian cardiologist Vakil on rauwolfia in the treatment of hypertensive disease. Vakil (1949) mentioned that the sedative action of this drug turned out to be a "blessing in disguise" for many of his patients. Wilkins (1952) became interested in rauwolfia, studied it and introduced it into Western cardiology in February, 1952—exactly when the first psychiatric use of CPZ was reported in Paris. Wilkins too found the sedative action of rauwolfia advantageous (Wilkins, 1952), and so did many other American cardiologists. But American psychiatrists showed no interest. Perhaps psychiatrists, in the United States as in Europe, lacked interest in another sedative or hypnotic because they had already enough "sedatives and hypnotics."

Cardiologic reports were not responsible for the introduction of rauwolfia into Western psychiatry. This took another accidental reading and it happened in New York on a spring Sunday in 1953 when the American psychiatrist Nathan Kline read the *New York Times*. By then, glowing accounts had arrived in the United States, first from France and then from other European countries, that the disturbed wards of mental hospitals in Europe had been transformed by CPZ. Now the *New York Times* brought good news from Bombay: at the VI. Gujarat and Saurashtra Provincial Medical Conference, held March 14–16, 1953, a special prize was awarded to Dr. R. A. Hakim for his paper "Indigenous Drugs in the Treatment of Mental Diseases." The indigenous drugs were from the plant *Rauwolfia serpentina*, the special prize was a gold medal, and says Kline, "In view of the tremendous paucity of pharmacological methods of treating mental disease our interest increased" (Kline, 1954).

The paucity was indeed tremendous in 1953: There was only one drug, CPZ, and by then it had revolutionized psychiatry. No such feat was ever attributed to rauwolfia, though it had been used ever since antiquity. Of course, psychiatric revolutions are rare—but so are gold medals.

The first highly effective antianxiety drug came from the United States: meprobamate. It was synthesized in 1950 (Ludwig and Piech, 1951), somewhat earlier than CPZ, and these two drugs share some clinical distinctions: Meprobamate has retained its importance for neurotic patients, just as CPZ has for psychotic patients; as CPZ was preceded by another phenothiazine derivative, so was meprobamate preceded by another propanediol derivative, mephenesin, a muscle relaxant with beneficial effects in anxiety states. The first pharmacologic study of meprobamate appeared in 1954 (cf. Berger, 1954, and Margolin and Kletzkin, Chapter 22)—four years after its synthesis—and the first clinical article in 1955 (Selling, 1955). But from then on rather quickly, meprobamate became very valuable to its takers—and its makers.

Before this eventful year drew to a close the first new stimulants arrived, pipradrol in the United States, methylphenidate in Switzerland, and—CPZ embarked on another ocean voyage westward across the Pacific to Australia.

D. 1955

The neurologist Fabing, who introduced pipradrol in 1954, brought psychiatry three additional gifts: (1) azacyclonol (Frenquel), the gamma isomer of the mild stimulant pipradrol, has an opposite effect—it is antipsychotic and is chiefly effective in postoperative psychoses; (2) bufotenine, named for its occurrence in the skin of toads, is hallucinogenic; and (3) the term "ataraxics."

The psychiatrist Osmond, contributor of the terms "hallucinogens" and "psychedelics," reported his self-experiments with the ancient Aztec drug ololiuqui, from the seeds of *Rivea corymbosa* (morning glory). Up to that time only the ancient Aztecs, the modern Mexican Indians, and Osmond had experienced psychologic effects after taking ololiuqui seeds. It is known that in other natural hallucinogens, like cannabis and cocaine, psychoactivity varies greatly with factors pertaining to the plant (geographic area, specific crop, particular batch or sample) and with the mode of intake too. This suggests that the psychoactivity of Mexican *Rivea corymbosa* varies from that grown in Cuba. Also, the mode of intake is important: Ololiuqui seeds are very hard, and it appears that in order to be psychoactive, they must be mixed with saliva and consequently either thoroughly chewed or taken pulverized, but not in capsules or swallowed whole.

The psychoactive principle of ololiuqui seeds was studied in 1937 by Santesson, who presumed that it was an alkaloid, but it defied chemical identification for twenty-three years—until 1960, when Hofmann analyzed Mexican ololiuqui seeds and isolated some LSD derivatives, the first such ergot alkaloids to be found in plants higher than mushrooms.

Studies with hallucinogens (see Cohen, Chapter 39), particularly with mescaline or LSD, became now much more frequent, rather suddenly if one considers that mescaline was in psychiatric use since 1894 and LSD since 1947. What happened? Cannabis (marijuana), another hallucinogen, antedates even mescaline by fifty years. Moreau de Tours used it then chiefly to study cannabis-induced mental symptoms, but he used it in treatment of psychotic patients too. Mescaline and LSD were at first used in therapy of mental patients more often than in self-experimentation or in normal volunteers. In therapy of psychotic patients hallucinogens were rather disappointing, but they are valued as drug aids in psychotherapy and in research: either to study the effects of hallucinogens in varying doses on artistic expression, chiefly painting, or on perception, of music too—whereas playing of instruments is not suitable for study because these drugs disturb coordination—or, in psychiatric research to induce psychosislike states in normal individuals in the hope that such "model psychoses" might reveal etiologic factors of schizophrenias.

Model psychoses are usually self-terminating in about 6–38 hours. The drug-induced symptoms disappear gradually. An earlier and quick termination is often necessary or desirable, when hallucinogens are used as drug aids in psychotherapy too. A trustworthy antidote is essential for such termination!

It has been known since Homer that drug-induced psychoses can be reversed or even prevented by another drug. In modern psychiatry barbiturates were used for this purpose. They were easier to obtain than Homer's "moly," but not always as effective. CPZ was the first modern dependable antidote. Here too, it replaced barbiturates and became the drug of choice to shut the "doors of perception" or delusion, though reserpine and azacyclonol served as antidotes too. CPZ intensified research with hallucinogens and made the use of these drugs in psychotherapy safer. Furthermore, by stimulating the introduction or synthesis of other drugs, CPZ added another function to hallucinogens, LSD in particular. LSD became the test drug for newly introduced antipsychotic and antianxiety drugs and the standard drug of comparison for other hallucinogens, with the blocking efficacy of CPZ for LSD serving as standard comparative. This is how CPZ pulled LSD from the horizon of psychiatric interest to the zenith of psychopharmacology—and LSD stayed there.

Here is its background. LSD is a one-man drug: the Swiss chemist Albert Hofmann, who synthesized it in 1943, discovered its psychologic activity too—when he accidentally inhaled some of the drug on April 16, 1943 (Stoll, 1947). One week later he made a planned self-experiment and described this experience together with the effects of his fateful sniff of the week before, in his laboratory notebook. Though Hofmann took 0.25 mg, that is 5–10 times the normally effective dose, he suffered no lasting ill effects. In fact, he became famous, but this was a late result. At first there was no happening at all—his notes remained unpublished for another four years, until the drug was studied by other volunteers and in the treatment of patients: for the first time in 1947, four full years after its synthesis. The slow start of LSD is characteristic of chance discoveries and yet surprising because for well over a century psychiatrists had used less effective drugs with LSD-like effects, chiefly mescaline and cannabis. The advantages of a standardized synthetic drug, effective in minute doses, ought to have made LSD enticing from the start—but they didn't. Even after the first publication in 1947, studies on LSD were sporadic for a long time, and then they increased slowly until 1955, when LSD came into the limelight. The total number of publications on LSD for 1947 through 1949 was 5; for 1950: 3; for 1951: 10; for 1952: 16; for 1953: 18; for 1954: 28; for 1955: 98.

The first therapeutic use of LSD in the United States was in 1950, as a drug aid in psychotherapy—in Missouri (Busch and Johnson, 1950). Animal studies came later, the first in 1951 with LSD and mescaline in the fascinating spider test by Witt, who was then in Bern, Switzerland. From then on animal studies increased rapidly. Siamese fighting fish enjoyed unprecedented popularity: LSD left them plain Siamese fish—it took the fighting out of them; water put it in again. Spiders were less lucky: LSD made them weave webs not worth catching flies with. The effects of CPZ were so touchingly reported that "59" became a favorite of little spiders all over the world. Here it is, how it appeared in *The Spider's Mother Goose:* "Once upon a time there was a little spider. Its name was '59.' One day it took a drug that made it tired and tireder. But six days later all was fine." This story was first published in a psychiatric journal, with photos—of the web, without a portrait of "59"—but of course in much more detail (Witt, 1955). Next, came journalists: about 1956 it became fashionable to take LSD for an experience to write about, as a drug aid in psychotherapy or for both purposes combined. The resulting articles appeared in the free press. This publicity, together with events that started at a Boston tea party with little tea and lots of LSD, nearly cost LSD its clinical career and psychopharmacology one of its most important research drugs.

If LSD is a one-man drug, its discoverer is a multihallucinogenic man: in 1958 Hofmann isolated psilocybin and psilocin from Mexican mushrooms and in 1960 the psychoactive principles of ololiuqui. Psilocybin is valuable in research and perhaps as a drug aid in psychotherapy, like LSD (Hofmann, 1961).

Jacobsen, the Danish physician of disulfiram fame (1948), discovered the psychoactivity of benactyzine, studied it pharmacologically and introduced the new antianxiety drug into psychiatry. In 1956 the drug came to England, where its mildly antidepressant quality was first noted (Davies, 1956), and in 1957 it arrived in the United States. In 1958 it was found that benactyzine in combination with meprobamate is particularly effective in the treatment of depression (Alexander, 1958) and benactyzine is now chiefly so used, as Deprol.

Early in 1955 psychiatric CPZ therapy arrived in Russia and was equally well received there as everywhere else. CPZ brought great improvements in therapy and research (19). The changes in therapy were less radical than elsewhere because Russian psychiatry was already dominated by Pavlovian ideas—

whereas in other countries the success of drug therapy narrowed the gulf between biologic and psychodynamic factions of psychiatry.

In October, the first international meeting on "CPZ and other neuroleptic drugs in psychiatric therapy" was held in Paris. At the first psychiatric use of CPZ, the Val-de-Grâce group predicted that "the gamut of psychotropic drugs would soon enrich psychiatry," and a few months later these authors foresaw "extramural drug therapy after short-term hospitalization" (20). In less than three years both predictions had come true. The gamut of psychotropic drugs was visibly present.

E. 1956

The tranquilizer turmoil was on. Drugs came and went. Some went faster than they came. But many more had come than gone by then—at least 40 antipsychotic and antianxiety drugs, nearly half of them phenothiazines, 7 stimulants, and 18 hallucinogens. Some were old, some were new, and one was both: promazine, "the drug with a past" and a curiosity as drugs go in that it is clinically an offspring and chemically an ancestor of CPZ: as compound RP-3276, promazine had played a brief but glorious role in 1950 in the synthesis of CPZ in Paris—the psychiatric revolution was triggered by *one* chlorine atom!

F. 1957

The discoverer of a very important drug tells in his first report on the new drug how his discovery came about: seven years before, in 1950, a drug house asked him to investigate one of their compounds for its potential sedative-hypnotic action in mental patients. The expected sedative effects were disappointing, but he noticed that schizophrenic patients, who were excited, manic, or hallucinating, felt some relief and became less disturbed. He attributed no significance to the drug's "peculiar sedative action"—and terminated its trial.

Three years later he attended the CPZ meeting of November 28, 1953, in Basle. There he heard the reports of other Swiss psychiatrists, who by that time had nearly a year's experience with this drug and, even more important, he saw CPZ in action! "Why is it that hallucinations lose their threatening nearness, recede into distance and manic ideas cease to bother the patient? Other sedatives do not have such effects and this already seems to indicate that the sedative inhibiting effects alone cannot be the decisive principle that affects the disease." Because of his experience at the Basle meeting, he says in his report, and because this experience enabled him to see his observations of 1950 in an entirely different light, he began to investigate, early in 1954, once more, the very same compound whose clinical trial he abandoned in 1950, and other compounds of the same chemical group. His investigation lasted over three years. Several of the compounds he tried proved effective in the treatment of endogenous psychoses. The autonomic effects of these compounds were rather similar to those of phenothiazines and their sedative-hypnotic action appeared to be weaker. In all that time he found no compound that could fully replace

CPZ. One compound, however, had a property that is missing in CPZ and it had favorable effects in depressive states (6). It was imipramine, an excellent antidepressant and particularly important because safe antidepressants are rare.

International efforts to make a drug just like or even better than CPZ has resulted in several excellent drugs now available for the treatment of major mental illness: butyrophenones, other phenothiazines, and even an antidepressant, imipramine. Though one or another of the newer antipsychotics has advantages for certain patients or specific symptoms, CPZ is still unsurpassed and nearly peerless. Drug therapy is most dramatic in psychotic patients—but drugs for minor mental symptoms are equally important: They might prevent psychosomatic illness and in situations of acute stress they can be lifesaving.

For further reading and references see Appendices 1 and 2.

3

CROSS-CULTURAL USES OF PSYCHOACTIVE DRUGS (ETHNOPSYCHOPHARMACOLOGY)*†

Marvin K. Opler

I. Introduction

Most persons in modern societies consume drugs of one type or another through doctor's prescriptions, widespread drugstore sale of pain relievers, or grocery and liquor store sales of items like coffee, tea, tobacco, and alcoholic products. It is less known that drug usage is also common in a number of nonliterate societies and has been since prehistory and in modern times, such as hashish among urban slum dwellers of Egypt or India, and in special instances, substances such as peyote among the Indians, from Aztec Mexico to tribes of the North American plains. There are also the mushrooms used by Indians of southern Mexico containing psilocybin (cf. Cohen, Chapter 39), and

* The author wishes to acknowledge with thanks the suggestions of Dr. Richard E. Schultes of the Botanical Museum, Harvard University. This work was supported by a grant from the Wenner Gren Foundation for Anthropological Research, 1964, also gratefully acknowledged.

† The Editors have rearranged the authors' sections by broad pharmacological effects of the agents, and added tobacco and caffeine.

many other naturally occurring stimulants, hallucinogens, and depressants, only a few of which can be touched on here.

II. Stimulants

A. *Amphetamine Addictions*

F. Lemere (1963) described a high incidence of *amphetamine* addiction in Japan, apparently the result of widespread use of such energizers during World War II and easy availability of "pep pills" following the war (cf. Bloomquist, Chapter 38). In some countries, the United States, for example, energizers are alternated with barbiturates to produce, respectively, exhilaration and quiescence. Lemere's account indicated that chronic psychoses occurred in many of the Japanese addicts if the drug had been used for a long time with consequent organic brain damage. Other than the Japanese case there is little cross-cultural material on responses to amphetamine energizing, probably because of its urban rather than folk derivation and usage.

B. *Tobacco*

Probably the most widely used member of the *Solanaceae* family is *tobacco* (*Nicotiana tobacum*). Its first introduction into the many cultures of the world from the New World has largely been as a *medicine.* In the pre-Columbian Americas it was smoked in pipes, chewed, and snuffed, by itself or in combination with hallucinogenic snuffs.

Its origin in Europe as a *medicine* has been ascribed to Jean Nicot, French Ambassador to Portugal in 1559. He was said to have obtained it as a gift from friends in Florida, and grew it in a garden, from which it spread throughout Europe as a drug for skin ulcers, asthma, and many other ailments.

One item of interest here is the early claim that it was a "tranquilizer," since Jean Nicot was said to have told Catherine de Medici, Queen of France, that tobacco smoke led to "a quiet tranquility and great submissiveness of disposition, so that through its general use, Her Majesty's subjects would become easy to govern." A number of writers from that time also characterized it as having tranquilizing effects (see Larson *et al.*, Appendix 1).

In the middle 1860's accounts appeared on the use of tobacco for epilepsy, apoplexy, hysterical convulsions, sedative, Parkinson's disease, and other nervous system disorders (see Appendix 1). Much of this no doubt was due to suggestion and/or placebo effects, and the smoking of tobacco was not done for its depressant or excitatory effect, but more probably because of pleasure derived from labial and visual sensory effects, and in primitive societies for ritual purposes, such as the use among early American Indians, and in combination with hallucinogenic snuffs among South American tribes.

C. *Pituri*

The Australian aborigine's use of pituri (pitchuri) is similar to that of tobacco. It is used as leaves of the *Duboisia hopwoodii* (*Solanaceae*) a shrub or dwarf tree, peculiar to Australian deserts. The leaves are collected during the flowering stage and are dried and sometimes smoked over the fire. When later mixed with ash of acacia wood, a wad or quid of cigar shape and 2 inches long is prepared, which is carried around for occasional chewing. When not in use, the Australian native carries it behind the ear like a clerk's pencil. After considerable chewing, the remaining wad is finally swallowed. Pituri was also used in trade or barter outside its desert habitat and exchanged for valued objects such as boomerangs, red ochre paint, spears, and throwing sticks and later for blankets or other imported trade goods. In Australian tribes, the plant may be used by women, but its more common purpose was for reducing hunger or the need for water in the desert and in lessening the effects of fatigue through its brief stimulant properties. The active ingredient is nornicotine, which has actions similar to nicotine, although small amounts of scopolamine also are present.

D. Coca Leaf

The use of a cocaine produced by chewing *coca leaves* in South America's Inca civilization illustrates one typical way certain American Indians approached psychoactive agents. At the height of the Empire, a postal system existed with Indian runners carrying messages from one post station to the next. The Empire of 2000 miles north to south included the high Andes and was linked by suspension bridges over mountain passes requiring the runners to move at fast speeds in high altitude for many miles. Coca leaves were chewed as a nonaddictive agent by the runners to produce the characteristic sense of exhilaration and temporary high energy output. Since coca leaf chewing appears to involve a slow rate of drug release (contrasted with subcutaneous injections), no addictive effect was reported, although leaf chewing does have a possibility of psychological habituation. Certain rules were binding upon the runners to take the plant product in its raw state before the physical ordeal and then only later, while actually running. Because such running was arduous, the messengers were committed to their work only for a limited period. There were no hallucinations of a visual, auditory, or tactile type, as with modern cocaine addicts, probably because small-dose ingestion was followed by intense physical activity, and also because, typically, the weaker raw products were used "in the Indian way" for a serious purpose. Coca is also snuffed in the Amazonian region of Colombia. The active ingredient is cocaine.

E. Caffeine

Caffeine, theophylline, and theobromine are closely related methylated xanthene alkaloids which occur in plants the world over, which have been used as CNS stimulants since prehistory, usually as beverages. The commonest ones are *coffee,* from the bean of the tree *Coffea arabica,* which probably originated among the ancient Arabs, and which contains caffeine (from the Arab word for wine); *tea,* from the leaves of the tree *Thea sinensis,* which originated in China, and which contains caffeine, theophylline (from the Greek "divine leaf"), and theobromine (from the Greek "divine food"); *cocoa,* cacao, or chocolate, from the seeds of the *Theobroma cacao,* containing caffeine and theobromine, and which originated in South America; kola or gura nuts of the tree *Cola acuminata,* chewed by the natives of the Sudan, which contain caffeine and theobromine, and from which the cola "soft drinks" derived their name because they were originally made from these nuts; *yerba maté* or Paraguay tea, popular drink in South America, from *Ilex paraguayensis,* containing caffeine; *guarana paste* from *Paullinea cupana* in Brazil; and *Apalache* tea or Youpan, from another species of *Ilex* in Virginia and the Carolinas, both containing caffeine. The popularity of these drinks as stimulants, which brighten the intellect and dispel mental and physical fatigue, is testified to by the estimated consumption of over 5.5 million pounds of coffee per year in the United States alone. No doubt the consumption of tea in Asia greatly surpasses this. These stimulant plants thus are no doubt by far the most commonly used psychopharmacological agents aside from alcohol.

F. Khat (or Quat, Q'at, and Chat)

In Somaliland, Kenya, Abyssinia, Ethiopia, and the eastern parts of the Arabian Peninsula the leaves of the tree *Cathala edulis* are chewed for a mild stimulant effect. It is claimed that in Abyssinia its use is older than coffee, the oldest reference to it being in 1333. Like the coca of the Andes Indians, the plant is valued for its properties in combating fatigue. The Ameru people of Kenya who refer to this as "*miraa*" also value it as an energizer which led one chemist in Nairobi to the discovery that it contained active alkaloids in the bark and in the leaves. In the markets in Kenya, Ethiopia, and Aden, bundles of fresh leaves and twigs are sold to be used in making teas or for chewing. In Ethiopia it is also added to a fermented honey-mead, a potent intoxicant. Chemically the active constituents were comparable to the drug ephedrine, the most common one being pseudo-norisophedrine. Heavy use of khat was said to be harmful because of large quantities of tannin and other substances harmful to digestive processes.

The psychiatrist J. C. Carothers, writing on the excessive use of *miraa* as a cause of insanity, mentioned the chewing of plant stems and leaves, and the swallowing of the juice as producing auditory hallucinations and elated states in some subjects, and described these mild manias as related to a schizophreniclike behavior. Other accounts speak of highly excitable states of mind and these have been mentioned especially by writers commenting on the current drug use in Aden and Yemen among native tribal warriors. It is exported to Aden from Ethiopia in large quantities by air, and one report claims this export as the beginnings of the Ethiopian Airlines.

In Somaliland, the khat chewer obtains the product in markets where banana leaves are used as a sign or trademark, and are used to wrap the khat to keep it fresh. Somali poetry also exalts the properties of this plant. In Israel it is claimed that immigrating Jews from Yemen often plant new patches of khat when they first settle. While Moslem custom forbids the use of alcohol, khat gardens of the *Celastraceae* family of plants are cultivated in the lowlands and grow naturally in the highlands regions, and there are no cultural barriers to the use of the product.

The amphetamine-like alkaloids of the plant would be toxic in large amounts, but this is inhibited by tannins present. The proponents of khat point out that it is rich in vitamin C, and the World Health Organization estimated that 100 gm of fresh leaves and twigs may contain over 150 mg of ascorbic acid. Other vitamins are also present. In the Ethiopian and Moslem literature, khat is claimed to be an aphrodisiac. It can also produce loss of appetite, gastritis, and other gastrointestinal disturbances. Cirrhosis of the liver has been implicated, but has not been proved. The khat chewing is not done in isolation, but typically in groups. As a stimulant, it is probable that the substance leads to habituation more often than to addiction, and it is also possible that the group or social uses provide some barrier against drug dependency. High doses do produce uncoordinated and even paralytic states.

G. *Stimulants Used in Central Asian Folk Societies*

The medicinal properties of plants used in folk societies in the Soviet Union have been the subject of research of the All-Union Institute of Medicinal and Aromatic Plants under the U.S.S.R. Ministry of Public Health (V.I.L.A.R.). The V.I.L.A.R. project is a program which concentrates on seeking new medicinal plants which are then grown in a specialized botanical garden. Deriving from cultures in the Kazakhstan and Central Asian area, securinine and echinopsine have been developed as effective central nervous system stimulants by Russian scientists. Comprehensive pharmacological, neurophysiological, and chemical analysis of these products are made.

III. Hallucinogens*

A. *Peyote*

Among the hallucinogenic phenylethylamines, the most prominent in American Indian usage was derived from the buttons of the *peyote* cactus, *Lophophora williamsii.* The common term, mescaline, derives not from the mescal cactus but from the tribal name of the Mescalero Apaches, one of three eastern Apache tribes who used peyote buttons. The original peyote religious ritual was developed among Mexican Indian tribes, such as the Tarahumara, who passed it north of the Rio Grande to a great number of peoples in the Southwest, such as Apaches, Navajos, and Pueblo Indians, and to the many tribes of the Great Basin, such as Ute and Paiute, as well as to the Plains Indian areas. The original spread coincided with attempts to revive older cultural values after these various people were defeated and placed in the demoralizing conditions of early reservation life. Again, the peyote button in its raw state was regarded as a specific gift to Indians which should be approached only for the serious religious purposes of raising morale and also curing sick individuals who ask the cult for help.

* See Cohen, Chapter 39.

Later, in the Plains area, the Indians' Native American Church continued to import the buttons from Mexico under the banner of freedom of religion, while elsewhere nativistic peyote cults flourished separately in the Great Basin and among the Southwest tribes already mentioned.

Hallucinatory visions are possible, especially with color enhancement, and the ceremonies continue through the night with a closing part for greeting the sunrise in the morning. The buttons are chewed in raw state, or in mashed form, or prepared in soup.

With non-Indians, the effects of taking the refined chemical substance mescaline was described first by Arthur Heffter, then such writers and scientists as Aldous Huxley, Havelock Ellis, and S. Weir Mitchell, in relatively high dosages of 0.5 and 0.6 gm by mouth. With Indians, possibly depending on body weight and physical condition, as well as the size of the buttons, hallucinogenic effects are achieved by chewing from three to five or so buttons. The night-long ceremony accommodates 1 to 2 hours of nausea, sweating, and distortions of time and vision as the experience deepens. The closing songs in peyote rites may accompany peak experiences in hallucinatory visions in the early morning. Possibly partly because of the frequent occurrence of vomiting, the morning section of the ceremony is typically followed by a feast.

B. Marihuana and Hashish

These drugs are preparations from the *Cannabis sativa* or hemp plant known by many additional names such as *bhang, ganja,* and *charas.* The fertilized female flowers, and sometimes leaves and stems, are smoked for intoxicating effects, chiefly a sense of exhilaration with some distortion of perception of space and a loss of the sense of time. Nonchronic users have commented on an intense hunger for food, especially sweets, while other studies have indicated a lessening of sexual tensions. Besides the disorientation in space and time which is possible, protracted users report ataxia, drowsiness, and nystagmus (involuntary oscillation of the eyeballs). In the Middle East and North Africa where strong forms of the drug, called *hashish,* are often used by many persons taking large amounts from childhood on, chronic users may have psychotic experiences reflecting a depressive affect, with tachycardia and severe sweating (cf. Cohen, Chapter 39).

C. Siberian Native Use of Fly Agaric

Fly Agaric (*Amanita muscaria*) is a mushroom which grows throughout northern Europe and Asia and when eaten is reported to induce a few hours of semiconscious sleep followed by 3 or 4 hours of exhilaration and hallucinatory visions. As an energizer, its ingestion also induces great physical activity. Small doses are necessary because larger ones can produce delirium and convulsions followed by death. The main centers of its usage were among tribes of western and northeastern Siberia, the Ostyak, Vogul, Selkup, Ket, Chukchee, the Koryak, and the Kamchadal. Recent work by the Swiss pharmacologists. S. P. Waser and C. Eugster (see Waser in Efron *et al.,* Appendix 1) suggests that one active ingredient, *muscimol* (agarin), was not destroyed in the kidneys, but rather was excreted in the urine. Some of the Siberian tribes collected the urine after taking Fly Agaric and used it again. Besides muscimol, Fly Agaric also contains ibotenic acid and muscazon, some belladonna-like alkaloids, muscarine, acetylcholine, and possibly some hydroxyindoles such as bufotenine. The hallucinogenic action, however, may be due, at least partly, to the first three substances named above.

In ancient Indo-Aryan tradition mention is made of the cult of the *soma.* The plant was referred to in the Sacred archaic Sanscrit hymns of the *Rig Veda* as a divine inebriant, which became lost in legend. Other terms in the literature are derived from Haoma. A term sometimes used in the literature for this hallucinogen is *Soma puhari.* The Vedic hymns refer to an exhilarating and exciting effect. In the *Rig Veda,* Soma is also the name of an important deity. Marvelous and heroic deeds are attributed to him. This material has also been described as being "stored in jars or vats" and later used in ceremonies which produce exhilaration in the subjects. Recent research by Wasson (in Efron *et al.*) has indicated that Fly Agaric is the soma substance referred to in the *Rig Veda.*

D. Aztec Use of the Mexican Morning-Glory

The Mexican morning glory, *Rivea corymbosa,* of the Convolvulaceae family, is also known as the ancient Aztec narcotic ololiuqui. The brown lentil-like seeds, which are bitter in taste, may be mashed with a mortar and pestle. The Aztecs traditionally were allowed to take ololiuqui privately with only an Aztec doctor present for its pain-killing properties. Large amounts of the morning glory seeds, of which there are many species, including our own cultivated ornamental flowers, often contain an active hallucinogenic principle. E. C. Parsons, in 1926, in her study of "Mitla: Town of Souls" describes the drinking of an infusion of leaves or the eating of about 13 seeds as causing a trancelike sleep preceded by "intoxication" and leading into the state of visual hallucinations at its peak (in about three hours) during which the subject had visions which led him to perceive and locate lost objects.

E. Use of Narcotic Snuffs in South America

A potent narcotic snuff, commonly known as *epéna* and made from the bark of the *epéna* and *ama asita* (or *Virola*) trees is sniffed through blowpipe tubes by the Waika Indians of northern Brazil and several other South American tribes. One way of taking the snuff is done with the aid of a helper, who blows the material into the subject's nasal passages. The subject may be dizzy and retch at first, but soon marked hallucinations occur characterized by the subject's feeling that both he and the natural world around him have grown to enormous size.

Paricá, which is a similar product, is inhaled by the Pairoa, Tukáno, and other South American Indians of southern Venezuela. This product has three major ingredients, two of a type found in brain tissue: 6-methoxytetrahydroharman, found in the pineal gland, and 6-methoxyharmalan, which can be formed from melatonin, the principle hormone of the pineal. A third ingredient chemically similar in action to energizers having an intoxicating effect, namely, β-carbolines, which include harmine, harmaline, and tetrahydroharmine, which are monoamine oxidase inhibitors, thus acting as antidepressants or "energizers" (see Horita, Chapter 20; Crane, Chapter 50). Paricá has been identified as coming from several plants, notably species of virola (*Virola calophylla* Warburg in Colombia, Peru, Venezuela, and Brazil and *Virola calophylloidea* Markgraf, also in Colombia and Brazil), although other species of this plant may possibly be used. The Indian terms *ya-kee* and *ya-to,* come from native languages, as does the term paricá by which snuff is known among the Tukáno Indians in the Rio Negro-Uapes area of Brazil. The Tukáno Indians use paricá in addition to tobacco, coca, and *caapi* and make snuff from the fresh tree resin after drying and pulverizing it. In some admixtures the ashes from the bark of the wild cacao tree are added to the powder.

Another intoxicating snuff made from the leguminous seeds of *Piptadenia peregrina,* is called *yopo* by non-Tukanoan tribes principally inhabiting certain western tributaries of the Orinoco River in Colombia and Venezuela.

Ethnographic collections include sniffing tubes obtained from tribes of the Llanos region, the Negro River, and the Orinoco drainage. The Waika, mentioned above, reside in the Rio Negro drainage of Brazil bordering Venezuela. These people have no intoxicating drinks, but use the epéna resin in powdered form. The myristicaceous snuffs are now believed to be more widely used than either tobacco or the seeds of *Piptadenia peregrina* or *Anadenanthera,* including its bark. Other plants like *mashihiri* are also mixed with épena, the former being identified as *Justicia pectoralis stenophylla.*

Tubes throughout the region vary from the long blowpipe length to smaller tubular bones and Y-shaped or forked tubes, which can be operated by placing one end in the mouth and the other in a nostril. Those who have studied the use of the resin of the myristicaceous tree, virola, distinguish it from the separate use of snuffs made from the leguminous tree *Piptadenia peregrina,* which apparently is used in the Colombian regions of the Orinoco.

The most reliable chemical investigations so far have identified the snuffs as being indole derivatives. The occurrence of tryptamine derivatives related to serotonin is also of considerable interest because the latter compound is a much-studied brain amine. Disturbances in indole metabolism have been suggested in psychiatric studies as discussed elsewhere in this text. Unfortunately, experimental evidence for the psychoactive effects of paricá and bufotenine, its main constituent, is still meager. As for epéna and the various snuff inhalants, the reports indicate their use for prolonged periods, intermittently during 8–10 hours. The pharmacology of paricá has not been well studied, but it is generally accepted that it has stimulating and exciting effects on the users.

F. Harmine in Ayahuasca: Caapi

Besides *epéna,* various references are found in the literature for harmine substances from South America under the general name of *caapi.* Caapi is a woody climber known botanically as *Banisteria caapi,* of the family *Malpighiaceae,* which grows in the northwestern regions of South America. Several tribes, for example the Tukáno, Turianas, Guahibos, Zaparos, Augutéros, and Mazánes, make a drink of caapi stems for feasts and religious ceremonies. After a few drinks the Indians reach an excitatory stage for about ten minutes during which hallucinations occur. Shamans also use caapi drinks to produce visual hallucinations and dreams which are said to contain supernatural intelligence. Often recorded is a feeling of lightness or of taking an aerial voyage. The liana or vine grows to a height of several feet and attaches to the trunks of trees. It is found in Colombia, Bolivia, Ecuador, Peru, and also in southern Venezuela and western Bolivia. In the eastern part of this habitat, that is, in the Colombia, Bolivia, and Venezuela areas, the natives call the plant caapi, whereas in Ecuador and Peru its name is *ayahuasca* (meaning "deadman's vine"); those in southern Colombia use the designation *yagé* or *yajé.*

The alkaloid of caapi was originally called *telepathine.* Later this was identified as harmine and the earlier terms were dropped in the scientific literature.

G. Ibogaine

Ibogaine (Bogadin), is an alkaloid present in the roots of the shrub *Tabernanthe iboga* Baillon, indigenous to French equatorial Africa, which are chewed by the Oubanghi natives of the Gabon regions for its CNS excitatory effects during religious rituals. Its native name is *iboga.* Besides the religious experience of ecstacy, iboga is used to obtain increased physical powers or as a temporary stimulant. Probably, however, its chief and most active use was in secret societies for which the individual's vision of particular animals or birds is taken as an indication of a cult to which he should belong. The drug effects also have some slight anticonvulsant properties. The stimulant has been isolated as ibogaine hydrochloride.

H. Nutmeg and Mace

Two familiar spices, *nutmeg* and *mace,* come from the nutmeg tree *Myristica fragrans.* The main nutmeg tree of the family Myristicaeae was originally a native of the East Indian Archipelago, but is now cultivated throughout the eastern islands of Indonesia, the islands of Malaysia, in the Caribbean, notably on Grenada, and in Ceylon. There are also about one-hundred species, particularly in Malaysia and India. The use of nutmeg is well known in native Hindu medicine, where the nutmeg was prescribed for various fevers and respiratory tract diseases such as tuberculosis and asthma as well as for heart disease. Arab physicians used it for disorders of the digestive system, kidneys, and lymphatic system. In addition nutmeg was used for its sedative and analgesic effects and in smaller doses to produce a mild hypnotic state in hysterical children. The corresponding Malaysian practices designate nutmeg for use in functional mental disorders. In the Moslem world, additional uses included its analgesic effects. It also is mentioned as an aphrodisiac, a usage preserved even today among the men of Yemen. The production of the plant has more recently spread to the Caribbean. The Hindu designation in Ayurvedic medicine lists nutmeg as a narcotic fruit or *Mada shaunda.* Today in India this is added to betel chewing to obtain intoxicating effects. Space and time distortions similar to those caused by marihuana are commonly reported by various users of nutmeg in the American scene, especially by prisoners, musicians, and beatniks ("hippies"), though the latter seem to be far less frequent than with drugs like mescaline.

Pharmacological accounts also refer to volatile oils of mace, which is a covering within the husk but outside the nutmeg seed, as well as from the seed itself. In addition, nutmeg "butter" is composed primarily of triglycerides containing myristic acid as the principal compound. The pharmacological effects stem from the oil of the nutmeg. Myristicin, the most common active ingredient, has mild monoamine oxidase inhibitory activity, but this probably does not contribute to the intoxicating effect. There is evidence that the active components can be converted to amphetamine-like compounds *in vivo* which have potent mescaline-like hallucinogenic activity in man.

I. Jimson Weed

Jimson weed grows throughout the North American continent. It is not certain if it originated as an Old World species or is a New World plant. In the United States the commonest species are *Datura stramonium* or *D. meteloids;* all *Datura* are of Solanaceae family. In the Aztec literature a species of plant, *Datura,* was known as *toloa,* from which the Mexican term *toloache* is derived. The term toloache refers to a divine induction of sleep, and the plant found in the Valley of Mexico is still known by illiterate tribes of that region as a local anesthetic. The Aztec priests used a datura to "pacify" their sacrificial victims at the temples. The plant has an herbaceous stem and may grow to a meter in height with large single flowers occurring apically. In Germany and England, *Datura stramonium* is commonly known as thorn apple or spiny apple.

Pharmacologically the activity is due to an alkaloid mixture of atropine, scopolamine, and hyoscyamine. Large doses of it produce a central *excitation* which frequently is followed by depression and bulbar paralysis. Psychological effects of intoxication are psychotomimetic alterations in which one loses orientation and has visual hallucination. The plant is also dangerous to browsing animals through overintoxication. The English term Jimson weed derives from "James-town Weed," after the settlement in Virginia (Jamestown).

> In 1676 a rather hungry contingent of British redcoats arrived in Jamestown, Virginia, to quell an uprising known as Bacon's Rebellion. While bivouacked there, the soldiers gathered some young plants and cooked themselves a tasty potherb. They called the plants the James Town weed; botanists classify the species as *Datura stramonium.* The consequences of this historic meal are to be found in Robert Beverly's *History and Present State of Virginia:* "The James-town Weed (which resembles the Thorny Apple of Peru, and I take to be the Plant so call'd) is supposed to be one of the greatest Coolers in the World. This being an early Plant was gather'd very young for a boil'd salad, by some of the Soldiers sent thither, to pacifie the Troubles of *Bacon;* and some of them eat plentifully of it, the Effect of which was a very pleasant Comedy; for they turn'd natural Fools upon it for several Days. One would blow up a Feather in the

> Air: another would dart Straws at it with much Fury; and another stark naked was sitting in a Corner, like a Monkey, grinning and making Mows at them; a Fourth would fondly kiss, and paw his Companions and snear in their Faces, with a Countenance more antick, than any in a *Dutch* Droll. In this frantick Condition they were confined, lest they should in their Folly destroy themselves; though it was observed that all their Actions were full of Innocence and good Nature. Indeed, they were not very cleanly; for they would have wallow'd in their own Excrements, if they had not been prevented. A Thousand such simple Tricks they play'd, and after Eleven Days, return'd themselves again, not remembering any thing that had pass'd."
>
> The narcotic properties of the James Town, or Jimson, weed soon became known to the colonists, as they had been known to our southern Indians, perhaps for centuries. American Indians, both north and south of the equator, employed various forms of daturas in their religious ceremonies, often as a means of promoting visions. The Indians of Virginia used *Datura stramonium* to intoxicate the young men of the tribe during initiation ceremonies" [from *The Sciences* 3: 10 (1963)].

Among Indians of the American West whose religions included the vision quest, toloache and Jimson weed was used in organized ceremonies for initiates to obtain supernatural power. A. L. Kroeber reported that California tribes boiled another species of *Datura* leaves in salted water to gain strength in battle, good luck in hunting, and immunity from bear bites or snakebites. The Diegueno Indians used still another species in a puberty ceremony, whereas the Incas of Peru employed another datura as an anesthetic in surgery. However, the plant was also reported to have been used in ancient Greece by the priests of the temple of Apollo and by the women oracles at Delphi to induce semihypnotic delirium. A local datura is in current use (abuse) by the "drug-happy" element. Also, misuse of medicated cigarettes containing belladonna and stramonium for asthma, has been growing in the United States, Canada, and England.

Because of its chemical composition, the drug induces thirst, dilation of the pupils, and behavioral excitation. While some sedative and analgesic effects are noted, there are often accounts of excitation, hallucinations, and even convulsions and death, indicating that variations in dosage can lead to delirium in a wide spectrum of religious usage. In Moslem history, the drug was reported to produce stupor in the victims of criminal acts. During Mark Anthony's campaign against the Parthians in Asia Minor in A.D. 36, the troops resorted to eating unknown plants, one of which was "thorn apple" (which the Egyptians also knew). As a result, some of them "went mad and died, and whoever recovered forgot all that he hitherto had done and recognized nothing."

J. Mandrake

Also among plants of the potato family *mandrake,* an herb of the genus *Mandragora* (Solanaceae), has been listed since ancient times as a potent hallucinogenic agent, once termed a "drug of the devil." Thought to have been used in witchcraft, the mandrake root was also used as an aphrodisiac, analgesic, hypnotic, cathartic, and fertility-inducing agent in women. In fact the "male mandrake" was represented both in phallic root shape and in male human form to signify its use for love potions. One of the contemporary medieval authorities on witchcraft, de Lancre linked the concepts of magic, poison, and drug indiscriminately. It is now thought that the deliria evoked by drugs as well as the vivid pictures of "Witches' Sabbaths" were connected with such hallucinatory experiences. Among other constituents it contains belladonna alkaloids.

K. *Loco Plants (Effects on Animals)*

Both the Indians of the western United States and northern Mexico as well as the later cattle breeders in these regions classify certain plants of the pea family (*Fabaceae*) growing in the prairies as having strange effect (hence its inclusion here as an hallucinogen) on animals. These are the *locoweeds* or loco plants and they are known to have accounted for extensive mortality among cattle. There are several species such as the *Astragalus* and *Oxytropis* (commonly called locoweed). When the grazing animal has eaten a large amount, it becomes irritable and separates from the rest of the herd or else continues to feed hungrily on the plant. Reports indicate death occurs after "running loco," spastic paralysis, respiratory irregularity, and cramps, the death often caused by respiratory syncope. It is interesting that these plants were never utilized in human rituals by native peoples, although they had knowledge of their strange effects on animals.

IV. Depressants

A. *Metatabi or Matatabi*

Metatabi derives from the Asiatic woody vine *Actinidia polygama* of the family Actinidiaceae and for which the chief interest is, as in the case of locoweed reported above, in connection with animals. Both the Chinese and Japanese know of this plant as a sedative for large species of the cat family such as leopards and lions.

In addition, it contains a substance related to the volatile oil of *catnip* in the aromatic plant (*Nepeta cataria*). The Japanese regarded this as a general tonic for diseases of cat. The Chinese herbalists also used metatabi for colic which was given in solution in rice wine or sake. According to one Japanese report, it has a sedative action and it depresses the limbic system, especially the hippocampus and hypothalamus tracts, in doses of 10–15 mg intravenous. In addition, such doses in man may produce some anxiety, a distortion of body image, visual hallucinations involving body movement, but all of these effects without disorientation or loss of reality contact. No systematic neurophysiological, pharmacological, or neurochemical correlates of the behavioral effects of this class of compounds have been made, nor of the chemically related agents in catnip.

B. *Opioid Addiction*

Opium is prepared from the latex of poppy capsules (*Papaver somniferum*). The opium alkaloids belong chemically to two separate groups, the addictive alkaloids morphine, codeine, and thebaine, which are phenanthrene derivatives, and the nonaddictive alkaloids, which include papaverine, are isoquinolines, and exert their principal action on smooth muscle. The use of opium is often found in cultural situations where there are strict social curbs on individualized and independent activities. Overseas Chinese living in metropolitan slums such as in Hong Kong have been targets of the opium trade, although the more violent acting out behavior from heavy alcohol use is not tolerated in this group. Similarly in Negro urban populations of the United States where prejudice and discrimination provide social barriers, opioid addictions may occur. In neither the overseas Chinese nor the Negro ghettos do any sizable proportion of slum dwellers become addicts. In fact, the sale of opium has been found to be even more widespread under conditions of colonialism where the target population is provided easy accessibility to the destructive effects of the drug. The Bureau of Narcotics in a 1963 report noted that since 1955 addicts have numbered less than fifty thousand and notes an addition of about eight-thousand persons annually along with an equally large annual reduction. The property of morphine in reducing pain or providing a euphoric sense of mental clouding has never been reported to vary from one cultural situation to another.

C. *Cross-Cultural Discovery of an Antipsychotic Agent, Reserpine**

Two widely separate primitive systems of medicine, one in India and the other in Nigeria, independently discovered for the world the uses of reserpine. In both instances, one deriving from Ayurvedic medicine in India and the other from cult practices of tribal Yoruban curing priests, this plant was used for hypertension in continuative small doses and for confusional and catathymic outbursts in larger doses intended to sedate the patient. The Yoruban native curers also placed the patient in shackles attached to the feet, but with reserpine they were able to remove these within 24–28 hours and proceed with other methods of psychotherapy.

While India is usually credited with the discovery of reserpine, and, indeed, the Indian herbalists and practitioners of the Ayurvedic System of Medicine first made known this product, spearheading the use of "wonder drugs" and tranquilizers in the modern world, this was only because fewer contacts were made with Yoruban herbalists by ethnobotanists and pharmacologists. The Yoruban practice of using tranquilizers is equally sophisticated in matters of dosage varying with age and body weight of the patient and his degree of excitatory behavior. As is well known, reserpine therapy has been used cross-culturally for agitated states, whether or not associated with toxic or confusional syndromes, and has been employed in epileptic psychoses as well as those due to mental deficiency, where psychomotor disturbances are predominant. Reserpine was equally useful in West Africa in acute manic states and in the above-mentioned confusional and catathymic excitement found more typically in Nigeria, where a West African species of rauwolfia was used in the raw state.

* See Caldwell, Chapter 2; Laborit and Sanseigne, Chapter 18.

D. *Kava, A Ceremonial Drink in Polynesia*

The plant *Piper methysticum*, a shrub of the pepper family, is used in Polynesia in a brew made from the root or the root is simply chewed. Originally the drink was made by village virgins chewing the root and spitting out the saliva stimulated by the material, and collecting it. The dry powder can be mixed with water to produce a pungently tasting beverage. Captain Cook describes the ceremonial use of passing around bowls of kava in formal greetings in Fiji. Native use is most moderate, but excessive ingestion is said to produce scaly skin, eye trouble, and weight loss.

The central nervous and peripheral effects of kava are believed due to the pyrone content of the plant, but this is contended (see Efron *et al.*).

Chemical and pharmacological studies of kava have indicated that the main pharmacological action is similar to that of CNS relaxants of the mephenesin type, but relatively inactive compared with modern synthetic products. The effects produced include a pleasant, relaxing, soporific effect accompanied by an enjoyable parethesia (see Efron *et al.*, for pharmacological effects). While kava drinking does produce clear reactions, such as a slight numbing of tongue and throat, and while the odor, taste, and sensation can be acquired without becoming addictive, the ceremonial drinking in the cultures of Fiji, Tonga, and Samoa derives its importance from the role of kava in the social, political, and ceremonial life of these people (see Efron *et al.*).

E. *Widespread Use of Alcohol in Primitive Cultures**

Of all psychoactive agents used in human societies, *alcohol* is the most widespread. Tribes of all areas of the world, except for Oceania and much of North America, made various forms of alcoholic drink. In the island areas of the Pacific, betel nut chewing and kava drinking took the place of alcohol; and in North America, many aboriginal tribes, lacking corn and other starchy products in agriculture, likewise did not make fermented drinks, with some exceptions, for example, the eastern Apache tribes who raided the Pueblos for corn and made corn liquor or *tiswin*.

If one considers peasant cultures with agricultural economies around the world, practically all of them have alcoholic beverages, and indeed their craft in making these drinks accounts for the great traditions in wine making or in the preparation of our present-day hard liquors. In most societies, primitive, peasant, and modern, drinking behavior is considered important in the social order. Thus, in certain oriental cultures (China, Japan), women are not encouraged to drink at all except under strictest supervision. There is no known sex difference in affinity to alcohol, or in proneness to addiction. Biochemical theories of alcoholism which ignore the differential use and rates of alcoholism by sex are extremely naive in the absence of such anthropological insights.

In a complex modern society, drinking behavior does vary among classes and other social groups, not for biological reasons but because of cultural varia-

* See Mendelson, Chapter 40.

tions within the whole society. The same is true in comparisons of alcohol use among modern nations (cf. Mendelson, Chapter 40). If one focuses more closely on drinking in single societies, such as the role of beer (*tesguino*) in Tarahumara culture, we find that tesguino has a sacred character somewhat analogous to the use of kava in the Pacific, or tobacco as used in rituals of North American Indians. Similarly, the Kofyar of northern Nigeria believed that the way to the supernatural was with beer in hand. By contrast the Hopi Indians banned drinking from their villages for many years, while their linguistic cousins, the Aztecs, believed that worshippers should get dead drunk at every religious ceremony.

Even more discriminating uses may be found in India, where libations are offered to local village deities, but never to the classic pantheon of gods. Japanese, who center drinking in the male sex, believe in binge drinking, but each outburst is planned for carefully and is widely spaced from previous alcoholic holidays. The literature reports that Jews, southern Italians, and Chinese are peoples having low rates of alcoholism, whereas Sweden, modern France, the United States and Irish émigrés represent high-rate situations. In one society, beer or wine drinking may be a typical mode of social interchange for males; but in a country like Sweden it may serve as a general social lubricant in a highly formalized system of etiquette. In numerous Central and South American societies, the cultural pattern may insist that men drink to a state of drunkenness as a social outlet. The Camba of eastern Bolivia, some 80,000 in all, reserve for men the right to celebrate by drinking and in part justify the prolonged convivial states with the idea that alcohol has medicinal value as an internal parasiticide. Typically, however, where alcohol has ritual or nutritive qualities attributed to it in the culture, its drug effects will be played down and the "escapist" or anxiety-relieving qualities of the depressant will be minimized. At any rate, cultural variations in drinking are noted by anthropologists more often than similarities, and the case for cultural patterning is further strengthened by historical, ethnic, and preliterate studies.

When one considers that drugs like alcohol may become psychologically addictive, and may produce chronic effects on the organism through protracted intake, it is clear that the element of cultural patterning in such cases has immense importance.

V. Toward Social, Psychological, and Pharmacological Classification*

Recently there has been a resurgence of interest in naturally occurring psychoactive drugs which influence behavior. One reason, though possibly not the most important, lies in the rapidity with which a number of such products have become available to modern urban populations, including the youth of our cities. The popular use of many of the above products has led to considerable confusion in the public mind regarding their proper classification and control. Many of the accounts in mass media like newspapers and magazines are mislead-

* See Part VIII, "Drug Abuse and Related Problems."

ing. This circumstance has led the author, while conducting a survey for a program in cross-cultural uses of psychoactive drugs, to study the uses of such products as marihuana, dimethyltryptamine (DMT), mescaline, and LSD in an urban area of approximately 600,000 people. It was found in this urban study that popular use of such preparations was strictly separated in the public mind of one group from opioid derivatives like morphine and codeine; that such products were classified by others as narcotics such as heroin; and that the use of barbiturates was likewise considered as being a felony. Further, the users of popular drugs like marihuana and LSD were not found to be initially college or high school students at all, although this occurred to a relatively small extent after the fad had begun. Finally, the initial users, besides not being students, were not even youthful in age, but ranged in age from 30–50 years old.

Within the category of "psychedelic" users just indicated, besides the relatively older age of first initiates, there are also different social categories to be discerned, such as the esthetes, the political nonactivists who are nevertheless socially rebellious, and the sensation seekers, who are mainly curious. Considering the widespread national interest in certain migrations of young and middle-aged persons to California centers of these "cults," sociological parallels have been sought with mass hysteria movements of the past, such as the Children's Crusades, the Dancing Manias, or tarantulism. While these latter movements may serve to illustrate a popular, faddist phenomenon which is common to both situations, the parallel does not include use of a drug in the earlier instances. Far more revealing, I think, are other similarities, including drug use, between the "pot" party of esthetes or self-exploring individuals and the Peyote cults which spread throughout Indian reservations in more recent times. In both of the latter drug-using social functions, we must remember that they occurred in times when social demoralization had spread widely through both the Indian reservations and also through the Bohemian or youth groups.

In both settings, also, cultural revivalism is a repeated theme. Each form of cult reacts against the dominating "Establishment," whether this is viewed as encroachment by white people or as middle-class engulfment. In both instances, a relatively mild and nonaddictive form of drug such as marihuana or peyote becomes the occasion for a social and ideological movement stressing the reestablishment of group and cultural purposes with the drug simply claimed to stimulate self-exploration in the service of this goal. Thus the Indian peyote users felt they were avoiding cultural breakdown, just as the drug cultists claim they are expanding horizons and renewing esthetic acuity at a time when wars, pollution, urban ugliness, and economic self-interest are strongly in evidence. Both, also, allude to new intellectual and social revivals, religious themes, and group solidarity.

Some comment should be made on the pharmacological agents used in primitive and folk materia medica. It must be remembered that two such elements, alcohol and tobacco products, have long been used in our society, the first chiefly from European peasant sources and the second from the American Indian. Alcohol is the chief hypnosedative on the list.

The antipsychotic agents were developed as a result of the discovery of reserpine. Anticonvulsants should be added to this classification, but almost nothing has been done with such agents in primitive materia medica.

The psychoanaleptics which alter behavior by causing an elevation or increase of mental activity may be represented by the mild stimulants such as caffeine. Although the latter has widespread social uses, the chief religious cult activities (with the exception of kava) are represented in a longer list of psychodysleptics which alter behavior by causing a sharp variation in mental activity.

For a fascinating and thorough overview of ethnopsychopharmacology the reader is referred to the recent very excellent monograph edited by Efron, Holmstedt, and Kline, "Ethnopharmacologic Search for Psychoactive Drugs" (see Appendix 1).

For further reading and general references see Appendices 1 and 2.

PART II

SOME BASIC ANATOMICAL AND PHYSIOLOGICAL CONSIDERATIONS

4

FUNCTIONAL NEUROANATOMY OF THE HYPOTHALAMUS*†

James N. Hayward

I. Introduction

This chapter reviews some general concepts of the architectural, chemical, and functional makeup of the brain as related to drug action. Functional neuroanatomy of the hypothalamus was chosen as an introductory section because the diencephalon is a crossroads for many of the central monoaminergic and cholinergic pathways to be discussed. Furthermore, the hypothalamus contains well-recognized neurosecretory neurons (hormone-producing nerve cells) and is also one of the most frequently studied CNS sites of drug action.

Pharmacological agents acting on the hypothalamus may affect feeding, drinking, thermoregulation, cardiovascular regulation, neuroendocrine function, and behavior. This somatovisceral integrative center of the forebrain, representing only 0.4% of brain volume in man, contains secretory, "receptor," and effector

* This work has been supported in part by NIH Grant NB-05638-04.

† Information used in the text comes from recent papers, abstracts, and unpublished results; however, only general reviews are listed in the bibliography.

neurons forming a syncytium with ascending and descending fiber tracts on either side of the third ventricle. Synaptic interactions between hypothalamic neurons and axons from midbrain, olfactory, neocortical, and limbic forebrain neurons provide the anatomical basis for such physiological integration. Drug actions on these neural elements remain complex and incompletely understood.

II. Form and Function

A. *Neurosecretory Neurons*

Hormone synthesis, transport, storage, and release into the circulation by the magnocellular nuclei, supraoptic and paraventricular, of the hypothalamus are well established. These neurons, and perhaps all nerve cells, have the dual capacity for electrical transmission and chemical secretion. The peptide hormones, vasopressin and oxytocin, are produced in the perikarya in electron-dense membrane-bound vesicles (1000 Å), transported down the unmyelinated axons, and stored or released into the bloodstream from the nerve endings in the posterior pituitary gland. A less well-documented group of hypothalamic secretory neurons, the parvicellular nuclei, probably discharge their chemical "releasing factor" into the vicinity of the portal vessels for regulation of anterior pituitary function.

Synaptic transmission within the mammalian central nervous system is generally considered to be by chemical rather than electrical means. The chemical types of transmitters, their modes of production, the morphological sites of transmitter storage and release, and the similarities of synaptic "neurosecretion" with supraoptico-neurohypophysial neurosecretion remain uncertain.

B. *"Receptor" Neurons*

Feedback regulation of hypothalamic visceral-endocrine function requires some central "sensor" neural element for detecting the blood levels of the factor being regulated. Nerve cells specifically sensitive to physical and chemical changes in the blood, such as temperature, osmolality, or hormones, are localized in the hypothalamus. Drug action on hypothalamic functions may "reset" such receptor neurons with a subsequent alteration in the level of physiological regulation.

C. *Neural Connections: Cholinergic and Monoaminergic Tracts*

The early discovery of biogenic amines in the hypothalamus (22) and the subsequent demonstration of acetylcholine and acetylcholinesterase in hypothalamic nuclei prepared the way for recent studies on a complex system of chemically specific nerve fibers emanating from the lower brain stem and coursing upward to stream through and to the hypothalamus. The tools for exploring these chemical pathways are histochemical marking techniques as well as lesions and chemical blocking agents. As a result of these anatomical and other pharmacological studies, cholinergic and monoaminergic mechanisms have been proposed for feeding, drinking, body temperature regulation, hormone secretion, and emotional behavior.

D. *Hypothalamic Island*

Recently, surgical isolation of the ventral hypothalamus–median-eminence region from the rest of the brain has been accomplished to create a deafferented hypothalamic island with an attached pituitary gland. With careful surgery the circulation entering the hypothalamic island from the base of the skull remains intact, allowing long-term studies on independent local hypothalamic control of anterior and posterior pituitary secretions. Much evidence of local hypothalamic drug action on neuroendocrine mechanisms in mammals has been derived from such preparations.

III. Body Water and Energy Balance

A. *Water Intake and Output: Osmoreceptors*

The neurosecretory activity of the neurohypophysis for the regulation of vasopressin (antidiuretic hormone, ADH) release depends primarily upon the solute concentration of the plasma. Hypothalamic "osmoreceptors" apparently detect hypertonicity of the plasma, accelerate the firing rates of the supraoptic neurons, and release vasopressin from the posterior pituitary gland. Vasopressin circulates to the renal tubule, where reabsorbtion of solute-free water results in concentrated urine and retention of water by the kidney. Experimental evidence suggests that a major stimulus for drinking is also hyperosmolality of the plasma. The hypothetical "osmoreceptors" (23) are therefore involved in water conservation by the kidney and water intake by the behavioral act of drinking. Drugs may modify body fluid balance by altering drinking, vasopressin release, or renal function. Nicotine and cholinomimetic agents enhance release of ADH, while hydrocortisone, epinephrine, and ethyl alcohol inhibit release of vasopressin from the neurohypophysis. Diuresis in the cold and antidiuresis in the heat may be the result of a shift in blood volume or water loss by sweating, respectively. Shifts in blood volume and alterations in arterial blood pressure can cause ADH release and induce drinking.

B. *Feeding and Energy Balance: Glucoreceptors*

Five factors appear to be critical in the neural regulation of feeding: blood levels of glucose, fatty acids, and amino acids, body temperature, and gastric distension. Several experimental maneuvers, including lesions, electrical recording, brain heating and cooling, and drug injections into the brain have defined regional hypothalamic mechanisms for feeding and satiety. A "feeding" center appears to be organized in the lateral hypothalamus and a "satiety" center in the ventromedial area. Unit activity in the satiety center is responsive to changing levels of blood glucose, while gastric distension can inhibit single neuron firing in the lateral hypothalamus. Ventromedial lesions produced by electrolysis or by administration of gold thioglucose result in obesity. It is presumed that the "glucoreceptor-satiety center" inhibition of the lateral hypothalamic feeding center has been eliminated with the subsequent excessive eating.

IV. Autonomic Mechanisms

A. *Temperature Regulation: Thermoreceptors and Endogenous Pyrogen*

Heat- and cold-sensitive nerve cells are located close to the third ventricle in the preoptic area. Local heating of this region initiates the autonomic adjustments for heat dissipation, i.e., peripheral vasodilatation, sweating, panting, and decreased motor activity. Local cooling of preoptic neurons induces heat-retaining and heat-producing activity, i.e., peripheral vasoconstriction, piloerection, increased motor activity, and shivering. Shifts in body temperature resulting from intraventricular or intracerebral biogenic amines have led to a "chemical" theory of body temperature regulation. However, similar effects on body temperature by cholinomimetic and anticholinergic agents, as well as species differences in the responses to intracranial biogenic amines, preclude a simple specific chemical (monoaminergic or cholinergic) theory of temperature regulation.

Bacterial and steroid fevers probably result from the release of a protein substance from white blood cells called leukocyte endogenous pyrogen. This protein circulates to the preoptic area and alters the activities of these neurons, thus resetting the "thermostat." Autonomic mechanisms for heat production and heat retention are activated by such hypothalamic action of endogenous pyrogen with peripheral cutaneous vasoconstriction, shivering, and piloerection. The mechanisms of drug action in fever, such as with acetylsalicylate, appear to be a competitive inhibition of the action of pyrogen on preoptic neurons with return to the "normal" setting of body temperature regulation and a defervescence of fever. Actions of psychopharmacological agents on body temperature may involve such preoptic neurons as well as other central and peripheral neural sites.

B. *Cardiovascular Regulation: Blood Pressure and Muscle Vasodilatation*

Drug action on peripheral vascular resistance and arterial blood pressure may involve those hypothalamic sites known to regulate the cardiovascular system. Recently a cholinergic vasodilator outflow to muscles has been described in certain species with its origin in the cerebral cortex, a station in the hypothalamus, and a final common pathway in the intermediolateral columns of the spinal cord. Behavioral components of "flight" and fight" and vasoconstriction of the skin and viscera accompany such increased muscle blood flow during the "defense reaction" induced by electrical stimulation of the hypothalamus. Pharmacological agents such as morphine may differentially block the behavioral component of such hypothalamic stimulation without preventing the increased muscle blood flow.

V. Neuroendocrine Aspects

A. *Adenohypophysis: Releasing Factors and Portal Vessels*

Nervous control of the anterior pituitary gland by the hypothalamus involves a vascular link rather than a direct nervous pathway such as occurs in the posterior pituitary gland. Nerve cells in the hypothalamus produce chemical substances (releasing factors) which are discharged from nerve terminals into the primary capillary loops of the portal vessels, picked up, and transported down the hypophysial stalk in the portal blood to circulate among the cells of the pars distalis. The synthesis and release of these "releasing factors" by these parvicellular neurosecretory neurons of the infundibular region is modified by neural signals and by circulating humoral factors. Each of the trophic pituitary hormones (adrenocorticotropin, ACTH; growth hormone, STH; follicle stimulating hormone, FSH; luteinizing hormone, LH; and thyroid stimulating hormone, TSH) is thought to be under direct specific control by an appropriate hypothalamic releasing factor, RF (corticotropin releasing factor, CRF; growth hormone releasing factor, STH-RF; follicle stimulating releasing factor, FSH-RF; luteinizing hormone releasing factor, LHRF; and thyroid hormone releasing factor, TSH-RF). The chemical structure of these releasing factors is not yet known. Increased flow of releasing factors over pituitary cells probably causes increased synthesis and release of pituitary trophic hormones. One pituitary hormone, prolactin or lactogenic hormone (LTH) is under inhibitory control by the hypothalamus. Prolactin inhibitory factor (PIF) normally prevents release of prolactin from the pituitary. Maneuvers which cause abnormal lactation, such as pituitary stalk section or antipsychotic drug (reserpine) treatment, probably depress production and release of PIF by hypothalamic neurons. Pituitary cells are then released from inhibitory control and hypersecretion of prolactin ensues.

B. *Humoral Feedback Control of Adenohypophysis: "Long" and "Short" Loops*

Drugs may act on endocrines at any one of four levels: CNS, hypothalamic final common neurosecretory pathway, pituitary gland, and peripheral endocrine gland. For example, the antifertility 19-norsteroids (oral contraceptives, the "pill") appear to act upon all four of these levels, although the hypothalamic and pituitary sites appear primary in prevention of ovulation in the mammalian female. Hypothalamic hormone-sensitive "receptor" neurons have been shown to act as sensors of blood levels of specific target gland hormones (hydrocortisone, estrogen, progesterone, testosterone, thyroid hormone) and to modulate the discharge of releasing factors into the portal vessels. This "long" negative and positive feedback loop is supplemented by a "short" negative feedback system involving direct action of pituitary hormones (ACTH, FSH, LH, TSH, LTH) on the hypothalamus. Many target gland hormones can also act directly on the pituitary gland to alter secretion. The complex interactions between the nervous system and these multiple negative and positive feedback loops underlie the circadian (daily) rhythms of endocrine gland secretions.

VI. Hypothalamus and Behavior

If we recognize that the hypothalamus is directly involved in feeding, drinking, sex, and sleep, it is obvious that such a pleasant sequence of events relates to much of the total behavior of the organism. Chemical or electrical stimulation of the hypothalamus can alter both endocrine gland secretion as well as feeding, drinking, and sleeping behavior. Castration abolishes mating behavior in some species, while focal estrogen implantation into the hypothalamus will restore such activity. Neuronal firing patterns in the hypothalamus may be altered by changes in blood tonicity and temperature, by visual, auditory, and tactile sensory stimuli, as well as by transitions from waking to sleeping behavior. Pharmacological agents may alter mood, sexual receptivity, hunger drive, and sleep-waking cycles by direct local effects on the hypothalamus or by indirect central and peripheral neural actions.

For further reading, see Appendices 1 and 2.

5

CENTRAL CHOLINERGIC PATHWAYS AND THEIR BEHAVIORAL IMPLICATIONS*

Alexander G. Karczmar

I. Introduction

A. Criteria for the Existence of Chemical Cholinergic Transmission

To satisfy the ultimate criterion for the existence of chemical transmission at a neuron-to-neuron or neuron-to-neuroeffector site, the release of the transmitter and its physiological action at the postsynaptic membrane must be demonstrated at a single synapse, or in a homogeneous synaptic population. Several types of indirect evidence may lead to the acceptance of a synapse as being chemically operated. First, apparently, no such synapse may function without showing a synaptic delay. Second, the application of the transmitter as a drug

* Recent published and unpublished results from the author's laboratory described in this chapter were supported in part by Public Health Grants CC0041-08 from the Communicable Disease Center, NB01308-01107, 2TIGM77-06-08, and 1 ROINB00455-01-02 from the National Institute of Health, and by Grants 1792 and 17-176 from the Illinois Mental Institute.

should cause pharmacologic phenomena analogous to the physiological events exhibited upon presynaptic stimulation. Third, pharmacological analyses with appropriate blockers and facilitators should affect in an identical manner the events induced by presynaptic stimulation and those evoked by the application of the putative transmitter as a drug. Fourth, anabolic and catabolic enzymic systems, concerned with the production and dissipation of the putative transmitter, should be demonstrable at the site in question. An important consideration is that the chemically operated synapses may be differentiated morphologically from electrical junctions (cf. Aghajanian, Chapter 7).

The discovery by Del Castillo and Katz (cf. 24,25) of the miniature potentials and of their relationship to the synaptic vesicles, at the skeletal myoneural junction, and subsequently at the cholinergically operated sympathetic ganglia as well as in the central nervous system may be considered as an important link. These spontaneous potentials recorded at quiescent synapses could be considered as units of chemical activity, as they were related as "quanta" to the full-fledged, impulse-generated postsynaptic potential. That the synaptic vesicles constitute the most likely source of such quanta was borne out by the biochemical analysis of the nerve ending material. In the brain, as well as in the peripheral nervous system, the isolated vesicular fraction contains various biogenic amines: acetylcholine (ACh), serotonin (5HT), norepinephrine (NE), dopamine (DA), and histamine. The enzymes concerned with their synthesis also are found in the nerve terminals, either in the vesicular fraction or in the mitochondria, while catabolic enzymes were generally found in a separate fraction. Of particular importance is the presence of cholinesterase (ChE) and choline acetylase (ChAc), the latter being located presynaptically. The work of De Robertis and of Whittaker (for refs. cf. 24,25, App. 1, Chapter 4) indicated that the vesicles may be neurochemically specific; large granulated vesicles and smaller, smooth ones, which contain, respectively, ACh and NE. Still other types of vesicles may be specific for histamine and for various amino acids.

This evidence strongly supports Dale's hypothesis for central chemical transmission in certain synaptic contacts. Moreover, some evidence strongly favors the presence of central cholinergic transmission.

B. Morphologic and Related Requirements for a Chemically Transmitting Synapse

The development of electron microscopy of the brain (cf. Aghajanian, Chapter 7) which led to the discovery of the so-called synaptic vesicles and their biochemical analysis, have markedly advanced our knowledge of brain function in the past few years.

A chemically operated synapse is characterized by asymmetrical thickenings of the opposed membranes, the presence of vesicles of various types at the presynaptic site, and of a subsynaptic web at the opposite site. Two types of synapses may be recognized, one of which seems to be found generally on dendritic spines and surfaces, and is characterized by a synaptic cleft con-

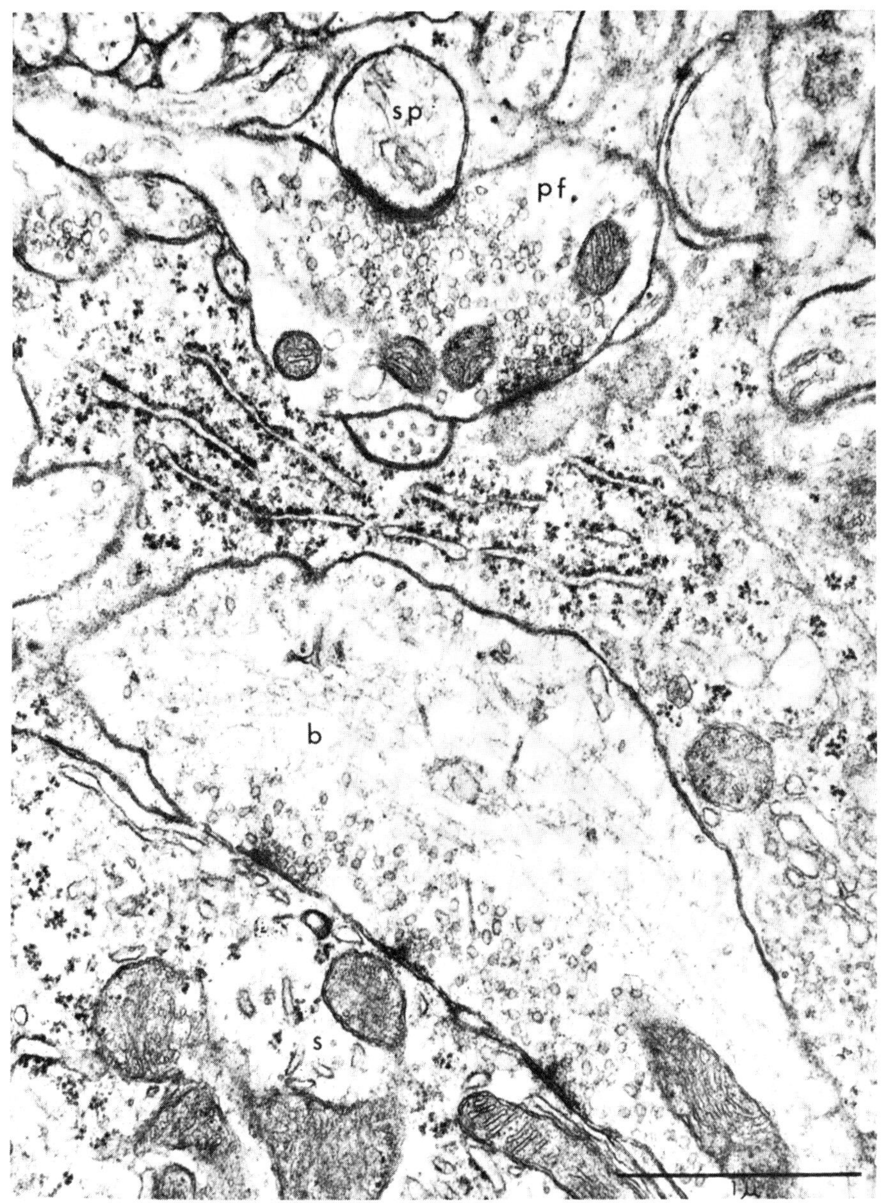

Fig. 1. Central excitatory and inhibitory synapses as seen in electron microscopy. Mouse cerebellum perfused in glutaraldehyde: (1) Axodendritic spine synapse. Parallel fiber (pf) synapsing with a spine (sp) from a Purkinje cell dendrite. Notice the aggregation of the synaptic vesicles in the presynaptic portion of the synapse and the marked density of the postsynaptic membrane. (2) Axosomatic synapse. Basket axon (b) synapsing with the soma (s) of a Purkinje cell at three points. Notice that the density of the postsynaptic membrane is less marked than in the case of the spine synapse. Parallel fibers are known to form type I excitatory synapses, while basket cell axons form type 2 inhibitory synapses. Notice the differences in the size and shape of the synaptic vesicles among these two types of synapses. The author is most grateful to Dr. L. M. H. Larramendi for the permission for the use of this figure, obtained in Dr. Larramendi's laboratories.

taining extracellular material (Fig. 1). The second type is found on cell bodies and dendritic surfaces, has a narrower cleft, and contains less dense extracellular material.

On the basis of neurophysiological evidence, type 1 and type 2 synapses are thought to be generally excitatory and inhibitory, as they depolarize and hyperpolarize, respectively, the postsynaptic membrane. However, functionally, the type 1 terminal may also be inhibitory: some of the type 1 synapses are axo-axonic and are superimposed on a presynaptic terminal and inhibit the transmission originating in the terminal as they depolarize it and depress its transmitter output.

It is important to mention that there are peripheral and central synapses which differ morphologically from the two types mentioned. Electron microscopy has shown that they have very narrow or no synaptic clefts, and it may be presumed that they are electrically operated.

Why should structures, thus described, predicate chemical transmission? In the case of peripheral synapses, where the release and the postsynaptic action of the transmitter were demonstrated, such structures could be readily demonstrated. Second, the synaptic gap necessitates a transmitter for the synaptic passage of the impulse, and electrophysiological data clearly indicated that the synapses in question cannot be electrically excitable. The synaptic delay is also a consequence of the synaptic gap and it does not obtain at electrical synapses.

The presence of the synaptic vesicles at the sites of the presumptive chemical transmission should be stressed; their relation, already described, to the miniature potentials at the peripheral cholinergic and certain central synapses, is a significant component of this reasoning.

Evidence strongly favors the existence of central cholinergic transmission. This evidence is particularly concerned with ACh content of synaptic vesicles in certain brain neurones as well as with the presence of ChE and choline acetylase (ChAc): moreover, certain data suggest that some of the excitatory synapses of type 1 may be considered cholinergic.

II. Functioning of a Cholinergic Synapse

The metabolism of a cholinergic synapse is concerned specifically with ACh, although energy metabolism and the bioenergetics of the synaptic membranes such as those related to the sodium pump and maintenance of membrane polarization are, of course, important. ACh synthesis depends on ChAc, magnesium, and adenosine triphosphate (ATP). Catabolism of ACh depends on cholinesterases (ChE's). ChE's are a family of enzymes. Butyrylcholinesterase (BuChE) is preponderant generally in the glia, and acetylcholinesterase (AChE) in the synapse proper, although some neurons contain BuChE as well. Subtypes of these two enzymes, as well as their isozymes and related ChE's such as arylesterase, are also present in the nervous system. Because of its kinetics, AChE is particularly adapted to hydrolyze in milliseconds the highly concentrated

ACh that is conveyed during impulse from the pre- to the postsynaptic membrane. Pre- and postsynaptic AChE is present in the brain.

Upon reaching the terminals, the presynaptic nerve action potential depolarizes their membranes and presumably ruptures those synaptic vesicles that are juxtaposed to it, causing the release of ACh. This release depends on the ionic milieu and is blocked by high Mg^{++} or low Ca^{++} within the terminal. The location and the density of the synaptic vesicles may depend on the intensity of activity, and may lead to either transmitter exhaustion or mobilization. Normally, a single impulse reaching a synaptic knob may liberate a "packet" of ACh containing about 8000 molecules.

ACh may not be released in one burst. According to the "percussion" hypothesis of Koelle (cf. 24,25,27), an initial priming burst, lasting a small fraction of a millisecond, initiates a positive feedback action upon the terminal and a mass

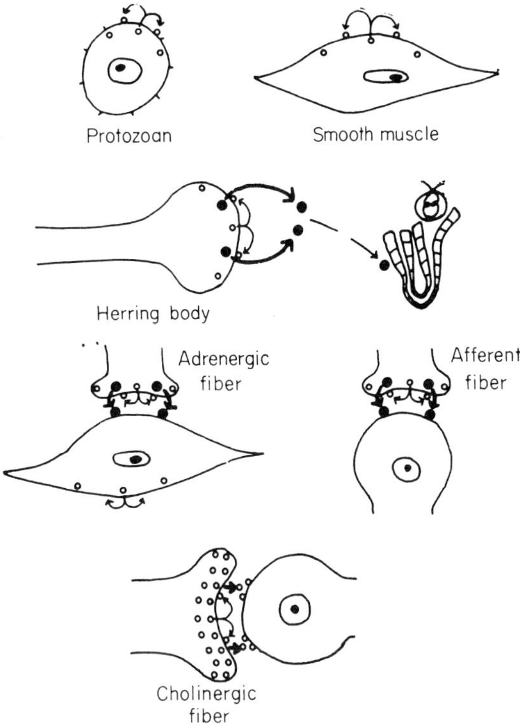

Fig. 2. Diagrammatic representation of Koelle's "percussive" hypothesis of the action of acetylcholine, showing: direct influences of acetylcholine localized to its sites of liberation (protozoans, smooth muscle); indirect influences of acetylcholine through liberation of hormones acting at remote sites (from Herring bodies) and of neurohumoral agents acting at adjacent sites (from adrenergic and primary afferent fibers); direct influences of acetylcholine at adjacent sites as a neurohumoral transmitter (from cholinergic fibers). From Koelle (27).

release of the transmitter. Koelle suggests that the same priming mechanism may lead to a release of other substances, such as NE or epinephrine, from neighboring neurons or from chromaffin cells. This, in turn, may alter the response of the postsynaptic membrane to ACh. Release of polypeptides from the same terminal also is possible via this mechanism, as in the case of the hypothalamicohypophyseal axis (Figs. 2 and 8).

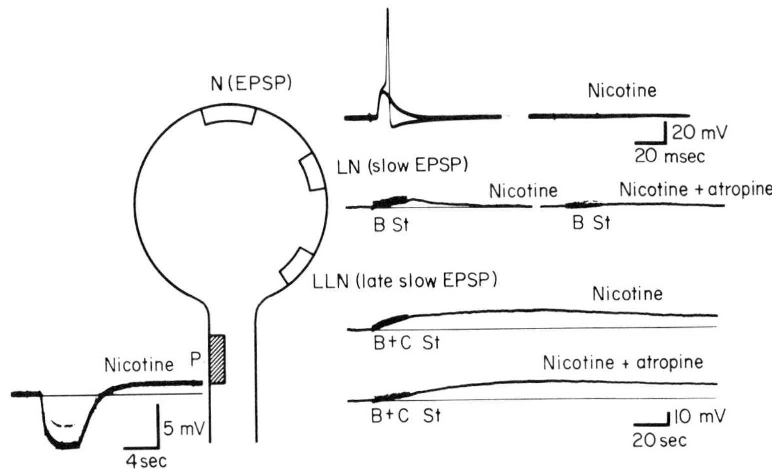

Fig. 3. Potentials obtained at the postsynaptic site following presynaptic stimulation. The original tracings were obtained in the frog sympathetic ganglion, but it is probable that corresponding membrane changes arise at the cholinergic synapses in the central nervous system. Negative excitatory potential [(N) EPSP; first row, right] is blocked by a large dose of nicotine (second tracing) or by ganglionic blocking agents; it arises at site N. The "slow" (LN) and "late slow" (LLN) EPSP's (three lower right rows) may arise upon stimulation of presynaptic terminals arising from two types of cholinergic neurons, B and C. LN is blocked by atropine but not by nicotine (third and fourth rows, right); LLN is not blocked by atropine or nicotine (third row, right). N, LN, and LLN were recorded by means of intracellular microelectrodes. Left record illustrates positive (P) hyperpolarizing potential, which is increased by anti-ChE's and blocked by atropine but not by nicotine (external electrodes). The diagram illustrates sites at which the various potentials arise; note that for various neurophysiological reasons the P site was assumed to be located at the axon hillock. From Koketsu and Nishi (25a).

Other membrane actions, depending on transmitters other than ACh, were recently described for the central nervous system. These important actions are inhibitory. One type of inhibition is presynaptic and due to depolarization of the nerve terminal. Another type of inhibition is concomitant with posthyperpolarization, which was described as emanating from Gray's type 2 synapses (Fig. 1). This inhibitor effect is presumably due to the release of an amino acid such as γ-aminobutyric acid (GABA) or glycine. The resultant inhibitory postsynaptic potential (IPSP) is related to the increase in postsynaptic concentration of chloride and potassium. It is of interest that the stimulation of a cholinergic terminal may also induce hyperpolarization (Fig. 3). Two expla-

TABLE I
Sites and Mechanisms at a Cholinergic Synapse [a]

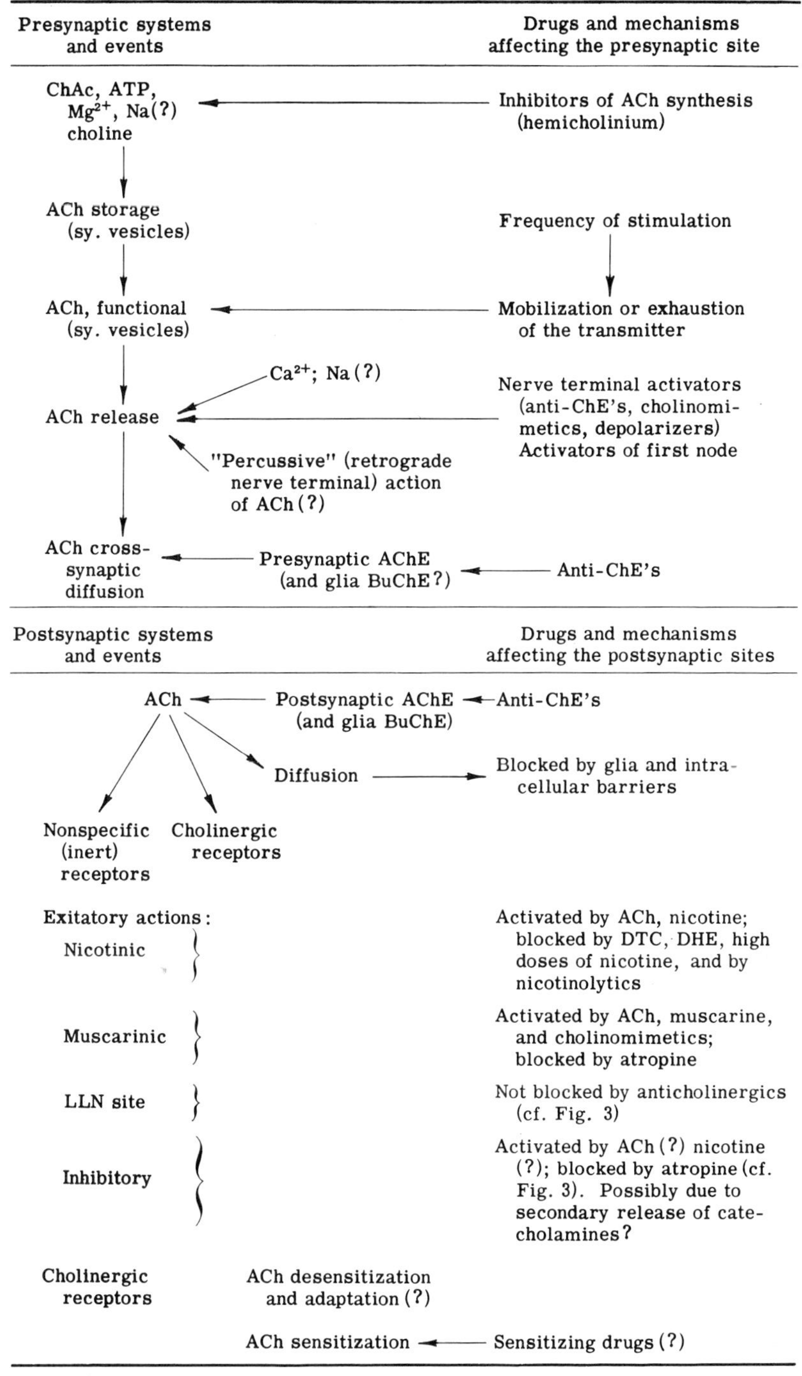

[a] This scheme is based mostly on the results of the studies of peripheral cholinergic synapses, but it should apply also to central cholinergic synapses.

nations may be proposed at present for this "cholinergic" IPSP. First, ACh may act directly on a specialized inhibitory cholinoceptive receptor. The second possibility is that ACh may cause the release of catecholamines, for example, from chromaffin granule cells present in the neighborhood of many synapses, or of other inhibitory substances which in turn hyperpolarize the postsynaptic membrane (see Figs. 2 and 8).

The cholinergic receptors responsible for the postsynaptic events differ from each other. This heterogeneity may arise within one postsynaptic membrane, which is then mosaic in nature, or between different cholinoceptive neurons. These receptors are differentiated pharmacologically and perhaps neurophysiologically. The muscarinic receptors are readily blocked by atropine and related drugs, but not by curarimimetics; the converse is true in the case of nicotinic receptors. Cholinergic synaptic transmission may be coupled with two ionically related excitatory phenomena, muscarinic and nicotinic, and with a directly or indirectly induced inhibitory process.

A cholinergic synapse is thus a complicated system, which the author has described elsewhere as a "little brain" (Table I, Fig. 3). Several mechanisms modulate its function: (1) the positive feedback of Koelle and other nerve terminal responses; (2) the negative feedbacks due perhaps to cholinergic hyperpolarization; (3) mobilization of the synaptic vesicles; (4) ionic influences; and (5) configurational receptor changes which may lead to sensitization of the postsynaptic membrane, while, conversely, adaptation to high levels of ACh and ACh desensitization may also occur (Table I) (cf. 24). Altogether, the modulation of transmission in the central nervous system need not depend entirely on an interplay between various transmitters and pathways.

III. Cholinergic Transmission in the Central Nervous System

A. *Modern Techniques Applicable to the Study of Central Synapses*

A number of classical methods are employed in the study of cholinergic synapses. ACh is generally determined by bioassay methods. ChAc is evaluated by bioassaying ACh or measuring the latter by means of radioisotope techniques.

The bioassay method for ACh is capable of detecting 10^{-8} to 10^{-19} M amounts, depending on the assay organ. The chemical methods are at present much less sensitive, and are generally inappropriate for the measurement of brain ACh. However, a gas chromatography technique, presumably sensitive at picogram levels, has very recently been developed by B. Holmstedt and D. J. Jenden to chemically and specifically demonstrate ACh in milligram amounts of mammalian brain.

Histochemical (see below), manometric, and titrimetric methods are employed for the measurement of ChE's. Conventional and microelectrode methods are employed for neurophysiological and neuropharmacological evaluations. Three novel, recently developed techniques require special mention.

1. The Multibarrel Micropipette

The five-barrel micropipette was designed originally by Eccles *et al.* (29) to record spontaneous and drug-induced neuronal firing. It consists of a central recording microelectrode and four contiguous microelectrodes filled with appropriate solutions of drugs in their salt forms. The drugs are ejected electrophoretically

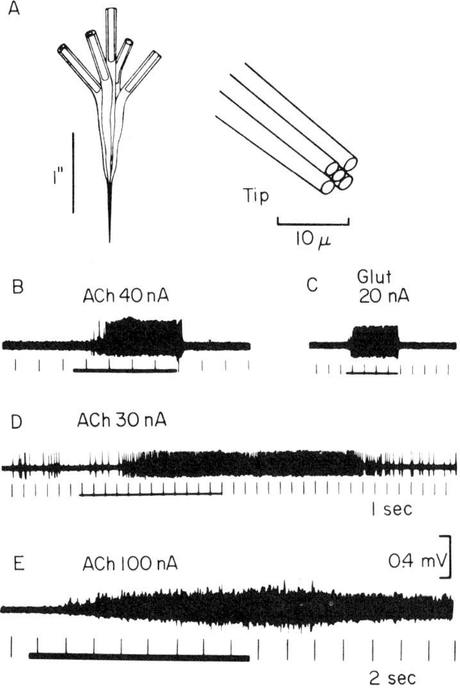

Fig. 4. Multibarrel pipette and typical neuronal responses to electrophoretic drug application. (A) The diagram of the glass five-barrel micropipette, with an enlarged view of the tip. From Curtis (cf. 24,25). (B–E) Comparison of muscarinic and nicotinic neuronal spike response recorded extracellularly from, and following administration through, the antibarrel pipette: (B) the response of the Renshaw cell to ACh, 40 nA; (C) the response of a cortical neuron (Betz cell) to *l*-glutamate, 20 nA; (D) the response of a cortical neuron (Betz cell) to ACh, 30 nA; (E) the response of a hippocampal neuron (field CZ 3) to ACh, 100 nA.

Compare the rapid onset and powerful response of the Renshaw cell to ACh and of a cortical cell to glutamate (B and C, respectively) with the delayed and relatively weak response to ACh of the cortical and hippocampal neurons (D and E, respectively). Modified from Biscoe and Straughan, and Krnjević (cf. 24,25).

(iontophoretically) by suitable currents. The diameter of the recording electrode is less than 0.5 μ for intercellular, and 1–3 μ for extracellular recording. Usually the neuronal spike is recorded extracellularly, and the spike frequency plotted automatically by appropriate equipment (Fig. 4). In actual experiments, acidic amino acids such as homocysteic or aspartic acids are employed in one barrel as nonspecific neuronal excitants. The other barrels may contain ACh, NE, and other appropriate agents. When cholinoceptive neurons are found, their response to ACh as compared to that of the excitatory amino acids, is analyzed pharmacologically, by using, for instance, physostigmine, atropine, and dihydro-β-erythroidine (DHE). The method is most useful when it can be applied to neurons which have been identified by their responses to specific afferent and efferent stimulation. This has been achieved in the case of the Renshaw cell, and, at the brain level, with the Betz cells and with certain neurons of the cerebellar cortex.

When such an identification is possible, and when the pharmacological analysis indicates a similarity of the neuronal response to the synaptic stimulation, on the one hand, and to ACh, on the other, the presence of cholinergic transmission at the synaptic site in question is very likely. However, cholinoceptivity alone cannot by any means be considered synonymous with cholinergicity of their transmission.

2. The Chemitrode Technique

In contradistinction to the electrophoretic technique, the related "chemitrode" method introduced by Delgado (cf. 26) serves to activate cell populations. Double cannulae are employed to inject liquids or to push crystals into the subcortical target areas, after which behavioral or electrical responses are evaluated. The interpretation of these responses may sometimes be difficult since they may be due not to the direct action of the drug upon a specific subcortical site but rather on its action elsewhere following its diffusion into the ventricle.

3. Histochemical Identification of Cholinesterasic Pathways

Koelle developed a method to differentially identify AChE and BuChE sites (27) and to localize these enzymes in the central and peripheral nervous system. Subsequently, Shute and Lewis (28) combined histochemical, nerve section, and ablation techniques to trace ChE-containing pathways. This technique allowed: (1) the identification of ChE containing nerve fibers; (2) the determination of the pathway directions, as the enzyme accumulated "in the cut ends of axons and their terminals on the other side"; and (3) the partial determination of the source of synaptic ChE, as in due time after the section the stain disappeared entirely or partially, depending on whether it was pre- or postsynaptic, respectively. The method proved fruitful when combined with measurement of ChAc and ACh in the areas investigated. Used alone, it cannot be used to identify cholinergic synapses, since AChE is present at both pre- and postsynaptic sites, and since ACh, not ChE, is the ultimate criterion of the cholinergic transmission.

B. An Identified Central Cholinergic Synapse: The Renshaw Cell

In 1954, Eccles and his associates (29) provided pharmacological evidence for the cholinergic nature of a spinal synapse located between the motor axon collateral and the Renshaw cell (Fig. 5). ACh, nicotine, and certain cholinomimetic substances were effective in increasing the rate of, or initiating the discharge from, the Renshaw cell. Following treatment with anticholinesterases (anti-ChE's), the activation of a single synapse produced prolonged repetitive discharge. Applied electrophoretically, even the quaternary anti-ChE's, which cannot cross the blood-brain barrier when given intravenously, exhibited similar actions, while DHE and *d*-tubocurarine (DTC) decreased the early response

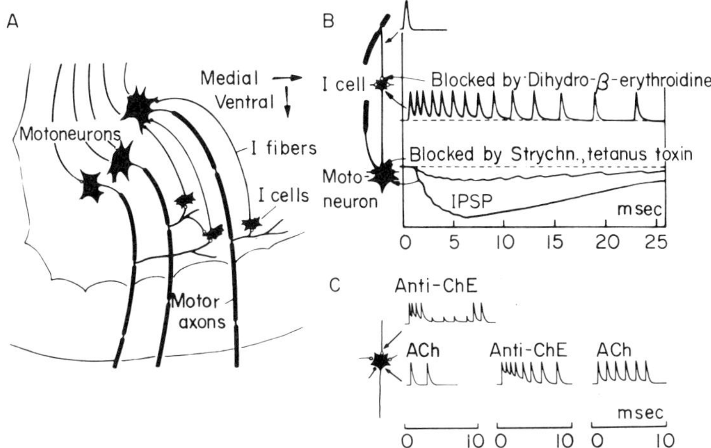

Fig. 5. (A) Drawing of recurrent inhibitory pathway from motor axon collaterals to Renshaw cells (inhibitory neurons or I cells) and thence to motoneurons. (B) Diagram summarizing the postulated sequence of events from an impulse in a motor axon to the inhibition of a montoneuron. All events are plotted on the time scale shown below and the corresponding histological structures are shown diagrammatically to the left (note indicator arrows). The four plotted time courses are from above downward for the following events: the electrical response of impulse in motor-axon collateral; the electrical response evoked in a Renshaw cell by the cumulative effect of acetylcholine at many synapses, showing impulses superimposed on a background depolarization; the IPSP generated in the motoneuron by the Renshaw cell discharge; and the aggregate IPSP evoked in a motoneuron that is bombarded repetitively by many Renshaw cells, which become progressively more asynchronous, so smoothing the latter part of the ripple. The structural diagram to the left shows converging synapses on the Renshaw cell and on the montoneuron. From Eccles (29). (C) Responses of the collateral nerve endings and of the Renshaw cell to anti-ChE's and to ACh (schematized). The upper repetitive response is that of the collateral to an anti-ChE as recorded extracellularly. It illustrates the responsiveness of the nerve terminals to cholinergic stimulants (29a). The three lower responses illustrate the Renshaw cell response to electrophoretic application of, in sequence, ACh, an anti-ChE, and, again, ACh. Note the intensified response to ACh following the anti-ChE. After Curtis, *et al.* (cf. 25).

to antidromic stimulation, and blocked the actions of nicotine and anti-ChE substances (see Fig. 5). Atropine was slightly effective, blocking the late Renshaw cell response to synaptic stimulation.

This summary of available data constitutes at the same time a model of evidence for establishing a CNS synapse as cholinergic. As noted, the criterion of collecting and identifying the transmitter following presynaptic stimulation of a nerve cell population could not be achieved in this case, as indeed in that of other putative central cholinergic synapses. However, other criteria were met. The responses of the Renshaw cell to presynaptic stimulation and to appropriate drugs were particularly affected in parallel. Collateral information such as the presence of AChE, ACh, and ChAc in the general area of the ventral horn, ventromedially to the motoneuron, i.e., in the region of the Renshaw cell, was also obtained. It should be added that certain difficulties have been encountered with regard to the histological localization and identification of the Renshaw cell. Several explanations, some of which eliminate the Renshaw cell, were offered, but the experimental support for these hypotheses is very incomplete at present (25).

The activated Renshaw cell releases an inhibitory transmitter, presumably glycine, and hyperpolarization of the motoneuron ensues (see Fig. 5). Thus, ACh is involved here in activating an inhibitory circuit and, as will be shown subsequently, ACh has an analogous role at several other brain sites.

In the amphibian spinal cord, pharmacological evidence in this laboratory led to the postulation of an interneuron which, when activated by ACh, depolarized the afferent nerve terminal (25). A presynaptic afferent inhibition may result, and thus, both the mammalian and the amphibian interneurons may participate in inhibitory circuits, although different types of inhibition, both post- and presynaptic, may be involved.

C. Status of Various Cholinoceptive Neurons as Parts of Cholinergic Pathways

1. The Cerebellum: Site of Probable Cholinergic Synapses

A relatively large number of cholinoceptive cells have been found by several investigators in the cerebellar cortex. It is generally agreed that at least some of the Purkinje cells respond. Whether granule or basket cells respond is controversial, due basically to difficulties of identification. Crawford and Curtis (Fig. 6) believed that only Purkinje cells respond to ACh and to several cholinomimetics, while other investigators believed that synapses between mossy fibers and the granule cells are cholinergic, and cited as supportive evidence the presence of AChE in and below the granular layer. In fact, all cerebellar afferent pathways contain AChE and should include cholinergic synapses (Table II). The cerebellar efferents do not appear to be cholinergic.

Crawford was unconvinced that the cholinoceptive response of the Purkinje cell indicates the presence of cholinergic synapses between the latter and either parallel or climbing fibers. He was disturbed by the long latency of the response of the Purkinje cell and the fact that cerebellar cortical potentials evoked by afferent stimulation were not readily blocked by either atropine or curariform drugs.

It appears that ACh must be involved in the function of the very important cerebellar system, and in the subtle two-way control that exists between cerebellar and the motor, sensory, cerebral, and reticular systems. However, one point should be stressed in this context: The activation of the Purkinje cell is dependent upon the level of its inhibition via the basket, stellate, or Golgi cells. Wherever the cholinergic cerebellar synapses are situated, the response

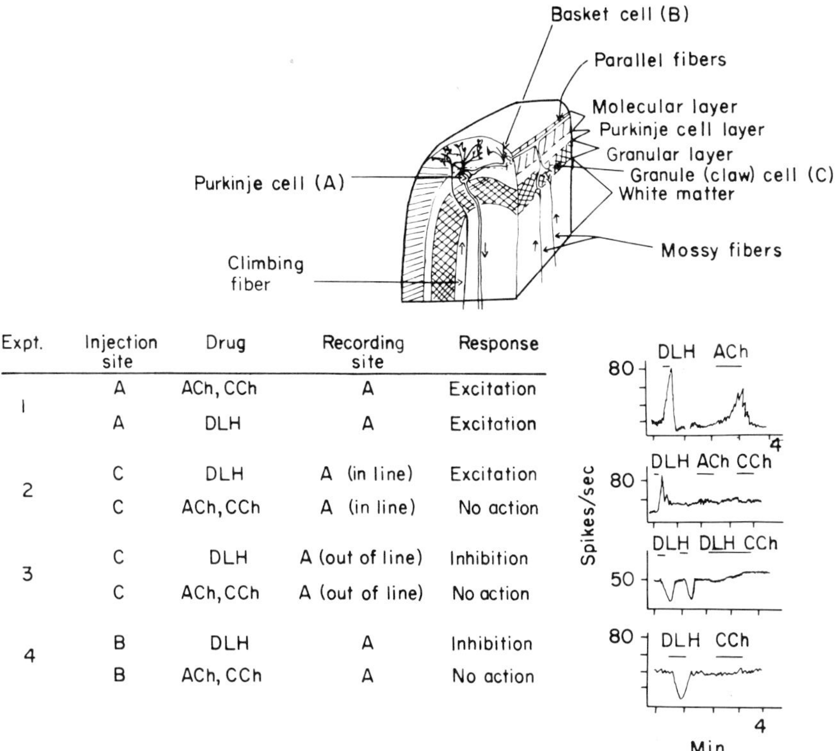

Expt.	Injection site	Drug	Recording site	Response
1	A	ACh, CCh	A	Excitation
	A	DLH	A	Excitation
2	C	DLH	A (in line)	Excitation
	C	ACh, CCh	A (in line)	No action
3	C	DLH	A (out of line)	Inhibition
	C	ACh, CCh	A (out of line)	No action
4	B	DLH	A	Inhibition
	B	ACh, CCh	A	No action

Fig. 6. Response of the cat cerebellar Purkinje cell to cholinomimetics, and to excitatory aminoacids applied electrophoretically at various sites.
Top: Schematic diagram of the cerebellar cortex and the arrangement (A–C) of recording and drug-ejecting multibarrel micropipettes. Purkinje cell (A), basket cell (B) and granule (claw) cell (C) are illustrated; the granule cell C is presented as being off-line with regard to the Purkinje cell A; thus, when stimulated, it excites the inhibitory basket cell; the in-line arrangement employed in the experiment 2 below is not illustrated. Also shown is the white matter with climbing and mossy fibers and the granular, Purkinje cell, and molecular layers. The two degrees of shading represent increasing concentrations of AChE. The arrows indicate afferent and efferent pathways. Lower left: Tabular summary of the responses of the Purkinje cells (recording site A) to drugs applied in four experiments as indicated under injection site. ACh, CCh and DLH, acetycholine, carbamylcholine, and DL-homocysteic acid, respectively. Lower right: Patterns of firing of the Purkinje cells obtained in experiments 1–4 (cf. lower left). The tracings represent frequencies (spikes/sec) as cumulated by the recorder. Electrophoretic injections indicated by horizontal markers; drugs in question indicated. Time (abscissa) in minutes. Adapted from Crawford *et al.* (cf. 25).

of the Purkinje cell depends on the level of its excitability. Moreover, if the cholinergic synapses are located at the terminals of the parallel fibers, they activate in parallel the Purkinje cell as well as the inhibitory interneurons.

It cannot be stated that the activity of the cholinergic synapses, if present in the cerebellum at all, simply facilitates the activity of its multiple junctions. This point is of importance whenever central cholinergic synapses are either present or putative. These synapses are only a part of a system, and the function

Table II

CHOLINESTERASE-CONTAINING PATHWAYS OF THE HINDBRAIN[a]

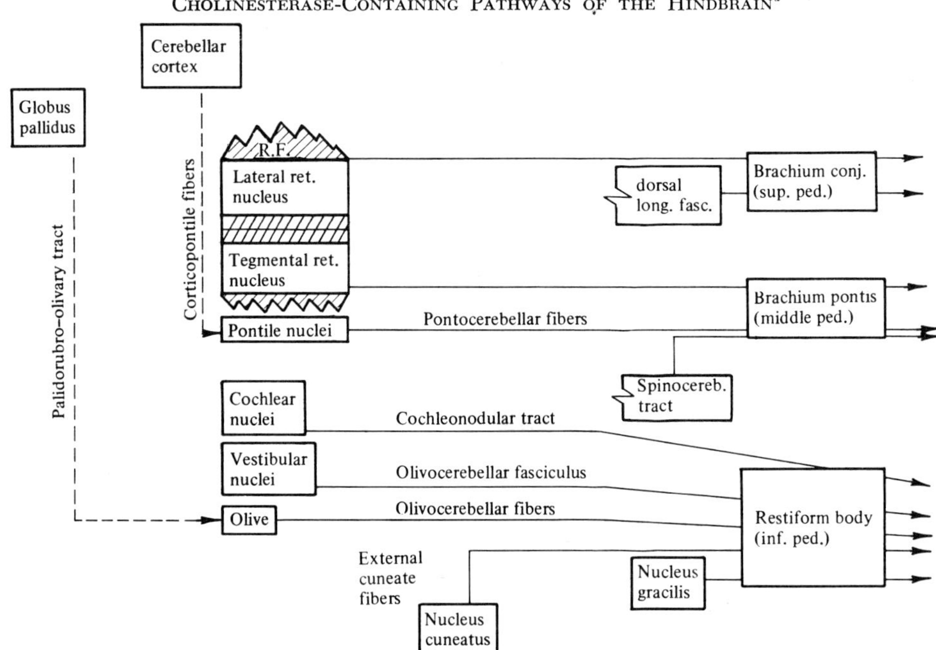

[a] Based on histochemical studies of Shute and Lewis (28). Only afferent pathways to the cerebellum indicated (efferents contain little or no ChE; cf. text). Cf. also Fig. 8.

resulting from the activity of this system cannot be directly correlated with the activity of its cholinergic synapses.

2. OTHER SITES WITH POSSIBLE CHOLINERGIC SYNAPSES

Varying proportions of cholinoceptive neurons have been found within the brain stem, the thalamus, the cerebral cortex, the caudate nucleus, and the hippocampus. In the case of the pyramidal Betz cells, 75% of the neurons tested respond to electrophoretic application of ACh and of cholinomimetics. When less well circumscribed sites were studied, the proportion of the cholinoceptive cells was found to be much lower. On the whole, the neurons in question seem to be muscarinic rather than nicotinic. They are excited by muscarine but not by nicotine, and they are blocked by atropine rather than by DHE. Thus, pharmacologically, these neurons resemble the cerebellar neurons rather than the Renshaw cell. ACh causes only depression of the spontaneous firing of some of the neurons. This is not the case with the Renshaw cell nor with the cerebellar Purkinje cell. Also, while it is difficult to compare the sensitivity of various cholinoceptive neurons to ACh, these subcortical cholinoceptive cells seemed less sensitive to ACh than the Renshaw cell.

In the view of Curtis and his associates, the delayed, frequently depressant and muscarinic character of the response of the neurons in question indicates that bona fide cholinergic synapses are not involved, the latter being characterized by the rapid and intense nicotinic response (see Fig. 4).

3. Cholinoceptive Cortical Pyramidal (Betz) Cells

It can be suggested that certain thalamic afferents form cholinergic synapses with at least some of the pyramidal neurons of the cortex. Indeed, their terminals contain vesicular ACh as well as AChE. The cholinoceptive cells are generally located in the primary sensory, including visual areas. They were identified neurophysiologically as Betz cells, although other pyramidal neurons may also be cholinoceptive. Moreover, late repetitive-unit firing evoked by specific afferent pathways via specific thalamic relays, and the potentials evoked in the somatosensory cortex by appropriate sensory or direct monosynaptic excitation, were blocked by atropine and hemicholinium, and increased by anti-ChE's. Finally, appropriate afferent stimulation and stimulation of the geniculate nuclei increased ACh output from the somatosensory and visual cortex, respectively, and this output was decreased by hemicholinium.

Krnjević hypothesized, therefore, that the synapses between the Betz cells and the pathways originating in specific thalamic nuclei, are cholinergic and that they are responsible for the late repetitive discharges (cf. 25). These pathways probably are distinct from those carrying primary afferent volleys but identical with those responsible for the projection activity and augmenting responses, as well as with the corticipetal pathways mediating arousal. Such a system may well fit the pharmacology of the reticular formation and certain behavioral responses to pertinent drugs, described below. In a still wider sense, this system may be the third relay junction and, as such, a part of the afferent relay systems.

However, the cells in question generally exhibit a delayed, muscarinic response perhaps not characteristic of cholinergic transmission (cf. above). Moreover, pharmacological studies with atropine and anti-ChE's do not always bring above consistent or expected results. Atropine, for instance, does not always block the cortical responses to the stimulation of thalamic relay nuclei. Finally, some cholinoceptive cells respond to other than specific thalamic stimulation.

It should be stressed that, as in the case of the cerebellum, the cortical excitatory synapses are a part of a complex system which includes both collateral and recurrent inhibitory circuitry. Thus ACh, if and wherever it activates such a system, must produce complex actions which cannot be considered simply as excitatory. Also, since many cortical cells are not cholinoceptive, as the distribution of ACh, ChAc, and AChE in the cortex is uneven, and since the activity of the latter is low in comparison to that of the caudate nucleus or of the medulla, many cortical areas probably do not contain cholinergic synapses.

4. The Thalamus

Neurons of the ventrobasal complex, of the lateral geniculate nucleus of the thalamus, and particularly the thalamicortical relay neurons are cholinoceptive. However, since the pharmacology of their cholinoceptive response differs from that of their response to somesthetic (via medial lemniscus) or optic tract stimulation, these sensory pathways are not considered cholinergic. Cholinergic synapses may be present at the termination of the cerebellofugal fibers at the ventrolateral thalamic relay neurons, since the latter respond to electrophoretic application of ACh, and since their response to appropriate presynaptic stimulation is blocked by atropine.

5. THE CAUDATE NUCLEUS

From 20 to 40% of the cells of the caudate nucleus respond to electrophoretic application of ACh and of cholinomimetics. Moreover, McLennan (cf. 24,25) found that both the pharmacologic responses of these cells and their response to the stimulation of nucleus ventralis anterior of the thalamus (VA) can be blocked by atropine. The caudate nucleus contains very high levels of ACh, AChE, and ChAc. Since stimulation of the VA releases ACh from the caudate nucleus, McLennan believed that there is a transmission pathway between VA and the caudate nucleus which terminates with a cholinergic synapse. This system seems different from the possible dopaminergic projection originating in neighboring thalamic nuclei (cf. Fuxe *et al.*, Chapter 6). The neurons in question exhibit muscarinic responses. Some of them respond to ACh by depression only. ACh also depresses responses to VA stimulation, and anti-ChE's affect the cholinoceptive response only slightly.

6. THE HIPPOCAMPUS

Up to 50% of the neurons of the hippocampal cortex, including the pyramidal and possibly also basket cells, are sensitive to ACh and to cholinomimetics. Their action is blocked by atropine but not by curariform drugs. The response is delayed, which is characteristic for muscarine-sensitive neurons. The activity of spontaneously firing hippocampal neurons and of those responding to septal stimulation can be increased by anti-ChE's. Additionally, studies of ChAc and AChE in normal and denervated hippocampus suggested that cholinergic fibers, possibly originating in the cells of the septum, reach the hippocampus via the fornix. They may terminate on the pyramidal cells, as well as on the cells identified as inhibitory by neurophysiological methods (perhaps corresponding to basket cells).

Basket cells, activated by the axon collateral of the pyramidal cell, send inhibitory fibers to the pyramidal soma. Thus, the neurophysiological, neurochemical, and electrophoretic data are amenable to alternative suggestions (see Fig. 7). Hippocampal pyramids may be activated by cholinergic fibers originating in the septum or in the commissure. The pyramids may in turn activate the inhibitory recurrent process, or the basket cells may be cholinergically activated, again producing inhibition, or alternatively, the basket cells may release ACh, which may act upon the pyramid as an inhibitory, hyperpolarizing transmitter.

7. THE HYPOTHALAMUS

Electrophoretically applied ACh exerts excitatory and depressant actions on the hypothalamic neurons. Moreover, unit activity of the neurons of supraoptic and paraventricular nuclei is increased by the intracarotid injection of ACh. Several areas, including the supraoptic nucleus, which may either receive or give rise to cholinergic transmission, contain neurons with varying amounts of AChE, as well as ACh and ChAc. Unfortunately, the cholinoceptive responses and the responses evoked by appropriate presynaptic stimulation have not been analyzed pharmacologically.

Shute and Lewis (28) proposed that the hypothalamic cells with a high AChE content represent relays of the ventral tegmental pathway as it leads from the midbrain to the forebrain, and are a part of a "cholinergic ascending reticular system." Actually, the cells in question arise in the areas of the afferent and efferent connections of the hypothalamus with the forebrain, midbrain, neocortex, and hypothalamohypophysial tract. However, many of the cells in these areas

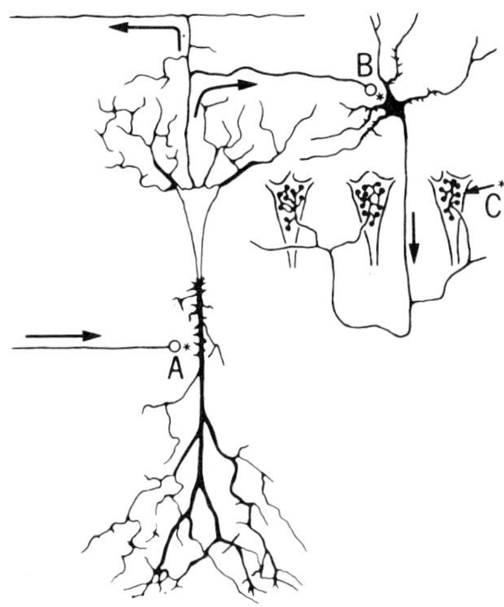

Fig. 7. Possible sites of cholinergic synapses in the hippocampus. Septal afferents (arrow) excite the pyramidal cell at A; the pyramidal neuron in turn activates via its axon collaterals (arrow) the basket cell (B), which sends inhibitory impulses (IPSP's) to the somas of three "off-line" pyramidal neurons (C). The open circles and stars indicate the action of the excitatory transmitter; the closed circles and the star (as to C) indicate the inhibitory action. ACh may act at either of the three sites (A–C; as a hyperpolarizer at C). Cf. text. Modified from Eccles (29).

do not stain for AChE, and moreover, some of the AChE-rich sites also are rich in DA and NE (cf. Fuxe *et al.*, Chapter 6).

D. Pharmacological Analysis of Central Cholinergic Mechanisms

The microelectrophoretic tests of the cholinoceptivity of single neurons coupled with pharmacological analysis of their responses to ACh and to appropriate presynaptic stimulation and with the measurements of AChE, ChAc, and ACh of the pertinent sites offer today the best approach for proving the existence of, and for localizing, central cholinergic synapses. The neuropharmacological effects of ACh, cholinergic stimulants and depressants, administered systemically or via the chemitrode, provide additional evidence for central cholinergic transmission. Since these data deal with neuronal systems and their interplays rather than with single neurons, they also provide information on the functional physiological meaning of cholinergic pathways.

1. Reticular Formation and the "Hypnogenic Center"

The reticular formation which extends from the medulla to the thalamus and reaches the cortex via the mesodiencephalic and diffuse thalamic system, is concerned with the wakefulness-sleep cycle, and with complex inhibitory and facilitatory processes extending both toward the cortex and the spinal cord. Generally, fast and low-voltage EEG results from activation of the reticular formation and accompanies behavioral alertness and goal-directed behavior. EEG slowing and synchronization may result from the interplay between facilitatory and inhibitory reticular systems, as well as from additional inhibitory circuitry emanating from the fronto-orbital cortex and from the thalamus. Indeed, the stimulation of the latter produces recruitment, augmentation, and synchronization. Depending upon this interplay, either slow, synchronized (spindle) or fast desynchronized (paradoxical) sleep may result. Certain synchronizing and augmenting activities accompany specific behavioral states. The EEG synchronization and increased voltage which occur after reinforcement (post-reinforcement synchronization, PRS) are important phenomena which occur after the goal-oriented and thus alert (EEG and behaviorwise) animal receives its award or has reached its temporary goal. Peripherally evoked cortical potentials (EP's) are increased at this time.

Chemitrode microinjection of ACh into bulbar, mesencephalic, pontine, or even rostral reticular formation produces electrocortical synchronization as well as hypnogenic action (cf. 26). This effect is identical with slow sleep, both behaviorally and with respect to the EEG. Moreover, the EP's are blocked or attenuated by ACh. This imitates one of the actions of the reticular formation, i.e., of blocking responses to sensory input as it induces sleep and inhibitory states. Two other hypnogenic areas have been explored. One of these areas is the "trophotropic zone" of the paramedian thalamic and anterior hypothalamic areas. The classical work of Hess (165) showed that low frequency stimulation of these sites induces sleep as well as a wide repertory of autonomic and behavioral responses. The other area comprises the forebrain system, which includes the preoptic region and the limbic midbrain system of Nauta. In this case, ACh and eserine produced, EEG and behaviorwise, slow sleep (cf. 26). As the system of Nauta connects with the hypothalamus and the reticular formation, the zones wherein ACh and electrical stimulation induces the slow sleep and appropriate EEG actions seem related.

The hypnogenic responses to ACh and in some cases to the electrical stimulation could be blocked by atropine. In fact, caudad direction of the hypnogenic influences could be demonstrated when the local application of atropine at the interpeduncular nucleus blocked hypnogenic action of rostrad applications of ACh (cf. 26). It was hypothesized that a cholinergic system regulates sleep and that this system is responsible for synchronizing and for attention-attentuating functions. Additional support for this hypothesis was the demonstration that the chemitrode application of NE to the pertinent sites induced EEG and behavioral effects opposite to that induced by ACh, but parallel with electrically or afferent stimulus-induced arousal mediated by the reticular formation and by the posterior hypothalamic ergotrophic zone of Hess.

The actions of certain cholinomimetics and of anti-ChE's must be, however, juxtaposed to those of ACh. Carbachol produces EEG and behavioral arousal when applied to sites at which ACh induces sleep, while a muscarinic substance, oxotremorine, produces an alert EEG pattern combined with sleep, i.e., the picture of paradoxical sleep. Anti-ChE's exhibit a number of interesting actions upon the reticular and related structures. These compounds, like carbachol, produce EEG alerting and the so-called divorce phenomenon, as there is no concomitant behavioral arousal. Anti-ChE's block recruitment, i.e., prevent augmentation and hypersynchrony of the cortical EEG, and prevent spindling. At high doses, these compounds produce convulsive spiking. Himwich (cf. 24) proposed that these actions of anti-ChE's were due to the presence of cholinergic synapses both in the reticular formation and in the diffuse thalamic system, constituting jointly an activating, cholinergic, diffuse mesodiencephalic system. However, amphetamine and other sympathomimetics produce similar EEG actions (cf. Stein and Wise, Chapter 23), and the drug-induced increase of either brain 5HT or NE, caused EEG effects resembling those of anti-ChE's, including, besides arousal, the lowering of the arousal threshold.

Atropinic substances, even when given in very small amounts to man or animal (20–50 μg/kg), produced synchronization and spindling, although again these EEG phenomena were not accompanied by frank behavioral sleep. Atropinics could also antagonize EEG alerting due to anti-ChE's.

Other interesting actions of atropinics and anti-ChE's are those concerned with PRS and certain related phenomena. The PRS, as well as the concomitant increase in cortical EP's, was blocked by atropinics, and this effect was antagonized by anti-ChE's, although, given alone, anti-ChE's prevented the PRS. Thus, alone, anti-ChE's exhibited desynchronizing actions both with regard to the PRS and to normal EEG patterns.

2. Suggested Cholinergic Mechanisms for Sleep and Related Phenomena

The dissimilar findings with anti-ChE's and carbachol, on the one hand, and ACh, on the other, as well as certain similarities between EEG actions of anti-ChE's and of sympathomimetics, appear puzzling. The effects of atropinics also seem inconsistent, for example, atropine-induced EEG synchronization is not accompanied by frank sleep, but the synchronization phenomena such as the PRS are blocked by atropine, and this effect of atropine is antagonized by anti-ChE's.

Some studies in the author's laboratories may provide an explanation for these contradictory findings. It was shown that the antagonism between anti-ChE's and recruitment depends on NE, as it did not occur after catecholamines were depleted, and as it was restored after DOPA was used to replenish the system with NE. It may be further speculated that anti-ChE's, but not ACh, may antagonize recruitment since the former induce repetitive activation of cholinergic synapses. Long-acting cholinomimetics such as carbachol and oxotremorine may act similarly. Thus, slow frequency thalamic stimulation or homologous physiological events which induce recruitment, spindling, and synchrony may be converted by anti-ChE's into a repetitive response favoring release of catecholamines. This speculation presupposes a cholinergic link in a basically adrenergic event, as proposed for certain autonomic events by Burn (cf. 24), who also suggested that slow frequency synaptic events lead to "pure" cholinergic events. In this vein, the recruitment should be a "pure" cholinergic event. The distinction between anti-ChE's and ACh would be then that the former induce fast, and the latter slow, sleep. While anti-ChE's do not produce frank hypnogenic action, their depressant actions, apparent in certain conditions, may be generally overpowered by the concomitant adrenergic release.

Thus, the EEG effect of anti-ChE's is not an example of pure arousal, and it consists of certain synchronizing and thalamic components, as well as activating components. Therefore, anti-ChE's may either antagonize the PRS, or induce the PRS and augment the EP, the type of action depending on conditions, as for instance on the presence or absence of atropine. The synchronization of the EEG and the relationship between PRS and EP may be also a matter of degree. It is of interest that in paradoxical sleep EP's are increased in spite of the fast EEG activity, and it is possible that anti-ChE's effect resembles the paradoxical sleep even to the extent of inducing an augmented EP response to afferent stimulation. This may explain the fact that atropinics block PRS as well as the PRS-augmented EP's.

3. Hypothalamic Actions of Cholinergics

As the hypothalamus contains cholinoceptive neurons, and in view of its autonomic and other functions, intrahypothalamic injection of ACh and related drugs should induce a wide variety of responses. Hypothalamic injections of some cholinergics cause thermic responses, and these may have behavioral correlates, as behavior is aimed at achieving thermoregulation.

The antidiuretic effect of cholinergic stimulants is of interest as it illustrates certain mechanisms of action available at cholinergic synapses. ACh, anti-ChE's, as well as cholinomimetics, cause the release of antidiuretic hormone (vasopressin and oxytocin), whether given intravenously or into the supraoptic nuclei. Two types of synaptic vesicles are found in the nerve terminals of the latter, small ones, which presumably contain ACh, and larger, hormone-loaded ones. Koelle proposed, therefore, that neurosecretory cells of the supraoptic nuclei are cholinergic and that hypothalamicohypophyseal fibers release ACh, which then acts via a "percussion" mechanism, liberating the hormones from the same terminals. ACh apparently does not affect the isolated posterior pituitary, and perhaps the hormonal release by endogenous or exogenous ACh occurs at a synapse between the supraoptic nuclei and cholinergic fibers arising in the lateral preoptic area.

Chemitrode experiments have proven to be of particular value in distinguishing between the feeding and drinking centers of the lateral hypothalamus. Electrical stimuli usually evoke and lesions usually block both thirst and hunger. ACh, muscarine, and carbachol produce drinking, the effect being potentiated by anti-ChE's. These actions are blocked by atropine, thus a muscarinic system may be involved (cf. 24). The system in question may be related to that controlling the release of the antidiuretic hormone since the stimulation of the thirst center occasionally causes the release of vasopressin. It is of interest that the overlapping hunger center responds to NE (cf. 24).

In the context of this review, the importance of the effects of cholinomimetics on thirst is primarily concerned with the role of thirst in behavior. The pertinent motivation may be not wholly concerned with the drive for satiation. In fact, the limbic system and several rhinencephalic structures including the amygdala have been shown to be concerned with motivation and affect associated with drinking rather than with hydration, and locally applied carbachol induces drinking in thirsty and in satiated animals alike.

4. Sensory Systems

AChE, ChAc, and ACh are present, usually at several relay levels, within the sensory system. In the case of the optic pathway, they appear first in the retina. Amacrine and bipolar cells contain ACh, and AChE abounds at their synapses with the ganglion cells (cf. 27). The lateral geniculate body, similarly to other thalamic nuclei, exhibits AChE, ACh, and ChAc, as well as cholinoceptive neurons.

ACh may participate in this pathway at several levels. The amacrine cells, interposed between the bipolar and ganglion cells, may be integrating or inhibiting the central passage of impulses initiated by light in the retina. Koelle (cf. 25) proposed that this integration is mediated by ACh, which releases percussively from the amacrine terminals, an inhibitory transmitter (Fig. 8). This effect may be blocked by strychnine, acting in this case pre- rather than postsynaptically, as classically demonstrated in the case of inhibitory action of the Renshaw cell at the motor neuron (see Fig. 5). Strychnine initiates rhythmic retinal discharge, and Koelle (25) based his suggestion of strychnine blockade of ACh release from the presynaptic terminal on his findings of such a block by strychnine of the ganglionic release of ACh. It should be added, however, that the more recent results did not indicate presynaptic actions of strychnine on the collaterals to the Renshaw cell.

ACh, physostigmine, and muscarine exert appropriate effects on the postsynaptic response of the lateral geniculate to the contralateral optic nerve stimulation (cf. 24). Sometimes these responses are blocked by curarimimetics, while atropine generally is ineffective. The doubtful status of cholinergicity of some stations in the thalamicocortical pathway has already been discussed. The responses of the somatosensory cortex to sensory stimuli increase the liberation of ACh in the cortex.

Thus, indirect evidence suggests the presence of cholinergic relays along the optic pathway, jointly with relays activated by other excitatory transmitters, as well as with inhibitory recurrent and/or collateral relays. Feldberg suggested that sensory (and motor) pathways alternate between cholinergic and noncholinergic neurons; it would be more appropriate to consider that these pathways have a hybrid nature (cf. 24).

Interesting results may be presented for the auditory system. AChE is present at some, but not all, relay stations of this system, according with the above-stated generalization. It seems to be present both in the auditory nerve and in the bundle of Rasmussen (cf. 27). It is concentrated at the lateral lemniscus and in the medial geniculate nucleus, but it is absent from the inferior colliculus.

ACh as well as several anti-ChE's given parenterally or electrophoretically, block the excitation of the afferent auditory axon by hair cells of the cochlea. The effect of the cholinergic stimulants resembles the responses to stimulation of the olivocochlear bundle of Rasmussen, which impinges via efferent axons

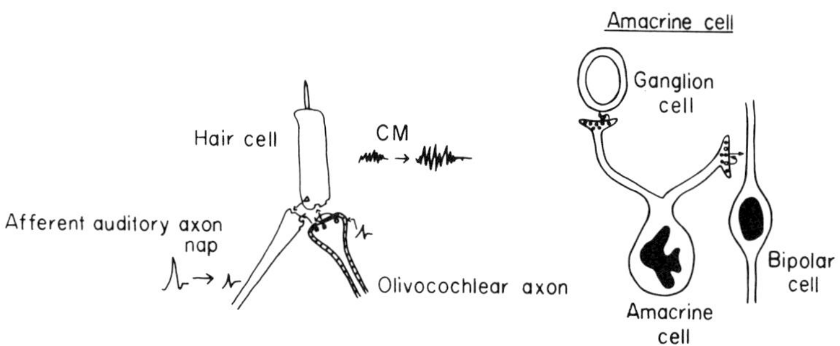

Fig. 8. Percussive release of inhibitory transmitters in the central nervous system, as proposed by Koelle (25).

On the left, diagrammatic representation of the proposed inhibitory function of olivocochlear axon (OCA). The hatched area of the axon symbolizes the presence of AChE. Normally, a nonidentified depolarizing transmitter (Δ) is released from the hair cell and excites the auditory axon. Classically, the stimulation of the OCA releases an inhibitory transmitter (□) which hyperpolarizes the hair cell and the auditory fibers, thus potentiating the cochlear microphonics (CM) and blocking the impulses (NAP) along the auditory axon; alternatively, the OCA action potential liberates ACh (O), which then releases percussively the inhibitory transmitter from the same terminal. On the right, similar representation of the proposed role of acetylcholine in the inhibitory function of the amacrine cell; the inhibitory transmitter (●) is released by acetylcholine (○). Koelle suggests that both in the case of OCA and of the amacrine cell, strychnine may block the release of ACh, besides, classically, competing with the action of the inhibitory transmitter at the auditory nerve.

upon the terminals of the afferent auditory axon as well as upon the hair cells. Anti-ChE's seemed also to prevent the behavioral responses to sound. However, while the stimulation of the olivocochlear bundle increases the cochlear microphonics, ACh and anti-ChE's suppress it. This may be explained as follows: The bundle of Rasmussen may activate a cholinoceptive interneuron, which releases a hyperpolarizing inhibitory substance; while the hyperpolarization of the hair cell membrane should increase the microphonics and inhibit the depolarization of the afferent terminal, exogenous ACh or anti-ChE's can depolarize the hair cell, thus blocking the microphonics. Another explanation may be that ACh produces in this case a hyperpolarization of the afferent axonal terminal of the auditory nerve.

Alternately, Koelle suggested that, as in the case of the amacrine cell, ACh released from the olivocochlear bundle terminals liberates via the percussion mechanism, an inhibitory transmitter from these very terminals (see Fig. 8). Strychnine and related substances blocks the responses to olivocochlear bundle stimulation (cf. 24,25) while neither atropine, DHE, nor DTC affect the olivocochlear inhibition of afferent axonal response to noise. However, if ACh acts percussively in releasing the inhibitory substance, strychnine but not atropine or curarimimetics may prevent this phenomenon. Thus, strychnine may block the inhibitory response to the stimulation of olivocochlear bundle both by a postsynaptic mechanism, and presynaptically (see Fig. 8).

5. Other Cholinergic Actions in the Central Nervous System

Certain central actions of cholinergic and anticholinergic drugs not directly pertinent to the behavioral aspects of this chapter will be mentioned briefly. Anti-ChE's and cholinergic stimulants affect monosynaptic flexor and extensor as well as polysynaptic flexor responses, and both depression and facilitation have been reported. Frequently, either type of action can be blocked by atropinics. Ultimately, anti-ChE's produce clonic and tonic convulsions, thus both spinal and subcortical mechanisms must be involved since the thalamic nuclei, the septum, and the hippocampus, all of which are affected by cholinergic stimulants and anti-ChE's, are a part of the centrencephalic epiliptogenic circuit.

A pronounced effect of cholinergic stimulants, anti-ChE's, and depressants on reflex control of respiration via the carotid body chemoreceptor system has been amply documented (cf. 24). Central medullary respiratory centers also are affected by these drugs. Ultimately, anti-ChE's induce respiratory failure, presumably due to the disorganization of the normal interplay between inspiratory and expiratory centers. Atropine rather than curarimimetics is capable of restoring the cycling function of the centers (cf. 24).

E. The Status of Central Cholinergic Transmission

The evidence with regard to cholinoceptive cerebellar, subcortical, and cerebral neurons obtained both with microelectrophoretic and chemitrode techniques; the presence in many areas of the brain of AcCh, ChAc, and ChE's; the widespread pharmacological and behavioral effectiveness of anti-ChE's, cholinergic stimulants, and blockers all demonstrate the importance of ACh in brain function. ACh may be involved in the wakefulness-sleep cycle, emotions, autonomic regulation and perception, as well as in certain behavioral patterns. It is of interest in this context that ACh is released from several brain areas following various types of activity, and that its levels vary from state to state. Yet, it should not be construed from the above alone that ACh can be thought of as the "hormone for behavior."

While cholinoceptive cells are found in many parts of the brain, they generally constitute a minority of the neurons tested. Furthermore, not every cholinoceptive cell need form a cholinergic synapse. The muscarinic response of a neuron may be interpreted as a nonspecific response, not indicative of the cholinergic innervation of the cell in question. Indeed, many cholinoceptive neurons respond also to catecholamines and 5HT and to the excitatory and inhibitory (hyperpolarizing) amino acids. This, incidentally, constitutes the phenomenon of the "mosaic" neuronal membrane. Even the classical cholinoceptive and cholinergic neuron, the Renshaw cell, responds synaptically to the inhibitory afferent stimulation homologously with its response to glycine.

In contrast to the relatively infrequent effect of ACh, the excitatory amino acids are almost always effective, and many noncholinoceptive neurons respond to catecholamines or 5HT. Nor should the case of inhibitory substances be forgotten. ACh is not the transmitter for classical post- and presynaptic inhibition, although under certain conditions it may exhibit inhibitory effects. Finally, it should be remembered that only the synapses between the motor axon collateral and the Renshaw cell have been proven to be cholinergic, although the direct demonstration of this fact is not available even for this site.

A special word of caution should be raised with regard to AChE as a marker of cholinergic synapses. The commonly carried out manometric or titrimetric studies of homogenates do not yield data on single neurons or on populations of physiologically homogeneous neurons. More relevant data can be obtained by means of histochemical and microanalytical techniques, and the findings led certain investigators to postulate cholinergicity of rather extensive pathways, including cerebellar-cerebrofugal, reticulocerebellar, and hypothalamic afferent and efferent systems (Fig. 9). Yet, the presence of AChE does not necessarily indicate that the neuron in question is cholinergic, i.e., that it releases ACh at its nerve terminals. Moreover, AChE may be an indicator of the "percussive" action of ACh and of the ultimate release of another transmitter, or of a modulatory rather than primary action of ACh. Also, ChE's may be related to processes not at all concerned with transmission or conduction (cf. 24,25).

The question of the functional significance of the central cholinergic transmission also should be raised. It has already been stressed that several putative central cholinergic synapses are parts of inhibitory circuitry. These synapses seem to activate interneurons, which in turn initiate both postsynaptic (as in the case of the motoneuron and possibly of cerebellar, cortical, and hippocampal systems) and presynaptic (as in the case of the amphibian spinal interneuron) inhibitory processes. The evidence for the cholinergically mediated release (via the percussion mechanism) of inhibitory transmitters, and even for the direct cholinergic inhibition (via hyperpolarization) also has been described. It may be suggested that a few cholinergic sites may effect widespread inhibition. Indeed, Eccles (29) suggested that the inhibitory pathways increase in importance along the neuroaxis, and also in the direction of phylogeny. This is not to be construed as saying that the stimulation of a cholinergic synapse may always, and only, lead to inhibition. These synapses form a part of "hybrid" pathways, operating via several transmitters, and involving excitatory and inhibitory systems. Therefore, whenever ACh initiates an excitatory process at a given synapse, the net process or behavior is unpredictable. In fact, depending on the pattern of mosaic responses and of the transmitters and pathways involved, no overt process may emerge at all.

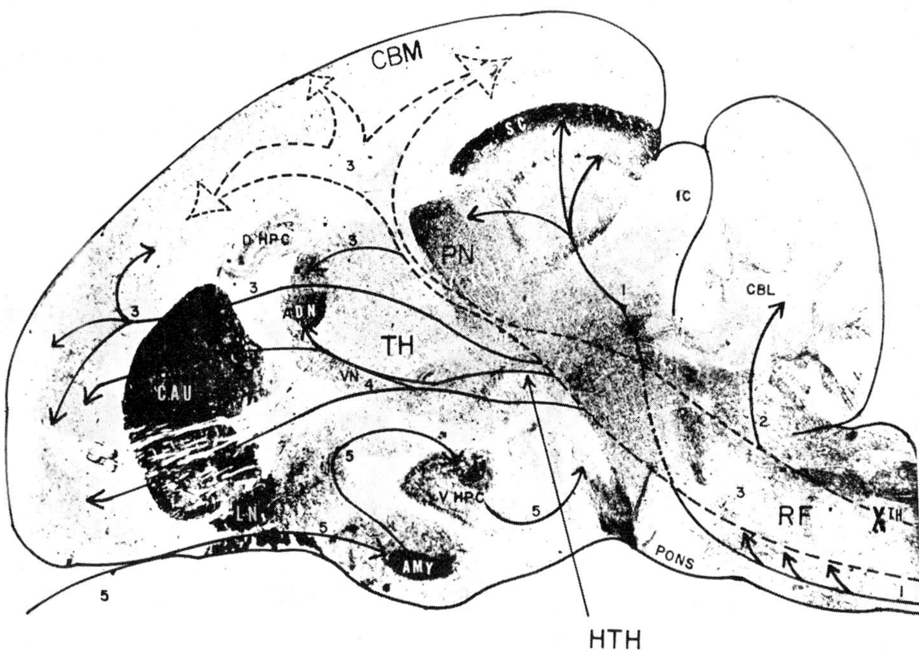

Fig. 9. Main localizations of ascending cholinergic pathways of the mammalian brain, as suggested by the distribution of AChE. A parasagittal section of the adult New Zealand albino male rabbit brain. The section has been subjected to Koelle's thiocholine histochemical procedure. Sixty minutes incubation time; no counterstain was used. The areas of dense concentration are representative of AChE localization. The arrows suggest some of the ascending cholinergic pathways. The area enclosed by the dotted line diagrams part of the ascending diffuse projection system. The hypothalamus (HTH) in this particular brain would lie medial to the section, and its relative position is shown by an arrow. (ADN) anterior dorsal nuclei of the thalamus; (AMY) amygdala; (CAU) caudate nucleus; (CBL) cerebellum; (CEM) cerebrum; (D HPC) dorsal hippocampus; (HTH) hypothalamus; (IC) inferior colliculus; (LN) lenticular nucleus; (PN) posterior nuclei of the thalamus; (PONS) pons; (SC) superior colliculus; (TH) central area of the thalamus; (V HPC) ventral hippocampus; (VN) ventral nuclei of the thalamus; (X^{TH}) motor nuclei of the X^{TH} cranial nerve. Pathways: (1) classical lemniscal pathways; (2) reticulocerebellar pathways; (3) diffuse projection pathways; (4) direct projection pathways; (5) olfactoamygdalo-hippocampohypothalamico "rhinencephalic" pathways. Figure used by courtesy of W. Van Meter.

IV. Behavioral Effects of Cholinergic and Anticholinergic Agents and Their Implications

A. *Adversive Vestibular Syndrome*

Several animal species responded by circus motions away from the injection site to unilateral intracarotid injection of anti-ChE's and related compounds or to their subcortical application, as shown first by Himwich and his group. This effect was associated with inhibition of AChE of the appropriate sites, and could be blocked by atropinics (cf. 24). The adversive syndrome was most likely concerned with the action on the vestibular and/or lateral posterior nuclei.

B. Pleasure Reward Center

Electrical stimulation of the lateral hypothalamus produces effects equivalent to those of reward or reinforcement, and animals with chronically implanted electrodes will press an electrode-activating lever for self-stimulation, as shown by Olds and his associates (cf. Scheckel, Chapter 16). The reward centers overlap with sites the stimulation of which induces adversive (avoidance) behavior and causes animals to prevent the shock by appropriate operant behavior. The reward center, but not the punishment sites, respond to cholinomimetics (cf. 24), and sympathomimetics block positive behavior. Recently, it was suggested on the basis of as yet incomplete evidence that the two systems may be mutually inhibitory, that both may contain ACh-activated synapses, and that NE may be involved in their inhibition (cf. 25).

C. Effects on Human Behavior

Cholinergic stimulants and anticholinergics were, and are, used in experimental or routine therapy. Disregarding their autonomic and somatic use, cholinomimetics have been evaluated in regressed schizophrenics. Atropinics are used in the therapy of endogenous or drug-induced (phenothiazine) Parkinsonism, as anesthetic premedication agents, in posttraumatic and postepileptic states, and, experimentally, in the treatment of selected psychoses. Moreover, accidental poisoning by anti-ChE's used as insecticides or rodenticides and by atropine occurs frequently.

Pfeiffer described a lucid moment evoked by arecoline in chronic catatonic schizophrenics, as well as alerting and awakening actions of deanol, which was mistakenly proposed to be a putative precursor of central ACh in normal subjects (cf. 24). Moreover, poisoning with anti-ChE's produces early excitement and restlessness. However, worsening or activation of schizophrenias have been reported with anti-ChE's and schizoid, depressive, and amnesic reactions, hallucinations and nightmarish dreams occur in normal subjects exposed chronically to anti-ChE insecticides.

Anticholinergics, given purposefully or ingested accidentally in overdose, present a complex symptomatology. Employed in the treatment of neurological sequelae of electroshock therapy (ECT), they decrease postshock euphoria and affect amnesia. It has been hypothesized that the ECT sequelae are due to the postconvulsive, increased central levels of ACh, and thus could be antagonized by the atropinics. However, overdoses of scopolamine, atropine, and several synthetic atropinics produce in normal subjects irritability, delusions, disorders of mood and consciousness, vivid visual hallucinations, and changes in sensory perception accompanied by EEG alterations. Some of this symptomatology is excitatory in nature, and it is noteworthy that several antidepressants, such as imipramine and benactyzine, possess marked atropinic properties. Many authors, however, have reported that atropinics produce drowsiness and depression, and it is also well known that "twilight sleep" results from the administration of combinations of scopolamine with opiates. The diversity of these findings may be explained partially by the fact that the effect of the atropinics depends on the behavioral and the EEG status of the subject.

D. Effects on Conditioned and Related Behavior

In experiments dealing with negative conditioning, animals must learn to operate a lever or to move away from a grid to avoid a shock (unconditioned) stimulus) after being warned by a conditioned stimulus. When the experiments involve positive reinforcement, the animals must learn an operant behavior for a reward, or find a solution to a maze problem (cf. Scheckel, Chapter 16).

It is generally agreed that anti-ChE's and several cholinomimetics such as arecoline, pilocarpine and tremorine, block the avoidance response without causing motor impairment or impairment of escape. Frequently, these effects are prevented by atropine, but not by quaternary anticholinergics, which do not penetrate into the brain. Russian investigators have proposed that activation of muscarinic synapses of the limbic system blocks the fear component of avoidance. However, nicotine blocks avoidance as well. Moreover, heightened anxiety, due to the drug, may impair appropriate avoidance-seeking behavior. Finally, anti-ChE's may produce amnesia, and thus may block the memory of the necessity to avoid.

Further complications arise from the fact that cholinergic blocking agents resemble cholinergic stimulants in their effect on avoidance. Particularly when relatively complex tasks based on discrimination are involved, anticholinergics effectively block conditioning. In fact, several psychotropic drugs used clinically as antianxiety agents, such as benactyzine and the antidepressant imipramine, exhibit potent atropinic actions and block avoidance in animals.

Another area of investigation is that concerned with learning and memory. Anti-ChE agents and cholinergic stimulants have been reported to both improve and to impair learning. However, high doses may impair, and low doses facilitate, learning. Paradoxically, atropinics frequently prevent learning. Furthermore, nicotinic and muscarinic substances may have different properties. Nicotine in small doses may improve learning, particularly in poor learners among animals. Nicotine also has a stimulant effect on the rate of operant behavior, distinquishable from that of amphetamine, as the latter particularly speeded up the slow rate behaviors.

As learning and memory are related processes, it is not surprising that controversial data have been reported on the effects of anti-ChE's and of related agents on memory as well. Anti-ChE's might have nonhomogenous effects on the memory processes, since they may improve the memory of almost forgotten tasks, but worsen the memory of a task learned more recently.

It is of interest in this context that atropinic substances, particularly atropine and scopolamine, consistently produced amnesic effects (also in man), and impaired learning and recall, although the impairment of memory may occur more readily with regard to such tasks as passive avoidance, but not to others. Generally, the retention of events learned under the influence of these drugs, and recall of tasks when drugs are administered *after* these tasks were learned, were both impaired. Paradoxically, atropinics may cause perseverance of responses of a certain type (freezing) in absence of reinforcement. As an amnesic, scopolamine is several times more potent than atropine.

An interesting effect of scopolamine is that it makes a redundant stimulus appear novel. Normally, a novel stimulus has a disrupting effect on goal-directed behavior, such as drinking, and this effect is attentuated following habituation to the stimulus. Pavlov postulated that "external inhibition" is concerned with the inhibition of conditioning due to novel, attention-shift-inducing stimuli, while "internal inhibition" causes habituation to redundant stimuli. Scopolamine prevents this habituation, the stimulus maintaining its disruptive effect on ongoing behavior. Also, atropinics frequently cause an increase in response rates in the course of conditioning, or reintroduces certain responses during extinction.

1. Implications of the Effects of Cholinergics and Anticholinergics on Conditioned Behavior

Several explanations have been offered with regard to the foregoing phenomena. The cholinergic system may block unrewarded behavior and prevent response to nonreinforced, redundant stimuli. The control by this system must be fluid and depend upon the condition of the organisms vis-à-vis its goal and on the state of reinforcement, as it should be possible for redundant stimuli to become relevant in certain conditions. For instance, after the reinforcement has been received, the cholinergic system activates synchronizing and inhibitory influences within the reticular formation (PRS), and facilitates and generalizes stimuli, as evidenced by the increase of certain phases of cortical EP's. Thus, the organism can pay attention to incoming stimuli for a short period following the reinforcement, thus preserving its flexibility and learning capacity.

Speculatively, atropinics may then act as follows: Responses normally inhibited by the cholinergic system and rarely occurring normally may appear following atropinics, and under certain circumstances centrally acting sympathomimetics and atropinics may reinforce each other. Moreover, the atropinics may impair performance when the latter depends on inhibition of wrong responses. For instance, the atropinics may disinhibit an animal which was taught not to press a wrong lever.

Thus, generally, the atropinics block discrimination learning and increase the tion or "freezing" effects of atropinics may be explained by their attenuation frequency of response to irrelevant stimuli. Similarly, the paradoxical antiextinc-cholinergic system is blocked, the animal continues to respond to stimuli which of the normal consequences of nonreinforcements so that when the inhibitory

The synchronizing tendencies of the cholinergic system inherent in these have become irrelevant. After reinforcement, anticholinergics exhibit a different type of action as they may block the cholinergically-induced synchronization (PRS) which relates to attention. This may explain perseverance of learned responses.

explanations of the atropinic action seem to be at odds with the desynchronizing and antirecruitment actions of anti-ChE's and of certain cholinomimetics. However, cholinergic stimulants may induce an unbalanced predominance of a part of this system concerned with maintenance of alertness, concomitant perhaps with release of NE and with its action on the facilitatory parts of the reticular formation, which is incompatible with EEG synchrony and with the PRS.

Some speculations involved the hippocampus. Theta hippocampal rhythms were thought to be associated with learning, acquisition of conditioned responses, and with orientation. Anticholinergics blocked, while physotigmine induced, these rhythms. These phenomena need not involve the hippocampus directly, since theta rhythm may originate in the posterior hypothalamicothalamic diffuse projection system. Moreover, the hippocampus exhibits a fast activity in response to a novel or indifferent stimulus, possibly originating in the midbrain reticular formation. This activity is also influenced by cholinergics and anticholinergics.

These conceptualizations may not be acceptable. They seem to offer explanations within which the facts may fit in a formal, abstract way. In experiments dealing with the postulated block by the cholinergic system of nonreinforced stimuli, excessive doses were frequently employed (for instance, 5–20 mg/kg doses of atropine were found necessary). Much smaller doses (a few μg in the case of scopolamine) suffice to block cholinoceptive responses of cells or systems (cf. 24,25); thus, it is not clear why such large doses should be necessary to block the proposed cholinergic "antiredundancy" system. In fact, these doses are capable of marked stimulation of the motor activity. In general, the motor effects of anti-ChE's, cholinergics, and anticholinergics may have influenced the operant behavior independently of their effects on fear, learning, or memory. In any event, to refer to those doses of atropine as "disinhibiting" appears to a pharmacologist as a glorification of a simple event. Neither does the pharmacologist require a special explanation when at this dose level atropine has an effect similar to that of amphetamine, or may synergize with the latter. In a different context, it should be stressed that the cholinergic drugs may affect sensory perception, as also indicated by some clinical data (cf. 24). Their effects on self-rewarding behavior also should be considered in the evaluation of their psychological actions.

It also should be stressed that only too frequently the explanations proposed hold for a particular procedure but not for another. Furthermore, the results of various investigators are frequently inconsistent. It is particularly disturbing that frequently cholinergic stimulants have been reported to produce effects similar to those of cholinergic blocking agents, hence it may be doubtful whether the cholinergic system is involved at all in the behavioral effects of either of these groups of agents.

Perhaps the most serious objection may be raised with regard to the puristic nature of some of the postulates made. As already pointed out, the circuits considered do not contain only, or even preponderently, cholinergic synapses. Other transmitters are involved as well, and the inhibitory circuitry, unrelated to ACh, is particularly important in the organization of behavior. Actually, ACh activation of any specific brain site opens up a Pandora's box, and simplified models are not tenable.

E. Cholinergic System, Adaptation and Intelligence

Krech, Rosenzweig, Bennett, *et al.* (cf. 24,25) have suggested or implied that changes in the cerebral cortex such as weight, thickness, ACh and ChE, may be related to inheritance, experience and environment, and may be correlated with adaptation and "intelligence" in the rat. This work has been criticized by many (cf. 24,25) and remains controversial. It is mentioned here only because it is cited frequently in general psychology and other texts, with perhaps less caution than its originators desired, as accepted fact, which it is not. Much further work is needed, especially to correlate the cholinergic system with all the others, known and unknown, in several species, especially primates. Nevertheless their reports have catalyzed much research.

V. Conclusions

The importance of the cholinergic system in the CNS cannot be overemphasized. It was the first system to yield the concept of chemical transmission. To date studies of it have offered some of the best research techniques in CNS biochemistry, histochemistry and neurophysiology. It is involved in such functions as respiration, water balance, motor activity, and behavior.

Both a paradox and a danger result from emphasizing the importance of the central cholinergic system. The paradox lies in the fact that relative to its importance, the system lends itself to very few therapeutic applications, being limited to antiparkinsonian therapy, minor aids in anesthesia, and minor use in psychopharmacology. The danger lurks in the exploitability of the cholinergic system for the purposes of generalizations. In fact, the limitations of its therapeutic manipulation should serve at the same time as a warning against the speculations that it generates. The therapeutic approaches to this system are limited because its broadness renders differential action within it difficult or impossible, and this very broadness should preclude overly simplified theories of its behavioral significance. Indeed, studies of the cholinergic system demonstrate admirably the cybernetic character of the CNS. The activation of a cholinergic synapse anywhere in the brain leads to an activation of multiple feedbacks, positive and negative, and to almost unpredictable reverberations throughout the brain.

This status may not continue forever. Differential therapeutic and behavioral manipulation of the cholinergic system may become possible some day. Whether it be so or not, to understand chemical transmission, one must understand the synaptic actions of ACh, and to understand the function of the brain, the interplay of cholinergic synapses with all the other synaptic systems must be first analyzed.

For further reading see Appendix 2.

6

CENTRAL MONOAMINERGIC TRACTS*

Kjell Fuxe, Tomas Hökfelt, and Urban Ungerstedt

I. Introduction

There is no doubt that the discovery of central neurons containing dopamine (DA), norepinephrine (NE), and 5-hydroxytryptamine (serotonin, 5HT), respectively, has been of great importance for the understanding of the mode of action of a large number of psychoactive drugs. The discovery of these new types of neuron systems was made thanks to the development of a very sensitive and specific histochemical fluorescence method for the demonstration of DA, NE, and 5HT. The method was introduced into neurohistochemistry in 1962 (30), and the results obtained on the central nervous system are summarized in this chapter.

The method is based on the discovery that the amines can be converted into strongly fluorescent compounds if exposed to formaldehyde gas, and if dried protein is present. The catecholamines (CA) are converted into strongly green fluorescent, 3,4-dihydroisoquinolines (420/480 mμ) with a secondary filter that cuts below 480 μ, whereas 5HT is converted into a yellow fluorescent 3,4-di-

* This work has been supported by the Swedish Medical Research Council (B69-14X-715-04A), "Stiftelsen M. Bergwalls Minne" and Knut and Alice Wallenberg Foundation.

hydro-β-carboline (420–525 mμ) with the same secondary filter as mentioned above.

II. The Main Characteristics of the Central Monoamine Neurons

Using this technique it was found that nerve cell bodies existed in the lower brain stem, containing low concentrations of CA and 5HT, respectively. The cell bodies (15–30 μ in diameter) were usually found to have a weakly to medium fluorescent cytoplasm with the fluorescence often concentrated in a perinuclear zone. These nerve cell bodies give rise to thin unmyelinated fibers (mainly between 0.2–1 μ in diameter) which are divided into very fine to fine terminal branches when they reach the brain area to be innervated. It is possible to see that the fluorescence in the terminals is concentrated on small enlargements of the terminal branches which vary mainly between 0.4–2 μ in diameter and which occur with frequent intervals (1–7 μ) along the axon. These enlargements contain extremely small amounts of amines, but on account of their small size almost enormous concentrations are reached. Almost the entire amine content of the brain is present in these enlargements or "varicosities," as Hillarp called them. The amines are in all probability localized in high concentrations in submicroscopic granules, and there is now good evidence that these granules correspond to the so-called dense core or granular vesicles as demonstrated in electron microscopic studies. Evidence has been obtained that these granules are produced in the cell bodies and transported down to the terminals via the axons. The main site of production is probably in the Golgi zone, which occupies most of the periventricular zone, where the highest fluorescence intensity is observed in the cell bodies (Fig. 1). These granules have an uptake-storage mechanism of amines which is highly sensitive to reserpine. At the level of the nerve cell membrane there exists another amine concentrating mechanism, which is not sensitive to reserpine and which is present in the entire neuron. This mechanism has been demonstrated and studied both *in vitro* using brain slices and *in vivo* using, e.g., intraventricular injections of unlabeled CA and 5HT.

The varicosities, which in all probability are the presynaptic structures, probably make both axosomatic (e.g., in the ventral horn) and axodendritic (e.g., in the neocortex) contacts with both nonamine-containing and amine-containing (CA and 5HT) neurons.

It is necessary to differentiate the DA nerve terminals from the NE nerve terminals by the use of a large number of pharmacological tests because the fluorescent compounds formed from DA and NE have identical activation and emission spectra. Thus, the DA nerve terminals recover their amine levels much more rapidly after initial depletion with α-methyl-*m*-tyrosine than the NE nerve terminals; the DA nerve terminals are not depleted of amines by treatment with a DA β-oxidase inhibitor; the DA nerve terminals do not, in contrast to the NE nerve terminals, remain fluorescent after reserpine treatment of α-methyl-dopa pretreated rats.

Since the nonterminal axons normally have such low amine concentrations

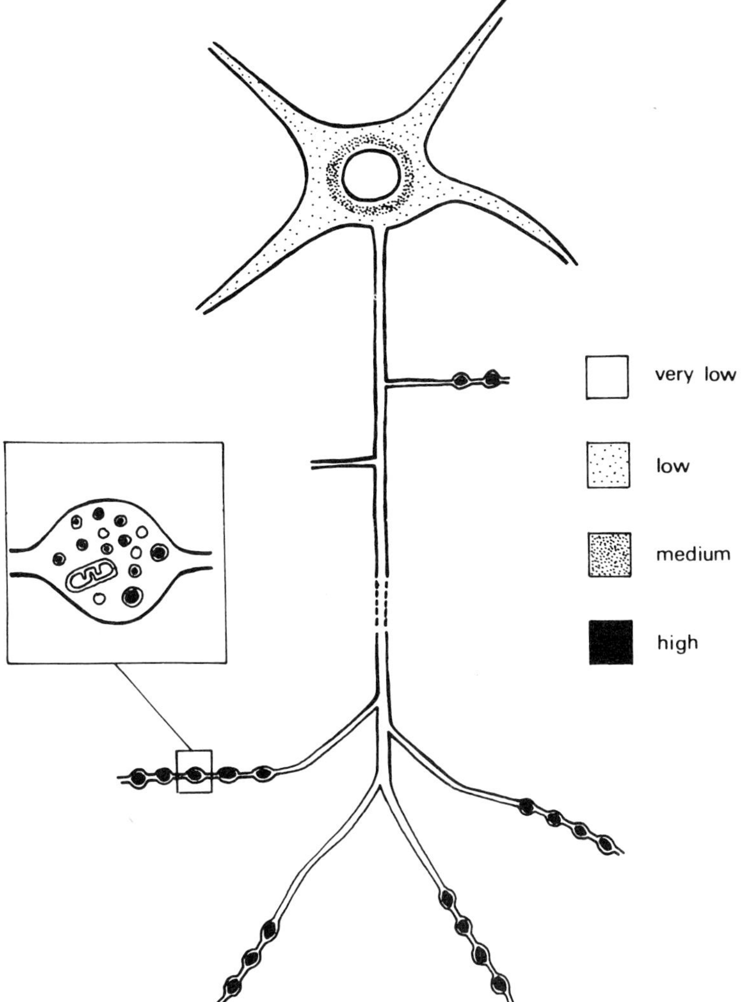

Fig. 1. Schematic illustration of the principal morphologic features of a central monoamine neuron. The concentration of amines in the different parts of the neuron is indicated by density of black dots. High concentrations are found in the varicosities of the terminal branches, which are filled with granular vesicles. Medium concentrations are found in a perinuclear zone, low concentrations in the remaining part of the cell body and very low concentrations in the nonterminal axons. Note the existence of collaterals.

that they cannot be visualized with the histochemical fluorescence technique, it is difficult to determine to which monoamine-containing cell bodies the various terminal systems belong. However, it has been possible to map out a large number of monoamine neuron systems, thanks to the development of certain pharmacological and experimental procedures (Fig. 2). The pharmacological procedure consists of increasing the amine levels in the entire monoamine neuron so that the nonterminal axons are also visualized. This procedure has proved most successful in the case of the 5HT neurons, since after monoamine oxidase inhibition these neurons become strongly yellow fluorescent in both cell bodies and nonterminal axons and terminals. The experimental procedure involves stereotaxic lesions in the terminal areas, tracts, or cell body area and subsequent study of the anterograde and retrograde degeneration in the monoamine neurons by way of histochemical and biochemical analysis of monoamines. This is the first time in neurohistology that it has been possible to map out special neurons

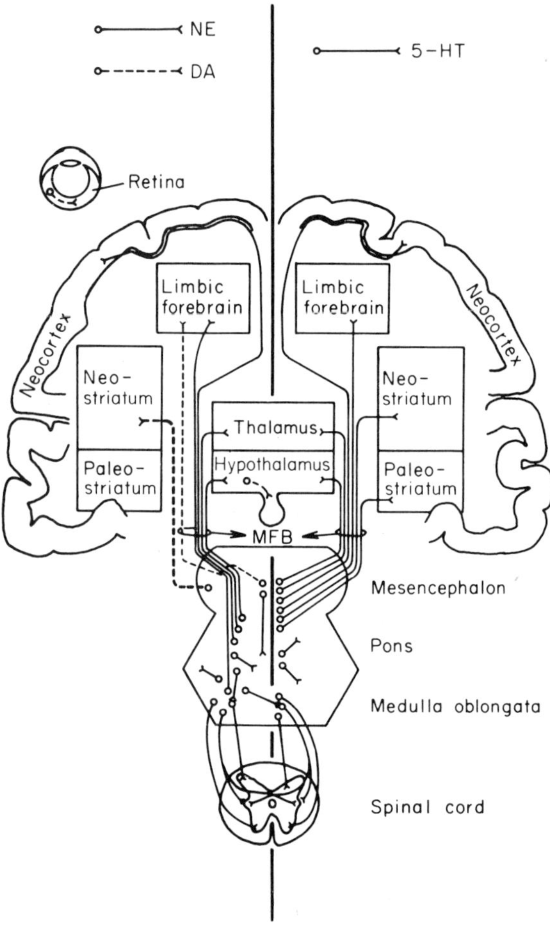

Fig. 2. Schematic drawing showing, in highly simplified form, the main monoamine neuron systems in the central nervous system.

by studying changes in the transmitter contents of neurons after lesions and drugs.

Because of the development of potent inhibitors of CA and 5HT biosynthesis, it is possible to study the state of activity, i.e., functional aspects in the various monoamine neuron systems, since the amine depletion obtained after inhibition of synthesis is highly dependent on the nervous impulse flow. Thus, an increased nervous impulse flow will result in a greater rate of amine depletion, whereas decreased impulse flow will result in a decreased rate of amine depletion. In view of this, the activity of the various monoamine neuron systems may be studied directly under the microscope under various physiological and pharmacological conditions by examining the rate of disappearance of fluorescence from the terminals after inhibition of synthesis.

III. Dopamine Neuron Systems and Their Possible Function

The systems discovered so far are two large ascending DA neuron systems and one small DA neuron system which converge onto the primary capillary plexus of the hypophyseal portal systems. The ascending fibers originate mainly from DA cell bodies situated in the zona compacta of the substantia nigra. The fibers mainly become aggregated in a bundle situated just medial and ventromedial to the lemniscus medialis in the area of the nucleus interstitialis descussationis tegmenti ventralis and of area ventralis tegmenti. This bundle lies dorsomedial to the ventral part of the crus cerebri in the H_2 area of Forel before it enters the rostral part of the crus cerebri. After entering the crus cerebri the tract soon diverges into the internal capsule to innervate the nucleus caudatus putamen. The DA nerve terminals are very densely packed and probably mainly make axodendritic contacts. It has been roughly calculated that the terminal system of one single nigroneostriatal DA neuron amounts to about one-half meter and contains about one-half-million varicosities. This probably means that a single neuron innervates a large number of nerve cells in the neostriatum. The divergence is undoubtedly of considerable functional importance. This system is of importance for normal posture and motor activation. The DA neurons are probably degenerated in Parkinson's disease, and the decreased DA neurotransmission in the corpus striatum is at least partly responsible for some of the symptoms (e.g., the rigidity) of this disease (see Hornykiewicz *et al.*, Chapter 46).

The other large ascending DA pathway innervates the nucleus accumbens and the tuberculum olfactorium. This tract probably has most of its cell bodies localized in the CA cell group surrounding the cranial part of the nucleus interpeduncularis, especially the dorsal part, since destruction of this cell group will cause degeneration of the DA nerve terminals in the areas mentioned above. The fibers ascend medial to the nigroneostriatal fibers but lateral to the ascending NA pathways. The possible function of this system is as yet unknown.

The DA nerve terminals in the external layer of the median eminence derive from fibers which originate mainly from DA cell bodies in the arcuate and anterior periventricular nuclei. Evidence has been presented that this neuron system participates in the regulation of gonadotrophin secretion, possibly by inhibiting the release of the luteinizing hormone and/or follicle stimulating hormone releasing factors from the median eminence.

During hypnosis with barbiturates DA neurons in general seem to have decreased activity. Furthermore, oxotremorine, which causes hypothermia and tremor, probably increases the activity of both the DA and NA neuron systems. The activation of the DA neurons seems to require a cholinergic link.

IV. Norepinephrine Neuron Systems and Their Possible Functions

Both descending and ascending NE neuron systems exist. The descending NE nerve fibers run down in the anterior and lateral funiculi and innervate the gray matter of the spinal cord. Close contacts are probably made with the cell bodies of motor neurons belonging to both flexor and extensor cell groups. There is a heavy innervation of the preganglionic sympathetic nerve cells and of the substantia gelatinosa. Probably, in the latter region, mainly dendritic contacts are made. The fibers are mostly derived from NE cell bodies present in the medulla oblongata, situated mainly in the lateral area of the nucleus

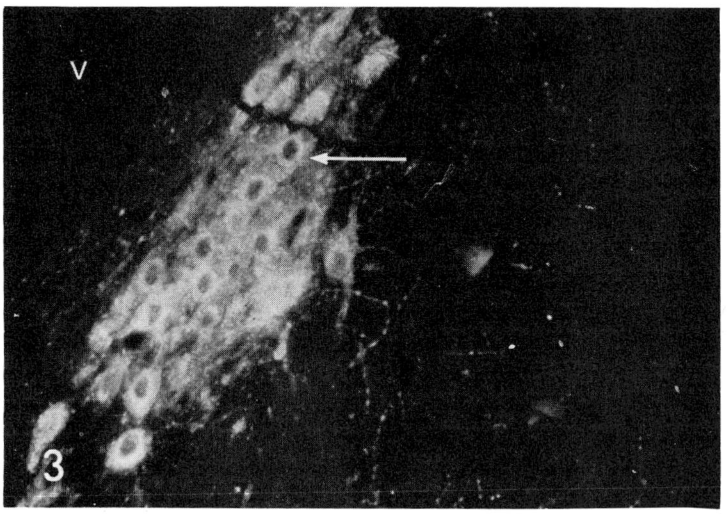

Fig. 3. NE cell bodies in the rat locus coeruleus. There is an accumulation of fluorescence in the cytoplasm, especially in a zone around the nucleus (arrows). (V) fourth ventricle. ×120.

reticularis lateralis. Some of these terminals seem to be able to inhibit normal transmission from flexor reflex afferents to dorsal roots, motor neurons, and ascending pathways resulting in blockade of short latency effects from the flexor reflex afferents.

The majority of NE nerve terminals in most areas of the telencephalon and diencephalon arise from axons ascending mostly in the medial forebrain bundle, and which are derived from NE cell bodies situated in the pons (locus coeruleus) and medulla oblongata (formatio reticularis). After leaving the rhombencephalon the NE fibers become aggregated in a lemniscus in the reticular tegmental midbrain running parallel to the longitudinal axis of the brain oriented in a dorsoventral direction, after which many of them reach the medial forebrain bundle by passing between the fasciculus retroflexus and lemniscus medialis.

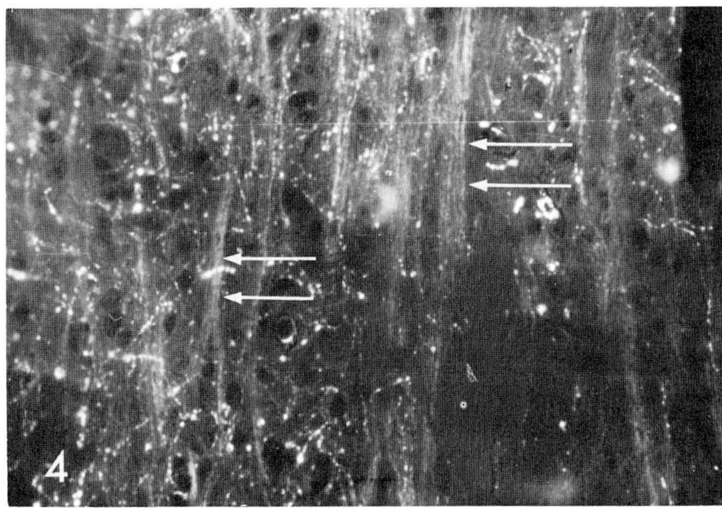

Fig. 4. Nonterminal NE-containing bundles of axons (arrows) in the medial forebrain bundle. They have a smooth appearance and exhibit only a weak green fluorescence due to very low amine concentrations. Also, varicosities with high concentrations can be seen. ×200.

The fibers innervate the limbic forebrain structures (for example the septal area, amygdaloid cortex, gyrus cinguli), the nucleus interstitialis striae terminalis, the preoptic area, the hypothalamus, and the neocortex. (Figs. 3, 4, and 5.)

The rest of the NE terminals (about 25%) in the telencephalon and di-

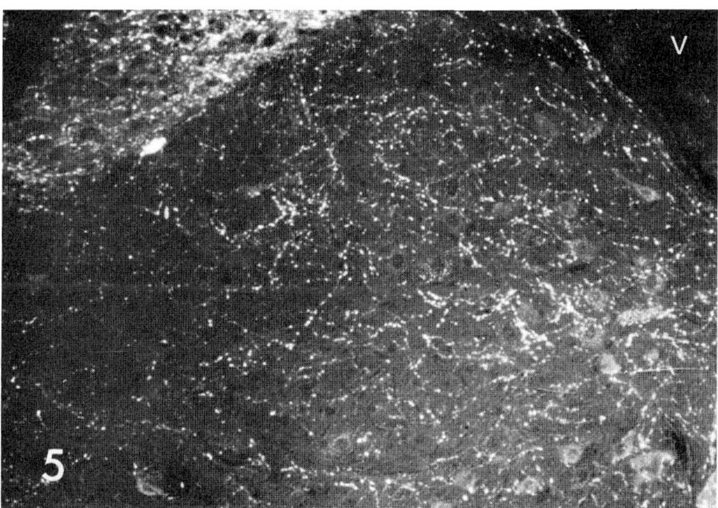

Fig. 5. A plexus of strongly fluorescent NE and 5HT nerve terminals is observed in the nucleus hypoglossus of rat. The terminals are characterized by the strongly fluorescent varicosities with their high amine concentrations. (V) fourth ventricle. ×120.

encephalon may arise partly from CA cell bodies localized to the area surrounding the nucleus interpeduncularis (group A10) (30).

The NE nerve terminals of the lower brain stem, including the cerebellum, probably arise from NE cell bodies in the medulla oblongata and pons, since destruction of all the CA cell bodies in the mesencephalon does not decrease their number in these areas of the brain. Recently, important data have been obtained with the help of large lesions between the mesencephalon and diencephalon which opens up new aspects concerning the morphology of the NE neurons. These findings support the view that a single NE neuron may simultaneously innervate, e.g., parts of the cerebellum and telencephalon (parts which lie far away from one another). Thus, the ascending NE neurons must give off many collaterals during their ascent, meaning that they may influence the activity in large areas of the brain. This is of great importance when analyzing how the NE neurons exert their effects in the brain, and how these effects may be changed by antipsychotic drugs.

Some of the NE fibers in the medial forebrain bundle reach the neocortex by turning dorsally into Broca's diagonal band, after which they run caudally in the cingulum giving rise to terminals making contact especially with the terminal parts of the apical dendritic tree of the pyramidal cells. The NE fibers to the hippocampal formation enter partly via the dorsal fornix and the fimbriae hippocampi. Some of the NE fibers reach the amygdaloid cortex area via the striae terminalis neurons as described here have hitherto not been discovered in the brain, and show that monosynaptic connections exist between the limbic forebrain areas and the neocortex, on one hand, and the reticular core of the lower brain stem, on the other hand.

It has been found that there is increased activity of both ascending and descending NE neurons under the influence of a hot but not a cold environment, under restraint stress, and during sham rage. These data indicate that the central NE neurons may participate in thermoregulation (the thermosensitive area in the anterior hypothalamus contains NE nerve terminals) in response to stress and in primitive emotional responses. The central DA neurons do not show any change of activity with these conditions. Data also exist to suggest that the various NE (and to a certain extent the DA) nerve terminals of the brain are activated during conditioned avoidance response. This suggests that conditioning mechanisms are also under the influence of CA neurons. Together, these data indicate that the NE neurons participate in the regulation of diverse fundamental mechanisms and influence activity in many areas of the brain. Evidence also exists that the NE neurons participate in the control of secretion of antidiuretic hormone, oxytocin, gonadotrophin, ACTH and growth hormone.

V. The Serotonin Neurons and Their Possible Function

In respect to 5HT neuron systems, descending and ascending pathways also exist. The descending 5HT pathways arise mainly from the lower raphe nuclei (i.e., nucleus raphe pallidus and nucleus raphe obscurus) and descend in the anterior and lateral funiculi to innervate the gray matter of the spinal cord. The fibers have a more superficial position in the white matter than the descending NE fibers. There is a heavy innervation of the sympathetic lateral column, and especially the ventral horn of the lumbosacral part. Close contacts are made with the cell bodies of the motor neurons. Data exist suggesting that release of 5HT from some of these terminals increases the flexor and extensor reflexes in the acute spinal animal, in the same way as release of NE from the NE nerve terminals. Therefore, descending monoaminergic pathways may be involved in the control of somatic reflexes. Some 5HT pathways also seem to increase excitability of all the motor neurons.

The ascending 5HT neuron systems originate mainly from cell bodies of the raphe nuclei of the lower brain stem, especially the nucleus raphe dorsalis and nucleus raphe medianus. Most of the axons ascend in the lateral hypothalamic area together with the NE axons and accompany them to the cortical areas and limbic forebrain structures.

The ascending 5HT neurons may also participate in the control of temperature regulation, since they show decreased activity when the animals are exposed to a low temperature and increased activity if the animals are exposed to a high temperature. It may be added that there probably is interaction between the NE and 5HT neurons because of heavy innervation of the lower raphe nuclei (containing 5HT cell bodies) by NE nerve terminals.

VI. Central Monoamine Neurons and Psychoactive Drugs

Because we now can visualize the transmitter substances, it is possible to study the effect of psychoactive drugs on the amine levels of the central DA, NE, and 5HT neurons directly with the microscope.

A. *Antipsychotic Drugs*

Reserpine causes a varying degree of amine depletion in the different terminal systems. For example, the neocortical NE nerve terminals are much more sensitive to reserpine than the hypothalamic NE nerve terminals. Also, within the same areas, there are terminals with varying degrees of sensitivity. The depleting effect of reserpine on the intraneuronal amine stores of the central catecholamine neurons is probably responsible for the pharmacologic effects of reserpine, such as sedation and decreased mobility.

Haloperidol and chlorpromazine, however, do not decrease the fluorescent intensity of the various DA, NE, and 5HT nerve terminals, although they cause similar pharmacological effects. Instead, certain cell groups in the medulla oblongata (A1) show increased fluorescent intensity. This may be due to increased production of amine storage granules. In turn, this is probably due to the fact that haloperidol and chlorpromazine block central CA receptors, which will result in a compensatory activation of the central CA neurons. Recently, increased activity has, in fact, been demonstrated in the central DA and NE neurons.

B. Antidepressant Drugs

Monoamine oxidase inhibitors such as pargyline, nialamide, pheniprazine, and tranylcypromine markedly increase the fluorescent intensity of the 5HT neurons, whereas the central CA neurons show only small increases (30). Therefore, the antidepressant effects of these inhibitors may be due mainly to an increased release of 5HT because of the marked accumulation of this amine.

In vivo and *in vitro* studies show that amphetamine in low doses can block the reserpine-resistant accumulation of CA into central NE and DA neurons, and markedly enhance the rate of its disappearance if the drug is given after the administered CA. The effects of amphetamine are probably due to release of extragranular amines. It is especially interesting to note the sensitivity of the neocortical NE nerve terminals to amphetamine, in view of the high psychomotor stimulation capacity of this drug.

Results from studies on the effect of imipramine-type drugs on uptake mechanisms in the central monoamine neurons have clearly indicated that desipramine and protriptyline selectively block the accumulation of fluorescence of administered catecholamines (DA and NE) into the central NE neurons. This is probably due to a blockade of the reserpine-resistant uptake-concentration mechanism situated at the level of the nerve cell membrane. The 5HT and especially the DA neurons are mainly unaffected by these drugs. These results indicate that the NE neurons are concerned in the regulation of affective states. This is supported by the fact that ethanol and acute doses of lithium (which may be a prophylactic agent against depressions and manias, cf. Schou, Chapter 51) probably increase the activity of the central NE neurons. However, 5-hydroxyindoleacetic acid levels in the cerebrospinal fluid are decreased in depressed patients, and imipramine and amitriptyline have little effect on the reserpine-resistant uptake-concentration mechanism of the central NE neurons, whereas the corresponding mechanism in the 5HT neurons is blocked to a large degree by these drugs.* Therefore, 5HT neurons are probably of even greater importance for the affective states.

For further reading see Appendices 1 and 2.

* Furthermore, prolonged lithium treatment probably decreases central 5HT neuro-transmission.

7

ELECTRON MICROSCOPIC ASPECTS OF NEURAL FUNCTION

G. K. Aghajanian

I. Introduction

It is now generally accepted that in the mammalian nervous system the transmission of impulses between neurons is chemically mediated (29). As a consequence of this belief, many investigations into the mechanism of action of neurotropic drugs deal directly or indirectly with some aspect of the synthesis, storage, release, and inactivation of substances suspected of being chemical transmitters, It has become common practice to assign cellular loci to these processes as a basis for conceptualizing possible sites of drug action. For example, a drug may be thought of as producing its effects by "releasing" a transmitter onto a receptor site. Quite different effects could result if a drug released the transmitter at a site distant from the receptor (e.g., at an intracellular site). Thus, the ultimate effect of a drug may depend critically upon its cellular locus of activity. In this context some familiarity with functional aspects of the fine structure of neurons becomes essential for understanding how a drug acts in the brain.

II. Fine Structure of Neurons: Nerve Endings

The fine structure of CNS tissue is unusual in several ways. There is remarkably little extracellular space evident in brain prepared for electron microscopy by standard fixation methods. The limiting membranes of neuronal and glial perikarya and their various processes are in uniformly close apposition, giving rise to the appearance of a tightly packed mosaic. The fine structure of neuronal perikarya per se does not differ appreciably from that of other cell types. Neurons, in common with most cells, possess nuclei, a "smooth" and "rough" endoplasmic reticulum, free ribosomes, mitochondria, lysosomes, etc. However, sites of interneuronal contiguity show a high degree of morphologic specialization, and the structural features of such sites will be emphasized since they ostensibly subserve the function of impulse transmission. With light microscopic methods the "bouton," "synaptic knob," or axonal "end foot" was long recognized to occur at regions of immediate proximity between an axon of one neuron and the dendrite or soma of another neuron. With the advent of electron microscopy the fine structural details of boutons or nerve endings could be observed for the first time. Under the electron microscope, nerve endings appear as terminal or *en passage* swellings of axons. The endings contain numerous vesicular structures, the so-called synaptic vesicles (Fig. 1). Synaptic vesicles in endings of inhibitory nerves seem to be slightly larger in diameter than those in excitatory endings (31). In addition to synaptic vesicles, mitochondria are also commonly found within nerve endings (see Fig. 1). These differ only in minor respects from mitochondria seen elsewhere. Portions of the limiting membrane of the nerve ending contiguous with the postsynaptic neuron appear "thickened" (see Fig. 1). Such morphologically specialized sites of contact are referred to variously as "synapses," "synaptic junctions," "junctional complexes," etc.

The functional significance of the various fine structural components of nerve endings is often assumed to be self-evident. It seems quite plausible, for example, that the "synaptic junction" is the morphologic counterpart of "synaptic transmission," or that "synaptic vesicles" are sites of storage and release of neurotransmitters. The fact is, however, that there is an enormous gap between an image seen with the electron microscope and phenomena on a chemical or physiological level, and there has been a great effort in recent years to link specific neural events (both chemical and physiological) to specific morphologic entities. Some highlights of this work, particularly that dealing with the nerve ending and its component parts, will be detailed here.

III. Synaptic Junctions

The physiological concept of the "synapse" emanates from early observations on the reflex arc which showed a temporal delay beyond that accounted for by nerve conduction alone and a unidirectional character of transmission. The morphologic concept of the "synapse" grew out of the neuron theory which, by postulating independent cellular units, created a need for explaining how

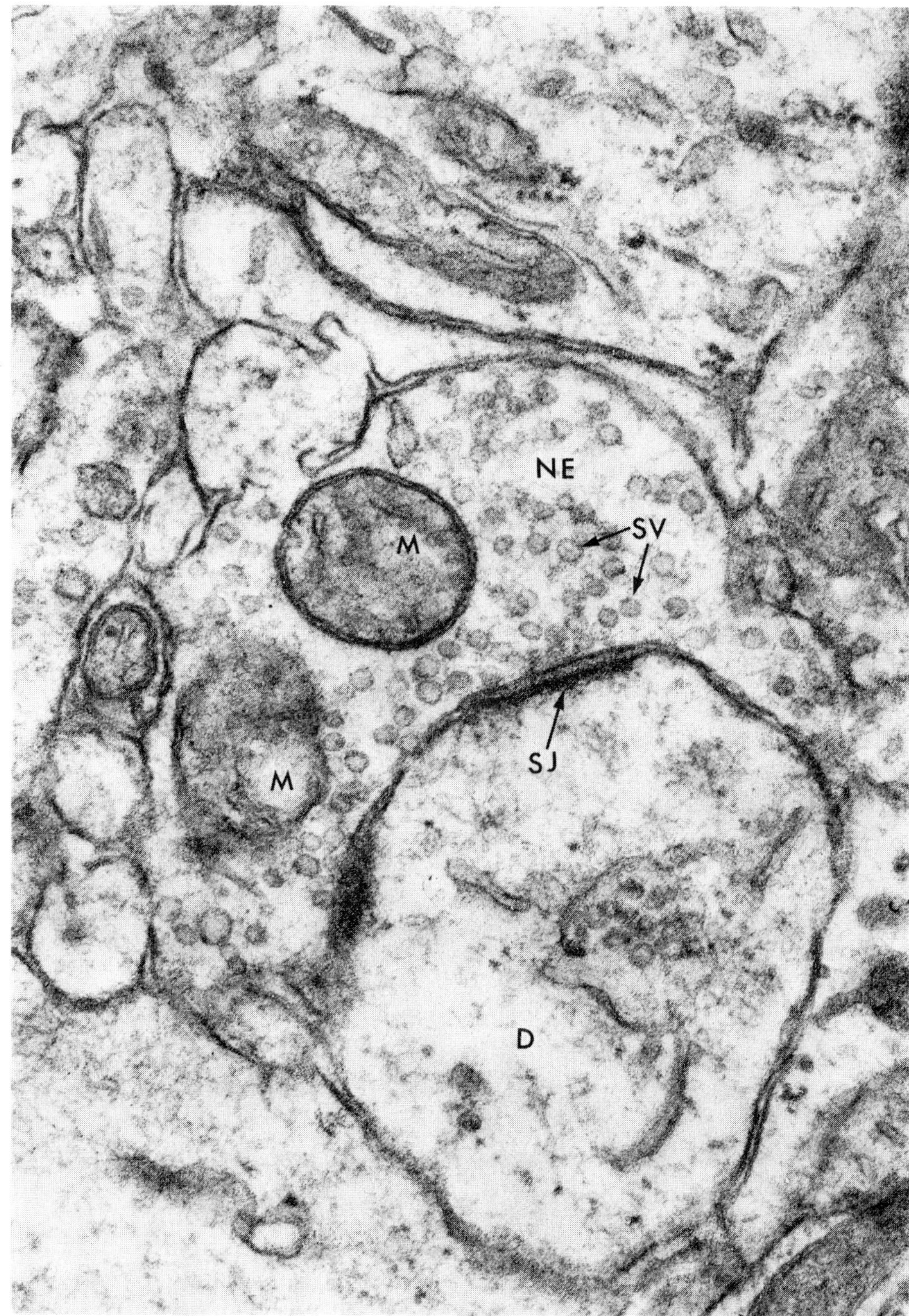

Fig. 1. Electron micrograph of a nerve ending in the paraventricular nucleus of the hypothalamus. The nerve ending (NE) shown in this micrograph forms a synaptic junction (SJ) with a dendritic process (D). Synaptic vesicles (SV) and mitochondria (M) are seen within the ending. The synaptic junction is characterized by a "thickening" along portions of the pre- and postsynaptic membranes. (Micrograph provided by G. K. Aghajanian and F. E. Bloom.) ×72,000.

impulses bridged the gap between separate neurons. It remained for electron microscopy to provide a suitable morphologic candidate for subserving the function of synaptic transmission, namely, the specialized zones of interneuronal contact (32). These zones, which may be called "synaptic junctions," are characterized by the presynaptic dense projections abutting against the inner surface of the presynaptic membrane, a cleft of approximately 200 Å separating the pre- and postsynaptic membranes in which some electron-opaque material can be seen, and a dense band within the postsynaptic cell or process (see Fig. 1). This complex of structures is often referred to as a region of "thickening" of the synaptic membranes, but recently it has clearly been demonstrated by a selective staining procedure that the material of the "thickening" is independent of the membranes. This material, which is arranged asymmetrically about the synaptic junction, appears to be composed in part of a dense deposit of basic proteins (33). Synaptic vesicles are usually clustered around the presynaptic dense projections.

The functional significance of the morphologically specialized contact zones is a subject of continuing speculation and controversy. The asymmetric distribution of the synaptic material and synaptic vesicles seems to be a morphological counterpart of the unidirectional nature of synaptic transmission. It is therefore tempting to assign the role of synaptic transmission to "synaptic" junctions. It must be realized, however, that there has been no *direct* proof of this proposition. Nevertheless, there are certain indirect lines of evidence which suggest that synaptic junctions are involved in transmission. For example, it has been shown that the rate of appearance of the synaptic material at junctional sites in developing rat cortex is closely correlated with the maturation of the EEG and behavior (34). Whether the synaptic material may facilitate transmission simply by an adhesive function or whether it participates in the process of transmitter release, activity, or inactivation remains a major unsolved problem.

IV. Neurotransmitters

There have been two principal histochemical approaches to the electron microscopic study of prospective neurotransmitters in brain: (1) subcellular techniques, by which chemical determinations are correlated with electron microscopically identified centrifugal fractions of homogenized tissue, and (2) histochemical staining and autoradiographic techniques utilizing intact tissue sections. Each approach has its advantages and limitations; subcellular methods permit precise chemical identification, while structural organization is preserved in methods using whole tissue. The major finding of the subcellular method has been the association of various potential transmitter substances (e.g., acetylcholine, serotonin, norepinephrine, and histamine) within density gradient fractions of brain homogenates that contain a high proportion of pinched-off nerve endings or "synaptosomes" (35,36). Synaptosomes are artifacts in the sense that they are formed during homogenization when nerve endings become detached from their axons. The detached nerve ending, which may retain a portion of the postsynaptic membrane as well as its content of vesicles and mitochrondria, can be partially separated from other substituents of the homogenate by means of centrifugation on a density gradient. This work with synaptosomes began before any of the other histochemical methods were in use and provided the first direct evidence that the various prospective transmitter substances were at least present in nerve endings. When the synaptosomes are ruptured by means of osmotic shock, the synaptic vesicles are liberated and can be isolated in a fairly pure fraction. It is significant that such vesicle fractions have a residual content of acetylcholine, serotonin, and norepinephrine despite the vigorous disruptive treatment. These findings are consistent with the long-standing hypothesis that synaptic vesicles contain neurotransmitters and are somehow involved in quantal or other forms of release.

The electron microscopic histochemistry of prospective neurotransmitters in whole tissue has thus far been rather limited in scope. The greatest success in localization has been with the monoamines (e.g., norepinephrine and serotonin). There is apparently an active uptake mechanism for these substances at the nerve ending membrane and this permits the introduction of radioactively labeled amines; the localization of the radioactive substances can then be studied with the technique of electron microscopic autoradiography. This approach was first used by Wolfe and coworkers (37) to localize tritiated norepinephrine in peripheral adrenergic nerves. Recently a similar approach was employed to identify sites of uptake of norepinephrine (38) and serotonin (39) in the brain. Glowinski and coworkers have shown that the intraventricular injection of norepinephrine, which circumvents the blood-brain barrier, leads to an uptake of the amine into the brain and an apparent mixing with endogenous norepinephrine (40). Electron microscopic autoradiography after such an intraventricular injection reveals an accumulation of tritiated norepinephrine over certain nerve endings in areas (e.g., paraventricular hypothalamus) that are rich in endogenous norepinephrine (Fig. 2). A high proportion of nerve endings with autoradiographic activity contain large (1000 Å) granular vesicles in addition to the more populous small (500 Å) vesicles with an agranular appearance. An accumulation of tritiated serotonin also occurs in nerve endings within the brain after an intraventricular injection, but with a regional pattern of distribution which differs from that of norepinephrine. This difference suggests some chemical specificity in monoamine uptake mechanisms (39).

The histochemical staining approach to the localization of transmitter substances in the central nervous system has not thus far been as successful as in peripheral nerves. Norepinephrine in peripheral adrenergic nerves has been repeatedly identified in relation to the granular contents of small (300–500 Å) vesicles within endings. In contrast, small vesicles in brain nerve endings, even in areas rich in endogenous norepinephrine, have not appeared to contain any granular material by the usual histochemical methods (i.e., fixation with osmium tetroxide). Recently, it has been reported that fixation with permanganate will demonstrate granularity in small vesicles of ending in areas high in norepinephrine (41). At best, however, histochemical methods for norepinephrine or other substances probably indicate only storage sites and do not reveal other significant compartments such as the postulated receptor sites. In addition, methods for the demonstration of possible neurotransmitters other than monoamines in whole tissue sections by electron microscopy are totally lacking. Since monoamine neurons represent less than one percent of all brain neurons, the magnitude of ignorance in this important area is clearly great.

V. Enzymes

As in the case of the neurotransmitters, studies on the electron microscopic localization of enzymes in nerve endings have utilized both subcellular and whole tissue methods. Enzyme activity associated with synaptosome fractions may be in one or more of the components of the pinched nerve ending including the trapped cytoplasm. The presence of cytoplasm within the synaptosome leads to the paradoxical situation where an enzyme may be particulate (i.e., found in synaptosome particles) and yet be soluble (i.e., not firmly attached to any structural component of the synaptosome). The vigor of homogenization and other conditions during preparation can influence apparent localization, thus giving rise to certain conflicting results and interpretations. Several of the enzymes significant for the cholinergic system have been studied by subcellular methods. Acetylcholinesterase seems to be a component of the synaptosome membranes since even after hypotonic disruption the enzymes remain with the synaptosome "ghosts" (35,42). However, the synaptic vesicle fraction, obtained after disruption of the synaptosomes, is virtually devoid in acetylcholinesterase activity. Choline acetyltransferase seems to be associated with the liberated synaptic vesicles, but this localization depends on species and method of preparation. By whole tissue histochemical methods it has been possible to demonstrate brain acetylcholinesterase at synaptic junctions but not in synaptic vesicles (43,44). These enzyme histochemical findings thus correlate with the pattern of localization obtained by subcellular fractionation methods.

Information about the electron microscopic localization of enzymes related to the monoamines has been derived almost entirely from subcellular methods. Monoamine oxidase, an enzyme which is involved in the inactivation of both the catecholamines and serotonin, appears to be a constituent of mitochondria, including those isolated from synaptosomes. Catechol-O-methyltransferase, however, is found in supernatant fractions. The localization of certain enzymes concerned with the synthesis of monoamines in the brain has also been studied. With mild conditions of homogenization most of the particulate decarboxylase activity is found in synaptosomes. The enzyme is readily solubilized, however,

---

Fig. 2. Electron-microscopic autoradiograph of hypothalamus after an intraventricular injection of H^3-NE. Clusters of autoradiographic grains (G), which appear as black, irregular coils, are seen superimposed on two preterminal axons in this field from the paraventricular hypothalamus. The grains are indicative of the intense radioactivity resulting from an accumulation of H^3-NE in the endings. Large, dense-core vesicles (DV) are characteristically seen in endings which take up H^3-NE (Autoradiograph provided by G. K. Aghajanian and F. E. Bloom.) ×33,000.

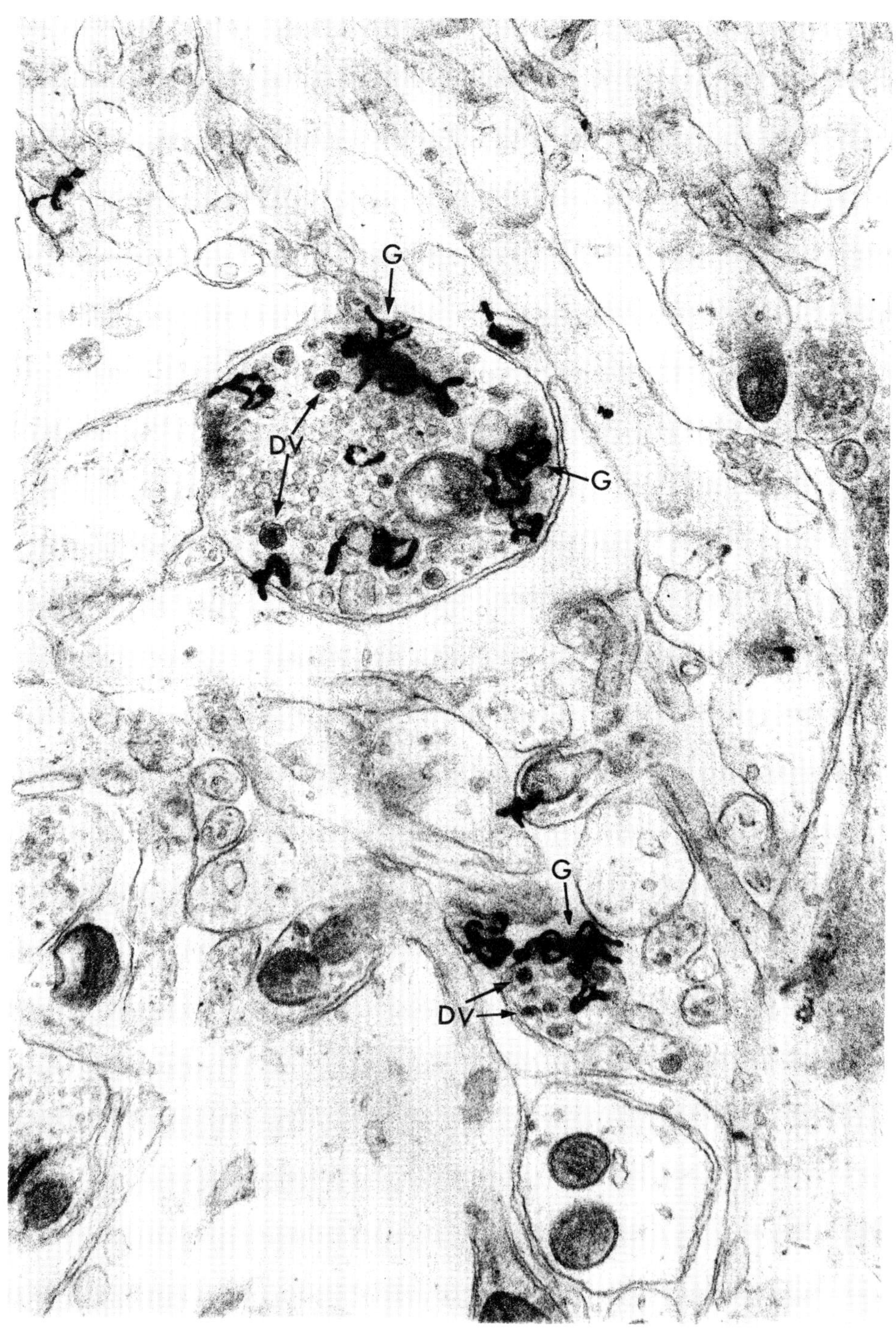

(Legend for Fig. 2 on facing page.)

when the synaptosomes are disrupted. Tyrosine hydroxylase also seems to be associated with synaptosome fractions (45), although it becomes solubilized readily with further disruption (46). Recently a Na^+ and K^+ dependent uptake mechanism for norepinephrine in synaptosome fractions has been described (47). This finding is of interest in relation to the fact that by subcellular fractionation methods a Na^+ and K^+ dependent adenosine triphosphatase has been shown to be present in the external membranes of synaptosomes but not in isolated synaptic vesicles (48). These findings correlate with results obtained with whole tissue enzyme histochemical methods; adenosine triphosphatase has been demonstrated at limiting membranes in the region of the nerve ending (49).

VI. Conclusion

In view of the foregoing discussion, how close are we to constructing a conceptual model which accurately represents the functional vicissitudes of transmitters at the nerve ending? Are neurotransmitters synthesized within the nerve ending, stored in synaptic vesicles, released at the presynaptic synaptic membrane to act at a receptor on the postsynaptic membrane, and then inactivated (either by enzymatic degradation or reuptake) at the junction? This model certainly provides a plausible view of what might be occurring, but it must be realized that the evidence in support of such a scheme is almost entirely circumstantial in nature. The attempts at correlating electron microscopy with functional aspects of transmission have yielded only a series of static glimpses of an underlying dynamic process. While there is good evidence that various prospective transmitter substances are synthesized and contained in nerve endings, there is as yet no direct information about how or where release may occur. Although synaptic vesicles are typically seen clustered about the dense projections at presynaptic membranes, the functional relationship of these structures is not readily apparent. Certainly interpretations other than that of transmitter release are conceivable for this observed proximity of vesicles and presynaptic membranes. Similarly, while it is tempting to regard the postsynaptic membrane as the site of attachment of transmitter to receptor, there are no experiments which bear directly on this point. There are relatively abundant data concerning potential sites of transmitter inactivation. For example, acetylcholinesterase is found at synaptic junctions, and this presumably would allow for the inactivation of acetylcholine released by cholinergic nerves. Exogenous monoamines are taken up into certain nerve endings, suggesting that endogenously released amines could be removed from sites of activity by a reuptake mechanism. In general, it may be noted that while there has been an accumulation of knowledge about sites of synthesis, storage, uptake, and degradation of substances that may be involved in neurotransmission, virtually nothing is known, on a morphologic level, about the crucial processes of release and receptor activity. Until the latter events can be approached by electron microscopic methods, our present formulation of the "model" nerve ending will remain incomplete with regard to its most significant functional aspects.

For further reading see Appendix 2.

8

THE BLOOD-BRAIN BARRIER AND OTHER MEMBRANE PHENOMENA IN PSYCHOPHARMACOLOGY

W. G. Dewhurst

I. Introduction

Many think of the blood-brain barrier as a definite structure like the Berlin Wall. However, the concept includes more subtle mechanisms than physical obstruction, while methods of entry may differ markedly from means of exit, so that an analogy with the Iron Curtain is more apt. The concept of a barrier arose when it was found that some substances present in the blood (even in high concentration) failed to penetrate the brain, whereas they reached other body tissues without difficulty. The substances barred included physiological metabolites such as epinephrine, pathological metabolites such as bile, and various drugs such as streptomycin and penicillin.

An understanding of the mechanisms at work is of much importance in psychopharmacology for several reasons. First, such knowledge is needed to ensure that particular agents reach the brain and act there rather than on the periphery. Second, the way drugs (and other agents) act on the brain is often inferred from changes in naturally occurring substances (e.g., amines) or their metabolites, and the ability of these natural products to pass the barrier must be known to assess experimental findings and to plan future studies. Third, there is growing evidence that the main action of many psychopharmacological agents is produced by alterations in membrane permeability or stability and the secondary consequences of this. Fourth, there is also growing evidence that some of the illnesses with which psychopharmacology is concerned show alterations of membrane permeability, and it is naturally important to know of such disturbances both to aid understanding of illness and to disentangle such effects from those produced by pharmacological agents.

II. The Structural Aspects

A. *Subdivisions*

The blood-brain barrier is frequently used as an umbrella term to cover all the phenomena arising at at least three physical interphases, namely, the blood-cerebrospinal fluid (CSF) barrier, the CSF-brain barrier and the blood-brain barrier proper. If glial cells are also considered, then three other interphases also exist (with blood, CSF, and brain). However, as far as biological significance is concerned, blood-neuron interchange is the one that matters, and the other intermediaries are of interest only insofar as they influence this.*

B. *Capillaries*

Turning now to the finer structural details, consider first the vascular part of the barrier. Brain capillaries, like those elsewhere, consist of endothelial cells resting on a basement membrane, and the cells are very similar to those of other vascular endothelium. However, three important differences distinguish brain from other capillaries. First, there is no evidence of perforation or fenestration, such as occurs, say, in the liver. Second, the basement membrane is often reduplicated to enclose "pericytes" (which may be of histiocytic or glial origin). Third, there is a layer of ATPase and ADPase activity in the basement membrane as well as the endothelial cells, and such a double layer is unique to brain capillaries. This obviously suggests active transport mechanisms. Externally extensions of glial cells ("feet") cover some 85% of the surface area, but their significance does not lie in physical obstruction (which would be trivial); they are probably concerned with active transport mechanisms.

C. *Interphases*

The *blood-CSF* interphase is generally taken to mean the blood-ventricular and blood-subarachnoid space junctions. In the ventricles this junction is specialized to form the choroid bodies. The capillaries are convoluted and closely apposed to a cubical ependymal epithelium which lines the ventricular cavity. These cells are similar to other secretory epithelium, and the whole structure

* To those consulting the literature, a word of warning on terminology is advisable. "Brain" may mean either the extracellular space around neurons and glia, or neurons, or glial cells. Such imprecision is partly derived from the methods used to investigate barrier phenomena, but can hardly be excused on such grounds. After all in common usage the "brain" signifies "neurons," *not* the holes surrounded by nerve and glial cells.

is believed to produce much of the CSF as well as possessing active resorptive capacities. The blood-subarachnoid space junctions are also specialized and comprise arachnoid villi which are protrusions of the subarachnoid space into the lumen of blood vessels. Much of the absorption from CSF to blood is believed to occur here, and it should be noted that this is the one site where no neuron, ependymal, or glial cells intervene between CSF and the vascular wall.

The *blood-brain* interphase is more extensive than originally thought. Woolam and Millen have shown by extensive microscopic studies that the blind invaginations of pia which the arteries entering the brain carry with them (Virchow-Robin spaces) end before the capillary level. This means that there is *no* general interchange between capillaries and subarachnoid space and the bulk of brain capillaries abut directly on glial or neuron cells, (or in the case of the choroid plexus on ependymal epithelium). Hence passage from blood to CSF requires passage through such cells, and this no doubt accounts for the many similarities between the blood-brain barrier and the blood-CSF barrier. The latter is in reality a blood-"brain"-CSF barrier.

The *CSF-brain* interphase comprises the CSF ependymal junction at the choroid plexuses already discussed and the extracellular fluid-brain junctions within the brain. These extracellular spaces consist of long tunnels, some 200 Å in diameter, with walls of interlacing bundles of nerve fibers and sparsely scattered nerve cell or glial cell bodies. The extracellular space is variously estimated at between 5 and 15% of the total brain volume. The narrowness of the spaces suggests that transcellular rather than intercellular transport occurs, and injected substances remain confined to the injection site and show little diffusion. There are slight differences in composition between extracellular fluid and the CSF, indicating that absorption and resorption are not confined to the choroid plexuses.

III. Functional Components

A. General Types

Structural considerations, besides being plagued with terminological ambiguity, are of limited value in telling us which substances will pass through. A functional approach provides a welcome clarification. Much work has been done on the barriers which different cells present, and Albert has summarized these into four types. In type 1 the barrier is a lipoprotein membrane and fat solubility is necessary for penetration. In type 2 a similar arrangement holds with the addition of molecules which can form complexes with anions to enable passive carrier transport. In type 3 there is active transport of substrates, often against a concentration gradient and consuming energy. In type 4 the membrane acts as a simple molecular sieve.

B. Types in Blood-Brain Barrier

Applying these types to the blood-CSF-brain interphases, we have already noted that capillary fenestration is absent in the brain and hence type 4 barriers do not occur. For foreign substances both the capillary and the neuron membrane act as type 1 barriers. For a few naturally occurring metabolites type

2 or 3 barriers exist. Thus L-amino acids are transferred from blood to brain by active transport, and similar mechanisms exist for glucose and some ions. Active transport also occurs in the reverse direction from brain (or CSF) to blood, and acids are rapidly ejected into the bloodstream. It will be apparent therefore that the "blood-brain barrier" consists of a variety of aids and obstacles to the passage of substances depending partly on the nature of the latter and the direction in which they are going. Although undeniably complex, we can still predict quite accurately how different drugs and metabolites will behave by the application of some simple principles.

IV. Factors Determining Passage through Lipoprotein (Type 1) Membranes

First, we can conclude that although drugs may pass various interphases between blood and neuron, *the sum effect is functionally that of a single type 1 barrier.* Here two requirements are important if a molecule is to pass. The first is *lipid solubility* (usually expressed as a partition coefficient between oil and water). It is readily determined by adding a substance to a mixture of equal volumes of olive oil, say, and water, shaking for a considerable time, separating the two phases, measuring the amount in the oil, and dividing this by the amount measured in water. Texts of physical chemistry should be consulted for details of experimental control necessary, but even without doing such estimations, it is still possible to predict fairly accurately the likelihood of entry to brain by some considerations of chemical structures. In a crude way the nearer a substance approaches water (HOH) in structure, the more water soluble it will be. Groups such as OH, COOH, NH_2 are hence called hydrophilic. Conversely, the nearer a substance approaches fat, i.e., possesses a long hydrocarbon chain as in palmitic acid ($C_{16}H_{32}O_2$), the more fat soluble (lipophilic) it becomes. It follows that replacement of the H in hydrophilic groups by alkyl groups largely negates water solubility. Thus OH is strongly hydrophilic, OCH_3 weakly hydrophilic, and OC_2H_5 lipophilic. Besides the ratio between carbon and oxygen (or nitrogen), a second factor is important. The hydrophilic groups OH, NH_2, and COOH are capable of *ionizing* (i.e., separating into two charged portions) when dissolved in water. Ionization strongly increases affinity for water, i.e., increases water solubility. The degree of ionization in turn depends both on its strength as base or acid and the pH of the solution (7.4 for blood).

Let us now apply these ideas to typical drugs important in psychopharmacology. For the sake of clarity we will consider first amphetamine, which has a relatively simple structure (cf. Usdin, Chapter 15). It is common knowledge, (even to the layman these days) that this substance can produce cerebral effects after inhalation or when swallowed in tablet form or aqueous solution (e.g., in coffee). This shows that it is water soluble and also sufficiently lipid soluble to pass the type 1 membrane of the gut wall, and also that of the blood-brain barrier. The part of the molecule conferring water solubility is the NH_2 group, and this effect is reinforced because at a physiological pH (7.4) this group exists as NH_3^+. In water the following reaction occurs:

$$R \cdot NH_2 + H_2O \rightleftharpoons R \cdot NH_3^+ + OH^-$$

Like the other amines considered in this paragraph, base strength is greater than that of ammonia. This means at pH 7.4 the equilibrium of the above reaction lies to the right, i.e., some 95% of the molecule is $R \cdot NH_3^+$. From this we may deduce that phenylethylamine and tryptamine (with two rings) are likely to have similar properties, which indeed they have (cf. Snyder, Chapter 9). Yet the addition of a single OH group to the molecule [e.g., 5-hydroxytryptamine (serotonin, 5HT)] or more [norepinephrine (NE)] diminishes lipid solubility so much that these substances are no longer active by mouth and do not penetrate the blood-brain barrier. The OH groups on the benzene ring are less than 1% ionized at pH 7.4 for their acidity is weaker than boric acid (equilibrium is to the left in $R \cdot O \cdot H + H_2O \rightleftharpoons R \cdot O^- + H_3O^+$).

Turning to larger molecules with three rings such as chlorpromazine and imipramine (cf. Usdin, Chapter 15), it can again be inferred that they will be sufficiently lipid soluble to penetrate the brain, as indeed they do. Unlike the amines discussed above, chlorpromazine is a much weaker base and at pH 7.4 is only some 50% ionized. The Cl^- substituent further enhances lipid solubility. The same is true for the four-ringed lysergic acid diethylamide (LSD-25). Yet even this large molecule may have its lipid solubility markedly reduced by substituting the diethylamide group with the more hydrophilic butanol amide. Although there is an additional lipophilic CH_3 at position 1, this substance (methysergide) has a brain/blood ratio approximately one-fifth that of LSD-25, whose ratio is approximately 1. As it happens, both are extremely potent substances effective in minute doses. With less potent substances such a difference in penetration can mean the difference between a useful and useless therapeutic agent. Reserpine (cf. Usdin, Chapter 15), with six rings, enters brain rapidly after intravenous injection and shows how effective CH_3 is in negating the effect of OH and COOH.

We can thus make a reasonably good forecast of lipid solubility from consideration of chemical structure, and because lipid solubility underlies passage through all type 1 membranes, as Professor Paton points out, "One arrives at the generalization that drugs which act on the central nervous system, drugs which are cumulative, and those which interfere with the biochemical processes within the cell will be active by mouth" (50).

V. Type 2 and 3 Membranes

Although the type 1 model holds for nearly all foreign substances, there is evidence that specific transport mechanisms exist for certain metabolites. Direction of movement is now particularly important. As far as entry *into* brain is concerned, the mechanisms are similar to those which operate from gut lumen across the gut wall. Thus, amino acids (which are water soluble and ionized) are taken into the brain far more rapidly than these physicochemical characteristics would indicate. Further, the mechanism shows specificity, as L-amino acids are transported more rapidly than the D-form, and the process consumes energy. There is evidence that such transport is linked with the sodium pump mechanism (Glynn, see Appendix 1).

Apart from this mechanism it is difficult for other acids to enter the brain. However, in the outward direction there is rapid clearance of acids from the CSF to the blood. It has been suggested that the outward flow of acids from CSF or brain to the blood deflects incoming acids and makes their entry more difficult. The active transport mechanisms from CSF-brain to blood have been likened to the mechanisms occurring between kidney tubule cells and the urine (*not* blood and tubules). It is not clear how far active transport mechanisms are concerned with bases, but in practice most physiological bases are catabolized to acid derivatives, and as we have seen, these are rapidly eliminated from brain-CSF to the exterior.

One portion of the blood-CSF barrier with specialized importance in active transport is the choroid plexus, and it is generally believed that the bulk of the CSF is formed at this site. As there are definite differences between the ionic composition of CSF and plasma, this indicates that active secretory processes must occur. Further, the range of permitted fluctuation of ions in the CSF is much narrower than that permissible in plasma, which again indicates an energy-consuming active transport mechanism controlling CSF production. It is, perhaps, less well known that the choroid plexus is also concerned with active reabsorption.

VI. Biological Significance of Barriers

Before considering the changes produced by disease or drugs in membrane barriers some of their normal roles will be noted. One obvious function is to contain more fluid parts of the cell while at the same time passing nutrients, keeping toxins out, and being selectively sensitive to stimuli. Cell containment is only effective, however, over a limited range of cell size. Enlargement beyond this point is physically unstable and necessitates a multicellular structure. A tissue response is now the sum of many discrete (or, in current jargon, digital rather than analogue) responses. This permits considerable subtlety of organization, as shown in the CNS mechanisms of convergence, occlusion, and so on. More important than organization, however, is specialization, which is not only possible between different types of cells but within the cell itself when subcellular units are isolated by membrane partition. Specialization has weaknesses, but overall it increases the total efficiency of the organism. Membrane partition also permits processes, otherwise incompatible, to occur within the same cell. A relevant example is the storage of amines with adenosine triphosphate in special storage granules. In this form they are immune from attack by monoamine oxidase, which is held behind the membranes of mitochondria. Thus amines can be accumulated at times of relative quiescence so that in an emergency large amounts are rapidly available. Without such storage the rate of amine supply would be limited by the rate of synthesis, which in an emergency might be fatal. We shall see that a variety of psychopharmacological agents may affect different points in the cycle by altering membrane permeability.

VII. Changes in Disease

It follows that changes in membrane permeability may have considerable effects, and such changes have been found to occur in a number of illnesses which are relevant in psychopharmacology. It may first be noted that the permeability of the blood-brain barrier is not static but changes with maturation. Young chicks, for example, allow the passage of catecholamines such as epinephrine and norepinephrine into the brain. At the age of 4 weeks or so the barrier matures, and after 2–3 weeks becomes impermeable to these amines, and thus similar to the blood-brain barrier of other animals including man. There is evidence also of maturational changes in human development, for if young infants become jaundiced (this may occur through rhesus [Rh] incompatibility), the bile gets into the brain particularly staining the basal ganglia (whence the name Kernicterus) and causes extrapyramidal dysfunction. Human adults, however, do not show this phenomenon during jaundice because the blood-brain barrier no longer permits bile to pass.

Apart from maturational changes gross rupture of the blood-brain barrier may occur, e.g., as a result of penetrating wounds, and after cerebrovascular accidents. The use of ^{203}Hg shows that such defects in the blood-brain barrier after strokes may last several months before functional continuity is restored.

More subtle changes can also occur. In phenylketonuria there is a defect of metabolism of phenylalanine (cf. Berman and Hsia, Chapter 27). The effects produced, however, may not only be due to the accumulation of toxic metabolites but may also be partly attributable to a deficiency of normal substrates for it has been shown that phenylalanine depresses the active transport of tyrosine through the blood-brain barrier.

In schizophrenia the amount of bromide found in the CSF relative to that in the plasma is less than in normal subjects, and salicylates and iodide behave similarly. This suggests that such substances are excreted more rapidly in schizophrenia than in normal controls.

Perhaps the most interesting findings so far are those occurring in depression. Radiosodium passes through the blood-brain barrier at a reduced rate in psychotic depression, though schizophrenics have normal exchange rates. The slow passage of sodium returns to normal when the patient is better. Depressed patients also show variations of salivary flow. Saliva is initially isotonic with plasma with a pH of 7.4, but as it flows along the ducts, sodium and bicarbonate are normally reabsorbed and the pH at the orifice is about 6.5. It has been shown that depressives when ill have a pH of near 7.4 at the orifice, but on recovery their pH returned to about 6.5. This gives further confirmation that membrane transport is reduced generally in severe depressive illness.

VIII. Changes in Barriers Produced by Drugs

Although not of direct therapeutic interest, it is worth mentioning that a variety of contrast media injected into the bloodstream can cause breaks in the blood-brain barrier. No bleeding or edema is evident and breaches are only revealed by the use of an acid dye such as trypan blue, which stains the central nervous system at the sites of the lesions. These "pure barrier lesions" may be produced either by metabolic inhibitors (such as heavy metals or agents blocking sulfhydryl groups) or by substances chemically similar to the dye indicators.

In recent years a more general (and more fruitful) approach has been concerned with the effects of various agents on cytoplasmic membranes. In such studies much use has been made of artificial models of lipid membranes as well as various preparations of red cells which are well suited to such work. Using such techniques it has been shown that various substances can decrease permeability of membranes, and such effects do *not* depend on structural specificity but rather on physical properties determining the amounts which can accumulate in a particular membrane. In many respects they resemble anesthetics. Their action in *decreasing* cell permeability has been called membrane stabilization. It is characteristic of these agents that in concentrations some 100 to 1000 times greater than those causing stabilization, cell membrane rupture may occur, i.e., they cause lysis. Thus they are biphasic in action.

Examples of membrane stabilization include a reduction of loss of potassium from red cells by promethazine and chlorpromazine and the inhibition of catecholamine release from various storage granules by cocaine, reserpine, chlorpromazine, and trifluoperazine. It has been calculated that maximum stabilization occurs with about one molecule of chlorpromazine per 100 $Å^2$ cell surface. Although results are well documented for phenothiazines and reserpine, the position of imipramine-like substances seems less well established, although it is usually accepted that their effects are due to a protection of natural amines from the action of monoamine oxidase by decreasing cell membrane permeability. A recent report comparing chlorpromazine and imipramine in depression emphasizes basically similar mechanisms of action. It is not unreasonable to speculate that the extrapyramidal effects of certain phenothiazines are sequels to the cell lysis component of biphasic action evident at high dosage.

IX. Conclusion

It is hoped that the preceding sketch will indicate something of the scope and importance of the membrane barriers possessed by cells. For those who wish to go further, the bibliography will show the way, both to mechanisms intricately intertwined (like the sodium pump, amino acid transport, adenosine triphosphate, and the receptor for norepinephrine) as well as others of beautiful simplicity (such as the "revolving door effect"). For readers who shudder at such prospects, remembrance of "Paton's principle" should be of practical profit. Whether the subject attracts or repels, however, there can be no doubt that membrane phenomena (of which the blood-brain barrier provides a specialized example) are fundamental in the physiology of the cell, may be widely disturbed in disease, and probably form the main site of action for the bulk of currently used psychopharmacological agents.

For general references and further reading see Appendix 1.

PART III

THE BIOCHEMISTRY OF MENTAL DISEASE AND SOME EFFECTS OF PSYCHOTROPIC DRUGS

9

CATECHOLAMINES, BRAIN FUNCTION, AND HOW PSYCHOTROPIC DRUGS ACT*

Solomon H. Snyder

I. Introduction

The catecholamines (CA) of importance in mammalian brains (Fig. 1) are dopamine and norepinephrine (NE). Chemically the term catechol refers to a benzene ring with two adjacent hydroxyl groups. In the past ten years there has accumulated a great body of research showing that the CA are neurohumors or neurotransmitters (chemicals transmitting information from the nerve ending of one neuron across a synaptic cleft to the cell body of another neuron) in regions of the brain that elaborate emotional behavior. It has also become clear that several important drugs used in psychiatry exert their clinical effects by affecting the synaptic action of the CA in the brain. Moreover, the effects of new drugs on human behavior sometimes can be predicted by a knowledge of how such chemicals interact with CA.

Suspicion that CA in the brain may be important to emotional function pre-

* The author is a recipient of a Research Career Development Award of the NIMH-K3-MH-33128. This work was supported in part by USPHS grants 1-R01-MH-13433 and 5-S01-FR-5378.

ceded knowledge that they were neurohumoral substances in the central nervous system. Much neurophysiological evidence has indicated that specific regions of the brain are concerned with the elaboration of emotional behavior. These areas include the hypothalamus and the limbic system of structures, including the amygdaloid nucleus, hippocampus, and central gray. It is interesting that these areas (which correspond to the rhinencephalon of various animal species) are phylogenetically older than the cerebral cortex which surmounts them. During the mid-1950's, chemical methods for the estimation of tissue concentrations of the CA were developed, and it became clear that NE and serotonin (5-hydroxytryptamine, 5HT) were localized in the brain areas concerned with emotional behavior. 5HT is a biogenic amine which like the CA may function as a neurohumor in the brain, but whose neurohumoral actions and relationship

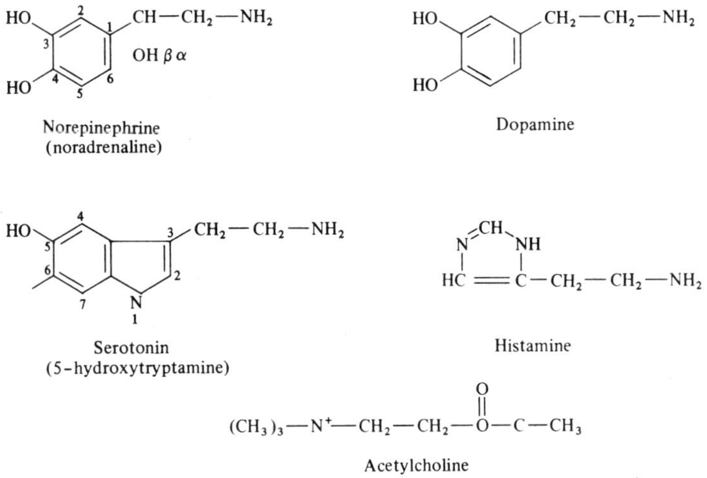

Norepinephrine (noradrenaline)

Dopamine

Serotonin (5-hydroxytryptamine)

Histamine

$(CH_3)_3—N^+—CH_2—CH_2—O—\overset{O}{\overset{\|}{C}}—CH_3$

Acetylcholine

Fig. 1

to psychotropic drug effects is less well established than for the CA. Also in the mid-1950's the first major antipsychotic, reserpine, was introduced into clinical usage. In 1957 it was found that reserpine depleted animal brains almost totally of their 5HT and CA contents. Acetylcholine, the best-known biogenic amine (see Fig. 1) has been known since 1927 to be a neurotransmitter. NE was already known to be the neurohumor at peripheral postganglionic sympathetic nerve endings. Knowledge of the depletion by reserpine of brain NE and 5HT prompted a great number of investigators to assume that these chemicals were neurotransmitters at synapses in the brain concerned with maintaining an alert state and that reserpine produced sedation by depleting them from their neuronal storage sites. It is only in the past three years, however, that criteria for a neurohumoral role in the brain have been fulfilled, more or less, by NE and the psychotropic actions of drugs related in a direct way to interactions with NE at synapses in the brain.

II. Catecholamine Metabolism

Much evidence indicates that some psychotropic drugs exert their clinical effects by affecting the actions of the biogenic amines at synapses in the brain. It is therefore important to understand the events at the central aminergic, especially noradrenergic, synapses. It is necessary to understand how the amines are released and subsequently inactivated at brain synapses. In the case of NE, these processes are virtually identical at peripheral sympathetic nerves and in the brain. Hence the abundant information about release, receptor action, and inactivation of NE at peripheral synapses can be used to help explain these phenomena in the brain.

III. Norepinephrine Biosynthesis

The principal precursor of the CA is the amino acid tyrosine (Fig. 2). Tyrosine, which has one hydroxyl (OH) group on its ring system para (directly

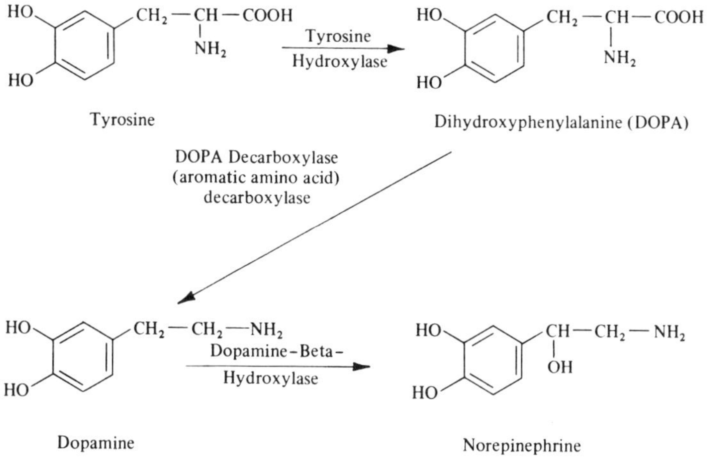

Tyrosine $\xrightarrow{\text{Tyrosine Hydroxylase}}$ Dihydroxyphenylalanine (DOPA)

DOPA Decarboxylase (aromatic amino acid) decarboxylase

Dopamine $\xrightarrow{\text{Dopamine-Beta-Hydroxylase}}$ Norepinephrine

Fig. 2

opposite) to the side chain, is hydroxylated adjacent to the first hydroxyl group to form an amino acid, 3,4-dihydroxyphenylalanine (DOPA). Tyrosine hydroxylase, the enzyme that carries out this reaction, is present principally in tissues with rich sympathetic innervations and in the brain. DOPA is then decarboxylated (the carboxyl or COOH group of the side chain is removed) by the enzyme DOPA decarboxylase to form 3,4-dihydroxyphenylethylamine (dopamine). Dopamine is hydroxylated on the β carbon (the side-chain carbon closest to the ring system, Fig. 1) to form NE by the enzyme dopamine-β-hydroxylase.

Dopamine is most highly concentrated in the corpus striatum of the brain, which contains large amounts of dopamine and very little NE. In order to determine whether drugs can affect the net synthesis of NE, it is essential to know which of the enzymic reactions just described is the "rate-limiting" step in CA synthesis. The rate-limiting step is the one whose relative activity controls the rate at which the end product, NE, will be formed. For practical purposes, the rate-limiting step can be assumed to be represented by the enzymic step whose inhibition stops the formation of NE *in vivo*. DOPA decarboxylase was the first of the enzymes described above to be studied in detail, and numerous inhibitors of this enzyme were developed. It was found, however, that even if DOPA decarboxylase was inhibited more than 90%, tissue levels of NE were not decreased. Hence DOPA decarboxylase cannot be the rate-limiting enzyme. In fact, DOPA decarboxylase is present in such excess that any DOPA formed by tyrosine hydroxylase is immediately decarboxylated to dopamine. Thus, measurable amounts of DOPA never accumulate in tissues, and under normal conditions DOPA cannot be detected at all in the brain or in the peripheral sympathetic nervous system. Inhibition of tyrosine hydroxylase by drugs such as α-methyl-*p*-tyrosine, however, results in a rapid lowering of brain NE and may cause sedation and anti-amphetamine effects in rats. α-Methyl-*p*-tyrosine inhibits NE synthesis, and tissue NE levels decline as NE is gradually discharged by nerve impulses and metabolized. Thus tyrosine hydroxylation is the main rate-limiting step in the biosynthesis of NE. Under certain circumstances, however, dopamine-β-hydroxylation also may be rate-limiting. After treatment with α-methyl-*p*-tyrosine, NE but not 5HT is depleted from the brain and, as already stated, sedation may ensue. *p*-Chlorophenylalanine is a compound which inhibits tryptophan hydroxylase, the rate-limiting enzyme in 5HT synthesis, resulting in depletion of 5HT but not of NE from the brain. It has been found that *p*-chlorophenylalanine causes insomnia in cats, just as does destruction of the serotonergic brain tracts. One might speculate that the noradrenergic and serotonergic brain tracts control sleep and wakefulness in a balanced sort of antagonism.

There are other ways, besides inhibiting specific enzymes, that drugs can affect the net synthesis of the CA. One way takes advantage of the relative nonspecificity of the enzymes of CA formation, a property which facilitates the synthesis of "false" neurohumors (see below). DOPA decarboxylase can decarboxylate many aromatic amino acids and therefore is called nonspecific "aromatic amino acid decarboxylase" (aromatic amino acids are ones which contain an aromatic ring, i.e., a ring of six carbons and possibly other atoms containing resonating electrons which are signified in diagrams by a double bond (=). Dopamine-β-hydroxylase will β-hydroxylate a great number of aromatic amines.

α-Methyldopa (Fig. 3) is a clinically used antihypertensive drug which can, but rarely does, precipitate psychotic depression in some patients. Both antihypertensive and possibly depressant actions can be attributed to effects on NE synthesis. Chemically, α-methyldopa is DOPA with a methyl group (CH_3) on the α carbon of the side chain, i.e., the carbon adjacent to the side-chain amine grouping. In the human or animal body, α-methyldopa also is decarboxylated by DOPA decarboxylase and the resultant α-methyldopamine is hydroxylated by dopamine β-hydroxylase to form α-methylnorepinephrine. The latter compound is then stored in synaptic vesicles which normally store NE. Thus, after α-methyldopa administration, α-methylnorepinephrine will displace erated because α-methylnorepinephrine is released instead and thus is called and replace NE in synaptic vesicles. Upon nerve stimulation, less NE is lib- a "false neurohumor" or transmitter. α-Methylnorepinephrine is less of a pressor (blood pressure elevating) agent than NE, so that after α-methyldopa treatment, for the same amount of sympathetic nervous discharge, there will be less total presser activity. Presumably, α-methylnorepinephrine acts as a false transmitter in the brain as well. If, as suggested by some, endogenous depression is related to a deficiency of NE at synapses in the brain, the production of an inactive false neurohumor by α-methyldopa could explain why it can cause depression.

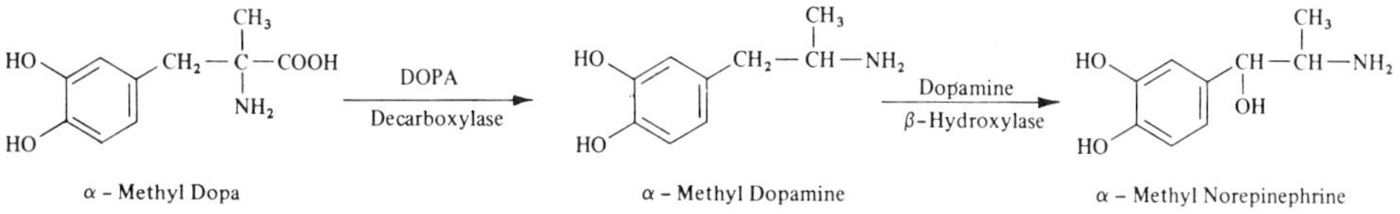

α - Methyl Dopa —DOPA Decarboxylase→ α - Methyl Dopamine —Dopamine β-Hydroxylase→ α - Methyl Norepinephrine

Fig. 3

Reserpine depletes NE almost totally from the brain and is well known to precipitate depressions which are clinically very similar to endogenous depressions.

IV. Synaptic Inactivation and Catabolism of Norepinephrine

The physiological inactivation of NE at adrenergic synapses is complex. There are two enzymes which degrade NE, monoamine oxidase (MAO) and catechol-*O*-methyltransferase (COMT). However, neither of them appears to represent the primary mode of NE inactivation at the synapse. The actions of NE liberated by nerve discharge are terminated primarily by reuptake of the liberated amine across the nerve membrane into the presynaptic nerve ending (Fig. 4). NE taken up in this way is rebound into the synaptic vesicles. The primary importance of the reuptake mode of synaptic inactivation is easily shown in the peripheral sympathetic nervous system. The effects of sympathetic nerve stimulation as well as administered NE are markedly potentiated by drugs which inhibit the reuptake process.

It has been found that when radioactive NE was injected intravenously into animals, it was highly concentrated by organs with a rich sympathetic innervation. If the sympathetic nerves to these organs were cut, the tissues no longer took up the radioactive amine. Centrifugation of tissue homogenates to isolate subcellular particles showed that the radioactive NE in peripheral sympathetic nerves was localized in small granules of the dimensions of the presumed synaptic vesicles. By similar techniques it was found that in the brain radioactive NE injected into the cerebral ventricles was taken up and concentrated in synaptosomes which could then be isolated by centrifugation as described earlier. Using these methods there was little difficulty in identifying drugs which interfere with the NE uptake process. Any drug which decreased the accumulation of radioactive NE by peripheral tissues or by the brain could be tentatively assumed to block the uptake mechanism. In this way, it was found that drugs such as imipramine and cocaine, which potentiated the effects of sympathetic nerve stimulation, are potent inhibitors of the uptake process. Cocaine is a CNS stimulant which can produce an euphoriant state, and imipramine is a well-known antidepressant.

The CA are metabolically degraded by the enzymes, monamine oxidase (MAO), and catechol-*O*-methyltransferase (COMT) (Fig. 5). MAO removes the side-chain amine (NH_2) group from NE and through an intermediate aldehyde results in the formation of 3,4-dihydroxymandelic acid. This enzyme is

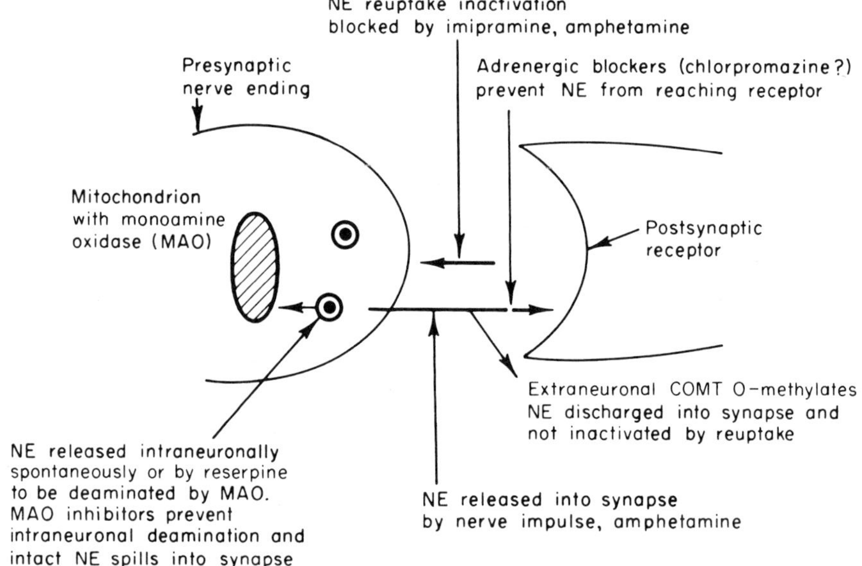

Fig. 4

called an oxidase because oxygen is required for the reaction and hydrogen peroxide is a product. COMT transfers a methyl (CH_3) group from the methyl donor S-adenosylmethionine to the *m*-hydroxyl group of the CA (the hydroxyl group which is closer to the side chain). MAO can act on any of a great number of amines. COMT acts on any catechol structure. Prior to excretion in the urine, the CA have usually been acted on both by MAO and COMT. A CA can be deaminated first and then *O*-methylated or vice versa. The resulting deaminated, *O*-methylated product is 3-methoxy-4-hydroxymandelic acid, usually referred to as vanillylmandelic acid (VMA). VMA normally is the major metabolic product of the CA in human urine and is excreted in excess in stress and in patients with phaeochromocytoma (tumor of the adrenal medulla), and because it can be easily measured, this can be used diagnostically in such cases.

Although monamine oxidase activity is present in many nonneuronal structures, as well as in sympathetic nerves in the periphery and noradrenergic nerves in the brain, the deamination of NE is primarily carried out by the MAO, which is localized in mitochondria of the noradrenergic nerve terminals which electron micrographs show to be located in close proximity to synaptic vesicles. COMT, however, is located extraneuronally. Under resting conditions, in the absence of nerve stimulation, NE slowly diffuses out of the synaptic vesicles and is deaminated by MAO within the nerve terminal (see Fig. 4) so that it leaves the neuron in an inactivated form. Once outside the neuron the deaminated product, 3,4-dihydroxymandelic acid, is then *O*-methylated. NE released by nerve stimulation is inactivated largely by reuptake into the nerve terminal from which it was released. NE which is released in a free form by nerve

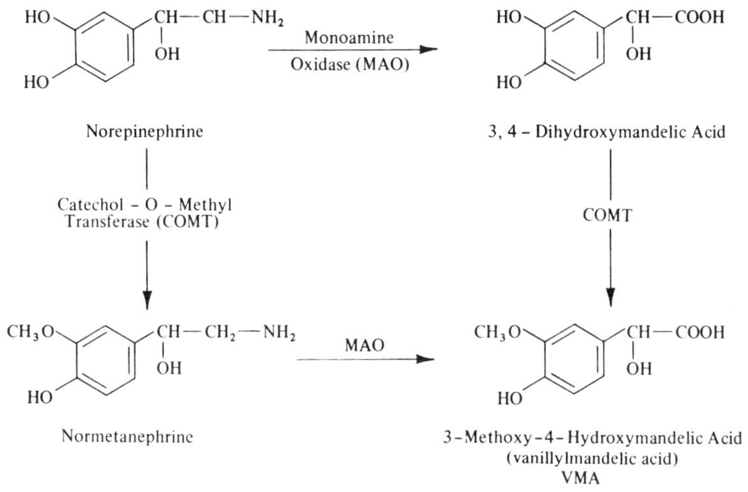

Norepinephrine

Monoamine Oxidase (MAO)

3, 4 - Dihydroxymandelic Acid

Catechol - O - Methyl Transferase (COMT)

COMT

Normetanephrine

MAO

3-Methoxy-4-Hydroxymandelic Acid (vanillylmandelic acid) VMA

Fig. 5

stimulation but not rebound by the nerve terminal is *O*-methylated to normetanephrine outside the neuron. Some of this normetanephrine is subsequently deaminated, but a large proportion is excreted in the urine unchanged. Thus, the amount of normetanephrine formed is an indication of the relative degree of sympathetic nervous discharge. This pattern of NE metabolism is the same in the brain and in the peripheral sympathetic nervous system.

V. Drug Action and Catecholamines

Before analyzing how psychotropic drugs may exert their actions via the CA, it is important to ascertain what sort of affective response is associated with the synaptic release of NE in the brain. This is, at the present state of knowledge, a difficult task. However, there is a considerable amount of circumstantial evidence that discharge of noradrenergic neurons in the brain is associated with "central excitation." Such excitation may be related to both positive and negative affects. Peripheral sympathetic activation occurs during emotionally intense experiences, such as anxiety, fright, anger, euphoric excitement. It is probable that noradrenergic brain tracts are the representation in the brain of the sympathetic nervous system, although there are some differences, e.g., antigenicity.

Experiments involving reserpine provided the first evidence implicating brain CA in the mediation of drug effects on behavior. As mentioned previously, it was found to deplete the brains of animals almost totally of their NE content; a dosage which depleted brain CA had a profound sedating effect. When inhibitors of MAO were administered to animals, there was an increase in brain NE levels and an associated central excitation. It was assumed, then, that lowering of brain CA content causes sedation and elevation of brain CA results in excitation. This formulation, however, fails to explain a number of observations. For instance, amphetamine, a well-known central excitant, lowers brain NE. Imipramine, an antidepressant, has no effect on brain CA levels.

Clearly, the actions of these psychotropic drugs cannot be explained solely by their effects on the *levels* of brain amines. The specific subcellular locus of action of the drug is important, as is also the effect of the drug on the metabolic pattern of the released amine. By considering amine synthesis, the intra- and intercellular area of amine release, and the effect of a given drug on NE inactivation and subsequent metabolism, it is possible to formulate convincing explanations of psychotropic drug action, which may predict the clinical effects of newly developed drugs.

A. *Reserpine*

Reserpine has a complicated ring structure containing an indole nucleus. Chemically it more closely resembles 5HT than NE and depletes the brain of both amines. Assuming that NE acting on central receptors results in behavioral excitation, the sedative properties of reserpine can be easily understood by examining the way in which it releases brain NE (see Fig. 4). Reserpine does not affect the presynaptic neuronal membrane from which transmitter molecules are discharged. It acts within the nerve terminal on the amine storage of synaptic vesicles to interfere with their ability to retain NE. NE leaks out of vesicles and is deaminated by MAO inside the nerve terminal and then leaves the neuron as the deaminated, inactive product. Thus, after reserpine treatment there is no intact NE available to act on postsynaptic receptors and sedation ensues. Chemical analyses have shown that reserpine administration to animals results in fewer *O*-methylated products of NE and a preponderance of deaminated metabolites. It is interesting that if a large dose of reserpine is administered rapidly to animals, there is an initial excitation prior to the sedation. In this situation, the amount of NE leaking out of the vesicles exceeds the deaminating capacity of the mitochondria in the nerve terminal so that a considerable amount of NE escapes deamination and crosses the synaptic membrane as the intact molecule to act upon the receptor. A similar excitatory effect can be observed after reserpine treatment if the animal has been pretreated with an inhibitor of MAO. Here, too, NE leaks out of the storage vesicles, is not deaminated, and leaves the neuron as the unchanged, active amine.

B. *Amphetamine*

Over the years, numerous modes of action have been proposed for this classic central stimulant. It was originally thought to have a direct action on postsynaptic receptors; others hypothesized it to act as an inhibitor of MAO. Amphetamine treatment of animals causes a lowering of brain NE but not of brain 5HT; the reduction is considerably less marked than occurs after reserpine (about 30% reduction with amphetamine as opposed to 90% reduction with reserpine for equivalent doses). Again we observe the apparent paradox that two drugs with opposite pharmacological effects (sedation versus excitation) appear to possess the same biochemical actions (NE release). Recent evidence has clarified this problem and indicated the probable mode of action of amphetamine. The NE released by amphetamine is metabolized primarily by *O*-methylation, normetanephrine being the predominant metabolite. As mentioned above, this pattern of metabolic inactivation is usually associated with release of free active NE across the synaptic cleft onto the postsynaptic receptor. The free NE released at the synapse is inactivated, after acting on the receptor, predominantly by reuptake into the presynaptic nerve terminal. Some of the free NE, however, is *O*-methylated outside of the presynaptic neuron. Thus, by knowing that NE released by amphetamine is metabolized primarily by initial *O*-methylation rather than by deamination, one can assume that the amine was released in a free, active form from the presynaptic membrane so that it could act on the postsynaptic receptors. Carlsson *et al.* (51) showed that a major mechanism of action of amphetamine is by inhibition of uptake of monoamines by the neuronal membrane, and by the storage vesicles at higher concentrations.

C. *Imipramine*

Imipramine, its demethylated derivative desmethylimipramine, and related compounds such as amitryptiline and its demethylated product, nortriptyline, appear to be the most effective antidepressant drugs. These drugs are not inhibitors of MAO as were the earliest antidepressants and do not affect the levels of brain CA in animals. However, imipramine is a very potent inhibitor of the reuptake process of inactivation of NE released at the synapse, both in peripheral sympathetic nerves and in the brain. It therefore potentiates the actions of NE released by nerve discharge.

The antidepressant action of imipramine and related chemicals can be tested behaviorally by their ability to reverse the sedation produced in animals by reserpine. A great number of molecules similar to imipramine have been synthesized as potential antidepressants. There is a striking correlation between their ability to prevent reserpine sedation in animals when given prior to reserpine and their antidepressant activity in man. Because of this useful empirical relationship, the sedation observed in animals after reserpine treatment is now frequently referred to as the "reserpine model of depression." This is notable since, as we mentioned earlier, reserpine may precipitate depression in human subjects.

How does imipramine pretreatment reverse "reserpine depression"? In analyzing the interaction of these two drugs, it is important to note two factors which appear to be crucial to this interaction: (1) Imipramine must be given before reserpine, since if given after reserpine, it is unable to prevent the resultant sedation; (2) the more rapid the release of the CA produced by reserpine, the more effective is imipramine in reversing sedation. An accelerated release of brain CA can be produced by giving a larger dose of reserpine, by administering reserpine intravenously, or by giving a reserpine-like drug, such as tetrabenazine, which acts more rapidly than reserpine.

These two considerations suggest that imipramine reverses the reserpine-induced sedation by inhibiting the inactivation of whatever free, active NE is released by reserpine. As discussed earlier, with large doses of reserpine or with a fast-acting reserpine-like drug, NE can leak out of the storage vesicles at a rate which exceeds the deaminating capacity of the mitochondria in the nerve terminal, and leave the nerve ending in active form. Imipramine would potentiate the excitatory action of such released amine. To reverse the reserpine sedation, it is important that NE be released rapidly; if not, it would be all deaminated before leaving the nerve ending. There would, consequently, be no free, active NE to be potentiated by imipramine. Imipramine must be administered prior to reserpine; if given after reserpine, the phase of rapid initial release of free NE would have passed and only deaminated products of norepinephrine would be emerging from the nerve ending. Hence, here too, there would be no intact NE available to be potentiated by imipramine.

D. *Monoamine Oxidase Inhibitors (MAOI)*[*]

The first clinically useful antidepressant drugs were the MAOI. Since these were all hydrazine structures, it was thought by some that their antidepressant action might be related not to MAO inhibition, but to some other biochemical effect of the hydrazine grouping. However, since that time several nonhydrazine inhibitors of MAO have been found to be potent antidepressant drugs. Moreover, several studies have shown that the antidepressant action of these drugs is related to the extent to which they inhibit MAO. Normally, MAO degrades only NE which leaks out of vesicles inside the nerve terminal and is therefore not concerned with the actual physiological inactivation of synaptically released NE. However, it is possible that after inhibition of MAO, NE which accumulates within the nerve terminal may flow over the synaptic membrane, across the synaptic cleft, and onto postsynaptic receptors.

VI. Summary

Recent investigations have related the characteristic actions of several psychotropic drugs to effects on the disposition and metabolism of brain CA. Reserpine appears to effect sedation by releasing NE within the nerve terminal so that it is inactivated by deamination before leaving the neuron. Sedation occurs

[*] Cf. Horita, Chapter 20; Biel, Chapter 21.

after NE has been gradually depleted in this way from the brain. Amphetamine, however, releases brain NE across the synaptic membrane in an active form onto postsynaptic receptors. It also inhibits uptake of monoamines by the neuronal membrane. Imipramine-like antidepressants act by inhibiting NE reuptake by the nerve terminal, thus potentiating the actions of synaptically released CA. MAOI exert their antidepressant effects by causing an accumulation of NE in the nerve terminal with possible spillage of some accumulated CA across the synaptic cleft (cf. Fuxe *et al.*, Chapter 6; Klerman and Paykel, Chapter 49; Biel, Chapter 21).

It is interesting that extensive investigations have failed to reveal a clear link between CA disposition and the important antipsychotic actions of the phenothiazine drugs. It is thought that the phenothiazine drugs may have an antiadrenergic action at the postsynaptic receptors. However, such antiadrenergic effects are shared by numerous other drugs which lack the antipsychotic properties of the phenothiazines.

For further reading and references, see Appendices 1 and 2.

10

THE BIOCHEMISTRY OF AFFECTIVE DISORDERS

H. Weil-Malherbe

I. Introduction

When the two major functional psychoses, schizophrenia and manic-depressive insanity, are compared, the latter will appear much less alien and bizarre to most observers than schizophrenia. Everybody has experienced moods of depression and moods of elation and we can, without too much effort, identify to some extent with the exaggerations manifested by the patients suffering from this disease. The symptoms of schizophrenia, on the other hand, often appear, at least superficially, too absurd and incomprehensible for a psychodynamic interpretation. Most of us would therefore be inclined to associate schizophrenia with a more somatic and manic-depressive psychosis with a more psychogenic etiology. Yet, in spite of prodigious efforts, no unequivocal evidence for a somatic etiology of schizophrenia has so far been established, whereas evidence obtained in recent years strongly points to a link between endogenous affective disorders and a malfunction of certain neurohumors.

The concept that "melancholia" is due to an excess of black bile and therefore has a somatic origin goes back to the Hippocratic doctrine of the four body fluids. In modern times the constitutional studies of Kretschmer (52) and the genetic studies of Slater (53) and others have indicated the involvement of hereditary factors, but only recently has a specific theory been proposed in terms of chemical mechanisms.

II. The Catecholamine Hypothesis of Affective Disorders

The catecholamine hypothesis of affective disorders postulates, briefly, that endogenous depression is due to a functional deficiency of brain catecholamines and that mania is due to an overactivity of the sympathetic centers.

Most of the evidence is indirect and based on the action of three groups of drugs, i.e., reserpine and drugs related to reserpine, monoamine oxidase (MAO) inhibitors (iproniazid, nialamide, pargyline, etc.), and the tricyclic antidepressants, such as imipramine and amitriptyline. The mechanism of action of these drugs is assumed to implicate the brain neurotransmitter amines, especially norepinephrine. This subject has been adequately covered elsewhere in this text (Synder, Chapter 9; Fuxe *et al.*, Chapter 6; Laborit and Sanseigne, Chapter 18; Horita, Chapter 20; Biel, Chapter 21; Klerman and Paykel, Chapter 49; Frohman, Chapter 11).

When we consider these three groups of drugs, they are all seen to interfere with some aspect of transmitter function, as discussed elsewhere in this text in detail. Reserpine is known to inactivate, probably irreversibly, the vesicular binding sites. Absence of binding results in the rapid depletion of transmitter stores. Inhibition of MAO, however, increases the transmitter levels, primarily in the intraneuronal cytoplasm, but secondarily also in the extraneuronal space. As for the tricyclic antidepressants, they have been shown to inhibit the uptake of transmitter across the neuronal membrane and thus prolong the exposure of the receptor to extraneuronal, released transmitter. They therefore potentiate the effects of norepinephrine, and perhaps also those of serotonin, both peripherally and in the central nervous system. Their central effects depend on a well-stocked and functional norepinephrine store in the brain. When this store is selectively depleted or blocked by adrenergic blocking agents, imipramine loses its power of counteracting the central effects of reserpine, such as sedation, ptosis, and hypothermia. In accordance with this mechanism of action, imipramine therapy reduces the output of 4-hydroxy-3-methoxymandelic acid (VMA) and increases the excretion of normetanephrine (10). Both of these results are expected from the reduced transport of released norepinephrine across the neuronal membrane, since the formation of VMA depends on access to the intraneuronal MAO, whereas the formation of normetanephrine is increased by prolonged exposure of norepinephrine to catechol-*O*-methyltransferase, whose activity seems to be concentrated in the extraneuronal space.

Both MAO inhibitors and tricyclic antidepressants interfere with a phase of transmitter inactivation and therefore potentiate transmitter activity, but they do so by different mechanisms. Their effects are therefore additive, and combination of the two may lead to serious and even fatal reactions.

The hypothesis that some forms of depression are associated with a disturbance of brain norepinephrine function is thus based on the following arguments:

1. A drug-induced deficiency of brain catecholamines in animals is usually associated with sedation and inertia, whereas high levels are associated with overactivity and arousal.
2. Prolonged administration of reserpine, known to deplete brain catecholamines in animals, is liable to precipitate a severe depression, even suicide, in human beings. Intervention of depression has also been described as a side effect of treatment with α-methyldopa (54), a precursor of a "false transmitter" and thus an agent specifically depleting brain norepinephrine stores, and with propranolol (55), a highly active blocking agent of β-adrenergic receptors. The inference is that causation of depression is correlated with a depletion and functional inactivation of brain norepinephrine.
3. Severe stress of a mental or physical nature often acts as a trigger for the onset of endogenous depression (56). Such stresses have been shown to reduce catecholamine levels in animal brain.
4. MAO inhibitors and imipramine-like drugs are so far the most effective antidepressant agents. Both are antagonists of reserpine and potentiators of norepinephrine. The inference is that the antidepressant effect is correlated with the potentiation of norepinephrine activity.
5. Electric convulsion therapy, which is still widely and successfully used in the treatment of depression, is known to stimulate the sympathetic nervous system and produce a massive discharge of catecholamines.
6. Amphetamine, though no longer used as an antidepressant because of its side effects and the danger of addiction, has marked euphoriant and alerting effects. Its action is complex but is due, at least in part, to the release of norepinephrine combined with an imipramine-like blockade of the neuronal uptake (cf. Stein and Wise, Chapter 23; Fuxe *et al.*, Chapter 6; Biel, Chapter 19; Snyder, Chapter 9).

On the basis of the catecholamine theory of depression, administration of dopa, the precursor of norepinephrine, should be the sovereign therapy, yet dopa therapy has, on the whole, been disappointing. This is partly due to distressing side effects, such as nausea, vomiting, acute hypertension, anxiety and insomnia, partly to the transitory nature of the improvement. Occasionally dopa produces dramatic effects and may even precipitate a manic reaction.

The metabolism of catecholamines in affective disorders has been studied by the determination of urinary excretion rates. While these studies bear little direct evidence on the hypothesis, they do show changes in the excretion of catecholamines and their metabolites, supporting the possibility of an involvement of central sympathetic activity. When the excretion of catecholamines was studied in patients with the cyclic form of manic-depressive disease, high excretion was associated with the manic phase and low excretion with the depressive phase, but catecholamine excretion in depression is not always low. In a group of depressed patients those suffering from reactive or neurotic depression were found to excrete normal norepinephrine amounts which did not vary greatly during the course of the illness. Patients suffering from endogenous (psychotic) depression, however, excreted extremely variable amounts of norepinephrine, which fluctuated between very low and very high values (57). Recently it was reported that the concentration of norepinephrine in the CSF of depressed patients is increased compared with controls suffering from lumbar root syndromes or alcoholism. Higher values were found at the height of the depression than at its beginning or after its termination (58).

III. Indole Metabolism in Affective Disorders

Although the evidence for an involvement of serotonin in the pathogenesis of affective disorders is less conclusive than that for an involvement of catecholamines, such a possibility cannot be excluded. The ingestion of large doses of tryptophan was found to enhance the antidepressant effect of MAO inhibitors but to be without effect in the absence of MAO inhibitors or in conjunction with imipramine. This is probably due to the accumulation of tryptamine which, like many other amines, has an arousal effect, possibly as a result of the displacement and release of transmitter amines. 5-Hydroxytryptophan, the immediate precursor of serotonin, has also been tried in combination with MAO-inhibitors for the treatment of depression, but with inconclusive results.

The excretion of tryptamine in depressed patients was found to be decreased (in the absence of MAO inhibition), that of xanthurenic acid tended to be increased. This might suggest an activation of tryptophan pyrrolase, an enzyme known to be activated by corticosteroids. Elevated levels of corticosteroids are, in fact, observed in depressive illness.

The excretion of 5-hydroxyindoleacetic acid (5-HIAA), the main metabolite of serotonin, has also been investigated in affective disorders, with conflicting results. In a case of cyclic manic-depressive illness the excretion was low during the depressed phase and high during the manic phase. 5-HIAA was found to be decreased in the CSF of both depressed and manic patients.

IV. Mineral Metabolism in Affective Disorders

A number of studies have produced evidence suggesting a disturbance of the electrolyte and water distribution in affective psychoses. In cyclic insanity the excretion of water, sodium, and potassium was found to have a tendency to fluctuate in phase with the mood changes, a higher rate of excretion being found during the manic phase. In depressed patients the levels of plasma sodium were found to be unusually variable, suggesting decreased homeostasis. The ratio of sodium to potassium in the urine was decreased and there was a tendency toward sodium retention (59).

More recently isotope techniques have been used to study the electrolyte metabolism in affective disorders (57,60). These studies demonstrated an increase of the so-called residual sodium not only in depression but also, and even more markedly, in mania. To all intents and purposes the residual sodium may be regarded as equivalent to the intracellular fraction of sodium, although it includes a certain amount of sodium bound loosely in bone. It has also been claimed that there is a compensatory loss of intracellular potassium, but the evidence for this effect is not sufficiently convincing at present.

The increase of intracellular sodium and the decrease of intracellular potassium (if such exists) are in the direction of the concentration gradients and indicate an increase in the membrane permeability for ions such as might result from an increased energy demand or an insufficient energy supply.

The electrolyte changes in affective disorders are of particular interest in view of the successful treatment of mania by the oral administration of lithium salts (cf. Schou, Chapter 51). Lithium salts, in therapeutic doses, have no effect on the levels of sodium or potassium in plasma, but they do affect the distribution of sodium in the tissues. After 7 days of lithium medication a large decrease of exchangeable sodium was observed, apparently mainly at the expense of the intracellular fraction. Lithium salts also affected the distribution of chloride ions. Lithium is thus believed to correct the increase of intracellular sodium seen in mania. Although lithium has not been very successful in the treatment of depression, it has been found valuable as a prophylactic treatment in cases of recurrent depression.

The possibility that the administration of lithium affects the function of the brain transmitter amines is at present under active investigation in several laboratories. In rats lithium changed the metabolism of isotopic norepinephrine injected intracisternally: the ratio of labeled deaminated catechols to labeled normetanephrine was increased in comparison with untreated rats (61). This may be interpreted as indicating an increase of the intraneuronal inactivation of norepinephrine at the expense of its extraneuronal metabolism. Such an effect would be the antithesis of the effect of MAO inhibitors and of imipramine.

V. Glucose Utilization in Depression

A decrease of glucose tolerance, signaling an inhibition of glucose utilization, was among the earlest biochemical changes described in depression. The significance of this observation has, however, been criticized, mainly because the rate of absorption from the alimentary tract is an uncontrolled factor when the oral glucose-tolerance test is used. A physiologically valid measure of glucose utilization is obtained when glucose is administered intravenously and the exponential part of the blood sugar curve is analyzed. In more recent studies such techniques were used; moreover, interference from other factors, such as age, sex, malnutrition, obesity, was reduced as much as possible, but the patients suffering from depression were still found to have a significantly decreased glucose tolerance. This change persisted for some time after recovery indicating a process of long-term adjustments (62).

The question arises whether the decrease in glucose tolerance can be attributed to the rise of corticosteroid levels which has been observed in depression, but, unlike the change in glucose tolerance, the increases in corticosteroids usually respond promptly to clinical improvement. They are presumably the unspecific consequence of mental stress and are also found in other forms of mental disease or states of emotional stress. Significant though they are, the changes in the plasma level of corticosteroids found in depressed patients do not exceed the normal range and are quantitatively insufficient to account for the decrease in glucose utilization. This does not, however, rule out the hormonal origin of the effect. Treatment of depressed patients with inhibitors of MAO has been reported to improve their glucose utilization, and this may be connected with a potentiation of insulin, an effect which has been attributed to MAO inhibitors.

For further reading and references, see Appendix 1, which also contains a recent review by the author, with a comprehensive bibliography. See also Appendix 2.

11

POSSIBLE BIOCHEMICAL MECHANISMS OF SCHIZOPHRENIA

Charles Frohman

I. Monoamines and Other Small Molecules

The hope of discovering a biochemical defect in schizophrenia has motivated many investigators. After the discovery of the mechanism of action of reserpine, the earliest antipsychotic drug used to treat schizophrenia, all compounds known to be or thought to be involved in nerve transmission came under systematic study. As discussed elsewhere in this text, it was found that reserpine acted by releasing much of the bound serotonin (5-hydroxytryptamine, 5HT) and bound norepinephrine (NE) present in the brain, quieting the patient by possibly altering nerve transmission in the midbrain. Both 5HT and NE have been implicated in nerve transmission in the midbrain. Therefore, studies of indoles (precursors of 5HT) and catecholamines (compounds related to NE) were strongly suggested. The observation that some distant analogs of 5HT, and catecholamines such as LSD and mescaline, etc., caused symptoms which resembled some of those found in schizophrenia, made work with the indoles even more interesting (cf. Cohen, Chapter 39). Woolley synthesized 5HT antagonists and produced hallucinations in human subjects by injecting those analogs. The interest in 5HT spread to other physiological indoles and to their precursor in mammalian metabolism, the heterocyclic amino acid, tryptophan. Many workers have studied the excretion of indole derivatives in the urine of schizophrenic patients. They found that various unusual tryptophan derivatives, e.g., hydroxylated skatoles, not evident in the urine of control subjects, appeared in the urine from schizophrenic patients. Other workers have shown that tryptophan loading in the diet produces a number of different abnormal indole metabolites in the urine from schizophrenic patients, enhancing the possibility that indole metabolism may be a significant area of study in schizophrenia. However, the presence of some of these abnormal metabolites has not always been confirmed when other laboratories repeat the studies, and may be due simply to intestinal microorganisms.

Beside 5HT, another compound released by reserpine is also active in nerve transmission, especially in the integrative portion of the brain. This is NE, a methylated epinephrine derivative. Hoffer (63) suggested that adrenochrome, an oxidation product of epinephrine, might be responsible for psychotic symptoms. He synthesized adrenochrome, administered it to volunteers, and claimed that they then showed psychotic symptoms. Attempts by others to repeat this were unsuccessful. Axelrod (64) demonstrated that epinephrine was disposed of not only by oxidation but also by methylation of the hydroxyl groups on the phenol portion of the molecule. Pollin, Cardon, and Kety (65), hypothesizing that the ratio of oxidized to methylated catecholamines might be related to schizophrenia, administered simultaneously a potent methylating agent, methionine, and an amine oxidase inhibitor, iproniazid, to schizophrenic patients. The amine oxidase inhibitor would prevent the oxidative destruction of any methylated catecholamines formed by action of the methionine. In a number of the subjects thus treated, severe exacerbation of symptoms resulted. Since this treatment resulted in an increase in methylated catecholamines and a decrease in oxidized catecholamines, this work seemed to indicate that if catecholamines were involved in the disease, it was more likely that this involvement occurred through the methylated products rather than through the oxidized products. In support of this position, Friedhoff demonstrated that easily discernible amounts of a derivative of methylated catecholamines, 3,4-dimethoxyphenylethylamine (DMPEA) or "pink spot," so called from its color reaction on paper chromatograms (see Cohen, Chapter 39), were found in urine from schizophrenic patients, but not in the urine of control subjects. Upon administering DMPEA to trained rats, Bergen found that it produced marked behavioral effects. The DMPEA-pink spot idea is, however, challenged. Hoffer (66), claimed that administration of a methyl acceptor, niacin, to schizophrenic patients caused an improvement in symptoms. While not definitely proven, it still remains a distinct possibility that derivatives of tryptophan or catecholamines, particularly the methylated derivatives, may play a role in the disease. This must await chemical analyses of biopsies of brain tissue or from very fresh autopsy material.

II. Plasma Protein Factors

In another entirely different research trend, Haavaldsen, Lingjaerde, and Walaas (67) in Norway discovered that serum from schizophrenic patients decreased the carbohydrate uptake of rat diaphragm. They next isolated a protein from the serum of schizophrenic subjects which had the same effect as the whole serum. This protein was an α- or β-globulin. Working independently, Heath and his co-workers (68–70) in New Orleans isolated a protein from serum of schizophrenic patients which they claimed produced schizophrenic symptoms for a short time in injected control subjects. They also reported that the same protein produced EEG changes in monkeys. He called this compound taraxein. While they originally claimed that this protein was an α-2-globulin, they now state that the protein is a γ-globulin. It is not completely clear whether the protein described by their recent work is identical to the compound which Heath earlier called taraxein and identified as an α-2-globulin. In any case it is claimed that this γ-globulin is an antibody to some protein present only in the septal area of the brain. Fluorescent antibody techniques have indicated that the septal area of the brain is uniquely affected by this protein. When the protein was tagged with a fluorescent antibody, it could be seen attached to the cells in the septal area of the brain. When injected into monkeys, the protein was claimed to produce catatonia (68,69). Heath and Krupp (70) recently elaborated on this in more detail. Heath felt that this was very significant in view of his earlier claims that abnormal EEG patterns were obtained from deep implanted electrodes in the septal area of the brains of schizophrenic patients. The work with EEG patterns could never be completely confirmed by other workers. This is consistent with his earlier observations that the septal area of the brain of schizophrenic subjects produced an abnormal EEG pattern when measured with deep implanted electrodes. In view of the earlier claims that taraxein (the compound which induced psychotic symptoms in control subjects and abnormal EEG patterns in the septal area of monkey brains) was an α-2-globulin, it is difficult to understand why a gamma globulin should have the same activity. It would appear that more data are necessary to confirm Heath's very interesting findings.*

Winter and Flataker (71) also made a protein extract from schizophrenic patients' plasma which, when injected into rats, impaired the rats' rope-climbing skill. Bergen and Pennell (72), working with their own plasma protein extract, have shown that trained rats perform a rope-climbing reward task less efficiently when injected with a protein isolated from plasma from schizophrenic patients than when they are injected with a similarly prepared fraction from the plasma of control subjects. This is the same effect they obtained when injecting the animals with DMPEA. They claimed that their protein extract is also an α-globulin. We (73) isolated a protein from plasma of schizophrenic patients which we found to inhibit cellular oxidation, as evidenced from the increased ratio of (compared to nonpatient plasma fractions) lactate to pyruvate in chicken erythrocytes which had been incubated with the plasma protein.†

* *Editor's note:* Milhailovic and Janekovic in Yugoslavia (70a) claimed that various brain areas, particularly hippocampus and caudate nucleus, have specific antigenicity and antibodies to them which, when injected intraventricularly, caused EEG disturbances in these specific areas and behavioral deficits in cats and monkeys. This work remains to be confirmed.

† *Editor's note:* Frohman does not include in his discussion nor his table the work of Ryan, Durell, and Brown at the National Institutes of Mental Health, Bethesda (73a), who say the

This protein also increased the accumulation of several amino acids by cells. It is an α_2-globulin. Krasnova (74), working in Moscow, was not only able to repeat this work but was able to isolate a second protein from plasma from schizophrenic patients which decreased the eosinophil response of rabbits to stress. Turner found a protein factor in the serum from schizophrenic patients which causes the agglutination of rabbit erythrocytes, but it is very questionable that this protein is related to schizophrenia. A comparison of properties of the various protein factors reported for schizophrenia is shown in Table I. Various laboratories have reported on blood-borne factors in schizophrenia, but it is not yet clear whether or not they are studying the same protein molecule. It can be seen from Table I, however, that the protein factors produced by most groups have many common properties.

In an attempt to investigate the possibility that the protein from two groups was identical, Bergen prepared blood extracts from his own subjects, assayed them for activity using his own procedure (rat climbing time delay), and gave them to us for study. Similarly, we prepared blood extracts from our subjects, assayed them (using the L/P ratio and glutamic acid uptake), and gave them to Bergen.

Each laboratory then used its own procedures to assay the other's blood extract. Predictions of activity by the two laboratories were highly correlated $r = 0.74$). These results suggest that the two laboratories were studying the same blood-borne factor (75).

We found that this protein is particularly effective in increasing the accumulation of three different amino acids by cells (76). Again, using chicken erythrocytes as a tool, we found that schizophrenic plasma (and the α_2-globulin extracted from the plasma) increased the rate of uptake of glutamic acid, tryptophan, and phenylalanine into the cell. In the presence of plasma from schizophrenic subjects, glutamic acid accumulated in chicken erythrocytes to a level almost twice as high as in the presence of plasma from control subjects. This accumulation is probably the result of a decrease in the rate of efflux of glutamic acid rather than an effect on the influx rate. Tryptophan and phenylalanine accumulation are affected in somewhat the same manner as glutamic acid, while passage of many other amino acids is not affected.

It should be pointed out here that the α_2-globulin which causes the change in amino acid transport was elevated in only about 60% of schizophrenic patients.

L/P effect of the factor is caused by heterogenic antibody, which causes a complement-linked lysis of the erythrocytes and an associated stimulation of anaerobic glycolysis. A wide variability of this effect among plasmas of schizophrenics and controls occurred, and the difference was not statistically significant. They discuss this disparity in more recent, equally negative studies (73b), and review negative findings by others, not mentioned by Frohman. Kety in a review on current biochemical approaches to schizophrenia (73c) reviews the literature, including the above, and points out that the possibility remains to be ruled out that the titer of this antibody is more closely related to a history of chronic hospitalization and greater exposure to a variety of antigens, stress, diet, etc., than to the presence of schizophrenia. Frohman is, however, careful to point out in the conclusion of his chapter that the L/P factor has not been proven to be directly related to the etiology of schizophrenia.

Table I
Characteristics of Plasma Fraction in Schizophrenia

	Indicator	Protein	Type	Lipid	Molecular weight	Lability	Protection	Small molecule
Bergen and Pennell (Boston)	Rat climbing	+	alpha 2	+	High	++++	Vitamin C or H_2	+
Ehrensvaard (Stockholm)	O_2 of an amine	+	alpha or beta	?	High	++++	Vitamin C or glutathione	+
Frohman (Detroit)	L/P ratio	+	alpha 2	+	400,000 ±50,000	++++	Vitamin C or H_2	–
Heath (New Orleans)	Monkey behavior	+	gamma	?	?	–		?
Saunders (Buffalo)	Rat climbing	+	alpha 2 or beta	+	800,000	++++	Vitamin C	?
Turner (New York)	Rabbit erythrocyte agglutination	+	?	?	High	+	?	?
Krasnova (Moscow)	L/P ratio	+	alpha or beta	+	?	++++	–	?
Walaas (Oslo)	CHO uptake	+	alpha or beta	+	High	++++	Glutathione	?

The rest had normal levels of the protein. Many other physiological and biochemical defects can be correlated with the elevated factor (Table II).

Patients with elevated factor levels showed little or no stage IV sleep (characterized by slow delta waves) during a full night's EEG recording, while patients with normal factor level and control subjects showed around 18% of a night's sleep in stage IV. The high factor patients were also poorer at differentiating between two different weights and at being able to locate portions of their own body blindfolded. They also conditioned less easily, and had an abnormal EEG response to photic stimulation (77). In the latter case, an increase in the frequency of the photic impulses caused an increase or no change in the energy of the resulting EEG instead of the energy decrease found in control subjects. Considering all these differences between the two groups of schizophrenic patients, it is quite possible that the high factor patients represent a different disease than do the low factor patients.

Table II

Comparison of the Biologic Correlates between the Groups of Patients with the High L/P Ratio (Group I) and Low L/P Ratio (Group III)

Variable	Group I patients (high L/P ratio)	Group III patients (low L/P ratio)
1. Stage-IV sleep	Reduced	Similar to controls
2. GSR conditioning	MUCH POORER	Approaches controls
3. Arm to arm discrimination (proprioception)	POORER	Similar to controls
4. Averaged photic responses	LOWER AMPLITUDES LONGER LATENCIES	Similar to controls
5. Energy content in EEG (frequency analysis)	INCREASED (with photic stimulation)	DECREASED (with photic stimulation)
6. Animal avoidance learning	?	LEARN QUICKER
7. Work output task	VERY POOR	Approaches controls
8. Clinical findings		LESS STABLE FAMILIES PREMORBID PERSONALITY DISTURBANCE

If this effect on amino acid transport occurs in neural cells, then a unified theory of biochemical defects in schizophrenia can be advanced which incorporates results from work on protein factors and theories involving indoles and catecholamines.

Of the amino acids whose rate of passage changes in the presence of the factor, trytophan is a precursor of 5HT and many other biological indoles, phenylalanine is a precursor of NE and other catecholamines, and glutamic acid forms γ-aminobutyric acid (GABA), another compound which has been said to be involved in nerve function. If more tryptophan, phenylalanine, and glutamic acid are entering a schizophrenic person's cells, then production of the normal metabolites of these substances may also be increased. Excessive amounts of neurotransmitters such as 5HT, NE, and GABA very likely could disturb nerve transmission. It is interesting to speculate that, since reserpine causes a decrease in the cellular levels of 5HT and NE, the tranquilizing action of this drug might be explained on this basis. Similarly, chlorpromazine, an antipsychotic drug widely used in schizophrenia, has been reported to decrease the *rate of accumulation* of amino acids in cells.

The excess of these amino acids in the cell may also cause overproduction of some of their minor metabolites. This would explain the frequent and recurrent reports of unusual indoles and catecholamines in the urine of schizophrenic subjects. Thus, the recent report of Himwich that bufotenine (*N,N*-dimethyl-5HT) is present more often in urine of schizophrenic subjects, and that of Friedhoff that DMPEA is also present in the urine of schizophrenic subjects, might be explained. Bufotenine has been shown to be a potent hallucinogen. Since bufotenine and DMPEA are both manufactured by methylation of their precursors, this might also explain the exacerbation of symptoms in schizophrenia brought about by increasing methylation as reported by Pollin, Cardon, and Kety (65) and the ameliorating effect of niacin (a methyl acceptor) as reported by Hoffer.

Attractive as these speculations might seem, it must be made quite clear that at the present time they are only working hypotheses and that much more data must be obtained before any portions of them can be proven. To be sure, much more data are necessary to definitely prove the involvement of a protein-factor in schizophrenia. That there is an α_2-globulin elevated in the blood of many schizophrenics cannot be disputed. However, it has not been proven that this α_2-globulin or any of its biochemical or behavior effects are directly related to the etiology of schizophrenia. In fact it is quite clear that if a relationship between the α_2-globulin and schizophrenia does exist, it is not a simple one-to-one relationship. We found elevated levels of the protein factor in many of the parents of schizophrenic subjects with high level of the factor (78). These parents are not schizophrenic. Therefore, if the factor were to be connected with the etiology of schizophrenia, it would be necessary to hypothesize the interaction of this factor with some other factor or condition not present in the parents of the schizophrenic subjects. However, with the increasing amount of data indicating biochemical differences in schizophrenia, it is quite possible that there are some chemical defects involved in the disease, and that these defects may involve a protein factor and/or the metabolism of catecholamines or indoles.*

For further reading and references, see Appendices 1 and 2.

* It also will be necessary to isolate, purify, and characterize such factors from various brain areas and their subcellular components, from schizophrenic patients versus normals.

12

METABOLIC EFFECTS OF SOME PSYCHOPHARMACOLOGICAL AGENTS IN BRAIN *IN VITRO*

J. H. Quastel

It is now well known that disturbances in brain function may be brought about by a variety of neurotropic and psychopharmacologic agents among which are:

1. Substances that affect, directly or indirectly, the energetics of brain cells by interference with oxidative phosphorylation or by inhibitory effects on stimulated brain cell metabolism. Such compounds include a wide variety of anesthetics, psychotropic compounds, alcohols, aldehydes, and steroids.
2. Substances that interfere with the influx of ions or of metabolites (e.g., amino acids or vitamins) into the brain cells, i.e., substances that block transport reactions at the brain cell membranes.
3. Substances that affect the store or level of pharmacologically active amines in brain cells.
4. Substances that interfere in a specific manner with brain enzyme systems, e.g., amine oxidase, amino acid decarboxylase, and nicotinamide adenine dinucleosidase (NADase).

Such substances exert effects on brain metabolism *in vitro* and some of these are the subject of discussion in this chapter.

I. Significance of Cerebral Energy Metabolism for Brain Function

The brain, which normally derives its energy almost entirely from oxidative processes, consumes oxygen at a rate which is among the highest in the body, and it has been calculated that during the first four years of life more than half of the total oxygen consumption of the body is by the brain. Brain is highly vulnerable to oxygen lack, a continuous supply of blood being essential for the normal functioning of this organ. The high rate of oxygen consumption by the brain is presumably essential for the maintenance of those processes required for brain function, e.g., the maintenance of ionic gradients and the electrical activity of the brain, the synthesis and storage of chemical transmitters, the maintenance of the phospholipid activity of brain cell membranes, and so on. Clearly, any factor that interferes with brain oxygen consumption, or with the metabolic systems in the brain dependent on oxygen consumption, will affect brain function and mental activity. Among such factors are a variety of psychotropic drugs. Even high oxygen pressures have mental effects, inducing convulsions, a fact known since 1878. A constant, rather than a rich, supply of oxygen is essential for the normal functioning of the brain, an observation that points to the importance of the regulation, within certain narrow limits, of respiratory activities in the central nervous system and of the various metabolic events dependent on respiration.

There is little change in the oxygen consumption of the brain with change of rate of blood flow unless this is reduced below 50% of its normal value. Thus, in spite of the fact that the cerebral blood flow in man increases from the normal value of 54 ml/100 gm/min to 93 ml/100 gm/min under conditions of 5–7% CO_2 inhalation, the rate of cerebral oxygen consumption remains at 3.3 ml/100 gm/min. The rate of cerebral oxygen consumption is, however, definitely affected in a number of pathological conditions where there is but little change in the rate of flow (79). In various types of coma there is a large decrease in the rate of cerebral oxygen consumption. Similarly, in experiments on the metabolism of the brain in monkeys it has been shown that, under barbiturate anesthesia, there is a fall of 50% in the rate of oxygen consumption in animals whose reflexes are absent and which have to be artificially supplied with oxygen. Although cerebral oxygen consumption is depressed by over 30% in pentothal anesthesia and in acute alcoholic poisoning, no detectable changes in cerebral oxygen consumption occur in sleep, or during mental arithmetic exercises, or in patients with schizophrenia. It should not be concluded, however, that where there is no fall in overall consumption of the brain, there are no physiological changes in that organ. It is known, for example, that the electrical activity of the brain as shown by the electroencephalogram (EEG) in sleep differs from that in coma. During ischemia and hypoxia of the brain, which can cause functional paralysis followed by irreversible damage due to lack of oxidative energy, the first mental disturbances and alteration of EEG coincide with diminution of total cerebral oxygen consumption.

Rapid biochemical changes take place in the brain following interference with its oxidative mechanisms. After an ischemia of ten minutes the brain adenosine triphosphate (ATP) content drops to 15% of the normal. Deprivation of oxygen, or interference with brain oxidations, does not have identical effects on different parts of the nervous system. For example, cyanide or carbon monoxide poisoning have selective effects, resulting in more consistent degeneration of neurons in the globus pallidus and parts of the cerebellum and cerebral white matter than elsewhere in the brain. Again, it is known that under anoxia there is a decrease in efficiency of ocular movements, attributed to diminished oxygen supply to subcortical as well as to cortical tissue. It is believed that changes in eye movements may be used to detect early effects of oxygen deprivation. The cerebral vasodilatation and increased blood flow known to occur in anoxia cannot fully compensate for the effects of the diminished oxygen tension. The result is an impairment of sensory and mental function and integration, the cortical cells apparently suffering more than other parts of the central nervous system.

The results of studies of rates of cerebral oxygen consumption *in vivo* both in health and disease lead to the conclusion that a fall in the rate of oxygen consumption is associated with functional cerebral disturbances, but that a constancy of the rate does not necessarily imply that there is no change in the functional activity of the brain. Moreover, it is evident that local changes may occur in various parts of the central nervous system that may have far-reaching effects on the behavior of the brain, but which are not reflected by any marked change in its overall oxygen consumption.

II. Measurements of Brain Metabolism *in Vivo* and *in Vitro*

Estimates of *in vitro* respiratory rates of whole brain are approximate to the values found *in vivo* in conditions of diminished functional activity but are considerably less than normal values *in vivo* (about one-half). It is evident that respiratory rates of brain tissue *in vitro* (in the form of brain slices) examined in normal physiological media do not reflect the rates obtained in the brain *in situ*. Nevertheless, it is possible by stimulation of the isolated brain tissue by alteration of the cationic concentration in the medium surrounding the brain tissue, or by electrical stimulation, to increase the respiratory rates to approximately those found *in vivo* (80,81). The application of a drug, protoveratrine, at low concentrations (e.g., 5 μM) to the isolated brain tissue has a like effect.

There is a close similarity between the effects of cationic stimulation of brain metabolism (either by increased potassium ion concentrations in a sodium medium or by increased sodium ion concentrations in a potassium medium or by absence of calcium ions from a normal medium) and those due to electrical stimulation, and it appears that both methods of stimulation have a common basis of action, namely, cationic displacements at the brain cell membrane. What is important to realize is the fact that the stimulated respiration, brought about by both methods, has the magnitude of brain respiration *in vivo* and possesses some of the characteristic features of brain reactions *in vivo,* such as response to drug action. It must be borne in mind, however, that isolated brain slices, under the best experimental conditions obtained so far, do not show, and cannot be expected to show, all the electrophysiological responses to stimulation associated with brain *in vivo.* Nevertheless, even as an approximation to the *in vivo* conditions, they are able to yield useful biochemical data bearing upon the properties of the functioning brain.

The stimulation of respiration *in vitro* that takes place on application of electrical impulses or by changed cationic fluxes at the cell membrane occurs only in brain slices, and not in brain homogenates or minces, and it is evident that the brain cells must be intact for stimulation to take place. Moreover, the stimulation is specific to certain areas of the brain. The stimulation of respiration is now known to consist of an increased rate of turnover of the citric acid cycle in brain mitochondria, due apparently to the increased quantities of adenosine diphosphate (ADP) (and phosphate) that are formed as a result of changed cationic fluxes at the brain cell membrane. The stimulation of the activity of membrane ATPase, which is both Na^+ and K^+ dependent, is probably the major reason for the increased brain cell concentration of ADP. Increase of the level of ADP leads to an increased rate of mitochondrial respiration as it controls the rate of oxidation of reduced nicotinamide adenine dinucleotide ($NADH_2$) and, therefore, the level of NAD, which in turn partly controls the speed of the citric acid cycle.

Application of electrical impulses leads to an increased influx of sodium ions in the brain cell. Increased concentration of potassium ions in the medium bathing the brain slices leads to the retention of high potassium ion concentrations in the brain cell, or to the influx of potassium ions. Both conditions lead to the increased activity of membrane-bound ATPase, which is a controlling factor in the stimulation of brain respiration *in vitro* (82,83). Deprivation of calcium ions from the incubation medium also leads to an increased influx of sodium ions into the brain cell.

The stimulated respiration of isolated brain, which may be regarded as mainly an ADP- (or phosphate-) controlled respiration, is highly sensitive to drugs having potent effects on brain function, for example, anesthetics, alcohols, and "tranquilizers."

Only oxidation of substances that enable stimulation to take place, e.g., glucose or pyruvate, is affected appreciably by these neurotropic drugs at pharmacologically active concentrations. Substantial suppressions of stimulated respiration by anesthetics take place at anesthetic levels. When the oxidation of mitochondria (even liver mitochondria) is stimulated by the addition of ADP, it is the stimulated oxidation which is more inhibited by anesthetics such as the barbiturates than the unstimulated oxidation. Moreover, this suppression occurs at anesthetic concentrations. The drug acts in this way as it is able to suppress ADP-controlled $NADH_2$ oxidation. This well-known fact has made amobarbital, for example, a very useful tool for the study of those phases of cell respiration in which

$NADH_2$ is involved and is an illustration of the conclusion made over twenty-five years ago that anesthetics such as the barbiturates inhibit a process playing an intermediate role between cytochrome oxidase and a flavoprotein concerned with the oxidation of $NADH_2$.

As the biological oxidation of $NADH_2$ in the cell is accompanied, and indeed controlled, by the phosphorylation of ADP to ATP, it follows that the anesthetic is also inhibitory to oxidative phosphorylation. It is the latter process that is of importance in the interpretation of some of the action of a variety of drugs on brain function. Inhibitions recorded with brain cortex slices represent effects on the entire brain cortex. Local inhibitions will be higher if there is localization of the site of action, or of absorption, of the anesthetic or neurotropic drug. It is known that these drugs have differential effects on brain cells, and neurons of different animal species do not all have the same sensitivities to anesthetics. For example, respiration of human brain cortex is more sensitive to luminal than that of rat brain cortex.

III. Effects of Anesthetic Agents on Brain Metabolism *in Vitro*

It was demonstrated over thirty years ago that barbiturates and other anesthetic drugs affect metabolism of isolated brain tissue and that there is a parallelism between the hypnotic activities of anesthetics of the same chemical type and their abilities to suppress brain respiration *in vitro*. The anesthetics suppress, at the concentrations tested, brain respiration *in vitro* in the presence of glucose or pyruvate but not that in the presence of succinate; so it is evident that not all respiratory processes are equally sensitive to the drugs. The concentrations of anesthetics required to accomplish marked inhibitory effects on the metabolism of brain tissue, examined in standard physiological media, are relatively large compared with those needed to induce the unconscious state. Relatively recent work carried out with cation-stimulated, or electrically stimulated, isolated brain slices or with brain mitochondria preparations has shown, however, that the anesthetics, at the low concentrations which are pharmacologically active, bring about marked inhibitions of certain respiratory processes. The concentrations of barbiturates that inhibit mitochondrial respiration are in close agreement with the anesthetic levels.

Cerebral respiratory stimulation (cationic or electrical) is highly sensitive to barbiturates and other anesthetics, and it is now known that amobarbital (0.5 m*M*) not only suppresses potassium-activated brain cortex metabolism but has a like effect on sodium-activated brain metabolism as well. The stimulated respiration is also more inhibited by ethanol and higher aliphatic alcohols, and by chlorpromazine (CPZ), than the unstimulated respiration. In fact, it had been shown some years earlier that the increment in the rate of oxygen uptake of frog nerve, carrying impulses at the rate of 50 impulses/second, is highly narcotic sensitive. The suppression of cationic, or electrical, stimulation of brain respiration by anesthetics and some analgesic drugs may be explained in either of, or both, the following ways: (1) inhibition of electron and energy transfer in mitochondrial metabolism; (2) inhibition of the cation movements at the membrane, thus affecting the ADP/ATP ratio in the brain cell and thereby the rate of the ADP-controlled mitochondrial respiration.

Similarity of biochemical behavior by different drugs does not necessarily result in similar clinical effects, for these must clearly depend on the sites in the nervous system at which the drugs act.

Local anesthetics, such as procaine or cocaine, inhibit electrically stimulated brain cortex respiration *in vitro* much more effectively than potassium-stimulated respiration. There is reason to believe that these drugs attach themselves to sites in the brain cell membrane in such a manner as to prevent the influx into the cell of sodium ions following the application of electrical impulses. The manner, however, in which these drugs combine with membrane sites is still unknown.

Recent work has shown that procaine (1 m*M*) or cocaine (0.2 m*M*) blocks the influx of sodium ions into the brain cell during electrical stimulation. This is demonstrated by the finding that the rate of cerebral oxidation of acetate, which is suppressed by the influx of sodium ions during electrical stimulation, is increased by the addition of the local anesthetics. Amobarbital (0.25 m*M* or 0.5 m*M*), however, has no such effect. In fact, its addition diminishes still further the rate of cerebral oxidation of acetate found during electrical stimulation. Yet procaine, cocaine, and amobarbital, at the concentrations mentioned, greatly suppress the electrically stimulated rate of cerebral oxygen uptake. These drugs, therefore, act on the brain cell either at different sites or on different mechanisms (see Fig. 1).

The results that have been obtained do not imply that all cells in the brain are equally affected by a neurotropic drug at the concentrations which cause mental changes nor that a depression of *total* brain respiration by an anesthetic should necessarily ensue. They do imply, however, that the affected cells can no longer carry on their normal biochemical and functional behavior and, therefore, that those parts of the nervous system controlled by the activities of the affected cells will also be affected, with resulting disturbances in the nervous system as a whole that will vary according to the location and neurophysiological significance of the affected cells. Moreover, it does not follow that the biochemical changes undergone *in vivo* by the brain as a whole, in the presence of the neurotropic agent, will be similar to those shown by the relatively few drug-affected cells; for the biochemical effects found in the brain as a whole, in the presence of a neurotropic agent, may be simply a reflection of the diminished, or changed, total cerebral activities due to the paralysis of the relatively small proportion of cells that are directly affected by the drug. Lack of realization of this fact has given rise to a good deal of confusion. It had been thought that the chemical consequences of exposure of brain tissue *in vitro* to a neurotropic agent should be identical with those found on examining the brain *in vivo* after administration of the agent and vice versa. This, however, is not a correct deduction. Depression of the functional activity of certain parts of the brain following the inhibition there of some aspect of metabolism (by an anesthetic, for example) will lead to lessened stimulation of many nerve cells in various parts of brain that are not directly affected by the drug. It will, therefore, lead to higher levels there of a number of substances [such as ATP or of acetylcholine (ACh)] than occur in the drug-affected cells, where the syntheses of these compounds have been inhibited by the neurotropic agent and which can no longer exert their normal function of stimulating various dependent nerve pathways.

The attachment of the drug to neuronal membrane constituents that results in changed cation movements and consequent metabolic disturbances in the cell may, perhaps, by its alteration of the electrical character of the membrane, be considered to be the direct cause of the changed functional state of the brain cell. If it could be shown that the changed electrical properties accompanying anesthesia or anoxia do, in fact, always precede the metabolic disturbances, it would be logical to conclude that the known metabolic effects of anesthetics, at narcotic concentrations, on electron or energy transfer might be a consequence of the initial electrical changes. Experiments, however, seem to indicate that the reverse is the case, i.e., that electrical changes may be a consequence of, or at any rate follow, metabolic changes. Thus it has been shown, in experiments on rats (84), that under anoxic conditions, following nitrous oxide anesthesia, the electrical activity of the cortex continues normally until about 70% reduction of the pyridine nucleotide present has taken place. Then there occurs an abrupt halt in electrical activity. When the anoxia is removed by oxygen administration, the oxidation of the reduced pyridine nucleotide recommences, and as the level of the nucleotide rises toward a higher degree of oxidation, the electrical activity is restored. It was concluded that the cortical electrical activity that still takes place, following the reduction of pyridine nucleotide, depends on the stores of high energy intermediates which are formed during oxidative phosphorylation and that reoxidation of reduced pyridine nucleotide is a necessary condition for the resumption of electrical activity.

The significance of the inhibitions by barbiturates, and other anesthetics, at narcotic concentrations, of biosynthesis of ATP is related to the resultant interference with neuronal mechanisms of great importance to the brain cell. Such mechanisms include the establishment of ionic gradients, the biosynthesis of ACh, the influx of amino acids, amines, cell nutrients, and other processes.

IV. Effects of Anesthetics on Electron, and Energy Transfer

The barbiturate amobarbitol, as well as the hypnotic chlorobutanol, suppresses the rate of oxidation of reduced nicotinamide adenine dinucleotide ($NADH_2$) by the cytochrome system. As it is now well known that the biological oxidation of $NADH_2$ is accompanied, and indeed in the cell is controlled, by the phosphorylation of ADP to ATP, it follows that the anesthetic is also inhibitory to oxidative phosphorylation. The suppression of $NADH_2$ oxidation by amobarbitol has the double effect of suppressing the citric acid cycle (as the rate of this is dependent on the supply of acetyl-CoA, which is formed by oxidation of pyruvate by NAD) and the formation of ATP.

The barbiturates, and other hypnotics, suppress, at low concentration, oxidative uptake of phosphate, i.e., ATP formation. The interference of these drugs with ATP synthesis in the brain is shown by their suppression of ACh synthesis and by their inhibitor effects (e.g., those of 4 m*M* pentobarbitol on ^{32}P incorporation (from labeled phosphate) into phosphoproteins or organic phosphorus compounds in cat brain slices respiring in the presence of glucose. This is also shown very well, using rat brain cortex slices, by the suppression by amobarbitol (0.5 m*M*) of glutamine biosynthesis, a reaction which is ATP dependent. The suppression of glutamine biosynthesis which occurs in slices of rat brain cortex, whose respiration has been stimulated by increased potassium ion concentration, is also shown by chlorobutanol (2 m*M*), tribromoethanol (0.1 m*M*), and other alcohols, and also by salicylates (5 m*M*).

The effects of these drugs on oxidative synthesis of ATP and, therefore, among other reactions, on the synthesis of ACh, especially that bound by subcellular particles, to be drawn upon during the functional activity of the nerve cell, may account for a diminished rate of recovery of the cell to its normal condition. This slowing of recovery is presumably one of the factors responsible for the paralysis of the nerve cells, or of the centers specifically affected by the drugs.

Thus, one way by which an anesthetic may suppress the functional activity of a brain cell is by suppression of the rate of biosynthesis of substances needed for brain function that require mitochondrial ATP (or other high energy phosphates) for their formation. A neurotropic agent that is not an anesthetic may have similar effects, but presumably it acts at sites in the nervous system distinct from those at which anesthetics have their optimal effects.

V. Anesthetics and Adenosine Triphosphatase

With liver mitochondria, the rate of oxygen uptake may be depressed in the presence of barbiturates by more than 50% with no depression of the ratio of phosphate esterified to oxygen consumed (i.e., the P:O ratio). Thiobarbiturates, however, depress the P:O ratio, a fact to be correlated with their activation of ATPase, in contrast to the lack of effect of the oxybarbiturates. Amobarbitol suppresses the activity of ouabain-sensitive cardiac microsomal ATPase (in the presence of Mg^{++}, Na^{+}, and K^{+}), but only at concentrations exceeding 2 m*M*, 50% inhibition occurring at 4 m*M*. The fact that amobarbitol at concentrations that abolish cationic or electrical stimulation of brain cortex respiration has but little inhibitory effect on the ATPase, which has been implicated in the active transport of Na^{+} and K^{+} across membranes, makes it unlikely that the drug operates mainly at low concentrations on sodium- or potassium-active transport at the cell membrane. In general, there seems to be little or no correlation between the effects of anesthetics on stimulated brain respiration and those on the activity of membrane-bound ATPase.

VI. Brain Metabolism and the Sodium Pump

The active uptake of potassium ions into the brain cell is sodium dependent, and, indeed, the presence of sodium ions is essential for various phenomena in brain tissue that are brought about by increased potassium concentrations in the medium surrounding the brain, e.g., stimulated respiration, stimulated phosphate incorporation into phospholipids and phosphoproteins, or stimulated synthesis of ACh. Amino acid transport is sodium dependent, and the transport of acetate or citrate in the brain *in vitro* is also highly sodium dependent. It is evident from these facts, as well as from those concerning the effects of ouabain, that conditions underlying sodium and potassium transport at the neuronal membrane, i.e., the operation of the sodium pump, greatly influence the kinetics of brain metabolism. It follow, too, that drugs that affect cationic equilibria at the neuronal membrane will also affect brain cell metabolism.

VII. Effects of Acetylcholine

In this connection some effects of ACh may be noted. This substance causes depolarization of the postsynaptic membrane with an increase of permeability to sodium and potassium ions. ACh, in the presence of eserine, stimulates the incorporation of ^{32}P into phospholipids of brain cortex slices with but little apparent effect on the rate of oxygen consumption, an increased rate of turnover of phosphate in the phospholipid taking place. The stimulation occurs in those areas of the brain containing cholinergic synapses, and it has been suggested that the stimulation by ACh is connected with the active transport of Na^+ across the postsynaptic membranes of cholinergic neurons. Sodium ions are essential for the stimulation, which can be abolished by a metabolic inhibitor such as malonate or by anesthetics at low concentrations. Ethyl alcohol is also an effective inhibitor. The metabolic effects of ACh on phospholipid metabolism resemble those due to increased potassium ions, or diminished calcium ions, in the medium surrounding the brain tissue. A reasonable hypothesis is that the ACh effect is mediated partly, if not wholly, by electrolyte changes at the cell, or synaptic, membrane in the cholinergic neuron, which in turn affects ATP formation and thereby phosphate turnover in the phospholipids. Such an explanation would be consistent with the observation that both atropine and hyoscine inhibit ACh stimulation of phosphate incorporation into phospholipids (presumably by competition for an ACh receptor site), but not potassium stimulation.

The presence of a high concentration of potassium ions brings about a depression of the rate of active transport of amino acids at the brain cell, and the depression of the rate of active transport of glycine is proportional to the depression of the ATP level. ACh reverses the inhibitory action of high potassium ion concentration on amino acid transport, and it has been suggested that it acts by promoting the influx of sodium ions which have a controlling effect on the amino acid influx. The effect of ACh is specific, being enhanced by the presence of eserine, which itself is without effect. It cannot reverse the inhibitory action of ammonium ions, ouabain, L-glutamate, or L-glutamine on glycine transport into the brain. Its effect is not given by choline or hemicholinium at equivalent concentrations.

VIII. Ouabain and Brain Metabolism *in Vitro*

It is now well known that ouabain, as well as other cardiac glycosides, inhibits cationic fluxes at the cell membrane without depressing respiration or glycolysis. They must act, therefore, by means other than those bringing about energetic changes. Ouabain, at concentrations of 10^{-5} M or less, suppresses the influx of glutamate and of creatine into the brain cell, depresses stimulation of respiration by potassium, abolishes glutamine biosynthesis, perhaps by suppressing ammonia transport to the site of glutamine biosynthesis, and suppresses the active transport of ascorbic acid and thiamine into the brain cell. It also suppresses acetate and citrate metabolism in brain *in vitro*. It is evident that there is a close association between membrane transport phenomena and the various processes occurring at the membrane that cause ATP breakdown. What is also evident is that interference with the transport process leads to leakage of amino acids and other substances concentrated in the cell. Ouabain can cause considerable depletion of the brain cell of amino acids and of creatine. Ouabain accomplishes these effects by its suppression of the activity of the membrane-bound, sodium- and potassium-sensitive ATPase, which has a controlling effect on the active transport into the brain cell of amino acids and a variety of nutrients and cell metabolites.

IX. Tetrodotoxin and Brain Metabolism *in Vitro*

Tetrodotoxin, a potent neurotoxin found in the Japanese puffer fish and elsewhere, suppresses at concentrations as low as 0.3 μM, action potentials in a variety of excitable tissues, including frog myelinated nerve fibers and lobster and squid giant axons. It is considered to be a specific blocker of sodium conductance. While it has no effect on the rate of respiration of rat brain cortex slices incubated in a physiological glucose medium, tetrodotoxin completely blocks the stimulation of respiration that occurs on application of electrical impulses (85). It has, however, no effect on potassium-stimulated respiration of brain cortex slices. These results are interpreted as indicating that with electrical stimulation there is an increased influx into the brain cell of sodium ions (86) which by their accelerating effect on the activity of membrane ATPase results in an increased rate of respiration controlled by ADP. Tetrodotoxin suppresses, because of its combination with a specific membrane component, this response of the brain cell to an applied electrical impulse. With high K^+, the flux of potassium ions which activate the membrane ATPase, and thereby activate brain cell respiration, is unimpeded by tetrodotoxin.

X. Effects of Acetylsalicylate

One of the most noteworthy effects of acetylsalicylate, when added to brain cortex slices respiring in a glucose phosphate medium, is an increased rate of leakage of amino acids and other substances from the brain tissue into the surrounding medium. This effect of acetylsalicylate is doubtless a consequence of the fact that it inhibits the influx of amino acids (e.g., glutamate) into the brain tissue. It also inhibits the influx of creatine into the tissue. As transport processes are ATP dependent, they are inhibited by acetylsalicylate, which, by its uncoupling effect on cerebral oxidative phosphorylation, diminishes the cell level of ATP. The effect of acetylsalicylate in bringing about an increased leakage of amino acids from the brain tissue is greatly enhanced under metabolic conditions where the cell content of ATP has fallen from the normal level (e.g., in the presence of high K^+ or NH_4^+ or glutamate), or when the phosphocreatine reserve has diminished to such an extent that it is unable to maintain the normal level of ATP (through the operation of creatine phosphokinase).

XI. Effects of Chlorpromazine and Allied Substances on Brain Metabolism

As mentioned earlier, CPZ at low concentrations reduces enhanced brain cell respiration due to electrical or cationic stimulation, the former being the more sensitive process. It also uncouples phosphorylations, at relatively high concentrations, associated with the oxidation of $NADH_2$ by the cytochrome system and of ferrocytochrome c, its effect varying according to the site in the brain, the hypothalamus being the most sensitive. It is evident that CPZ can bring about suppressions in the brain of oxidative synthesis of ATP. Moreover, the addition of CPZ (0.1 mM) to guinea pig brain slices brings about changes in the labeling of lipid phosphorus in the presence of ^{32}P, namely, decreases of phosphatidylethanolamine and phosphatidylcholine and an increase of phosphoinositide; with higher concentrations there is a considerable decrease in labeling of lipid phosphorus.

CPZ differs from the barbiturates in bringing about progressive inhibitions of brain respiratory processes and in its high binding power with tissue proteins. It also affects cell permeability, diminishing uptake of circulating labeled norepinephrine (NE) into heart and adrenal medulla. CPZ (0.1 mM), and also reserpine, cause complete release of particle-bound epinephrine in adrenal gland preparations. Several other phenothiazine antipsychotics resemble CPZ in this respect. Possibly, such effects on brain transport phenomena are due either directly to combination with specific membrane constituents or indirectly to suppression of formation of ATP that controls transport at the cell membrane. New evidence indicates that, at concentrations of 0.05 mM, it blocks sodium influx following electrical stimulation, a fact pointing to its combination with a specific membrane component. A drug related chemically to CPZ is imipramine, but whereas the former is classed as an antipsychotic agent, the latter acts as an antidepressant. Recent results show that the two drugs behave very similarly, although with a quantitative difference, on brain preparations, and it seems evident that, at their effective pharmacological concentrations, they have but little inhibitory effect on mitochondrial respiration. In this respect, they resemble the aliphatic alcohols. The two drugs also behave similarly in bringing about a stimulation (at low concentrations) of the rate of incorporation of phosphate into brain phospholipids, without affecting the oxidative metabolism of brain slices. The evidence suggests that their effects are located at possibly different sites on the brain cell membrane, but the nature of these sites is at present unknown.

XII. Effects of Aliphatic Alcohols and Aldehydes

The presence of ethanol at small concentrations diminishes the rate of oxygen consumption of rat brain cortex slices respiring in a glucose-phosphate medium when this has been stimulated by the presence of increased concentrations of K^+ or by the application of electrical impulses. The inhibitory effects of the alcohols increase markedly as the length of carbon chain increases and with increase in concentration. The stimulation of brain cortex respiration (brought about by K^+ or electrically) is diminished, or abolished, by concentrations of alcohols that have little or no effect on the unstimulated respiration. *N*-Pentanol is much more effective than ethanol in effecting an inhibition of stimulated respiration, and there seems to take place a rapid establishment of equilibria between the alcohols and the components that influence the brain respiratory system. Brain mitochondria respiration is relatively insensitive to concentrations of alcohols that considerably depress stimulated rat brain slice respiration. It would appear that aliphatic alcohols exert their effects on brain cell respiration at the brain cell membranes.

Acetaldehyde is a potent inhibitor of brain slice respiration, its inhibition of potassium-stimulated respiration occurring at a very much lower concentration than that at which ethanol produces the same effect. The stimulation of brain respiration due to K^+ is abolished by acetaldehyde at concentrations that have no observable effect on the unstimulated respiration. Acetaldehyde and *N*-valeraldehyde, at equivalent concentrations, have almost equal inhibitory effects on potassium-stimulated rat brain cortex respiration. The inhibitory effects of the aldehyde do not increase sharply with increase of their concentration, in contrast to the effects of the corresponding alcohols. The aldehydes, also in contrast to the alcohols, inhibit brain mitochondrial respiration as markedly as they inhibit brain cortex respiration. The results obtained with the aldehydes do not support the view, however, that the corresponding alcohols exert their inhibitory effects on brain respiration by preliminary conversion to the aldehydes.

The aldehydes derived from the pharmacologically active amines are also highly inhibitory at low concentrations to brain respiration, that corresponding to tyramine, viz. *p*-hydroxyphenylacetaldehyde, being sufficiently potent to inactivate succinic dehydrogenase.

Many of the results recorded so far in this chapter are summarized in Fig. 1.

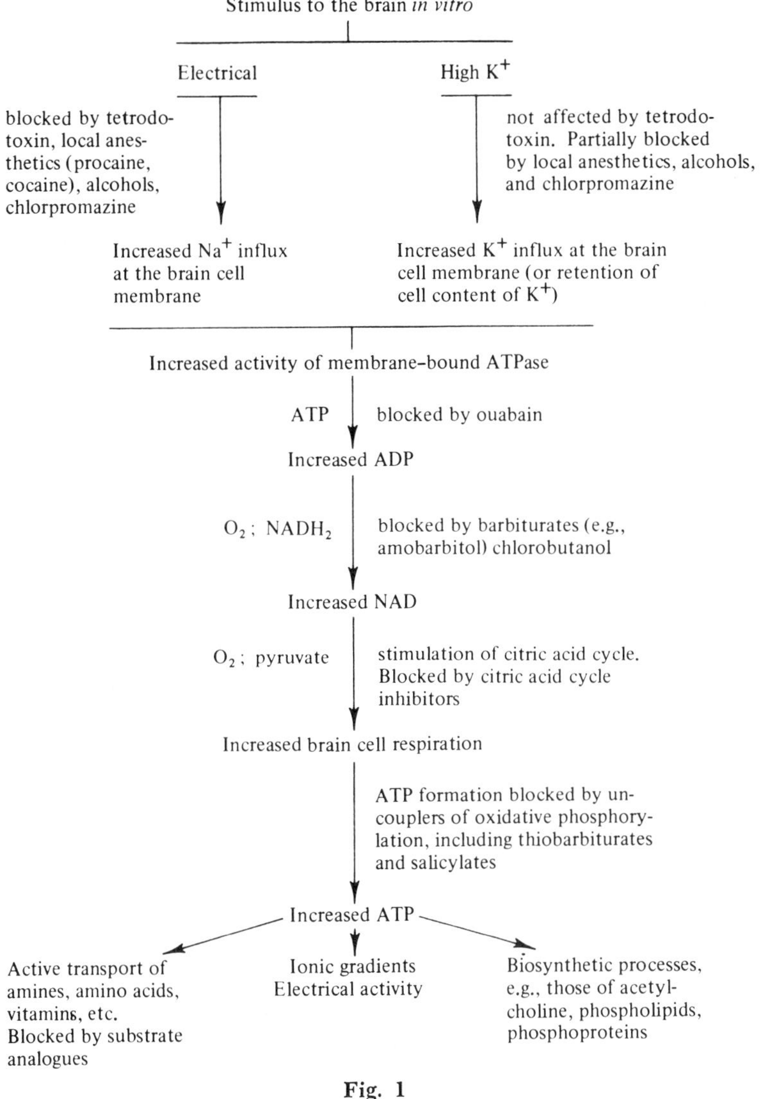

Fig. 1

XIII. Effects of Some Specific Inhibitors of Brain Transport Reactions

Mention has been made of the transport processes involving the pharmacological important amines. Active transport of amino acids into the brain is a sodium-dependent process which is suppressed by ouabain. It is evident that the process is largely controlled by the activity of the membrane-bound ATPase. The cell concentration of ATP is also a controlling factor because under a variety of experimental conditions the extent of accumulation of glycine in the brain *in vitro* is proportional to the level of ATP in the brain.

ACh undergoes active transport into the brain *in vitro,* the process being blocked by the presence of eserine or atropine. As experiments with ACh have usually been carried out with eserine to inhibit cholinesterase, it was once thought (erroneously) that ACh is not actively transported into the brain cell.

Choline also undergoes active transport into the brain *in vitro,* but this process is not affected by eserine. It is, however, blocked by the choline analogue, hemicholinium, which is without effect on the active transport of ethanolamine or serine.

Ascorbic acid undergoes active transport at the brain cell membrane, and this process is blocked by certain steroids in a specific manner, for they do not affect the active transport of amino acids in the brain cortex *in vitro.*

Another example is the block of active uptake of thiamine (vitamin B_1) into the brain cell by a thiamine analogue, Amprol, which induces neurological disturbances in animals in which it is injected.

XIV. Effects of Some Drugs That Are Amino Acid Decarboxylase Inhibitors

Decarboxylation of glutamate to form γ-aminobutyrate, which may play an important role in brain function as an inhibitor of neuronal excitation, and the removal of γ-aminobutyrate by transamination with α-ketoglutarate, are processes that take place in the brain. It is to be expected that drugs affecting these processes will also affect the level of γ-aminobutyrate in the brain *in vitro.*

Hydroxylamine is a potent inhibitor of glutamic decarboxylase and γ-aminobutyrate transaminase. Injection of hydroxylamine into cats markedly reduces duration and spread of electrically induced after-discharges and results in increasing cerebral levels of γ-aminobutyrate.

Aminooxyacetic acid is a more potent inhibitor than hydroxylamine and in duces a more prolonged increase in the brain content of γ-aminobutyrate. It is able to protect animals against seizures induced by thiosemicarbazide.

Both hydroxylamine and aminooxyacetic acid block metabolism of γ-aminobutyrate in the brain cell and affect the rates of amino acid formation from glucose. The results are consistent with the conclusion that these drugs act by combining with pyridoxal phosphate, a necessary coenzyme for amino acid decarboxylation.

Interference with amino acid decarboxylation *in vitro* may be brought about by amino acid analogues such as α-methylamino acids (e.g., α-methyltryptophan or α-methylhistidine). 2-Hydroxy- and 2,5-dihydroxytryptophan are reported to be inhibitors of 5-hydroxytryptophan decarboxylase. *In vivo* inhibition of dihydroxyphenylalanine decarboxylase can be brought about by administration of α-methyldihydroxyphenylalanine (α-methyldopa).

The amino acid precursors of the catecholamines undergo decarboxylation through a pyridoxal phosphate linked decarboxylase, e.g., DOPA decarboxylase which is also regarded as a catalyst for the decarboxylation of 5-hydroxytryptophan. This enzyme is competitively inhibited by α-methyldopa which will bring about a rapid fall in cerebral dopamine and NE. However, it is thought that the decrease of NE in various tissues by α-methyldopa may be related more to a displacement or release mechanism than to an inhibition of DOPA decarboxylase, and that its effect in diminishing cerebral serotonin (5-hydroxytryptamine, 5HT) may not be entirely confined to inhibition of the decarboxylase.

XV. Effects of Hydroxylase Inhibitors

Cerebral oxidations (by hydroxylases) are important for the conversion of phenylalanine to tyrosine and thence by decarboxylation to tyramine or in the conversion of tryptophan to hydroxytryptophan and thence to 5HT. The hydroxylases involved in these reactions are distinct from each other and are widespread (i.e., not only in mammalian tissues but in bacteria and in toads). They probably represent rate limiting factors in the formation of tyramine and 5HT from the relevant dietary amino acids. Tyrosine hydroxylase is the enzyme responsible for conversion of tyrosine to 3,4-dihydroxyphenylalanine (DOPA). This initial step in the biosynthesis of catecholamines is possibly rate-limiting for the overall conversion *in vivo.* The enzyme has greatest activity in such tissues as adrenal medulla and brain, which have high concentrations of catecholamines. Brain tyrosine hydroxylase, which is concentrated largely in nerve endings, differs, however, in certain respects from adrenal tyrosine hydroxylase, in being particle bound, insensitive to cofactors (such as 2-amino-4-hydroxy-6,7-dimethyltetrahydropteridine) and possessing a lower Michaelis constant for tyrosine. There is evidence, however, indicating that tyrosine hydroxylase may occur outside the granules containing catecholamines.

Dopamine-β-hydroxylase, which converts dopamine to NE, is located in portions of the central nervous system (hypothalamus and caudate nucleus) and in the adrenal medulla and is to be found largely in the catecholamine-containing granules. Its distribution differs from that of tyrosine hydroxylase.

Tyrosine and catechol derivatives have significant inhibitory effects on tyrosine hydroxylase; among the former is L-α-methyl-*p*-tyrosine and among the latter is 3,4-dihydroxyphenylacetamide. Amino acid analogues of tyrosine form a larger group of tyrosine hydroxylase inhibitors; among these are L-phenylalanine, 3-iodo- and 3-bromo-DL-phenylalanine, and 3-iodo-*L*-tyrosine. New results show that 5-halotryptophans are potent inhibitors of brain tyrosine hydroxylase (87). *p*-Chlorphenylalanine is an inhibitor of tryptophan hydroxylase *in vitro* and *in vivo* and effectively depletes brain 5HT.

For general reviews and further reading and references see Appendices 1 and 2.

PART IV

STRUCTURE AND METABOLISM OF PSYCHOTROPIC DRUGS

13

CHEMISTRY OF PSYCHOPHARMACOLOGICAL AGENTS

F. J. Petracek

I. Introduction

Even a brief review concerning the chemistry of the psychopharmacological agents should begin from a historical perspective. The first "chemical" experience with these agents probably predates any recorded history. Indeed, the indigenous use of plant extracts for medicinal purposes might be considered a benchmark of any societal grouping which is regarded as having a culture. Although "tranquilizers" are often considered a product of recent cultures, the employment of plant extracts for their psychic effects was known to be prominent in primitive societies. Thus a good deal of native experience for the extraction and processing of stimulants, hallucinogens, and "tranquilizers" was in hand long before chemistry became a formal discipline (cf. Caldwell, Chapter 2; Opler, Chapter 3).

From the latter part of the eighteenth century the isolation and characterization of the alkaloids (organic bases obtained from the plants) became a systematic effort. A number of medicinally useful alkaloids became articles of commerce long before modern structural theory or notation existed, e.g., morphine (1805), strychnine (1820), atropine (1831). Somewhat later, from 1860 onward, the structural notation of organic compounds was developed, and synthetic organic chemistry itself grew rapidly as a specialized area of chemistry. By 1900 many of the important bond-forming reactions and the building blocks (the reagents and catalysts) had been described in the chemical literature.

After 1900 the structures of many of the alkaloids became known. Organic chemists employed and developed numerous degradation (or bond-breaking reaction) methods which cleaved the complex naturally occurring molecules into more easily identifiable chemical units. Finally, as the individual structures became known, there arose the challenge to reconstruct, to synthesize, from readily available reagents, the identical structures which had been produced by the vegetable kingdom.

These two parallel chemical efforts of organic chemistry, natural products chemistry and synthetic chemistry, together formed the chemical groundwork of psychopharmacology. The isolation of reserpine (I) and the synthesis of chlorpromazine (CPZ) (II) were landmarks in medical research and treatment.

Novel psychopharmacological agents are developed from the investigation of novel chemical structures. While there is virtually no limit to the structural variations possible by synthesis, the numbers of new alkaloidal structures from plants is limited. In fact the progress in synthetic chemistry has been such that the living plants are no longer a unique source for complex heterocyclic alkaloid-like structures. Nonetheless, the plant kingdom remains as a rich reservoir of new compounds, as illustrated by the symposium on the "Ethnopharmacologic Search For Psychoactive Drugs," edited by Efron *et al.* (88). A measure of the present potential of synthesis is provided by reserpine. This truly formidable array of C. H, O, and N atoms has been synthesized by a route which has been adapted to commercial production. No important psychopharmacological agent from a plant source has been marketed since reserpine and other similar rauwolfia alkaloids. The preponderant effort in the search for new compounds of clinical advantage has now shifted to the synthetic area.

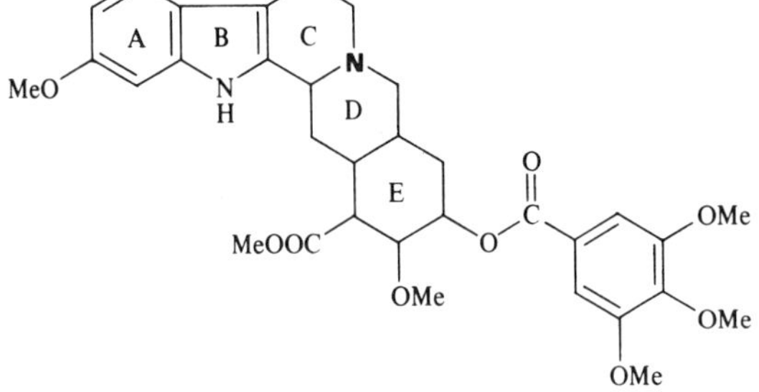

Reserpine
(I)

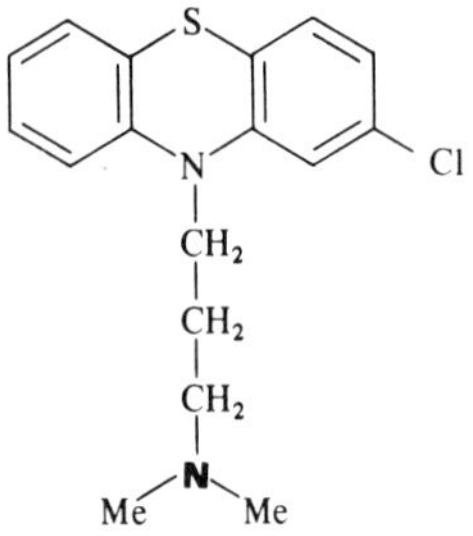

Chlorpromazine
(II)

A historical summary of the chemical basis for psychopharmacology should also include comment on such other phases of natural product chemistry as the isolation and structural elucidation of the neurotransmitters. The discovery of this group of compounds stimulated an outpouring of pharmacological observations and research (cf. Snyder, Chapter 9). Thus, the discovery of the major neurotransmitter amines—acetylcholine (III), norepinephrine (IV), serotonin (V)—led to outstanding isolation and identification studies.

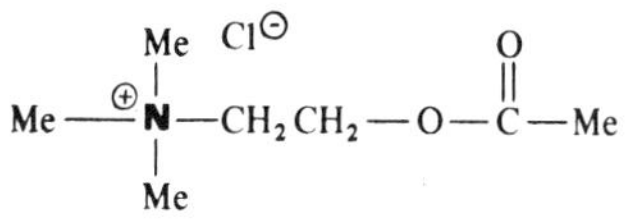

Acetylcholine chloride

(III)

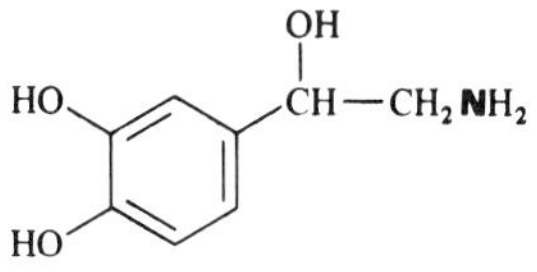

Norepinephrine

(IV)

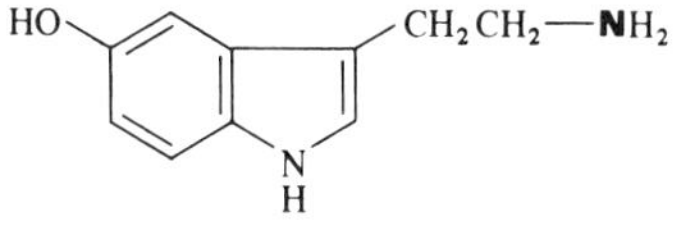

Serotonin

(V)

Other compounds which have been demonstrated to be important in CNS functions are dopamine, tyramine, histamine, and tryptamine. These brain amines have often provided the starting points for the development of rationales for the action of many of the psychopharmacological agents.

II. General Structural and Chemical Properties

The psychopharmacological agents do not fall neatly into a single chemical category. Nonetheless, many of those considered in this text can be defined as lipophilic organic bases,* and it is useful to consider the important structural features of this psychopharmacological model. The lipophilic part of the molecule is usually an *aromatic* group, a planar system of atoms containing a conjugated ring system of double bonds. Although consisting mainly of carbon atoms, other elements, most frequently nitrogen and sulfur, can be appropriately substituted to maintain the aromatic nature of the system. Some important examples of ring systems, other than the familiar benzene, are indole (rings A and B of reserpine), pyridine (nialamide), and the three-ring phenothiazine system [chlorpromazine (CPZ)].

Positioned one to four atoms from the lipophilic aromatic section of most of these molecules are basic nitrogen atoms (see Table II). This basic amine nitrogen may be part of a complex heterocyclic system, as in reserpine or it can be attached to an aliphatic side chain as in CPZ. This bridging chain usually consists of methylene groups, e.g., the trimethylene chain $—CH_2CH_2CH_2—$, and it adds to the lipophilicity or fat-soluble character of the entire molecule. In structures such as reserpine and CPZ which contain two nitrogen atoms each, it is important to distinguish the basic nitrogen from that which is nonbasic.†

* Some notable exceptions, e.g., meprobamate, are discussed briefly in Section IV,H.

† In this chapter the basic nitrogen atom is boldfaced to distinguish it from several neutral-type nitrogens.

This generalized three-sectioned model (*aromatic-chain-amine*) of a psychopharmacological agent is valid for the majority of stimulants, "tranquilizers," and hallucinogens. However, it is not restricted to psychopharmacological agents, being descriptive as well of the antihistamines, anticholinergics, and local anesthetics. Since this model serves to describe so many major classes of drugs, it appears initially to have little value. Actually, it serves to emphasize that these many clinically distinguishable drugs are not grossly different in structure. The psychopharmacological agents are really not unique chemical entities. Many were derived structurally from the historically older anticholinergic and antihistaminic classes. Awareness of the structural similarities between separate clinical categories of drugs should increase an understanding of the complete spectrum of the activity, particularly side effects, observed with any particular drug (see warning, Section V).

A. *Relationship of General Structure and Chemical Properties to Drug Action*

Before examining the individual chemical and physical properties of each of the subdivisions of the psychopharmacological agents, some of the possible ways in which these properties affect drug action will be reviewed. Frequently, the action of a drug is considered only in a restrictive sense as being the result of the specific interaction of a drug molecule at the site of action (receptor) in a tissue or cellular substrate. Preceding this event, however, a CNS drug must be absorbed from the gastrointestinal tract and transported into the brain (cf. Goldenberg and Fishman, Chapter 14), where the receptor site-drug interaction itself occurs. Following this, the drug is metabolized and excreted. In all of these processes the chemical and physical properties of the individual drug are important. Some of those properties which relate directly to these separate biological processes, which together constitute drug action, are solubility (both in lipoid and aqueous systems), partition behavior between lipoid and aqueous phases, base strength of the amine segment, the overall molecular shape, and, in somes cases, the nature and distribution of the electronic charge of the aromatic segment.

The following discussion deals with some of the important chemical and physical properties of each of the three structural segments of the *aromatic-chain-amine* model insofar as they bear on CNS drug activity.

1. Basic Amine Group

The basic amine nitrogen, present in most of the known psychopharmacological agents, plays a key role in several of the separate physiological processes which together result in drug activity. The amine group acts as a base by virtue of its ability to accept a proton (H^+) from the physiological solvent system. The acidity, or the protonating ability, of this system is constantly changing as the drug molecule proceeds from absorption to final excretion. Amphetamine is used to illustrate this protonation process (Scheme 1).

The uncharged free base form of amphetamine is shown as the base (VI), while the charged ammonium form is shown as the salt (VIa). The solubility characteristics are markedly different. The free base is an oil, insoluble in water and soluble in ether (lipophilic), while amphetamine salts, e.g., the sulfate salt, is a crystalline water-soluble, ether-insoluble substance. Therefore, a difference in partition behavior would be expected in a physiological system consisting of a lipid phase and an aqueous phase, depending on the fraction of the base in the protonated, water-soluble form.

The extent to which a base, such as amphetamine, is protonated to its ammonium form depends on two variables: its own inherent strength as a base (pK_a)* and the pH of the medium in which it is dissolved. For example, for an organic base with $pK_a = 8$ in a medium with pH = 7.3 (average of 7.0–7.6, small intestine), half of the drug is in the readily absorbed un-ionized form.

At pH = 3 (e.g., in the secreting stomach) the ratio of the polar protonated form to that of the uncharged free base would be $10^5/1$. Therefore, in the stomach (pH 3–7) the basic psychopharmacological agents are virtually completely ionized, while in the GI tract (pH $\cong$ 7.3) the un-ionized free base is a major species. The uncharged species of a drug is absorbed much better than the polar charged form, and the lipophilic amines, existing largely as the free bases in the gastrointestinal tract beyond the stomach, are more

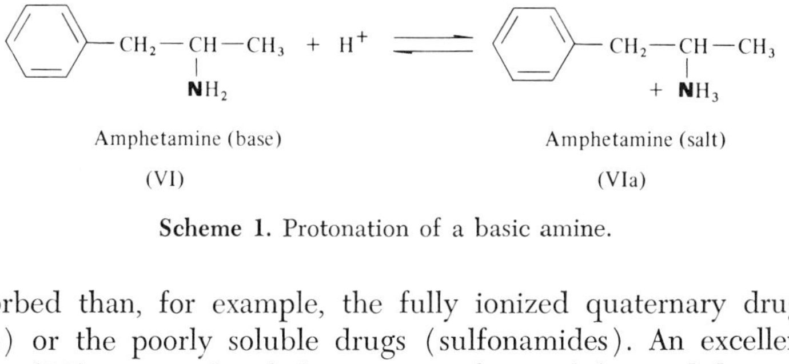

$$C_6H_5-CH_2-CH(NH_2)-CH_3 + H^+ \rightleftharpoons C_6H_5-CH_2-CH(\overset{+}{N}H_3)-CH_3$$

Amphetamine (base) (VI) — Amphetamine (salt) (VIa)

Scheme 1. Protonation of a basic amine.

easily absorbed than, for example, the fully ionized quaternary drugs (hexamethonium) or the poorly soluble drugs (sulfonamides). An excellent review by Schanker (89) gives a detailed treatment of ionizability and drug absorption and transport.

Although the amine group is important in absorption, its key role is played at the site of drug action. Acting directly with membrane surfaces and proteinaceous enzyme regulatory structures, the amine center of the molecule is presumed to trigger or inhibit a particular physiological response. Unfortunately, drug-receptor interactions are not directly observable at the molecular level. Therefore, evidence for the presumed importance of the ionized form of the amine is indirect. For example, conversion of the amine group in amphetamine to a neutral amide results in a loss of stimulant activity.

The amine function of the psychopharmacological agents appears in a variety of individual structural forms. However, the base strengths of most drugs of this type are similar, and thus the balance of charged and uncharged forms at physiological pH's remains comparable whether the amine nitrogen is hetero-

* pK_a values are now in general use rather than pK_b values; $pK_a = 14 - pK_b$. The pK_a values of the basic psychopharmacological agents are in the range of 8–10. The pK_a, values for many common drugs can be found in such handbooks as the *Merck Index*.

cyclic (reserpine), aliphatic (CPZ), primary (amphetamine), or tertiary (CPZ). The inherent chemical stability of most of the psychopharmacological agents is good in contrast, for example, to penicillin, where acid lability inactivates most of the drug before absorption occurs.

Most of the amine groups in the psychopharmacologically active molecules are either secondary (R—**NH**—R′) or tertiary (R—**N**—R′R″). Generally the amines of the depressant and "tranquilizing" group are tertiary, while the stimulant agents are more often primary or secondary amines (Table I).

TABLE I

Amine Substitution and CNS Effect

Amine type / CNS Effect	Primary	Secondary	Tertiary
Stimulants	Amphetamine Phenelzine Parnate	Methylphenidate Nialamide Pipradol Methamphetamine	
Antidepressants		Desipramine Nortriptyline	Imipramine Amitriptyline
Antipsychotic and antianxiety agents			Chlorpromazine Reserpine Diazepam Chlordiazepoxide Hydroxyzine Benactyzine Haloperidol

Amine metabolism has been and is now being studied extensively. The *N*,*N*-dimethyl group is subject to mono-*N*-demethylation as well as di-*N*-demethylation. The active *N*-demethylated form of imipramine, desimipramine, was discovered by a study of its metabolic products. The primary amines can be oxidized to acids. Some of the tertiary amine groups are oxidized to the *N*-oxide function ($R_3N \rightarrow O$). (Cf. Goldenberg and Fishman, Chapter 14.)

2. The Aromatic Group

The aromatic segment found in almost all of the psychopharmacological agents assumes even more structural variety than the amine function. Several of the more important attributes of this group relevant to CNS activity deserve comment.

The aromatic group is almost without exception lipophilic in nature and, since it is usually the largest segment, it confers this solubility property upon the entire molecule. Thus it plays a key role in absorption and transport to the CNS centers. Because of this lipophilic group, the psychopharmacological agents are able to pass from the circulatory system through the blood-brain barrier to the CNS centers where the specific activity is elicited. Although the blood-brain barrier is not a single identifiable anatomical structure, it has been established operationally as being lipid in nature, preventing the passage of polar molecules (e.g., some amino acids and quaternary ammonium salts), and allowing the passage of nonpolar molecules.

Because the aromatic grouping is usually the largest portion of the molecule, it also dominates the overall steric pattern, and the steric arrangement of all drug molecules, the CNS agents as well as others, is known to be a critical feature affecting drug activity. Although aromatic rings with conjugated systems of double bonds (e.g., phenyl or indolyl) are essentially planar, they can be joined by one or more atoms to give a new aromatic structure which diverges from a strictly planar shape. Thus certain tricyclic compounds may assume a "butterfly" shape. Although these slightly varied planar configurations may not greatly influence solubility or partition behavior, a marked change in effect would be possible at receptor sites with rigid steric requirements for the receptor site-substrate "fit."

Since aromatic centers are areas of high electron density, charge transfer complexes are generally considered to be an important mode of binding, but a great deal of caution must be exercised when relating electronic properties of a molecule with the degree of drug activity. A particular electron-attracting group (e.g., $—CF_3$) may enhance activity when it is a substituent on one series of CNS agents, while it can have the opposite effect in another series. These substituent groups modify other important properties of the molecule as well as the electronic density such as shape, solubility, and metabolic vulnerability. Therefore, correlations of substituent groups with pharmacological activity in one structural series *cannot* be applied uncritically to another series. (See Section V.) Some real progress is being made in separating the electronic and solubility effects relevant to drug action (90). This kind of multiparameter mathematical analysis requires precise biological data, which is particularly difficult to obtain in many CNS screening methods.

Difficulties in synthesis sometimes limit the availability of substituent groups in specific positions of the aromatic nucleus; still the variation of substituent groups on the aromatic part of the parent molecule has been an important part of the effort in the synthesis and screening of psychopharmacological agents.

The presence of the aromatic group greatly aids the analysis of drug concentrations in biological fluids. The conjugated systems often have unique ultraviolet and fluorescent spectra which can often be used to detect concentrations of a drug at very low levels. For example, fluorescence spectrometry is used to measure as little as 4–5 ng (0.004–0.005 μg)/gm tissue of 5HT and NE in brain centers when studying the effect in test animals of the various CNS agents on the release or uptake of these chemical neurotransmitters.

The aromatic nucleii are very often the most susceptible centers for metabolic attack. Enzymic hydroxylation of the aromatic rings followed by conjugation to form the glucuronides and sulfates is a common metabolic pathway (cf. Goldenberg and Fishman, Chapter 14).

3. The Aliphatic or Alicyclic Connecting Chain

The spatial relationships between the aromatic and the amine groups are known to be critical variables in the activity profiles of the psychopharmacological agents. Together these spatial relationships constitute the so-called geometry of the molecule. Much of this geometry or shape is determined by a group of connecting atoms between the aromatic and amine segments. This arrangement of connecting atoms, or chain, limits the distance between the aromatic and amine groups, and, in many cases, defines a rigid shape for the molecule. The chain may consist simply of methylene groups, as in amphetamine and CPZ, or a more complicated arrangement such as ring C of reserpine.

CPZ provides an example of the influence of the length of the connecting chain on activity. Addition of a single methylene group, giving a four-carbon chain between the phenothiazine nucleus and the amine, causes a loss of antipsychotic activity. Removal of a methylene group changes the antipsychotic activity to antihistaminic activity. With reserpine a change in shape only of the bridge (ring C) causes a loss of activity (Table II lists some of the connecting chains).

TABLE II

Aromatic (Ar) - Amine (-**N**<), Bridging Groups

Drug Name	Ar - (bridge)-**N**<
Chlorpromazine	Ar—CH_2—CH_2—CH_2—**N**<
Amphetamine	Ar—CH_2—CH_2—**N**<
Haloperidol	Ar—C(=O)—CH_2CH_2—CH_2—**N**<
Hydroxyzine	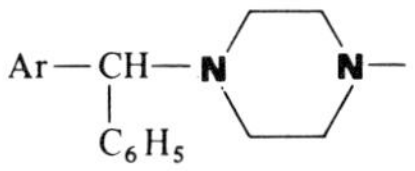 Ar—CH(C_6H_5)—**N**(piperazine ring)**N**—

Considerable structural variation is possible with each of these major chain types. However, the extent of variation is usually less than that carried out with the aromatic and amine groups.

III. Molecular Properties and Receptor Theory

It has been emphasized that the chemical and physical properties of a drug influence *all* of the parameters—absorption, transport, receptor response, metabolism—which together determine the drug's activity. Nonetheless, the events which occur at the receptor site are of key importance to a real understanding of drug action.

The complexity of the central nervous system, coupled with inadequate tools for observation, are formidable barriers to rapid advances in gaining information about molecular interactions between CNS drugs and receptor sites. However, general considerations which have been proposed concerning receptor-site theory probably apply to the CNS system as well. Gill (91) has written an excellent review of the hypotheses concerning drug-receptor site interactions.

For the present purpose it is sufficient to note that a receptor site is very likely a discrete arrangement of atoms which forms a complex with the drug molecule in a precise manner by utilizing several types of weak bonding forces. Even slight changes in the structure of the drug molecule would be expected to affect the delicate balance of the drug-receptor complex, and changes in one part of the molecule could be more critical than in others in affecting this complex. In addition, these receptor sites, which interact with the drug molecule, are themselves only a part of the extremely complex anatomical, chemical and electrical systems comprising the central nervous system. Therefore, extrapolations and conclusions based on structure-activity studies must be viewed with much more caution in the case of the central nervous system than in other areas.

IV. Chemistry of Major Psychopharmacological Agents

A. *Rauwolfia Alkaloids*

The rauwolfia alkaloids were marketed for clinical use, first as hypotensives, in 1952. The first pharmaceutical preparations were a purified alkaloid fraction (alseroxylon) and even the powdered whole root (*Rauwolfia serpentina* Benth) which had already been used for hundreds of years in India. Soon thereafter the main active constituents, reserpine (Ia), deserpidine (see tables in Usdin, Chapter 15), and rescinnamine were isolated and characterized. Reserpine is the most widely used of the chemically available crystalline alkaloids (cf. Laborit and Sanseigne, Chapter 18).

Although these alkaloids are much more complex in structure than most synthetic psychopharmacological agents, the three principal structural groupings are present. A *basic nitrogen* atom in ring C is separated from the aromatic indole system by a *chain* of two methylene groups (positions 5 and 6 in Ia). In addition, the active antipsychotic alkaloids possess in rings D and E a unique variety of structural groups. Reserpine also contains six asymmetric centers, adding greatly to a structural complexity not present in most synthetic CNS agents. Its acid salts are less water soluble and more lipophilic than the corresponding salts of most of the other CNS agents.

Soon after the structural elucidation of reserpine was completed, the Nobel laureate R. B. Woodward (Harvard) devised a total synthesis which in the final stages (forming rings C and D) consisted in joining the indole portion (VII) (rings A and B) to a ring E fragment (VIII) containing all the substituents properly oriented (shown in Scheme 2). This synthetic scheme has been used by other investigators to obtain derivatives of reserpine, unavailable from the plant, so that the important points of structure/activity relationship could be examined (92).

Reserpine is a good example of a psychopharmacological agent in which the *shape* is the most critical feature of the compound. The overall chairlike shape of reserpine is shown graphically, as A, Scheme 3. The hydrogen atom at position 3 (see Ia) can be removed and replaced on the opposite face of the molecule, a chemical process called *inversion.* Inversion of the configuration at the C-3 position causes a rotation of part of the molecule (rings A, B, and C) relative to the other part (rings D and E), giving the inactive 3-isoreserpine (B in Scheme 3). Thus, although the chemical groupings of the molecule are identical, the change in the overall shape is responsible for a difference in activity.

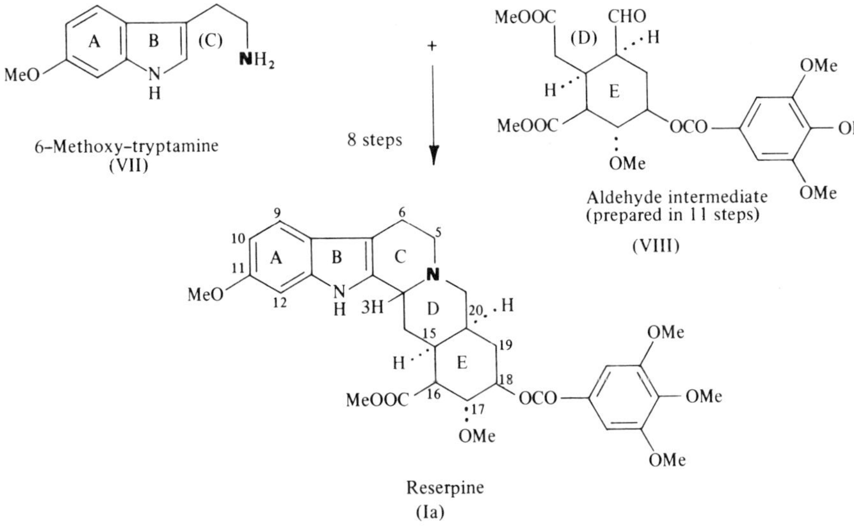

Scheme 2. General plan of Woodward's 19-step synthesis of reserpine.

Reserpine is optically active (positions 3, 15, 16, 17, 18, and 20 are asymmetric, hence 2^6 or 64 optical isomers are theoretically possible). The naturally occurring form rotates plane polarized light to the right (dextrorotatory) and is often referred to as *d*-reserpine [also written (+)-reserpine]. The complete mirror image, *l*-reserpine, obtained by synthesis, lacks the antipsychotic activity of the d-form.

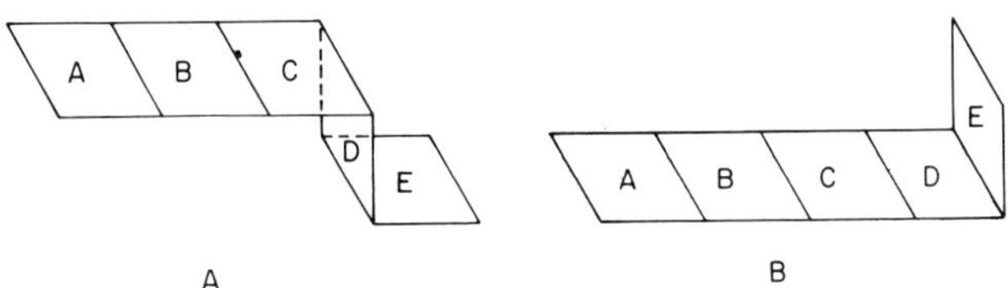

Scheme 3. (A) general shape of rings A–E in reserpine; (B) general shape of rings A–E in 3-isoreserpine.

This is not unexpected when we recall that the biological substrate (the postulated receptor site mentioned earlier) is formed from optically active chemical groupings (e.g., amino acids, sugars).

Many structurally simpler compounds based on the reserpine structure have been synthesized, but none of these compounds has shown typical reserpine-like activity. Some separation of hypotensive and antipsychotic activity has been achieved by synthetic variation of the trimethoxybenzoyl group at position 16.

B. Phenothiazines; Thioxanthenes

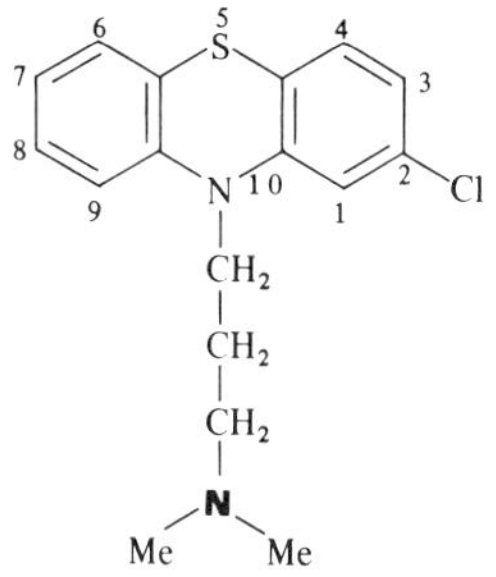

Chlorpromazine.
2-chloro-10-[3-(dimethylamino)-propyl]-phenothiazine

(II)

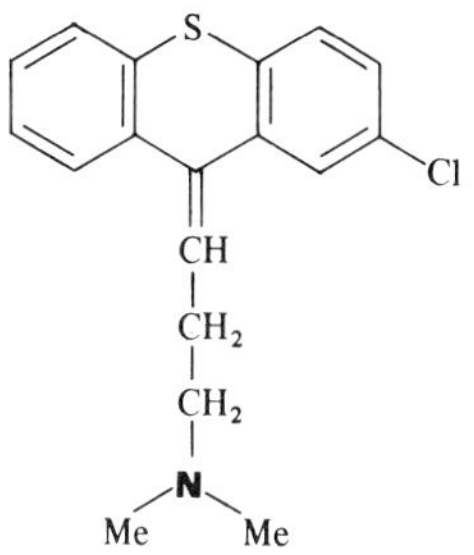

Chlorprothixene.
trans-2-chloro-10 (3-dimethyl-aminopropylidene)-thiaxanthene.

(X)

The development of CPZ (II) illustrates the most widely used approach to drug development. Instead of extracting an already formed active compound from a plant source, laboratory syntheses are used to modify structurally, and thereby improve, a parent structure which has an activity worthy of further investigation.

The molecular progenitor of CPZ was the antihistamine, promethazine (XI), which contains an aminoethyl (2 C atoms) side chain attached to the neutral nitrogen atom of the phenothiazine nucleus. When this aminoethyl side chain was extended by a methylene group to give an aminopropyl "tail," the strong antipsychotic activity appeared. Thus CPZ (II) emerged as a major antipsychotic agent the year following the clinical development of the rauwolfia alkaloids.

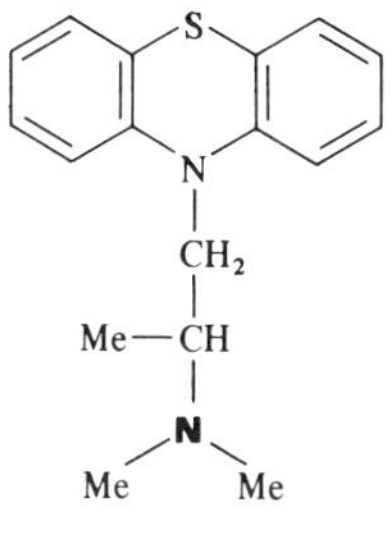

Promethazine.
10-(2-dimethylamino-1-propyl) - phenothiazine

(XI)

Today, fifteen years later, this parent structure is still under intense synthetic, pharmacological, and clinical investigation. For example, the thiaxanthenes (X) and the tricyclic antidepressants (see Section IV,C) resulted directly from the initial CPZ researches. During the ensuing fifteen years, thousands of analogs and related compounds have been prepared and tested.

Although these aminopropyl aromatic tricyclic compounds are usually oils in the form of the free bases (unprotonated), the acid salts are high-melting point, crystalline, colorless solids. The salts are the usual marketed forms.

Most of the clinically useful bases are tertiary, but extensive variation in the particular type of tertiary amine function is possible without loss of activity (see Table III).

TABLE III

Amine Base Groups in Phenothiazines

Generic name	Structure
Chloropromazine	$-N(Me)-Me$
Mepazine	3-piperidyl, N—Me
Fluphenazine	—N(piperazine)N—CH_2CH_2OH
Prochlorperazine	—N(piperazine)N—Me
Dixyrazine	—N(piperazine)N—CH_2CH_2—O—CH_2CH_2—OH
Methophenazine	—N(piperazine)N—CH_2CH_2—O—C(=O)—(3,4,5-trimethoxyphenyl: OMe, OMe, OMe)
Pipamazine	—N(piperidine)—C(=O)—NH_2

The aromatic portion of the phenothiazine antipsychotic agents contains the two phenyl groups joined in the ortho positions by a sulfur atom and a very weakly basic nitrogen. This nitrogen is such a weak base ($pK_a \simeq 2$) that it does not exist in the positively charged "onium" form under physiological pH conditions. Both N and S atoms allow resonance interaction between the two phenyl groups, thus conferring aromatic properties on the phenothiazine system. This system is shaped like a folded plane slightly bent at the N–S axis (XVI).

Almost all the marketed antipsychotic phenothiazines and thiaxanthenes are substituted in the 3-position with groups ranging from —Cl (the most common) to the $—SO_2N(CH_3)_2$ radicals. In general, increased antipsychotic activity is related to increased electron-attracting power of the group in the 3-position. It should be emphasized again that this generalized rule is valid only for the phenothiazine system.

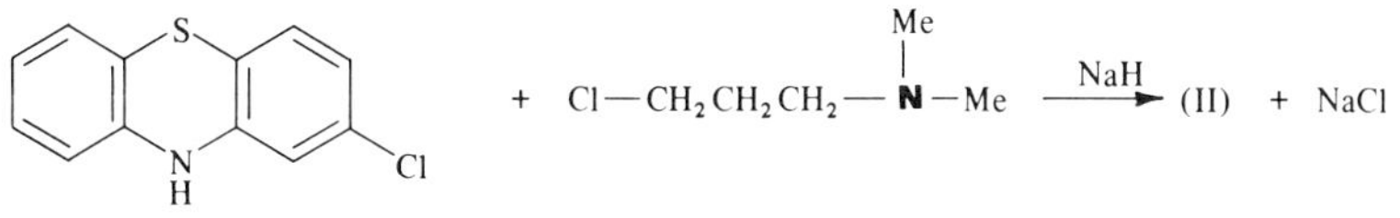

(XII) + $Cl—CH_2CH_2CH_2—N(Me)—Me$ (XIII) $\xrightarrow{NaH}$ (II) + NaCl

Scheme 4. Chlorpromazine synthesis.

The most commonly employed synthesis of the 10-aminopropyl phenothiazines, and indeed of all the related tricyclic antipsychotics and antidepressants, consists of joining the separately prepared aromatic nucleus with an aminopropyl derivative. The aminopropyl derivative (e.g., XIII) bears some group (—Cl or —Br) which reacts with the aromatic —NH— (as in XII), forming the new bond (Scheme 4).

However, many other general reactions of the same formal description are used. For example, the final step of one thiaxanthene synthesis (Scheme 5) utilizes the Grignard reaction of the ketone XIV with XV to form the intermediate (in brackets), which is then dehydrated to the final product.

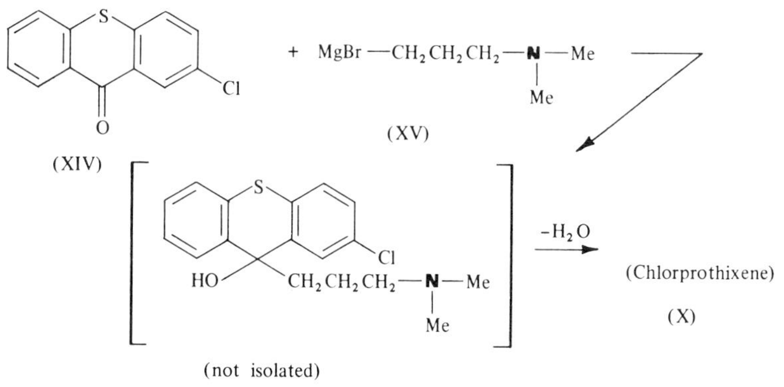

(XIV) + $MgBr—CH_2CH_2CH_2—N(Me)—Me$ (XV) → [HO, $CH_2CH_2CH_2—N(Me)—Me$ (not isolated)] $\xrightarrow{-H_2O}$ (Chlorprothixene) (X)

Scheme 5. A thioxanthine synthesis.

Another form of geometrical isomerism is illustrated by chlorprothixene (X). Since the molecule is not symmetrical with reference to the double bond, both *cis* and *trans* forms of X are possible. Chlorprothixene is the *trans* form, where the amine group of the side chain is situated on the opposite side of the double bond with respect to the aromatic —Cl group.

Some of the tricyclic antipsychotic agents and antidepressants contain optically active centers in the side chain and therefore these can exist as (+) and (—) optical isomers. If optically active reagents are not used in the synthetic steps, then a one-to-one ratio of (+) and (—) isomers is obtained, and ordinarily these are not separated in the marketed form. In several cases, the separated optically active (+) and (—) forms have been tested pharmacologically and the (—) form has shown more activity than the (+) form. Along with other considerations, this has led Gordon (1968; see Appendix 2) to suggest XVI as the preferred conformation (geometrical arrangement) of this typical phenothiazine structure at the receptor site, where A—B—C represent the complementary segments of the receptor site. (See Fig. 5.)

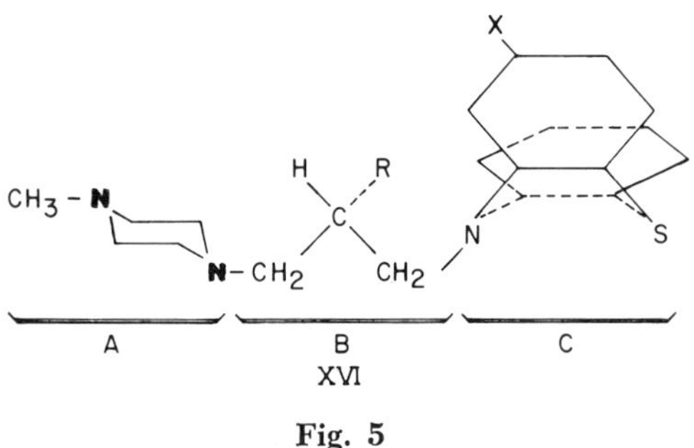

Fig. 5

Many additional active structures related to II and X have been prepared with atoms other than nitrogen and sulfur as the bridging elements. Aromatic rings other than phenyl, e.g., pyridyl, have been substituted with retention of antipsychotic activity. Thus the prototype phenothiazine system is no longer unique. Nonethless, few other structures have initiated and sustained so much medicinal chemical research as the parent molecule, CPZ.

C. Tricyclic Antidepressants

There are no major structural or chemical differences between the tricyclic antidepressants and the phenothiazine-type antipsychotic agents. The separate classification comes at the pharmacological and clinical stages of testing.*

These two classes differ mainly in the composition of the bridging atoms between the two phenyl groups. In addition, the present clinically available antidepressants usually lack a substituent group on the position corresponding to the 3 position in the phenothiazine system of CPZ.

* The tricyclic antidepressants are grouped as isosteres of the tricyclic antipsychotics. Isosteres are structures whose important spatial features are similar, although their molecular structures are not identical or even closely related.

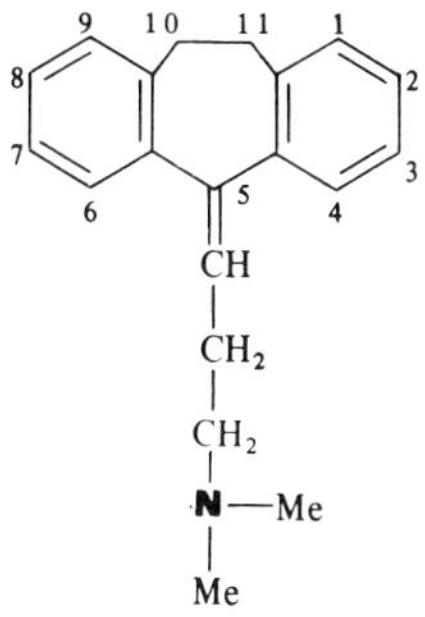

Amitriptyline.
5-(3-dimethylaminopropylidene)-10, 11-dihydro-5H-dibenzo[a, d] cycloheptatriene.

(XVII)

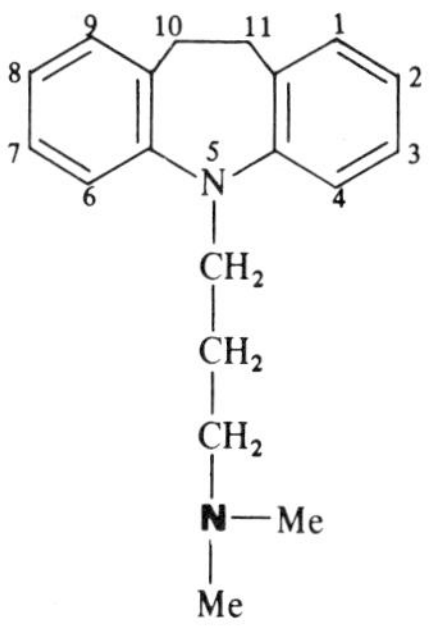

Imipramine.
5-[3-(dimethylamino)propyl]-10,11-dihydro-5H-dibenzo[b,f] azepine.

(XVIII)

Because of the close chemical similarity, it is not unexpected that the syntheses of XVII and XVIII would be similar to those employed for CPZ (II) and chlorprothixene (X). The three-ring partially aromatic systems are constructed separately and then the aminopropyl side chains are attached by procedures similar to those referred to in Section B.

TABLE IV

Tricyclic Structures*

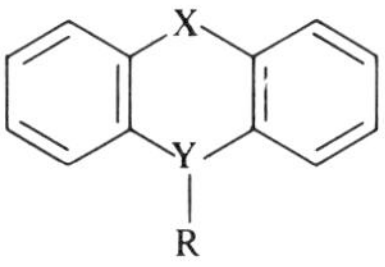

R = —C—C—C—N— system

X	Y—R
$-CH_2-S-$	$-N(R)-$
$-O-$	$-N(R)-$
$-S-$	$-CH_2-N(R)-$
$-CH_2-S-$	$-CH_2-N(R)-$
$-CH_2-CH_2-$	$-CH_2-N(R)-$
$-NH-$	$-C(=O)-N(R)-$

* From Jucker, 1963.

Metabolic studies demonstrated that the mono-*N*-demethylated derivatives of XVII and XVIII to be the "active metabolites," and these have since been marketed as nortriptyline and desipramine. It is of interest to point out that, whereas mono-*N*-demethylation is a common metabolic reaction, by contrast it is not an easily performed chemical transformation *in vitro.*

The aminopropyl side chain is present in almost all of the clinically useful antipsychotics and antidepressants of the tricyclic type. However, numerous other tricyclic systems with different bridging groups (X and Y, Table IV) for rings 1 and 3 have been synthesized and are presently under investigation both as antipsychotics and antidepressant agents. Some of these are shown in Table IV (see also Klerman and Paykel, Chapter 49). These few examples indicate that the possible variations are numerous and additional synthetic and clinical studies will continue in the search for improved drugs.

D. The 1,4-Benzodiazepines

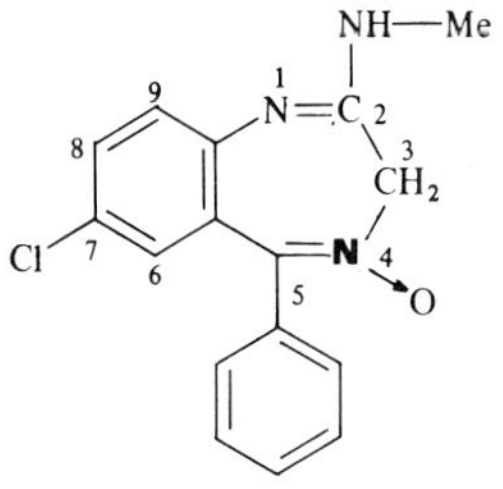

Chlordiazepoxide.
7-chloro-2-methylamino-5-phenyl-3H-1,4-benzdiazepine-4-oxide

(XIX)

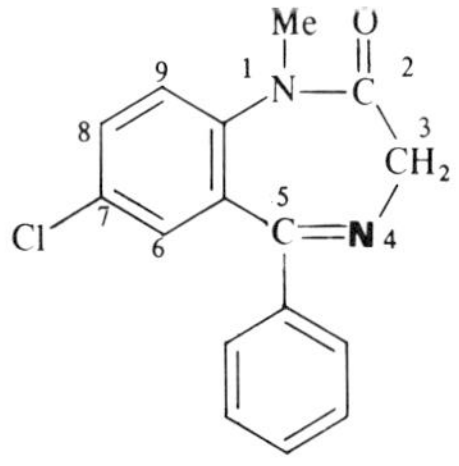

Diazepam.
7-chloro-1,3-dihydro-1-methyl-5-phenyl-3H-1,4-benzodiazepine-2-one

(XX)

In 1960 the 1,4-benzodiazepines were introduced clinically as a novel structural class of antianxiety agents. In some respects the chemical discovery of this new class of compounds was unexpected. In a study aimed at developing new CNS structures Sternbach *et al.* (94) intended to synthesize a quinazoline *N*-oxide. An unexpected chemical rearrangement took place in the final step of the sequence and chlordiazepoxide (XIX) was isolated instead. The correct structure was soon recognized, and in the course of general screening its anticonvulsant and sedative properties became known.

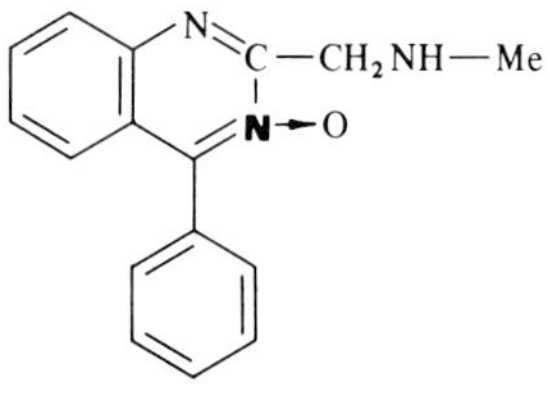

(XXI)

Both chlordiazepoxide and diazepam syntheses start with the aminobenzophenones (XXII). From these, one route uses a one-step reaction with α-chloracetyl chlorides to complete the cyclization as shown in Scheme 6.

The benzodiazepines, like the rauwolfia alkaloids and the tricyclic propylamines, can also be described as aromatic lipophilic amines. An interesting feature which distinguishes them is the proximity of the basic N atom (shown in boldface) to the aromatic systems, separated from either the benzo or phenyl group by one carbon rather than the usual chain of two or three atoms.

The development of diazepam followed from studies of the structure/activity relationships of the earlier chlordiazepoxide, which indicated that neither the *N*-oxide or the methylamino group of XIX was critical for retention of activity. The 7-chloro substituent, however, enhances activity markedly. The unsaturated 4,5-C=N-system is also a requirement for high activity since when reduced to —CH_2—N, the typical anticonvulsant activity is greatly diminished.

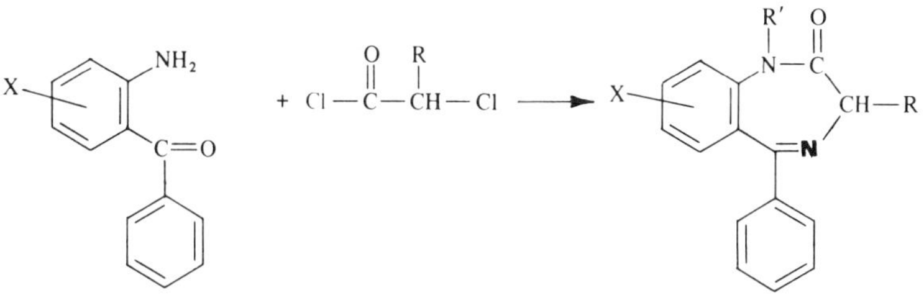

(XXI)

(XX): X = 7 —Cl, R′ = —CH_3 R = —H
(diazepam)

(XXII)

Scheme 6. A 1,4-benzodiazepine synthesis.

Considerable synthetic and clinical effort is still in progress on compounds of this class or closely related series. It is of interest to note that the quinazoline (XXI) originally desired was eventually prepared by Sternbach and found to be inactive. The initial major effort has been reviewed (94).

One of the more recent developments has been the clinical introduction of oxazepam, which lacks the N—CH_3 of diazepam (XX), but has in addition an —OH group at the 3-position.

E. Diphenylmethyl Alkylamines

One group of antianxiety agents contains the diphenylmethyl radical (the aromatic section) attached to an aliphatic or heterocyclic group which holds the basic amine group. Two of this type, benactyzine (XXIII) and hydroxyzine (XXIV), are shown here. Like CPZ these were developed from earlier antihistamine and anticholinergic prototype molecules.

The relationship of this class of antipsychotics to the older anticholinergics may prove in the end to be more than historical. It has been proposed that these antipsychotic agents, with known peripheral anticholinergic action, may act *centrally* by affecting cholinergic pathways. In this context, it should be emphasized that we know very little about the mechanism of action at the molecular level for *any* of the psychopharmacological agents.

The syntheses for the diphenylmethyl type are uncomplicated, employing well-known starting materials and reactions to give crystalline, water-soluble acid salts. This diphenylmethyl class is actually closely related to the tricyclic class, lacking only a second bridge to form the central ring.

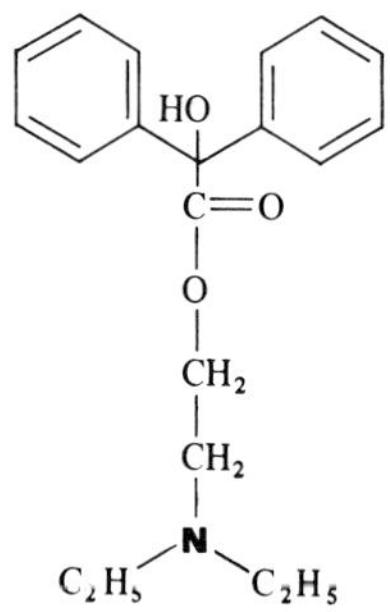

HO
C=O
O
CH_2
CH_2
N
C_2H_5 C_2H_5

Benactyzine.
β-diethylaminoethyl benzilate

(XXIII)

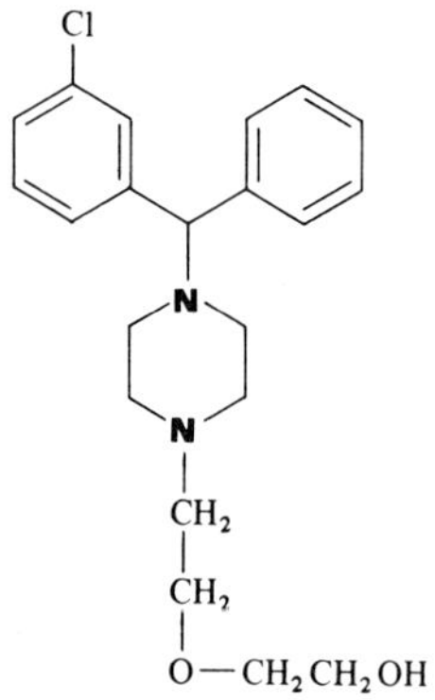

Cl
N
N
CH_2
CH_2
$O-CH_2CH_2OH$

Hydroxyzine.
1-(p-chlorobenzhydryl)-4[2-(2-hydroxy-ethoxy)-ethyl] piperazine

(XXIV)

Another clinically known member of this class is identical to benactyzine (XXIII), except for a hydrogen in place of the hydroxyl group (adiphenine). Buclizine has this general structure also.

F. Phenethylamine Stimulants and Monamine Oxidase Inhibitors

There is a large group of psychostimulants, the phenethylamines (e.g., VI and XXVI) and the monamine oxidase (MAO) inhibitors (XXV), which are

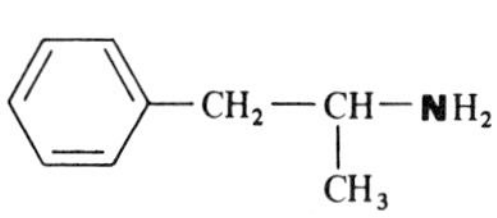

$CH_2-CH-NH_2$
CH_3

Amphetamine.
α-methyl-phenethylamine

(VI)

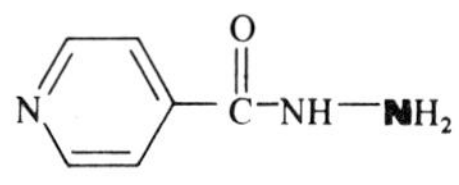

O
N C-NH-NH₂

Isoniazid.
isonicotinic acid hydrazide

(XXV)

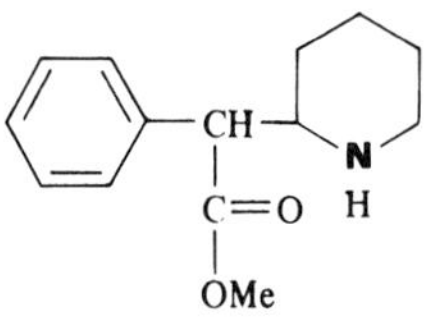

CH
N H
C=O
OMe

Methylphenidate.
α-phenyl-2-piperidineacetic acid methyl ester

(XXVI)

generally simpler in structure than the previously discussed compounds. Although the pharmacological mechanism of action probably differs, these two groups have in common either the —C—C—N arrangement or a group isosteric with it such as the CO—NH—NH_2 group in place of —CH_2—CH_2—NH_2. Compounds of this class are less lipophilic than the psychopharmacological agents discussed above, which contain at least two aromatic rings. Both the salts and free bases are more water soluble. In addition, the clinically useful members of this class seldom have substituent groups on the aromatic ring.

The development of the MAO inhibitors (XXV)* stemmed originally from the observation that the antitubercular drug iproniazid, an isopropyl derivative of isoniazid (XXV), caused CNS stimulation. Other compounds more closely related to amphetamine soon followed to the clinic (cf. Horita, Chapter 20).

Because of toxicity problems, the MAO inhibitors, particularly the hydrazine (—NH—NH—) type, are of little present chemical and clinical interest. The syntheses of these relatively simple structures are not complicated.

G. *Butyrophenones*

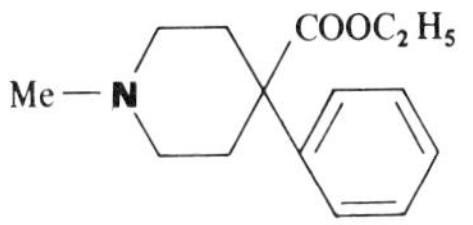

Meperidine
N-methyl-4-phenyl-4-carbethoxy-piperidine

(XXVII)

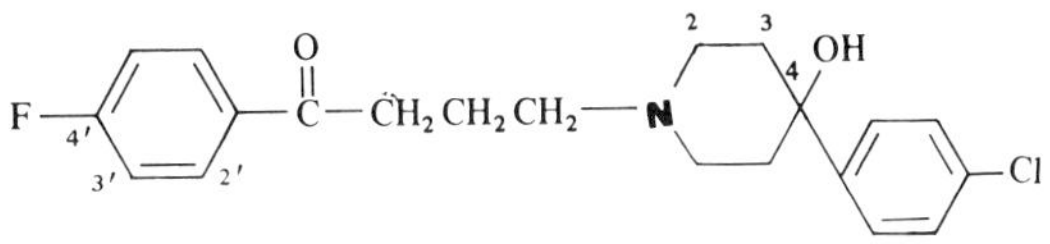

Haloperidol
4-[4-(*p*-chloro phenyl)-4-hydroxy-piperidino]-4′-fluorobutyrophenone

(XXVIII)

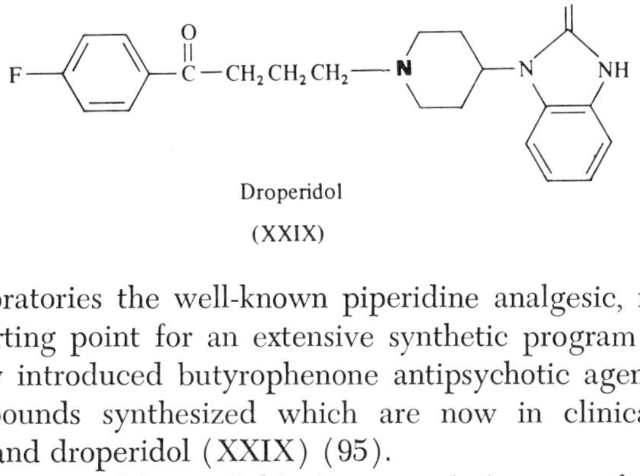

Droperidol

(XXIX)

In the Janssen Laboratories the well-known piperidine analgesic, meperidine (XXVII), was the starting point for an extensive synthetic program eventually leading to the recently introduced butyrophenone antipsychotic agents. Among several of 5000 compounds synthesized which are now in clinical use are haloperidol (XXVIII) and droperidol (XXIX) (95).

The butyrophenones are readily available by several three- or four-step sequences which lead to the crystalline free bases or hydrochloride salts. All of the more active compounds contain the *p*-fluorobutyrophenone segment attached to either of three cyclic amine bases—piperidine, piperazine, or tetrahydropyridine. The opposite position of the cyclic base is usually substituted with

* Only the boldfaced N atom in isoniazid (XXV) is comparable in base strength to that of amphetamine. The nitrogen next to the carbonyl group is neutral and is isosteric with the —NH_2 bearing carbon atom of amphetamine.

a combination of a polar group and a phenyl ring. This position, as in the piperidyl and piperazinylphenthiazines, allows more variation without loss of activity than is possible in the *p*-fluorobutyrophenone part. A structural correlation has been drawn between the butyrophenones, reserpine, and the cyclic base phenothiazine antipsychotic agents (95).

H. Other Nonbasic Psychopharmacological Agents

Sections IVA to IVG have covered the major groups of psychopharmacological agents which can be described by the *aromatic-chain-amine* model proposed at the outset (see Section II). It is interesting to note also that most of the hallucinogenic agents, e.g., LSD, mescaline, psyilocybin, and some alkoxy-substituted amphetamines, can also be described by this model.

There are notable exceptions, however. Meprobamate, for example, has neither an aromatic grouping nor a basic nitrogen atom. Another exception is phenaglycodol. Among the hallucinogenic agents, tetrahydrocannabinol (marihuana, hashish; see Cohen, Chapter 39) is a phenol (a weak acid) rather than a basic compound.

Future developments might well be in totally new structural areas quite unrelated to the lipophilic amines discussed above, e.g., the tetrahydrocannabinols.

V. Summary

Any system of classification employed in discussions of CNS agents runs the risk of oversimplifying an exceedingly complex situation. It seems that, prevented from substantial progress in understanding the CNS system because of its complexity, many authors are tempted to propose hypotheses for mechanisms of action based on structural comparisons only. For example, although LSD and serotonin are *structurally* related, they may be *pharmacologically* unrelated. Structural relationships should certainly be used to advance ideas in the CNS field. *However, it should be emphasized that this practice is often abused through ignorance* and this abuse can actually impede meaningful progress toward understanding the role of CNS agents in altering behavior.

Even a brief review such as this indicates that already a prodigious cooperative effort of the various disciplines, from chemical synthesis to clinical investigation, has gone on in psychopharmacology. In spite of this, however, our understanding of how CNS drugs act at the molecular level is still largely unclear or at best based on tentative hypotheses. Therefore, it seems safe to conclude that the work of the first fifteen years is really only a beginning.

For further reading see Appendix 2.

14

METABOLISM OF PSYCHOTROPIC AGENTS

Harry Goldenberg and Vivian Fishman

I. Introduction

The introduction of reserpine and chlorpromazine in the early 1950's had a profound effect on psychiatric therapy by demonstrating that emotional disorders are amenable to drug treatment. Chlorpromazine has enjoyed unusually wide acceptance, and in the intervening years it has become the prototype for the synthesis of hundreds of new experimental drugs. Referring to Table I (top figure), it may be noted that this antipsychotic agent consists of a three-ring, phenothiazine nucleus containing a chlorine atom at position 2 and a dimethylaminopropyl side chain at position 10. By substituting other groups for the halogen in the nucleus or by replacing the terminal aliphatic nitrogen with a heterocyclic amine group, many pharmacologically active phenothiazine derivatives have been obtained. Some of these compounds, such as perphenazine, trifluoperazine, thioproperazine, and fluphenazine, are five to twenty times more potent than chlorpromazine.

Several interesting classes of psychotropic drugs result from alterations in the phenothiazine nucleus itself. Replacing the nuclear nitrogen atom with a

TABLE I

Key to the Metabolism of Chlorpromazine[a]

$CH_2CH_2CH_2N(CH_3)_2$

N 1 Cl

9 8 7 6 S 5 4 3 minor

Metabolite	Structure	Formed By
Nor_2CPSO	$CH_2CH_2CH_2NH_2$; N; Cl; S→O	Didemethylation, sulfoxidation
CPNO	O; $CH_2CH_2CH_2N(CH_3)_2$; N; Cl; S	N - Oxidation
2 - Cl - PhzSO	N; Cl; S→O	Side-chain degradation sulfoxidation
7-HO-CP glucuronide or sulfate	$CH_2CH_2CH_2N(CH_3)_2$; N; Cl; RO; S; $R{=}C_6H_9O_6$ or SO_3H	7-Hydroxylation, glucuronidation or sulfation
N-Acetyl-7-HO-Nor_2CP	$CH_2CH_2CH_2NHCOCH_3$; N; Cl; HO; S	Didemethylation, *N*-acetylation, 7-hydroxylation
3-HO-Nor_1CP glucuronide	$CH_2CH_2CH_2NHCH_3$; N; Cl; S; OR; $R{=}C_6H_9O_6$	Monodemethylation, 3-hydroxylation, glucuronidation

[a] Arrows indicate reactive sites in the chlorpromazine molecule. More than forty metabolites of chlorpromazine are excreted by man. The six derivatives illustrated here give a bird's-eye view of the various transformations to which the drug is subjected during its passage through the body.

carbon atom bearing a double bond in the side chain results in a new series of antipsychotic agents called thioxanthenes. The thioxanthene analog of chlorpromazine is chlorprothixene. If the sulfur atom of promazine is replaced with an ethylene group ($—CH_2—CH_2—$), a new compound, imipramine, is obtained which acts as an antidepressant rather than antipsychotic. The structural resemblance between phenothiazines, thioxanthenes, and imipramine (an iminodibenzyl derivative) is pointed out only to facilitate our discussion of their metabolism since structure-activity relationships are dealt with in detail elsewhere. Analogies will be noted later in the metabolic disposition of these psychotropic drugs.

The purpose of this chapter is to consider the metabolism and excretion of two classes of drugs, *viz.* the antipsychotic, and the antidepressant agents. Due to limitations of space, our discussion will be restricted to the following drugs: chlorpromazine, promazine, miscellaneous phenothiazine compounds, reserpine, chlorprothixene, imipramine, and iproniazid.

II. Antipsychotic Agents

A. *Phenothiazines*

Unsubstituted phenothiazine was used in veterinary practice as an anthelmintic for a decade prior to the introduction of chlorpromazine. Phenothiazine is a ten-membered ring structure whose position numbers are similar to those in the chlorpromazine molecule (Table I). The metabolism of this anthelmintic has been reviewed by Clare *et al.* (96). It is pertinent to note that the positions *para* to the nitrogen atom of phenothiazine, *viz.* 3, 5, and 7, represent biologically active sites in the molecule. Hydroxylation occurs at the 3- and 7-positions, and S-oxide (sulfoxide) formation occurs at the 5-position. Phenothiazine sulfoxide is found in the aqueous humor of the eye in calves treated with phenothiazine, and was identified by Clare *et al.* (96) as the photodynamic agent responsible for the development of photosensitized keratitis in these animals.

Studies on the effect of light and of oxidants on phenothiazine derivatives (particularly chlorpromazine) have led to the detection of free radical intermediates, which result from the loss of an electron (97). It has been proposed by these authors that drug metabolism proceeds *in vivo* via a free radical mechanism. The tendency for phenothiazines to yield colored solutions in oxidizing media serves as the basis of a number of rapid urine tests for phenothiazine and related drugs (98).

1. Chlorpromazine

The metabolism of chlorpromazine has been under study for more than a decade. Despite this, its biological fate in man is not yet completely defined. While the urinary unconjugated metabolites have been identified and quantitated, information on the conjugates is incomplete. A review of the literature also reveals a dearth of data on blood levels of the parent drug and its derived products.

The origin of these problems lies in the following factors. As we shall soon see, chlorpromazine has high biological reactivity. The drug is rapidly cleared from blood and excreted in urine in the form of forty or more metabolites. It is doubtful whether human urine contains, on average, more than 0.1 or 0.2% of the parent drug after oral intake. Not all of the urinary products have been identified, due to lack of specific standards for reference purposes. Carrying out meaningful blood studies requires sophisticated techniques for the resolution and detection of nanogram quantities of closely related metabolites. These techniques have not been developed to the point where blood levels can be routinely used either to control drug dosage for optimal clinical response or to detect potentially toxic products.

The three major pathways for the metabolism of chlorpromazine are sulfoxidation, side-chain demethylation, and ring hydroxylation. The first pathway was established by Salzman and Brodie (99), who isolated chlorpromazine sulfoxide from dog urine and determined its excretion values from ultraviolet absorption measurements (275 mμ) of urine extracts. Chlorpromazine sulfoxide values of 10–14% (dog) and 5% (man) were reported, expressed as percent of dose. No evidence was given in this paper for demethylation of chlorpromazine. Two years later Ross *et al.* (100) demonstrated that rats administered chlorpromazine-(*N*-methyl)-^{14}C expire the label as $^{14}CO_2$, which is indicative of demethylation. Working with dogs, Walkenstein and Seifter (101) obtained chromatographic evidence for monodemethylation of promazine, as revealed by the excretion of nor$_1$promazine* and its sulfoxide in urine. The authors found no indication of didemethylation. Fishman and Goldenberg (102,103) reported that the CPSO present in human and dog urine is accompanied by its two desmethyl derivatives, viz. nor$_1$CPSO and nor$_2$CPSO. The sum of the three sulfoxides was calculated to be 5.9% for human urine and 11.3% for dog urine. These values are in good agreement with the "CPSO" values obtained by Salzman and Brodie, which suggests that their method measures total sulfoxide rather than CPSO. Nor$_2$CPSO appears to be a major metabolite in human urine (3.7%) but a minor one in dog urine (1.1%).

Further studies by Fishman *et al.* (104,105) led to the isolation of CPNO, 2-Cl-Phz and 2-Cl-PhzSO from human and dog urine. The second and third compounds represent products of side-chain cleavage. By quantitating the three compounds it was deduced that N-oxidation and side-chain degradation represent minor pathways of metabolism.

In independent studies Johnson *et al.* (106) also identified 2-Cl-Phz and 2-Cl-PhzSO in human urine. More recently, Rodriguez and Johnson (107) have isolated an intermediate degradation product, 2-Cl-Phz-10-propacid, from an extract of acidified human urine. The formation of this compound is consistent

* Key to abbreviations: nor$_1$, desmonomethyl; nor$_2$, desdimethyl; CP, chlorpromazine; CPSO, chlorpromazine sulfoxide; CPNO, chlorpromazine-*N*-oxide; Phz, phenothiazine; PhzSO, phenothiazine sulfoxide; propacid, β-propionic acid; P, promazine; PSO, promazine sulfoxide; PNO, promazine-*N*-oxide.

with the following proposed series of transformations in the side chain of chlorpromazine:

$$\rangle N-CH_2-CH_2-CH_2-N(CH_3)_2 \rightarrow \rightarrow \rangle N-CH_2-CH_2-CH_2-NH_2 \rightarrow$$

CP Nor$_2$CP

$$\rangle N-CH_2-CH_2-CHO \longrightarrow \rangle N-CH_2-CH_2-COOH \rightarrow \rightarrow \rangle N-H$$

2-Cl-Phz-10-propacid

The various chlorpromazine metabolites discussed above are unconjugated* and, with the exception of 2-Cl-Phz-10-propacid, they are extractable from alkaline urine into organic solvent. Resolution of these products is obtained by two-dimensional thin layer chromatography using the solvent systems indicated in Fig. 1. Nor$_1$CP appears in the chromatogram and represents a minor metabolite. Nor$_2$CP is either absent, or present in such small quantities as not to be readily detected. The dark spots are trace phenolic substances which bear the hydroxyl group in the 7-position. They are identified in the legend to Fig. 1. We estimate that human subjects receiving a daily oral regimen of 300–1200 mg chlorpromazine excrete 8 to 9% of the drug in unconjugated form.

There is marked disagreement in the literature as to the percent of chlorpromazine (total) which can be recovered from urine. For subjects on daily medication the following values have been recorded: 5–20%, 15–20%, 58%, 21–70%. However, most authors agree that the average ratio of conjugated to unconjugated products is 3:1. Assigning a value of 8–9% to the unconjugated compounds,

* 2-Cl-Phz and 2-Cl-PhzSO also appear in the glucuronide fraction (Fig. 2).

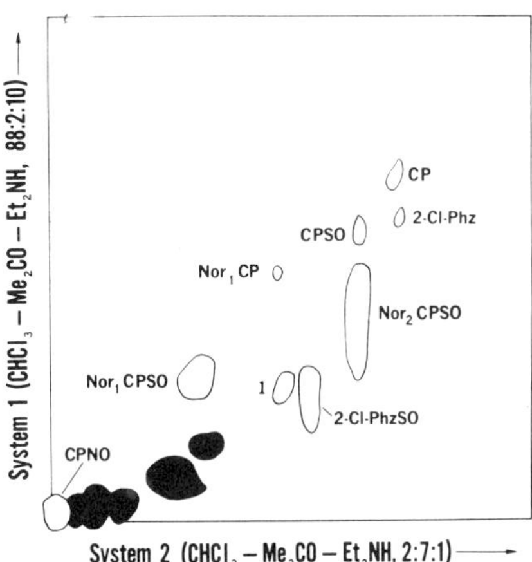

Fig. 1. Thin layer chromatogram of unconjugated chlorpromazine metabolites extracted from human urine (105). Nor$_2$CP and 2-Cl-Phz-10-propacid are not shown in this figure. Key to symbols: CP, chlorpromazine; nor$_1$CP, nor$_1$chlorpromazine; CPSO, chlorpromazine sulfoxide; nor$_1$CPSO, nor$_1$chlorpromazine sulfoxide; nor$_2$CPSO, nor$_2$chlorpromazine sulfoxide; CPNO, chlorpromazine-*N*-oxide; 2-Cl-Phz, 2-chlorophenothiazine; 2-Cl-PhzSO, 2-chlorophenothiazine sulfoxide; dark spots, 7-hydroxychlorpromazine, 7-hydroxy-nor$_1$chlorpromazine, 7-hydroxy-nor$_2$chlorpromazine, 7-hydroxychlorpromazine sulfoxide, L4, L5.

the total excretion is calculated to be about 35% of the drug intake. This value is almost identical with the average excretion of 37% recently reported (108).

Identification of the conjugated metabolites of chlorpromazine has proven to be a formidable task, resisting the efforts of most workers. Forrest and Piette (97) stated that "after 10 years of intensive clinical use of . . . chlorpromazine, the major urinary drug metabolites of the phenolic, polar fraction, have not been unequivocally identified, despite the fact that this drug was the subject of many metabolic investigations in numerous laboratories, and more data on

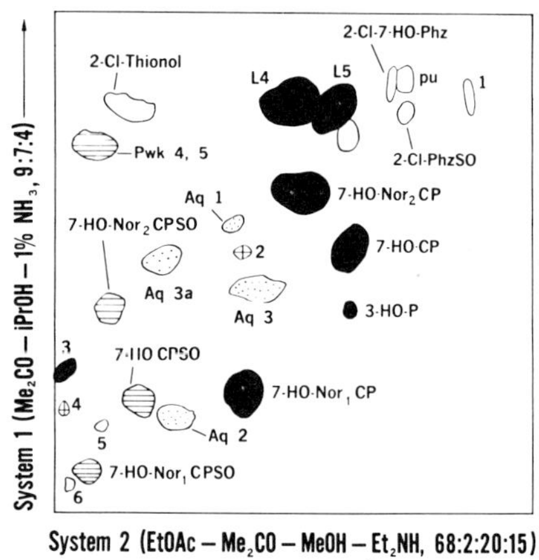

Fig. 2. Thin layer chromatogram of chlorpromazine metabolites isolated from the glucuronide fraction of human urine (105). Key to symbols: 7-HO-CP, 7-hydroxychlorpromazine; 7-HO-Nor$_1$CP, 7-hydroxy-nor$_1$chlorpromazine; 7-HO-Nor$_2$CP, 7-hydroxy-nor$_2$chlorpromazine; 7-HO-CPSO, 7-hydroxychlorpromazine sulfoxide; 7-HO-Nor$_1$CPSO, 7-hydroxy-nor$_1$chlorpromazine sulfoxide; 7-HO-Nor$_2$CPSO, 7-hydroxy-nor$_2$chlorpromazine sulfoxide; L4, *N*-acetyl-7-hydroxy-nor$_2$chlorpromazine (?); L5, *N*-acetyl-7-hydroxy-nor$_1$chlorpromazine (?); Pwk 4, L4 sulfoxide; Pwk 5, L5 sulfoxide; spot no. 3, 7-hydroxychlorpromazine-*N*-oxide; spot no. 2, 3-hydroxychlorpromazine; 2-Cl-PhzSO, 2-chlorophenothiazine sulfoxide; 2-Cl-7-HO-Phz, 2-chloro-7-hydroxyphenothiazine; 2-Cl-Thionol, 2-chlorothionol; spot no. 1, 2-chlorophenothiazine-7-one; 3-HO-P, 3-hydroxypromazine; Aq 1, Aqua 1; Aq 2, Aqua 2; spot no. 6, Aqua 2 sulfoxide; Aq 3, Aqua 3; spot no. 5, Aqua 3 sulfoxide; Aq 3a, Aqua 3a; spot no. 4, Aqua 3a sulfoxide.

its metabolic fate and type and amount of oxidative derivatives are available than for any other phenothiazine compound."

Lin *et al.* (109), Posner (110), and others suggested that the conjugates of chlorpromazine are, for the most part, hydroxylated (phenolic) compounds bound to glucuronic acid. Cleavage of the bond was obtained by hydrolysis with acid or with β-glucuronidase. Beckett *et al.* (111) showed that sulfuric acid conjugates are also present in urine, albeit in smaller amount.

Most of the metabolites in the urinary glucuronide (aglycone) fraction were identified by Fishman and Goldenberg in a two-year study. The results appear in three papers (105,112,113). According to these workers, position 7 represents the major site of hydroxylation. Eleven phenols of this configuration are given in Fig. 2. Note that the compounds reflect ring hydroxylation, demethylation, sulfoxidation, N-oxidation, and probably N-acetylation. A small amount of the 3-isomer was also detected, along with a trace of 3-HO-P. It is of interest that several phenothiazines, principally 2-Cl-PhzSO and 2-Cl-Phz, were identified among the aglycones. Their simultaneous presence in the unconjugated fraction suggests that side chain degradation is followed by partial conversion to the glucuronide conjugate, probably at the ring N atom.

About thirty of the forty compounds listed in the legends to Figs. 1 and 2 were identified. The most serious deficiency was the failure to identify the seven "aquas," so called because of the blue-green spots obtained when the chromatoplate is stained with acid. These spots do not appear in dog urine. Noting that synthetic 3,7-dimethoxychlorpromazine also produces a blue-green color, the authors suggested the 3,7-dioxy configuration as a possible assignment for the aquas. Support for the 3,7-positions comes from Coccia and Westerfeld (114), who report that an aqua-staining diphenol, identified as 3,7-dihydroxychlorpromazine, is obtained by incubating either 3-HO-CP or 7-HO-CP with rat liver microsomes. Evidence for the 7,8-positions has recently been given by Daly and Manian (115). Working with rabbit (not rat) liver microsomes containing an hydroxylation-methylation system, the authors obtained O-methyl-7,8-dihydroxychlorpromazine from either 7-HO-CP or 8-HO-CP. On this basis they propose a 7,8-configuration for the diphenols in (human) urine. This proposal seems inconsistent with their observation that 7,8-dihydroxychlorpromazine and its methylated derivative give a blue-purple reaction with acid, not an aqua color. Also, by their own observation, the analytical method used in the study is specific for vicinal dihydroxy compounds (catechols), and would not detect 3,7-dihydroxy derivatives if present.

a. *Pharmacological Activity of Chlorpromazine Metabolites.* Considering the variety of derivatives produced by chlorpromazine, various workers in the field have sought to determine whether the activity of the drug is mediated through a metabolite. Posner *et al.* (116) compared known and model metabolites of chlorpromazine (and promazine) on the basis of behavioral as well as pharmacological tests. High activity was shown by Nor_1CP, CPNO, and by hydroxylated derivatives. CPSO had greatly reduced activity, in confirmation of earlier reports. Manian *et al.* (117) have demonstrated that 3-HO-CP and 7-HO-CP have pharmacological activity similar to chlorpromazine. According to Bolt and Forrest (118), 7-HO-CP is a normal storage product of chlorpromazine in human tissues. 7-HO-CP may, however, also be involved in the hyperpigmentation and corneal opacities sometimes seen in chronically dosed patients (119).

b. *Blood Metabolite Levels.* The possibility that the clinical response to chlorpromazine is related to the pattern of its metabolism has intrigued many workers, and studies along these lines have been reported from the laboratories of Forrest, Huang, Wechsler, and Hollister. However, most studies to date have dealt with urine, whose metabolite content may not reflect the clinical reponse as accurately as the drug pattern in blood.

Reports on chlorpromazine metabolite levels in blood are fragmentary, due to analytical problems resulting from their low concentrations. Huang and Ruskin

(120) reported that most of the circulating drug is present in the glucuronide rather than in the unconjugated fraction (12.7 μg vs. 0.76 μg/ml serum). Wechsler *et al.* (121) disagree, stating that only small amounts of aglycones are released after enzymatic hydrolysis. Using a gas chromatograph equipped with an electron capture detector, Curry and Marshall (122) report the presence of CP, Nor_1CP, Nor_2CP, and CPSO in the blood of psychiatric patients receiving medication. A more sensitive assay based on electron capture is the subject of a recent paper by Hammar and Holmstedt (123). These authors prepared the trifluoroacetyl derivatives (of the desmethyl metabolites) for injection into the gas chromatograph and detected CP, Nor_1CP, Nor_2CP, and 2-Cl-Phz-10-propacid.

2. Promazine

Few laboratories have studied this drug, yet its metabolism is more clearly defined than that of chlorpromazine. We have already alluded to the work of Walkenstein and Seifter (101), who demonstrated that promazine is transformed by animals to yield Nor_1P, PSO, and Nor_1PSO. Goldenberg and Fishman (113a) reported the results of an extensive study of the metabolism of promazine in man and animals. By use of thin layer and paper chromatography, the authors detected the parent drug and 27 metabolites in human urine, many of which were then identified and quantitated. The results are given in Table II. As noted, 33% of the drug was accounted for in the urine, distributed as follows: 14 unconjugated compounds, 15%; 10 glucuronide conjugates, 15%; 4 sulfate conjugates, about 3%. Nor_2PSO and Nor_1PSO were the principal unconjugated metabolites, while a series of 3-hydroxy sulfides (3-HO-P, 3-HO-Nor_1P, L4, and L5) were the principal aglycones isolated from the glucuronide fraction. The promazine metabolites reflect sulfoxidation, mono- and didemethylation, ring hydroxylation, *N*-oxidation, side-chain degradation, glucuronide and sulfate conjugation, and probably *N*-acetylation (L4 and L5).

In this study the metabolism of promazine was found to be markedly species-dependent. Dogs excreted only 13% of the drug, primarily in the unconjugated fraction. Rabbits excreted 10–13% in the urine, primarily as 3-HO-P (free and bound). In both animals there was detectable but minimal didemethylation, as compared with man, in whom didemethylation represents a major route of metabolism.

In view of the evidence for dihydroxylation of the chlorpromazine nucleus, it is noteworthy that diphenols have not been detected among the metabolites of promazine. As we shall note later, dihydroxylation is also not seen in the imipramine nucleus. Promazine and imipramine are comparable in that their nuclei are symmetrical and unsubstituted in the first and third rings. Chlorpromazine possesses a chlorine atom which may serve to activate the nucleus for dihydroxylation by human liver microsomes.

3. Miscellaneous Phenothiazine Compounds

Levomepromazine has been used in psychiatry for treatment of patients who have developed toxic reactions to chlorpromazine. Its metabolism was studied by Allgen *et al.* (124). Analysis of human urine revealed small amounts of

Table II
URINARY EXCRETION OF PROMAZINE AND ITS METABOLITES IN MAN[a]

Class	Compound	%	Total (%)
Nonphenols	nor_2promazine sulfoxide	6.3	
	nor_1promazine sulfoxide	5.2	
	promazine sulfoxide	0.7	
	promazine-N-oxide	0.8	
	promazine	0.2	
	nor_1promazine	0.4	
	nor_2promazine	trace	
	phenothiazine	0.01	
	phenothiazine sulfoxide	0.2	14
Free phenols	3-hydroxypromazine	trace	
	3-hydroxy-nor_1promazine	0.5	
	3-hydroxy-nor_2promazine	trace	
	L_4 and L_5	trace	1
Glucuronides	L_4 and L_5	5.5	
	3-hydroxypromazine	3.7	
	3-hydroxy-nor_1promazine	3.1	
	3-hydroxy-nor_2promazine	0.9	
	3-hydroxypromazine sulfoxide	NA	
	3-hydroxy-nor_1promazine sulfoxide	NA	
	3-hydroxy-nor_2promazine sulfoxide	NA	
	phenothiazine	0.1	
	phenothiazine sulfoxide	0.2	15
Sulfates	3-hydroxypromazine	NA	
	3-hydroxy-nor_1promazine	NA	
	3-hydroxypromazine sulfoxide	trace	
	3-hydroxy-nor_1promazine sulfoxide	trace	3
	Grand Total		33

[a] Expressed as % of oral dose.
[b] NA = exact value not available
L_4 = N-acetyl-7-hydroxy-nor_2promazine
L_5 = N-acetyl-7-hydroxy-nor_1promazine

unoxidized drug, about 1% of the dose; sulfoxides, 10%; and about ten polar metabolites. There was no evidence in feces for either sulfoxides or glucuronic acid conjugates. The sites of hydroxylation of the polar metabolites were not determined.

Perphenazine metabolism was examined by Huang and Kurland (125). The drug contains a piperazine ring in the side chain. It is relatively potent and is used in about one-fifth the average daily dosage of chlorpromazine. The authors studied the average daily excretion of drug in five patients, with the following results: unchanged perphenazine, 1%; sulfoxide, 12.7%; and glucuronide conjugates, 30%.

Thioridazine is probably the only drug for which sulfone formation has been demonstrated *in vivo*. The metabolism of thioridazine is complicated by the presence of a second sulfur atom, located in the methylmercapto group at position 3 of the phenothiazine ring. Using labeled drug administered to rats, Zehnder *et al.* (126) identified as metabolites the ring sulfoxide (the 5-oxide), the side chain sulfoxide (position 3), the disulfoxide, and the disulfone. It should be noted, however, that the metabolites determined in rat urine represented only 1–2% of the administered radioactivity. Demethylation of the side chain (position 10) was extensive, approximating 30–40% of the drug dose. The drug was excreted into rat bile in the form of glucuronide conjugates, and eliminated primarily in the feces. In a later publication Eiduson and Geller (127) reported a different distribution of metabolites in human subjects. After administration of a single oral dose of labeled thioridazine to psychiatric patients, the following excretion pattern was observed: urine, 30% of oral dose; feces, 50%; bile, 60%. In contrast to the other phenothiazine tranquilizers, little or no glucuronide-conjugated material was found in urine.

B. Chlorprothixene

This drug was first introduced in Europe in 1959 and later in the United States. Its structural similarity to chlorpromazine was pointed out in the introduction to this chapter. The double bond between the side chain and the carbon atom of the thioxanthene ring is essential for central activity, producing an electron distribution similar to that of the phenothiazine compounds. Chlorprothixene differs chemically from chlorpromazine in the greater stability of its solutions, and in its decreased sensitivity to light.

There is a limited literature on the metabolism of chlorprothixene. The sulfoxide was first identified by Allgen *et al.* (128) as a major metabolite in human and animal urine. Using thin layer chromatography, Huus and Khan (129) have also detected the sulfoxide, the nor$_1$sulfoxide, unchanged drug, and additional unidentified metabolites in the nonconjugate fraction of animal urine. The properties of one unidentified metabolite were suggestive of nor$_1$chlorprothixene or its *N*-oxide. The authors isolated the aglycones from dog urine and observed two products of unknown structure. In contrast, rat urine appeared to be devoid of phenolic metabolites.

Chlorprothixene disappears rapidly from the bloodstream. In rats given chlorprothixene orally the drug and its sulfoxide appear within 15 to 30 minutes in liver, lung, and kidney, and in smaller amounts in brain, skeletal muscle, spleen, and fat tissue. The sulfoxide is excreted in bile and feces as well as in urine.

Wallace (130) has recently described a sensitive ultraviolet spectrophotometric method for chlorprothixene in biological specimens. In this procedure the drug and its unconjugated derivatives are extracted into heptane and subsequently oxidized to products having an absorption maximum at 233 mμ. According to the author, the sensitivity of the method permits determination of the drug in urine 3 days after ingestion of a single 50 mg dose. In this study, human subjects voided 7% of the drug (as heptane extractables) during a 72-hour period.

C. *Reserpine*

The roots and extracts of *Rauwolfia serpentina* have been used as tranquilizers for many centuries. Rauwolfia contains a number of alkaloids, but it was not until 1952 that reserpine was isolated and shown to be the principal active ingredient. Reserpine contains two components, methyl reserpate and trimethoxybenzoic acid (TMBA), which are joined via an ester linkage. The pharmacological activity of the drug is lost when the bond is split by hydrolysis. This occurs during the metabolism of reserpine, under both *in vivo* and *in vitro* conditions.

Animal studies have demonstrated a species difference in the metabolism of reserpine. In the rat, oral administration of the drug leads to hydrolysis in the intestinal mucosa. This is followed by the appearance of methyl reserpate in the tissues, urine, and feces. Administration of the drug via the intravenous route leads to much lower levels of methyl reserpate. Little methyl reserpate appears in the dog with either oral or parenteral administration. This is attributed to a lack of significant hydrolytic activity in the gastrointestinal tract of the animal. The species difference between rat and dog probably accounts for the greater resistance of the rat to the effects of reserpine. Reserpine is also rapidly metabolized by the mouse, with 30 to 40% of the labeled drug appearing in the urine, as free TMBA, within four hours of administration. The ability of the liver of different animals to split reserpine has been studied, and found to have no relationship to the sedative effect of the drug.

In addition to the metabolites discussed above, reserpine is transformed by the rat or guinea pig to syringic acid, syringoyl methyl reserpate, and CO_2.

Human subjects receiving a daily oral dose of 0.5 mg reserpine excreted 6.4% as methyl reserpate (131). Only 2 of 31 subjects had measurable amounts of free reserpine in the urine. Numerof *et al.* (132) indicate that schizophrenics metabolize reserpine in a manner similar to normals.

Reserpine releases serotonin (along with other biogenic amines and other substances) from its binding sites, resulting in an increase of serotonin blood levels. Many workers report that the effect of reserpine correlates better with the amount of serotonin in blood than with the reserpine level. The apparent tendency for reserpine to disappear from the body before sedation runs its course has led Brodie to call reserpine a "hit and run" drug. Nonetheless, careful analysis suggests that traces of reserpine actually do persist in blood, liver, and brain for weeks after administration of the drug. It has, however, not been possible to relate the intensity of drug action to the concentration of reserpine in the brain.

III. Antidepressants

A. *Imipramine*

Imipramine consists of an iminodibenzyl nucleus with a dimethylaminopropyl side chain affixed to the ring N atom. This drug was introduced into clinical practice in 1959 and has enjoyed substantial acceptance as an antidepressant.

The urinary excretion of imipramine was first examined by Herrmann *et al.* (133–135), who demonstrated side-chain demethylation, ring hydroxylation at position 2,* and glucuronide conjugation. In 1962 there appeared reports from other laboratories of the presence of imipramine-*N*-oxide and iminodibenzyl in urine. The latter metabolite reflects complete scission of the side chain of imipramine, comparable to the formation of phenothiazine from promazine.

Crammer and Scott (136) have recently detected a new series of imipramine metabolites in human urine and plasma. These derivatives are apparently hydroxylated at position 10 of the nucleus, in the ethylene bridge of the seven-membered ring. A similar transformation has been reported in the ethylene bridge of amitriptyline. If we include these new imipramine metabolites, 13 products would appear to be present in the unconjugated fraction, as follows:

Imipramine	2-HO-Nor$_2$imipramine
Nor$_1$imipramine	2-HO-Iminodibenzyl
Nor$_2$imipramine	10-HO-Imipramine
Imipramine-*N*-oxide	10-HO-Nor$_1$imipramine
Iminodibenzyl	10-HO-Nor$_2$imipramine
2-HO-Imipramine	10-HO-Iminodibenzyl
2-HO-Nor$_1$imipramine	

There is at this time no evidence for simultaneous hydroxylation at positions 2 and 10. Rupture of the iminodibenzyl nucleus, resulting from cleavage of the ethylene group, is a distinct possibility and may explain the existence of radiolabeled "nonextractables" in the studies of Christiansen *et al.* (137).

The glucuronides of 2-HO-imipramine and its nor$_1$-derivative have been characterized and represent major urinary excretion products. According to the literature, at least four and possibly six other glucuronides appear in the conjugate fraction. On this basis the total number of imipramine derivatives voided in urine approximates twenty.

According to Herrmann (135), human subjects excrete 11% of their daily drug intake in the form of unconjugated compounds. The work of Christiansen suggests that the level of conjugated compounds is more than twice the nonconjugates, giving a total of 35% of the drug accounted for. This value is similar to the average excretion of promazine and chlorpromazine derivatives in urine.

A rapid color test for imipramine and its metabolites has been developed (98). Although semiquantitative, the test is useful for confirming drug intake by recalcitrant patients.

B. Iproniazid (MAO Inhibitor)

Iproniazid is one of a group of "psychic energizers" whose activity is attributed to an inhibition of monoamine oxidase activity. Other drugs included in this group are nialamide, isocarboxazide, phenelzine, pheniprazine, and tranylcy-

* Position 2 in the iminodibenzyl nucleus is para to the ring N atom and equivalent to position 3 in the phenothiazine ring.

promine. The inhibition of MAO causes an accumulation of endogenous amines, among them brain serotonin. The consensus is that the clinical effects of the MAO inhibitors are due to the increased serotonin levels, rather than to the drugs per se. As a result, primary interest in the literature has not been directed to the metabolism of the MAO inhibitors, but instead to their effect on the metabolism of monoamines.

According to Koechlin *et al.* (138), the metabolism of iproniazid proceeds by two routes, viz. oxidative dealkylation and hydrolysis, as follows:

$$\text{(1) Iproniazid} \xrightarrow{\text{oxidative}} \text{isoniazid + acetone} \longrightarrow CO_2$$
$$\downarrow$$
$$\text{(2) Iproniazid} \xrightarrow{\text{hydrolytic}} \text{isonicotinic acid + isopropylhydrazine}$$

The first route is regarded as a mechanism for inactivation of the drug. In the second sequence the isopropylhydrazine released is an active MAO inhibitor.

Tracer studies by Koechlin showed that the isopropyl group in iproniazid is ultimately oxidized to CO_2, resulting in elimination of 79 to 90% of the radioactive dose within 72 hours. Oxidation rates of the drugs appeared to vary markedly between individuals. Within the same time interval (72 hours), 10 to 13% of the administered radioactivity appeared in the urine. Of this, about 2 to 3% was attributed to unchanged iproniazid. Chromatographic studies revealed the presence of metabolites whose identities were not determined.

In this study the blood and plasma levels reached a first, sharp peak in about two hours and a second, broad peak in 20 to 40 hours. The initial peak represents a buildup of the parent drug, while the secondary peak probably reflects the release of labeled carbon from the metabolized drug into the carbon anabolic pool.

For further reading and references see Appendices 1 and 2.

15

CLASSIFICATION OF PSYCHOPHARMACA

Earl Usdin

I. Apologia

As is true for many papers on the classification of psychopharmaca, this one will start with an apologia. There are no universally accepted definitions of terms and there are no clear-cut lines of demarcation between the various classes of drugs with psychotropic action. Below is a partial list of terms used to describe the action of these compounds:*

antianxiety	antiphobic (AA)	ataraxic (AA)
antidepressant	*antipsychotic*	depersonalizing (H)
antidepressive (AD)	anxiolytic (AA)	depressant (AA)
antineurotic (AA)	ataractic (AA)	energizing (AD)

* For consistency, those terms in italics are used wherever possible throughout this text [See Preface to this volume and Section VI].

hallucinogenic	psychoeffective	psychotaraxic (H)
neuroleptic (AP)	psychoenergizing (S)	psychotherapeutic
neuroplegic (AA)	psychohibitor (AA)	psychotomimetic (H)
neurotropic (AA, AP)	psycho-inhibitor (AA)	psychotonic (AD)
pherenotropic	psycholeptic (AA)	psychotoxic (H)
phrenotropic	psycholytic	psychotropic
psychedelic (H)	psychomimetic (H)	relaxant (AA)
psychic energizing (S)	psychomotor stimulant (S)	*stimulant*
psychoactive	psychopharmaceutical	taraxic (H)
psychoactivator	psychopharmacological	thymerethic (S)
psychoanaleptic (AD)	psychosolytic	thymoanaleptic (AD)
psychochemical	psychososomimetic (H)	thymoleptic (AD)
psychodysleptic (H)	psychostimulant (S)	tranquilizing (AA)

Some of these terms are synonymous and others, even though they indicate somewhat the same general type of action, are so different in action that they cannot even be classed as synonyms (and even synonyms differ at least in nuances of meaning). Having confessed to the inadequacy of the classification, I have divided the compounds in the tables which follow into five classes: antipsychotics (AP), antidepressants (AD), antianxiety drugs (AA), stimulants (S), and hallucinogens (H). In the above list, the terms have been associated with these classes when possible. Some authors discuss neuroleptics as if they were tranquilizers, whereas other authors discuss them as if they were energizers; according to Pöldinger (139), they are tranquilizers which have mood elevating components. Jacobsen (140) summarizes many of the schemes proposed for the classification of psychopharmaca.

II. Compounds Included in Tables

The data contained in these tables have been obtained both from the published literature and from manufacturers or distributors and are condensed from a recent book entitled "Psychotropic Drugs and Related Compounds" (141). Whereas the previous publication included all compounds which had been reported to have any psychotropic action as well as chemically related compounds, this chapter includes only those psychotropic compounds which are listed in one of the following references (142–145).

III. Arrangement of Compounds

Several systems have been proposed for classifying psychotropic compounds. The system used here is according to chemical structure: phenothiazines and related compounds, indoles, other heterocycles, aromatic compounds, and aliphatic compounds. Other systems can be based on pharmacological action; an example would be as follows:

1. Antipsychotics
   a. *Phenothiazines*
      I. *Aliphatic subgroup*
      II. *Piperidyl subgroup*
      III. *Piperazine subgroup*
   b. *Thioxanthenes*
   c. *Reserpine and derivatives*
   d. *Miscellaneous*
2. Antidepressants
   a. *Tricyclics*
      I. *Iminodibenzyl derivatives*
      II. *Dibenzocycloheptadine derivatives*
   b. *Monoamine oxidase inhibitors*
      I. *Hydrazines*
      II. *Nonhydrazines*
3. Antianxiety Agents
   a. *Benzodiazepines*
   b. *Piperidines and piperazines*
   c. *Miscellaneous heterocycles and aromatics*
   d. *Carbamates*
   e. *Miscellaneous aliphatics*
4. Stimulants
   a. *Phenylalkylamines*
   b. *Miscellaneous*
5. Hallucinogens
   a. *Harmine and derivatives*
   b. *Lysergic acid derivatives*
   c. *Miscellaneous heterocycles*
   d. *Glycollates*

IV. Synonyms, Trade Names, and Manufacturers

An attempt has been made to include every synonym or trade name ever published in connection with each compound. Whenever possible, trade names have been associated with the company using them. In a few cases, the same name has been used for more than one compound. The inclusion of the name of any company does not imply that this company is necessarily still supplying the compound, but only that it has supplied it at some time, either according to publications or according to private communication. In some cases, manufacturers have questioned the use of certain names in connection with their compounds, but all synonyms have been included which have been seen in any literature references. The addresses of the manufacturer or distributor are given in one of the appendices of Usdin and Efron (141).

V. Structures and Chemical Names

To conserve space, the structures of the phenothiazines, the reserpine derivatives, and the phenylethylamine derivatives are given as parent compounds plus details of side chains.

There is a lack of a uniform system of nomenclature for chemical compounds: *Chemical Abstracts* uses one system (there is a conflict even within *Chemical Abstracts*); most American and British workers use IUPAC recommended numbering; in Germany, the most popular system is the one used by Beilstein. In addition, there are at least three other numbering systems in common use. Unfortunately, the literature rarely indicates which numbering system is being used, and time factors precluded the author from determining uniform chemical names for the compounds. Thus, in most cases, the chemical names are those which have been published or those supplied by the manufacturer.

VI. Psychotropic Actions and Doses

As discussed in Section I, five actions have been stressed: antipsychotic (AP), antianxiety (AA), antidepressant (AD), stimulant (S), and hallucinogenic (H). *There is no intent to imply that this action is either the only action which the compound has or even that it is necessarily the major action resulting from administration of the compound.* Since the author has been compelled in many cases to interpret reported results into one of the broad classes, it is recommended that the reader go back to the original source [listed with each psychotropic action in Usdin and Efron (141)] in any case where question arises on a reported action.

The dose values given in the tables are not included here for treatment purposes, but only to give an indication of the levels which have been used. Unless otherwise stated, the dose is that which has been recommended for oral administration. The actual dose which is given is dependent, of course, on the patient, whether it is an initial dose or a maintenance dose, etc. *It is strongly suggested that appropriate original references be checked before accepting any dosage.*

VII. Abbreviations

AA	Antianxiety
AD	Antidepressant
AP	Antipsychotic
bid	Two times per day
CNS	Central nervous system
deH	DeHaen, P. (145)
H	Hallucinogen
im	Intramuscular
iv	Intravenous
kg	Kilogram
MAOI	Monoamine oxidase inhibitor
Med	"Medindex" (146)
mg	Milligrams
ND	"New Drugs; Evaluated by the A.M.A. Council on Drugs," 2nd ed. (142)
PDR	"Physicians' Desk Reference to Pharmaceutical Specialties and Biologicals," 20th ed. (143)
P	Pöldinger, Walter (147)
po	By mouth
S	Stimulant
qid	Four times per day
sc	Subcutaneous
symp	Sympatholytic
tid	Three times per day
USD	"United States Dispensatory and Physicians' Pharmacology," 26th ed. (148)
USP	"Pharmacopeia of the United States of America," 17th rev. (144)
μg	Micrograms
$>$	More than
$<$	Less than

For further reading and references see Appendices 1 and 2.

Table I
CLASS: PHENOTHIAZINES

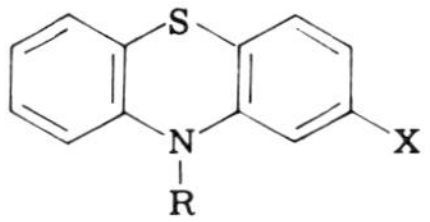

(Phenothiazine ring: S; N–R; X at position 2)

Compound	Synonyms, Trade Names, Manufacturers	Structure	Psychotropic Action and Dose	Listing
Acepromazine	Notensil, Plegicil (Clin-Byla), acetylpromazine, Acepromizina, Anatran, Lisergan, Plegicin, Plegicyl, acetopromazine, Atravet, Anergan, AY-57062 (Ayerst), 1522-CB, WY-1172, Soprotin (Knoll) (Cr. Barnes, Benger), SV-1522, acetazine (Gt. Britain), Plegecyl, acepromazina, Notesil, Soprintin (Knoll), Soprontin (Knoll), Atsetozin (Russian), Acethylpromazin, Notenquil	**—X:** $-C(=O)-CH_3$ **—R:** $-(CH_2)_3N-(CH_3)_2$ **10-[3-(Dimethylamino)propyl]-phenothiazin-2-yl methyl ketone**	AP; 75–150 mg; 20–30 mg/im or po/tid	
Acetophenazine maleate	Acetoperphenazin(e), Phenthoxate, SCH 6673 (Schering), Tindal maleate (Schering), acephenazine	**—X:** $-C(=O)-CH_3$ **—R:** $-(CH_2)_3-N$(piperazine)$N-(CH_2)_2-OH$ · dimaleate **10-{3-[4-(2-Hydroxyethyl)-1-piperazinyl]propyl}phenothiazin-2-yl methyl ketone maleate**	AP; 80 mg; 40–80 mg	ND; PDR; USD

Carphenazine	MDS-92 (Wyeth), Proketazine (Wyeth), WY-2445 (Wyeth), Carfenazina, carfenazine	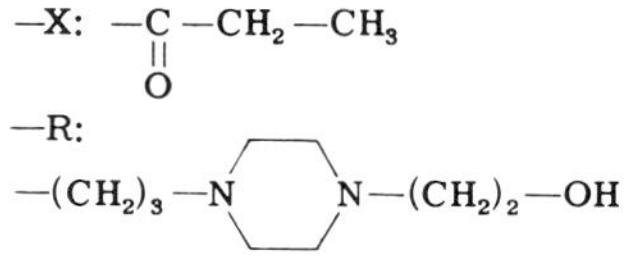 —X: $-\underset{\underset{O}{\parallel}}{C}-CH_2-CH_3$ —R: $-(CH_2)_3-N\langle\rangle N-(CH_2)_2-OH$ · maleate 4-[3-(2-Propionyl-10-phenothiazinyl) propyl]-1-piperazine-ethanol maleate	AP; 25–50 mg/ tid; 25–400 mg	deH; ND; PDR; USD
Chlorpromazine	A 2601(SKF), Amblictine, Aminasin, Aminazina (Gosfarmprom), Aminazid(e), Aminosine, Amphiectil, Ampliactil (Rhodia), Ampliactyl, Amplictil (Rhodia), chlorbomasin, chlordeazin, Chlor-Promanyl (Maney), chlorpromazini hydrichloridum, chlorpromazimium, clorpromazina, clorpromazine, Contamin, Contomin, CPZ, Elmarine (El.-Marion), Fenactil, Hebanil, Hibanil (Rh.-Poulenc, Leo), Hibernal (Leo), Hibernol, HL 5746, Hybanil, Hybernal, Klopromex (Dumex), Klorpromazine, Klorpromex, Largactil (Rh.-Poulenc, Farmitalia, M&B), Largactyl, Largaktyl, Maitran (Farmitalia), M&B 2378 (M&B), Megaphen (Bayer), Novomazina, Novomazine, Nuerpromazin(e), Opromazin, Phenactyle, Phenathyl, Plegomazin(e), Prazil, Prodinyl (RIT), Promactil, Promazil(e), Promazol (Zambon), Propaphen (Rodlebon), Propaphenin (Rodlebon),	—X: —Cl —R: $-(CH_2)_3-N(CH_3)_2 \cdot HCl$ **2-Chloro-10-[3-dimethylamino) propyl]-phenothiazine hydrochloride**	AP; 10–25 mg/ tid or qid; 12.5–50 mg/ im; 20–50 mg/iv; 75–500 mg; 25–125 mg	Med; ND; PDR; USP; USD; P

Table I (*Continued*)

Compound	Synonyms, Trade Names, Manufacturers	Structure	Psychotropic Action and Dose	Listing
	Prozil, Prozin (Luso), RP-4560 (Rh.-Poulenc), Sanopron, SKF-2601(SKF), Thenatyl, Thorazene, Thorazine (SKF), Torazina, Wintermain, Wintermin (Shionogi), Klorpromex (Dumex), Amphactil, Clordelazin (Rumanian), Neuroplex, Promazina, Psicarmon, Rauctil, Chloropromazine	(See page 199)		
Fluphenazine dihydrochloride	Anatensil, Anatensol (Squibb), Antasol, Antensol, Flufenazine, Flumazine, Flumezin(e), Lyogen (Byk-Gulden), Lyogen forte (Byk-Gulden), Moditen (Squibb), Modixen (Squibb), Noditen, Omca (Heyden, Squibb), Pacinol, Permitil (White), Prolixin(e) (Squibb), Sevinal, Sevinol (Schering), Siqualine, Siquoline, S 94, SQ 4918 (Squibb), Tensofin, Trancin (Schering), Transin, Vespazin(e), SQ 4889, Sch 6894, Fulmezine, Sevinon (Schering), Dapotum (Heyden), Valamina (Schering), Prolixene, flufenazina, trifluofenazina	—X: $-CF_3$ —R: $-(CH_2)_3-N\langle\rangle N-(CH_2)_2 \cdot OH \cdot 2\,HCl$ 4-[3-(2-Trifluoromethyl) phenothiazin-10-yl] propyl-1-piperizine-ethanol dihydrochloride	AP; 0.25 mg/ bid or tid; 0.5–20 mg	Med; ND; PDR; USD
Fluphenazine enanthate	SQ 16,144 (Squibb), Prolixin andante (Squibb), Moditen enanthate (Squibb), OF (Squibb, France), Moditen-retard (Squibb, France)	—X: $-CF_3$ —R: $-(CH_2)_3-N\langle\rangle N-(CH_2)_2-O-C(=O)-(CH_2)_6CH_3$ 4-[3-(2-Trifluoromethyl) phenothiazin-10-yl]-propyl-1-piperazine-ethylheptanoate	AP; 25–75 mg/ sc	

Mepazin(e) hydrochloride	Lacumin(e) (Lundbeck), Mepasin, Mepazin, MPMP, P-391, Pacatal (Warner, Promonta), Pacatol, Pacazine, Pactal (Warner), Paxital, Pecazinum, pecazin(e), Papital, Nothiazine, Promozen, Ravenil, Seral, mepazina, pecazina	**—X: —H** **—R:** **$-CH_2-$** (piperidine ring) **N—CH_3 · HCl** **10-[(1-Methyl-3-piperidyl) methyl]-phenothiazine hydrochloride**	AP; 25 mg/tid or qid; 75–400 mg; 50–600 mg	Med; ND; USD
Methotrimeprazin(e)	ARC-VI-C-5 (Addiction Res. Center, NIMH), Bayer 1213 (Bayer), CL-34,467 (Lederle), Dedoran (Shionogi), Hirnamin(e) (Shionogi), levomeprazin(e), levomepromazin(e), levopromazine, Levoprome (Lederle), mepromazine, methotromeprazine, methoxyphenothiazine, methoxytriḿeprazine, Minozinan (Rh.-Poulenc), Monozinan, Nauroctil (M&B), Neotonzil, Neozine (Rhodia) Neurocil (Bayer), Nirnamine, Nirvan (United Drug), Nomizan (Rh.-Poulenc), Nozinan (Rh.-Poulenc, Mexos), RP 7044 (Rh.-Poulenc), Sinogan-Debil, Veractil (M&B), Vetactil	—X: $-OCH_3$ —R: $-CH_2-CH(CH_3)-CH_2-N(CH_3)_2$ 10-[3-(Dimethylamino)-2-methylpropyl]-2-methoxyphenothiazine	AP; 25 mg/po or im; 25–1000 mg	deH; Med; USD

Table I (*Continued*)

Compound	Synonyms, Trade Names, Manufacturers	Structure	Psychotropic Action and Dose	Listing
Perphenazin(e)	Chlorperphenazin(e), chlorpiprazin, chlorpiprozin(e), Decentan (E. Merck, Bracco), Dezentan, Etaperazine, Etapirazin, Ethaperazine, Fentazin(e) (A&H), Grenolon, Perfenazin(e), Thilatazin, Tranquisan, Trilifan (Schering, Citrane), Trilafon (Schering), Perphenan, PZC, SCH-3940 (Schering), Chlorpiperazin, Clorpiprozin, Perfenacin, clorpiprozina, Calmazina, Metid, Neuropax, perfenazina, Perfenil, T 57, Trilafan	—X: —Cl —R: $—(CH_2)_3—N$ (piperazine ring) $N—(CH_2)_2—OH$ $\cdot 2\,HCl$ **4-[3-(2-Chlorophenothiazin-10-yl) propyl]-1-piperazine-ethanol dihydrochloride**	AP; 2–16 mg/bid or qid; 5–10 mg/im; 5 mg/kg/im/bid; 48 mg; 2–64 mg	Med; ND; PDR; USD
Prochlorperazine	Bayer A 173 (Bayer), Capazine, chlormeprazine, chlorperazine, Compazina, Compazine (SKF), Dicopal, FI 5685, Meterazin(e), Nipodal (Bayer), Niprodal, Novamin(e) (Shionogi), Hypodal, prochlorpemazin(e), Prochlorpremazine, Procloropemazina, Procloropromazina, proclorpemazine, proclorperazina, proklorperazine, propazine, RP-6140 (Rh.-Poulenc), Sedovomin (Cosma), SKF-4657 (SKF), Stemetil (M&B, Rh.-Poulenc, Farmitalia, Rhodia), Stementil, Stemmetil, Tamatil (Rh.-Poulenc), Tementil (Rh.-Poulenc, Rhodia), Temetil, Timental, Tematil	—X: —Cl —R: $—(CH_2)_3—N$ (piperazine ring) $N—CH_3$ · dimaleate or · ethanedisulfonate 2-Chloro-10-[3-(4-methyl-1-piperazinyl)propyl]phenothiazine dimaleate or ethanedisulfonate	AP; 5–16 mg/bid or qid; 150 mg; 90 mg; 25–250 mg	Med; ND; PDR; USP; USD

Promazin(e)	A 145 (Bayer), Agazergil, Ampazin(e) (Xavier), Apacergil, Alophen, Centractil (Astra), Centractyl (Astra), Eliranol, Esparin, Lemazina, Lemezina, Lete, Linarol, Liranol (Wyeth), Lirinol, Medoprozine, Neohibernex, Neurolax (Rigaux), Neuroplegil (Gentili), Delazine, Intrazine (Intra Med.), Phentractyl, Piarine, Prazine (Wyeth), Nogepha, Proma, Promacina, Promantine, Promanyl (Maney), Promatine, Promazionon, Promilene (Lepetit), Promoton (Galma), Promwill, Propasine, Propazin(e), Protactil, Protactyl (Asche, Wyeth), Pro-Tan, Pro-Tran (Mowatt), Prozine, RP 3276 (Rh.-Poulenc), Sediston (Serono), Sinophenin (DDR), SKF 3406 (SKF), Sparine (Wyeth), Starazine, Statazine, Talofen (Pierrel), Talophen, Tomil, Verodon, Verophen (Bayer), WY 1094 (Wyeth), Verofen (Bayer), Medeprozin, Sterazin, Calmotal, Varophen	—X: —H —R: $-(CH_2)_3-N(CH_3)_2 \cdot HCl$ **10-[3-(Dimethylamino) propyl]-phenothiazine hydrochloride**	AP; 10–200 mg/po or im; 50–150 mg/kg; 25–1000 mg/kg	Med; ND; PDR; USD
Thiopropazat(e)	Artalan, Chlorophenothiazine, Dartal (Searle), Dartalan (Searle), Dartan (Searle), Dartilan, SC 71055, tiopropazate, thiopropazote, tiopropazato, SC 7105	—X: —Cl —R: $-(CH_2)_3-N\langle piperazine \rangle N-(CH_2)_2-O-C(=O)-CH_3$ $\cdot 2\,HCl$ **4-[3-(2-Chlorophenothiazin-10-yl)-propyl]-1-piperazinethyl dihydrochloride**	AP; 2–10 mg/tid or qid; 6–60 mg	Med; PDR; USD

Table I (*Continued*)

Compound	Synonyms, Trade Names, Manufacturers	Structure	Psychotropic Action and Dose	Listing
Thioproperazine	RP-7843 (Rhone-Poulenc), SKF-5383 (SKF), Majeptil (Rhone-Poulenc, M&B), Vontil (SKF), Cephalmin (Shionogi), Thioperazin(e), IC 5911 (Ives), Sulfenazin (USSR), tioproperazina, tioperazina, thiopropemazin(e), Mayeptil (Rhone-Poulenc)	—X: $—SO_2—N(CH_3)_2$ —R: 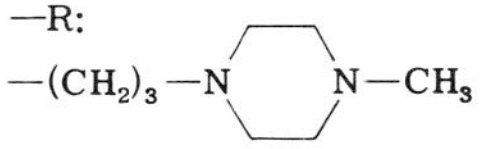 $—(CH_2)_3—N$ (piperazine ring) $N—CH_3$ · methanesulfonate *N*,*N*-Dimethyl-10-[3-(4-methyl-1-piperazinyl) propyl]phenothiazine-2-sulfonamide methanesulfonate	AP; 20–60 mg; 200 mg	
Thioridazin(e)	Mallorol (Sandoz), Malloryl, Meleril, Mellaril (Sandoz), Melleretten (Sandoz), Melleril (Sandoz), Mellerette, TP-21 (Sandoz), tioridazina	—X: $—S—CH_3$ —R: 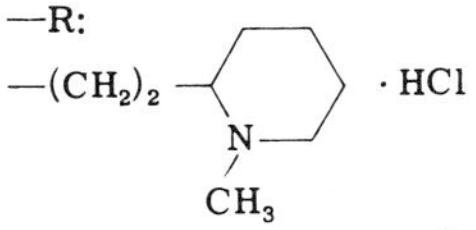 $—(CH_2)_2—$ (piperidine ring, N—CH_3) · HCl 2-Methylmercapto-10-[2-(*N*-methyl-2-piperidyl) ethyl]-phenothiazine hydrochloride	AP; 10–100 mg/ tid or qid; 50–800 mg	Med; ND; PDR; USD
Trifluoperazin(e)	Eskazine, Eskazinyl (SKF), Jatroneural (Rohm & Haas), MC-4703, SKF 5019 (SKF), Stelazine (SKF), Terfluzin(e) (Theraplix), Tranquis, trifluoroperazine, trifluperazin(e), trifluro methylperazine, Trifluzine, Triftazin, Triphthasine, Yatroneural, Triflurin (Maney, Canada), Triftazin (Russian)	—X: $—CF_3$ —R: 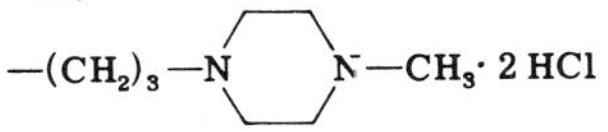 $—(CH_2)_3—N$ (piperazine ring) $N—CH_3 \cdot 2\,HCl$ **10-[3-(4-Methyl-1-piperazinyl)-propyl]-2-(trifluoromethyl)-phenothiazine dihydrochloride**	AP; 2–40 mg; 2–15 mg	Med; ND; PDR; USD

Triflupromazin(e)	Adazine (Upjohn), Esprivex, Flumazin(e), Fluomazina (Savio), Fluopromazine, Fluorofen (Savio), MC 4703 (Squibb), MS 4703, Nivoman (Heyden, Squibb), Psyquel, Psyquil (Heyden), Siquil (Squibb), SKF 4648 (SKF), Syquel, trifluoromethylpromazin(e), Triphentizine, Vespral (Squibb), Veprin (Squibb), Vetame, Visprin, Vespril, Me 4703, Aristofen, Neuro Padil, Plegal, Flurofen	—X: $—CF_3$ —R: $—(CH_2)_3—N(CH_3)_2 \cdot HCl$ 10-[3-(Dimethylamino) propyl]-2-(trifluoromethyl)phenothiazine hydrochloride	AP; 20–150 mg; 5–40 mg/im; 1–8 mg/iv; 100–800 mg; 50–300 mg	ND; PDR; USD
Trimeprazine	Temaril (SKF), methylpromazine, Repeltin (Bayer), Theralen(e) (Leo, Theraplix), alimemazin(e), RP-6549 (Rhone-Poulenc), Panectyl (Rhone-Poulenc), Vallergan (M&B), Teralene (Farmitalia, Rhodia—Brazil), Alimezine (Daichy), SKF 5277 (SKF), Valledrine (M&B), Levopromazine, Theralin (Theraplix), Bayer 1219 (Bayer), Vallergal, Variargyl, Alimenazine, Teralene, Nedeltran, Temaril, Temaryl	—X: —H —R: $—CH_2CH(CH_3)CH_2N(CH_3)_2$ · ½ Tartrate 10-[3-Dimethylamino)-2-methylpropyl] phenothiazine tartrate	AP; 400–600 mg; 50–300 mg; 100–200 mg/im	

Class: Phenothiazine Analogues and Isosteres

Amitriptylin(e)	Adepril, Elavil (Merck), Horizon, Laroxyl (Roche), MK 230, Prohepta-diene (Res. Inst. Prague), Redomex (Labas), Ro 4-1575 (Roche), Saroten (Wm. Warner, Lundbeck), Sarotex (Lundbeck), Seroten, Triptanol, Triptisol (Merck), Tryptanol, Tryptisol (Lundbeck), Tryptizol (Merck), Uxen, amitriptilina, Triptizol, R 8788, Sch 7172, N750, Elatrol (Assia-Zori), Larozyl (Roche, Sweden), damilen(e) (Russian)	$CH—(CH_2)_3—N(CH_3)_2 \cdot HCl$ 5-(3-Dimethylaminopropylidene)-10, 11-dihydro-5*H*-dibenzo[*a*, *d*]-cycloheptatriene hydrochloride	AD; 10–50 mg/bid/po or iv; 20–30 mg/im; 100–300 mg	Med; ND; PDR; USD

Table I (*Continued*)

Compound	Synonyms, Trade Names, Manufacturers	Structure	Psychotropic Action and Dose	Listing
Chlorprothixene	Chlorprotixen, Chlorprotixin, N 714, N 7714, O.C. 1131-1417 (Merck), Quinlan, Quinlun, Ro 4-0403 (Roche) = mix of *cis* and *trans*, Ro 4-0403/4 = *trans*, free base, Ro 4-0403/8 = *trans*, HCl salt, Solatran (Warner), Tactaran, Taractan (Roche), Taractaran, Tarasan (Roche), Tarazan, Truxal (Lundbeck, Tropon), Truxaletten (Tropon), clorprotixene, Trictal	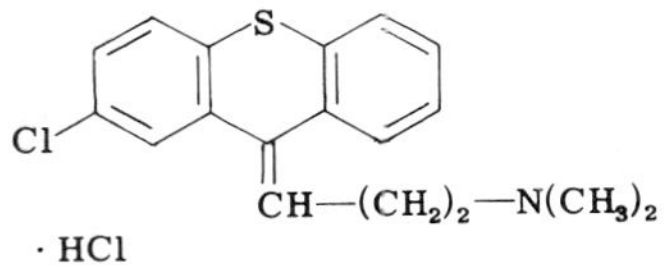 Cl; S; CH—$(CH_2)_2$—$N(CH_3)_2$ · HCl 2-Chloro-9 (3-dimethylamino-propylidene)thioxanthene hydrochloride	AP; 15–30 mg/tid; 30–100 mg/im; 25–300 mg/qid	Med; ND; PDR; USD
Desipramine	Desmethylimipramine, DMI, G-35020 (Geigy), GMI, JB 8181 (Lakeside), norimipramine, Norpramin (Lakeside), Pertofran(e) (Geigy), Pertofrina (Hässle), Ex 4355 (Lakeside), demetilimipramina, Pentrofane, desmetilimipramina	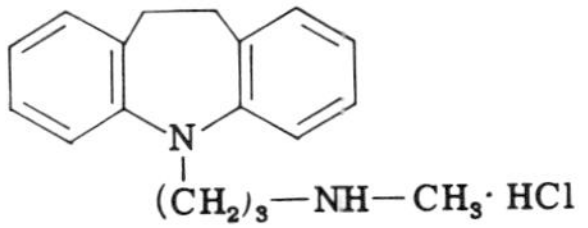 N; $(CH_2)_3$—NH—CH_3· HCl 10, 11-Dihydro-5-(3-methylaminopropyl)-5*H*-dibenz-[*b*, *f*] azepine hydrochloride	AD; 25 mg/tid; 75–200 mg	deH; Med; ND; PDR; USD
Imipramine	Berkomine (Berk), Deprinol, DPID, Eupramin (Jugodijetetika), Irmin, Imizin(e), Melepramin (Ver. Heil), Meliprimin(e) (Egyt), Nelipramin, Promiben, Surplix, Tofranil (Geigy), Iramil (Knoll, Australia), Antideprin (Rumanian), Dynaprin, Timolet	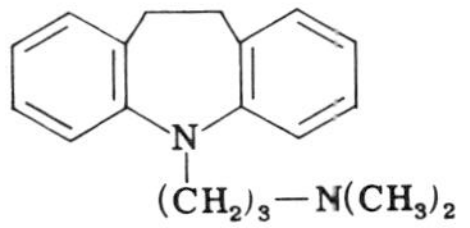 N; $(CH_2)_3$—$N(CH_3)_2$ 5-[3-(Dimethylamino) propyl]-10, 11-dihydro-5*H*-dibenz-[*b*,*f*] azepine	AD; H (at high dose); 100–300 mg/po or im; 100 mg; 30–300 mg	Med; ND; PDR; USD

Nortriptyline	Acetexa (Lilly), Allegron (Dista), Allergon (Dista), desitriptyline, desmethylamitriptyline, Aventyl (Lilly), Arentyl, Lilly 38489 (Lilly), Noritren, Nortrilen (Tropon), Sensival, Vividyl (Lilly-Italy), Norzepine (Bial), L38489, Psychostyl (Lilly-France), nortriptilina, desitriptilina	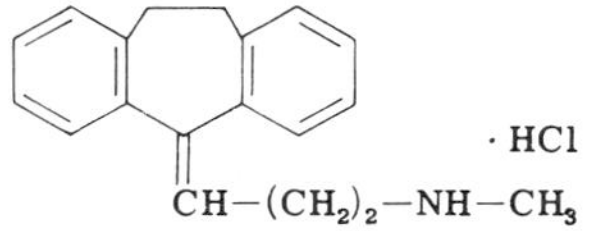 $=CH-(CH_2)_2-NH-CH_3 \cdot HCl$ 5-(3-Methylaminopropylidene)-10,11-dihydro-5*H*-dibenzo-[*a*,*d*]cycloheptene hydrochloride	AD; 20–100 mg; 50–150 mg	deH; Med; ND; PDR; P
Opipramol	Ensidon (Geigy), G33040 (Geigy), piperaziniminostilbene, Insidon (Thomae, Geigy), Nisidana, Dinsidon, RP-8307, Nisidan	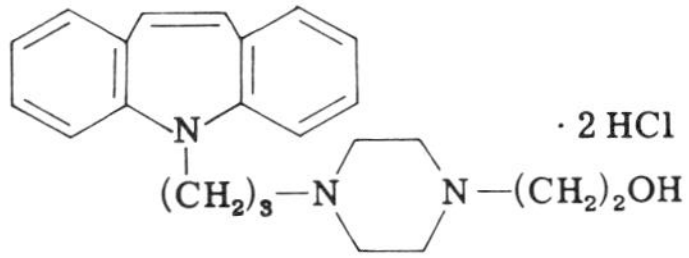 $N-(CH_2)_3-N(piperazine)N-(CH_2)_2OH \cdot 2HCl$ 4-[3-(5*H*-Dibenz[*b*,*f*]azepine-5-yl) propyl]-1-piperazinethanol dihydrochloride	AD	
Thiothixene	P 4657B (Pfizer), Navane (Roerig), tiotixene, thiothixine (*cis* isomer)	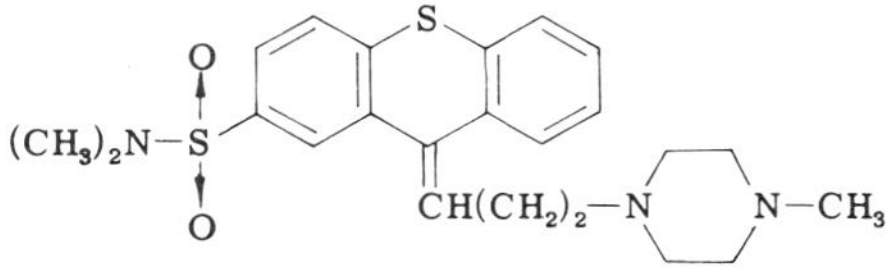 $(CH_3)_2N-SO_2-$; $=CH(CH_2)_2-N(piperazine)N-CH_3$ *N*,*N*-Dimethyl-9-[3-(4-methyl-1-perazinyl)-propylidene]thioxanthene-2-sulfonamide	AP; 3–20 mg	Med; PDR; USD
Trimepramine	Trimiprimine, trimeprimine, RP 7162 (Rhone-Poulenc), Surmontil (Rhone-Poulenc, M&B), FI 6120 (Farmitalia), trimeproprimine, IC 6001 (Ives), IL 6001 (Ives), trimipromine, Stangyl, trimepropimine, trimipramine	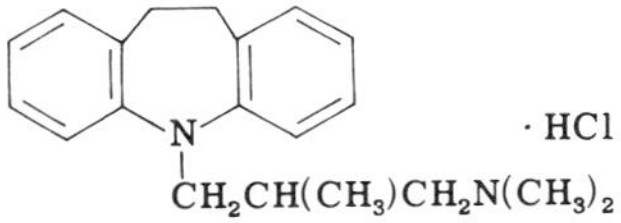 $N-CH_2CH(CH_3)CH_2N(CH_3)_2 \cdot HCl$ 1-(3-Dimethylamino-2-methyl-propyl)-10,11-dihydro-5*H*-dibenz[*b*,*f*]azepine hydrochloride	AP; 30–300 mg	PDR; USD

Table I (*Continued*)
CLASS: RESERPINE AND DERIVATIVES

X N H N $CH_3O—C(=O)$ A OCH_3

Compound	Synonyms, Trade Names, Manufacturers	Structure	Psychotropic Action and Dose	Listing
Deserpidine	A-11025, Canescine (Penick), dereserpine, desmethoxyreserpine, Harmonyl (Abbott), Lilly 22641 (Lilly), Raunormine, recanescine	—X: —H —A: —O—C(=O)— [3,4,5-(OCH_3)₃-phenyl] 11-Desmethoxyreserpine	AP; 0.5–3 mg; 0.25 mg/tid or qid	Med; PDR; USD
Rescinnamine	Anapral, Anaprel (Servier), Moderil (Pfizer), Raupyrol (Schweizerhalle), Raurescin(e) (Columbus), Recitensina (Sclavo), Rescaloid (Hässle), Rescamin, Rescidan, Rescisan (Pharmacia), Reserpinine, Resipal, Tenamine (Hiss), Normorescina, Rescin, Rescinpal, Rescitens, Scinnamina, Tuareg	—X: —OCH_3 —A: —O—C(=O)—CH=CH— [3,4,5-(OCH_3)₃-phenyl] 3,4,5-Trimethoxycinnamoyl-methyl reserpate	AP; 0.25–1.0 mg; 5–15 mg/im; 0.5–2 mg	PDR; USD

Reserpine	Alserin, Anquil, Apoplon, Ascoserpina, Banasil (Ulmer), Benazyl, Bioserpine, Crystoserpine (Smith-Dorsey), Cystoserpine, Elserpine (Canright), Escasper(e), Eskaserp (SKF), H520, Helfoserpin, Interpina, Key-Serpine (Key), Kitine (Superior), Lemiserp (Lemmon), Loweserp (Lowe), Neo-Antitensol, Purserpin, Quiescin (Organon), Raucap (Ethical), Raugal, Raudiford (Squibb), Raulen (Maney), Rauloydin (Tutag), Raumorin(e), Raunova, Raupoid, Raurine (LDW), Rausan, Raused (Squibb), Rausedan, Rausedyl, Rauserpol (Bika), Rausingle (Columbus), Rautrin, Rauvilid, Rauwipur, Rauwoleaf, Rawilid, Reserbal (Richter), Reserlor (Taylor), Resercen (Central), Rauserpine, Reserp, Reserpamed, Reserpene, Reserpex (ICP), Reserpil, Reserperin, Reserpina, Reserpinum, Reserpoid (Upjohn), Reserpur, Rezerpin, Residin(e), Resine (Kirkman), Respital (Premo), Restran (Cole), Riserpa, Rivasin (Guilini), Roxel, Roxinoid (Merck), Roxynoid, Sandril (Lilly), Sandron, Sedaraupin(a) (Böhringer), Sederaupin, Serfin (Parke-Davis), Seripur, Serolfia (Ascher), Serpalan (Lannett), Serpanray (Panray), Serpasil (Ciba), Serpasol, Serpate (Vale), Serpazil,	—X: $—OCH_3$ —A: $—O—C(=O)—C_6H_2(OCH_3)_3$ (3,4,5-trimethoxyphenyl) Methyl-18-*O*-(3, 4, 5-trimethoxybenzoyl) reserpate	AP; 1–5 mg; 3–9 mg; 0.1–2.0 mg; 2.5–5.0 mg/im; 3–9 mg	Med; PDR; USP; USD; P

Table I (*Continued*)

Compound	Synonyms, Trade Names, Manufacturers	Structure	Psychotropic Action and Dose	Listing
	Serpazol, Serpen (Haag), Serpena, Serpentil, Serpentin(a), Serpicon (CMC), Serpil, Serpiloid (Riker), Serpine (Pit.-Moore, Rowell), Serpivate, Serpivite, Serpoid (Canfield), Sertabs (Tablerock), Sertina (Testagar), Temposerpine (Lepetit), Tenserpin, Unilord (Taylor), Vio-Serpine (Rowell), Austrapine (CSL), Rivased, Tempo-Reserpina, Serfolia	(See page 209)		
CLASS: BENZODIAZEPINES				
Chlordiazepoxide	Contol, Decacil, Equibral (Ravizza), Librium (Roche), metaminodiazepossido, methaminodiazepoxide, Novosed (Neo Bologna), Psichial (Lang), Reliberan (Geymonat), Reposal, Rilax (Hanover), Ro 5-0690 (Roche), Seren Vita, Sonia (Simes), T112L, Viansin (Farmacosmici), Libritabs (Roche), Timosin (VEB), Droxal (Bernabo), Lentotran (Patria), Napoton (Terapia), elenium (Polish), clordiazepossido, Ansiacal, Bent, Benzodiapin, Cebrum, Endequil, Kalmocaps, Labican, Lixin, Mildmen, Psicofar, Psicosan, Psicoterina, Smail, Viopsicol	Cl; N; NH—CH_3; N; O; C_6H_5; · HCl 3*H*-1,4-Benzodiazepine-7-chloro-2-(methylamino)-5-phenyl-4-oxide hydrochloride	AA; 5–20 mg/ tid or qid; 50–100 mg/ iv/tid or qid	Med; ND; PDR; USD

Diazepam	Apaurin (Krka), La III (Roche), Horizon (Yamanouchi), Ro 5-2807 (Roche), Valium (Roche), WY-3467, Vival (Apothekernes), Cercine (Takeda), Apozepam (Apothekernes), Vatran (Valeas), Sonacon (Chugai)	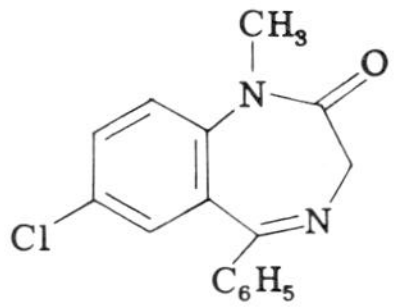 7-Chloro-1, 3-dihydro-1-methyl-5-phenyl-2*H*-1, 4-benzodiazepin-2-one	AA; 2–10 mg/ tid or qid; 6–30 mg; 6–60 mg	Med; ND; PDR; USD; P
Oxazepam	8092 CB, Rondar (Wyeth), Serax (Wyeth), Serenid-D (Wyeth), Seresta (Wyeth), WY-3498 (Wyeth), Propax (Cipan), Aplakil (Aristegui), Adumbran (Thomae; Boehringer), Ansiolisina (Effepi), Praxiten (Wyeth-Germany), Serpax (Wyeth-Italy), Limbial (Chiesi), Z 10-TR	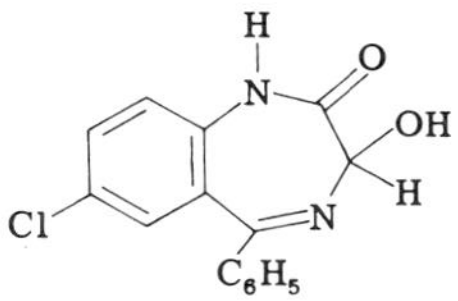 7-Chloro-1, 3-dihydro-3-hydroxy-5-phenyl-2*H*-1, 4-benzodiazepine-2-one	AA; 10–30 mg/ tid or qid	deH; Med; ND; PDR; USD
CLASS: OTHER HETEROCYCLIC COMPOUNDS				
Azacyclonol	Ataractan, Calmeran, Frenoton, Frenquel (Merrell), Frequel, Mer 17 (Merrell), Phrenoton, γ-pipradol, Psychosan	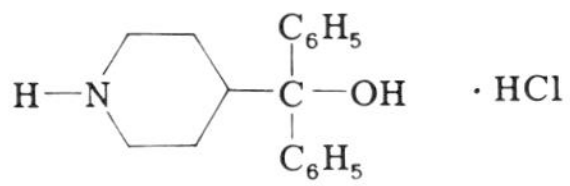 α, α-Diphenyl-4-piperidine-methanol hydrochloride	AA; anti-H; no effect; 20–800 mg; 100 mg/iv/ 6x/day	PDR; USD; (anti-H)

Table I (*Continued*)

Compound	Synonyms, Trade Names, Manufacturers	Structure	Psychotropic Action and Dose	Listing
Buclizine	Aphilanor (Ucepha), Buclizinum (NFN), Histabutazine (DCI), Histabutyzine (DCF), Longifen(e) (UCB), Neo-Istafene (UCB), Postafen(e), Retamin(e) (NDKF), Softran (Stuart), Stopcold-N (UCB), UCB 197 (UCB), UCB 4445 (UCB), Vibazin(e) (Pfizer)	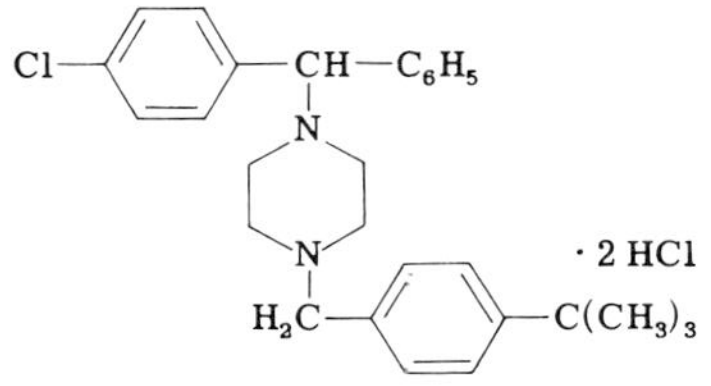 1-(*p*-*tert*-Butylbenzyl)-4-(*p*-chloro-α-phenylbenzyl)piperazine dihydrochloride	AA; 50–150 mg; 10–100 mg	ND; (weak AA)
Chlormezanon(e)	Banabin, chlormethazon(e), chlormethazanon(e), Fenarol, Rilaquil (Guidotti), Trancopal (Sterl.-Win., Bayer), WIN 4692 (Sterl.-Win.), Clorilax (Drumond), clormetazanone, Bisina, Miorilax, Mio-Sed, Rexan, Rillasol, Rilax, Tanafol, Tiazanone	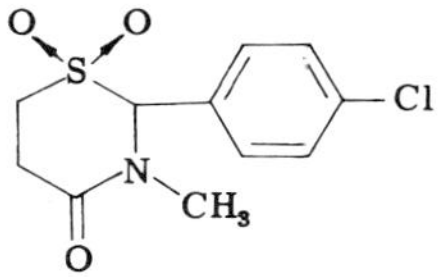 4*H*-1,3-Thiazin-4-one, 2-(*p*-chlorophenyl) tetrahydro-3-methyl-1,1-dioxide	AA; 100–200 mg/tid or qid; 600–800 mg	Med; ND; PDR; USD
Dehydrobenzperidol	Dridol (Leo), Deidrobenzperidolo, Innovar-Vet, R 4749 (Janssen), Droperidol (Ortho), Thalamonal (Werfft, Janssen, Orion), R 4910 (oxalate), R 6400 (succinate), R 7481 (HCl) (Janssen), Innovar (McNeil), Vetkalm (Impfstoffe), Leptofen (Erba), Inappin (Oryx), (Lind. and Riemer), Droleptan (Le Brun), Inapsin, Innovan (Johnson & Johnson), Inoval (Johnson & Johnson), Leptunal (Leo), Depridol	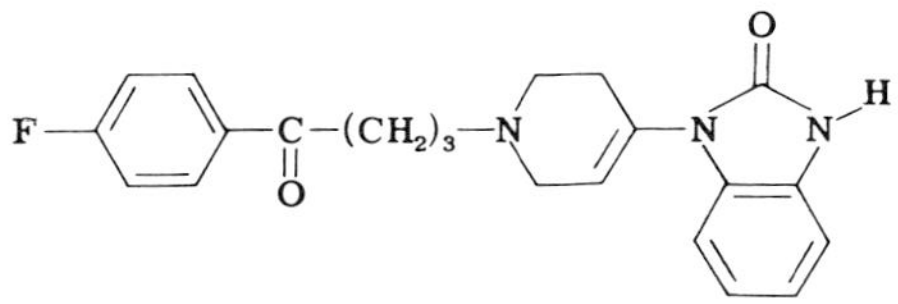 1-{1-[3-(*p*-Fluorobenzoyl)propyl]-1,2,3,6-tetrahydro-4-pyridyl}-2-benzimidazolinone	AA; 5–50 mg	

Ditran	JB-329 (Lakeside)	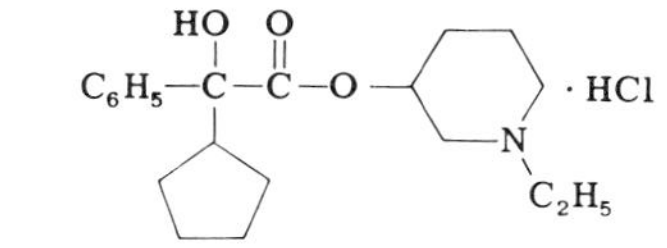 and 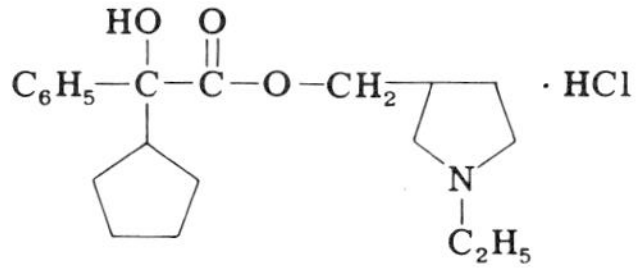 *N*-Ethyl-2-pyrrolidylmethylphenylcyclopentyl glycolate hydrochloride and *N*-ethyl-3-piperidyl phenylcyclopentyl glycolate hydrochloride	H; 5–10 mg; 15 mg	
Glutethimide	Doriden(e) (Ciba), Elrodorm, Ondasil, C 11511, Gimid, Glutäthimid, glutetimide, Noxyron, Sarodormin	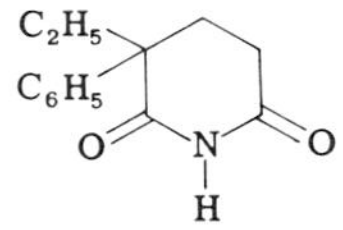 2-Ethyl-2-phenylglutarimide	AA; 250 mg/tid; 375–750 mg	
Haloperidol	R 1625 (Janssen), Halopoidol, Serenelfi (Janssen), Serenase (Janssen, Lind. Riemer, Orion, I.L.F.I., A.C.F.), Serenace (Searle), Aloperidin (Janssen), Halopidol (Johnson & Johnson), Vesalium (Janssen, Orion) Halol, Aloperidon, R 1630 = HCl (Janssen), R 2401 = oxalate (Janssen), R 2420 = HBr (Janssen),	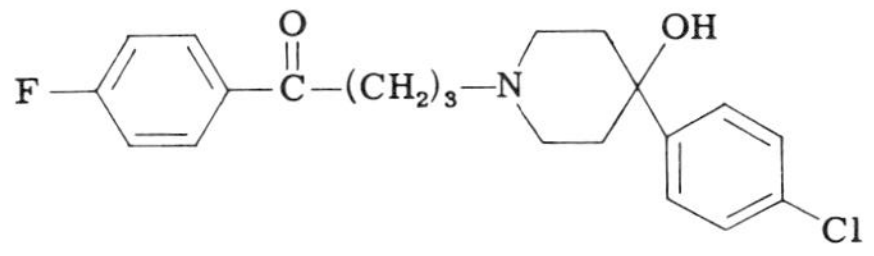 4′-Fluoro-4-{1-[4-hydroxy-4-(4′-chloro)-phenylpiperidino]}butyrophenone	AP; 0.5–7.5 mg; 3–9 mg	

Table I (*Continued*)

Compound	Synonyms, Trade Names, Manufacturers	Structure	Psychotropic Action and Dose	Listing
	R 2429 = sulfate (Janssen), R 2171 = cyclohexane sulfamate (Janssen), (Werfft, Leo, ACF, I.F.L.), Haldol (Janssen, McNeil, Leo), Aldol, Sernel (Portugal), Sernàs, Galoperidol (Russian), aloperidolo, Halopal (Johnson & Johnson-Argentina), Pernox (U.V.A.), Ukolind (Lindopharm)	(See page 213)		
Harmaline	(Penick)	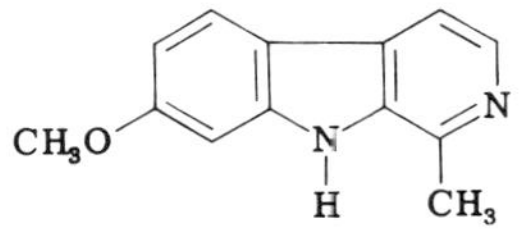 CH_3O, N, H, CH_3, N 4, 9-Dihydro-7-methoxy-1-methyl-3*H*-pyrido-[3, 4-*b*]-indole (Penick)	H	
Harmine	Banisterine (Penick), yageine, telepathine, leucoharmine, (Pitman-Moore)	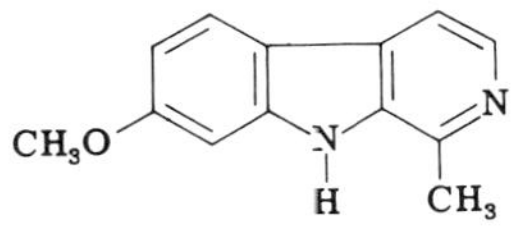 CH_3O, N, H, CH_3, N 7-Methoxy-1-methyl-9*H*-pyrido[3, 4-*b*]indole	H; 150–250 mg/iv	

Hydroxyzin(e)	Atara, Atarax (Pfizer, Harvey, UCB), Ataraxoid (Pfizer), Atarazoid, Aterax (UCB), Hychotine (Ucepha), hydroxine, Idrossizina, Masmoran (Pfizer), Neo-Calma (Chimoin), NP 212, Pamozine, Parenteral, Paxistil (Pfizer), Placidol, Plaxidol, Tran-Q, Traquizine (Pfizer), U.C.B. 4492 (UCB), Vistaril (Pfizer, Hausman), Neurozina, Fenarol, Equipoise (Pfizer, England), Atazina, Deinait	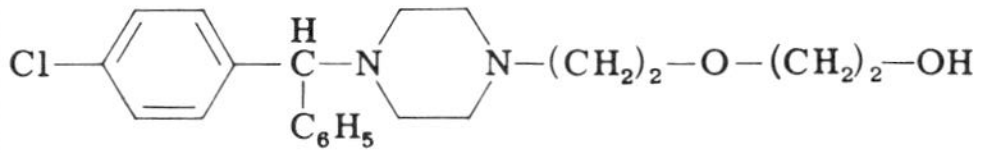 2-{2-[4-(*p*-Chloro-α-phenylbenzyl)-1-piperazinyl]-ethoxy}ethanol	AA; 50–200 mg; 25–100 mg/bid or tid; 20–100 mg/im; 50–75 mg/iv; 30–400 mg; 20–100 mg/tid	Med; ND; PDR; USD
Iproniazid	Marsilid (Roche), Iprazid, Ipronid, Marsalid, IIH, Ro 2-4572 (Roche), Rivivol (Zambeletti), Ipronin	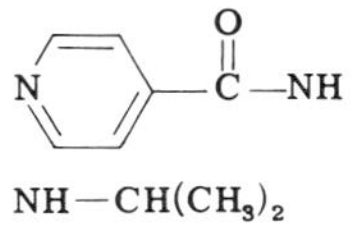 1-Isonicotinyl-2-isopropylhydrazine	AD; 50–150 mg; 10–50 mg	
Isocarboxazide	Benazid, BMIH, Enerzer, Maraplan, Marplan (Roche), Marplon, Ro 0831/1 (Roche), Ro 2-3773, Ro 5-0831/1, Isocarbossazide	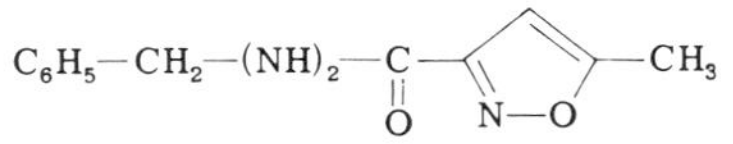 1-Benzyl-2-(5-methyl-3-isooxazolyl-carbonyl) hydrazine	AD; 10–30 mg; 75 mg; 30–90 mg	PDR; USD; P
Lysergic acid diethylamide	Delysid (Sandoz), LSD-25, lysergide, Lysergamid (Spofa)	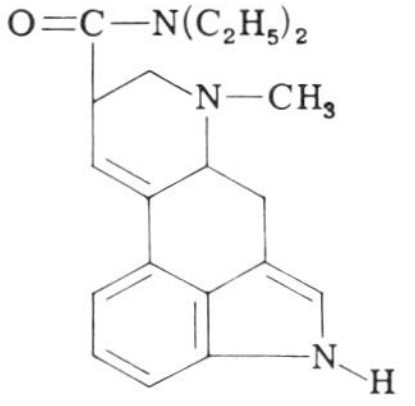 *N*, *N*-Diethyllysergamide	H; 0.025–0.075 mg/po, im, or iv	

Table I (*Continued*)

Compound	Synonyms, Trade Names, Manufacturers	Structure	Psychotropic Action and Dose	Listing
Meclizine	Navicalm (Squibb, UCB), Itinerol (Galencia), Bonine (Pfizer), Postafen(e) (UCB, Pfizer), Bonadoxin (Pfizer), Meclozine (D.C.I.), Histamethizine (DCF), Ancolon (BDH), Sea-Legs (BDH), Siguran, Subari, Suprimal (ACF), Monamin(e) (Nordisk-Droge), Travelon (ACF), Histamethine, Histametizyn, Neo-Istafene, Neo-Suprimel, Parachloramine, Peremesin, Sabari (Lori), UCB 5062 (UCB), Vomisseis (ILF), Ancolan, Bonamine (Pfizer), Chiclida (Torrents), Histametizine (DCF), UCB 170 (UCB), Bonadettes (Pfizer), Neo-Suprimal, Calmonal (Heyden), meclozine	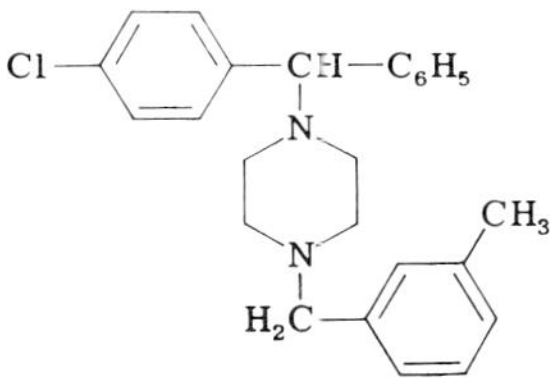 1-(*p*-Chloro-α-phenylbenzyl)-4-(*m*-methylbenzyl) piperazine	AA	
Mephenoxalone	AHR-233 (Robins), Control, Dorsiflex (Medial), Ekilan (Szabo), Lenetran (Lakeside), Methoxydone (Robins), Metoxadone, Moderamin (OM), Oxazolidinone, Placidex (Toraude), OM-518 (OM, Lakeside), Repoise, Szabo Tranquilizers (Szabo), Trepidone (Lederle), mefenoxalone, Valans, Tranpoise	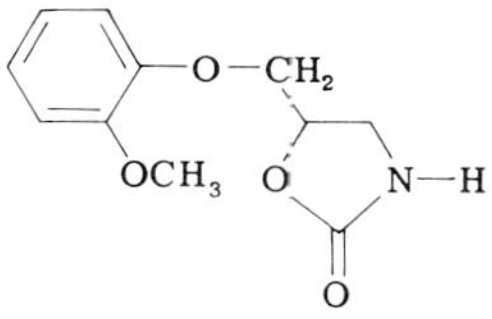 5-(*o*-Methoxyphenoxymethyl)-2-oxazolidinone	AA; 400 mg/qid; 800–1600 mg	ND; USD

Methylphenidate	C 43-IIC, Centedrin(e), 4311/b Ciba (Ciba), Meridil, Phenidylate, Rilatin, Ritalin(e) (Ciba), Ritalina, metilfenidato, fenilidato, fenidilato, methyl phenidylacetate, C-4311/b	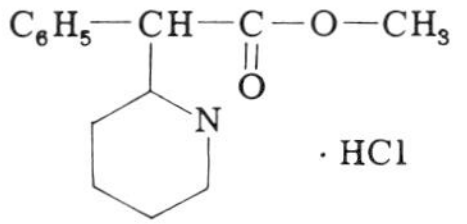 $C_6H_5-CH(C_5H_9NH)-C(=O)-O-CH_3 \cdot HCl$ Methyl α-phenyl-2-piperidine-acetate hydrochloride	S; 10–60 mg; 10–20 mg/bid or tid; 10–50 mg/iv, im, or sc; 60–160 mg; 5–15 mg	Med; ND; PDR; USD; P
Methyprylon	Noludar (Roche), Noctan, Dimerin, Nodular, Ro 1-6463 (Roche), metiprilone	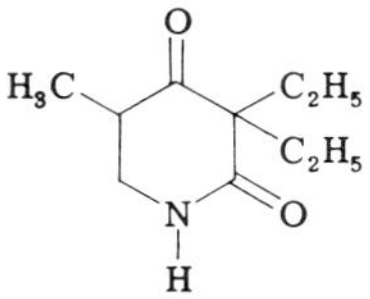 3,3-Diethyl-5-methyl-2,4-piperidinedione	AA; 200–400 mg	
Modaline Sulfate	W 3207 (Warner)	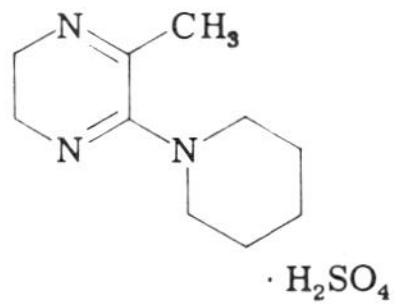 $\cdot H_2SO_4$ 2-Methyl-3-piperidinopyrazine hydrogen sulfate	AD; 15 mg; 60 mg	
Nialamide	Espril (Saba), Niamid(e) (Pfizer, Harvey), Nuredal, Nyazin (Galenika), P 1133, Surgex (Firma), BEIH, Delmoneurina, Isalizina, Mygal, Niaquitil, Psicodisten	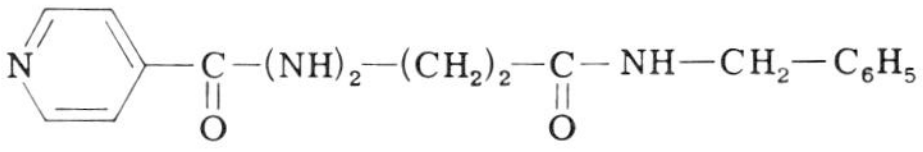 $C_5H_4N-C(=O)-(NH)_2-(CH_2)_2-C(=O)-NH-CH_2-C_6H_5$ 2-[2-(Benzylcarbamyl) ethyl]hydrazide isonicotinic acid	AD; 75–100 mg; 25–150 mg; 75–500 mg	Med; ND; PDR; USP; USD; P

Table I (*Continued*)

Compound	Synonyms, Trade Names, Manufacturers	Structure	Psychotropic Action and Dose	Listing
Oxanamide	Quiactin (Merrell)	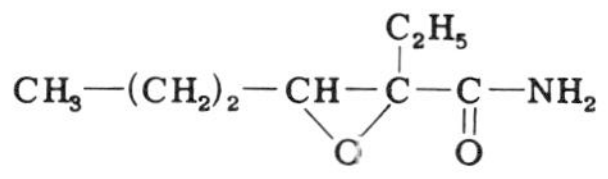 $CH_3-(CH_2)_2-CH-C(C_2H_5)-C(=O)-NH_2$ (epoxide O bridging CH–C) 2, 3-Epoxy-2-ethylhexanamide	AA; 1600 mg; 400–1600 mg	ND; PDR; USD
Pemoline	Kethamed (Medo-Chem.), Stimul (Pharmacia, Kingshill), PIO (Pharmacia), Hyton (Pharmacia), Volital (Labs for Applied Biology, London), P 10 (Japanese), FWH-352, Deltamine (Aron), LA 956 (Aron), CS-293, H 3104, A-13397 (Abbott), Myamin (Dainippon), phenyliso-hydantoin, PT 360, Ronyl (Rona), Tradon (Beiersdorf), Dantromin (Organica), Azoksodon (USSR), pomolin(e), phenoxazol(e), phenyl-pseudohydantoin, Pondex, PW/135, Pioxol, Azoxodon (Russian), Sigmadyn, F.I.O., Yhl, fenoxazol	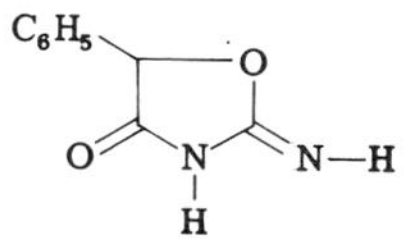 C_6H_5; O; N–H; N; H; O 5-Phenyl-2-imino-4-oxo-oxazolidine	S; 10 mg; 20–40 mg	
Phencyclidine	Sernyl (Parke-Davis), PCP, CI 395 (Parke-Davis), Sernylan (Parke-Davis)	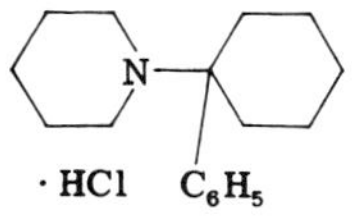 N; $\cdot$HCl C_6H_5 1-(1-Phenylcyclohexyl)-piperidine hydrochloride	H; 5–10 mg/bid	

Phenmetrazine	Preludin (Geigy, Böhringer), Psychamine A, Antapentan, McN-R-747-11, A 66, Anorex, Anoran, Cafilon, Delgacerol, Fenmetrazin, Minadit, Oxazimerdine, Phenmetralinum, R 381–382.	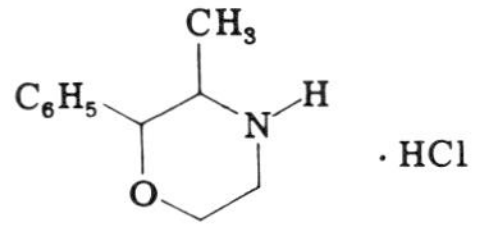 3-Methyl-2-phenylmorpholine hydrochloride	S; 12.5–25 mg/ bid or tid	
Phenytoin	Diphenylhydantoin, Alepsin, Aleviatin, Antilepsin, Anti-sacer, Auranile, Causoin, Citrullamon, Citrulliamon, Comital, Denyl, Difenin, Difhydan, Di-hydan, Dihydantoin, Dilantin (Parke-Davis), Dillantin, Dintoin, Dintoina, Diphantoine, Diphedal, Diphedan, Diphenin, Diphentoin (Massengill), Diphenylan, Epamin, Epanutin, Epelin, Epifenyl, Convul (Foy), Dilantin Sod. (Parke-Davis), Diphenylan Sod. (Lannett), Epilan, Epilantin, Epinat, Eptal, Eptoin, Fenantoin, Fenitoina, Fentoin, Fenytöine, Gerot-Epilan-D, Hindatal, Hidantina, Hydantal, Hydantin, Hydantoin, Hydantoinal, Idantoil, Idantoin, Lepitoin, Minetoin, Neoshidantoina, om-Hydantoine, Oxylan, Phanatine, Phenatoin(e), Silantin, Sodantoin, Sodanton, Solantin, Solantoin, Toin, Solantyl, Tacosal, Zentropil, Comitoina, Dihydan soluble, Diphenylhydantoin sodium, Silantin Sod., Denyl Sod., Phenytoin Soluble, Dihycon (CMC), Hidantal, Sanepil	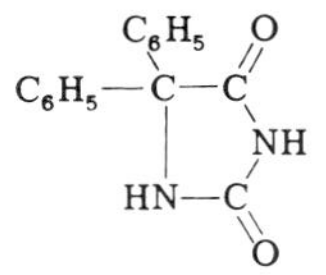 5,5-Diphenylhydantoin	AA; 100–600 mg	

Table I (*Continued*)

Compound	Synonyms, Trade Names, Manufacturers	Structure	Psychotropic Action and Dose	Listing
Pipradrol	Alertol, CP, Dol, Gadexyl, Gerodyl (Gea), Leptidrol (Kabi), Luxidine (Pierrel), Meratran (Merrell), Meretran, MRD-108, MRE 108, PBH, pipradol, Pipral, Piridrol, Metadin (Euro), Detaril	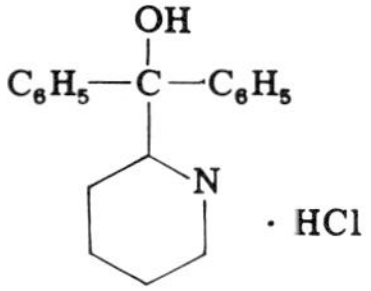 OH; C_6H_5—C—C_6H_5; N; · HCl **α, α-Diphenyl-2-piperidine methanol hydrochloride**	S; 7.5 mg; 3–7.5 mg; 1 mg/bid–2 mg/tid	ND; USD
Triperidol	R 2498 (Janssen), R 3000—free base (Janssen), trifluperidol, Psicoperidol (Lind. & Reimer), (I.L.F.I.), McN-JR-2498 (McNeil), (Le Brun), (Yoshitomi), (I.F.L.), (Oryx), flumoperone, Psychoperidol (Andrews)	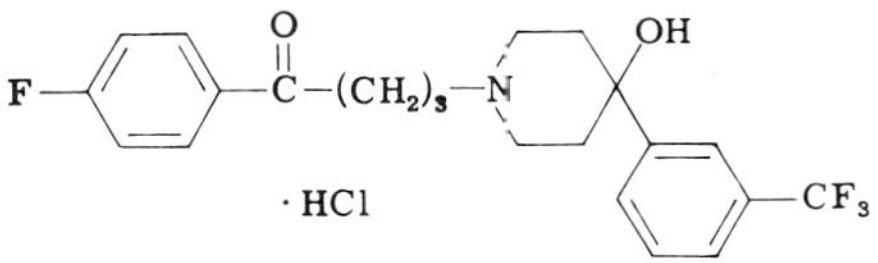 F; O; C—$(CH_2)_3$—N; OH; CF_3; · HCl 4′-Fluoro-4-[4-hydroxy-4-(3′-trifluoromethyl-phenyl)piperidine]butyrophenone hydrochloride	AP; 5 mg/iv; 2.5–5 mg/po	

CLASS: PHENYLETHYLAMINE DERIVATIVES

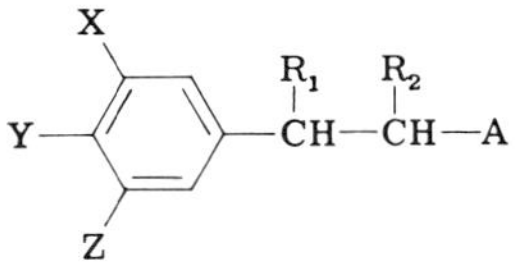

X; Y; Z; R_1; R_2; —CH—CH—A

Compound	Synonyms, Trade Names, Manufacturers	Structure	Psychotropic Action and Dose	Listing
Amphetamine phosphate	Actemin, Aktedron (Chimoin), Dynaphenil, Monophos, Racephen, Raphetamine phosphate (Stras)	—X: —H —Y: —H —Z: —H —R_1: —H —R_2: —CH_3 —A: —NH_2 · H_3PO_4 α-Methylphenethylamine phosphate	S; 25–50 mg	ND; USD

Amphetamine sulfate	Acetdron, Adipan, Adiparthrol (Medial), Aketdrin, Alentol, Allodene, Amfetamine, Amphamed, Amphatamin, Amphate, Amphetaminum, Amphezamin, Ampohoids-S, Anara, Anfetamina, Astedin, Benzafinyl, Benzamphetamine, Benzebar, Benzedrina, Benzedrin(e) (SKF), Benzedryna, Benzpropamine, Betafen, Betaphen, Bluzedrin, Centramina, Deoxynorephedrin, Didrex, Dietamine, Durophet, Elastonin, Euphobine, Euphodine, Euphodyn, Fabedrine, Fenamin, Fenara, Fenopromin, Halloo-Wach, Ibiozedrine, Isamin, Isoamin, Isoamyn(e), Isomyn, Leodrin, Levonor, Linampheta, Mecodrin, Mimetina, Monetamine, Noclon, Noirydrine, Norephedrane, Oktedrin, Oraldrina, Ortedrine, Ortenal, Orthedrin, Percomon, Pharmamedrine, Phenamin(e), Phenedrin(e) (Specia), Profamina, Profetamine, Propenyl, Propisamine, Psychedrine, Psychedrinum, Psychedrina, Psychoton, Raphetamine, Rhinalator, Sedolin, Simpamina, Simpamine, Simpatedrin, Stimulan, Symatedrine, Sympametin, Sympatedrine, Theptine, Vapedrine, Zedrin	—X: —H —Y: —H —Z: —H —R_1: —H —R_2: —CH_3 —A: —NH_2 · H_2SO_4 **α-Methylphenethylamine sulfate**	S; H on repeated doses; 5–40 mg; 10–20 mg/im or iv	Med; ND; PDR; USP; USD

Table I (*Continued*)

Compound	Synonyms, Trade Names, Manufacturers	Structure	Psychotropic Action and Dose	Listing
D-Amphetamine sulfate	Actedron, Adjudets, Adrizine, Afatin, Afettine, Albemap, Am-Dex, d-Amfetasul (Pit.-Moore), Amitrene, Amphedrin(e) (Van Pelt & Brown), Ampherex, Amphex, Amsustain (Key), D-Ate, Betafedrina, d-Betaphedrine, Carrtime, D-Citramine, Dadex, DAS, Dephadron, Desoxyn, Dexaline, Dexalme, Dexalone, Deamed (Medo-Chem), Dexamphetamine, Dexedrina, Dexedrine (SKF), Dexoval, Dex-Sule, Dexten, Dextenal, Dextroamphetamine, Dextroanfetamina, Dextro-Profetamine, Dextrosule, Diocurb, Domafate, Dynaphenyl, Elastonon (Nordmark), Ephadren, Evrodex, Hetamine, Lentanet, Maxiton, Obesedrin, Obesonil, Pellcaps, Phenpromin, Phetadex, Proptan(e), Psychodrine, Revidex, Sympamin, Sympamina-D, Synatan, Tanphetamine, Tempodex, Zamine	D-α-Methylphenethylamine sulfate	S; 5–50 mg	USD
Methamphetamine	A 884, Adipex, Amedrine, Amphedroxyn (Lilly), Apamine, Corvitin, Daropervamin, Deofed, Depoxin, Desamin(e), Desfedran, Desoxedrine, Desoxo-5, desoxyephedrin(e), Desoxyfed, Desoxyn(e) (Abbott), Desoxyphed, Destim, Desyphed (Sterl. Win.), Desyphen, Detrex, Dexophrine, Dexosyn, Dexoval (Vale), Dexstim, Dextim, DOE	—X: —H —Y: —H —Z: —H —R_1: —H —R_2: —CH_3 —A: —NH—CH_3 ·HCl *N*, α-Dimethyl phenethylamine hydrochloride	S; H (at large iv dose); 2.5–5 mg/bid or tid; 10–15 mg/iv/bid; 15–30 mg/im/bid; 2.5–10 mg; (for H: 40–60 mg/iv)	Med; ND; PDR; USP; USD

	(Breon), Doxephin, Doxyfed (Raymer), Drinalfa (Squibb), Effroxine, Efroxine (Maltbie), Erba, Estimulex, Eufodrin, Eufodrinal, Euphodrinal, Gerobit, Gerovit, Hiropon, Isophan, Isophen (Knoll), Kemodrin, Lanazine, Metamine, Metamfetamina, Metamsustac (Pharmax), Methamphin, Methedrinal, Methedrine (Bur. Wel.), Methoxyn, methylamphetamine, methylbenzedrin, Methylisamin, Methylisomin, Methylisomyn, Methylpropamine, Miller-Drine, Neodrin, Neopharmedrine, Noradrin, Normadrine, Norodrin (Endo), Norodrin, Oxydess, Oxydrene, Oxydrin, Oxyfed, Pervitin (SKF, Temmler, Zilliken), Phedoxe, Phedrisox, Philopon, Pisichergina, Premodrin, Psiquergina, Psychergine, Psykoton, Semoxydrine (Massengill), Soxysympamine, Stimdex, Syndrox (McNeil), Tonedrin, Tonedrone, Vonedrin(e), Madrine (Langley), metamfetamina, desossiefedrina, Psichergina	(See page 222)		
Phenelzine	Alacine, Alazine, Cavodil, EP 411, Fenelzina, Kalgan, Monofen, Monophen, Monoten, Nardelzine (Warner), Nardil (Warner), Phelazin, Phenaline (Substantia), Phenelzin, Phenalzine, S 1544, Stinerval (Wander), W-1544A, Phenodyne (Assia-Zori), fenizin, MAO-Rem	—X: —H —Y: —H —Z: —H $—R_1$: —H $—R_2$: —H —A: —NH—NH_2 · H_2SO_4 **Phenethylhydrazine sulfate**	AD; 20–75 mg; 45–90 mg; 15 mg/tid or qid; 45–150 mg	deH; Med; ND; PDR; USD; P

Table I (*Continued*)

Compound	Synonyms, Trade Names, Manufacturers	Structure	Psychotropic Action and Dose	Listing
Pheniprazine	Catron (Lakeside), Cavodil (Benger), PIH, Catroniazid(e) (Lakeside), RUN, phenylisopropylhydrazine, Catran, Catrol, Katroniazid, Katroniz, β-phenylisopropyl hydrazine, JB 516, Katron, Phenizin, Miral, Castron, Phenazine, Psicosten, feniprazina, fenilisopropilidrazina	C_6H_5—CH_2—CH(CH_3)—NH—NH_2 (α-Methylphenethyl) hydrazine	AD; 3–12 mg	
Tranylcypromine	Parnate (SKF), Parstelin, SKF 385 (SKF), Transamine, Tylciprine (Theraplix), tranilcipromina, trancylpromine	—X: —H —Y: —H —Z: —H —R_1: —CH_2: —R_2 —A: —NH_2 ½ H_2SO_4 2-Phenylcyclopropylamine sulfate	AD; 20–30 mg; 20–40 mg; 10–60 mg	Med; ND; PDR; USD

CLASS: OTHER AROMATIC COMPOUNDS

Compound	Synonyms, Trade Names, Manufacturers	Structure	Psychotropic Action and Dose	Listing
Benactyzine	A 4540-1-1, Actozine (Maney), Aktozin, Amisil, Amitacon, Amitakon, Amizil, Amizyl, Amyxil, Amyzil, Arcadin (Boots), AY-5406-1 (Ayerst), Beatilin, Beatilina (Maggioni), Benacticina, Benactizina, Benactizinum, Benactina, Benactyne, Bensytyl, Cafron (Camden), Cedad (Recordati), Cevanol (ICI), Destendo, Diazil, Diphemin, Fobex, Gevanol, Ibiotyzil, Lucidil (Smith & Nephew), Lucidyl, Nervacton, Nervatil,	$(C_6H_5)_2$—C(OH)—C(=O)—O—$(CH_2)_2$—$N(C_2H_5)_2$ · HCl β-Diethylaminoethylbenzilate hydrochloride	AA; H, at high dose; 1–3 mg/tid; 40–200 mg	ND; USD

	Neuractil, Neurobenzile, Neurolepton, Nutinal (Boots), Parasan (Medicinalco), Paratil, Parazan, Parpon, Phobex (LDW), Phoebex, Procalm, Savitil, Stoikon, Suavetil, Suavitil (MSD, Schweizerhalle, Glaxo), Suavtil, Surfen, Svavitil, Tranquillactine (Labater), Tranquilline, Valladan, Win 5606, Ester 22, Sedansina, Finalin	(See page 224)		
Captodiame	Suvren (Ayerst), Covatix (Gödecke), (Lundbeck), captodiamine, Covatin(e) (Lundbeck, Warner), Covatrix, N 68, AY 55074 (Ayerst), captadiamine, captodramin, Covantix (Germany), Covantine (Austria, Norway, France), Souvrain, Vovatine (Bailly)	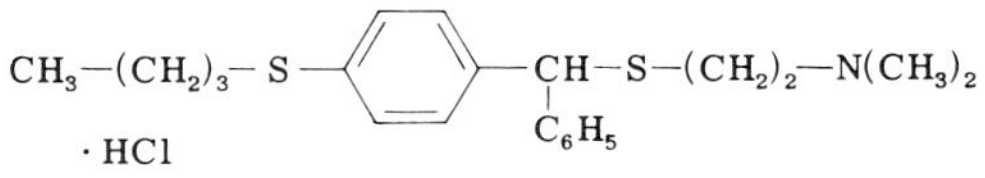 $CH_3-(CH_2)_3-S-C_6H_4-CH(C_6H_5)-S-(CH_2)_2-N(CH_3)_2 \cdot HCl$ 2{[*p*-Butylthio)-α-phenylbenzyl]thio}-*N*,*N*-dimethylethylamine hydrochloride	AA; 100 mg/ tid-qid	
Deanol	Atrol, Bitonal (Ind. Gal.), Cy-37 (Choay), Deaner (Riker), Dianol, Dienol, Dimethaen, Pabenol (Gentili), Recrein, Stimulest, DMAE	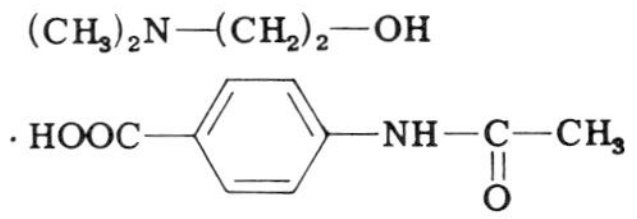 $(CH_3)_2N-(CH_2)_2-OH \cdot HOOC-C_6H_4-NH-C(=O)-CH_3$ 2-Diethylaminoethanol *p*-acetylaminobenzoate	S; 50 mg; 25–400 mg	Med; ND; PDR; USD
Hydroxyphenamate	AL 0361 (Armour), hidroxifenamate, Listica (Armour), P-301, phenylbutamate, Tensifen, oxyfenamate	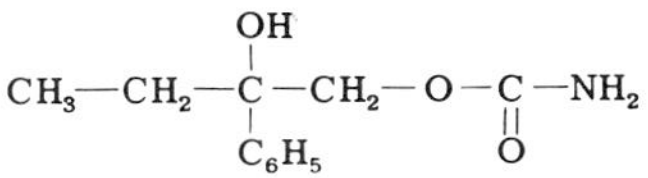 $CH_3-CH_2-C(OH)(C_6H_5)-CH_2-O-C(=O)-NH_2$ 2-Hydroxy-2-phenylbutyl carbamate	AA; 400–800 mg	ND; USD

Table I (*Continued*)

Compound	Synonyms, Trade Names, Manufacturers	Structure	Psychotropic Action and Dose	Listing
Mephenesin	A 1141 (Abbott), Atensin, Avosyl (Schenley), Avoxil, Avoxyl, BDH 312, BYK-M 1 (Byk), Cresoxydiol, Cresossidiolo, Creoxypropanediol, Curythan, Daserd (Evron), Daserol (Evron), Decontractil, Decontractyl (Robert), Diloxol (Carnrick), Dioloxal, Dioloxol (Carnrick), Findolar, Findolor, Glukresin, Glykresin, Glotol (U.S. Standard), Kinavosyl (Schenley), Kresoxypropanediol, Lissephan, Lissephem (Abbott), Mefensina, Memphenesin, Mephedan (Daniels), Mepherol (Bryant), Mephesin, Mephin, Mephson (Tutag), Mianesina, Moctynol (Moore), Myanesin (BDH), Myanol, Myocain(e), Myocuran, Myodetensin, Myolax (Key), Myolysin, Myopan, Myopen, Myoserol, Myoten (Central), Myoxyl, Myoxane (Ascher), Nephelor (Taylor), Noctynol, Oranixon (Organon), Prolax (Cole), Proloxin (Lannett), Relaxant (Hart), Relaxar (Bouty), Relaxil (Egger), Relaxyl (Zef), Renarcol (Byk), Rhex "Hobein" (Hobein), RP 3602, Sansdolor, Saserol, Seconesinz, Sinan (Warren-Teed, Fulton), Spartoloxin (Spartan), Spasmolyn (Heun), Sq 1156, Stilalgin, Thioxidil (Normand),	CH_3 (ortho on benzene ring) $-O-CH_2-CH(OH)-CH_2OH$ 3-(*o*-Tolyloxy)-1, 2-propanediol	AA; 100–200 mg/tid or 5x a day	Med; PDR; USD (primarily used as a muscle relaxant, but also used as AA)

	Thoxidil (Normand), Tokerol (Squibb), Tolansin (Phys. Drug), Tolax (Stu. & Case), Tolcil, Tolhart (Hart), Tolosate (Brewer), Toloxyn (Delta-Pharm), Tolserol (Squibb), Tolseron, Tolsil (Pharmaseal), Toxulexin (Miller), Tolulox (Miller), Tolyspaz (Chicago), Torulox, Walconesin (Walker), cresossi-propandiolo, Tolofren, Xeral, *o*-tolylglycerol	(See page 226)		
Methocarbamol	Robaxin (Robins), Neuraxin (Robins), Etroflex (Etro), Lumirelax (Lumiere), Tresortil (Gia), AHR 85 (Robins), Miolaxene (Lepetit), Metocarbamol, Miowas (Wasserman), Robaxan (Robins in Philippines), Relax (I.O.N.), Myolaxene, Robaxine (Medial), Robinax (Robins in India), Robaxon (Robins in Sweden), Guaiphensin carbamate, guiacol-gliceriletere monocarbammato, Metofenina, metocarbamolo, Miorilas, Perilax, Reflexyn	$C_6H_4(O{-}CH_3){-}O{-}CH_2{-}CH(OH){-}CH_2{-}O{-}C(=O){-}NH_2$ 3-(*o*-Methoxyphenoxy)-1, 2-propanediol-1-carbamate	AA; 1000–1500 mg	
Methoxypropanediol	Reorganin (Brunnengraber), Resyl (Ciba), Tulyn (Tutag), XL 90, Myoscain-E, Myoscaine (Holzinger), Guaiamar, Guiaphenesin, Guanar, Guayanesin, Miorelax, MY 301, Myocaine, Oresol, Oreson, Respenyl (Crookes), guajacol-α-glycerinether, Resil, Gaiamar, Tolseron, Sirotol (Brunnengraber), Tolyn, metossi-propandiolo, metfenossidiolo, guaicuran, guaiacolglicerinetere	$C_6H_4(O{-}CH_3){-}O{-}CH_2{-}CH(OH){-}CH_2OH$ 3-(*o*-Methoxyphenoxy) propane-diol-1, 2	AA; 150–200 mg; 500–3000 mg	

Table I (*Continued*)

Compound	Synonyms, Trade Names, Manufacturers	Structure	Psychotropic Action and Dose	Listing
MO-1255		$C_6H_5CH_2-N(CH(CH_2)_2)-C(=O)-OCH_2CH_3$ Ethyl-*N*-benzyl-*N*-cyclopropylcarbamate	AD	
Pargyline	A 19120 (Abbott), Erytonal, Eusdatine (Abbott), Eutonil, Eutonyl (Abbott), MO 911, Pargiline, pargilina	$HC{\equiv}C-CH_2-N(CH_3)-CH_2-C_6H_5 \cdot HCl$ *N*-Methyl-*N*-2-propynylbenzylamine hydrochloride	AD; 75–150 mg	PDR; USD (primarily used as antihypertensive)
Phenaglycodol	Acalmid, Acalo (Lilly), Alterton (Pierrel), Atadiol (Tosi), Fenaglicodolo, Phenglykodol, Remin, Sinforil (Roussel), Stesil, Ultran (Lilly)	$Cl-C_6H_4-C(CH_3)(OH)-C(CH_3)_2(OH)$ 2-(*p*-Chlorophenyl-3-methyl-2, 3-butanediol	AA; 300 mg/tid or qid; 400–1200 mg; 300–1500 mg	ND; PDR; USD
Phenyltoloxamine	PRN (Bristol), Bristamin(e) (Bristol), Histionex (Strasenburgh), Phenoxadrine (Clin-Comar), Antin, C 5581 H, Bistrimin, Harv-Amine, Bristain	$C_6H_4(CH_2-C_6H_5)(O-(CH_2)_2-N(CH_3)_2)$ *N*, *N*-Dimethyl-2-[(α-phenyl-*o*-tolyl) oxy]-ethylamine	AA; 25–200 mg/tid; 300–800 mg	

Class: Aliphatic Compounds				
Ectylurea	A 18285, Actine, Astyn, Ectida, Ecton, Ectyda, Ektyl, Ektylcarbamid, Euplacid, Levanil (Upjohn), Levil (I.B.I.), MA 110, Nestyn, Neuroprocin (Minerva), Nostal, Nostin, Nostyn (Ames), Pacetyn, Tranzer, U 8771, ectilurea, Cronil, Crotural, Distessol, Neocrosedin	$CH_3-CH=C(CH_2-CH_3)-C(=O)-NH-C(=O)-NH_2$ *cis*-(2-Ethylcrotonoyl)urea	AA; 150–300 mg/tid or qid; 450–1200 mg	ND; PDR; USD (used primarily as a sedative but also used as AA)
Emylcamate	*tert*-Hexanol carbamate, Kabi-295 (Kabi), MK-250, Nucital, Nuncital (Kabi), Psicoplegil, Restetal (Kabi), Statran, Striatran (Merck), emilcamato	$CH_3-C(C_2H_5)(C_2H_5)-C(=O)-NH_2$ 1-Ethyl-1-methylpropylcarbamate	AA; 200 mg/tid or qid; 600–800 mg	Med; ND; USD
Ethchlorvynol	Arvynol, Ethchlorvynol, Ethochlorvynol, ethychlorvynol, Normoson, Placidil, Placidyl (Abbott), Serenesil, etclorvinolo, Normonson	$CH_3-CH_2-C(OH)(CH=CH-Cl)-C\equiv CH$ 1-Chloro-3-ethyl-1-penten-4-yn-3-ol	AA; 100–200 mg/bid or tid; 200–800 mg	PDR; USD (used both as sedative and as AA)

Table I (*Continued*)

Compound	Synonyms, Trade Names, Manufacturers	Structure	Psychotropic Action and Dose	Listing
Meprobamate	Amepromat, Anathymon, Andaksin, Andaxin(e), Aneural (Wyeth), Aneurol, Aneusral (Asche), Aneuxral, Ansiatan, Ansietan, Ansil, Ansiowas, Anural, Apascil, Arpon, Artolon (Roter), Ataraxine, Atraxin, Ayermate (Ayerst), Biobamat, Brobamate, Calmax, Calmiren, Casil, Cirpon (Tropon), Cirponyl, Cyropon (Tropon), Dapaz, Diveron, Dormabrol, Ecuanil (Wyeth), Edenal, Epikur, Equanil (Wyeth), Equatrate, Equilium, Equinil, Equitar, Erina, Gadexyl, Gagexyl, Harmonin (Takeda), Hartol (Fontoura-Wyeth), Holbamate (Sap), Letyl (Etro), Madiol, Margonil, Mepamtin, Mepantin, Mepavlon (ICI), Meposed (Vernleigh), Mepranil, Meprin, Meprobam, Meproban, Meprocompren (MBK), Meprodil (Streuli, Lederle), Meprosa, Meprosan, Meprosin, Meprospan (Wallace), Meprotabs (Wallace), Meprotan, Meprotaps, Meprozine, Miltamato (Vitax), Miltann, Miltuan, Miltown (Wallace), Morbam, Multaun (Lederle), Neo-Tran, Nephentine (West-Ward), Nervonus, Oasil (Simes), Orlevol, Orolevol, Pan-	$CH_3—CH_2—C(CH_3)(CH_2—O—C(=O)—NH_2)_2$ 2-Methyl-2-*n*-propyl-1, 3-propanediol dicarbamate	AA; (sedative, not AA); 200–2000 mg; 400 mg/tid	Med; PDR; USD

	calma, Panediol, Pan-Tranquil, Paxin (Pierrel), Perequil (Lepetit), Pentranquil(e) (Lepetit), Perequietal, Perquietil, Placidon, Prequil, Probamato, Probamyl, Procalmadiol, Procalmadol, Procalmidol, Procarbamide, Promato, Proquanil, Quaname (Wyeth), Quanane (Wyeth), Quanil (Wyeth), Reostral, Restenil (Kabi), Restenyl, Restinal, Restinil (Kabi), Sadanyl, Sedanyl, Sedazil, Setran (Wallace, Cipelli), Shalvaton, Sowell (Cophar), Tensol, Tensonal, Trankvilan, Tranlisant, Tranquil, Tranquilan, Tranquiline, Tranquilsan, Tranquisan, Trelmar, Urbil, Urbilat (Hor-Fer-Vit), Zirpon, Klort (Lemmon), Protran (Carrtone), Fas-Cile (Schliksup), Tamate (Merrell), Meptran (Reid-Provident), Estasil, Meprodiol, Pankalma, Quietidon, Sedoquil, Sedoselecta, Selene, Solevione, Mendel, Stensolo, Apasil	(See page 230)		

Table I (*Continued*)

Compound	Synonyms, Trade Names, Manufacturers	Structure	Psychotropic Action and Dose	Listing
Methylpentynol	Dormison (Schering-USA), Oblivon (Schering-England), Hesofen (Hässle), Atemorin (Scherer), Allotropal (Heyl), Atempol (Norgine), Riposon (Recordati), Somnesin (BDH), Util (Leo), Apridol, Imnudorm, Pentadorm, Antistress, Seral, Dalgol, Formison, Dormidin, Dormigen, Dormiphen, Hexofen, Methylparafynol, Meparfynol, Dorison, Dormalest, Perlopal (Robisch), Insomnol (Medo-Chem), Mecarol, Oblevil, Melpintol, Mepentamato, Mepentil, Metilpentinolo, Noxokratin, Olvadon, Comesa, Pentydorm, Pentyrest, Placidal, Sedapercut, Sintyal, Trusono, Quietal, Dormosan, Methylpentynolum, Dormosan, Dormocit, Immudorm, Insomnol, Macarol, Aniphor, metilparafinolo	$CH_3—CH_2—C(CH_3)(OH)—C≡CH$ **3-Methyl-1-pentyn-3-ol**	AA; 250–1000 mg	
Tybamate	Benvil (Beecham), Nospan (Wallace), Solacen (Wallace), tibamato, Tybatran (Roche, Robins), Effisax (Maggioni), Idalene, W-713	$H_2N—C(=O)—O—CH_2—C(CH_3)((CH_2)_2—CH_3)—CH_2—O—C(=O)—NH—(CH_2)_3—CH_3$ **2-Methyl-2-propyltrimethylene butylcarbamate carbamate**	AA; 250 mg; 750–2000 mg	deH; Med; ND; PDR; USD

PART V

THE PHARMACOLOGIC BASIS OF PSYCHOPHARMACOTHERAPY

16

PRECLINICAL PSYCHOPHARMACOLOGY

Carl L. Scheckel

I. Introduction

A. Relations between Animal and Human Psychopharmacology

There is close interaction between clinical research on humans and laboratory studies of animals. This interaction has facilitated both the foundation and growth of psychopharmacology. While animal studies have the advantage of being suitable for rigorous and objective experimental control, clinical work offers the advantage of uncovering subtle or unusual drug effects for which the animal experiment frequently makes no provision. When a new type of drug effect is seen in the clinic, the experimentalist can then develop new test procedures to measure some unique effect of that drug in animals. Also, the animal test can be used to elucidate modes and sites of action of drugs and to find among newly synthesized agents other clinically useful drugs. Simultaneously, other animal procedures can be developed to test drugs already known to be clinically useful, resulting in the suggestion of new uses for these older agents. In this way the clinician and the laboratory experimenter do their own work independently, but provide each other with information that is mutually advantageous and permits the progress of all phases in the field of psychopharmacology. Until now, however, the most crucial aids to progress, in what became totally new areas, have been provided by careful and observant clinicians.

B. New Drugs Motivate New Research

Despite the fact that most major developments have had their origin in the clinic, preclinical psychopharmacology has continued to grow in number of investigators as well as laboratories, its areas of application, its acceptance by other disciplines, and in general popularity. It must be asked why this has happened. The answer is simple: the existence of clinically useful drugs. The fact that many drugs do exist for the useful and effective treatment of a variety of behavior or mental disorders in man has served to force psychopharmacologists to develop new and better ways of studying these drugs in animals. One area where this is particularly true involves studies on the effects of drugs on conditioned behavior in animals. After it became known that chlorpromazine (CPZ) had antipsychotic activity in man and that it also suppressed conditioned foot shock avoidance behavior in rats, it was assumed that all "tranquilizers" would affect conditioned avoidance behavior in rats. Fortunately, it took only two to three years to dispel this misconception, because it was subsequently demonstrated that meprobamate and chlordiazepoxide had ("tranquilizing") antianxiety activity in man even though these drugs had no significant effect on conditioned avoidance behavior in rats.

This presented a challenge for psychopharmacologists, especially for those who espoused conditioning techniques for preclinical drug evaluation. In the first years when the antianxiety effects of meprobamate and chlordiazepoxide were being observed in the clinic, it was also known that these drugs had the interesting ability to abate aggressive or attack behavior in wild animals, especially monkeys. However, these drugs had no effect on the conditioned behavior procedures in general use at that time. A major effort followed to design animal tests that would be sensitive to the unique effects of these antianxiety drugs (cf. Margolin and Kletzkin, Chapter 22). By now, of course, this particular problem has been acceptably solved, and there are presently many published papers showing specific effects of meprobamate, chlordiazepoxide, and similar drugs on various kinds of conditioned behavior in animals (cf. Margolin and Kletzkin, Chapter 22). However, it was the psychotropic drugs in therapeutic use that motivated the careful studies leading to this advance in methodology. As newer drugs are developed, they continue to provoke new research efforts. Current challenges are provided by the imipramine-type (tricyclic) antidepressants (cf. Klerman and Paykel, Chapter 49), and lithium carbonate (cf. Schou, Chapter 51).

II. Preclinical Pharmacology and Conditioning Behavior

A. Pharmacologic Tests

There are several relatively standard pharmacologic procedures for testing potential psychotropic drugs, most of which do not employ conditioned animal behavior. Indeed, some tests do not measure (psychologically defined) behavior at all. However, each drug must be tested in many of these procedures simply to learn as much as possible about the drug and also to look for possible relations between basic pharmacologic or physiologic actions and behavioral effects. Many times what seems to be a behavioral effect is actually a manifestation of toxicity, hypotension, muscle relaxation, etc. For example, much is learned from determining the LD_{50} (the lethal dose killing 50% of the animals) at various times after administration of the drug by different routes and noting the symptoms that precede death. If the intraperitoneal or subcutaneous LD_{50} is nearly equal to the oral LD_{50}, it is concluded that the drug is easily absorbed from the gastrointestinal tract. If death is preceded by convulsions, one may expect that sublethal doses produce general excitation or stimulation of locomotor activity. In such case, the increased motor activity does not necessarily indicate that the drug will be a useful stimulant in man since the animal test may only reflect sublethal toxicity.

Symptoms preceding death can also indicate the mechanism of drug action. Animals may die of intense sympathetic or parasympathetic stimulation, suggesting that the drug may be acting via adrenergic or cholinergic mechanisms. These effects can be further investigated using responses of isolated tissues such as the spleen, heart, ileum, or iris. Similar peripheral mechanisms are explored by measuring effects on the cardiovascular system of cats and dogs and by determining whether the drugs augment or antagonize the effects of catecholamines, serotonin, acetylcholine, or histamine. CPZ, for example, reverses the hypertensive effect of epinephrine; imipramine enhances the effect of norepinephrine, while chlordiazepoxide is relatively inactive on the peripheral autonomic system. This kind of information raises the as yet unanswered question of whether or not there is any relation between peripheral autonomic effects and the central nervous effects resulting in altered behavior or mood.

There are other general pharmacologic tests used to study psychotropic agents in mice and rats: (1) spontaneous motor activity as recorded by jiggle cages, interruption of light beams, or similar devices; (2) ataxia, as measured by a falling response or inability to walk on a rotating cylinder; (3) potentiation of CNS depression, as measured by prolongation of barbiturate sleeping time or alcohol; (4) blockade of tremors, CNS excitation, and convulsion caused by the administration of tremorine, metrazol, strychnine, 5-hydroxytryptophan, and electroconvulsive shock.

Still other tests measure a drug's ability to prevent electric foot shock-induced fighting in mice, to produce a muscle relaxation, hind limb relaxation, analgesia, anorexia, writhing, emesis, diuresis, or to alter gastric motility. All of the presently used psychotropic agents have one or more of the above effects. Essential is a wide margin between the dose producing interesting pharmacologic effects and the dose causing neurotoxicity or death. Figure 1 shows the doses of four widely used drugs that possess pharmacologic activity (prevention of fighting, antagonism of strychnine convulsions, and muscle relaxant action) at doses significantly lower than those causing death in mice. The drugs shown in Fig. 1 are, of course, well-known psychotropic agents by now, but they were not

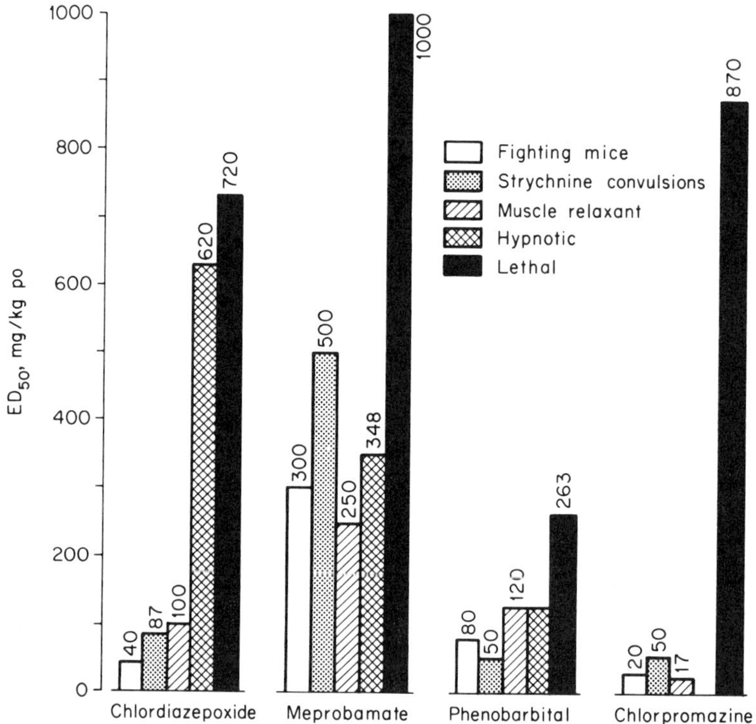

Fig. 1. Effects of four psychotropic drugs on mice in standard pharmacologic tests. (Ordinate: ED_{50} = dose effective in 50% of the subjects.)

always so, and any newly synthesized compound with equivalent activity would certainly be worthy of additional study on animal and, subsequently, human behavior.

Although there are some investigators who believe that behavioral drug effects can best be evaluated by human observers looking at animals and subjectively scoring changes in gross behavior, behavioral pharmacology (or psychopharmacology) has come more and more to mean the study of behavior using conditioning techniques.

B. Conditioning Behavior

1. Pavlovian Conditioning Techniques

Pavlovian (classical) conditioning techniques have not been widely used in this country to study drug effects; the fundamental procedure is described briefly so that the other techniques may be seen in contrast. In Pavlovian conditioning a subject is presented with a neutral stimulus, i.e., a stimulus that has no meaning or motivational properties in itself. This neutral stimulus (light, tone, bell, etc.) is then paired with another stimulus, the unconditioned stimulus, which by itself is capable of eliciting some reaction from the subject. For example, the unconditioned stimulus may be a puff of air directed at the eye, and it elicits the response of an eye blink. A neutral stimulus (e.g., buzzer) is presented just before or simultaneously with the puff of air. Initially, the buzzer causes no relevant behavioral effects, but after it has been repeatedly presented with the puff of air, the buzzer alone is able to elicit an eye blink. When this happens, the buzzer is called the "conditioned stimulus." This is a general consequence of classical conditioning: A neutral stimulus, by repeated association with an unconditioned stimulus, acquires the ability to elicit the response that was normally provoked only by the unconditioned stimulus. In other words, the animal is conditioned to make a specific response to a previously meaningless or irrelevant stimulus. The response the animal makes to the conditioned stimulus is termed the conditioned response. (The conditioned response is very similar to the unconditioned response, but there are subtle physiological differences.) The response made to the unconditioned stimulus is called the unconditioned response because this response is not dependent on the conditioning process: It occurs naturally, automatically, or autonomically.

Two points should be realized about classical conditioning: (a) The subject has no control over what stimulus will be presented or when it will be presented; (b) the subject cannot control the type of response it makes nor whether or not it will make it.* Pavlovian conditioning, thus, exerts very rigorous control over behavior, and the behavior conditioned typically concerns an autonomic or reflex nervous mechanism.

The extent to which Pavlovian conditioning controls subtle forms of human behavior and disease is still unknown. One can speculate, however, that the control is extensive, and it is only regrettable that drugs known to affect human behavior have not been extensively studied using classical conditioning techniques.

2. Instrumental Conditioning

The principal difference between classical and instrumental conditioning is the control the subject has over the presentation of the unconditioned stimulus. In instrumental conditioning the subject's behavior determines whether or not it receives the unconditioned stimulus, whereas in classical conditioning the subject cannot control this stimulus. This difference is illustrated in the following two experiments.

In the first experiment classical conditioning is used. A buzzer is sounded just before and contiguous with an electric shock to the foreleg of a dog.* The electrodes are placed on the dog's leg so the shock itself provokes leg flexion. After repeated pairings the leg flexion occurs when the buzzer sounds, but even with the leg flexed in response to the conditioned stimulus (buzzer), the unconditioned stimulus (shock) is still presented. Thus, shock is given regardless

* *Editor's notes:* That this is true in an absolute sense is doubtful, and particularly dubious in relation to extrapolation to man. For some cogent observations in this respect, see Efron (149).

Investigators working with animal behavioral tests must take into consideration many subtle variables which may lead to misinterpretation of effects of drugs, such as: sex odors left in mazes—handedness may affect maze performance or lever pushing; drugs may have an analgesic or sensory enhancing effect which alter electric shock thresholds—they may have an effect on neuromuscular transmission or a direct motor effect and thus affect activity.

of the response made. In instrumental conditioning the same conditioned stimulus (buzzer) may be used and the same conditioned response (leg flexion) required. In this instance, however, the presentation of the buzzer serves as a warning that shock is imminent, and if the conditioned response is made during the warning buzzer, shock is not given. Only if the conditioned response is not made does the shock occur. The animal is thus conditioned to avoid the shock.

An additional feature of instrumental conditioning not possible using the classical technique is the selection of the conditioned response. In classical conditioning the conditioned response must be practically identical to the unconditioned response, whereas in instrumental conditioning the two responses can be quite different. For example, in the instrumental conditioning experiment described above the subjects could have been conditioned to avoid shock by wagging their tails, nodding, or waving their heads, or pulling a rope, or almost any other response chosen by the experimenter.

One of the first instrumental conditioning procedures used to study psychotropic drugs was actually quite similar to a Pavlovian conditioning procedure—so similar, in fact, it is typically referred to as "*classical* avoidance" even though it is not essentially Pavlovian. It was employed to distinguish between the behavioral effects of chlorpromazine and barbiturates. Rats were placed in a box having a grid floor through which electric shock could be delivered to the rats' feet.† In the center of the box was a vertical wooden pole which the rats could climb to avoid or escape the shock. Periodically a buzzer was sounded and was followed by foot shock. The animals could avoid the shock by climbing the pole when the buzzer came on or, if they failed to do this, they could escape the shock by climbing the pole when the shock was on. After several trials the rats were conditioned to avoid the shock with the pole-climb response. When drugs were tested in this procedure, there was a clear and qualitative difference between CPZ and barbiturates or hypnotics. CPZ blocked the conditioned avoidance response (pole climbing during the buzzer) at a dose well below the dose that interfered with escape responding. Barbiturates and hypnotics, however, only blocked avoidance responses at the same doses that caused noticeable ataxia or prevented the escape. Therefore, CPZ had a selective effect in that it blocked only one type of behavior, whereas the barbiturates simply produced a general slowing of all behavior.

This result shows an important pharmacologic effect of CPZ, but it also illustrates a significant feature of conditioning techniques. Namely, one specific type of behavior can be brought under the experimenter's control; this behavior can be defined with precision, and the effects which drugs have on it may be measured objectively.

3. Operant Conditioning

This technique is similar to instrumental conditioning insofar as the subject makes responses to alter the environment, to make it less aversive or more rewarding. However, operant procedures are more versatile and the principles

† See Editor's footnote for p. 239.

more general than instrumental conditioning. Actually, the principles of operant conditioning are broad enough to include instrumental conditioning as a special case.

The main tenet of operant conditioning is that "reinforcement" controls behavior. This means that an animal performs an action because it is reinforced for doing so. Furthermore, the particular kind of behavior performed is determined by the consequences of that performance, i.e., the type of reinforcement obtained. There are basically two types of reinforcers, positive and negative. A positive reinforcer is a reward such as food or water given to a hungry or thirsty animal when it makes an appropriate response. A negative reinforcer is a punishment, typically electric shock,† presented when the animal does not make the appropriate response. In general, animals learn to respond to obtain rewards and to remove or avoid punishments in a reliable and predictable manner. Indeed, behavior can be so exquisitely controlled by reinforcement that the experimenter can decide in advance what type of behavior he wishes to study and then reinforce the animal only when it performs the behavior specified by the experimenter.

A great variety of different behaviors can be conditioned depending on the purpose of the research. The type, the degree of complexity, and the subtleness of the behavior brought under experimental control are limited only by the skill and imagination of the experimenter using this technique.

Experiments are typically done with the animal in a chamber called a Skinner box. The box contains a grid floor through which electric shock can be delivered to the animal's feet, a food-pellet dispenser that can provide rewards, lights and a loudspeaker for presenting visual and/or auditory stimuli, and one or more levers that the animal may press. The animal is conditioned to press the lever to obtain rewards or avoid punishment. Behavior is recorded and counted in terms of lever presses.

A lever may seem to be an inordinately simple device for measuring behavioral response, but it is quite adequate. In general, experiments are automatically controlled by appropriately connected relays, transistors, or a computer. The lever in the box is connected to a switch, the position of which can be sensed by the automatic controls. The lever thus acts as an interface, translating the animal's behavior into something electronic circuits can recognize. Accurate automatic programming and recording of experiments is also of importance. Behavior is usually conditioned to occur at precise times, rapidly, or under other rigorously defined conditions, and repetitively. Human control could break down from inability, fatigue, or impatience. It should also be realized that an animal that is hungry or receiving foot shock emits many different responses in rapid succession and pressing the lever may be only one of these. The animal must learn which of these many responses is producing the reinforcement, and the experimenter must teach it by presenting the reinforcer immediately after the correct response (lever press) occurs and before another response has time to occur. Furthermore, he must do all this hour after hour, week after week, with relentless consistency. The invaluable aid of automated instrumentation is obvious.

† See Editor's footnote to p. 239.

The arrangement of times or circumstances when lever pressing (responding) produces reinforcement is called the "schedule of reinforcement." There are many known schedules for studying different behaviors, and new ones are constantly being developed to study other kinds of behavior. Perhaps the simplest schedule is continuous reinforcement (CRF) where each and every lever press produces a food pellet regardless of how rapidly or slowly the animal responds. On a fixed ratio (FR) schedule several responses may be required for each reward. For example, an FR 2 schedule requires the animal to make two responses for one pellet, and on FR 25 the subject must make twenty-five responses. Without too much difficulty rats will work on FR 25, pigeons and squirrel monkeys will make several hundred responses for one reward, and rhesus monkeys will go above FR 1000.

4. Effects of Drugs on Food Rewarded Behavior

In the initial studies of drug effects on conditioned behavior, there was a tendency to lump all FR schedules, and even all food reward schedules, together, as if they measured fundamentally the same kind of behavior. Even within different FR schedules, however, it was found that the same dose of the same drug had different effects depending on the FR value. For example, drugs such as amobarbital have no significant effect on low FR schedules, but curiously increase the (already normally fast) response rate of high FR schedules. Noting these unexpected drug effects, behavioral theorists were quick to point out that if behavior is changed (by changing the schedule), the drug effect is also altered. At that time, however, there was no specific information on what was critically different between high and low ratios.

Two other types of positive reinforcement schedules are frequently used: differential reinforcement of low rate (DRL) and fixed interval (FI). As the name implies, on a DRL schedule the subject is rewarded for responding slowly. After making one response the subject must withold making another for some period, e.g., 20 seconds. If the subject responds too soon, it is not rewarded, and the possibility of reward is again postponed for another 20 seconds. Consequently, the subject is never reinforced if it responds too rapidly. If the animal consistently waits 20 seconds or longer between responses, every response is rewarded. The frequency distribution of the times between consecutive responses (interresponse time, IRT) from a well-trained rat gives a relatively normal distribution with a slight negative skew and mode of about twenty seconds. Antipsychotic drugs and hypnotics have rather unspecific depressant effects on this type of behavior. Antianxiety drugs, however, increase the response rates when tested in this procedure.

FI is similar to DRL in that it ostensibly measures timing behavior or temporal discrimination. Claims that a particular test measures only one psychological function, however, must be made with extreme caution. What appears to the human observer as a simple lever-pressing task may be a complicated ordeal for the animal doing it. (To ascertain the animal's reaction to a test, another lever can be placed in the box. The animal can use this lever to turn the experiment off for a while or conversely to turn it on. Studies of this kind have shown that subjects will not only work to obtain food and avoid shock, but they will respond to turn off food-reward schedules as well as to turn on shock or the possibility of obtaining shock.) Simple tests that apparently measure only one function may measure other, not so obvious, functions with much greater sensitivity. Consequently, interpreting drug results only with reference to the most simple and obvious factors can result in confusion. For example, antianxiety agents are known to increase response rates on DRL and FI. If these schedules are regarded as measures of how well the subject discriminates the passage of time, then the conclusion must be that these drugs disrupt timing behavior. However, antianxiety drugs also *improve* performance on traditional tests that apparently measure memory. It is therefore tempting to conclude these drugs improve memory. Since timing behavior involves memory, the two conclusions are quite imcompatible, and an alternate interpretation must be sought. This can usually be gained from very close inspection of the animal's behavior.

Behavior on an FI schedule can be analyzed with relative ease, because the responses leading to a single reward are spread out over a relatively long period of time. On this schedule the subject is rewarded for the first response made after a given (fixed) time (interval) has elapsed since the preceding reward. The value of the FI can be set at any reasonable time, e.g., 5 minutes. Thereby the animal can obtain food once every 5 minutes provided it is in the process of responding when the reinforcement becomes available. Subjects do attempt to obtain the reward as quickly as possible by responding at increasingly high rates as the interval advances. As soon as the response produces the food, the rate of lever pressing decreases to about zero for a short time (called the post-reinforcement pause) after which responding again begins to increase at a positively accelerated rate until the next reinforcement.

Antipsychotics and hypnotics typically decrease responding on DRL and FI. Antianxiety agents increase the overall response rate and virtually eliminate the postreinforcement pause—as soon as the subject receives one pellet, it quickly begins to press the lever again instead of waiting.

The ability of antianxiety drugs to increase responding on FI schedules is noteworthy, partly because these drugs are generally regarded as sedative agents; and they do cause muscle relaxation, drowsiness, and ataxia as measured in other pharmacologic tests. More important, perhaps, is the fact that these drugs decrease the amount of time the subject spends in the pause after reinforcement. The normal lack of responding during the pause can be regarded as a measure of the subject's *aversion* to working in this procedure. Decreased pausing may therefore indicate that antianxiety drugs render the procedure to be less aversive to the subject.

5. Drug Effects on Shock Avoidance Behavior

While aversive components of reward schedules are probably very critical for the animal subject, they are usually ignored by the human experimenter because the latter has a much more straightforward and unambiguous means of administering punishment, viz. delivering electric shock. While shock can be given under a variety of complex circumstances, there are basically two different types of shock avoidance schedules in general use: discrete avoidance and continuous avoidance.

Discrete avoidance procedures are quite similar to the instrumentally conditioned avoidance behavior used by Cook and Weidley described above. Periodically (every 1 or 2 minutes) an animal is presented with a discrete trial during which it can avoid shock, escape shock, or fail to escape shock. Each trial consists of 5 seconds of warning noise followed by 5 seconds of foot shock. The animal may avoid shock by pressing the lever during the noise or escape the shock by pressing the lever after the shock has come on. Animals are trained until they avoid shock on more than 90% of the trials given during 5-hour sessions. As in the conditioned avoidance procedure of Cook and Weidley (150), CPZ-type antipsychotics have a specific effect in blocking avoidance responses at doses which do not interfere with escape responses; the animals are sufficiently sedated so they do not avoid, but their ability to respond and turn off the shock is unimpaired. In contrast, doses of hypnotics that impair avoidance behavior also impair escape behavior. Antianxiety drugs have no characteristic or important effects on this behavior. Of course, at high doses these latter drugs depress lever pressing, but this is due most likely to muscle relaxation and ataxia and not to a behavioral effect per se. This interpretation is supported by results of Heise and McConnell (151) using a modified discrete trial avoidance precedure. They inserted a 5-second delay, or silent gap, in between the warning noise and the shock. In this case rats could avoid shock by responding either during the noise or the gap periods. When given small doses of CPZ, the subjects did not press the lever during either the noise or gap but did respond to escape the shock. Hypnotics continued to eliminate all behavior as they did in the unmodified test. This procedure was, however, more sensitive to the sedative effects of antianxiety agents. When given moderate doses of chlordiazepoxide or meprobamate, rats frequently did not respond during the noise, but they still avoided the shock by responding in the silent gap.

Although discrete avoidance procedures are most useful in studying CPZ-like drugs, they have the disadvantage of not providing a good measure of stimulant drug activity. CPZ itself, for example, at very low doses has a stimulant effect not seen in the discrete avoidance procedure. The continuous avoidance schedule is sensitive to both stimulant and depressant drug effects. On the continuous avoidance schedule no external warning cue preceding the shock is provided. The subjects must simply respond in a continuous fashion to postpone an ever-impending shock (152). If the animal does not respond, it is shocked at regular intervals, e.g., once every 20 seconds. Each time the subject responds it postpones the shock for a longer interval, e.g., 40 seconds. If the animal responds at a constant rate higher than one response every 40 seconds, it is never shocked; but whenever it waits longer than 40 seconds, it receives a shock, and the shock is then repeated every 20 seconds until another response is made. The duration of the shock can be extremely brief or it may last for several seconds. Heise and Boff (153) described a continuous avoidance procedure using two levers and a relatively long (5 second maximum) shock duration. Rats pressed an avoidance lever to postpone the shock, but if the shock came on, they could press the other (escape) lever to turn it off. In the nondrugged state these subjects make approximately 210 avoidance responses per hour, receive about five shocks per hour, and escape all shocks. This schedule is particularly useful in evaluating drugs since the response rate is low enough to be significantly increased by small doses of stimulants, but still high enough to be depressed by small doses of sedatives.

Stimulants such as *d*-amphetamine, methylphenidate, and cocaine increase the rate of avoidance responding in a dose-related manner. Drugs having primarily depressant effects include chlordiazepoxide, CPZ, morphine, hydroxyzine, levorphanol, phenobarbital, trifluoperazine, methyprylon, hexobarbital, chlorprothixene, zoxazolamine, emylcamate, pentobarbital, chlormezanone, meprobamate, and ethyl alcohol (153). Although all of these drugs depressed continuous avoidance behavior in rats, they have qualitatively different effects in man: psychotropic agents, nighttime sedatives, hypnotics, and muscle relaxants. Heise and Boff, therefore, attempted to show that these drugs have some qualitative differences in rats in this procedure. Differences between drug categories were shown by measuring the ratio between the dose of a drug having a minimal depressant action (the dose that just significantly increased the number of shocks received) and the dose that severely depressed behavior (the dose causing escape failures). A large ratio (about 4.0) indicates the intensity of sedation is gradually increased over several doses. A small ratio (about 1.0) indicates the drug has an all-or-none effect: The animal responds normally at one dose, but if the dose is increased only slightly, behavior is completely suppressed. Psychotropic drugs characteristically have high ratios, reflecting the fact that both experimentalists and clinicians can carefully control the degree of sedation in their subjects by proper adjustment of the dose. Sedatives or nighttime sleep inducers have intermediate ratios (about 2.0), indicating little separation between the dose causing mild sedation and the dose producing frank drowsiness. Hypnotics and muscle relaxants have a ratio of about 1.0.

6. Effects of Drugs on Conflict Behavior

Another useful method for studying drug effects in animals is a conflict procedure. This involves the simultaneous delivery of both a reward and punishment when a response occurs. In this procedure, hungry subjects are basically conditioned to work for a food reward, but when they make the response required to obtain food, they are also punished with shock. Subjects are motivated (by hunger) to approach the lever and respond for food, but they are also motivated to avoid the lever because the response produces irritating or painful shock. The subjects are thus in an approach-avoidance conflict. Investigations of the effects of drugs on this behavior may seem particularly appealing because conflict is a predicament well appreciated by the human observer. Experiments on this behavior, however, must be dealt with carefully since conflict involves both food reward and shock avoidance behavior, and drugs are known to independently affect reward schedules and avoidance schedules where no conflict is apparent. If a drug is shown to reduce (or attenuate) conflict behavior, it may achieve this effect by: (1) reducing shock avoidance; (2) increasing food rewarded behavior; (3) reducing a portion of behavior called "conflict"; or (4) a general change in locomotor activity.

In one study of the factors involved in conflict behavior, rats were trained to discriminate between two tones while working for food (154). When a high tone (2000 cps) was presented, rats pressed a right-side lever once for a food reward and, when a low tone (400 cps) occurred, a response on the left lever was rewarded. Tones were presented in random order and spaced 1 minute apart during 3-hour test sessions. A correct response terminated the tone and, if the subject did not respond correctly, the tone was terminated automatically after 15 seconds. Two aspects of behavior were measured: (1) the percent of correct responses and (2) the response latency, i.e., the time from the onset of a tone to the occurrence of a correct response. During this first part of the study, subjects quickly learned to respond correctly to both tones on nearly all trials with a response latency of less than 3 seconds on each trial. At this point punishing shock was introduced. Each time the subject responded correctly on a low-tone trial there was a probability of 0.1 that the response would produce foot shock in addition to the food pellet. Thus, all correct responses to the low (conflict) tone produced food, but 10% of these responses also delivered shock. (The trials on which shock could occur were distributed randomly, and no cue was available as to whether any given correct response to the conflict tone would be shocked.) Correct responses to the high (approach) tone produced only food just as during the initial training. After repeated exposure to these conditions, the subjects responded on every approach trial with a latency of about two seconds. On the conflict trials, however, they failed to respond on about seventy percent of the trials and, when a response occurred, its latency was about ten seconds. Thus, occasional punishment and the conditioned expectation (threat) of a punishment produced a large change in the subject's behavior during the low (conflict) tone. This procedure, therefore, permitted an almost simultaneous evaluation of drug effects on simple approach behavior and approach-avoidance conflict behavior where the response requirement (one lever press) was the same for both behaviors. The effects of several doses of meprobamate on this behavior are shown in Fig. 2. This drug markedly reduced the response latency on conflict trials, while having no effect on simple approach behavior. There also was a slight increase in the number of conflict trials responded to under various doses of this drug. Other antianxiety drugs such as chlordiazepoxide and diazepam caused marked reduction in response latencies to the conflict tone, and they also significantly increased the number of conflict trials responded to at doses having no effect on approach behavior. These three drugs, therefore, had a specific effect on conflict behavior in that they reduced the tendency of the animal to withhold a response that was equivalent in all respects except for the aversive component. CPZ, in contrast, had no significant effects on these behaviors, and at the highest dose tested it caused marked sedation and the animals did not respond on any trials.

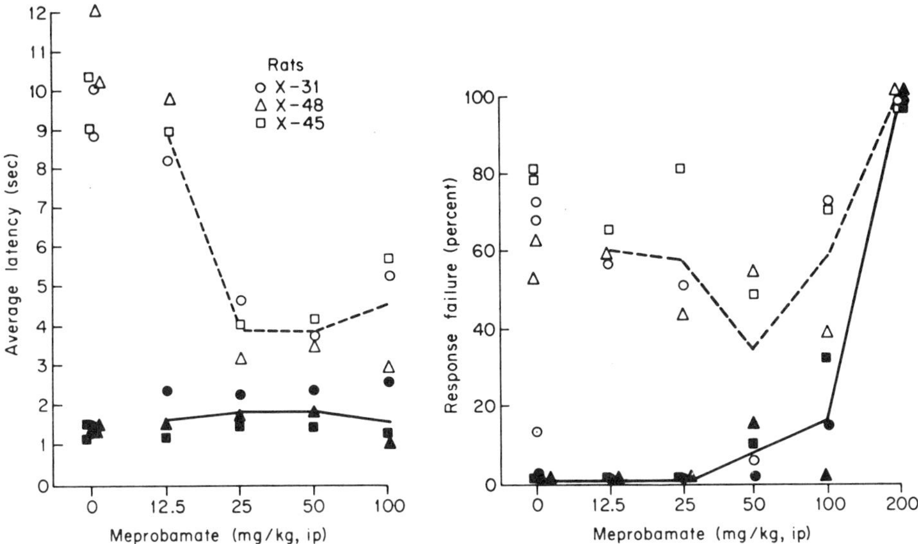

Fig. 2. Effects of meprobamate on discrete trial approach and approach-avoidance behaviors in rats. (Dashed line) approach-avoidance trials; (solid line) approach trials. [Reprinted from Heise, C. A. (214) with permission of Pergamon Press.]

7. Examples of Newer Techniques

a. Delayed Response. Many drugs alter conditioned behavior in distinct ways as described above. However, these behaviors are relatively simple and do not push the subject to the limit of its abilities. Requiring animals to perform at near maximum ability allows us to test the effects of drugs on reasonably complex behavior. One way of measuring complex behavior is to force the subject to remember something in a delayed response situation.

In one study (155) rhesus monkeys were placed in a large box containing three levers. Above each lever was a 1-inch diameter disc that could be illuminated with a red, green, or white light. Normally the discs were white, but every 2 minutes a sample stimulus was presented at the center disc. The sample was either red or green light which remained on for a maximum of 10 seconds. The subjects were trained to press the lever under the samples, and this response started a delay interval during which all lights were turned off. After the delay only the side lights came on; one side was red and the other green. The animal's task was to press the lever under the side disc that was the same color as the sample had been (match the sample). Correct matching responses were rewarded with a 190-mg banana pellet. Incorrect responses simply terminated the trial with no reward. The duration of the delay interval (the time that the subject had to "remember" the color of the sample) varied as a function of the animal's performance. At the start of each 3-hour session the delay was set at zero seconds, but every time the subject made correct matching responses on two consecutive trials at one delay, the delay presented during the next trial was automatically increased. Whenever a subject failed to match correctly or failed to respond to the sample, the delay interval in the next trial decreased. Thus, as the subject performed correctly, the problem became more difficult, but errors or a failure to respond to the sample made the problem somewhat easier.

The effects of two hallucinogenic drugs, LSD and bufotenin, and amphetamine on this behavior are shown in Fig. 3. All three drugs reduced the level of performance, but in different ways. Amphetamine reduced performance by increasing the number of times the subject failed to respond to the sample stimuli, indicating a possible anorexic effect. The hallucinogens, however, decreased the performance by increasing the frequency of incorrect matches. This suggests that these latter drugs disrupt memory, visual discrimination, or some other visual process.

b. Electronic Analysis of Vocalizations. One index of mood changes in humans is a change in speech. When a person is excited, his speech is rapid and high pitched; the converse is true for depression. It was proposed, therefore, that drugs which alter emotional states in man might change vocalizations in monkeys. Discrete cries were evoked from individual squirrel monkeys before and after various drugs and were recorded on a standard tape recorder. The cries were elicited by reaching for (but not touching) each monkey with a gloved hand (153). Recordings of the vocalizations were then analyzed by Kersta (156).

Reaching toward nondrugged monkeys consistently evoked a loud high-pitched screech. Frequency and intensity spectrographic recordings of a representative monkey are shown in the left side of Fig. 4. The upper half of Fig. 4 shows a bar spectrogram and the lower half a contour spectrogram of the vocalization. The bar spectrograms show the different frequencies (from 0 to 7000 cps in 17 cps steps not discriminable in the print) contained in the screeches and how the frequency spectrum changed with time. The contour spectrograms show the intensity of the screech both as a function of time and frequency. Each contour line represents an intensity increase of 6 db, moving from the white background of the Fig. 4 to the darkest portion of the spectrogram. The darkest parts of the spectrograms from nondrugged subjects are arrived at by crossing eight contours, indicating that the most intense cries were between 48 and 54 db above threshold (re: 0.0002 dynes/cm^2). All vocalizations or combinations thereof had a duration of less than 2.4 seconds, which is the total amount of time shown along the abscissa. The time from the beginning of the spectrogram to the onset of the cry was an artifact of the tape recording and does not represent the latency of the response.

The duration of the discrete cries from nondrugged monkeys averaged about 400 msec (range 200–800 msec). The bar spectrograms from nondrugged animals show that the energy of the cry was mainly randomly distributed (not organized into discrete frequency bars), but tended to concentrate around 2000 and 3500 cps. The right-hand spectrograms of Fig. 4 show the effects of diazepam 45 minutes after oral administration.

Diazepam increased the duration of the cry, but did not change the intensity

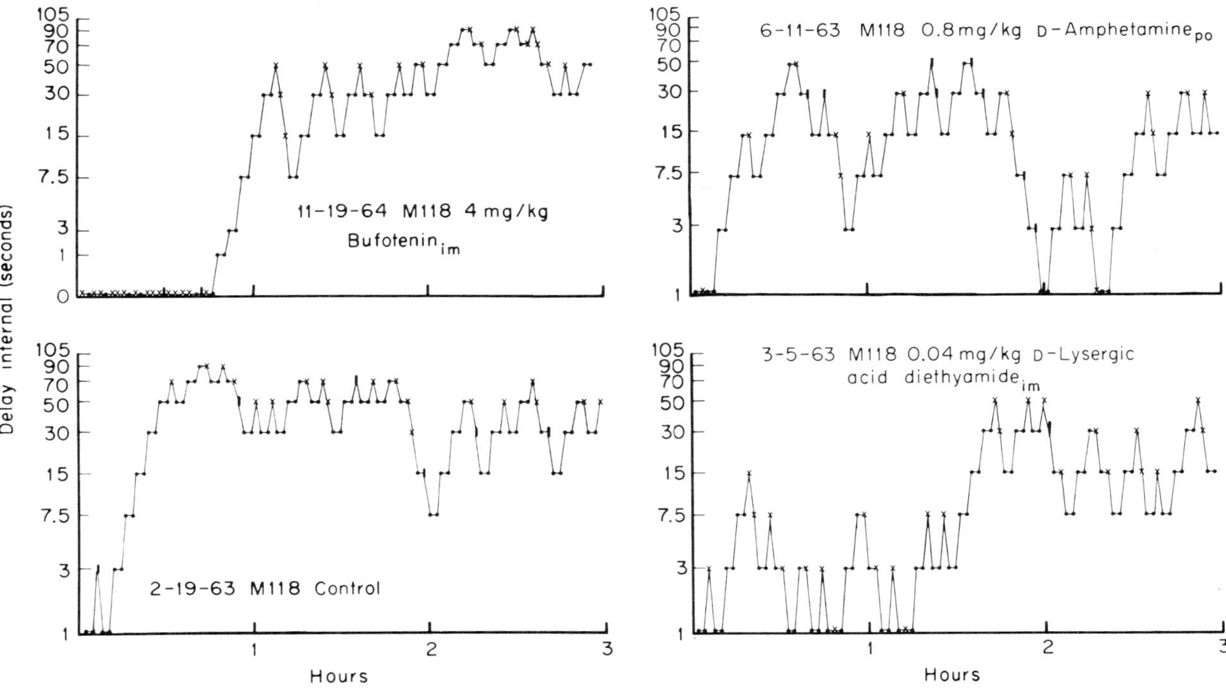

Fig. 3. Effect of bufotenin, amphetamine, and LSD on delayed matching behavior in rhesus monkeys. (Filled circle) correct match; (cross) incorrect match; (vertical line) no observing response.

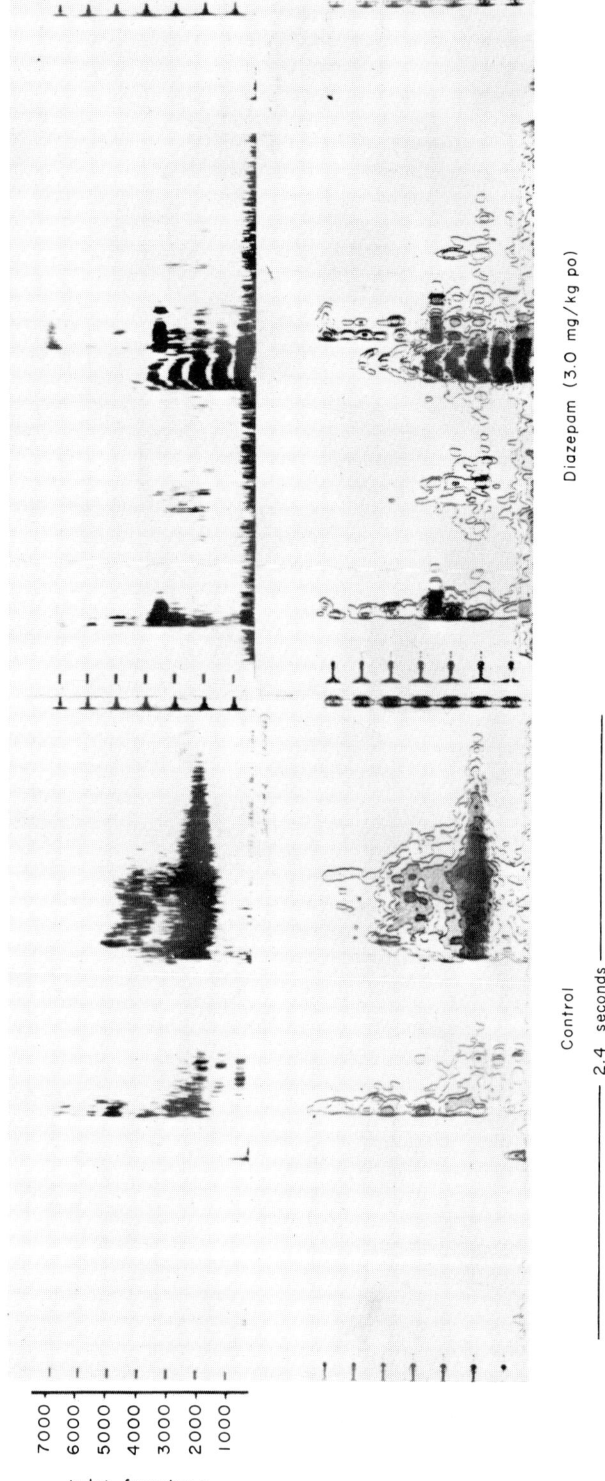

Fig. 4. Spectrograms of vocalizations of a squirrel monkey before (control) and 45 minutes after diazepam. [Reprinted from Scheckel, C. L., and Boff, E. (1967) *In* "Neuro-Psycho-Pharmacology" [H. Brill *et al.*, eds.] p. 789, Exerpta Medica Foundation, Amsterdam, with permission of the publisher.]

of the cry. Most interestingly, diazepam increased the patterning or vocal energy (as opposed to consonant energy, e.g., random noise). As can be seen, under diazepam the cry contained several discrete frequency bars, which appear in the center of the drug spectrogram. These bars parallel each other in their rate of change over time, first showing a rapid increase in frequency, then a flattening followed by a decrease in frequency. The rapid increase in the bar frequencies is indicative of stimulation or excitation in human subjects.

III. Prediction of Clinical Effects from Animal Studies

After a drug has been shown to have interesting and definitive activity in man, techniques can usually be devised to measure some unique or characteristic action of that drug in animals. To make a meaningful and valid correlation between drug effects in animals and man, however, is difficult, but to predict the effect a totally new drug will have in man, based on animal studies alone presents an even greater problem. While there are no foolproof solutions to this problem, several reasonable attempts have been made.

A. *Empirical Categories: Hypnotics, Antipsychotics, Antianxiety Agents*

The empirical approach is the most direct, the least complex, and perhaps the most parsimonious. The main reasoning is this: Different classes of drugs are known to have qualitatively different effects in humans. Therefore, attempts are made to demonstrate qualitatively different effects of these drug classes in animals—regardless of the test used to show such differences. Thus, in man CPZ-type drugs produce a different effect than pentobarbital-type drugs, and chlordiazepoxide and meprobamate have still a third type of activity. Amphetamines of course, have another action; the effect of antidepressants such as imipramine and MAOI's are different from amphetamine effects in man. Animal tests were therefore developed to show measurable behavioral differences between CPZ-type drugs and pentobarbital-type hypnotics and to show further differences between CPZ- and chlordiazepoxide-type drugs.

After the effects of standard drug classes were established in animal tests, new synthetic compounds were tested in these procedures, and their effects were compared with the standard drugs. Thus, if a new compound selectively blocked avoidance responses in rats on a discrete trial avoidance schedule, the compound was predicted to have CPZ-like action in man. Similarly, if a new drug attenuated conflict or increased FI responding in rats, the drug would be proposed as a chlordiazepoxide-type antianxiety drug in man.

The advantage of the empirical approach is that it is not restricted by any preconceptions, and it can be applied to any behaviorally active drug. Considering that so little is known about the fundamental causes of anxiety or psychosis, this approach is surely a safe one. Its disadvantage is that it is unlikely to discover anything that is significantly new or different. As stated earlier, these tests were developed to measure some unique effects, in animals, of drugs that were already known to be effective in humans. These tests can therefore be used to develop more potent chloridiazepoxide-type antianxiety drugs or other CPZ-type antipsychotics. This does not mean that the tests are bad; they have already demonstrated their utility, but they are inadequate for the exploration of new problems and need to be changed. The direction in which they should be changed, however, will only be known after more is learned about the behavioral and biochemical genesis of mental illness.

B. Behavioral Categories: Active and Passive Avoidance

While empirical investigations of drug action did not lead to the proposal of any theories of how drugs affect behavior, some studies have provided a basis for some generalizations and predictions. Some of the more important findings are as follows: (1) Antipsychotics selectively block avoidance responses in the discrete and continuous avoidance procedures, whereas these behaviors are not significantly affected by antianxiety drugs except at high doses causing side effects; (2) antianxiety agents attenuate conflict behavior and increase food reinforced behavior on FI and DRL schedules, while antipsychotics have nonspecific depressant effects on these behaviors. If only schedules that involve shock avoidance are considered, it is seen that both types of drugs reduce avoidance behavior, but the avoidance behavior reduced by antipsychotics is quite different from the behavior attenuated by antianxiety drugs. For example, in discrete avoidance the animal must actively press a lever to avoid shock, and this behavior is selectively reduced by antipsychotics. In a conflict procedure the animal must avoid shock by withholding the lever response, but it does not withhold responses when treated with antianxiety drugs. The former procedure may be called "active avoidance," whereas in conflict there is "passive avoidance." Thus, the two drug categories can be distinguished on a very general basis: Antipsychotics selectively reduce active avoidance behavior, and antianxiety drugs reduce passive avoidance. The converse is also true: antipsychotics do not reduce passive avoidance, and antianxiety drugs do not reduce active avoidance. While this distinction holds for a variety of animal species in many tests involving active or passive avoidance, the clinical significance of the distinction is not well understood. The beneficial effects of antianxiety drugs on phobias would certainly be an example of a reduction of passive avoidance in man. Can the schizophrenic symptoms reduced by antipsychotics be manifestations of active avoidance behavior? Is schizophrenia a pathological form of social active avoidance?

While the above distinction between active and passive avoidance in animals concerns the avoidance of electric shock, the argument can be extended to procedures which do not have such an obviously aversive element. Schedules like FR, FI, and DRL are seemingly motivated only by food reinforcement, but they may also have aversive aspects. On FR and FI, for example, animals are rewarded with food, but they are typically only rewarded when they work fast and hard. Consequently, the reward is associated with a large expenditure of energy. The latter can be aversive, and this aversiveness is probably reflected by the postreinforcement pause, viz. the animal withholds responses that reinstate an aversive (hard work) condition. (The same behavior is seen in humans. After very hard work, pursual of a business contract, completing a term paper, or ending a political campaign, the individual takes a rest, or just "gets away from it all." He essentially absents himself from an environment that has a conditioned association with hard or prolonged work.) This is another example of passive avoidance behavior. The effects of antianxiety drugs on FR and FI behavior of animals are especially interesting in this context. In these tests antianxiety drugs decrease or eliminate pausing and increase the overall response rate suggesting that these drugs reduce passive avoidance behavior on the food reinforced schedules. The passive avoidance component of DRL behavior is perhaps even more obvious. On DRL the subject is reinforced for spacing responses at least 20 seconds apart and, if the subject responds prematurely, it is not rewarded but punished because the premature response postponed the availability of food for another 20 seconds. Thus, the subject must learn to withhold (avoid) premature responses at the same time it is learning to make responses to obtain food. Viewed in this way, DRL is a conflict schedule, as it involves both responding (approach) and the withholding of a response (passive avoidance). Since antianxiety drugs increase rates of DRL, it is possible that they do so by reducing the passive avoidance component of this schedule.

It can be concluded that antianxiety drugs reduce all types of passive avoidance behavior in animals, even in cases where an obvious aversive stimulus (electric shock) is not present. It could even be proposed that when behavior that has no discernible aversive component is increased by antianxiety drugs, the behavior does in fact have some aversive element that could be uncovered by more intense behavioral analysis. In this way drugs may serve to define critical elements of behavior not otherwise sufficiently characterized by psychological tests. It is conceivable, for example, that drugs may be developed for the specific diagnosis of different psychopathologies, just as nalorphine is currently used to uncover narcotic addicts.

For further reading and references see Appendices 1 and 2.

17

PHARMACOLOGY OF PHENOTHIAZINES

L. Valzelli and S. Garattini

I. Introduction

The phenothiazine derivatives had been studied since 1944, mainly for their antihistaminic properties, but it was not until chlorpromazine (CPZ) was synthesized in 1950 that it was noted that this was the first molecule of this category possessing a nonhypnotic depressant activity on the central nervous system. The use of this drug in psychiatric practice led to a completely new approach to mental illness, introducing the concept of pharmacological control of psychotic symptoms. Because of this, CPZ and its derivatives were first classified as "major tranquilizers," whereas more recently these drugs have been better defined as "antipsychotics." Despite the number of other phenothiazines which have been synthesized, CPZ is still widely used because of its wide spectrum of antipsychotic and other activities. It possesses properties of the other phenothiazine derivatives and can be taken as the prototype in this series (for history, see Caldwell, Chapter 2).

II. Peripheral Pharmacological Properties

In addition to its typical antipsychotic activity on the central nervous system, CPZ also possesses a wide spectrum of pharmacological properties, including adrenergic blocking, anticholinergic, antihistaminic, and antiserotonin effects, as well as weak spasmolytic activity. It is also able to induce hypothermia. Its cardiovascular effects, especially the hypotensive response, are an expression of both central and peripheral actions of the drug.

The adrenergic blocking effect of CPZ is one of its chief effects. It blocks or reverses hypertensive responses to epinephrine administration in laboratory animals, whereas the pressor effect of norepinephrine is diminished but not reversed. In addition, the carotid sinus reflexes and the pressor responses normally present on stimulation of the cut central end of the vagus nerve are completely blocked. CPZ is twenty times more effective than promethazine, another representative of the phenothiazine group, in protecting animals against the toxicity of large doses of epinephrine and norepinephrine.

The metabolic effects of epinephrine are not affected, although CPZ itself is mildly hyperglycemic. Its anticholinergic effects are mild, both on the response of isolated guinea pig ileum to acetylcholine and in respect to its hypotensive action in the dog. The antihistaminic activity of CPZ is slight. The drug is a hundred times less active than promethazine in protecting guinea pigs against the toxicity of injected histamine, and forty times less active in protecting them against a histamine aerosol. Its antiserotonin activity is illustrated by its antagonism of the effect of serotonin (5-hydroxytryptamine, 5HT) on the blood pressure of the spinal cat, its antagonism to the stimulating activity of 5HT on the isolated rat colon, and the edema produced by 5HT injected subcutaneously in the rat. The cardiovascular effects of CPZ include the following: (1) There is a dose-dependent decrease in blood pressure, sometimes accompanied by a compensatory tachycardia; (2) the drug does not antagonize the increase in heart rate following intravenous administration of epinephrine, and can itself induce an increase in cardiac frequency; (3) CPZ produces an increase of the coronary outflow as measured on the isolated and perfused rabbit heart, and promethazine is about twice as effective in this respect; (4) a ventricular block can be obtained in the dog after repeated administration of CPZ; (5) it is also effective in inducing dilation of peripheral vessels, with an increase of the blood flow. The respiratory effects of CPZ are such that low doses stimulate respiration, while larger doses induce temporary apnea.

Other effects of CPZ include a weak spasmolytic action, diminishing the tone of the amplitude of the spontaneous movement of isolated small intestine of rabbits. It can also induce some local anesthesia, being somewhat slightly more effective than promethazine and twice as effective as meperidine. CPZ has a powerful antiemetic effect due to depression of the chemoreceptor emetic trigger zone. It also has a hypothermic effect due to its action on the temperature regulatory nuclei of the hypothalamus, the magnitude of which depends on the ambient temperature.

Large doses of CPZ have hormonal regulatory effects, e.g., induction of pseudopregnancy in rats. Similar effects have been reported in women, probably due to an interference with release of pituitary gonadotrophin as a result of hypothalamic depression. Other phenothiazines possess the same effect to a lesser or greater degree. CPZ can diminish the urinary excretion of several estrogenic hormones. It also has a lactogenic effect.

CPZ and other phenothiazines have a melanocyte-stimulating effect in amphibians, which is of interest because this activity seems to be correlated with their clinical efficacy. CPZ possesses some neuromuscular blocking activity, possibly not due to competitive inhibition, since it is not reversed by neostigmine, but probably the result of direct action on the muscle.

III. Activity on the Central Nervous System

CPZ and most other phenothiazines do not modify the monosynaptic and the polysynaptic reflexes of the spinal cat, whereas only monosynaptic reflexes are depressed in the intact animal. As a consequence, the effects of these drugs on postural mechanisms are to be accounted for by its effect on the central nervous system.

CPZ has been shown to have a different kind of CNS depression than that of the usual sedative or hypnotic substances. This action is mainly on the brain-stem structures associated with the arousal system of the brain. The core of this system is the reticular formation of the brain stem, which projects diffusely to all areas of the cerebral cortex, hippocampus, and many other structures, receiving in turn impulses from the main sensory pathways, with collaterals in the brain stem and midbrain. To sum up, CPZ has little or no direct depressant action on the reticular formation, but selectively depresses afferent input to this area.

The brain-stem reticular activating system maintains the wakeful state by means of a tonic facilitatory effect on the brain. Consequently sleep, anesthesia, and coma can be attributed to a reduction or blockade of this facilitatory effect. According to this point of view, the reticular formation can be considered as an important central regulatory mechanism in many cerebral functions, and it can be assumed that all the influences exerted on this particular brain structure can affect other parts and functions of the brain.

In respect to brain electrical activity, CPZ and other phenothiazine derivatives do not affect the spontaneous activity of isolated cortex, and the changes in the electrocorticographic records of intact animals are due to the action on brain-stem structures. The effect of CPZ on the human electroencephalogram (EEG) is relatively slight, consisting mostly of an increased synchronization of cortical activity. More pronounced changes are evident in epileptic patients, in whom the drug augments paroxysmal discharges and spike-and-wave complexes. CPZ induces high voltage discharges in the hippocampus and in the amygdala, followed by a typical EEG defined as rhinencephalic seizure patterns. With large doses the seizures spread from the hippocampus to the cerebral cortex.

In respect to animal behavior CPZ induces a general reduction in motor activity, together with a lack of interest in the environment and decreased responses to external stimuli. These modifications of general behavior are not accompanied by an impairment of motor ability and coordination at lower dosages. At higher dosages or with chronic use, animals become cataplectic (they may remain rigidly in unnatural positions in which they are placed). Certain phenothiazine derivatives selectively depress emotional defecation in animals in an open field, but have little effect on motor performance, e.g., thioridazine, while CPZ and prochlorperazine inhibit both of these functions equally.

More specific aspects of behavior such as sociability and hostility are respectively increased and decreased by CPZ administration. In particular, aggressive behavior is markedly inhibited by small doses of the drug in monkeys, mice, and other animal species, including man. CPZ also reduces the increased locomotor activity induced in laboratory animals by administration of CNS stimulants, such as amphetamine and amphetamine-like drugs, and antagonizes the effects of the administration of lysergic acid diethylamide (LSD). However, phenothiazine derivatives in general potentiate the effects of barbiturates, and other depressants, such as alcohol, causing a marked increase in the duration of sleeping time.

Phenothiazine derivatives greatly affect learning processes, abolishing conditioned responses in various species of laboratory animals. CPZ has a marked action on conditioned avoidance responses, inducing a delay in acquisition, but has only a slight effect in extinction. Perphenazine acts similarly, predominantly depressing conditioned avoidance responses and motor activity. The depressant effects of these drugs on conditioned and motor performance in animals seem, however, not to be due to their general tranquilizing effect, but to the extrapyramidal symptoms which are produced by inducing motor movement disorders (dyskinesias), which interfere with the animals' motor performance in response to rewarding or aversive stimuli.

In other conditions defined as "experimental neurosis," induced by conflictual conditions, the administration of phenothiazines restores normal behavior almost completely.

IV. Other Phenothiazines

There are individual pharmacological differences among the many phenothiazines which cannot be completely covered here. However, a few of these will be mentioned.

Promazine possesses all of the basic properties of CPZ, but has a particularly strong antiemetic activity. Promethazine is a powerful antihistaminic agent also possessing marked adrenolytic, anticholinergic, and anticonvulsant activity. Diethazine is an antihistaminic, analgesic, and adrenolytic agent with minor atropine-like properties. It also has a hypnotic action. In addition, it can relieve the symptoms of Parkinson's disease by an as yet unknown mechanism. Mepazine possesses in general the same spectrum of effects as CPZ, but is less potent and does not have analgesic activity. Thioridazine is a potent adrenergic blocking agent, whereas trifluoperazine has the same cardiovascular effects as CPZ, but lacks parasympatholytic or anticonvulsant properties. Finally, perphenazine, a very potent antiemetic, is similar to CPZ, but has very little hypotensive action.

For reviews of the pharmacology of CPZ, and more detailed discussions of the pharmacology of other phenothiazines please refer to the appendices.

18

PHARMACOLOGY OF OTHER ANTIPSYCHOTIC DRUGS

Henri-Marie Laborit and Alain Sanseigne

I. Reserpine

A. *Introduction*

Rauwolfia alkaloids appeared in the modern treatment of psychoses around 1953, slightly later than the phenothiazines. Their therapeutic use, however, goes back to much earlier times, since Hindu medicine refers to the utilization of rauwolfia-type plant extracts in the treatment of hypertension, insomnia, and insanity (cf. Caldwell, Chapter 2).

It was not until 1954 that Schlittler *et al.* isolated reserpine, an alkaloid from the resin fraction of the extract, which was then considered the active principle responsible for the sedative action. This in turn led Wilkins (1954) to investigate the product in the treatment of hypertension, while Bein established that in low doses the drug had a sedative effect on rabbits, though the animals could be aroused by stimulation, being in this respect different from the action of barbiturates and more akin to the effect of chlorpromazine (CPZ) in man, as reported by Laborit and his associates in 1952. Lastly, in 1954 Kline reported his initial observations with the product in psychiatry.*

* Cf. Caldwell, Appendix I for Chapter 2, for the above references.

B. Absorption, Fate in the Body, and Elimination*

Rauwolfia alkaloids are rapidly absorbed in the intestinal tract and diffuse readily after parenteral administration. In 1959, Williams identified the main metabolites of reserpine as: methyl reserpate, trimethoxybenzoate, syringic acid, and methyl reserpate syringoyl. ^{14}C-labeling of the carboxyl group on the side chain of reserpine established that 70% is excreted as reserpine in the feces and 5% as trimethoxy benzoate in the urine, regardless of whether administered orally or intravenously.

Reserpine vanishes rapidly from circulation and is probably stored in adipose tissues; it then reappears in the blood as trimethoxy benzoate. Although traces of reserpine can be detected in the blood as late as six weeks after injection, it is believed that the therapeutic action is not predicated on blood concentrations. Moreover, the substance is known to diffuse uniformly throughout the various areas of the brain.

C. Preparation and Dosage

The powdered whole extract of *Rauwolfia serpentina* is usually available in tablets of 50 and 100 mg. The average daily dose is 200–400 mg, equivalent to 0.5–0.7 mg of purified reserpine. The sedative and antihypertensive fraction of the extract is available in 2-mg tablets. Daily doses range from 2 to 4 mg. Reserpine is manufactured in capsules of 0.25, 0.5, and 0.75 mg; in drops (2 mg/ml), in injectable solutions (5 mg in 2 ml and 25–50 mg in 10 ml), as well as in tablets (0.1, 0.2, 0.25, 1, 2, 4, and 5 mg). In the treatment of hypertension, the dose ranges from 0.05 to 0.5 mg per day. In psychoses, the dose may attain 5 mg by the oral route and 10 mg by intramuscular injection. Other rauwolfia alkaloids also used in psychiatry are: rescinnamine (0.25 to 0.5 mg/day), deserpidine (0.1 to 3 mg/day), and syrosingopine, mostly used in hypertension.

D. Pharmacologic Activity

1. Central Nervous System

"Under low doses, the animals are tired and subdued, while with larger doses they sleep quietly," wrote H. J. Bein in 1954 (cf. Caldwell, Chapter 2); he observed the reversible hypnotic action previously reported for CPZ, thus differentiating between antipsychotics and the classical anesthetics and hypnotics. The preservation of the pupillary corneal reflex and the pain reflex indicates the absence of analgesic action. Reserpine lowers the reactive threshold to pain stimuli. It has no anticonvulsant action and in fact lowers the threshold to convulsive electroshock seizures. It prolongs the duration of afterdischarges following hippocampal stimulation. Reserpine affords no protection against strychnine, picrotoxin, nicotine, or cardiazol. Conversely, it inhibits caffeine-induced stimulation, but does not interfere with the stimulant activity of dextrorotatory

* Cf. Goldenberg and Fishman, Chapter 14.

amphetamines. Like CPZ, reserpine lowers the ability of conditioned animals to respond to stimuli. Also, like the phenothiazines, reserpine in elevated doses is capable of causing an extrapyramidal syndrome and even a pseudo-Parkinsonian syndrome (cf. Hornykiewicz *et al.*, Chapter 46).

2. Amine Depletion*

Pletscher *et al.* (157) showed that reserpine decreases the level of endogenous 5-hydroxytryptamine (serotonin, 5HT). Holzbauer and Vogt (158) showed that it also decreases the levels of norepinephrine (NE) and other biological amines. Thereafter, numerous investigators attempted to link such depletion with the drug's effect on behavior. A single reserpine dose can deplete catecholamine and 5HT reserves in the brain and peripheral organs for a period of days or weeks.

Some investigators attributed the effect of reserpine on behavior to its depletion of 5HT (159). Conversely, Carlsson *et al.* (160) are of the opinion that catecholamine depletion is the reason for the drug's action on behavior. Dopamine (DA) can antagonize the effect of reserpine on 5-hydroxytryptophan (5HTP). Finally, others hold that the central effects of reserpine are linked to mechanisms other than catecholamine and 5HT depletion.

It is likely that reserpine acts by a variety of diverse mechanisms. It is certain that phenothiazines, which possess similar central effects, do not deplete cerebral reserves of catecholamines or 5HT. Therefore, it is much more likely that the antihypertensive action of reserpine is related to the decrease of catecholamines in tissues and peripheral organs and that this hypotensive response is not evidently related to reserpine's central action. Reserpine not only depletes granular catecholamine stores but also reduces their *in vivo* and *in vitro* activation in tissues. This phenomenon is possibly related to a decrease in adenine nucleotides, observed at the level of the granules. Reserpine would therefore depress the active transport which should be compensating the depletion, by diffusion of the catecholamines, but this reserpine-induced depletion is blocked by cold, which cannot be readily reconciled with the theory of decreased active transport. Conversely, hypersensitivity to injected catecholamines would seem to be related to the depletion of storage sites, similar to that following resection of a nerve. It is quite probable that reserpine interferes by one or more as yet unknown mechanisms with the metabolic processes which are a factor in numerous secondary reactions that cannot be explained by catecholamine depletion, and might actually be a contributing factor in the depletion itself.

On the electroencephalogram (EEG), 15 minutes after intravenous injection of 2 mg/kg of reserpine, all stereotaxic leads show activation of dominant motor cortex potentials, with occasional bursts of peak-wave activity. This tracing contrasts with the slow pattern, which becomes evident several hours later. Within a few hours, reserpine-treated rabbits present an EEG pattern of slow waves and spindles, particularly marked in the caudate nucleus. Auditory stimulation causes cortical desynchronization, but only its duration, along with reticular

* Cf. Snyder, Chapter 9.

activation of the caudate nucleus and the appearance of theta waves from the hippocampus and thalamic nuclei. A nociceptive stimulus (for example a 60-cps stimulation of the sciatic) will induce generalized theta waves in all leads and cause a marked, though transient, fall in blood pressure.

It seems logical to suppose that this desynchronization is an expression of the train of impulses which reach the cortex by lemniscal pathways. The fact that there is no prolongation reflects an inhibition of extralemniscal pathways, indicative of a stimulation of the multisynaptic neuronal activity of the brain stem by neuromodulators (NE and 5HT), which are no longer available to perform this function after administration of reserpine.

By depriving the neurons of their neuromodulator reserves, reserpine also depletes the neuronal metabolic activators in the posterior hypothalamus. This results in a predominance of anterior hypothalamic activity, evidenced by the appearance of slow waves and cortical spindles, showing little activity at the level of mesencephalic reticular formations.

In reserpinized animals, the administration of a gaseous mixture of 50% CO_2 and 50% O_2 causes hypotension rather than hypertension. The initial phase of theta waves, visible for some seconds in the normal animal, fails to materialize and the slow waves appear earlier (10 seconds, instead of 40). Upon discontinuation of the CO_2, the epileptogenic activity increases.

3. Neuromodulators

Under normal conditions, epinephrine, NE, DA, and 5HT do not permeate the blood-brain barrier. After reserpine has depleted the brain levels of these different neuromodulators, their precursors 3,4-dihydroxyphenylalanine (DOPA) and 5HTP may be injected in an attempt to resupply materials capable of reactivating cerebral synthesis of these substances.

In an animal reserpinized 12 hours earlier, intravenous injection of 25 mg/kg DOPA reactivates in all leads the slow pattern characteristic of reserpine within 1 minute following the injection. The hippocampus and lateral thalamus seem the least responsive. Under the same conditions, an injection of 5HTP (20 mg/kg), infused at a rate of 2 mg/kg/min provokes a generalized low-voltage pattern in all leads 45 to 60 minutes later, though increasing markedly the cerebral 5HT levels.

Infusion of 50 mg/kg DOPA and 30 mg/kg 5HTP at the rate of 3 mg/kg/min to an animal treated with reserpine will cause within a few minutes signs of systemic excitation, with tremors and hyperpnea associated with a flattening of the EEG record in all stereotaxic leads. The pattern is interspersed with bursts of dominant hippocampal electric activity. This, in turn, is followed by dominant theta waves from the hippocampus. After a few minutes, the tracing flattens out and the animal dies.

The action of 5HTP, with or without DOPA, resembles acute anoxia. It has been shown that under conditions of anoxia the same leveling of the tracing is related to a reduction of 70% or more in nicotinamide adenine dinucleotide (NAD) and nicotinamide adenine dinucleotide phosphate (NADP) and that the EEG is reactivated upon attaining a certain degree of oxidation of pyridine nucleotides by the administration of oxygen. We have established, however, that the reducing action of 5HT is probably responsible for some of its pharmacological properties.

Under the circumstances, this action is particularly effective in the treatment of convulsive seizures induced by hyperbaric oxygenation, as we showed in 1957 (161), and that reserpine enhances convulsions triggered by O_2 under pressure.

4. Overall Considerations

The effect of CPZ on behavior has often been likened to that of reserpine. CPZ, however, prevents the release of neuromodulators from their storage granules, while reserpine depletes the reserves of the latter. The functional results are identical, but with the difference that in the case of replenishment without possibility of release (CPZ), the cellular elements will be less responsive to injected neurohormones, whereas in the case of depletion (reserpine), their sensitivity will be enhanced. We must add that in the case of CPZ the action on metabolism and the antagonism toward oxidative processes, probably resulting from interference with the chain of intramitochondrial carriers, afford a partial explanation of the central effect achieved. In the case of reserpine, the metabolic and membranous processes involved are not yet known.

There is still no explanation available as to the biological mechanism by which reserpine leads to a depletion of neuromodulator reserves. It would seem to us, at least in relation to isolated organ function of reserpinized animals, that reserpine exerts a direct pharmacologic action on the cellular metabolic function of which the changes in granular membrane permeability would only be a consequence. In such cases, one cannot admit, lacking further evidence, that all reserpine-induced functional disturbances of central or peripheral character, are exclusively due to the depletion of catecholamine and 5HT granular reserves.

II. Other Major Antipsychotics

A. *Butyrophenones*

These constitute a group of substances synthesized by Janssen in 1958 (see Appendix 1). Initial clinical findings were presented by Divry, Bobson, and Collard in 1958 (162).

1. Haloperidol

Its acute toxicity is greater than that of CPZ, since the LD_{50} is 20 mg/kg by the intravenous route, but the product is active in very low doses. Chronic toxicity seems low, and mice receiving 110 mg for 15 days presented no histological lesions. A daily dose of 10 mg/kg to rats for 134 days caused neither mortality nor habituation.

As for the vasomotor system, haloperidol causes no change in the arterial pressure of rats, but induces hypothermia. At high doses it depresses ventilation in dogs. The product is neither adrenolytic nor cholinolytic, but rather antihistaminic. In reference to behavior, a dose of 0.16 mg/kg causes sedation in rats with reduction in spontaneous motility; 2.5 mg/kg causes catalepsy and convulsions. The drug inhibits the conditioned flight reflex in the rat, along with the response to unconditioned stimuli. It potentiates phenobarbital in mice, but is unable to prevent cardiazol or strychnine convulsions.

Toxicity is low, and the spread between LD_{50} and therapeutic doses considerable. The drug possesses a measure of analgesic activity. On the whole, although it is a potent antipsychotic, it has not been judged superior to CPZ by many investigators.

a. Indications. Therapeutic effectiveness is most pronounced in manic patients and in acute stages of schizophrenia, while the poorest results are achieved in depressive psychoses. The product would therefore seem to be indicated in syndromes attended by agitation, hyperactivity, hallucinations, and paranoid delirium, but not in depressions. In the opinion of European investigators, this is the most potent agent currently available in the treatment of manic syndromes.

b. Side effects. They are akin to those reported for other antipsychotics and are essentially characterized by the appearance of an extrapyramidal syndrome. This entails akinesia, hypertonicity, spasms, and paresthesia. There may be slight arterial hypotension, particularly orthostatic, perspiration, salivation, loss of appetite, and loss of weight, which are the main signs of an autonomic syndrome.

c. Dosage. The dosage range is the lowest for any of the current antipsychotics. For intravenous administration: 1–5 mg per injection; orally: 7.5–15 mg per day. Peak oral doses appear to be in the range of 30 mg per day, and those given intramuscularly, 2–25 mg per day.

2. Triperidol

This product is related to haloperidol, the difference consisting in a CF_3 group on the phenyl nucleus instead of CL. This drug seems to be the most potent of the series. Although its acute toxicity is lower (LD_{50} = 26 mg/kg intravenously in mice), it exerts a greater catatonizing effect. Pharmacologically it is very similar to the preceding substance. The drug is a potent antagonist of apomorphine, while it potentiates barbiturates.

a. Indications. Its sedative action is weaker than that of haloperidol and at low doses, it actually exerts a stimulant effect. Unlike haloperidol, it is free of depressant effects and appears indicated in the treatment of hebephrenic and apragmatic forms of schizophrenic psychoses.

b. Dosage. Dosage is 1–5 mg per day. Side effects are those caused by high doses of antipsychotics, notably somnolence and drug-induced Parkinsonism.

3. Haloanisone

This is a fluorinated, nonchlorinated compound in which piperazine was substituted for piperidine. It has no anticonvulsant action, but is an antagonist of apomorphine; it potentiates barbiturates, reduces motility in mice at a dose of 1 mg/kg. At doses above 5 mg/kg, the product causes an excitomotor syndrome, characterized in mice by sudden jerks and in dogs by tremor.

a. Indications. Its sedative action is often remarkable in psychoses associated with agitation. It would at times seem opportune to potentiate this effect with low doses of phenothiazines, which by themselves would be ineffective. The drug has been credited with a potent antihallucinatory action.

b. Dosage. This ranges from 20 to 100 mg per day. Side effects are similar to those of the preceding products, except that their incidence seems to be rather frequent.

B. Chlorprothixene

This drug resembles CPZ, except that the nitrogen in the central nucleus is replaced by a carbon and a double bond at the start of the lateral chain gives rise to an isomer. It is the *trans* form that is used therapeutically. A chlorine atom occupies the same position as in CPZ. The toxicity of the product appears to be twice as high as the toxicity of CPZ: the LD_{50} for mice is 28 mg/kg intravenously and 140 mg/kg orally. Its action on behavior resembles both the antipsychotics and the tranquilizers in that a high dose is necessary to induce catatonia. It inhibits the conditioned light reflex in rats at half the dose of CPZ. It potentiates barbiturates and nonbarbituric hypnotics as well as analgesics. It induces hypothermia, is antipyretic and acts as an antagonist of apomorphine. Its anticonvulsant action is limited. The drug's effect on the EEG is similar to that of CPZ. It is a hypotensor and an accelerator of the heart rate. It antagonizes epinephrine, acetylcholine, histamine, and 5HT.

1. Indications

This drug would appear to be indicated in the treatment of endogenous depressive as well as manic syndromes. It is also used as an antiemetic. The occurrence of extrapyramidal symptoms is open to discussion and, unlike the antipsychotics in general, there seems to be little tendency to somnolence. Some changes in blood pressure and pulse rate have been reported, together with variations in the temperature curve. The dosage is 90–150 mg per day intramuscularly, 60–90 mg per day intravenously, and 120–180 mg orally.

C. Reserpines

Along with total rauwolfia extracts, which have not proven superior to reserpine in psychiatric use, other alkaloids have recently been included in therapy.

Rescinnamine and reserpidine are pharmacologically similar to reserpine, but present no evident therapeutic advantages.

D. Synthetic Reserpines

Tetrabenazine is a benzoquinolizine derivative and, like reserpine, it lowers the tissue concentration of 5HT and enhances the excretion of its catabolite,

5-hydroxyindole acetate (5-HIAA). It also decreases the NE content of the brain.

The acute toxicity of tetrabenazine is ten times smaller than that of reserpine, and its chronic toxicity is low. Excretion is faster than with reserpine and does not exceed 8 hours, while sedation under reserpine persists for several days.

Tetrabenazine decreases the avoidance reaction in rats in about the same doses as CPZ. It reduces aggressiveness in animals and depresses general activity. No gastric lesions were found in rats after administration of tetrabenazine, while 90% of those treated with reserpine presented extensive hemorrhagic lesions of the stomach. The product reduces food intake in rats; a similar effect has been observed in humans. It seems to activate slightly the release of NE and 5HT from peripheral storage sites.

Side effects are relatively slight, with little hypotensive action and few digestive disorders. In man, a Parkinson-like syndrome has been reported, but it clears up on withdrawal of therapy. The EEG shows activation of the alpha rhythm without an increase in the number of spindles; however, the onset of temporal peaked-wave bursts calls for reduced doses in epileptics.

Dosage. Treatment can be initiated with 50 mg intravenously and continued intramuscularly or orally, inasmuch as the subcutaneous administration is painful. The dosage ranges from 75 to 300 mg per day in three or four divided administrations. The dose may reach as high as 600 mg per day in men, while 180 mg seems adequate for women.

The *activity* of the drug is most outspoken in hallucinations. In acute psychoses, the drug works fast to relieve anxiety.

III. Conclusions

To conclude this brief review, we believe that we should begin by differentiating between the antipsychotic action of CPZ and that of reserpine, both at the biochemical and the neurophysiological level. Neither product prevents cortical desynchronization upon stimulation of the sciatic nerve, for instance. This desynchronization, however, lasts only as long as the stimulus itself and is an expression of inhibition of the ascending reticular activating system. Direct stimulation of the reticular system under CPZ is associated with a cortical desynchronization, thus suggesting that the inhibition operates at the level of the synapses between the mesencephalic reticular formation and the ascending pathways.

It may be postulated that wherever neurons and neuroglia contain catecholamines, then CPZ, on the one hand, will render impermeable the membranes of the storage granules and thus prevent their release, while reserpine, on the other hand, will initially promote such release, but then prevent renewed storage of catecholamines. In either case, the catecholamines can no longer perform their function.

The incoming train of impulses to the cerebral regions which release acetylcholine will cause the nicotinic effects of acetylcholine to trigger the physiologic release of catecholamines from their storage granules. These in turn will play a regulating role on the activity of adjoining nerve cells.

In the limbic system, the same physiological mechanism will promote the release of 5HT, which is stored there in abundance. This is most likely the cause for the appearance of theta waves characteristic of hippocampal electric activity. Both CPZ and reserpine will inhibit this action, the one by preventing 5HT release, the other by depleting the storage granules and preventing replenishment. Both will lower the threshold of hippocampal excitation, thus prolonging after-discharges following direct stimulation.

Conversely, at the level of the corpus striatum, reserpine-induced depletion of DA will have the same catatonic effect on the extrapyramidal system as CPZ. The pathological Parkinsonian syndrome is associated with DA depletion from the striatum (cf. Hornykiewicz *et al.*, Chapter 46).

At the level of the intralaminary thalamic nuclei, diffuse low frequency (8 cps) cortical desynchronization is observed. The system appears to be essentially cholinergic. CPZ and reserpine promote the recruiting response at low frequencies, but raise considerably the threshold to desynchronization at high frequencies.

Lastly, the distinction between the anterior, predominantly glycolytic hypothalamus, and the posterior, predominantly oxidative, portion provides a clue to the prevalence of the so-called trophotropic action of the two antipsychotic drugs. CPZ and reserpine alike depress the responsiveness of the posterior hypothalamus to direct stimulations.

These experimental considerations are of more than theoretical interest. The reduced excitability of the thalamic system undoubtedly plays a role in the decreased attention caused by antipsychotics, whereas in the case of antianxiety agents this system appears to perform a focalizing action. Decreased excitability of the reticular formation to impulses of peripheral origin is also doubtlessly very important. Alerting signals favoring flight or defensive reactions arise from the reticular formation of the brain stem traversing the inner capsule on the way to the cortex. This would account for the fact that defense reactions are depressed by CPZ and reserpine. The decreased excitability of the posterior hypothalamus certainly contributes to the depression of these reactions.

In concluding this presentation, we should like to emphasize a concept which has often helped us in neuropsychopharmacology. This has to do with our observation that so-called tranquilizing drugs used in neuroses generally reduce the excitability of the limbic system to direct stimulation, whereas the drugs used in psychoses tend to augment the reactivity. If one admits that the function of this system is an element essential to both affective behavior and memory, then this observation would seem to afford fruitful deductions.

For further reading and references see Appendices 1 and 2.

19

NON-MONAMINE OXIDASE INHIBITOR ANTIDEPRESSANTS STRUCTURE–ACTIVITY RELATIONSHIPS

John H. Biel

I. Introduction

The stuctural evolution of the non-monamine oxidase inhibitor (non-MAOI) antidepressant drugs and the subsequent revolution in the therapy of mental depression is a direct outgrowth of the molecular modification by the medicinal chemist of the antihistaminic drugs and the postulate advanced by the early investigators that the control of brain function and the emotional state is the result of an interplay between certain endogenous chemical neurotransmitter hormones similar to that prevailing in the peripheral nervous system, where acetylcholine and norepinephrine may act synergistically or mutually antagonistically in mediating autonomic nerve impulses (163–165).

The early antihistaminic drugs were essentially ethylenediamine derivatives where one of the nitrogens was substituted by two bulky aromatic groups and the other nitrogen by two methyl groups (I and II).

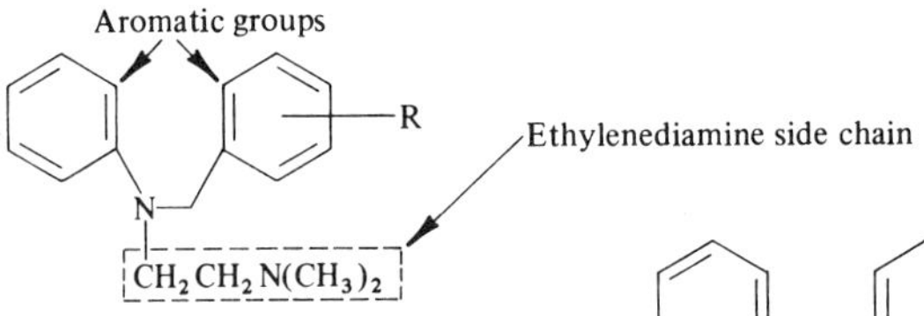

Aromatic groups

Ethylenediamine side chain

$CH_2CH_2N(CH_3)_2$

Phenbenzamine

(I)

R=H, Cl, OCH_3

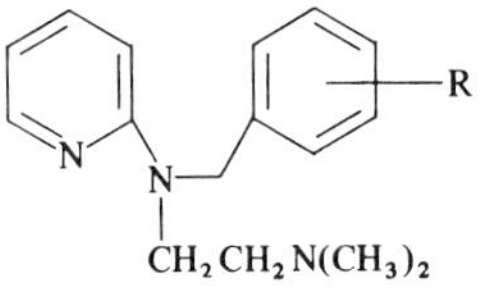

$CH_2CH_2N(CH_3)_2$

Tripelennamine

(II)

The aromatic nitrogen could be substituted by an isosteric "CH" group (III) with an increase in the antihistaminic activity.

Methylidenyl group

$CH_2CH_2N(CH_3)_2$

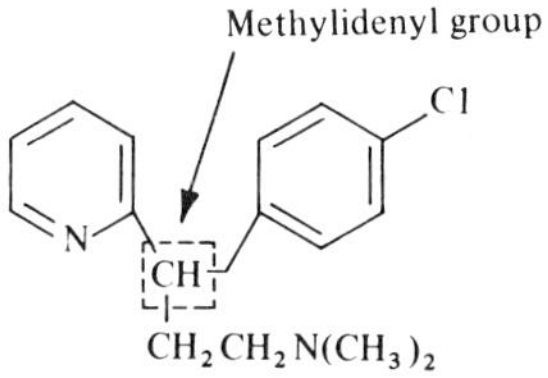

Chlorpheniramine

(III)

We shall see later that the replacement of an aromatic nitrogen by a methylidenyl group became one of the major molecular modifications in the tricyclic antidepressant and psychotropic drug field.

One of the outstanding central side effects of the antihistaminics was stimulation in the animal and sedation in man—a dichotomy which led many pharmacologic investigators astray in failing to forecast clinical antidepressant properties in man for drugs which displayed a "tranquilizer" spectrum in animals.

The joining of the two aromatic groups in I by a sulfide bridge (IV) produced a highly potent and long-lasting antihistaminic with an even greater degree of central depressant (sedative) activity. Replacing the isopropyl by an *n*-propylene side chain (V) reduced the antihistaminic activity markedly but accentuated the psychoactive properties; the addition of a 2-chloro substituent in one of the phenyl rings yielded the first antipsychotic tranquilizing drug (chlorpromazine) (VI), which represented a major breakthough in the chemical treatment of mental illness, particularly the psychoses (see Caldwell, Chapter 2).

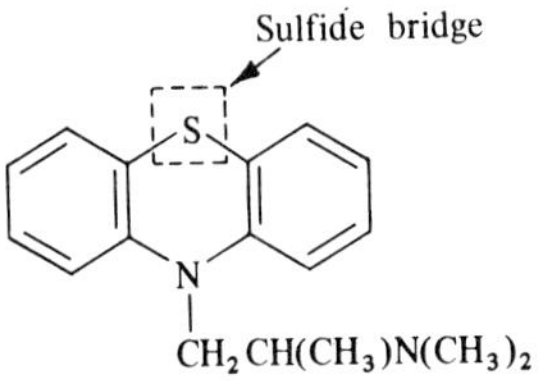

Sulfide bridge

$CH_2CH(CH_3)N(CH_3)_2$

Promethazine

(IV)

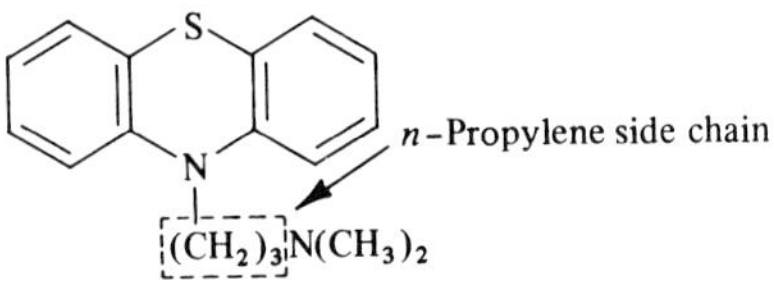

n-Propylene side chain

$(CH_2)_3N(CH_3)_2$

Promazine

(V)

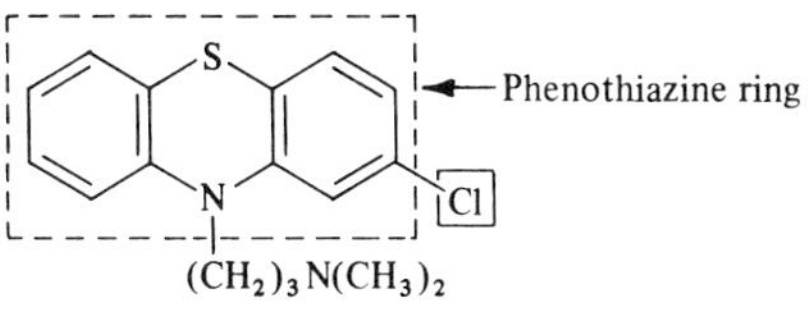

Phenothiazine ring

Cl

$(CH_2)_3N(CH_3)_2$

Chlorpromazine

(VI)

Thus, the "freezing" of two phenyl groups into a rigid conformation and the change from an isopropyl to an *n*-propylene side chain (thereby separating the ring and terminal nitrogens by three methylene groups) produced compounds with important psychotherapeutic properties acting selectively on the hypothalamic structure in the midbrain without disturbing the higher centers, which would have resulted in physical and mental incapacitation.

The transition from the antihistaminic to the psychotherapeutic drugs was made possible, therefore, by these structural alterations:

1. The joining of two aromatic groups into a bridged tricyclic system.
2. The change from an aminoethylene to a aminopropylene side chain (the three-carbon distance between the two nitrogens, i.e.,

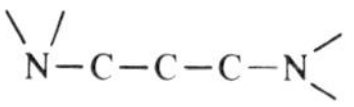

$$\rangle N{-}C{-}C{-}C{-}N\langle$$

was of crucial importance to CNS activity).

3. The addition of an electronegative group (Cl, CF_3, $COCH_3$, $CH_3S \rightarrow O$, SO_2NMe_2, CN) which greatly intensified antipsychotic and other psychoactive properties.

II. Structure–Activity Relationships of the Tricyclic Antidepressants

The isosteric replacement of sulfur with an ethylene bridge by Schindler and Häfliger (166) in structure V yielded the first major antidepressant drug imipramine (VII). This change from a "flat," two-dimensional (phenothiazine)

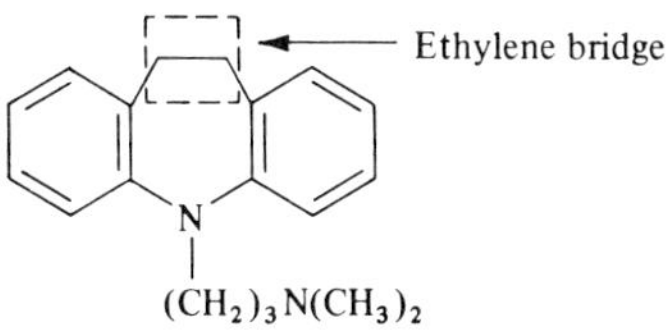

Ethylene bridge

$(CH_2)_3N(CH_3)_2$

Imipramine

(VII)

to a "skewed," three-dimensional ring system (iminodibenzyl) proved to be of paramount importance in the evolution of the antidepressant drugs from their parent structures.

On the basis of its pharmacologic spectrum imipramine was considered a weak antipsychotic agent and hence went unnoticed for several years. It was Kuhn

(166) who first discovered the therapeutic action of imipramine in the treatment of endogenous depressions and his pioneering work represented a major advance in the chemical treatment of the depressed state. It sparked a vast chemical and pharmacological effort to synthesize analogues of imipramine and devise new methods of animal testing which would have clinical relevancy. An excellent and comprehensive review by Häfliger and Burckhardt (168) covers the chemistry, pharmacology, and clinical effects of the iminodibenzyl and related derivatives until 1963. A treatise dealing with the correlation of chemical constitution and clinical efficacy of psychoactive drugs has been published by Stach and Pöldinger (169).

Further structural refinements which produced certain qualitative and quantitative changes in the biochemical, pharmacological, and clinical spectrum of the tricyclic antidepressants were the replacement of the ring nitrogen by a carbon atom (VIII) and the elimination of one of the *N*-methyl groups in the terminal amino group of imipramine to yield desipramine (IX) (170).

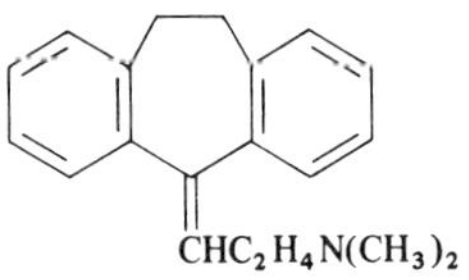

$CHC_2H_4N(CH_3)_2$ — Amitriptyline (VIII)

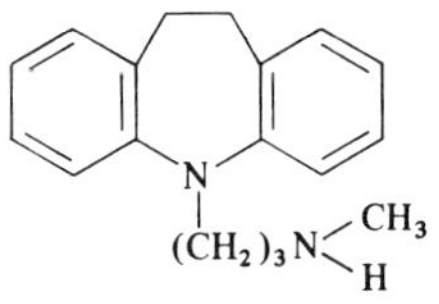

$(CH_2)_3N(CH_3)H$ — Desipramine (IX)

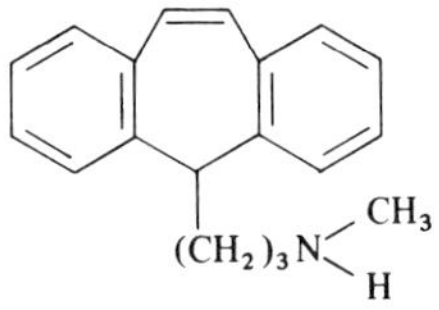

$(CH_2)_3N(CH_3)H$ — Protriptyline (X)

Amitriptyline (VIII) is an efficacious antidepressant with a high incidence of somnolence, which is absent in imipramine; the latter drug is more of a *stimulant* antidepressant.

The slow and variable onset of action of imipramine, its orthostatic hypotensive effects especially in the elderly, and its paradoxical effects in animal vs. human pharmacology prompted this author and his associates to synthesize the desmethyl analogs of imipramine (IX) and a closely related analog of amitriptyline (X). The structure-activity rationale was based on the fact that in the sympathomimetic series the *N*-methyl analogs (XI) of methamphetamine and epinephrine (XII) were devoid of their central and vascular stimulant properties, respectively, and it was reasoned that a similar parallelism might exist among the tricyclic antidepressants.

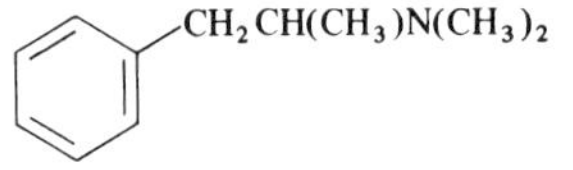

$C_6H_5CH_2CH(CH_3)N(CH_3)_2$ — *N*-Methylmethamphetamine (XI)

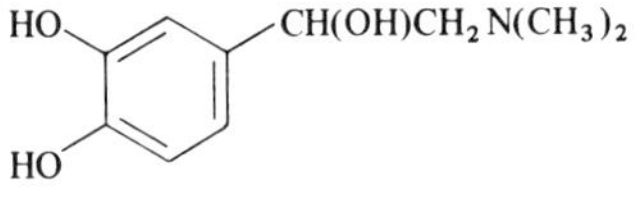

$(HO)_2C_6H_3CH(OH)CH_2N(CH_3)_2$ — *N*-Methylepinephrine (XII)

At about the same time it was demonstrated that in rats (but not in mice, guinea pigs, or rabbits) imipramine is converted to desipramine (IX) and that it is the *metabolite* which is responsible for the antidepressant activity of imipramine; hence, the delayed action of imipramine was ascribed to the slow accumulation of normethyl compound in the body (171).

In the clinic, desipramine had a more rapid onset of action than imipramine (170,172); side effects were less severe and their nature also different as compared to imipramine.

From these basic structual prototypes, a vast array of related analogs evolved which were classified by Pöldinger (139) according to their clinical activity spectra and chemical structures:

A. *Mood-Elevating Antidepressants*

Imipramine

(XIII)

Dibenzepine

(XIV)

B. *Antianxiety—Sedative Antidepressants*

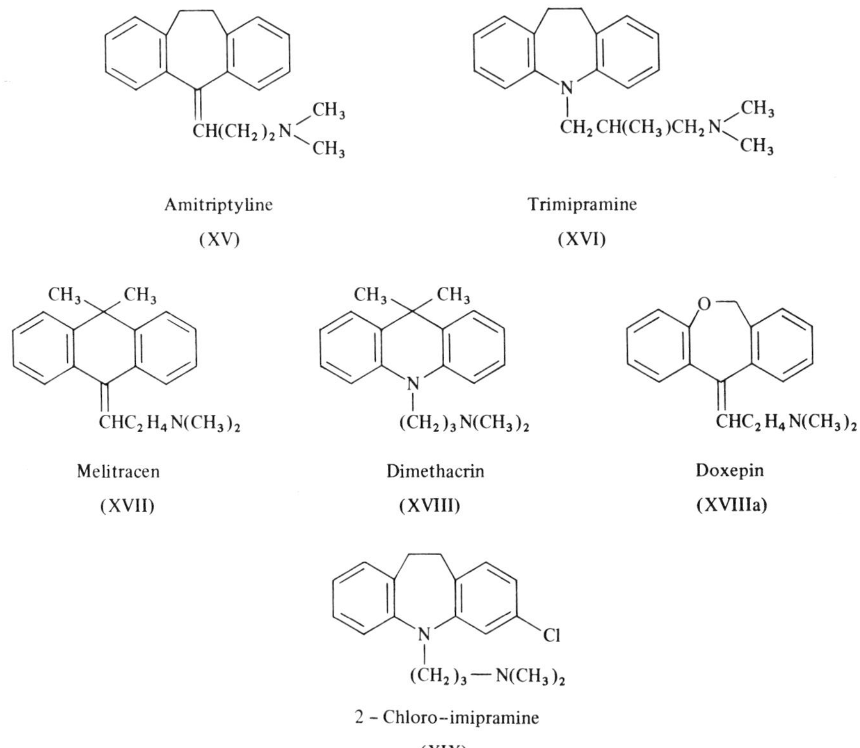

Amitriptyline (XV)

Trimipramine (XVI)

Melitracen (XVII)

Dimethacrin (XVIII)

Doxepin (XVIIIa)

2 - Chloro-imipramine (XIX)

C. *Stimulant Antidepressants*

The structures shown below, as well as the MAO inhibitors are used in the inhibited, withdrawn (anergic) depressed patients. They also have a greater tendency to exacerbate psychotic symptoms:

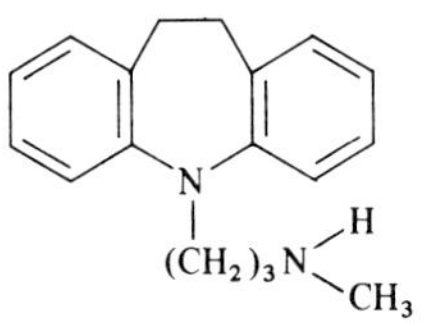

Desipramine

(XX)

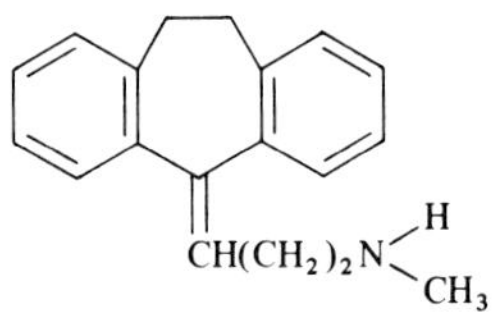

Nortriptyline

(XXI)

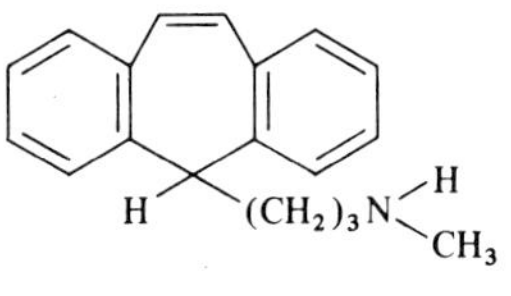

Protriptyline

(XXII)

D. *Phenothiazines and Phenothiazine Analogs with Mood-Elevating Properties*

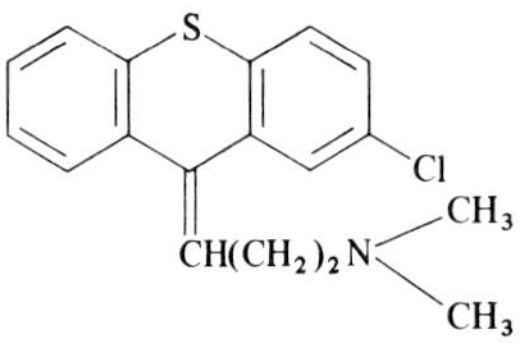

Chlorprothixene

(XXIII)

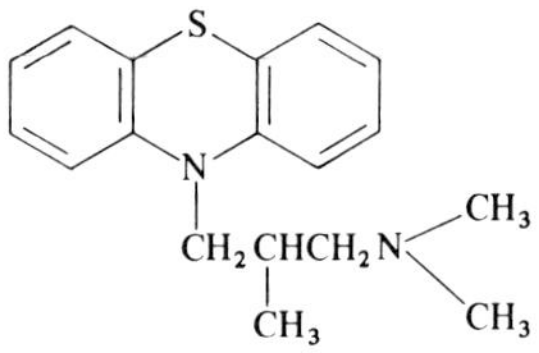

Levomepromazine

(XXIV)

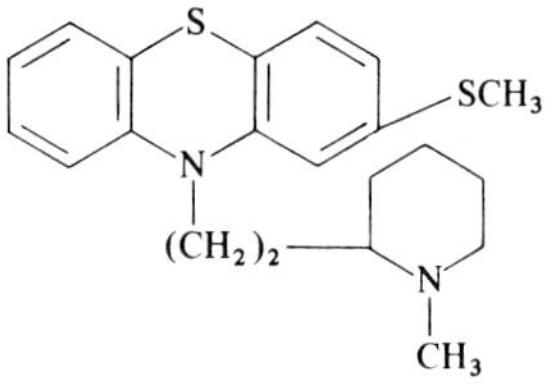

Thioridazine

(XXV)

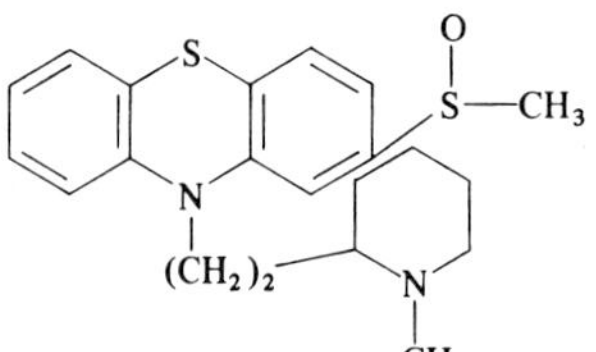

Mesoridazine

(XXVI)

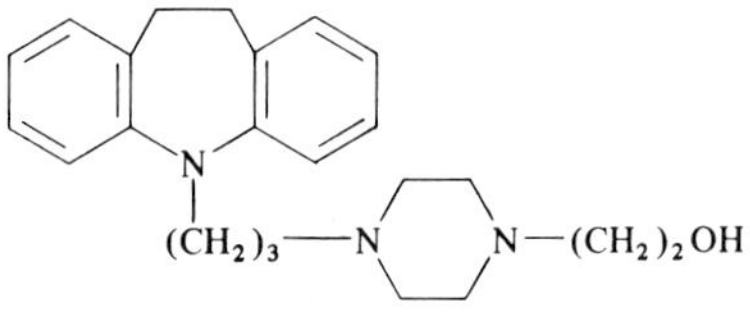

Opipramol

(XXVII)

It should be noted that the "stimulant" antidepressant drugs are generally *secondary* amines, i.e., they have a terminal monomethylamino group. The "sedative" antidepressant drugs have a *tertiary* terminal amino group (i.e., dimethylamino); in addition, some of them also have a flatter ring system (XVII; XVIII) or an electronegative substituent (chlorine) in the 2-position (XIX).

A terminal dimethylamino or monomethylamino group appears to be crucial to afford a predominantly antidepressant-acting drug. It might be inferred from this that metabolic demethylation to a secondary amine is required for therapeutic efficacy in mental depression.

III. Mechanism of Action of Antidepressant Drugs

A. *Enhancement of Adrenergic Transmission*

Increased strides have been made toward arriving at a biochemical basis for endogenous depression. This has been discussed elsewhere in this text to some extent. The argument runs somewhat as follows: Reserpine causes a depression in 15% of the patients which cannot be distinguished from a true endogenous depression. Biochemically, this "model" depression is accompanied by a 50% drop in the urinary excretion of amine metabolites, indicating that the neurotransmitter amines are *released* intracellularly by reserpine and *metabolized* intracellularly by MAO without ever exerting a physiologic effect at the adrenergic nerve endings. During treatment with imipramine, urinary normetanephrine increased and vanillylmandelic acid (VMA) levels decreased starting at the time of the period of improvement. The decreased VMA excretion is thought to be due to the decreased intracellular degradation of norepinephrine (NE) by MAO brought about by the ability of the antidepressant drugs in preventing the reuptake of "active" (extracellular) NE at the cell membrane into intracellular storage. The reuptake of physiologically active NE by the cell represents one of the main pathways of NE inactivation. Extracellular ("active") NE is metabolized by catechol-*O*-methyltransferase (COMT) to normetanephrine at the adrenergic synapse. Schanberg *et al.* (61) demonstrated that imipramine and desipramine, but not chlorpromazine (CPZ), slowed the disappearance of previously administered ^{3}H-normetanephrine. Additional evidence is provided by the classical experiments of Murad and Shore (173), which showed that pretreatment of rats with four tricyclic antidepressants greatly potentiated the ability of tetrabenazine to release ^{3}H-metaraminol from adrenergic stores in heart and brain. Metaraminol is not metabolized by either MAO or COMT, but resembles NE with regard to storage, release, and reuptake by the adrenergic cells. Glowinski *et al.* (174) studied the effects of desmethylimipramine, pheniprazine, and amphetamine on the disposition and metabolism of ^{3}H-NE and ^{3}H-dopamine in various regions of the rat brain. Deaminated metabolite levels were "severely reduced," while ^{3}H-normetanephrine levels were "strikingly elevated." Meisch *et al.* (175) demonstrated that desipramine, but not reserpine, can block the β-hydroxylation of ^{3}H-α-methyldopamine and ^{3}H-α-methyltyramine, suggesting that hydroxylation takes place *inside* the cell membrane and not in the reserpine-sensitive storage sites.

Metabolism of Norepinephrine (NE)

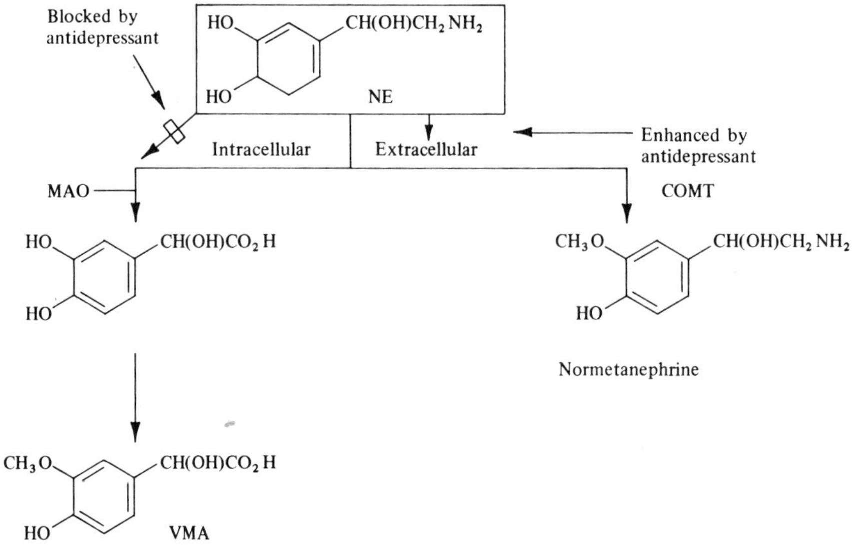

Blocked by antidepressant

HO, HO — $CH(OH)CH_2NH_2$ — NE

Intracellular | Extracellular

Enhanced by antidepressant

MAO → HO, HO — $CH(OH)CO_2H$

COMT → CH_3O, HO — $CH(OH)CH_2NH_2$

Normetanephrine

↓

CH_3O, HO — $CH(OH)CO_2H$

VMA

For a critical review of the role of biogenic amines in mediating the effects of the antidepressant drugs, the reader is referred to Schildkraut *et al.* (176).

B. Blockade of Cholinergic Transmission

An alternate or additional mechanism of antidepressant drug action which would implicate blockade of central cholinergic responses was proposed originally by Biel *et al.* (177). It was based primarily on the fact that certain potent central anticholinergic drugs, such as Ditran (XXVIII), were capable of producing long-lasting remissions in a variety of depressed patients and that many potent thymoleptic drugs could antagonize all of the parasympathetic side effects of reserpine. Thus far, all of the clinically effective thymoleptic drugs display considerable anticholinergic properties, both centrally and peripherally. For a review of the experimental evidence the reader is referred to Biel (178).

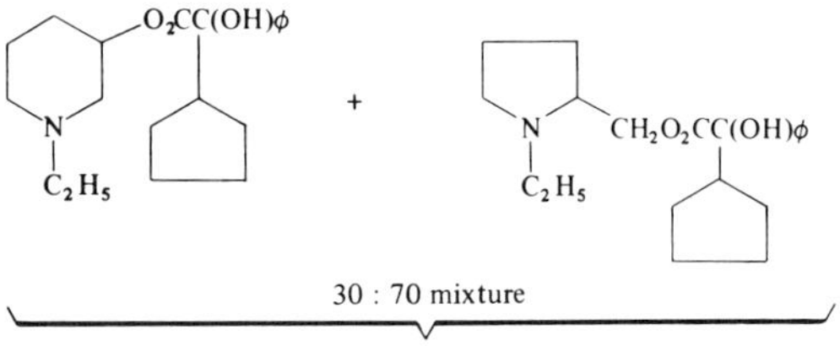

$O_2CC(OH)\phi$ — N — C_2H_5 + N — C_2H_5 — $CH_2O_2CC(OH)\phi$

30 : 70 mixture

Ditran®

(XXVIII)

IV. Conclusions

On the basis of currently available biochemical and pharmacological data, the mechanism of the antidepressant action of the tricyclic agents may be due to their ability to: (1) enhance central adrenergic transmission by inhibiting intracellular reuptake of centrally released (by sympathetic stimulation) norepinephrine and (or) dopamine and (2) inhibit central cholinergic transmission by lowering brain acetylcholine levels or blocking the effects of this neurotransmitter. Both mechanisms would mutually reinforce each other and exert an overall synergistic effect.

A third mechanism has recently been invoked by Carlsson *et al.* (179), which is based on the selective inhibition by imipramine (VII) of cellular reuptake of serotonin and α-methyl-*m*-tyramine by serotoninergic neurons. Both desipramine (IX) and protriptyline (X) were inactive in this test.

V. Structures of Newer Antidepressant Drugs in Advanced Pharmacological or Early Clinical Testing

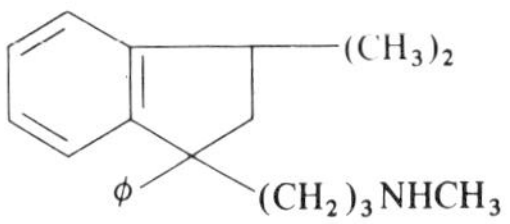

$-(CH_3)_2$, ϕ, $(CH_2)_3NHCH_3$

Lu 3-057a

(XXIX)

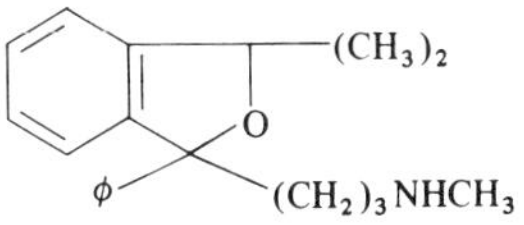

$-(CH_3)_2$, O, ϕ, $(CH_2)_3NHCH_3$

Lu 3-010

(XXX)

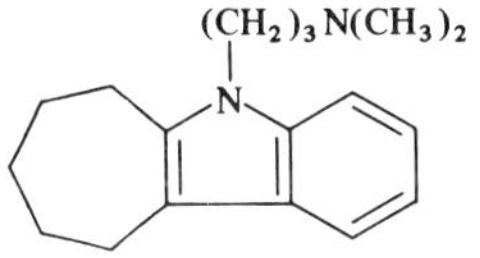

$(CH_2)_3N(CH_3)_2$, N

Pramindole

(XXXI)

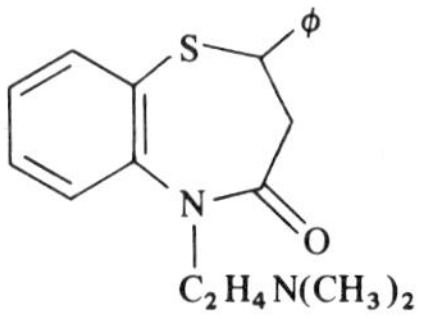

S, ϕ, N, O, $C_2H_4N(CH_3)_2$

Thiazesim
SQ 10, 496

(XXXII)

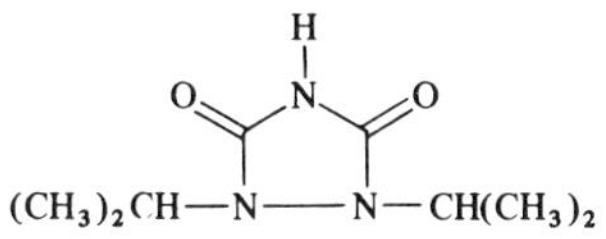

H, N, O, O, $(CH_3)_2CH—N——N—CH(CH_3)_2$

A - 10749

(XXXIII)

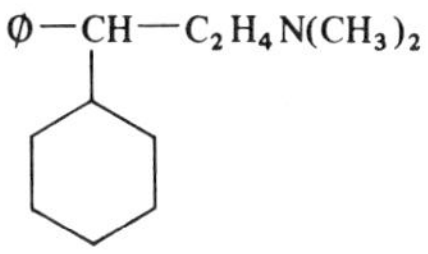

$\phi—CH—C_2H_4N(CH_3)_2$

Gamfexine
WIN 1344

(XXXIV)

Compound XXX is of particular interest, since it represents a major structural departure from the tricyclic antidepressant drugs, yet is as effective as protriptyline (X) in inhibiting cellular reuptake of ^{3}H-metaraminol and ^{3}H-norepinephrine in the mouse heart and twice as active as X in antagonizing the effects of reserpine and potentiating norepinephrine responses. In contrast to protriptyline, the drug (XXX) was devoid of any anticholinergic properties. No clinical data are as yet available on this drug.

For further reading and references see appendices.

20

PHARMACOLOGY OF MONAMINE OXIDASE INHIBITOR ANTIDEPRESSANTS

A. Horita

I. Introduction

The past decade has seen the introduction of a number of psychoactive drugs whose mechanisms of action have been based around the biogenic amines. Among these are the inhibitors of the enzyme monoamine oxidase (MAOI), which have found clinical significance as antidepressant agents. The basis of their therapeutic efficacy is presumably associated with the inhibition of this enzyme and the consequent increase in brain levels of the amines.

The discovery of monamine oxidase (MAO) as an enzyme capable of degrading catecholamines led to the speculation that it was the primary pathway for terminating responses induced by sympathetic stimulation. Much of the earlier work with the potentiation of catecholamine responses either through drugs or denervation was based upon the reduction of MAO activity. Thus, the amphetamine-like drugs exhibited some MAO-inhibitor activity at relatively high doses, and this was thought to contribute to their pharmacological actions. The concept of MAO inhibitors as psychoactive drugs is also not new, for over twenty-five years ago various investigators suggested that the stimulant action of amphetamine was due to its action on the enzyme. However, all of the experimental results were not compatible, and it was not until the discovery of the newer MAOI that further significance of MAO inhibition was realized (180,181).

II. Monoamine Oxidase

A. *Properties of MAO*

Monoamine oxidase is an enzyme which deaminates a variety of natural and synthetic amines having the general structural requirement of $R—CH_2—NH_2$. Not possessing a high degree of specificity, R may represent a ring or straight-chain structure within certain limits. The process of deamination as carried out by this enzyme consists of the following steps:

$$R—CH_2—NH_2 + O_2 + H_2O \xrightarrow{\text{MAO}} R—\overset{\overset{\displaystyle O}{\|}}{C}—H + H_2O_2 + NH_3$$

$$2R—\overset{\overset{\displaystyle O}{\|}}{C}—H + O_2 \xrightarrow[\text{Dehyd.}]{\text{Ald.}} 2R—\overset{\overset{\displaystyle O}{\|}}{C}—OH$$

The initial step is that of deamination with the formation of the corresponding aldehyde plus ammonia; the aldehyde is further metabolized to the carboxylic acid derivative by a second enzyme, aldehyde dehydrogenase. In the intact animal and in man one generally recognizes the extent of MAO activity by the amount of the carboxylic acid derivatives found in biological fluids.

Some of the common substrates for MAO include 5-hydroxytryptamine (5-HT, serotonin), the catecholamines (especially dopamine), tyramine, tryptamine, phenethylamine, and kynuramine. While all of these compounds fulfill the structural requirement of $R—CH_2—NH_2$ as indicated above, the addition of an α-methyl group renders a compound inactive as a substrate for MAO. In fact, some of the α-methylated derivatives of substrates become relatively active inhibitors. For example, phenethylamine and tryptamine, which are substrates, are converted to inhibitors of MAO upon becoming their α-methylated analogs.

In most species of animals the liver has the largest amount of MAO activity, although the enzyme is distributed widely throughout the body. Generally, higher amounts are found in structures richly innervated by sympathetic nerves such as the heart and spleen as well as in the nerves themselves. The brain differs in that it does not have a homogeneous distribution of the enzyme, the greatest activities being localized in the midbrain region.

Within the cell (see Aghajanian, Chapter 7) the enzyme is localized mainly in the mitochondrial fraction, thus constituting one of the particulate enzymes. All mitochondria, however, do not appear to be endowed with MAO, for structures containing large numbers of mitochondria, such as skeletal muscle, may be relatively poor in MAO activity. It is possible that tissue MAO activity is really a function of sympathetic nerve innervation; i.e., the mitochondria of sympathetic nerves contain the major part of MAO in order to control the storage of adrenergic transmitter substance(s) at these sites. Such a view is supported by the fact that MAO activity decreases markedly in sympathetically innervated organs after postganglionic sympathectomy.

B. Possible Functions of MAO

MAO has been designated frequently as the primary pathway for the destruction of the sympathetic transmitter, much like that given to acetylcholinesterase, the enzyme responsible for the breakdown of acetylcholine. However, the rate of action between the sympathetic transmitter and MAO is manifold slower than in the case of the esterase-acetylcholine interaction. Recent evidence suggests that there are at least three mechanisms of catecholamine inactivation, and MAO appears to be related more to the control and regulation of endogenous stores of the amines rather than to the exogenous catecholamine levels. This may be seen by the fact that after MAO inhibition the pharmacological actions of exogenously administered epinephrine or norepinephrine (NE) are not potentiated significantly. However, the contents of endogenous amines in various tissues, both in the bound and free forms increase. The mechanism of this phenomenon may be explained on the blockade of amine catabolism while biosynthesis is unaffected by the drug, resulting in a net increase in amine levels. Whatever its exact status, MAO represents an important pathway in the overall metabolism and control of biogenic amine function.

III. Inhibitors of MAO

A. Preiproniazid Period

Prior to 1955 no potent and long-acting inhibitors of MAO were known. Drugs such as cocaine, amphetamine, methylene blue, certain amidine, and choline-*p*-tolyl ether were shown to possess anti-MAO activity *in vitro,* but generally their pharmacological properties did not coincide with the enzyme-inhibiting potencies. Among these agents amphetamine and its related compounds have probably received the greatest attention, for these were the agents that produced the therapeutically desirable central stimulant action. Mann and Quastel (182) were the first to propose that this stimulant action might be related to the inhibition of MAO. They postulated that endogenous amines were normally metabolized to form aldehydes possessing CNS depressant activities, and that amphetamine might antagonize these by inhibiting MAO. However, the introduction of the irreversible inhibitors of MAO has resulted in a modification of this attractive hypothesis.

B. Iproniazid and Hydrazine Compounds

The concept of brain MAO inhibition and CNS stimulation was revived with the discovery of iproniazid. Originally introduced as an antitubercular drug, iproniazid was found to possess powerful and irreversible activity as a MAOI. It was then that the possible relationship between enzyme inhibition and pharmacological activity was seen. Since that time a vast number of hydrazine derivatives have been examined for anti-MAO activity, and less than a dozen of these were found to be of clinical value. Some of these include drugs such as iproniazid, pheniprazine, phenelzine, isocarboxazid, and nialamide (see Usdin, Chapter 15).

The hydrazine-type inhibitors of MAO act on the enzyme in an irreversible manner. The exact mechanism of inhibition is not well understood, but appears to involve an initial oxidative step, possibly a metal ion of the enzyme, prior to the irreversible inhibition. Once inhibition is complete, recovery of enzyme activity to normal levels requires periods of several weeks, apparently through the biosynthesis of new enzyme.

The process of MAO inhibition as produced by some of the secondary hydrazine compounds, such as iproniazid, isocarboxazid, and nialamide, appears to require an initial transformation of the compound to the active form, possibly the corresponding primary hydrazine derivative. Thus, iproniazid is converted to isonicotinic acid plus isopropyl hydrazine, the latter acting as the MAOI. Primary hydrazines, such as phenelzine and pheniprazine, probably act directly with the enzyme to exert the irreversible blockade.

Although all of the hydrazine compounds ultimately appear to exert their anti-MAO activity in the same manner, each has its characteristic properties. Space does not permit an extensive description of each, and the reader is recommended to the references (183–190).

C. Newer Nonhydrazine Inhibitors

While the hydrazine compounds produced both anti-MAO and antidepressant actions, they also demonstrated other biological effects such as inhibition of diamine oxidase, decarboxylases, and other pyridoxal-dependent enzymes, as well as nonspecific effects on liver and nerve tissue. These effects do not contribute to the desirable psychopharmacologic effects of the MAO inhibitors. In fact, the side effects of certain hydrazine compounds were so severe that they have been withdrawn as therapeutic agents. Such unwanted actions resulted in the search for inhibitors of the nonhydrazine type, and these efforts culminated in the discovery of compounds such as tranylcypromine, pargyline, modaline, and MO-1255, compounds unrelated in chemical structure but all possessing potent anti-MAO activity. Like the hydrazine inhibitors, these compounds also are of the irreversible type and produce effects of long duration.

1. Tranylcypromine

The compound 2-phenylcyclopropylamine represents a chemical structure very similar to that of amphetamine. Because of this likeness, it possesses many of the pharmacological properties of the latter agent, such as the CNS stimulant and peripheral sympathomimetic actions. However, its most outstanding effect is its anti-MAO action. Unlike amphetamine, tranylcypromine exerts an irreversible and long-acting blockade of the enzyme at low dosage levels. The inhibitor resembles the hydrazine-type block, but the molecular mechanism is probably different.

2. Pargyline

This compound, chemically designated as *N*-benzyl-*N*-methyl-2-propynylamine, could not have been predicted as a MAOI by mere observation of its molecular structure. Yet pargyline exerts a specific and irreversible inhibition of MAO, and because of its relative lack of other direct actions, it is fast becoming a choice for MAO inhibition in experimental investigations. Clinically, it finds utility as an antihypertensive agent, although it may act also as an antidepressant.

3. Others

Two other compounds are worthy of mention as MAO inhibitors. These are modaline (2-methyl-3-piperidinepyrazine) and MO-1255 (ethyl-*N*-benzyl-*N*-cyclopropylcarbamate), both of which have undergone clinical trials as either antihypertensives or antidepressant agents. MO-1255 is of special interest in that thus far it is the only MAOI which appears to lack the antihypertensive action in man.

IV. Biological Effects of MAO Inhibitors

The MAO inhibitors produce a multitude of biological actions, some of which are related to the inhibition of the enzyme, while others appear to be direct actions of the compounds. Still other effects are poorly understood and may involve other enzymes or mediator substances. An attempt will be made here to differentiate the biological effects exerted as a result of MAO inhibition from other actions and to separate brain effects from peripheral actions.

A. *Effects Related to MAO Inhibition*

1. CNS Effects

The administration of MAO inhibitors in experimental animals as well as in man causes an increase in measurable levels of various amines. The extent of change in amine levels exhibits considerable species variation. In many species both the catecholamines and 5HT levels in brain rises after MAO blockage, but in the cat, dog, and frog 5HT but not NE levels rise. The exact nature of these differences is not well understood, but it would appear that in the latter animals MAO does not play a major role in the metabolism of NE. Also in these animals the inhibitors do not produce the excitatory or antidepressant action as seen in the rat, rabbit, mouse, etc. Thus, there is some correlation between the increase in brain NE levels and the antidepressant activity of these agents. It may therefore be presumed that the antidepressant quality of these agents in man depends upon the alteration of NE levels in the brain. However, we cannot neglect the possible role of 5HT in this effect, for some clinical work has demonstrated the potentiated reponse to MAO inhibitors when administered together with the precursor of 5HT, 5-hydroxytryptophan.

If we may assume that NE is the major amine involved in the antidepressant actions of the MAO inhibitors, it follows that inhibition of MAO results in a decreased metabolism. This results in the presence of greater amounts of bound and free NE, the latter of which is the active form of the mediator. Since NE is localized primarily in the midbrain portion of the brain, the inhibition of MAO results in the greatest increase of this amine in this area.

Brain amine levels do not demonstrate a dose-response relationship with the inhibitors. It is first necessary to inhibit the enzyme almost to completion before the amine levels begin to increase, indicating that there exists a large reserve of MAO present in this organ.

The terms "antidepressant" and "psychic energizer" have been coined to classify the MAO inhibitors and to differentiate them from other stimulant drugs such as the amphetamines, caffeine, methylphenidate, and the analeptic–convulsant-type agents. The psychoactivating processes have been described for many species of animals, and these generally include effects such as increased excitation, mydriasis, rapid respiration, increased motor movements, hyperthermia, and other signs of central and peripheral sympathetic stimulation. These effects arise only after larger or repeated doses of the drugs, and usually a time lag is observed. Pharmacological signs appear after the brain levels of norepinephrine rise and subside when NE levels fall.

Inhibition of brain MAO not only causes an increase in level of monoamines but also prevents the depletion or release of the amines normally produced by several depleting agents such as reserpine and tetrabenazine. In so doing, the MAO inhibitors also antagonize the depressant actions of these depleters, which suggests that MAO is also involved in some manner with the release of the biogenic amines.

Other CNS effects of the MAO inhibitors include the anticonvulsant activity against both electrical shock and drug-induced seizures. Although brain amines may be involved, this effect may not be an anti-MAO function. In any case, it is presently only of passing interest; it is not of clinical significance.

2. Peripheral Effects

While most of the attention has been directed to the central nervous system, the effects of the MAO inhibitors on the peripheral structures is equally interesting and important. Many tissues and organs behave in a manner similar to the brain in exhibiting a rise in amine levels and in the prevention of their release by reserpine and related depletors. In producing this effect the inhibitors attenuate or reverse the typical reserpine syndrome, such as hypotension, ptosis, and diarrhea.

a. Antihypertensive Action. One of the most interesting actions of the MAO inhibitors is their antihypertensive effect in man. Some controversy exists as to its mechanism and whether it is related to MAO inhibition. Although an absolute relationship between the antihypertensive effect and enzyme inhibition is not available, it may be significant that all of the clinically used MAO inhibitors do possess the property of producing a postural hypotension. One experimental drug, MO-1255, has been claimed to be devoid of the hypotensive effects; however, a complete pharmacological and clinical evaluation of this agent is not yet available.

The mechanism by which MAO inhibitors exert their antihypertensive effect has been the subject of much speculation. It has been suggested that this effect is produced through sympathetic ganglionic blockade, through adrenergic nerve terminal blockade, or through the displacement of adrenergic nerve mediator by a "false transmitter," which forms as a result of MAO inhibition. This last hypothesis is of interest, for after MAO inhibition it is possible to detect in tissues considerable amounts of octopamine, which arises through the beta hydroxylation of tyramine. According to the hypothesis, the octopamine is taken up by adrenergic nerve terminals and displaces the natural mediator. Release of the octopamine supposedly reduces sympathetic activity since this "transmitter" is much weaker as a vascular or cardioactive substance, and this results in the hypotensive action.

Very recently another related view of the possible mechanism of adrenergic nerve blockade and antihypertensive action of MAO inhibitors was suggested by Costa and Neff (191). They have uncovered evidence that the biosynthesis of NE is controlled by a feedback mechanism in which NE levels themselves control the rate of biosynthesis by regulating the activity of tyrosine hydroxylase, the enzyme converting tyrosine to 3,4-dihydroxyphenylalanine (DOPA). When MAO inhibitors are administered, NE levels rise due to their decreased breakdown, and this increase acts to autoregulate its own biosynthesis. With the decreased formation of NE from tyrosine less of the mediator is stored in the adrenergic nerve granules, and octopamine levels rise due to the shunting of more tyrosine to this pathway. This reduced formation of NE results in a dampening effect on sympathetic function and, consequently, a hypotension.

Whatever the actual mechanism of the antihypertensive action produced by the MAO inhibitors may be, these compounds have aided greatly toward the understanding of adrenergic nerve biochemistry and pharmacology.

b. Antianginal Action. Another of the peripheral effects of many of the MAO inhibitors is their antianginal property. This effect is demonstrable only in man, and accordingly it is difficult to interpret or investigate properly. More of its characteristics will be discussed in a later part of this chapter. As with the antihypertensive action it is still uncertain as to whether this effect is related to the MAO inhibition, the increased levels of biogenic amines, or to an effect totally unrelated to MAO inhibition. However, the fact that only the inhibitors demonstrate this phenomenon points to a relationship with the enzyme and its inhibition.

B. Effects Unrelated to MAO Inhibition

It is not a simple matter to describe in a general manner the actions which are unrelated to MAO inhibition. Most of these effects may be considered as direct actions attributable to the drug molecules themselves rather than to enzyme inhibition. Consequently, depending upon the chemical structures, the responses will vary from drug to drug. Aside from acting as possible clinical side effects, these secondary actions are relatively unimportant.

Compounds with structural configurations related to the sympathomimetic amines tend to produce CNS and autonomic stimulation, much like amphetamine and related compounds. Thus, phenelzine and tranylcypromine (and pheniprazine, which is now only an experimental drug) possess the phenethylamine nucleus and exhibit both CNS and cardiovascular stimulation independent of MAO inhibition.

Other unrelated actions which have been reported in the literature are: ganglionic blockade, adrenergic blockade, local anesthesia, neuromuscular blockade, and antithrombic activity.

V. Interactions of MAO Inhibitors with Other Substances

A. Interactions with Other Drugs

Since the introduction of the MAO inhibitors into clinical medicine, there has resulted a growing list of interactions which occur between these compounds and other unrelated agents (192,193). Some of these could have been predicted from earlier experimental studies, but an increasing number of unexpected interactions have become prevalent. Many of these are of the potentiative type, and these occur with drugs such as the tricyclic antidepressants (such as imipramine), central stimulants (such as caffeine, methylphenidate), CNS depressants (barbiturates, phenothiazines, analgesics), certain antihypertensive drugs (reserpine, methyldopa), and even with certain foods and beverages. The mechanism of some of these paradoxical responses involve directly or indirectly the inhibition of MAO, such as the reversal of reserpine, the potentiation of methyldopa, amphetamines, and imipramine-like compounds.

Possibly the first serious interaction in man between MAO inhibitors and such drugs was that with imipramine. Upon changing from a MAO inhibitor to imipramine it was found that extreme symptoms of hyperthermia, excitation, hypertension, etc., occurred. This was later confirmed as a consistent finding in experimental animals and could be explained on the basis of excess catecholamine activity in the central nervous system. This interaction, being related to the inhibition of MAO, could occur even several days after the inhibitor was withdrawn since, as mentioned earlier, they are irreversible in action and require considerable time before adequate resynthesis of MAO can occur.

Many of the other interactions listed above are not the result of MAO inhibition. The ability of several of the MAO inhibitors to inhibit the drug-metabolizing enzymes in the liver microsomes of various animals has been well documented. The potentiation of drugs such as the barbiturates, analgesics, and phenothiazines may be related, at least in part, to the inhibition of their metabolism, resulting in higher and prolonged blood levels. A number of other drug interactions have been recorded with the MAO inhibitors. However, it is not possible to understand their mechanisms without further studies.

B. Interactions with Foods

Perhaps the greatest paradoxical interaction that occurred with the MAO inhibitors was the cheese-and-wine reactions in patients treated with tranylcypromine. Later this was extended to other foodstuffs as well as other MAO inhibitors. The food-MAO inhibitor action at first appearance was puzzling, but it soon became apparent that the common denominator in the foods involved was the substance tyramine, a sympathomimetic amine possessing potent cardiovascular activity and which is an excellent substrate of MAO. In normal individuals the tyramine in such foods and beverages is rapidly destroyed by the MAO in liver and other tissues, but after inhibition of MAO sufficient blood levels of tyramine are reached to produce marked cardiovascular crises. The tyramine content of foods such as cheeses and wines is quite high and presumably arises through the bacterial decarboxylation of tyrosine. From these observations it may be predicted that ingestion of any foods containing tyramine or other vasoactive amines which are substrates of MAO may lead to the paradoxical interactions described above.

C. Interactions with Biological Substances

In addition to the possible interactions with other drugs the MAO inhibitors may in certain instances interact with body constituents, such as cells and their fractions, plasma protein, metals, and biochemical metabolites. This is especially true with the hydrazine-type compounds which tend to be highly reactive. The common example of such a reaction is that between a hydrazide and pyridoxal (vitamin B_6) and other aldehydes to form hydrazones, which may result not only in a deficiency of pyridoxal but also in the formation of other toxic products.

For further reading and references see appendices.

21

MONAMINE OXIDASE INHIBITOR ANTIDEPRESSANTS: STRUCTURE-ACTIVITY RELATIONSHIPS

John H. Biel

I. Introduction

The emergence of the monamine oxidase (MAO) inhibitors as a new class of therapeutic agents in the treatment of mental depression was the result of the convergence of three separate and seemingly unrelated events.

During the use of iproniazid (I) in tubercular patients, Selikoff and Robitzek (194) noted certain mood-elevating properties which appeared to occur inde-

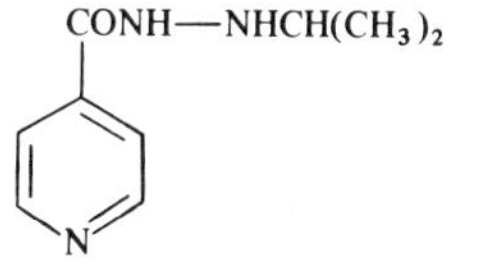

CONH—NHCH$(CH_3)_2$ [pyridine ring, 4-substituted]

Iproniazid

(I)

pendent of the degree of improvement of the disease. It was further observed by these investigators that the drug markedly potentiated the pressor activities of some standard sympathomimetic amines.

At about the same time Zeller and Barsky (195), who had been interested in the inhibition of the enzyme MAO for several years, discovered the potent monamine oxidase inhibitor (MAOI) properties of iproniazid. The two events, however, went unnoticed until Brodie *et al.* (196) demonstrated an actual rise in brain monoamine (norepinephrine and serotonin) levels and Loomer *et al.* (197) responded to this discovery by giving the drug to depressed patients and demonstrated its efficacy as an antidepressant agent. These findings taken together suggested to Brodie that the antidepressant effect of iproniazid was not a direct one but the result of an accumulation of brain monoamines which in the presence of the enzyme inhibitor did not undergo metabolic degradation.

Further support for Brodie's hypothesis came from the evaluation of the hydrazine isostere (II) of methamphetamine (III), which had been designed and

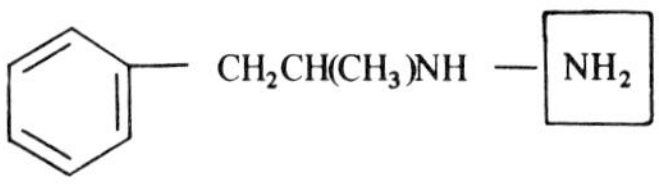

C_6H_5—$CH_2CH(CH_3)NH$—NH_2

JB - 516
(Pheniprazine)

(II)

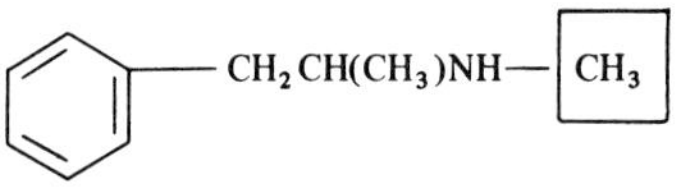

C_6H_5—$CH_2CH(CH_3)NH$—CH_3

Methamphetamine

(III)

synthesized by Biel *et al.* in 1958 (cf. 185) for the purpose of intensifying and prolonging the therapeutic effects of amphetamine.

Brodie found that compound II, even though structurally unrelated to iproniazid, was ten times as potent as the latter drug in raising brain monoamine levels in his *in vivo* preparation. These findings correlated well with Horita's demonstration *in vitro* that II was approximately forty times as effective as iproniazid as an MAOI (198). Clinical investigations then showed pheniprazine (II) to be a highly efficacious antidepressant drug in man.

The summation of the above findings sparked an intense effort in search for MAO inhibitors as a new mode of therapy for the mentally depressed. (See Crane, Chapter 50 for historical and clinical aspects.)

II. Structure–Activity Relationships of the MAOI

The reader is referred to exhaustive reviews dealing with the chemistry, biochemistry, pharmacology, and clinical applications of both the hydrazino and nonhydrazino MAOI's (185,188,190,199). This chapter will be confined to a summary of the major structure-activity principles that emerged during the decade of a rather intense research effort by industry, government, and academic institutions.

A. The Hydrazine MAO Inhibitors

1. Alkylhydrazines

While hydrazine and methylhydrazine are inactive as MAOI's, optimum potency is achieved already with ethylhydrazine and isopropylhydrazine (cf. Tables I and II).

TABLE I

Alkylhydrazines, *in Vitro* MAO Inhibition

Alk—NH—NH_2

Alkylhydrazine	Concentration (moles/liter)[a]
H	Inactive
CH_3	Inactive
C_2H_5	5×10^{-6}
n-C_3H_7	5×10^{-5}
i-C_3H_7	5×10^{-6}
Iproniazid	5×10^{-4}
JB-516	5×10^{-6}

[a] Concentration of drug which produced a 50% inhibition of serotonin metabolism in rat liver homogenates.

TABLE II

Higher Alkylhydrazines, *in Vitro* and *in Vivo* Inhibition

Alk—NH—NH_2

Alkylhydrazine	Reserpine[a] reversal (mg/kg)	ED_{50}[b] (moles/liter)
$CH_3CH(C_2H_5)$	30	8×10^{-6}
CH_3CH—	30	1.1×10^{-5}
$CH(CH_3)_2$	30	1.4×10^{-5}
$(C_2H_5)_2CH$—	10	5.4×10^{-6}
CH_3CH—$CH_2CH(CH_3)_2$	3	4.6×10^{-6}
CH_3CH—$CH_2CH_2CH_3$	1	4×10^{-6}
ϕCH_2CHCH_3 (JR - 516)	1	2×10^{-6}
Iproniazid	100	6.7×10^{-4}

[a] Threshold dose of drug (sc, mice) which reversed normal effects of reserpine.

[b] Concentration of drug which produced a 50% inhibition of serotonin metabolism in guinea pig liver homogenates (200).

Further alkyl substitution to yield symmetrical or unsymmetrical *bis*-alkylhydrazines resulted in a sharp drop in MAO inhibition and trisubstitution abolished activity. Cycloalkyl and hydroxyalkylhydrazines were generally less potent than isopropylhydrazines. Due to the toxicity properties of this class of compounds, none of them ever reached the clinic.

2. Aminoalkylhydrazines

Only the monoaralkylaminoethylhydrazines exhibited potent MAOI properties (Table III).

TABLE III

Aralkylaminoethylhydrazines, MAO Inhibitory Properties

$$R'—\phi—Y—N(R'')—C_2H_4NHNH_2$$

R'	R''	Y	*In vitro* activity[a] (% inhibition) $10^{-6}M$	$10^{-5}M$	Reserpine[b] reversal (mg/kg)
H	CH_3	CH_2	70	100	8
H	H	$CH_2CH(CH_3)$	-	100	20
H	ϕCH_2	CH_2	-	Inactive	Inactive
H	CH_3	CH_2[c]	-	-	40
p-CH_3O	CH_3	CH_2	87	97	8
p-Cl	CH_3	CH_2	40	100	8
m-Cl	CH_3	CH_2	13	100	10
o-CH_3O	CH_3	CH_2	-	-	20
m-CH_3O	CH_3	CH_2	30	100	20
O-Cl	CH_3	CH_2	77	-	4
O-CH_3	CH_3	CH_2	60	82	8
3, 4-CH_2O_2	CH_3	CH_2	41	89	8
p-F	CH_3	CH_2	-	-	8
H	CH_3	-	65	100	3
JB-516	$\phi CH_2CH(CH_3)NH—NH_2$	-	65	100	4
H	ϕCH_2	CH_2	-	-	0
o-CH_3S	CH_3	CH_2	9	100	40

[a] Rat liver homogenates.

[b] Threshold dose of drug (sc, mice) which reversed normal effects of reserpine. The drug was administered 2 hours prior to reserpine administration.

[c] Propyl- instead of ethylhydrazino side chain.

The presence of the *N*-methyl group on the aryl or aralkylamino moiety appeared to be necessary to achieve optimum activity. Alkylation, arylation or aralkylation of the hydrazino moiety resulted in a sharp activity drop.

3. Aralkylhydrazines

This class of compounds yielded the most potent MAO inhibitors, as illustrated in Tables IV and V. It is interesting to note in this connection that the hydrazine

TABLE IV

Effect of Chain Length on MAO Inhibition[a]

Ph—Y—NH—NH_2

Y	*In vivo*[b] potency (Iproniazid = 1)	*In vitro* percent of inhibition 10^{-5} *M*	10^{-6} *M*	Analeptic activity[c] (mg/kg)	LD_{50} (mg/kg) (sc, mice)
–	< 1	–	–	None	–
CH_2—	40	100	21	60[d]	68
CH_2CH_2—	4	50	30	None	102
CH(CH$_3$)—	20	–	–	None	–
CH(OH)—CH_2—	8	0	–	None	–
CH(C_2H_5)—	< 2	65	5	None	–
CH_2—CH(CH$_3$)—	40	100	60	1.0	95
CH(CH$_3$)—CH_2	16	80	25	None	–
CH_2CH_2CH(CH$_3$)—	20	100	80	None	–
Iproniazid	1	25	0	None	–
Amphetamine	–	–	–	1.0	20

[a] Biel *et al.* (201).

[b] Drug administered to mice intraperitoneally 2 hours prior to the intraperitoneal administration of 5.0 mg/kg of reserpine.

[c] 5.0 mg/kg (intraperitoneally of reserpine administered to mice 3–4 hours prior to the administration of the drug.

[d] Convulsions occurred at this dosage.

TABLE V

Effect of Nuclear Substitution[a]

R—Ph—$CH_2CH(CH_3)NH$—NH_2

R	*In vivo* potency (Iproniazid = 1)	*In vitro* potency percentages of inhibition 10^{-5} *M*	10^{-6} *M*	Analeptic activity (mg/kg)	LD_{50} (mg/kg)
p-OCH_3	8	100	10	10 (?)	118
3, 4-$(OCH_3)_2$	4	65	15	–	130
3, 4, 5$(OCH_3)_3$	2	50	5	–	100
3, 4-CH_2O_2	20	100	55	15	100
o-Methyl	20	100	45	12	114
p-Isopropyl	4	95	25	–	108
m-Chloro	20	100	49	3	84
6-H	4	86	–	8	–
Iproniazid	1	25	0	–	–

[a] Biel *et al.* (201).

isosteres (IV and V) of certain sympathomimetic amines afforded highest MAO inhibition:

C_6H_5—CH_2—[NH]—NH_2 isostere of: C_6H_5—CH_2—[CH_2]—NH_2

(IV) β - Phenethylamine

C_6H_5—$CH_2CH(CH_3)NH$—[NH_2] iosotere of: C_6H_5—$CH_2CH(CH_3)NH$—[CH_3]

(V) Methamphetamine

There was a second parallelism between the two series. Just as nuclear or side-chain substitution with hydroxy or methoxy groups markedly decreased CNS activity in amphetamine, so was MAOI potency greatly impaired by similar structural maneuvers in the hydrazine series.

Alkyl or aralkyl substitution on either nitrogen of the aralkylhydrazines decreased or abolished activity, particularly with respect to substitutions on the NH moiety (cf. Tables IV, V, VI).

TABLE VI

Effect of *N*-Alkylation[a]

$PhCH_2$—$CH(CH_3)$—$N(R_1)$—$N(R_2)(R_3)$

R_1 R_2 R_3	*In vivo* potency (Iproniazid = 1)	*In vitro* percentages of inhibition 10^{-5} *M*	10^{-6} *M*	Analeptic activity (mg/kg)	LD_{50} (mg/kg)
H H CH_3	3	–	–	10	126
H CH_3 CH_2	8	–	–	15	109
H H $CH(CH_3)_2$	2	–	–	50	269
H CH_2SO_3Na	16	100	–	–	–
H H CH_2SO_3H	20	–	–	–	–
H 1,2,3,4THIQ[b]	2	–	–	None	–
H H $CH(CH_3)CH_2Ph$	2	12	0	–	–
$PhCH_2N(CH_3)$—NH_2	2	6	0	None	–

[a] Biel *et al.* (201).

[b] $N(R_2)(R_3)$ = tetrahydroisoquinolino.

Summarily, it may be stated that the aralkylhydrazines represent one of the most potent structural types of MAO inhibitors. The salient features for optimum activity are (a) an unsubstituted phenyl ring, (b) an ethyl or propyl side chain between the phenyl and hydrazine moieties, with a methyl group on the α-carbon atom (thus, α-methylphenethylhydrazine and α-methyl-α-phenylpropylhydrazine are probably the most powerful agents among the hydrazine MAO inhibitors), and (c) a monosubstituted hydrazine group. Alkylation, hydroxyalkylation, aminoalkylation, and aralkylation of the aralkylhydrazino nitrogen markedly reduce activity. The effect of acylation of the terminal hydrazino group on MAO inhibitor activity will vary with the nature of the acyl group and the "tightness" of the hydrazide linkage. Acylation of the proximal hydrazino nitrogen results invariably in loss of activity.

As far as toxicity properties are concerned, certain nuclear substitutions such as *n*-butoxy, phenoxy, and alkylthio groups will tend to reduce at least the acute toxicity of the parent compound. Acylation of the terminal nitrogen may, in some instances, decrease the chronic toxicity manifestations of the unsubstituted parent drug. Thus, a toxic benzylhydrazine can be turned into a useful antidepressant drug by converting it to the hydrazide of 5-methylisoxazole-3-carboxylic acid (IV). Replacing the phenyl group with such heterocyclic

H_3C — [isoxazole ring, O, N] — $CONH—NHCH_2\phi$

(IV)

moieties as pyridyl, furyl, thienyl, and benzodioxan greatly lowered activity.

4. Hydrazides

An ideal antidepressant MAOI would be one that is transported quickly to the brain and, hence, could be given in a small enough dose to avoid major peripheral toxicity or other undesirable side effects. Acylation of an active alkyl or aralkylhydrazine led to a number of active hydrazides which were less toxic than the "free" hydrazines and superior to iproniazid in activity. A few examples are listed in Table VII.

TABLE VII

$RCONH—NH—CH(CH_3)_2$

R	Activity (Iproniazid = 100)
4-Pyridyl[a]	100
2-Pyridyl	191
2-Thienyl	192
$CH_3CH(NH_2)$—	253
$(CH_3)_2CHCH_2CH(NH_2)$—	200
$HOCH_2CH(NH_2)$—	189
$HO_2CC_2H_4CH(NH_2)$—	250

[a] Iproniazid.

Generally, the L-amino acid hydrazides provided optimum activity, with the glutamyl derivative exhibiting the greatest potency and affinity for brain tissue.

The pivalic acid derivative (VI) of benzylhydrazine deserves mention because of its selective affinity for cardiac rather than brain tissue.

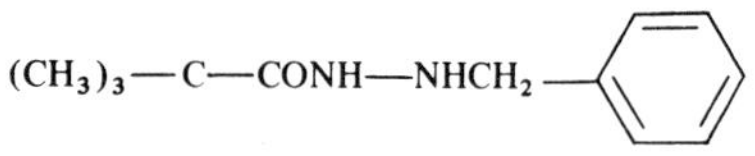

$$(CH_3)_3—C—CONH—NHCH_2—C_6H_5$$

Tersavid

(VI)

In general, a ring-unsubstituted benzyl or α-methylbenzylhydrazino moiety afforded the most potent hydrazides. One of them, isocarboxazide (VII), dis-

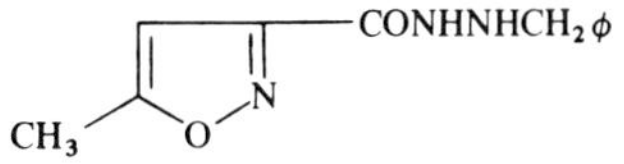

CONHNHCH$_2\phi$ (5-methylisoxazol-3-yl; CH_3, O, N)

Isocarboxazide

(VII)

played from seven to thirty times the potency of iproniazid in various tests. Comparative activities in animals relative to iproniazid of some clinically effective MAOI's are shown in Table VIII.

TABLE VIII

Comparative Activities of Some Clinically Effective MAO Inhibitors[a]

Drug	Relative activity	Structure
Iproniazid	1.0	 4-pyridyl—$CONHNHCH(CH_3)_2$
Nialamide	1.8	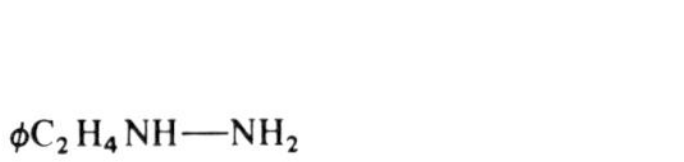 4-pyridyl—$CONHNHC_2H_4CONHCH_2\phi$
Isocarboxazide	3.1	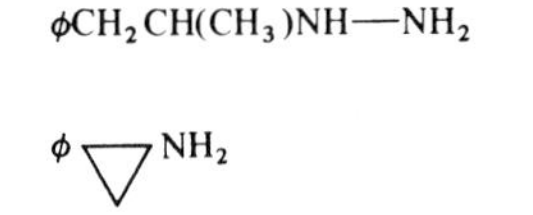 5-methylisoxazol-3-yl—$CONHNHCH_2\phi$
Phenelzine	18	$\phi C_2H_4NH—NH_2$
Pheniprazine	31	$\phi CH_2CH(CH_3)NH—NH_2$
Tranylcypromine	45	ϕ—cyclopropyl—NH_2

[a] Based on tryptamine potentiation test (202).

5. Conclusions

Potent MAO inhibitors were found among four main classes of hydrazine derivatives: (1) alkylhydrazines, (2) aminoalkylhydrazines, (3) aralkylhydrazines, (4) hydrazides. The most potent compounds were usually characterized by structural simplicity. Increased substitution usually resulted in decreased activity. Thus isopropylhydrazine, phenylisopropylhydrazine, and benzylaminoethylhydrazine provided the most active enzyme inhibitors. The aralkyl derivatives displayed a greater affinity for brain than for liver MAO. The reverse was true for the alkyl and aminoalkylhydrazines. Decreased toxicological symptomatology and greater organ selectivity could be achieved by acylating the more active hydrazines (isopropyl- and benzylhydrazine) with an acyl group which would form a sufficiently stable hydrazide linkage to transport the hydrazine to the desired target site, but would then be sensitive to metabolic breakdown in order to release the active metabolite. Particularly outstanding acyl groups which fulfilled some of these criteria (at least in animals) were privalyl, α-glutamyl, 5-methyl-3-isoxazolylcarboxyl, nicotinyl, and *N*-benzylcarboxamidoethyl. Without the acyl groups some of the more potent hydrazines could not have been introduced into clinical medicine because of toxicity problems. This is a very striking example of how systematic molecular modification can convert a highly potent but toxic compound into a clinically safe and effective therapeutic agent.

In the same vein, 1-benzyl-2-(D-ribonoyl)hydrazine was comparable to iproniazid in activity and tissue distribution; however, the LD_{50} could not be reached at 4000 mg/kg (intraperitoneal, mice). Hence, the "metabolic hooks" provided by the acyl portion afforded a marked decrease in the toxicity of aralkylhydrazines.

B. The Nonhydrazine MAO Inhibitors

The nonhydrazine MAO inhibitors have been reviewed most comprehensively through 1963 by Zirkle and Kaiser (188), and the reader is referred to this excellent chapter for background material.

Potent MAO inhibitors have been discovered among the following classes of amines: harmala alkaloids, cyclopropylamines, propargylamines, indolealkylamines, amino pyrazines.

1. The Harmala Alkaloids

The methoxy-substituted harmanes (VIII) are potent, short-lasting, and reversible MAOI's. Their receptor affinity was clearly demonstrated by Horita

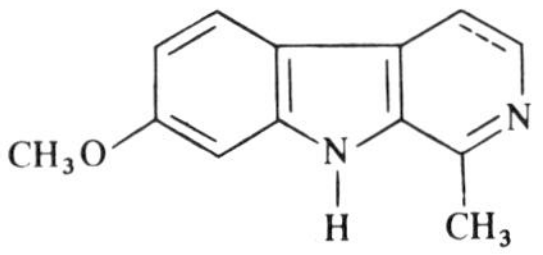

CH_3O N N H CH_3

Harmine, harmaline

(VIII)

and McGrath (203), who showed that prior administration of harmaline was capable of blocking the potent, irreversible MAOI properties of pheniprazine (α-methylphenethylhydrazine) (II).

Small changes in the structure of this group of alkaloids can alter radically their CNS properties. Thus, 6-methoxyharmalan is a potent serotonin antagonist, and the trimethoxybenzamidomethyl derivative (IX) a potent central *depressant.*

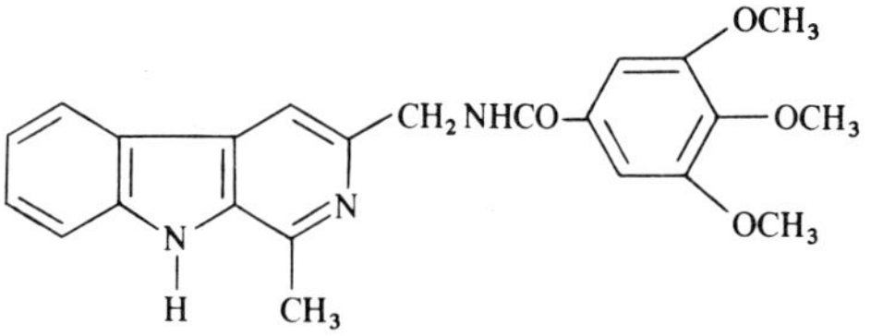

(IX)

The reversible nature of the MAOI properties of the harmala alkaloids and the ubiquity of their central and peripheral side effects have precluded their therapeutic exploitation.

2. The Cyclopropylamines

The impetus to the investigation of this class of MAOI's was given by Burger and Yost (204) with their synthesis of a "cyclized amphetamine," 2-phenylcyclopropylamine (X), which had 5000 times the MAOI activity of the "open chain" amine. Since the only structural variable between amphetamine and X is the

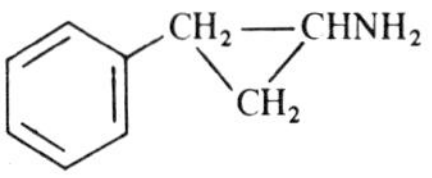

Tranylcypromine

(X)

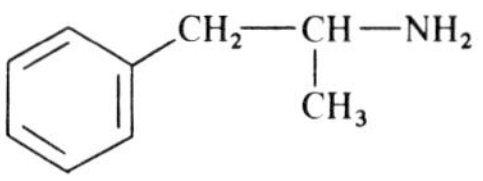

Amphetamine

(XI)

cyclopropyl ring, the latter moiety is presumably responsible for the potent, irreversible MAOI activity of tranylcypromine. The "retracted" methylene group exposes the amino moiety and allows the latter to enter more readily into interaction with cell receptors. Furthermore, the cyclopropane ring per se can interact with receptors, being so much more reactive than the isopropyl group in amphetamine. The "freezing" of the conformation of this modified amphetamine molecule would favor a better and more permanent receptor fit.

Table IX illustrates the comparative pharmacologic and clinical properties of amphetamine, the "cyclized" amphetamine, and *N*-aminoamphetamine (II).

TABLE IX

Comparative Activities of Three Antidepressants[a]

	$C_6H_5CH_2CHNH_2$ CH_3	$C_6H_5CH—CH—NH_2$ CH_2	$C_6H_5CH_2CHNH—NH_2$ CH_3
Pharmacology			
Pressor	Yes	Yes	Yes
CNS stim.	Potent	Moderate	Moderate
C.A.R.[b]	Blocks	Blocks	?
MAO inhibition	1	5000	1000
Tolerance	Yes	No	No
Clinical Activity			
Antidepressant			
Neurotic	Mild	Potent	Potent
Psychotic	Inact.	Weak	Moderate
Onset	Fast	Fast	Slow
Duration	Brief	Moderate	Long
Postdrug depression	Yes	No	No
Antihypertension	No[c]	Variable	Potent
Angina pectoris	No[c]	No[c]	Striking pain relief
Appetite	Decreased	?	Increased
Liver toxicity	No	No	Yes

[a] Taken from Biel (205).
[b] Conditioned avoidance response.
[c] Contraindicated.

Particularly noteworthy are the spectacular increase in MAOI activity, the abolition of tolerance and anorexia, and the lesser sympathomimetic effects of the amphetamine variants. The lack of liver toxicity and shorter duration of action distinguish the phenylcyclopropylamine from the *N*-amino amphetamine (pheniprazine).

The inherent sympathomimetic effects of tranylcypromine (X) were mitigated further without loss of MAOI potency, by converting the free amine to its 5-pyrrolidone-2-carboxamide (XII).

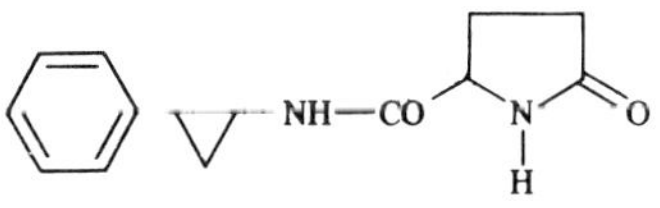

NH—CO N H O

(XII)

$NHCO_2CH_2\phi$

(XIII)

The benzylcarbamate derivative (XIII) was shown to be twice as potent *in vivo* as the free amine, suggesting that the acyl moieties might facilitate transport of the active molecule to its target site, where it is presumably cleaved and can interact with the cell receptors.

Other cyclopropylamine derivatives with potent MAOI properties are shown here (XIV–XVII):

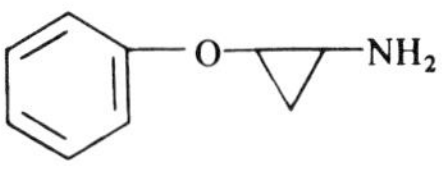

O—NH$_2$

(XIV)

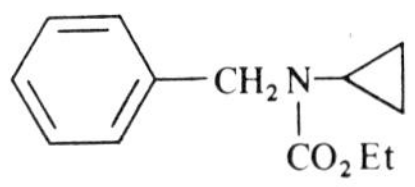

CH_2N—
CO_2Et

(XV)

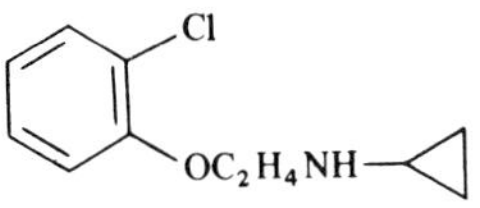

Cl
OC_2H_4NH—

(XVI)

$CH_2N—C_2H_4NH$—
CH_3

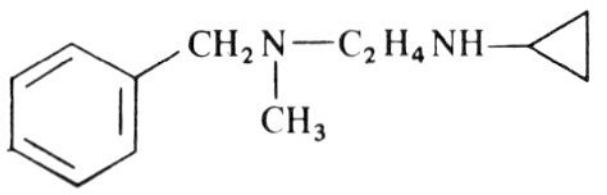

(XVII)

Compound MO-1255 (XV) has been claimed to be an active antidepressant in man devoid of cardiovascular side effects, which would make it rather unique among MAO inhibitors.

It may be seen from these examples that receptor attachment may take place over a relatively wide area of the surface of the enzyme molecule, provided that the necessary "anchoring" groups are present, i.e., a phenyl group, a reactive side chain, and the amino group. One would expect from this structural variety of active compounds that different types of agonist-receptor complexes would form which could trigger also a modified set of pharmacologic responses. Unfortunately, no clinical data are available on most of the above compounds to make valid comparisons concerning differences in their *therapeutic* spectra.

3. The Propargylamines

The discovery of the MAOI activity of propargylamine (XVIII) led Swett and his collaborators (206) to synthesize a large number of derivatives which culminated in the introduction of pargyline (XIX) as a clinical antihypertensive agent with lesser antidepressant properties.

$CH{\equiv}C{-}CH_2NH_2$

Propargylamine

(XVIII)

$\phi CH_2N{-}CH_2C{\equiv}CH$
CH_3

Pargyline

(XIX)

The attachment of an amphetamine side chain (XX) apparently increased the central stimulant and MAOI effects of XIX. Indanyl and tetrahydronaphthylamine analogs (XXI; XXII) were twenty to forty times as potent as XIX as MAOI's.

4. The Indolealkylamines

The replacement of a phenyl by an indole ring in amphetamine resulted in the development of α-alkyltryptamines with moderate MAOI and antidepressant properties. The structures are depicted as follows:

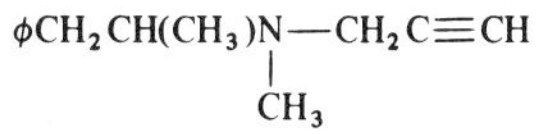

$\phi CH_2CH(CH_3)N(CH_3)—CH_2C\equiv CH$

(XX)

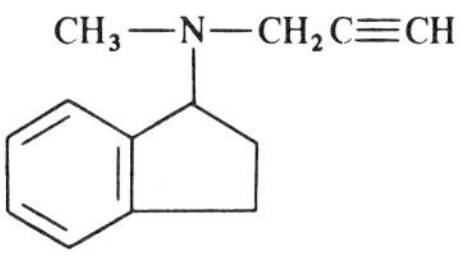

$CH_3—N—CH_2C\equiv CH$

(XXI)

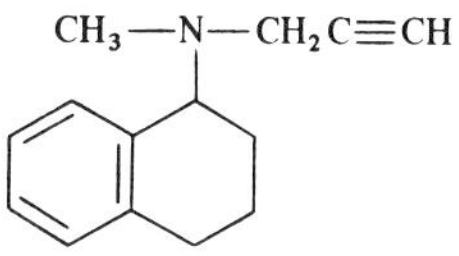

$CH_3—N—CH_2C\equiv CH$

(XXII)

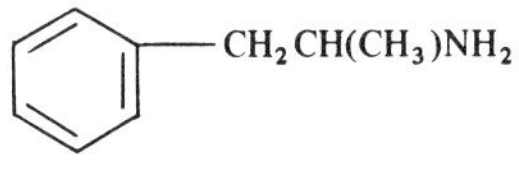

$CH_2CH(CH_3)NH_2$

Amphetamine

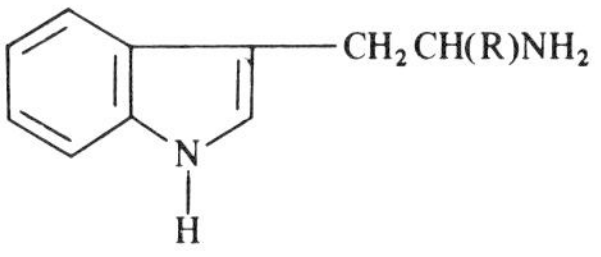

$CH_2CH(R)NH_2$ N H

(XXIII)

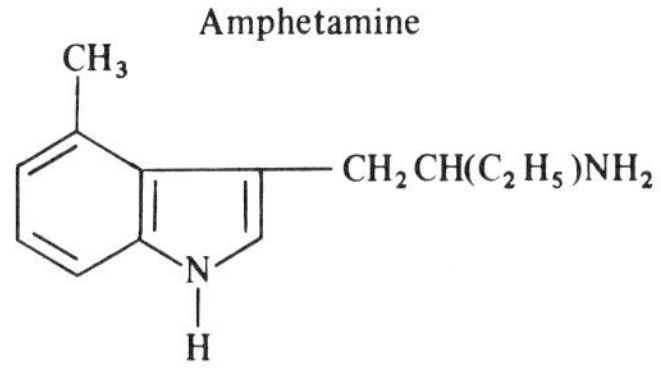

CH_3 $CH_2CH(C_2H_5)NH_2$ N H

MP - 809

(XXIV)

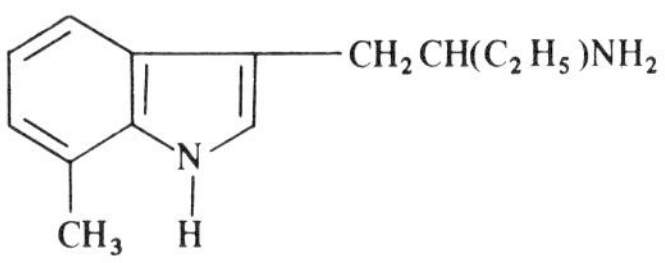

$CH_2CH(C_2H_5)NH_2$ N CH_3 H

(XXV)

Compound XXIII where R is methyl produced hallucinogenic effects. Etryptamine (XXIII; R = C_2H_5) is devoid of these side effects and was marketed for a while as an antidepressant in the treatment of neurotic depressions; however, blood dyscrasias found in a few cases and thought to be drug related prompted withdrawal of this antidepressant from the market. Compound XXIV has been claimed to be an active antidepressant in man, and its 7-methyl analog (XXV) is several times as potent as etryptamine (XXIII) as an MAOI both *in vitro* and *in vivo*. No clinical utility has been revealed for the compound.

An excellent review of the chemistry and pharmacology of the indolealkylamines has been published by Heinzelman and Smuszkovicz (207).

The "cyclization" of the alkylamine side chain to a pyrrolidine ring has yielded a number of interesting compounds (XXV–XXVIII) which display a variety of pharmacologic responses: CNS stimulation, tryptamine and nicotine antagonism, and suppression of mouse fighting behavior.

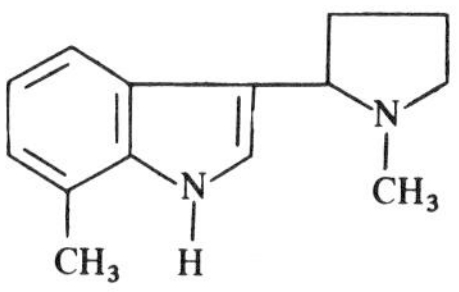

N CH_3 N CH_3 H

(XXVI)

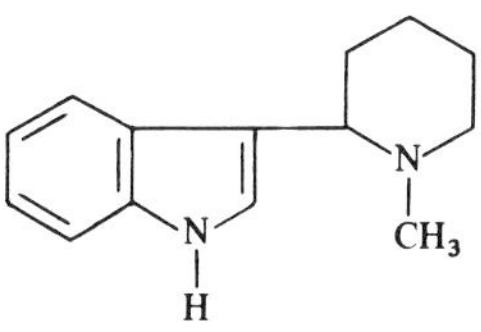

N CH_3 N H

(XXVII)

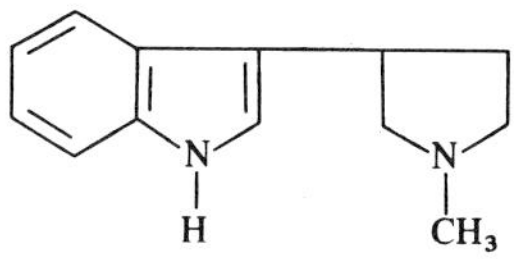

(XXVIII)

As MAOI's, XXVI and XXVIII were approximately one-hundredth and one-tenth as potent as pheniprazine, respectively.

5. The Aminopyrazines

The structure-activity relationships of this drug group have been reviewed comprehensively by Zirkle and Kaiser (188). One of the agents, modaline sulfate (2-methyl-3-piperidinopyrazine hydrogen sulfate) (XXIX), is about four to six times as potent as phenelzine (β-phenethylhydrazine) as an MAOI.

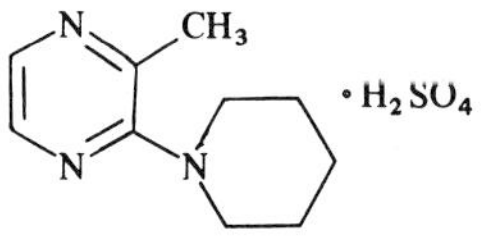

$\cdot H_2SO_4$

Modaline

(XXIX)

The presence of a 2-alkyl and a 3-*N*,*N*-disubstituted amino group is crucial to the retention of MAOI activity.

In its antidepressant spectrum, the drug seems to display effects common to both the MAOI and imipramine-like agents. Its rather severe orthostatic hypotensive properties in man may limit its ultimate clinical utility.

For further reading see Appendices 1 and 2.

22

PHARMACOLOGICAL PROPERTIES OF ANTIANXIETY DRUGS

S. Margolin and M. Kletzkin

I. Introduction

Several general reviews covering the pharmacology of antianxiety agents have recently appeared (208–219). This chapter deals primarily with pharmacological properties of antianxiety agents which influence the brain in terms of neurophysiological function and psychological aspects of behavior. A clarification of terminology appears warranted with the objective of expressing anxiety in both neurophysiological and psychopharmacological terms. The two most widely prescribed drugs, meprobamate and chlordiazepoxide, are representative of the antianxiety class of "tranquilizers." As they have been most thoroughly investigated, they provide a more complete background for considering the pharmacological actions of the antianxiety agents.

With the appearance of the antianxiety agents in the 1950's, substances became available that did not induce in patients the "sweet dreaming-waking state" of the barbiturates, the opium alkaloids, alcoholic ferments, or ether. There was no euphoria, and the associated feeling of "release" from recognition of the immediate environment. The first very widely prescribed antianxiety agent was meprobamate, and it remains a reference standard for drugs in this pharmaceutical classification.

The antianxiety agents appear to have their primary pharmacological action in those deeper regions of the brain associated with emotionality, and associated with the subconscious elements in human behavior. An expanding body of evidence indicates that subcortical structures may play a role even more important than that of the cortex in the determination of psychological or behavioral characteristics.

The evidence at this time suggests that the major sites of action are subcortical. The diencephalon has been recognized for some time as the regulator of autonomic nervous system activity; and visceral expressions of emotion, such as pallor, blushing, increase of blood pressure and pulse rate, are mediated by the hypothalamus. Electrical stimulation of the ventral hypothalamus in the waking, mobile cat causes mydriasis, horripilation, generalized sympathetic excitation, clawing, fighting and running movements, high-pitched growling, and other pseudo-affective manifestations.

Although an organic cause of anxiety has not been established, other central neurophysiologic processes underlying anxiety may exist in the midbrain reticular formation and the diffuse thalamic-reticular projections. Their role in alerting the organism may also provide the emotional tone to the incoming sensory impressions, thus determining their ultimate perception and the memory of the experience. The neurophysiologic studies of the hypothalamus and rhinencephalon suggest an even more prominent role in the integration of emotional and visceral activity, and thus the secondary somatic symptoms of anxiety.

II. Psychopharmacologic Effects of Antianxiety Agents

An antianxiety agent is a substance which relieves anxiety and produces calmness, peacefulness, serenity, placidity, or ataraxia. Numerous central CNS depressants, some stimulants, and a few drugs with no generally recognized actions on the central nervous system may relieve anxiety. The antianxiety agents modify psychologic states in recommended dosages which distinguish them from sedative-soporific drugs. They are preferred in the treatment of nervous tension states, mild depression, psychosomatic disorders, etc.

Mammalian animal research, as well as human pharmacologic data, have established that the antianxiety agents do not, in contrast to sedative-hypnotics, readily induce deep coma or general anesthesia. Clinically, a much greater degree of soporific effect is regularly observed with the sedative drugs.

Many pharmacologic agents employed historically in the management of anxiety reactions may be widely known for other significant properties. For example, narcotics such as morphine or opium may be effective in relieving anxiety, but they tend to impair perceptual, cognitive, and other mental functions. They also have a marked addiction liability which prevents their use as tranquilizers in a modern Western society.

The antianxiety drugs are generally recognized as specific for the relief of anxiety. That this specific effect is not due to an overall sedation, such as provided by ethyl alcohol, barbiturates, or chloral hydrate, is supported by the absence of impaired performance. Although ethyl alcohol or the barbiturates may cause tolerance followed by physical dependence (barbiturate or alcoholic addiction), physical dependence rarely occurs with antianxiety agents. They are different from the sedatives in that their action is not primarily sedative, hypnotic, or depressive of mood.

The antianxiety agents can exert potent actions on various subcortical structures: (1) the reticular system of the brain stem, including the medulla, midbrain, and diencephalon, (2) the hypothalamus, and (3) the limbic system, particularly the amygdala and hippocampus, as with meprobamate and chlordiazepoxide. In contrast, barbiturates act more strongly on the higher than on the primitive centers in the medulla oblongata; consequently, therapeutic doses which depress the cerebral cortex may alter the pulse rate, blood pressure, and respiration.

Sherrington gave a general indication of the existence of cardiac changes in learned experiences. Moreover, the alterations in heart rate which accompany an aversive conditioned reflex have been observed in humans as well as laboratory animals. Meprobamate and chlordiazepoxide diminish the associated tachycardia, while leaving the motor component unaffected. This property suggested their use in cardiac patients who are overreactive and anxious. By diminishing the exaggerated cardiac reactivity triggered by mental agitation, they can lessen cardiac stress.

Animal and human toxicity findings support the concept that deep anesthesia or narcosis are usually not seen after even large doses of antianxiety agents as compared to barbiturates, chloral hydrate, and other sedative-hypnotic drugs.

Meprobamate and chlordiazepoxide are members of a distinct class of antianxiety drugs that act similarly in laboratory pharmacological experiments, in experimental operant conditioning situations, and in electrophysiological studies of the central nervous system. Phenobarbital may act like these drugs in most behavioral experiments, but has quite different effects upon the central nervous system. Effects of the phenothiazines and barbiturates on behavior, and on the central nervous system are qualitatively different from the antianxiety drugs.

No single mechanism of action has been discerned in types of behavior affected by the antianxiety drugs. These drugs possess anticonvulsant and muscle relaxant properties, tame or reduce fighting in aggressive animals, and increase the amount of food eaten by deprived animals. Experiments on response-contingent punishment ("conflict") suggest that the antianxiety drugs may specifically attenuate passive avoidance behavior (learning *not* to respond).

Jasper and his colleagues confirmed the high specificity of the response of single thalamic neurons in conscious man. Their studies showed that under conditions existing in an operating room, tactile stimuli or movements of joints elicit regularly reproducible and constant responses in certain thalamic cells, which reflect accurately the location, the intensity, or the direction of change in a given stimulus. Individual cells within the sensory portion of the thalamus (ventrobasal complex) continue to respond in the same manner to peripheral stimulation, whether the patient is aware of such stimuli or not.

Clinical observations indicate that an amputated limb may be represented by a phantom limb, often with pain to which the patient exhibits exaggerated emotional reactions. Similarly, exaggerated painful emotional reactions occur following a lesion of primary sensory pathways in the thalamus, the well-known thalamic syndrome. Loss of normal sensation from the hand due to a lesion of its nerve supply may be replaced by a hand which is excruciatingly painful to the slightest touch, causalgic pain. Such observations suggest that central brain mechanisms upon which conscious sensory experience depends must have the capability of being activated independently of the information arriving over normal sensory input channels. Many central neurons, even in specific sensory systems, show much continuous activity in the absence of deliberate stimulation. Sensory receiving areas of the cerebral cortex, under conditions compatible with perceptual awareness, are not rigorously stimulus bound and may be activated independently of specific sensory information. Their subliminal activation in different states of vigilance alters the nature of their response to specific stimuli, and may suddenly cause aberrant behavior or anxiety.

For every patient each significant (emotion-arousing) memory or symbol has its own specific physiologic pattern in the emotional circuit; the neurophysiologic sensations resulting from the activity of that pattern are the emotional components of that memory or symbol. Bremer noted that stimulation of hypothalamic or adjacent regions, in the free-moving cat, induces a display of rage and aggressiveness unaccompanied by any manifestation of immediate memory. The same emotional outburst, when evoked by a natural stimulation, would have been followed by a long-lasting behavior disturbance. Thus, among the various neurophysiologic factors upon which memory retention and recall depends, it may be useful to consider the input by which the cerebral machinery has been put into action. Behavioral conduct involving apparently the same patterns of efferent impulses may differ radically in regard to the laying down of memory traces. These findings in the cat remain consistent (neurophysiologically and behaviorally) with those observed in human studies.

Some neurological syndromes, such as phantom limb, causalgia, and the thalamic or Dejerine-Roussy syndrome, have features reminiscent of certain psychiatric aberrations, namely, that the reaction to a stimulus or social situation appears grossly exaggerated and disproportionate to the input intensity.

III. Experimental Neuropharmacology and Psychopharmacology

The investigator evaluating chemicals as psychotherapeutic agents is handicapped by the lack of laboratory versions of the clinical syndromes to be remedied. No ready techniques exist for provoking in animals (or in humans) good models of specific psychiatric disorders. Although "bizarre" behavior can be produced in mammals, as by bilateral temporal ablations in monkeys, such abnormalities are not easily matched with human aberrations. The pharmacologist is left, therefore, with empirically, often fortuitously derived drugs whose therapeutic effect in humans is known, but whose mechanism of action is not; and a large body of information is limited to the pharmacological effects on animals. From this he tries to extract pharmacological activities relevant to therapeutic effects in humans, to devise new tests for examining these properties, and to consider what meaning proposed mechanisms of action might have for our concepts of mental disease.

Animal pharmacology characterizes the actions of meprobamate and chlordiazepoxide in specific laboratory tests. Understanding of the experimental methodology may clarify some of the clinical effects. The tests may be considered in three groups: (1) simple tests which depend on selective depression of the central nervous system; (2) more elaborate tests of CNS function depending upon neurophysiological measurements; and (3) behavioral tests.

The first group of tests are quite simple, do not require surgery or preliminary training of animals, and do not depend upon interaction of a test animal with another. They identify muscle relaxation, locomotor activity, anticonvulsant effects, potentiation of sedation or hypnosis, and other easily measured properties. As these effects are readily observed and biometrically evaluated in human subjects, it is possible to objectively measure relief of muscle spasm of central origin, insomnia, and certain convulsive disorders.

Of methods for determining muscular relaxation, the one most widely used measures the incidence and duration of loss of righting reflexes following administration of a drug. Graded doses of the drug are given to groups of laboratory animals, most commonly mice and rats. The animals are placed on their backs, and the number which fail to right themselves can be used to calculate the dose that will produce loss of righting reflexes in 50% of animals. This method measures marked muscular relaxation, but others are sensitive to smaller amounts of drug and distinguish less profound relaxation. A rotarod test measures drug effects by the length of time that a mouse can walk along a rotating rod before falling off. In the traction test, a mouse is suspended from a horizontal screen by his front paws. Response is measured by ability to touch the screen with his hind paws. The length of time an animal remains on an acutely inclined screen, or the angle in degrees at which it slides off a tilted board are suitable measures of muscle relaxant effects of drugs. In such experiments the antianxiety drugs show muscle relaxant effects correlated with the dose, and the physical demands upon the skeletal muscles.

The effects of antianxiety agents on the amount of movement of an animal have been studied in a variety of activity measuring devices. They may record movement by interruption of light beams, by the jiggling of a suspended cage, or related principles. The animals may be in a normal state, or may have been made hyperactive by pretreatment with a stimulant drug such as methamphetamine or mescaline. Meprobamate and chlordiazepoxide in adequate dosage can reduce locomotor activity in either type of trial.

A variety of drugs, including antianxiety or antipsychotic agents, antihistaminics, etc., can increase the duration of sleep produced by barbiturates. Most commonly, hexobarbital is preferred. Animals receiving hexobarbital plus a subhypnotic dose of an antianxiety agent sleep longer than those receiving the hypnotic alone.

The antianxiety agents may possess anticonvulsant properties. The most common methods of causing experimental convulsions use electroshock, strychnine, pentylenetetrazol, but photic flicker, intense sound, spinal asphyxia, nicotine, carbon dioxide, veratramine, morphine, procaine and other local anesthetics, benzodioxanes, and thiosemicarbazide have also been tried.

After these gross unsophisticated tests, a deeper understanding of the pharmacological actions requires more elaborate neurophysiological analysis. The muscle relaxant action of meprobamate-like drugs has been studied in terms of specific spinal reflexes, demonstrating that their site of action lies within the central nervous system rather than at the neuromuscular junction. The monosynaptic knee jerk remains unaffected, but depression of the more complex polysynaptic flexor and crossed extensor reflexes occurs. Confirmation of this finding appears in electromyographic studies of decerebrate rigidity. In such preparations, a transection made through the brain stem of the cat at the level of the colliculi prevents rostral inhibitor influences from modulating the predominantly facilitatory discharges of the brain stem behind the transection. This results in profound contraction of extensor muscles, and the appearance of intense electromyographic activity easily recorded from the limbs. Small doses of antianxiety agents abolish this experimental spasticity.

The procedures thus far described have yielded useful information about the muscle relaxant, anticonvulsive and sedative properties of antianxiety drugs, but little about "tranquilizing" action. To approach this problem a review of our knowledge of systems of the brain which may be involved in mental disturbance and by implication by targets for antianxiety agents can be helpful. Those portions of the brain include the cerebral cortex, the reticular activating system, and the limbic system.

Depression of the cerebral cortex, even at low doses, is characteristic of the sedative-hypnotic barbiturates. The electroencephalographic changes are accompanied by parallel behavioral changes. Since cortical depression with concomitant behavioral depression, drowsiness, sensory and motor impairment, etc., is undesirable with therapy with antianxiety agents, it is important to ascertain whether antianxiety agents produce cortical depression. If they do, how does the dose which causes cortical depression relate to that which has other neurophysiological effects? Although high doses of antianxiety agents may cause cortical depression, they affect the limbic system at much lower doses, thus allowing for "tranquilization" without sedation. Since the reticular activating system is intimately involved in maintaining a high level of consciousness and awareness, the same considerations would apply for the cerebral cortex. The characteristic alterations in the electrical activity of the cerebral cortex and hippocampus which can be produced by electrical stimulation of the reticular activating system is depressed by low doses of barbiturates. However, antianxiety agents do this only in relatively high doses. Electrophysiological recordings from the reticular formation itself, both for spontaneous as well as evoked activity, are in agreement with recordings taken at the cortex, but provide more direct measures of reticular function. Here again the generalized depressant effect of barbiturates contrasts with the more selective action of antianxiety agents.

At present, the limbic system seems the most likely candidate for a neural substrate of psychiatrically interesting behavior. A generally acceptable catalog of this system includes the hippocampal formation, septal region, portions of the orbitofrontal cortex, cingulate gyrus, parts of the thalamus, hypothalamus, ámygdala, and certain other structures. Intervention in the limbic systems of experimental animals by suitably placed lesions, or by electrical stimulation, produces alterations in behavior involving fear, aggression, sexuality, and other activities of a motivational nature. In man, behavioral disturbances, often of a psychopathic nature, accompany temporal lobe epilepsy. In man and laboratory animals disturbances in memory have been observed with manipulation of temporal lobe structures.

In animals with electrodes placed in various limbic structures, spontaneous electrical activity of these regions is essentially unaltered by meprobamate or chlordiazepoxide. However, if electrical stimulation is used to initiate long-lasting abnormal discharge activity in hippocampus or amygdala, then these drugs can drastically curtail those afterdischarges. Moreover, this occurs at doses which have little or no effect upon the electrical activity of the cerebral cortex, or of the ascending reticular formation. Thus, these agents fulfill certain requirements already specified for an antianxiety agent. They can control abnormal activity in a region of the brain strongly suspected of involvement in aberrant behavior at a dosage level which fails to depress the activities of the brain implicated in consciousness, intellectual processes, or sensorimotor performance.

Behavioral techniques for studying antianxiety agents may be discussed under two headings. Tests in the first group involve interaction of animals with their own or an alien species, and measure the reduction in spontaneous hostility or in experimentally induced aggressive behavior. Tests in the second group often involve a considerable amount of preliminary training and usually measure the effects of drugs on some shaped and stabilized behavior.

Both meprobamate and chlordiazepoxide have been shown to reduce the spontaneous hostility of monkeys, cats, dogs, hamsters, rabbits, or the fighting that occurs when a new mouse is introduced into an established cage group. These drugs also reduce the kind of viciousness induced in rats by lesions of the septum. Fighting can be elicited by introducing mice which have been isolated for 2 or 3 weeks into a small area, and otherwise peaceful mice can be made to fight by applying electric shocks to their feet or by pinching their tails. Both kinds of fighting are reduced by the antianxiety agents.

The conditioned avoidance response is probably the most widely used test for psychotropic drugs. The animal is required to make a response such as pressing a lever to avoid being shocked. If the response is not made before onset of shock, it must be made to end the shock. Often he is required to make the response during the presentation of a given signal (discriminated avoidance). In other cases, he may be required to press the bar more or less continuously without any external signal or stimulus presented. In this situation each response postpones the shock for some predetermined time, and so long as responses are made before the expiration of that period, shock will be avoided. In addition to bar pressing, pole climbing and shuttle responses (moving from one side of the test chamber to the other) have been used. None of the antianxiety agents have much effect on the performance of conditioned avoidance responses unless doses that produce motor impairment are reached. Antipsychotic agents of the phenothiazine type reduce avoidance responses, causing the animals to receive shocks.

In the discriminated avoidance, an animal often anticipates the warning signal and responds prematurely. This secondary conditioning, which is a generalized response to the test chamber, is blocked by meprobamate, but the response to the warning signal is not affected. In the "modified trace" classical avoidance a time gap of several seconds is allowed to elapse between the end of the warning signal and the onset of shock. Both meprobamate and chlordiazepoxide increase responding during the "gap." Thus in these aversive situations antianxiety drugs do not interfere with an adaptive learned response, but the secondary conditioned response which occurs at an inappropriate time is eliminated.

When the correct response is rewarded, usually by food or water, i.e., positively reinforced, meprobamate alters the rate of responding. When an animal is given no external signals but is required to space his bar presses according to some specific time interval, low stable rates of pressing are established. If, for example, the animal successfully refrains from bar pressing for 18 seconds, he will enter a 3-second period during which each bar press will be rewarded. He must then restrain himself for another 18 seconds in order to receive an additional 3 seconds of rewarded responding, and so on. In this differential reinforcement of low rates, treatment with meprobamate produces increased responding during the payoff period.

Conditioned suppression studies use aversive stimuli to suppress ongoing behavior. If, during the course of lever pressing for reward, a time period is signalled indicating a forthcoming unavoidable shock, then lever pressing during this period is suppressed. Both meprobamate and chlordiazepoxide antagonize the suppression, allowing the animal to continue working for a reward during this period, despite the unavoidable shocks. In some experiments the aversive stimulus is made contingent upon performance of a specific response, that is, ongoing behavior is suppressed by punishing it. For example, cats were shocked for touching a mouse, thus suppressing this behavior. After meprobamate the cats continued to attack mice despite shocks. Another variation of this technique is an approach-withdrawal situation where thirsty rats receive electric shocks when they attempt to drink from their usual trough. These shocks decrease the number of drinking attempts, and cause the rats to approach and withdraw in a characteristic manner. After treatment with meprobamate very few of these approach-withdrawal maneuvers are seen, and the rat drinks despite the shocks.

In the conflict situation devised by Geller, animals are trained to bar-press on a variable interval schedule. At 15-minute intervals a tone is sounded and a continuous reinforcement schedule, which rewards each bar press, goes into effect. Conflict is introduced by delivering an electric shock with each reward while the continuous reinforcement schedule is in force. This results in very few bar presses being made during this high payoff period. Meprobamate and chlordiazepoxide increase the number of shocks the animal will take, and the amount of feeding during the suppression period.

Rats are readily trained to jump from a Lashley stand to one of two doors facing them. The correct door opens on impact and the rat is rewarded. The incorrect door stays closed and the rat falls. The doors may be distinguished in various ways. However, if the problem is made unsolvable so that no way of identifying the correct door is available to the rat, he becomes disturbed. If compelled to jump, he develops a position habit, that is, he will jump to one of the doors exclusively, regardless of its being open or shut. If at this time the problem is made solvable by consistently identifying the open door, the rat nevertheless persists in his fixated behavior. However, such rats when treated with meprobamate or chlordiazepoxide can learn the correct solution.

Finally, in a classical Pavlovian conditioning situation where a motor defensive response has been learned, autonomic concomitants of emotional stress are observed. These may be cardiac or antidiuretic, and are reduced by antianxiety agents without impairing the motor response.

The antianxiety agents have emerged as a group of compounds characterized by a constellation of neuropharmacological, psychopharmacological, and therapeutic activities which distinguish them from the antipsychotic agents such as the phenothiazines, and from the sedative-hypnotic agents typified by the barbiturates. The antianxiety agents, in addition to their muscle relaxant and anticonvulsant effects; (1) control abnormal electrophysiological activity in various components of the limbic system at doses which have little or no effect on the cerebral cortex, (2) do not depress conditioned avoidance or Pavlovian defensive responses, but do overcome the suppression of performance caused by response-contingent punishment, thereby enabling an animal to work for reward under behaviorally disabling conditions, and (3) reduce anxiety, tension, and the symptoms arising from these, thus allowing patients to continue at their normal activities without causing sleepiness or motor incoordination.

For further references and reading see Appendices 1 and 2.

23

BEHAVIORAL PHARMACOLOGY OF CENTRAL STIMULANTS

Larry Stein and C. David Wise

I. Classification of Stimulant Drugs*

Drugs classified here as *behavioral stimulants* include: (1) the amphetamines and related phenethylamine derivatives (e.g., methamphetamine, phentermine, mephentermine, methyphenidate, pipradol), (2) cocaine, and (3) caffeine and related xanthine derivatives. The behavioral stimulants are to be distinguished from the *analeptics* (respiratory stimulants), picrotoxin and pentylenetetrazol, and from the convulsant drugs, such as strychnine. The behavioral stimulants are also to be distinguished from *antidepressants* of both the monoamine oxidase (MAO) inhibitor type and the tricyclic type. Neither the analeptics nor the antidepressants produce the characteristic stimulation of alertness, mood, and activity of animals or normal human subjects that typifies the action of the behavioral stimulants. Although amphetamine has some analeptic activity, it is considerably less effective than picrotoxin, particularly in its ability to increase respiration that has been depressed by barbiturate drugs. Amphetamine also

* Cf. Biel, Chapter 24.

has antidepressant activity, but the short duration of its action in this regard renders it unsatisfactory for the treatment of the chronically depressed.

II. Behavioral Effects of Amphetamine

From the viewpoint of the experimental psychologist, perhaps the most interesting action of amphetamine is its ability to facilitate goal-directed or operant behavior (220). We use the term "facilitation" rather than "stimulation" because we think it is more accurate to speak of amphetamine as facilitating or enhancing the tendency to perform operant responses rather than stimulating or instigating them. This distinction is not merely a terminological one, but it has relevance for and seems to be consistent with our neurochemical theory of the mechanism of central action of amphetamine. Amphetamine also exerts other central stimulating action, e.g., hyperactivity, active sniffing. These actions of amphetamine should be distinguished from its facilitating action on operant behavior, and it remains to be seen whether they are mediated by similar or different biochemical mechanisms.

Experimental findings in animals seem to be consistent with the idea that amphetamines have a facilitating effect on motivated or goal-directed behavior, if account is taken of the following: (1) that amphetamine depresses food and water intake, apparently by reducing hunger and thirst; (2) that some minimum tendency to respond is required for amphetamine facilitation; (3) that the facilitating effect of amphetamine will be less conspicuous when the tendency to respond is very great; (4) that moderate or optimum doses tend to facilitate behavior, but excessively high doses disrupt behavior; and (5) that the control rate of response is an important parameter in the dose-effect curve: i.e., amphetamine facilitates and disrupts high-rate behaviors at lower doses than it facilitates and disrupts low-rate behaviors.

A. Anorexic and Thirst-Inhibitory Effects of Amphetamine

Animal studies have shown that amphetamine decreases the intake of food and water. Observations suggest that amphetamine will have conflicting effects on behavior maintained by food or water reinforcement; that is, the drug will exert two opposing effects that will tend to cancel each other out. One effect will be the general tendency of amphetamine to increase rates of responding as suggested above, while the other will be a rate-decreasing effect not unlike that produced by satiation. Whether one effect or the other predominates in a specific case will no doubt depend on the dose, the species, and many other features of the situation.

If reinforcers other than food or water are used, it is relatively easy to demonstrate that amphetamine enhances the tendency to engage in operant behavior. For example, when behavior is maintained by the avoidance of negative stimuli (e.g., electric shocks), amphetamine reliably increases the rate of response over a wide range of conditions. Amphetamine also substantially increases the output of behavior maintained by positive reinforcement if electrical stimulation of the brain, rather than food or water, is used as the reward. Under the drug, rats exposed to cold respond at higher rates for heat reinforcement and monkeys respond at much higher rates for flashes of light.

B. A Minimum Tendency to Respond Is Necessary in Order to Obtain Amphetamine Facilitation

Increases in rates of response of rats with methamphetamine do not occur if tests are made on base lines of extremely low rate. In one test, the low rates are achieved by programming "no consequences" (no reward or punishment) to the lever press response for several days; in other tests, in which rats avoid shock to the feet by pressing a lever, methamphetamine was given very early in training, before the avoidance contingency had started to take effect. Strongly depressing the tendency to respond by prolonged extinction or discrimination training may also eliminate the facilitating effect of amphetamine.

C. The Facilitating Effect of Amphetamine Will Be Less Conspicuous When the Tendency to Respond Is Very Great

Self-stimulation* experiments in rats have shown that amphetamine may increase low and high rates alike, although low rates usually showed proportion-

* Self-stimulation means that animals learn to repeatedly and rapidly press a lever to electrically stimulate certain "reward" areas of the brain chronically implanted with electrodes, to yield positive reinforcement (221).

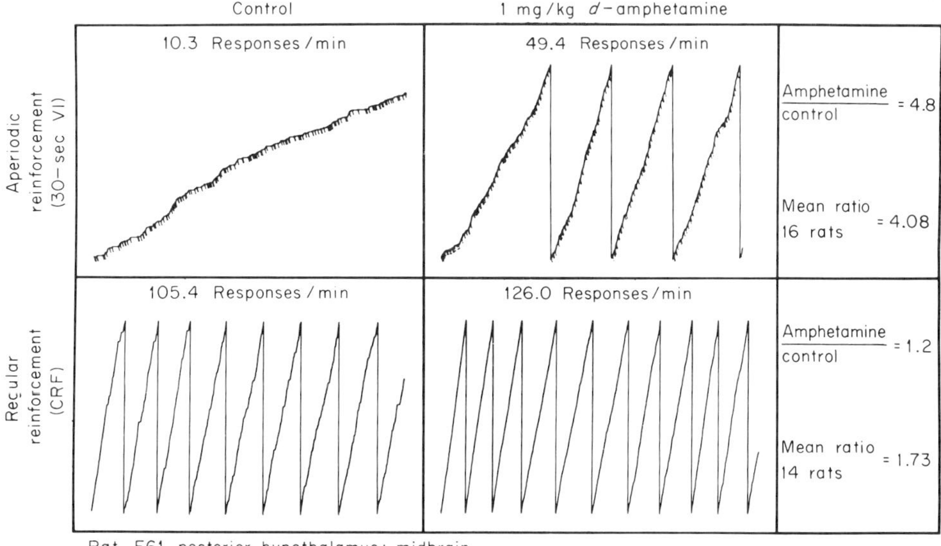

Fig. 1. Effects of amphetamine sulfate on high (regular reinforcement) and low (30-second variable-interval reinforcement) base-line rates of self-stimulation. Each record shows performance in a 90-minute test. Diagonal lines on variable-interval response curves indicate deliveries of the electrical reinforcement. Average augmentation ratios (amphetamine rate/control rate) of all animals tested are given at the right.

ately greater increase (220). If a high base-line rate of self-stimulation is generated by reinforcing every response (regular reinforcement schedule), and if a low rate is generated by presenting the same electrical reinforcement on an aperiodic basis, the latter can be increased over 300% by 1 mg/kg of *d*-amphetamine sulfate; the same dose produces an increase of only 20–70% in the regular reinforcement test (Fig. 1).

D. *Moderate Doses of Amphetamine Facilitate Behavior, but High Doses May Disrupt Behavior*

It has long been known from simple observation that very high doses of amphetamine will disrupt the normal pattern of ongoing behavior. Initially, such disruption was attributed to a toxic action, either peripheral or central or both. Peripheral factors may be largely excluded because *l*-amphetamine—which has equal potency to *d*-amphetamine in the periphery, but only 20–25% of its central activity—is less depressant than *d*-amphetamine. Furthermore, early experimental studies demonstrated depression of food-reinforced behavior at doses of amphetamine that have no debilitating peripheral effects. It is possible that these behavioral decrements were due to a central depressant action of *d*-amphetamine, but drug-induced anorexia could not be ruled out. Higher doses of amphetamine may depress behavior independently of an anorexic action. In one study, comparable base lines of response were established in two groups of monkeys working either for food or for escape from electric shock. In both groups, low doses of amphetamine increased the rate of response and high doses reduced it; indeed, the dose-effect curves for both types of behavior were almost indistinguishable. Because behavior maintained by escape from shock should be relatively insensitive to the anorexic effects of amphetamine, the similarity of the two dose-effect curves suggests that higher doses of amphetamine have a depressant action on behavior which is independent of anorexia.

E. *Control Rate of Response Is an Important Determinant of Facilitation and Depression by Amphetamine*

Studies in pigeons led to the suggestion that control rate of responding is an important factor, that sustained rates of responding are not susceptible to increase, but that very low rates or intermittent responding are readily increased. So susceptible are low rates to augmentation by amphetamine that striking increases in rate have been demonstrated even when the reinforcer was food. Amphetamine has long been known to increase the low rates of response emitted in extinction if extinction is not prolonged, or if partial reinforcement precedes extinction. Similarly, it has proved effective in programs that maintain low or erratic rates by infrequent reinforcement or by differential reinforcement of low rates.

These and related observations led Dews (221a) to suggest that low rates of response tend to be increased by moderate doses of amphetamine, whereas high rates of response tend to be decreased by high doses. This rule of thumb has had good predictive power in a number of subsequent experiments (222), but it also has failed to predict accurately in other experiments.

In one experiment a monkey was trained to avoid shocks under two programs. One program (Sidman avoidance) produced a low control rate of avoidance behavior and the other (fixed ratio avoidance) a high rate. As Dews' rule predicts, methamphetamine (0.25–2 mg/kg) sharply increased the low control rates generated by the Sidman program; however, contrary to prediction from the rule, the very high avoidance rates generated by the fixed-ratio program were not decreased. Similarly, Sidman (223) observed some years ago that amphetamine increased, rather than decreased, the "bursts" of high rate response that typically follow presentations of shock in a free avoidance situation. Finally, in a case of positively-reinforced behavior, Stein (220) found that a high control rate of self-stimulation was not reduced, and even was increased, by a 1 mg/kg dose of *d*-amphetamine sulfate (Fig. 1).

Not only are high rates sometimes increased by amphetamine but, and again contrary to Dews' rule of thumb, low rates are sometimes decreased. The most notable example of the latter is provided by experiments in which low rates are generated by punishment of behavior. A number of reports indicate that amphetamine does not increase the tendency to engage in behavior that has been suppressed by punishment and, in fact, even decreases it. This observation

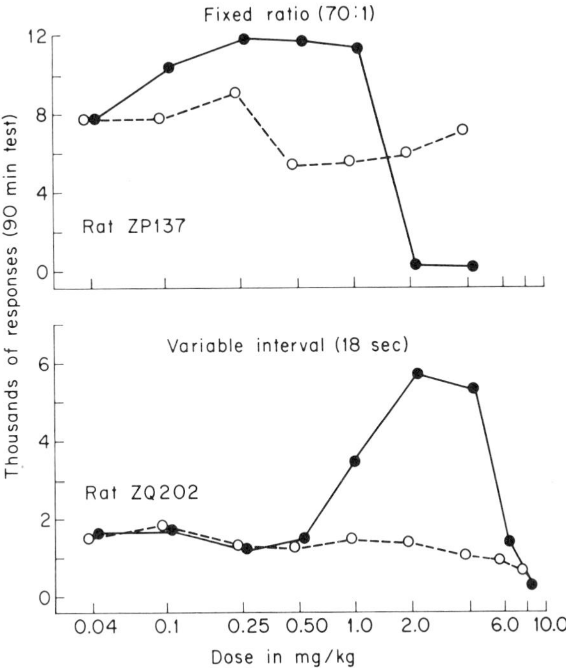

Fig. 2. Dose-effect curves showing effects of amphetamine on high (fixed-ratio) and low (variable-interval) base-line rates of self-stimulation. Note that amphetamine both facilitates and suppresses fixed-ratio behavior at lower doses than it facilitates and suppresses variable-interval behavior. (Solid line with filled circles) *d*-amphetamine; (dashed line with open circles) control (Unpublished data of Stein, Berger, and Margules).

has special significance from the point of view of theory and is treated in more detail below. Another example of reduction of low-rate behavior by amphetamine-like drugs is that pipradol decreases the rate of response in extinction if stimuli correlated with reinforcement are removed in the extinction test series, although the usual increase in extinction responding was produced by the drug if these stimuli were not removed.

It has been demonstrated directly that the control rate of response may determine the dose at which amphetamine causes facilitation or suppression of behavior. Rats with positively reinforcing hypothalamic electrodes were trained either on a program that produced a high base-line rate of self-stimulation (fixed-ratio schedule) or a moderate rate (variable-interval schedule). After control rates stabilized, the effects of a wide range of doses (0.04–10 mg/kg) of *d*-amphetamine sulfate were determined. In both groups, amphetamine caused response facilitation at low doses and response suppression at high doses. However, the threshold doses for both facilitation and depression were much lower in the high-rate fixed-ratio group than the low-rate variable-interval group (Fig. 2).

III. Biochemical Effects of Amphetamine

A. *Theories of Amphetamine Action**

Many biochemical hypotheses have been offered to explain the central stimulating effect of amphetamine. Early theories assumed that amphetamine produced its effect on the central nervous system by inhibiting MAO, thereby reducing the rate of formation of inhibitory aldehydes or retarding the destruction of catecholamines. More recently, it has been proposed that amphetamine acts directly on norepinephrine (NE) receptors in the brain by a mimicking action. Later, it also was suggested that amphetamine acts centrally by combining with serotonin (5HT) or tryptamine receptors in the brain. The evidence against these theories is summarized below.

In 1964, Stein (223a) proposed for the first time that the behavioral-facilitating action of amphetamine, like its peripheral sympathomimetic action, is mediated indirectly by the liberation of norepinephrine. This theory, now generally regarded as correct, has been independently validated by biochemical and pharmacological studies which are discussed below, and has been fully elaborated upon and documented by Wise and Stein elsewhere (223b).

1. Inhibition of Monamine Oxidase

The discovery of new and potent inhibitors of monamine oxidase (MAO) (e.g., iproniazid) have made it easy to test and reject this idea. Large doses of iproniazid, which largely or completely inhibit MAO in the brain, have no facilitating effect on self-stimulation and sometimes even inhibit it; smaller doses of iproniazid have no apparent effect on the rate of self-stimulation. A series of doses of iproniazid will increase the rate of self-stimulation, but the magnitude

* Cf. also Fuxe *et al.*, Chapter 6; Snyder, Chapter 9; Biel, Chapter 24.

of the effect is usually smaller than the maximum effect of amphetamine. The short-acting MAO inhibitor, harmaline, also fails to facilitate operant behavior. Moderate increases in rate are observed after injection of phenylisopropylhydrazine (JB-516) or tranylcypromine, but these inhibitors of MAO are closely similar in structure to amphetamine and may have a stimulating action for this reason; furthermore, although these drugs are much stronger inhibitors of MAO than amphetamine, they are much weaker stimulants. Most evidence to date indicates rather conclusively that the inhibition of MAO by amphetamine does not, by itself, account for its central stimulant action. It is important to point out that amphetamine is immune from attack by the enzyme and can therefore act for prolonged periods in the brain.

2. Direct Action on Serotonin or Tryptamine Receptors

If the behavioral facilitating action of amphetamine depends on the activation of 5HT or tryptamine receptors, one might expect an amphetamine-like facilitation of behavior after administration of 5HT or tryptamine. No such facilitation occurs, but 5HT does not penetrate easily into the brain and both it and tryptamine are rapidly metabolized by MAO. Levels of 5HT in the brain may be elevated by the combined administration of the amino acid precursor of 5HT, 5-hydroxytryptophan (5HTP), and a MAO inhibitor. Under these conditions, learned behavior is usually inhibited rather than facilitated. It also has been reported that low doses of 5HTP and a MAO inhibitor facilitated self-stimulation behavior; however, it was not assumed that such facilitation was necessarily due to an action on a 5HT receptor, and it was even suggested that the drug effect may have been caused by a release of NE. It has been suggested that the 5HT hypothesis could be tested by comparing amphetamine and α-methyltryptamine (a derivative of tryptamine resistant to MAO, which, in addition, has the same side chain as amphetamine). Although rats look excited after α-methyltryptamine, no facilitation of self-stimulation is observed. Furthermore, α-methyltryptamine does not counteract the inhibitory effect of reserpine on self-stimulation, whereas amphetamine is quite active in this respect. Finally, selective depletion of brain 5HT 24–72 hours after administration of *p*-chlorophenylalanine (which inhibits the biosynthesis of 5HT and thus depletes brain 5HT) has no effect on the rate of self-stimulation. Taken together, these results suggest that amphetamine does not facilitate operant behavior by an action on 5HT or tryptamine receptors, although it may produce excitement by this means.

The 5HT hypothesis is also weakened by evidence that links the central effects of amphetamine to the catecholamines. Amphetamine, of course, is similar in structure to NE; both are derivatives of phenethylamine, the basic structure of compounds possessing sympathomimetic activity. If amphetamine acts centrally by virtue of its phenethylamine structure, one might expect to see amphetamine-like facilitation of behavior after administration of phenethylamine. No facilitation of self-stimulation has been observed even at a dose of 10 mg/kg, but this negative result could be explained by the fact that phenethylamine is rapidly destroyed by MAO. Additional tests on phenethylamine have therefore been made after MAO was inhibited by iproniazid. Under these conditions, a strong positive effect is obtained that seems to resemble the facilitating action of amphetamine in all respects. This finding clearly favors the idea that a NE receptor, rather than a 5HT receptor, is somehow involved in the central stimulant action of amphetamine.

3. Direct Action on Norepinephrine Receptors

In the peripheral parts of the body, the sympathomimetic activity of amphetamine is now thought to be mediated by the liberation of NE. Several studies have shown, however, that amphetamine still exerts its behavioral effects in reserpine-treated animals. Indeed, it has even been reported that there is a marked enhancement of the activity-increasing effect of amphetamine 24 hours after reserpine. On the basis of these experiments, it has been suggested that in the central nervous system amphetamine acts primarily as a directly acting sympathomimetic amine.

An opposite view has been offered on the basis of studies of the interactions between reserpine and amphetamine in the self-stimulation test, which showed that large doses of reserpine weaken or shorten the response to amphetamine, although the initial intensity of the response may often be unaffected or even enhanced. Large decreases in the effects of amphetamine also are obtained if NE levels in the brain are depleted by α-methyl-*p*-tyrosine, an inhibitor of NE biosynthesis (Fig. 3) (227).

Time course studies of the interaction between amphetamine and reserpine provide further evidence on this point. It has been well established that the depletion of amines after reserpine follows a definite time course; total brain levels of NE drop to a minimum within 3–4 hours and recover only very slowly over the next several days. If amphetamine releases NE to produce central stimulation, its effect should decrease sharply after reserpine is given, reach a minimum at 3–4 hours, and then recover slowly. As expected, the stimulating effect of amphetamine drops off rapidly (though not as rapidly as do NE levels) within the first few hours after reserpine, reaches a minimum of about one-tenth of its normal action at 3 hours, and then recovers partially (although somewhat more so than do NE levels) at 24 hours. This apparent relationship between amine depletion and amphetamine activity is quite suggestive, and presumably might be even more compelling if the level of NE had been measured in the functional pools rather than total brain content.

4. Indirect Action by Release of Catecholamine

In addition to the findings with reserpine and α-methyl-*p*-tyrosine, other evidence supports the idea that the facilitating action of amphetamine on behavior is mediated by the release of NE from stores in the brain. First, it has been demonstrated that the facilitating effect of amphetamine on self-stimulation is strongly potentiated by MAO inhibitors. The potentiation is puzzling if it is assumed that amphetamine acts directly, because amphetamine itself is not destroyed by MAO, but the potentiation is easy to understand if amphetamine acts by releasing NE, a substance that is destroyed by the enzyme.

Second, amphetamine-like facilitation of self-stimulation and other behaviors

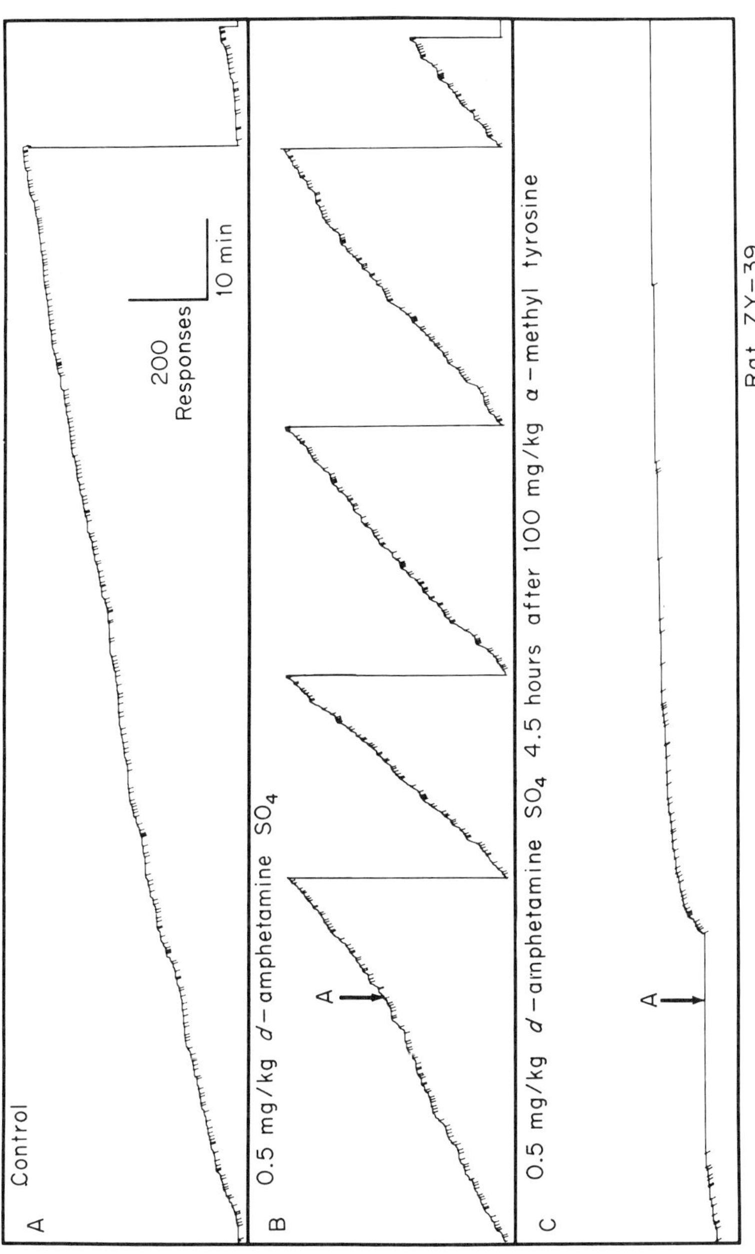

Fig. 3. Diminished effect of amphetamine after α-methyl-tyrosine.

are observed after administration of other substances that liberate NE rapidly from stores in the brain. α-Methyl-*m*-tyrosine is especially active in this respect. Similarly, a phase of amphetamine-like stimulation is sometimes observed to precede the inhibitory action of tetrabenazine; the stimulation is clearly revealed in animals pretreated with MAO inhibitors, presumably because the liberated NE is then protected from destruction. The effects of amphetamine and α-methyl-*m*-tyrosine are also enhanced by MAO inhibitors. These compounds, however, are also quite active in the absence of an inhibitor, presumably because of their ability to release NE rapidly and from strategically located stores close to the synaptic terminals.

Third, work of several investigators reveals that amphetamine lowers the NE content of the brain, although large single doses or smaller doses administered on a chronic basis are required for pronounced effects. It is interesting, furthermore, that *d*-amphetamine is three to five times more potent as a depleting agent than *l*-amphetamine, since this coincides with the relative central stimulating potency of these compounds. Curiously, these NE depleting doses of amphetamine increase the level of 5HT in the brain. If it is correct to assume that amphetamine acts centrally by releasing a transmitter, this observation is further evidence that 5HT is less likely to be involved than NE.

The pattern of NE metabolites found after the administration of amphetamine is consistent with the conclusion that the drug may release brain NE in a physiologically active form. When the endogenous stores of rat brain NE are labeled with radioactive exogenous NE, more normetanephrine and less deaminated catechol products are found after amphetamine. This result is in line with the idea that NE is released without exposure to intraneuronal MAO and is metabolized primarily by the extraneuronal enzyme, catecholamine-*O*-methyl transferase. It also has been shown that a single 5 mg/kg dose of *d*-amphetamine sulfate produced an increased turnover of NE in the brain stem of the rat, although repeated doses or a larger dose (15–20 mg/kg) have no such effect. In addition, amphetamine greatly augments the increase in NE turnover caused by electric shock stress.

Low doses of *d*-amphetamine partially block the accumulation of NE, but not dopamine, in the intact rat brain after the administration of *l*-dopa (to animals pretreated with reserpine and nialamide). The cortex and other forebrain areas are more sensitive to this effect of amphetamine than the brain stem. Although the results on NE accumulation are open to various interpretations, the observation that low doses of amphetamine may act selectively in the forebrain is important.

Finally, it has been demonstrated *in vivo* that NE can be released from specific areas of the brain by systemic injection of amphetamine. In these experiments specific regions of hypothalamus and amygdala were bathed in Locke's solution through a chronically implanted Gaddum-type push-pull perfusion cannula, and a radiotracer technique was used for the analysis of NE and its metabolites in the perfusate. Figure 4 shows the increased release of radioactivity produced by amphetamine in an amygdaloid perfusate. Figure 4 also shows that rewarding electrical stimulation of the medial forebrain bundle had the same NE-releasing

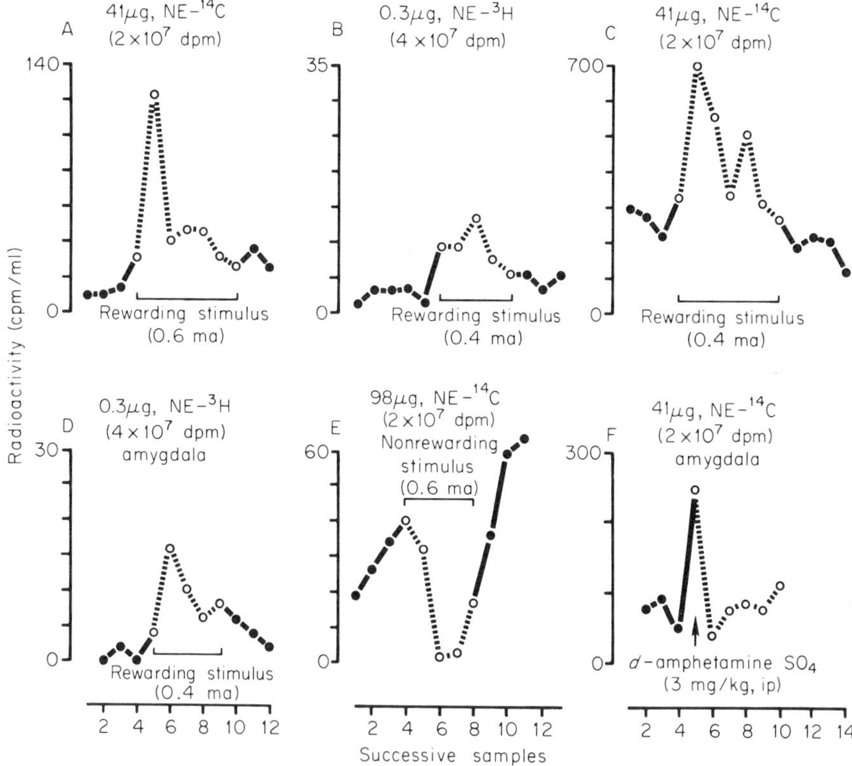

Fig. 4. Sample experiments illustrating effects of rewarding brain stimulation, nonrewarding stimulation, and amphetamine on the release of radioactivity into hypothalamic (A–C, E) and amygdaloid (D, F) perfusates. In (C), the monoamine oxidase inhibitor pargyline (50 mg/kg) was injected intraperitoneally 16 hours before the start of perfusion. The radioisotope tracer and dose used in each experiment is indicated.

effect as amphetamine, whereas punishing brain stimulation had the opposite effect and inhibited the spontaneous release of radioactivity.

IV. A Theory of the Behavioral Facilitating Action of Amphetamine

Biochemical and psychopharmacological evidence reviewed in the preceding section strongly supports the idea that the behavioral facilitating action of amphetamine is caused by the release of NE. The exact nature of the releasing action is still unclear; however, there is reason to believe that molecules of amphetamine do not simply displace molecules of NE from storage sites, but rather that the drug somehow potentiates the physiological release of NE. Whatever the actual mechanism, the effectiveness of such release would be increased both by the ability of amphetamine to inhibit MAO and by its ability to prevent reuptake of the released transmitter. As a result of this combination of properties, amphetamine clearly is well suited to augment transmission at central noradrenergic synapses. Hence, it is reasonable to speculate that amphetamine exerts its central stimulating action by augmenting transmission at those noradrenergic synapses whose activation facilitates goal-directed behavior.

Where are these synapses located? Two lines of evidence converge to support the idea that these synapses are formed by noradrenergic terminals of the medial forebrain bundle in the forebrain and diencephalon. First, behavioral studies suggest that the medial forebrain bundle is the major pathway of a brain system responsible for the facilitation or positive reinforcement of behavior. Self-stimulation studies of Olds (221) demonstrated that the electrical stimulation of the medial forebrain bundle serves as a powerful reward. Furthermore, we found that free stimulation of this structure facilitates operant behavior, and lesions disrupt it. The second line of evidence indicates that the medial forebrain bundle is evidently the only significant pathway through which noradrenergic fibers pass in order to reach higher levels of the brain. Using a new histochemical technique for visualizing NE at the cellular level, Hillarp *et al.* (224) have found a system of NE-containing neurons that ascend in the medial forebrain bundle and terminate at noradrenergic synapses in the forebrain and diencephalon. Other workers have demonstrated that lesions of the medial forebrain bundle cause extensive depletion of NE in the forebrain and diencephalon.

To summarize, the medial forebrain bundle evidently is the major fiber system in the brain for the facilitation of goal-directed behavior, and it also is the structure that contains the vast majority of noradrenergic fibers that form terminals in the forebrain. We therefore have proposed that moderate or optimum doses of amphetamine facilitate goal-directed behavior by enhancing the release of NE from terminals of the medial forebrain bundle in the forebrain. Whether this behavior-facilitating action of NE depends on the excitation of cells that facilitate behavior, or whether it depends on inhibition of cells that suppress behavior, is a question for further research to decide. However, much literature exists which demonstrates suppressor influences of the forebrain on behavior. Hence, it is likely that NE released by amphetamine acts mainly as an inhibitory transmitter which depresses the activity of behaviorally suppressant cell groups in the forebrain. In other words, amphetamine may facilitate behavior by a disinhibitory action.

If amphetamine acts by enhancing the release of NE from the medial forebrain bundle, then electrical stimulation of the medial forebrain bundle and the drug should produce similar effects on behavior. Such seems to be the case. Stimulation of the medial forebrain bundle and amphetamine both retard the extinction of food-reinforced behavior and facilitate the performance of a shuttle-box avoidance response. It also has been demonstrated that rewarding brain stimulation, like amphetamine, speeds up the low rate of response generated by a schedule in which only low rates are rewarded. Others have shown that monkeys and rats can be trained to perform a response for intravenous self-injection of amphetamine and related stimulant drugs in much the same way that they can be trained to work for electrical stimulation of the medial forebrain bundle; hence, both amphetamine and medial forebrain bundle stimulation have rewarding properties. Finally, medial forebrain bundle stimulation and systemically administered amphetamine both cause release of NE and its metabolites into amygdaloid perfusates in the unanesthetized rat.

A theory of the mechanism of action of drugs should account for features that limit, as well as produce, the drug action. As described earlier, amphetamine fails to facilitate behavior which either is insufficiently reinforced or is punished. If the medial forebrain bundle were the major site of action of amphetamine, as assumed above, it then would be logical to ask how conditions of insufficient reinforcement or punishment might affect this structure to limit its responsivity to the drug.

We have reviewed elsewhere evidence which suggests that the level of activity of the medial forebrain bundle is increased by rewarding stimulation [or, more precisely, by the input of stimulation which signals that reward is forthcoming (224a)]. Furthermore, there is reason to believe that activity of the medial forebrain bundle is inhibited by punishment (225). Hence, the input of rewarding and punishing stimulation may jointly determine the level of activity of the medial forebrain bundle. The same factors also determine whether or not amphetamine will be effective. It therefore is conceivable that the conditions of reward and punishment influence the action of amphetamine by regulating the level of activity of the medial forebrain bundle. According to this idea, amphetamine will facilitate behavior if the activity of the medial forebrain bundle exceeds some minimum level. Drug-induced facilitation will not occur if the activity of the medial forebrain bundle is reduced below this level. Such reduction could be caused either by insufficient reinforcement or by punishment. A strong feature of the theory is that it nicely accounts for the intriguing observation of Hill (226) that pipradol loses its facilitating effect on responding in extinction if stimuli associated with reinforcement are removed. Presumably, such removal of stimuli which forecast reinforcement would deactivate the medial forebrain bundle and thus eliminate the stimulant effect of the drug.

Finally, since we assume that the facilitating effects of amphetamine on behavior are mediated by NE, it would appear from the considerations above that the drug may influence the release of NE only if neurons are firing and not if they are in the resting state. This suggests that amphetamine does not simply displace NE from its storage sites, but instead potentiates the physiological release of transmitter from functional pools by nerve impulses.

For further reading, see Appendices 1 and 2.

24

STIMULANTS: STRUCTURE-ACTIVITY RELATIONSHIPS

John H. Biel

I. Introduction

The status of the central stimulants up to 1955 was perhaps adequately summed up by Goodman and Gilman (228) in the second edition of "The Pharmacological Basis of Therapeutics":

> Although central nervous system stimulants are sometimes dramatic in their pharmacological effects, they are relatively unimportant from a therapeutic point of view. It is not possible to stimulate the central nervous system for a long period of time, for heightened nervous activity is followed by depression, proportional in degree to the intensity and duration of the stimulation. Consequently, therapeutic excitation of the central nervous system is usually of brief duration and is reserved for emergencies characterized by severe central depression.

This statement was based, of course, on the action of those drugs available at the time for stimulation of the central nervous system. Such agents are picrotoxin, metrazol, strychnine, camphor, nikethamide, caffeine, and amphetamine.

II. Analeptics

Picrotoxin and metrazol were used most often in respiratory depression resulting from barbiturate poisoning. Metrazol and camphor were, of course, the forerunners to the electroconvulsive therapy of schizophrenia. The first four of these drugs produce central excitation only at the convulsive dose, the action of nikethamide is similar to that of picrotoxin, but it is a much less potent agent (229,230).

The central stimulant properties of caffeine are well known. However, this compound is of no value in the treatment of the emotionally depressed state.

More recent compounds which have displayed valuable respiratory stimulant properties in man without the danger of inducing convulsions are shown in Fig. 1.

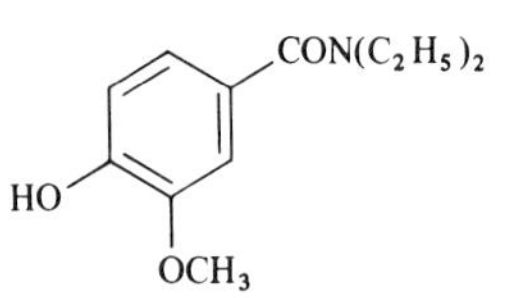

Ethamivan

(I)

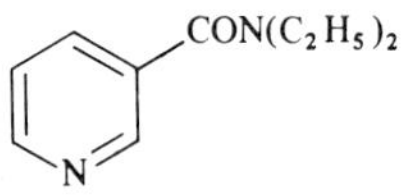

Nikethamide

(II)

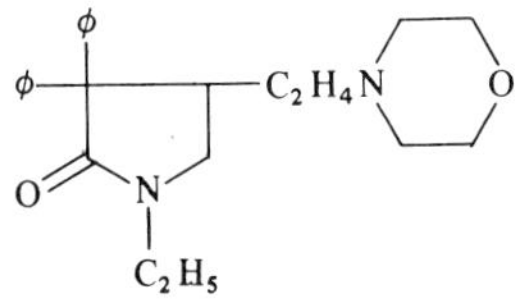

Doxapram

(III)

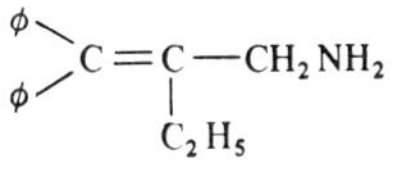

Gilutensin®

(IV)

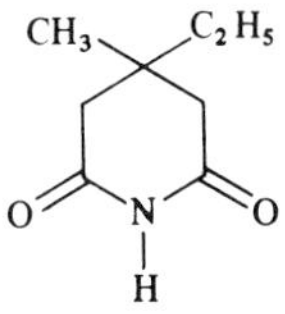

Bemegride

(V)

Fig. 1. Newer analeptic agents.

The structural relationship of ethamivan to nikethamide is obvious. Bemegride is of interest, since similar substitutions in the 3,3-position of the piperidine ring will produce such sedative drugs as VI and VII.

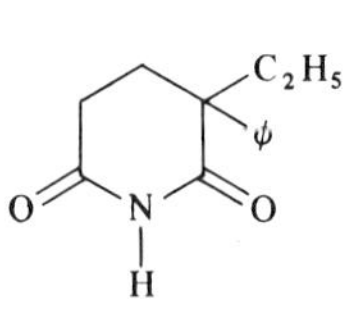

Glutethimide

(VI)

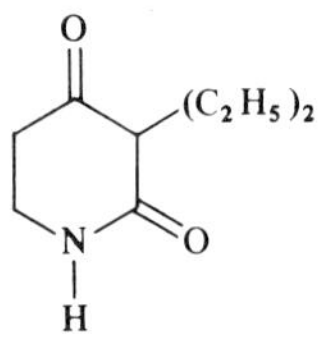

Methyprylon

(VII)

III. Sympathomimetics

A. *Amphetamine*

The systematic variations of the epinephrine structure by Barger and Dale (231) eventually led to the synthesis of a number of "stripped down" phenethylamines which accentuated some of the pharmacologic properties of this catecholamine and attenuated others. In this series, only one such compound, α-methylphenethylamine [amphetamine (VIII)], was found to produce mood-elevating and often euphoric effects in man. Credit for this discovery must go to Gordon Alles (232), who realized the clinical impact of his findings. To this day, amphetamine remains a useful drug in the treatment of minor neurotic depressions which may arise from a temporary environmental situation.

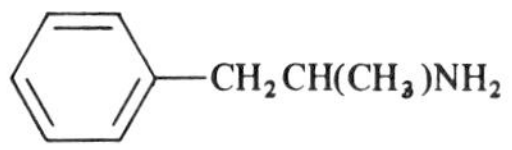

C_6H_5–$CH_2CH(CH_3)NH_2$

Amphetamine

(VIII)

Its main drawbacks are (a) a postdepressive phase following the mood-lifting experience, (b) the development of tolerance to the drug which requires administration of increasingly larger doses, (c) its appetite-depressant (anorexigenic) properties, and (d) its cardiovascular effects.

It is tempting to speculate at this point on the inability of amphetamine to influence the course of moderate to severe mental depressions. If such depressions are the result of some metabolic disturbance which prevents the accumulation of neuroeffector catecholamine at the receptor to the "critical level," amphetamine would be powerless in exerting its characteristic type of action. Some substance is lent to this speculation by recent experiments of Ingvarsson (233) in chronically severely depressed patients, in which intravenous administration of 50 mg of dihydroxyphenylalanine (dopa) every other day produced remissions within a few days. Discontinuance of dopa administration or lowering of the dose resulted in prompt relapse. These results are all the more remarkable in that these patients had been suffering from long-standing depressions which were resistant to presently available antidepressant therapy. It is of further interest that those patients who also suffered from asthma or parkinsonism experienced a relief of their symptoms following dopa therapy. Dopa is, of course, the precursor of dopamine and epinephrine, two catecholamines which are capable of reversing the symptoms of parkinsonism and asthma, respectively. Confirmation of Ingvarsson's interesting findings by other clinical investigators will be required before the above-proposed hypothesis can be embraced with any kind of enthusiasm.

What is still troublesome in explaining the mechanism of action of amphetamine is (a) the postdepressive phase which invariably follows the state of mood elevation, and (b) the development of tolerance to the central effects of the drug. Stein (see Chapter 23) would ascribe to amphetamine a central catecholamine-releasing action that would ultimately result in catecholamine depletion at the receptor site. At that stage, amphetamine would have to act, however, as a receptor-blocking agent to prevent the interaction of newly synthesized catecholamine with the adrenergic receptor. Recent evidence to support this assumption has been obtained by Fischer *et al.* (233a), who showed that the metabolite of amphetamine, *p*-hydroxyamphetamine (IX), is capable of acting as a

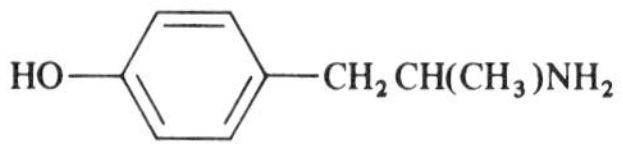

$$HO-C_6H_4-CH_2CH(CH_3)NH_2$$

(IX)

"false adrenergic neurotransmitter" which can compete with NE for the adrenergic receptor sites but is far less potent in eliciting the central adrenergic responses induced by NE.

The fact that brain catecholamine depletion by reserpine, tetrabenazine, and alpha-methyl-*m*-tyrosine does not affect the central effects of amphetamine may be explained on the basis that these agents empty only the larger "nonfunctional" storage pool of its catecholamine content and do not affect the "functional" pool. Furthermore, these substances interfere only with norepinephrine binding and not with the rapid biosynthesis of norepinephrine in the brain, which will continue to supply the "functional" pool with norepinephrine, thereby affording normal or even enhanced sympathetic output (234).

The mechanism of the central action of amphetamine continues to be explored, and the prevailing evidence points to multiple mechanisms involving catecholamine release, inhibition of cellular catecholamine uptake, monamine oxidase inhibition, and a direct intrinsic action (235). Dependence on amphetamine and other stimulant drugs, its clinical manisfestations, and treatment are the subject of two excellent reviews (236,237) (see Chapter 38).

B. Structurally Modified Amphetamines

To overcome the therapeutically limiting side effects of amphetamine a number of molecular modifications have resulted in the development of more selectively acting central stimulants which find some application in the treatment of mild reactive depressions, fatigue states, and general lassitude. All of these drugs incorporate a β-phenethylamine skeleton in the molecule (Fig. 2), and are generally characterized by being less potent stimulants and lacking the euphoric qualities of amphetamine. They are essentially devoid of the anorexigenic and potent cardiovascular properties of the parent drug and do not appear to elicit the postdepressive phase so characteristic of the amphetamine action. The incorporation of the β-phenethylamine moiety into a piperidine ring system is of interest since this system has served as a basis for other types of centrally active drugs such as the potent psychotomimetic agents, analgetics, surgical anesthetics, local anesthetics, anticonvulsants, sedatives, and powerful antipsychotic drugs (haloperidol types).

Drugs which are representative of the modified amphetamines (see Fig. 3) and belong to the class of the minor antidepressants are pipradol (X), methylphenidate (XI), Sch 5472 (XII), and W-1207 (XIV). Pipradol and methylpheni-

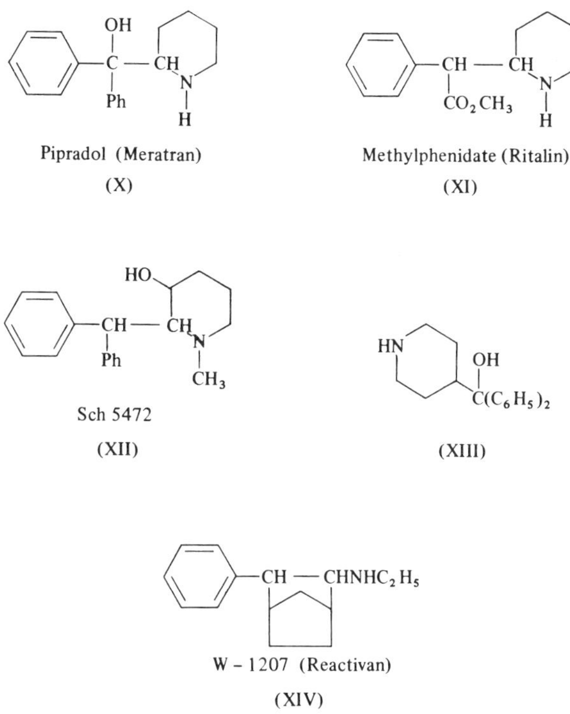

Fig. 2. Structurally modified amphetamine derivatives.

date are used in uncomplicated, reactive depressions. Unlike amphetamine, the drugs do not cause tolerance. The activity spectrum of Sch 5472 is qualitatively similar to that of methylphenidate, except that the drug is ten to twenty times more potent as a psychomotor stimulant. Doses as low as 0.25–0.75 mg per day have been found effective in combating exhaustion and fatigue. Unlike pipradol and methylphenidate, the drug increases learning behavior in rats. Compared with amphetamine, the dosage ratio for producing disorganized behavior versus increased wakefulness is considerably greater for Sch 5472. It is interesting that the 4-isomer of pipradol actually antagonizes the stimulant effects of the latter drug. The drug W-1207 appears to be more of a caffeine-like stimulant inasmuch as it seems to be devoid of any antidepressant properties.

IV. Indolealkylamines

Therapeutic efficacy has been claimed for a group of indolealkylamines in the treatment of neurotic depressions. The structures of the compounds are depicted in Fig. 3.

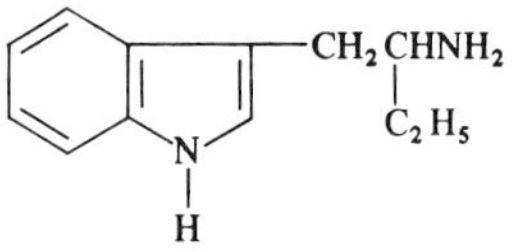

CH_2CHNH_2 / C_2H_5

Etryptamine (monase)

(XV)

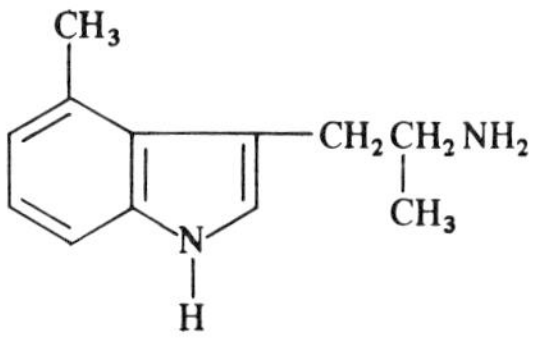

CH_3 ; $CH_2CH_2NH_2$ / CH_3

MP - 809

(XVI)

$CH_2CH(C_2H_5)NH_2$; CH_3

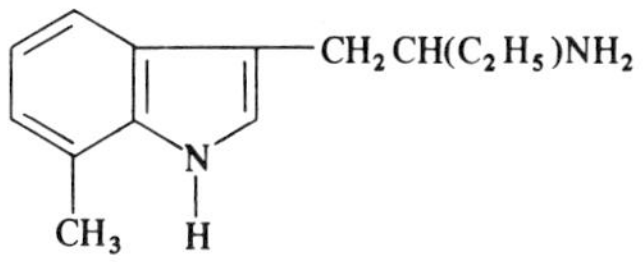

(XVII)

Fig. 3. Indolealkylamines with antidepressant properties.

Etryptamine (XV), originally marketed for its antidepressant properties, was withdrawn because of blood dyscrasias in a small percentage of cases. Although the drug displays monoamine oxidase (MAO) inhibitory effects in animals (238), its action in man is presumably not a consequence of this property since it is given in doses which produce no clinical MAO inhibition. The antidepressant action of MP-809 (XVI) has been described by Azima *et al.* (238a) but since the drug has not undergone widespread clinical investigation, its true therapeutic value remains in doubt. Only preliminary animal data are available for the potential activity of the 7-methylindole derivative (XVII), which appears to be more active than etryptamine.

The mechanism of action of this group of drugs appears to be unrelated to MAO inhibition or psychomotor stimulation since both of these properties are absent in man. Murphree *et al.* (239) report that etryptamine produced feelings of exhilaration in normal human volunteers, while α-methyltryptamine, the lower homolog, caused LSD-like symptoms of tenseness, restlessness, and general malaise. An excellent review of the chemistry and pharmacologic activities of indole compounds has been published by Heinzelman and Smuszkovicz (207).

V. Newer Experimental Compounds

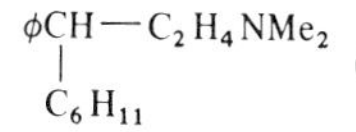

$\phi CH(C_6H_{11})—C_2H_4NMe_2$ (Win 1344)

Gamfexine

(XVIII)

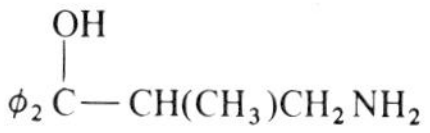

$\phi_2C(OH)—CH(CH_3)CH_2NH_2$

(U - 23,807A)

(XIX)

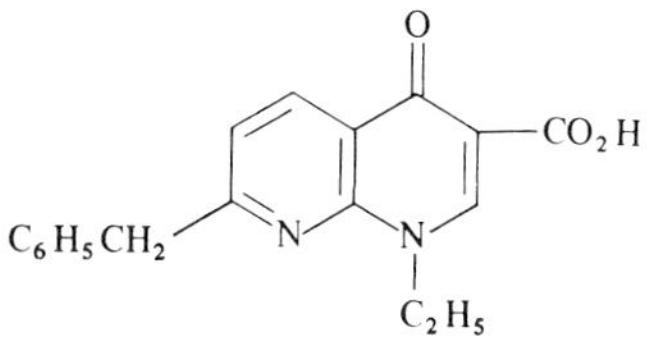

$C_6H_5CH_2$ … CO_2H … C_2H_5

(XX)

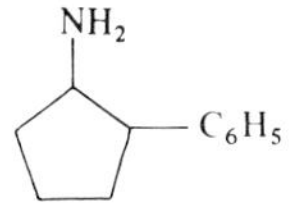

NH_2 … C_6H_5

Cypenamine

(XXI)

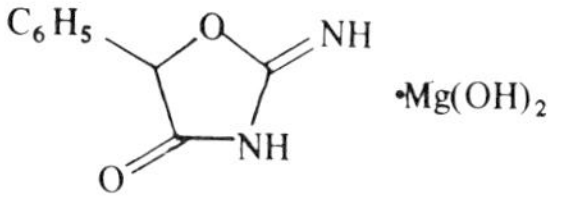

C_6H_5 … O … NH … NH … O $\cdot Mg(OH)_2$

Mg pemoline

(XXII)

C_6H_5 … O … $N(CH_3)_2$ … N … O

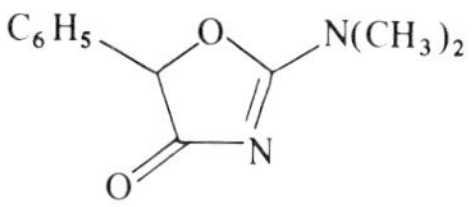

Thozalinone

(XXIII)

Win 1344 (XVIII) is capable of stimulating depressed patients. In combination with thioridazine, it works well in withdrawn schizophrenics. Gershon *et al.* (240) found the compound less efficacious than imipramine (37% vs. 54%). The stimulant properties of the drug often result in exacerbation of psychotic symptoms. Compound (XIX) has one-third the activity of amphetamine in increasing spontaneous motor activity. The effects of single oral doses in cats and dogs were still present after 24 hours. Unlike amphetamine, U-23,807A lowers body temperature and potentiates hexobarbital and ethanol narcosis at two and four-times the dose of chlorpromazine, respectively. The branching of the alkylene side chain virtually eliminates all peripheral anticholinergic effects. The l-isomer is now undergoing clinical trial. Preliminary reports indicate the drug to be inactive in neurotic, involutional, or reactive depressions.

The naphthyridine derivative (XX) was more potent than amphetamine as a central stimulant. Its effect was antagonized by reserpine and the α-adrenergic blocker, phenoxybenzamine. The compound is thought to act by either altering NE uptake or release from storage pools.

Cypenamine (XXI), a cyclized phenethylamine, produced some improvement in retarded children. Magnesium pemoline (XXII), originally hailed as a memory-enhancing drug by increasing RNA synthesis, appears to owe its effect to stimulating performance rather than memory or learning processes. A structurally related drug, thozalinone (XXIII), was ineffective as a clinical antidepressant agent.

VI. Conclusions

The therapeutic scope of the central stimulants, at least on the basis of the presently available drugs, remains limited. This is due to several factors. Those compounds which produce euphoria and a feeling of well-being are without exception psychotomimetic, as illustrated by such amphetamine variants as mescaline (XXIV) and DOM (XXV). Others that are more centrally stimulating

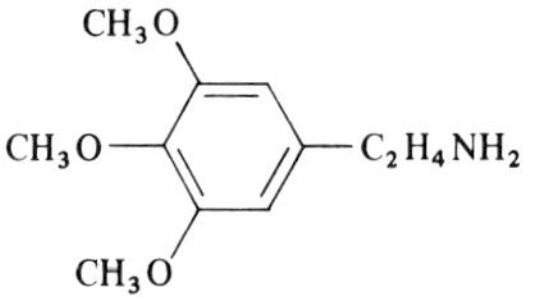

CH_3O, CH_3O, CH_3O, $C_2H_4NH_2$

Mescaline

(XXIV)

CH_3O, CH_3, OCH_3, $CH_2CH(CH_3)NH_2$

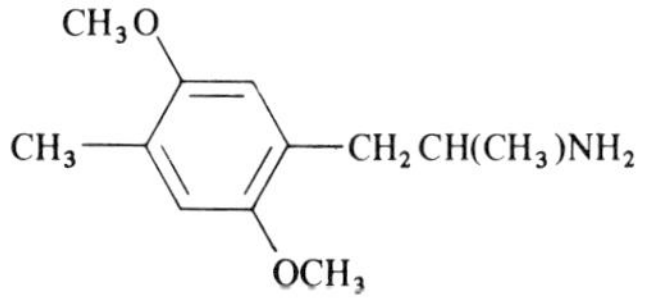

DOM (STP)

(XXV)

than mood-elevating may cause central side effects such as jitteriness, anxiety, and exacerbation of depressed symptoms. In addition, exaggerated cardiovascular responses and anorexia may restrict their utility even further. In the treatment of mild to moderate depressions, there is little evidence that the current central stimulants are of any great or lasting therapeutic value.

Drugs capable of increasing learning behavior, memory, and performance are still very much in the embryonic development stage, largely for want of clinically relevant animal testing procedures. Yet it is in this area that the central stimulants will ultimately find their role in human therapy.

For further reading and references see Appendices 1 and 2.

PART VI

GENETIC AND ENVIRONMENTAL ASPECTS OF DRUGS AND BEHAVIOR

25

PHARMACOGENETICS*

John L. Fuller

I. Introduction

The emergent science of pharmacogenetics is concerned with the relationships of inherited chemical and physiological variation to variation in response to drugs. The contribution of this science to clinical psychopharmacology is more potential than actual, since little is known regarding the degree to which genetics modifies the therapeutic efficacy of psychologically active drugs or contributes to undesirable side effects. However, animal experimentation demonstrates clearly that the genotype of subjects can significantly modify drug effects, and there are many examples in man of inherited variations in sensitivity to therapeutic agents. Genetic variability must therefore be kept in mind in the interpretation of clinical studies.

II. Genetic Background

A gene in the classical sense is now considered to be a macromolecule of deoxyribonucleic acid (DNA) which serves as the code for production of a

* This research was supported by PHS grant MH-01775 from the National Institute of Mental Health.

molecule of ribonucleic acid (RNA). RNA molecules in turn specify the sequence of amino acids in a polypeptide (messenger RNA), or serve as parts of the cellular machinery involved in protein synthesis (ribosomal and transfer RNA). Current texts on genetics and biochemistry should be consulted for details.

Genes in microorganisms have been classified functionally as structural or regulatory. Structural genes specify the amino acid sequences of proteins, which in turn serve in many roles in the organism. Regulatory genes turn other genes in the same cell off and on, in response to environmental stimuli. Regulation of gene action in multicellular organisms also involves hormones, so that the distinction between structural and regulatory function is blurred. A gene which specifies the structure of a hormone can indirectly regulate another gene in a different cell.

Many genes exist in variant forms. For example, an alteration in a portion of DNA which specifies messenger RNA will result in an altered protein. The functional effects of the change in protein structure may be minor, or they may cause death because an essential enzyme is inactivated or an essential cellular component misformed. Alterations in transfer and ribosomal RNA have more general effects on synthetic processes and are thus harder to detect. It should be emphasized that the discovery and analysis of genetic effects depends upon the existence of mutant genes and the comparison of organisms with different genotypes.

The phenotype of an organism is an expression of its genotype, but phenotypic variation may or may not be a reflection of genotypic variation. Such phenotypes as neuroticism may indeed be modified by genes, but geneticists would not expect to find genes specifically coded for neuroticism. The very phraseology sounds absurd. However, a phenotype which is dependent upon the activity of a specific protein can be shown in breeding experiments to correspond closely with one or a few genes. As an example, the enzyme glucose-6-phosphate-dehydrogenase (G-6-PD) in man is associated with at least two genes, one on the X-chromosome and the other on an autosome. The X-linked deficiency in G-6-PD is found predominantly among negroes and in peoples of Mediterranean origin. Red blood cells from persons with G-6-PD deficiency hemolyze upon exposure to the antimalarial drug primaquine, with serious consequences. The discovery and eventual explanation of primaquine sensitivity is a classical example of research in pharmacogenetics (241).

Many metabolic errors are known in man, and some are associated with a changed response to drugs. [For recent reviews see the Master Bibliography (241–244).]

Examples in animals of responses to drugs varying because of gene substitution at a single locus are uncommon. Sawin and Glick (245) found that certain strains of rabbits were refractory to atropine. The serum of these refractory animals contained an atropinesterase which was active *in vitro,* and which was not demonstrable in susceptible strains. Breeding tests demonstrated that enzyme activity was dependent upon the presence of an autosomal gene. In 25 heterozygotes for this gene the mean enzyme activity was 107 units (arbitrary scale) against a mean of 271 units in homozygotes. Thus, a double dose of the gene produced more than twice the activity produced by a single dose.

Evidence for variations in drug sensitivity among strains of animals is more common. Some "strain differences" in pharmacological response may turn out to be single-locus effects when appropriate breeding tests are carried out. Others appear to be genetically complex and to depend upon variation at two or more independent loci. Although the possibilities for biochemical analysis of genetic effects are much greater when a single locus can be isolated, it may be that multiple-locus differences are a closer model to the quantitative variation in drug responses found among so-called normal people.

Studies of strain differences in reaction to drugs affecting the nervous system are not commonly motivated by concern for better therapy of animals, but are motivated, rather, by the hope that a comparative approach will aid in understanding the causes of individual variations in drug response. An inbred strain is characterized by a constellation of physiological and behavioral characteristics which can be reproduced consistently. Genetic uniformity usually adds to the precision of pharmacological and behavioral experiments. Comparisons of strains can suggest correlations between pharmacological and psychological variables which may be generalized to other situations. The use of two or more strains in an experiment provides a means of detecting genotype-treatment interactions, situations in which identical treatment has different effects on animals of different genetic constitution.

III. Pharmacogenetic Studies in Man

Pharmacogenetic studies of psychiatric interest are rare, but the number will undoubtedly increase. Goldberg *et al.* (246) compared the outcome of drug therapy in white and negro schizophrenic patients. Data were gathered from nine hospitals collaborating in a Psychopharmacology Service Center survey. Only three of the hospitals had data suitable for the racial comparison. Males receiving a placebo improved more than similarly treated females; females improved more than males when phenothiazines were administered. Race differences were inconsistent, though negroes seemed to be helped more than whites by a placebo. The authors speculate that drugs are more effective against schizophrenias in which genetic vulnerability is important in etiology. Thus, they conclude, genetic factors in schizophrenia were more significant in white females than in the other patients. Racial differences may suggest a genetic explanation, but such conclusions are valid only when, as in primaquine sensitivity, a clearly defined gene is found to be the basis of the difference. Racial groups often differ widely in socioeconomic background, and environmental effects must be considered in the interpretations of studies such as that of Goldberg *et al.* Negro and white populations differ in the frequency of many genes, but their relationship to differences in phenothiazine response is speculative.

A proportion of patients who receive phenothiazines show disturbances of motor activity related to the extrapyramidal neural systems. Great individual differences in vulnerability to these undesirable effects have been observed. Myrianthopoulos *et al.* (247) compared the incidence of Parkinson's disease in the relatives of patients who showed Parkinsonian symptoms following phenothiazines and in the relatives of another patient group without such symptoms. Among 728 relatives (parents, siblings, grandparents, aunts, and uncles) of the index cases there were 13 cases of Parkinson's disease; among 777 relatives of the controls there were only three cases. The difference is significant, and supports the hypothesis that susceptibility to extrapyramidal disturbance during phenothiazine therapy is related to a genetic predisposition to degenerative disease of the basal ganglia.

A comparison of the outcome of drug therapy (primarily imipramine) in patients treated for depression showed concordance of clinical results in 40 out of 44 pairs of relatives (248). This degree of similarity between relatives is higher than would be predicted by any reasonable genetic hypothesis and, contrary to the author's conclusion, suggests that environmental correlations between the pairs play an important role in determining the amenability of depression to drug therapy.

Family studies and twin studies will be useful in behavioral pharmacogenetics providing that care is taken to avoid the biases often present in such investigations. Special designs (double blind, etc.) may be necessary when clinical improvement is being evaluated.

IV. Pharmacogenetic Studies in Animals

Table I summarizes very briefly a few studies of strain differences in response to drugs. It is probable that strain differences can be found in the response to any drug provided a sensitive measuring technique is used and a sufficient number of strains are observed.

Related to studies on strain variation in response to drugs are observations on genetic control of neurochemical characteristics. Genetic variations in brain catecholamines, serotonin, cholinesterase, and other systems have been demonstrated in mice (249,250). A difference in the amount of a physiologically active compound normally present in the body could be the basis for a difference in sensitivity to drugs such as cholinesterase inhibitors or monoamine oxidase inhibitors. To our knowledge such correlations have not yet been established.

V. Interpretation of Genetic Variation in Drug Response

Given the existence of genetic variation in response to drugs as shown in Table I, it is possible to search for a rational basis for the variation. Two types of explanation are possible: (1) Organisms may differ in rate of absorption, metabolism, or elimination of pharmacologically active compounds; (2) organisms may differ in the sensitivity of target systems to pharmacologically active compounds.

An example of the first type of mechanism is the tolerance to atropine of

Table I
SELECTED PHARMACOGENETIC STUDIES IN ANIMALS

Drug	Response	Subjects	Results	Reference
Hexabarbital	Sleeping time	Mouse strains 11 inbred, 1 random bred	Large interstrain variation. Non-inbred more variable.	Jay (1955)[a]
Pentylenetetrazol Pentobarbital Chlorpromazine *d*-Amphetamine	Activity	Mouse strains C57BL/6J, DBA/2, C3H/An, BALB/c	Significant strain differences. Not well related to a simple effect upon "arousal."	Meier *et al.* (1963)[b]
Chlorpromazine	Activity	Mouse strains C3HeB/J, A/HeJ, DBA/2J, C57BL/6J	Percent subjects inactivated by standard dose varied among strains.	Huff (1962)[a]
Chlorpromazine	Shock avoidance and escape	Mouse strains C3HeB/J, C57BL/6J, RF/J	Slope of dose-response curves varied. Drug affected conditioned activity more than basal activity.	Fuller (1966)[b]
Reserpine	Shock avoidance	Reactive and nonreactive rats	Slope of dose-response curve differed between stocks.	Broadhurst (1964)[a]
Ethanol	Sleeping time	Mouse strains BALB/cCrgl, C57BL/Crgl	BALB/c sleep 3 times longer. Duration sleep not related to brain alcohol concentration.	Kakihana *et al.* (1966)[a]

[a] See Appendix 1.
[b] Meier *et al.* (1963), see reference 251; Fuller (1966), see reference 252.

rabbits with atropinesterase. Atropine is inactivated before it can become effective. An example of the second variety of mechanism is primaquine sensitivity in individuals with G-6-PD deficiency. The enzyme-deficient red cells of these individuals are excessively fragile with the result that primaquine can precipitate an acute hemolytic reaction.

There are a few facts on which to base a judgment on the relative importance of differences in drug metabolism versus differences in target organ response in relation to psychotropic drugs. A good argument can be made for the importance of inherited patterning or intensity of reactions in determining sensitivity to drugs. Meier *et al.* (251) conducted experiments (on the interactions of genotype, drugs, and shock avoidance) with a hypothesis that drug effectiveness would be related to the general level of arousal of the mouse strains used. Although significant genetic effects were obtained, they found no simple relationship to their hypothesis, but admitted that their ordering of strains on an arousal scale was somewhat subjective.

Fuller (251a) measured the activity of four strains of mice in an hourglass chamber. The animals could be trained to increase activity by shocking them for failing to cross the center constriction each 20 seconds. They could also be trained to stay on one side by shocking them for crossing. Yoked controls received shocks whenever their trained mates made "errors," but could not themselves affect the schedule of shocks. Chlorpromazine depressed activity more in the trained mice than in their yoked controls, but no strain difference in the slope of the dose-response curve was found (in contrast with previous studies from the same laboratory). Dose-response relationships for chlordiazepoxide did differ between strains, but not between trained and control mice.

There may be no difference at the neuronal level between genetic and experiential determination of sensitivity to psychoactive drugs. Still the results of this experiment suggest that chlordiazepoxide acts upon a kinetic drive which has important genetic determinants but is relatively unaffected by training. Chlorpromazine seems specifically to depress some process in trained mice which is not developed in yoked controls and which is refractory to chlordiazepoxide. This has been tentatively identified as anxiety, which is more affected by differential experience than by differential heredity.

More facts must be gathered before such hypotheses as those of Meier and of Fuller can be evaluated (251,252). Their experiments are presented as illustrations of the uses of genetic stocks in comparative psychopharmacology. The full value of genetics to this area of research is still to be realized, but the start which has been made is encouraging.

For further reading and references see Appendices 1 and 2.

26

DEVELOPMENTAL PSYCHOPHARMACOLOGY*

Jack Werboff

I. Introduction

In contrast to traditional pharmacology with its approach limited to analysis of function in a target organ or system, psychopharmacology has forced the biological scientist to be more concerned with the integrated analysis of structure and function, particularly in relation to the central nervous system. Developmental psychopharmacology by its very nature has pushed this integration further. Indeed, an understanding of maturational phenomena in morphological, physiological, biochemical, and behavioral terms is required in order to understand the differential effects and mechanisms of drug action at various periods of development. It has been unfortunate that few investigators have taken advantage of the unique opportunity offered by the developmental problem to further their own area of special interest, and to demonstrate the integral nature of mind-body interaction. Yet, when one considers the requirements in terms

* Acknowledgment: This report was supported in part by Public Health Service Research Grants HD-01019 and HD-01082 from the National Institute of Child Health and Human Development.

of time, space, facilities, animals, and financial resources, the lack of progress in this area is more comprehensible. However, only through the integrated efforts of many different specialties will the important breakthroughs be made relative to the prevention and rehabilitation of behavioral abnormalities, and also to the enhancement of normal behavioral function.

II. Origins of Behavior

It is fairly common practice of behavioral scientists and laymen alike, including parents, to generally explain behavioral problems by circumstantial events occurring in close temporal proximity. When alteration of these circumstances fails to ameliorate the behavior, genetic or other biological factors are called upon as causative agents. For those of us interested in the behavioral end points of developmental psychopharmacology, such a view of behavioral causality is limiting. It is important to recognize that behavioral development proceeds on a continuum, not with its origin at birth, but long before with the evolution of man as an animal and species. Figure 1 illustrates this continuum of time periods.

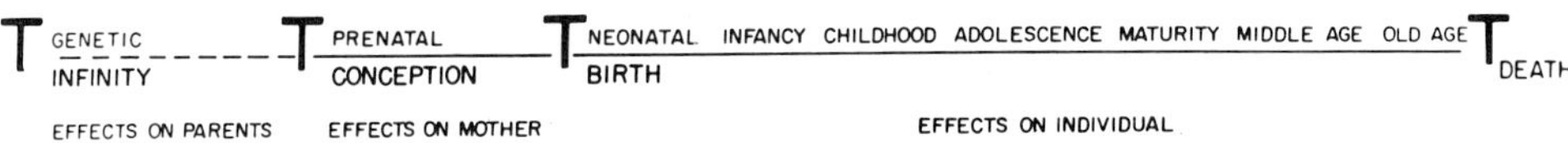

Fig. 1. Time periods relative to developmental psychology.

It should be pointed out that all behavior, at any point in time, is the culmination of the sum total of all the individual's life experiences from birth, the experiences imposed on the mother during the prenatal period, together with the experiences imposed on each of the parents prior to conception as well as their genetic heritage, which includes all of phylogenetic development. The term "experiences" is here widely defined as events occurring both internal and external to the organism, of which he may or may not be aware, but which have measurable effects at some level of biological organization. Such experiences acting through the individual, mother, or parents may be derived from a variety of environmental factors including psychic, personal, social, and, in the context of this chapter, a broad category of agents classed as pharmacological substances of which more will be discussed later. The effects are not only immediate on various specific biological substrates but may also have long-term or delayed effects on other biological or behavioral processes, depending upon the subsequent experiences and the genetic constitution of the individual. Thus, a behavioral problem expressing itself at any one of the seven age periods conceptualized was precipitated by current events, but the predisposing elements may have been present prior to conception by means of his genetic heritage, or by a series of chance events occurring to either of his parents affecting their germ plasm, or by events prior to birth occurring to his mother, or even by events early in postnatal life. An important consideration in this time continuum is that the earlier in development a particular event takes place, the greater the likelihood that it will affect the expression of undifferentiated systems, whether they be morphological, physiological, biochemical, or behavioral. Thus, the genetic potential as it governs every stage of development may be modified by events occurring prior to its ultimate expression.

This graphical or conceptual presentation of time periods in development should not be interpreted to support a theory of "critical periods." This theory based on embryological and morphological development has generated much interest in the behavioral sciences, where its application has implied that particular experiences must occur at specific times in development for subsequent behavior to unfold. The suggestion presented here is that every period of time is critical in the development of subsequent behavior. Unique events are occurring at every moment which shape the outcome of future development. However, there is not a specific relationship between an antecedent event and a subsequent behavior as the critical period theorists advocate.

It is not necessary to belabor the available knowledge that each age period has special requirements related to morphological, physiological, biochemical, and behavioral processes that would interact differently with psychopharmacologic agents. With this in mind, it is important to indicate a deficit in our research designs that fail to account for the carry-over effects of one set of experiences at one age to another set of experiences at another age. Most developmental research uses the *cross-sectional* method. This permits studying several age periods concurrently with the assumption that antecedent events would have been held constant. To be sure, this method is most expedient in terms of time and money. However, it can never provide the necessary answers to those questions concerned with long-term or delayed effects of particular pharmacologic experiences on biological and behavioral functions. To answer such questions requires *longitudinal* research, that is, following specific individuals for life with a satisfactory method of controlling or monitoring genetic background, environmental experiences, and periodically assaying biological and behavioral functions.

III. Animals and Man

The ultimate data in developmental psychopharmacology must come from studies of man. However, the requirements for obtaining reliable and valid information on the effects of drugs for longitudinal research as previously discussed almost precludes the study of man. Ethical, legal, and practical considerations prevent us from setting up experimental populations of humans with known genetic backgrounds and controlled environmental experiences. In work with humans, advantage must be taken of the unique opportunities that occasionally arise with clinical problems and populations such as epidemics of rubella, the thalidomide tragedy, inborn errors of metabolism, and isolated groups with endemic genetic or environmental disorders, in order to identify particular antecedent factors that govern development and later behavior. Such populations also permit the testing of methods, particularly drug therapy, that may ameliorate biological and behavioral defects found in these conditions.

In spite of the major and ever-prevalent criticism that one can never extrapolate animal data on drug effects to effects on man, it must be strongly argued that animal studies represent the only means to obtain cogent data relative to developmental psychopharmacology. These arguments would include the following: (1) The life span of certain animal species permits the complete study of developmental effects over the entire range from conception to death in a relatively brief time period; (2) through mechanisms of selective breeding, mutations, inbreeding, and crossbreeding, it is possible to create in the laboratory large numbers of relatively homogeneous animal populations for extensive longitudinal or cross-sectional study; (3) it is possible to manipulate and control environmental conditions of rearing and testing in order to set up usual and special conditions to evaluate their interactive effects with drug treatments; (4) it is possible to create special conditions within the animal, such as CNS lesions, to determine the mechanisms underlying drug-behavior effects; (5) from the large number of animal species available, it is always possible to select a given species and strain that possesses a unique biological or behavioral system comparable to man so that a given process or mechanism may be studied.

An extensive support of animal research programs must be continued and expanded by private and public resources in order to gain the great wealth of data available from animals before committing a drug to use with man in which the possibility exists of endangering not only the individual but also subsequent generations. Such views are currently being advocated by representatives of the Food and Drug Administration (FDA) and the Pharmaceutical Manufacturers Association (PMA).

IV. Behavioral Parameters

The research literature in psychopharmacology has suffered from the bias prevalent among behavioral scientists in this field that operant conditioning is the only important behavioral process worth studying and lever pressing the only reliable response. Although much can be said in favor of this view, this orientation has seriously handicapped progress in the developmental approach to psychopharmacology.

As a general rule, it should be pointed out that any behavioral parameter (i.e., learning, activity, emotionality, etc.) should be studied at every developmental period. To be sure, the ingenuity of the investigator to develop appropriate test instruments to measure these processes will be taxed, but it is not impossible, as the recent flood of publications in this area indicates. Research designs, methodology, and apparatus must take into account the unique sensory and motor and other physiological attributes of the organism at each maturational stage. For example, knowing that most infant mammals are poikilothermic requires a test environment to maintain body temperature or the animal will have reduced metabolism and manifest limited behavioral responsiveness.

Because there is no *a priori* information to predict that one or more aspects of behavior will be affected by a drug treatment, it is critical that a program of research in developmental psychopharmacology utilize a battery of maturational and behavioral measures to assess the effects of drugs at any period in the life span. Such a battery will frequently include assessment of the following: (1) morphological characteristics at birth, evaluation for congenital defects, and measurement of various body parts; (2) growth by taking weight at birth, weaning, and other age periods; this measure is frequently used as the best index of general health; (3) maturation of specific responses and reflexes during the first few weeks of life such as the rooting and placing reflexes and achieving an upright position and righting responses; and the maturation of specific sensory-motor capacities such as age at which eyes and ears open and their response to specific stimuli; (4) maturation of physiological rhythms such as homeothermic temperature regulation and circadian rhythm; (5) activity levels at various ages which may include recording of spontaneous activity in the home cage (recorded by a variety of transducers such as ultrasonic devices), or spontaneous activity in rotating wheels, open field, or other popularly used instruments; and the activity response in forced tests such as rotating rods and drums, or water submersion in which measures of exhaustion may be obtained; (6) motivational factors such as differential responses to positive and aversive stimulation at various ages with determination of threshold changes as a function of previous drug treatment; (7) learning measures with attempts to delineate performance; motivational, and cognitive aspects in acquisition and retention (it is possible to vary the complexity of learning from simple classical conditioning, through intermediate instrumental discrimination, to highly complex conceptual problems); (8) measures of emotionality using psychophysiological instrumentation for assessing the role of the autonomic nervous system; these techniques may be parallel to evaluating role of personality variables in man; (9) sexual development of specific organs and responses, and sex role, and reproductive efficiency for male and female, including maternal behavior; (10) psychopathological behavior related to CNS functions such as convulsive disorders.

In considering the categories of behavioral parameters described above, it is relatively easy to consider that an alteration in behavior resulting from a drug treatment may always represent a defect. However, this is not the case. It is very possible, and sometimes probable, depending upon the drug administered, the time of administration, and its specificity of action, that the behavioral changes resulting may be an enhancement or facilitation, and improve the ability of the organism to adapt to its environment. Furthermore, the complexity of behavior is such that changes may be seen at one developmental stage and not at another, or that one form of the behavior will be affected but not another. To explain these diversities of response again requires the development psychopharmacologist to consider the biological-behavioral interplay of morphological, physiological, and biochemical mechanisms to explain the drug-development-behavior interaction.

V. Drugs and Drug Action

In addition to the usual pharmacological compounds considered to have psychotropic qualities, it is important to delineate other classes of agents that may play an important role in developmental psychopharmacology. In this context every drug may have an effect on some aspect of behavior, depending upon circumstances of drug administration. Consider the effects of nutritional variables. It is certainly well documented that deficits and excesses of particular dietary components can cause a variety of biological and behavioral effects. In some instances, certain foods interact with particular drugs to cause death and debilitation. Thus, the long-term nutritional state of the organism and the immediate presence of specific dietary components could alter the metabolism and affect the physiological and behavioral action of a given drug. Furthermore, it is necessary to consider the presence of other "drugs" such as chemical additives in food, pesticides, and other environmental contaminants in food, air, and water that may interact with drugs differentially at particular developmental stages to alter the expression of behavior.

This discussion raises an issue related to the ecological understanding of drug action on behavior where it is necessary to consider events external to the organism as well as his inherent cycles and genetic constitution to fully explain developmental psychopharmacology. Such inherent cycles as the circadian rhythm are well known to alter drug metabolism and the behavioral and physiological effects resulting from drugs.

VI. Genetic Variables

Without duplicating the material of the chapter on pharmacogenetics, it is important to reiterate particular concepts that genetic variables such as degree of genetic heterogeneity and homogeneity, presence of mutant genes, polygenic control of behavior, etc. play a profound role in development, behavior, and psychopharmacology. One of the values of the approach of developmental psychopharmacology which is relatively unexplored is the possibility that drug administration early in the life of a developing organism may either modify the expression of the genetic predisposition or may even alter the respective germ plasm and result in new mutations. There has been considerable concern and alarm over the effect of chemical agents on our environment that are potential mutagens. The possibility that these result in defects has not been fully explored. Certainly with additional accumulation of knowledge in this area, it may be possible to modify the expression of defective genes and/or raise the limits of expression for "normal" genes.

VII. Prenatal Drug Administration

Since the time man started to understand and explain the world around him, folklore has perpetuated old wives' tales that experiences occurring during pregnancy will have an effect on the unborn child. In spite of the fact that congenital malformations were observed and reported for hundreds of years by medical practitioners, it wasn't until 1910 that a science of experimental teratology emerged from the biological disciplines related to embryology. Since that time, the experimental literature, supported by documented clinical observations, has recorded several hundred teratogenic agents which, when administered to pregnant animals (infrahuman and human), are known to result in disruption of pregnancy, fetal wastage, resorption, miscarriage or abortion, stillbirths, and an infinite variety of congenital malformations involving every organ system in the body. In recent years, it has been further suggested that teratogens may influence functional systems such as biochemical systems which result in syndromes called "inborn errors of metabolism" such as galactosemia and phenylketonuria. In addition, other functional systems involving behavior and adaptation have been implicated as being under teratogenic influences so that disorders such as mental illness and mental retardation may have their origins in prenatal development.

In spite of all that is currently known about teratology, misconceptions continue to be generated about prenatal development. It required a tragedy such as that recently seen with thalidomide to reawaken us to the fact that the fetus is vulnerable to insult. Perhaps our own psychodynamics misguide us to accept the notion that the fetus is protected in its amniotic environment from the cruel external world. We tend to justify this false conclusion by stating that there exists a placental barrier in the maternal-fetal relationship which wards off all evils. Certainly this is not the case. Although such a barrier exists, its function is limited. Molecules of almost all substances have been reported to cross this barrier either by means of simple physical diffusion or by some type of active transport system. Because of this fact, it is fairly well accepted that anything ingested by the mother will ultimately be found in the fetus.

A second major misconception is that the immature organism (fetus and newborn) have the same capacities as the adult to metabolize and detoxify noxious substances. As has been found for other environmental stressors, the newborn and fetus have not developed the mechanisms to detoxify and excrete noxious substances. This has been demonstrated for a variety of drugs such as amidopyrine, phenacetin, and hexobarbitone as well as for the life-saving antibiotics and drugs such as novobiocin, tetracycline, penicillin, and chloramphenicol.

Since the fetus is so vulnerable, what factors determine the type and extent of the teratogenic defect? Although this is not completely known, there is evidence to suggest that there is an inherited genetic predisposition. In animals, this predisposition can be seen by particular strains manifesting more defects than other strains after identical treatment. This genetic predisposition linked together with a particular teratogen, administered at a certain dosage level, and at a specific time during pregnancy results in the observed defect. Teratologists have argued that the teratogen is not as important as the time of pregnancy in which it is administered. Evidence for this viewpoint is found in the fact that a wide variety of teratogenic agents will produce the same defect (such as cleft palate) if administered at the same time of pregnancy. A minority viewpoint states that certain congenital defects are a result of the action of specific teratogenic agents. Neither one of these extreme positions answers all of the available facts. A compromise position combining the two viewpoints seems most tenable. A case in point would be the thalidomide incident in which a specific agent (thalidomide) administered at a special time in human pregnancy (days 28–42) resulted in particular defect (phocomelia).

Nowhere is the effect of specificity of teratogenic action as great as in the area of behavioral teratology. Here the underlying hypothesis is that teratogens have special affinities for particular developing fetal brain centers and that alterations in their development become manifest as alterations in behavior. Particularly at low dosages of teratogens, behavioral alterations are observed in the absence of gross morphological or structural defects. Since it is extremely difficult to predict *a priori* what types of behavioral changes will be seen after a particular prenatal treatment, it is essential to evaluate a variety of behavioral measures through an appropriate battery of behavioral or performance tests as previously described. Utilizing this approach, it would also be possible to find alterations in behavior which appear as improvements or facilitation in performance as well as behavioral defects.

A. *Hormones*

Hormones administered to pregnant rats have been found to result in behavioral improvements in their offspring. Desiccated thyroid hormone administered throughout pregnancy to rats produced better maze-learning ability of the progeny. Similarly, purified anterior pituitary growth hormone (somatotrophin) administered prenatally to rats enhanced performance of cortically mediated behavior and maturation of innate behavioral responses. Although not completely understood, one physiological action of the hormones was found to modify the pattern of cerebral cortical maturation as evidenced by neuronal hypertrophy, which was hypothesized to account for the observed behavioral improvement.

Of recent interest has been the administration of epinephrine and steroid hormones during pregnancy. These hormones simulate the behavioral and physiological effects in the offspring that have been produced by stressing the mother. In one series of studies, epinephrine to the mother produced alterations in the emotionality of the progeny similar to that produced by experimental anxiety to the mother. Further work on prenatal factors in the etiology of gastric ulcer showed that either psychic stress or epinephrine at the critical time of embryological differentiation of the gut resulted in ulcers in the offspring when they were subjected to stress as adults.

B. *Sedatives and Barbiturates*

Pharmacological compounds considered to be sedatives or barbiturates have been reported to result in a wide variety of behavioral defects in offspring after administration to pregnant animals. These behavioral defects persist for long periods, well after the drug has been metabolized and excreted. This would indicate permanent alteration to the developing nervous system. Alcohol, for example, given to pregnant rats, results in altered emotionality and defective learning of a maze. In addition, sodium bromide, a once widely used sedative, has been shown in rats to produce several types of learning defects (maze learning and reasoning) as well as decreased emotionality, and increased convulsive responses to an audiogenic stimulus. These compounds (alcohol and sodium bromide) were administered throughout the entire course of pregnancy so that a large accumulation of the drugs may have permeated all areas of the cerebrum and thus affect a wide variety of dependent behavioral functions. In other investigations, sodium barbital and sodium pentobarbital administered to pregnant rats and guinea pigs in the few days prior to delivery resulted in inferior learning ability on mazes and reasoning problems for the rat offspring, and neurological and maturational deficits for the guinea pig progeny. Whether or not these defects were a direct result of the drugs on the fetal nervous system is not known. It is highly possible that these drugs administered shortly before delivery could have interfered with the inception of normal respiration in the newborn and the resultant respiratory distress produced a secondary cerebral damage through anoxia, which then manifested itself in the behavioral defects.

C. Psychotropic Drugs

Psychotropic drugs are generally considered to be without many side effects; however, these drugs by their very nature have an affinity for the central nervous system. One would predict then that these drugs could influence the developing central nervous system of the fetus if ingested by the mother. Human clinical reports are somewhat equivocal. They suggest in some investigations with follow up of the offspring that chlorpromazine has no observable ill effects, while other reports state that chlorpromazine and reserpine are frequently associated with perinatal disturbances. The experimental animal literature is fairly well conclusive in reporting a variety of toxic and behavioral changes in the progeny after administration of these drugs to pregnant rats.

In one investigation reporting the effects of maternal administration to rats of drugs that altered serotonin level (reserpine, iproniazid, 5-hydroxytryptophan, and a benzyl analog of serotonin), it was observed that all behavioral consequences in the offspring were in the same direction, regardless of the pharmacological differences between the drugs. These drugs were found to be toxic for neonatal survival, and resulted in increased activity, emotionality, and audiogenic seizures. No effects were noted in motor maturation or in learning ability. The behavioral characteristics of the rats were likened to the syndrome of the hyperkinetic child. This syndrome is thought to result from a diencephalic defect of some type. The fact that these drugs did not alter motor maturation and learning ability (activities which are associated with cortical dysfunction), and that, regardless of the pharmacologic differences between the drugs, they resulted in similar behavior changes, suggests that the fetal development of the diencephalon was affected.

Subsequently, three psychotropic drugs (reserpine, chlorpromazine, and meprobamate) were studied in an attempt to delineate the specificity of the behavioral changes in the offspring with these drugs that operated through different cerebral mechanisms. All the drugs were found to result in increased neonatal mortality and affected general growth and development as measured by weight gain. Reserpine and meprobamate offspring weighed less, while chlorpromazine offspring weighed more than control offspring. Offspring of all drug groups were found to show decreased activity and emotionality, and resistance to audiogenic seizures. This was interpreted to indicate that all the drugs affected developing diencephalic centers in a similar manner. When evaluated for learning ability, only the meprobamate offspring showed learning defects, whereas the reserpine and chlorpromazine offspring did not. The fact that meprobamate is a barbiturate-type drug that affects cortical function while the others are primarily diencephalic warrants the interpretation that meprobamate altered the development and function of the cerebral cortex in addition to the diencephalic centers.

D. Mechanisms

Some consideration should be given in this discussion to the possible mechanisms that explain how a drug given to a pregnant mammal affects the behavior of her progeny. If one considers a direct action of the drug on the structures or processes mediating the behavior, then the drug may alter the germ plasm prior to birth, pass the placental barrier, and alter the developing embryological structures, or persist in the maternal organism and be secreted in the mother's milk to the newborn. However, the resultant behavioral alterations in the offspring may be an indirect effect of the drug. In this case, the drug creates conditions in the mother which alter the surrounding and sustaining internal environment of the fetus; thus, a condition such as anoxia, toxemia, or eclampsia may produce the morphological and behavioral changes in the offspring. The drug may also act indirectly by altering the mother's ability to care for her offspring after it is born so that the postnatal environment is not conducive to survival, adaptation, or normal development.

VIII. Neonatal Drug Administration

It is of interest to note that the majority of reports relative to neonatal drug administration are concerned with hormones, particularly gonadal, thyroid, and adrenal hormones. The hypothesis underlying this work is that alterations in hormonal status early in life determines the later mature expression of the same hormones via CNS mechanisms. Although the processes mediating these changes have not been elucidated, there is a body of experimental data supporting such an interpretation.

Of special significance is the role of the gonadal hormones, which serve both as *organizer* of sexual activity in the immature animal and as a *releaser* of sexual activity in the adult animal. When testosterone and estrogen are given to offspring of both sexes, the effects are seen on the opposite sex counterparts; thus, testosterone masculinizes (structurally and behaviorally) the female, while estrogen feminizes the male. Recent work has extended these results to show that other aspects of behavior, namely, aggression, associated with sex role in animals, is also altered in similar directions by neonatal gonadal hormonal administration. More work is needed to determine if other behaviors, whether or not they are related to sex role, also change with these hormones.

The absence of thyroid hormone in infancy has been shown to affect a variety of behavior and physiological functions such as retardation in the maturation of reflex phenomena, delayed myelinization, abnormal EEG's and reduced capacity for learning and remembering. It would appear that the effect of lack of thyroid is a generalized phenomenon rather than specific to these systems mentioned. Alterations in adrenal hormones are seen to parallel and possibly mediate the effects of early experience or stimulation in infancy. In general, these effects are to enhance behavior and physiological functions, in contrast to the effect of thyroid.

Several reports are available investigating the effects of chronic administration of chlorpromazine in infancy in several species, and following several behavioral parameters. In general, these studies are equivocal with little or no effects on later behavior. Similar findings exist for reserpine and deanol.

Although there is a dearth of publications relative to behavioral consequences of neonatal drug administration, there probably is a wealth of unexplored data resulting from testing in pediatric pharmacology relative to behavioral changes in the organism. Long-term behavioral study is necessary in evaluating effects of drugs at this time of development.

For further reading and references see Appendices 1 and 2.

27

NUTRITIONAL PSYCHOPHARMACOLOGY: INHERITED METABOLIC DISORDERS AND MENTAL RETARDATION

J. Berman and D. Yi-Yung Hsia

I. Introduction

Inborn errors of metabolism occur because of a mutation in DNA-directed protein synthesis, leading to a malfunctioning or absent enzyme, and thereby to abnormal metabolism. The consequential diseases and symptomatology depend upon the nature of the enzyme defect.

Nutritionally influenced mental retardation occurs in approximately twenty metabolic diseases. Therapy in these diseases assumes a knowledge of the pathological manifestations and biochemistry involved, making treatment with specific dietary management feasible. Usually the basis for treatment is based on one or more of the following suppositions: (1) a build-up of metabolites proximal to the enzymic block, (2) a decrease of metabolites distal to the block, (3) increases in metabolites from ordinarily minor secondary pathways, (4) inhibition of pathways unrelated to the involved enzyme system, and (5) an unusual enzyme structure causing a malfunctioning coenzyme-apoenzyme relationship. Within a biochemical pathway there are many possible sites for errors, each producing a unique disease, though symptoms may be similar.

Dietary measures consist of limitation of offending substances, supplementation of reduced metabolites, or administration of coenzymes to correct a malfunctioning factor. Therapeutic effectiveness is measured by correlating neuropathology, behavior, mental symptoms, and intelligence. Experimental data from animals made metabolically diseased can occasionally be used, but correlation at the cellular and molecular levels has not been possible. However, nutritional management is not always required in these diseases, for in many instances biochemically affected individuals remain asymptomatic without therapy.

The original paper by Garrod (see Appendix 1) described four genetic diseases resulting from enzymatic defects: alkaptonuria, albinism, cystinuria, and pentosuria. This list has grown markedly in the last few decades and presently accounts for hundreds of diseases and variations.

II. Conditions Treated by Dietary Means

A. *Phenylketonuria*

Phenylketonuria (PKU) is an excellent example of a nutritionally affected inborn error of metabolism since so much is known of its symptomatology, biochemistry, neuropathology, and treatment. Experimental "PKU" in animals has been extensively studied, and the findings have suggested possible explanations for the characteristic mental retardation in the human phenylketonuric.

PKU is described as a classical autosomal recessive disease occurring in about 1 out of 20,000 live births. The concentration of the enzyme phenylalanine hydroxylase is markedly reduced or totally absent in the phenylketonuric, resulting in abnormal phenylalanine metabolism. The consequent hyperphenylalaninemia and phenylpyruvic aciduria is associated with severe mental retardation which often necessitates institutionalization.

Psychological abnormalities occur in PKU and include hyperactivity, destructiveness, self-mutilation, impulsiveness, rage, and schizoid reactions with hallucinations, seclusiveness, and abnormal posturing as well as mental retardation. Seizures are common, and a large number have encephalographic abnormalities. Fine tremors and microcephaly are often observed, as well as increased muscular tone and tendon reflexes. Extraneural signs include pigmentary changes, eczema, musty odor, and slightly decreased body size.

Defects in myelinization and degeneration of white matter sometimes seen have been ascribed to developmental arrest, absence of myelinization, or demyelinization. The metabolism of cerebral lipids appears to be altered, but no general agreement exists as to which lipids are altered or to the significance of the alteration.

Recent studies have made us cognizant of other conditions which may be either variants of this disease or separate entities. Hypertyrosinemia, with associated hyperphenylalaninemia, is probably due to delayed maturation of one or more enzymes such as phenylalanine hydroxylase or *p*-hydroxyphenylpyruvic acid oxidase. It is common in infants of low birth weight, corrected by ascorbic acid administration, and is without sequelae. Hyperphenylalaninemia, with a blood phenylalanine of between 6 and 20 mg% and with normal blood tyrosine, apparently has no mental retardation and is another condition in which the genetic defect is unknown. There are still other individuals that seem to have classical PKU, but have normal mentality and/or normal urinary findings. Some of these cases have been postulated to have a phenylalanine transaminase deficiency.

In a collaborative study to investigate the causes for high phenylalanine with normal tyrosine in newborn screening programs, it has been shown that about one-quarter have persistent phenylalanine between 6 and 19.9 mg% and the remainder have phenylalanine greater than 20 mg%. Among untreated cases, normal mental development was found in approximately 20% of those with phenylalanine greater than 20 mg% and almost all of those with phenylalanine less than 19.9 mg%. In the remaining cases, low phenylalanine diet was useful in preventing mental deficiency, particularly when started under 30 days of age.

Since it has not been possible on a genetic basis to demonstrate independent segregation between those with high phenylalanine and those with low phenylalanine, we should for the time being view all instances of elevated phenylalanine levels as a single entity. Thus, the term phenylketonuria would include "hyperphenylalaninemia," "hyperphenylalaninemia without phenylketonuria," "persistent hyperphenylalaninemia," "phenylalaninemia," and "atypical phenylketonuria," but would exclude "atypical phenylketonuria with delayed maturation of phenylalanine transaminase" and "delayed maturation of phenylalanine hydroxylase."

1. Biochemistry

Phenylalanine hydroxylase and its cofactor tetrahydropteridine are needed to convert phenylalanine to tyrosine largely, if not exclusively, in the liver. The hydroxylase system itself is composed of two parts: a labile active cofactor-dependent enzyme and a stable enzyme. The stable enzyme is not directly involved in the reaction, but functions to keep the pteridine cofactor in an active form. The labile fraction is deficient in the liver of the PKU, but seems to be present in the normal humans as early as the 22nd to 24th week of fetal life. The enzyme deficiency produces abnormal concentrations of some metabolites, many of which have been implicated in producing the clinical manifestations of PKU.

The biochemical pathways of phenylalanine metabolism are depicted in Fig. 1. In PKU the concentration of blood tyrosine is normal or decreased. Blood phenylalanine is increased, as are urinary phenylpyruvic, phenylacetic and phenyllactic acids, *o*-hydroxyphenylacetic acid, and phenylethylamine. These metabolites result from increased phenylalanine metabolism along secondary pathways, and have been shown to be toxic to the developing animal brain *in vitro,* by as yet little understood mechanisms. These products can also inhibit

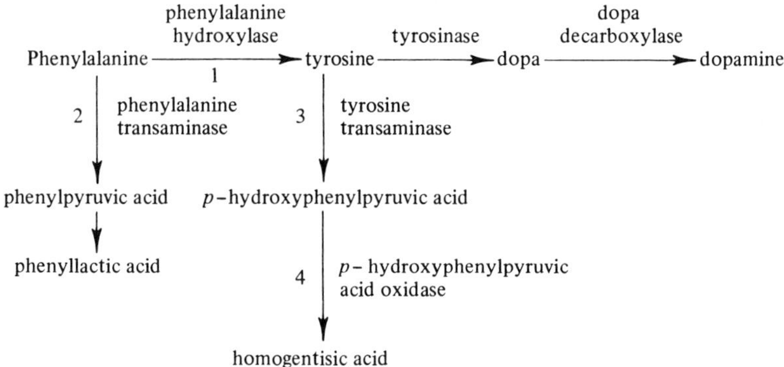

Fig. 1. Pathways of phenylalanine and tryosine metabolism and the defects in: (1) PKU, (2) hyperphenylalaninemia, (3) tyrosinosis I, and (4) tyrosinosis II.

enzymes such as dopa decarboxylase and tyrosinase (Fig. 2), which perhaps explains the decreased catecholamine and melanin production in the phenylketonuric.

Abnormal phenylalanine metabolism may also inhibit enzymes involved in the metabolism of amino acids other than phenylalanine. Liver tryptophan hydroxylase and dopa/5-hydroxytryptophan decarboxylase are two such enzymes. Cofactor inhibition has been found in mice, but no cases of either inhibitors or deficiency have been discovered in humans. Perhaps hyperphenylalaninemia is such a disease.

2. Treatment

At present, treatment consists of dietary control of phenylalanine intake. Several casein hydrolysate diets are available, one of which, "Lofenalac," is prepared by removal of phenylalanine by filtration, replacement of any other amino acids lost, and addition of vitamins and minerals. However, this may not be a totally satisfactory diet, since unknown nutrients may be lost. Dietary variation and supplemental calories may be obtained from other foods low in phenylalanine content. This regime controls the disease but does not cure it because the enzyme is still missing.

Evaluating the influence of dietary control on the intelligence of the phenylketonuric is more difficult. To be maximally effective, treatment must be administered within the first few weeks to months of life. If delayed, a loss of intelligence is likely. At best, a certain intelligence loss is often unavoidable and

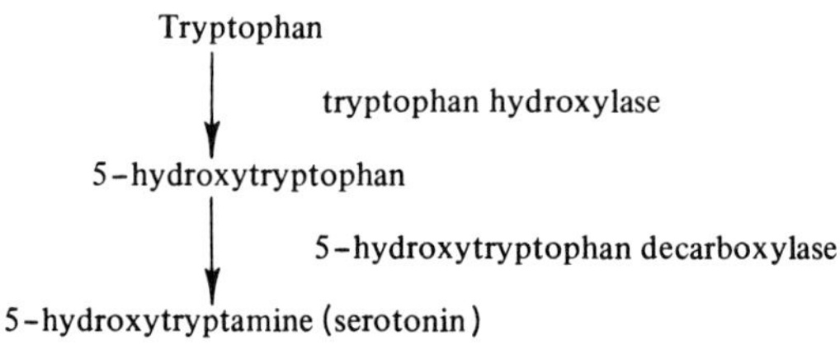

Fig. 2. Pathway of tryptophan metabolism to serotonin.

the average treated IQ is dull–borderline, 80–90. Whether this IQ level is maintained for long periods of time is unknown.

According to current thinking, dietary treatment is probably of no value and may even be detrimental among patients with phenylalanine levels of 20 mg% or less. Furthermore, a small but definite number of patients with phenylalanine levels of 20 mg% or more will develop normally even without treatment. However, in the remaining patients with phenylalanine levels of 20 mg% or more, low phenylalanine diet appears to be effective in reducing the mental defect seen in phenylketonuria, particularly when it is started before 30 days of age.

A concept is now emerging of an acquired PKU caused by embryonic *in utero* exposure to excessive phenylalanine. This concept stems from the observation that phenylketonuric mothers have given birth to both normal and mentally retarded children having normal blood phenylalanine levels. During the next fifteen years, the problem of the concept of acquired PKU will become more serious as treated phenylketonurics become of marriageable age. Placing the mother on a low phenylaline diet during gestation seems logical, but its effects on a growing fetus can be potentially disastrous. Pregnant rats on such a regime have a marked increase in the number of abortions. Mothers who are hyperphenylalaninemic, having blood phenylalanine levels of less than 20 mg% do not have retarded children. A logical approach would be to place PKU mothers on a modified diet adjusted to keep their blood phenylalanine levels between 12 and 20 mg%. It is hoped that future experimentation will resolve some of these problems. Perhaps total replacement of the missing liver enzyme will be attained, as first suggested by Linus Pauling, possibly by a planned viral infection specifically changing the genetic coding back to the normal state.

3. Experimental Approaches

The mechanisms by which mental retardation in PKU is produced are poorly understood, despite a relatively thorough knowledge of the biochemical pathways involved. Studies attempting to relate behavior to biochemistry are frequent, yet the results are equivocal. One of the major difficulties is that there is no animal in which PKU occurs spontaneously. Correlation of pathological, neurohistological, and biochemical findings with behavior has been attempted, but experiments relating these to nerve cell functions and to the effects of a low phenylalanine diet on the integrity of the central nervous system are rare. One method of study concerns the *in vitro* method of tissue culture. In all of the experimental data presented there has been no attempt to review all data, but rather an attempt has been made to give some of the approaches which have been applied. Many of these studies are highly speculative, and none should be taken as final.

Changes in neuroectodermal cells in tissue culture occur when excess phenylalanine is added to the media. The cells derived from newborn puppies are delayed in differentiation, migration, and overall growth. Nonneuronal mesenchymal control tissues are unaffected. These experiments point to the neuron as the target organ, which is essential in myelin formation.

Another method for the experimental study of PKU involves the dilute-lethal strain of mice which have an inherited malfunctioning of pigmentation and CNS manifestations similar to PKU. At the age of 2 weeks, marked locomotor symptoms begin, followed rapidly by convulsive limb movements, overbalancing, seizures, hyperphenylalaninemia, and death at 3 weeks. Myelinization occurs in normal sequence, but rapidly deteriorates and stops at 21 days. Phenylalanine hydroxylase is abnormal in that its cofactor pteridine is inhibited. This produces a situation analogous to that in the human and hence of great importance for further study. However, more recent reports have failed to confirm an enzyme deficiency or inhibition, although the biochemical abnormalities are demonstrable when the mice are challenged with a load of phenylalanine.

Recently, a phenylalanine analog (*p*-chlorophenylalanine) has been discovered which totally inhibits phenylalanine and tryptophan hydroxylase and produces "true" biochemical PKU in rats and mice, but behavioral studies have been equivocal. This drug, with its capacity to specifically inhibit phenylalanine enzymes, may lead us to the understanding of PKU at all levels.

The most frequent experimental approach at present utilizes diets high in phenylalanine, in an effort to simulate the human disease in animals. Unlike human PKU, phenylalanine hydroxylase is not deficient, but many abnormal signs and metabolic abnormalities appear.

Early studies with rats served to show a correlation between a diet high in phenylalanine (3.5–7%) and poor behavior as evidenced by inferior performance on image tests. It was soon realized, however, that there are many factors which could have influenced these results. Newborns should have been used rather than older animals since mental abnormalities in human PKU probably take place in the newborn period. Additional evidence suggests that the animals must be cleared of phenylalanine before testing, as phenylalanine itself may be nonspecifically toxic, accounting for poor behavior-test results. Furthermore, the proper behavioral test must be used because only two out of six tests in rats had reproducible results.

"PKU" monkeys and rats have abnormal myelinization in the cortical white matter and increases in glial elements in the cortical gray matter. Electron microscopy shows abnormalities in glial mitochondria, incomplete myelinization, and inconstant demyelinization. Cerebrosides are unchanged in PKU guinea pigs, however, and the choice of the animal could be an important factor in all of these studies.

Human PKU's have decreased levels of blood serotonin, urinary 5-hydroxyindoleacetic acid, and many other abnormalities of tryptophan metabolism and transport which disappear with treatment (see Fig. 2). This has led to a theory that one of the prime causes of mental retardation in PKU is due to abnormally low levels of brain serotonin.

Since liver tryptophan hydroxylase and 5-hydroxytryptophan decarboxylase is partially inhibited in experimental "PKU," many studies have been done attempting to correlate these changes with behavior. Significant decreases in brain serotonin are found to be associated with reduced mental ability in rats on the experimental diet. A causal relationship cannot be concluded, however, as individual brain serotonin measurements correlate poorly with individual behavior-test results. Animals with increased brain serotonin, after treatment with a monoamine oxidase inhibitor, also show decreased learning ability.

In another study, brain serotonin was increased by the use of the serotonin (5HT) precursor, 5-hydroxytryptophan (5HTP), and was associated with decreased learning ability. Decreased 5HT was associated with increased ability. It is difficult to validate these results since adult animals were used and were not cleared of phenylalanine prior to testing.

To correct these problems a further study was conducted, which attempted to reduce brain 5HT by the use of three independent mechanisms. The first method used was the standard phenylalanine diet; the second used reserpine which is known to deplete 5HT stores; and the last blocked the 5HT receptors by the use of chlorpromazine. The reduction in 5HT was then correlated with learning ability after the animals had been cleared of their respective 5HT depletors for 3 days. All three experimental classes produced decreased learning ability, and concurrent administration of 5HTP or another 5HT congener, melatonin, reversed the effect. Similar studies have failed to confirm these works, and it has been pointed out that not all animals were made phenylketonuric biochemically. At present, final conclusions on the importance of 5HT in PKU cannot be made, despite many attempts to link it to the mental manifestations. The biochemistry and neuropathology are obviously extremely complex. Perhaps the advances and mistakes learned from PKU can set the stage for a better understanding of the other inborn errors of metabolism.

B. Tyrosinosis

Tyrosinosis was first discovered in 1932 and presumed to be caused by a lack of the enzyme *p*-hydroxyphenylpyruvic acid oxidase (see Fig. 1). Recent reviews of the original biochemical data make many investigators feel that this disease was not due to an oxidase deficiency but rather to a deficiency of tyrosine transaminase (see Fig. 1). Since that time, no similar cases have been recorded. During the past few years, many patients have been discovered who have a true oxidase deficiency. This has led to confusion, as the newer disease was variably termed tyrosinosis, tyrosinemia, and hepatorenal dysfunction. The present discussion is limited to the oxidase enzyme deficiency which most people now call tyrosinosis.

The most common signs are hypertyrosinemia, tyrosyluria, cirrhosis, and de Toni-Debré-Fanconi syndrome, growth failure, and thrombocytopenia. Mental retardation is variable, but seems to increase with age. Hypermethioninemia is rarely present without severe liver involvement.

Inheritance is probably recessive, and in a population isolate in Canada, 41 cases were discovered for an incidence of 1 in 6000, making it nearly similar to phenylketonuria in this instance.

Transient tyrosinemia of infancy occurs in 0.1% of full-term and 50% of premature infants. This is a benign self-limiting variation caused by a combination of factors: delayed maturation of the enzyme, relative vitamin C (cofactor) deficiency, and increased amounts of dietary protein. A few of these infants do not respond to ascorbic acid and are presumed to have only delayed maturation of the enzyme.

Ascorbic acid is unable to correct any of the signs of true tyrosinosis. Proper treatment consists of a low phenylalanine and tyrosine diet. Vitamin D is added in large amounts when there is an associated Fanconi syndrome (osteomalacia, glycosuria, aminoaciduria, hyperphosphaturia), and combinations of these diets cause a fair improvement in many of the manifestations of the disease.

C. Branched-Chain Ketoaciduria

Maple sugar urine disease (MSUD) is one of the branched-chain amino acidurias, and like PKU it is treated by dietary restriction. The odor and taste of the urine is similar to that of maple sugar. It is recessively inherited, associated with severe mental retardation, and is usually rapidly fatal.

Symptoms include feeding difficulties, irritability, vomiting, rigidity, convulsions, and finally stupor and death within a few weeks of birth. Other cases

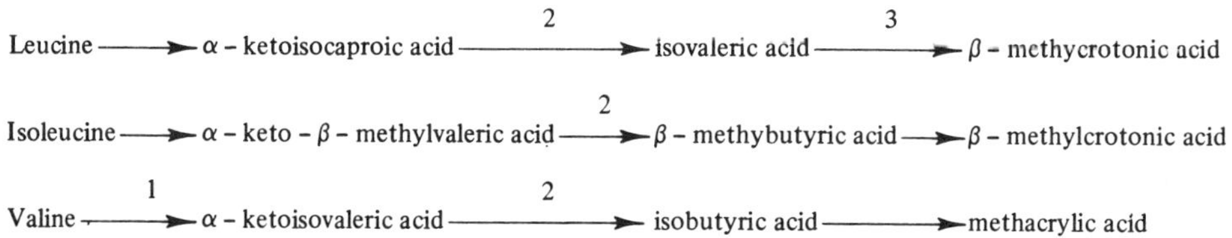

Fig. 3. Pathways in the metabolism of branched-chain amino acids and the defects in: (1) hypervalinemia, (2) MSUD, and (3) isovalericacidemia.

are now being recognized with milder symptoms and less severe biochemical alterations.

The primary abnormality in this disease is caused by a defect common to three amino acids (Fig. 3).

There is no general agreement on brain neuropathology, as only 10 patients have been studied, reflecting the rareness of the disease. There is also difficulty in obtaining necropsy specimens from patients similar in age and with the same systemic biochemical pattern and symptomatology. In most cases there is an excessive pallor and delayed formation of myelin, spongy, and edematous white matter and an increased size and number of astrocyte nuclei.

In two patients, brain cerebrosides, γ-aminobutyric acid (GABA), glutamic acid, and glutamine have been found to be low, with increases in branched-chain amino acids and water content. Serotonin was decreased, as were total lipids, total phospholipids, alkali-stable phosphorus, cholesterol, and neuraminic acids. The gray matter was relatively normal, and almost all of the changes were noted in the white matter. Another study concurred with respect to cerebrosides and water content, but no decrease in brain lipids was noted; cerebroside sulfatide and ceramide were normal, and there was no increase in branched-chain fatty acids.

MSUD like PKU is treated by the restriction of the offending amino acids prior to the biochemical block.

During the first year of life, the plasma levels of valine, isoleucine, and especially leucine are labile, causing severe problems with dietary management. After an initial stabilization period, variation can be accomplished by the addition of gelatin, arachis oil, and sucrose together with low-protein fruits, vegetables, and gluten free flour. The lability lessens with age, but new problems arise when the body's requirement for these amino acids decreases, causing a severe limitation in choice of foods available to the child. Nonadherence to the diet can rapidly produce symptoms such as acidosis, vomiting, dehydration, and death. This is unlike PKU, where high plasma levels are compatible with normal overt behavior. Brewer's yeast corrected an abnormal growth rate present in one case, despite adequate amino acid levels and other nutrients.

Two independent studies have found brain serotonin to be decreased by leucine. The most recent study found a significantly decreased learning ability on the rat image test as well. The rats used, however, were 4 weeks old, and the animals were not cleared of leucine prior to testing. Abnormal serotonin metabolism has now been found in histidinemia, galactosemia, and phenylketonuria, and thus its possible role in mental retardation must always be kept in mind.

Recent reports have indicated many variants of MSUD. Biochemically classical cases have been described with minimal symptoms, and mild forms with only partial absence of the decarboxylating enzyme. In addition, there are others who have hypoglycemia and no urinary odor. Finally, there is a variety with intermittent signs and symptoms which may be a genetically distinct entity.

There are at least two other diseases with abnormalities resulting from malfunctioning of the branched-chain amino acid pathways. Both are rare and probably recessively inherited. Isovalericacidemia has been reported in two cases from the same family, with a defect in leucine metabolism after the decarboxylation step (see Fig. 3). Hypervalinemia occurs as a result of a defect in transamination of valine and has been described in one case.

Of the two, isovalericacidemia is the milder, with some mental retardation and the constant and persistent smell of sweaty feet. Acidosis, vomiting, and lethargy are usually associated with a metabolic stress such as an increase in protein ingestion or infection and are corrected by limitation of protein intake. The deficit can be demonstrated in white cells, but the usual routine screening procedures and chromatography are of no value.

Mental retardation and physical symptoms are more severe in hypervalinemia. A low-valine milk has been used, but due to its late start (9 months) in the one case studied, no conclusions can be drawn from its failure to improve intelligence. Routine screening would detect this disease since abnormal metabolites are found in the blood and urine and the enzyme defect is present in leucocytes.

D. *Galactosemia*

Hereditary disorders of carbohydrates are usually not associated with mental retardation. The only exception is that of galactosemia, a recessively inherited disease whereby the ability to utilize galactose is lost. Early detection can result in avoidance of most of the symptoms by treatment with galactose-free diet.

1. Biochemistry

The major pathway for the incorporation of galactose into the body pool is via the hexose monophosphate shunt, involving four reactions (Fig. 4) of galactose to a utilizable glucose metabolite. A deficiency of galactose-1-phosphate uridyl transferase prevents reaction 2 (see Fig. 4), resulting in an accumulation of galactose-1-phosphate, which is believed to be responsible for many of the symptoms. The importance of these reactions in galactosemia is unknown. A small amount of exogenous galactose is needed in the production of endogenous galactose containing anabolites. The direct conversion of galactose-1-phosphate to UDP* galactose in step 7 can provide for galactolipids and mucopolysaccharides, which are the more important of the anabolites. The conversion of galactose to xylulose is a means by which galactose could enter

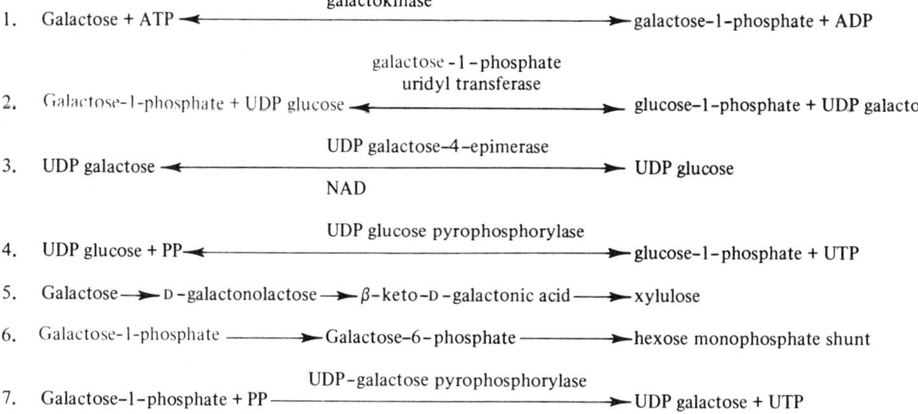

Fig. 4. Pathways in the metabolites of galactose.

the hexose monophosphate shunt (reaction 5), but its entrance in reaction 6 has not been proven.

2. Clinical

Severe disease is accompanied by vomiting, diarrhea, dehydration, jaundice, cataracts, hepatosplenomegaly, and mental retardation in addition to hypoglycemia, albuminuria, and a generalized aminoaciduria. In its milder form individuals may be entirely asymptomatic with no mental impairment or at worst suffer some postprandial abdominal discomfort. No disparity exists with regard to the enzyme, which is markedly reduced or absent in all cases.

At least two variants exist, Duarte and Negro, and one related abnormality associated with a galactokinase deficiency. A homozygous individual for the Duarte variant has 50% activity for galactose-1-phosphate uridyl transferase. He is symptom free and exhibits a single band† on electrophoretic examinations. His heterozygous parents have 75% activity and two electrophoretic bands,† which differ from normal individuals.

* Uridine diphosphate.

† 1 band indicates 1 enzyme or isoenzyme, 2 bands indicates 2.

It is unclear whether all galactosemic negroes belong to the Negro variant type, but to date there have been no Caucasians in this class. These individuals may be severely affected or relatively asymptomatic. All have a marked deficiency of transferase, yet some are able to normally catabolize a galactose load. A separate genetic allele or modifier gene has been postulated, though the usage of alternate pathways could account for many of these findings.

The galactokinase deficiency syndrome is similar to galactosemia in its clinical manifestations. It diverges in that mental retardation and aminoaciduria are absent and galactosuria occurs only after a galactose meal. These individuals have normal transferase levels and symptoms are related to the galactokinase deficiency (see Fig. 4, reaction 1).

3. Treatment

Removal of exogenous dietary galactose is the only effective therapy. Early treatment reverses the biochemical and clinical abnormalities. Late treatment may be unable to overcome severe cirrhosis or reverse mature cataracts; nevertheless, it should be attempted because some alleviation of symptoms may occur. In regard to mental retardation, reports vary in the evaluation of therapeutic effectiveness, despite early initiation of treatment. The final intelligence at best is probably slightly below normal, similar to the findings in PKU.

In the past, therapy consisted of a pudding made from lactose-free cereals, eggs, vegetable margarine, sucrose with added calcium, and vitamins. However, this provided too high a caloric intake, and diarrhea often ensued, necessitating a modification in the formula. More recent diets are derived from galactose-free milks such as Nutramigen and Dextrimaltose. Soybean preparations could be harmful as they contain stachyose, which when hydrolyzed include two molecules of galactose. The diet becomes easier to manage with age since the amount of galactose ingested relative to body weight decreases, and an improvement of galactose utilization occurs.

E. Disorders of Urea Biosynthesis

There are five sequential steps in the biochemical production of urea from ammonia, each of which is associated with an enzyme abnormality (Fig. 5).

The diseases involved in its metabolic pathway are hyperammonemia I and hyperammonemia II, citrullinemia, argininosuccinic aciduria, and lysine intolerance. All are associated with hyperammonemia, mental retardation, and treated with low-protein diets. Unlike PKU and MSUD, the amino acids which accumulate prior to the enzyme block do not appear to be responsible for the clinical manifestations. These amino acids are nonessential, and toxic symptoms are undoubtedly due to increased amounts of ammonia.

The following discussion is limited to the first four diseases, lysine intolerance being dealt with separately since its direct relation to urea production is tenuous. The limitation of ammonia is extremely difficult, since it arises from the deamination of amino acids. There are three possible means of regulating ammonia production. Ketoglutarate may be converted to glutamic acid and glutamine, which then affords ammonia for renal excretion. Glutamate could thus be admin-

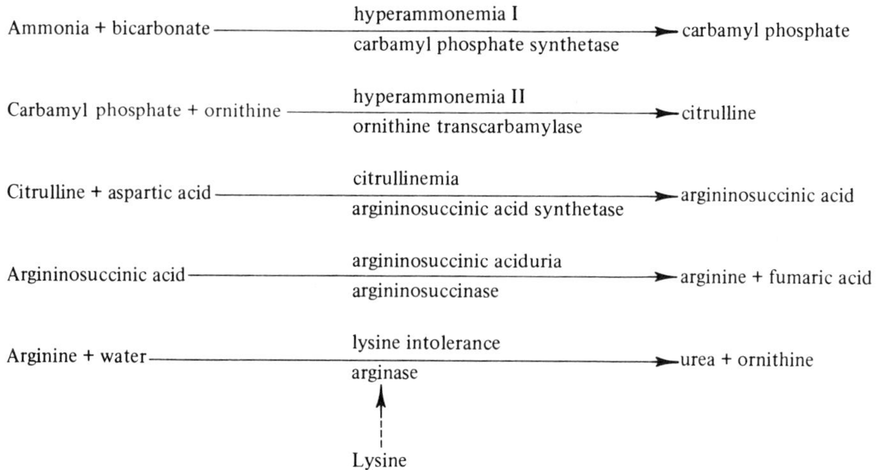

Fig. 5. Pathways in the metabolism of urea.

istered to facilitate this excretion. Another involves the use of ammonia for the synthesis of pyrimidines for nucleic acids. Both of these are ineffective in restraining blood ammonia levels, as pyrimidine synthesis is independently governed and the blood concentration of glutamine has an upper limit, after which its conversion from ketoglutarate ceases.

The last form of therapy is the administration of neomycin which, through its interference with bacterial production of ammonia, could theoretically decrease the ammonia load. Most experiments to date have found this ineffective. Thus, in all of these diseases we are left with restriction of protein as the only form of treatment since there are no means of reducing the blood ammonia level.

The biochemical production of urea is not completely understood. Alternate pathways have been proposed, as individuals affected with these diseases are able to provide normal amounts of urea despite their enzyme block. Enzyme deficiencies in these diseases should make the amino acids beyond them essential. However, most studies have not substantiated this, and a dietary supplementation of these amino acids does not help clinically.

Lysine intolerance and hyperlysinemia are two diseases of lysine metabolism neither of which has a known enzyme defect and yet are related to the urea cycle. Knowledge concerning the degradative steps of lysine metabolism is sparse, but the pathway which has been postulated to be affected in this disease is shown in Fig. 5.

Only one case of lysine intolerance has been reported. Periodic ammonia intoxication was noted, particularly after a protein meal, and was associated with abnormal muscular tonicity, episodic coma, hyperlysinemia, and hyperargininemia. Mental retardation and neuromuscular irritability were constant findings. Liver enzymes were normal, including carbamylphosphate synthetase, argininosuccinic acid synthetase, ornithine transcarbamylase, and arginase. A liver enzyme capable of degrading lysine, L-lysine: nucleotide adenine oxidoreductase was decreased. Since lysine is a potent inhibitor of arginase, it is possible that symptoms are produced by its inhibition. Thus, treatment consists of a diet low in protein and L-lysine.

Hyperlysinemia differs from lysine intolerance in that these patients have an associated aminoaciduria with no associated ammonia intoxication. The biochemical defect has been postulated to be a reduced ability to incorporate lysine into protein, which would preclude any effective treatment.

F. Histidinemia

One of the most distinguishing features of histidinemia as compared with the other inborn errors is the frequent findings of a speech defect. Mental retardation, growth failure, and fair complexion are mild and highly variable signs. If a causal relationship could be proven between the speech defect and histidine metabolism, an entirely new approach to mental retardation could evolve. The diseases previously discussed have an associated nonspecific mental retardation, making biochemical-pathological correlations difficult.

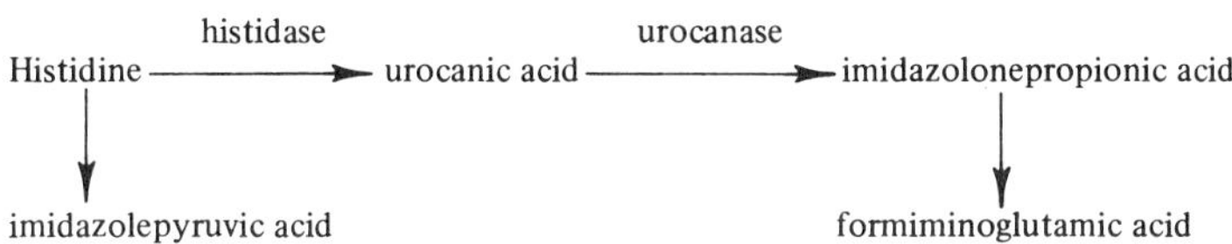

Fig. 6. Pathway in the metabolism of histidine.

Histidase is essential in the conversion of histidine to urocanic acid. This results in a histidinemia, histidinuria, imidazolepyruvic aciduria, and a decreased excretion of formiminoglutamic acid (Fig. 6).

Imidazolepyruvic acid gives a positive test with ferric chloride and Phenistix similar to that in PKU. Blood urine levels of histidine and the response to histidine loads are abnormal, and skin histidase activity is absent.

Removal of histidine from the diet causes blood and urine findings to revert to the normal state. It is not known what effect such a diet has on the speech defect, or the mental retardation. Until recently, histidine has not been considered essential for man, though it is for some animals. Diets low in histidine do not cause adults to become biochemically or clinically defective, but infants require it for normal growth.

III. Conditions Treated by Other Nutritional Means

A. Pyridoxine Dependency Syndromes

Cystathioninuria, pyridoxine dependency, xanthurenicaciduria, and pyridoxine-responsive anemia are diseases in which the symptomatology has been ascribed to a vitamin B_6 dependency in a single enzyme system. The coenzyme pyridoxal-5′-phosphate is derived from vitamin B_6, which exists in three forms:

pyridoxine, pyridoxamine, and pyridoxal. All three are intraconvertible and transformed by pyridoxal phosphokinase to their active coenzyme form.

A primary deficiency of vitamin B_6 produces a disease through the malfunctioning of multiple enzymes. Several enzyme systems, particularly the decarboxylases and transaminases, require vitamin B_6 for normal functioning. The most affected enzymes are those which have the least affinity for the coenyzme and/or whose needs are the greatest at that moment. This type of deficiency is not genetic and no different than the other vitamin deficiencies.

Only six cases of cystathioninuria have been reported with little agreement as to symptoms. Five of the six had mental abnormalities and two had thrombocytopenia. The others were associated with nephrogenic diabetes insipidus, PKU, acromegaly, and other congenital malformations. These cases have a mild increase of cystathionine in blood and a marked cystathioninuria, which are reduced after administration of high doses of pyridoxine hydrochloride (Fig. 7).

The normal requirement of vitamin B_6 is 0.5–1.5 mg/day. It has been postulated that the primary defect is the occurrence of an abnormally structured

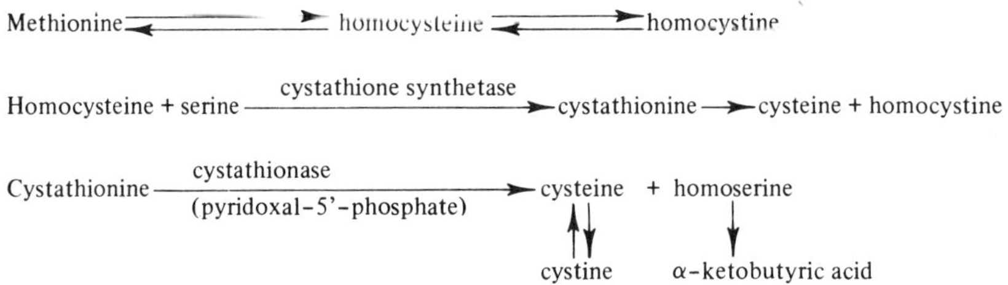

Fig. 7. Pathways in the metabolism of methionine and the defects in cystathioninuria and homocystinuria.

apoenzyme, causing an abnormal coenzyme-apoenzyme unit. Administration of large doses of vitamin B_6 (100–250 mg/day) results in a more normal relationship creating a functional holoenzyme.

Liver cystathionase activity has been measured, with minimal activity being present. *In vitro,* addition of excess pyridoxine fully corrected this deficiency, and a structural defect of cystathionase was deduced.

The role of cystathionine in the causation of symptoms and mental aberrations is not understood. Recently, however, evidence has been produced which shows that it may be a postsynaptic inhibitory agent. Whether mental retardation can be corrected or prevented awaits further studies. All cases reported to the present time, show little if any improvement in mentality on prolonged administration of pyridoxine. However, most were started relatively late after birth.

The pyridoxine dependency syndrome consists of convulsions and neurological manifestations which are alleviated by pyridoxine administration. Convulsions have been reported *in utero* and, without prompt treatment, death often occurs soon after birth.

Evidence is accumulating that the primary metabolic block is in the conversion of glutamic acid to GABA. Glutamic acid decarboxylase is a B_6-dependent enzyme and together with GABA is found primarily in the gray matter of the brain. GABA concentration increases after birth, and many studies associate its malfunctioning with audio- and photogenic convulsions. In addition, GABA can be a substrate for oxidative metabolism which is inhibited during pyridoxine dependency convulsions. Its administration during seizures can cause temporary alleviation of the convulsive state. Until recently, little hope was given for comparative organ studies, such as with cystathioninuria, because GABA was felt to be located only in the central nervous system. However, recent studies have found it to be present in renal tissue, and thus direct tissue assay may be feasible.

B. Homocystinuria

Most individuals affected with homocystinuria have mental retardation, dislocation of the lens, peculiar facies, abnormal gait, and skeletal deformities. Cystathionine synthetase (serine dehydrase) is deficient in the liver, prohibiting the normal formation of cystathionine from homocysteine (see Fig. 7). Symptomatology is highly variable, necessitating trials with multiple therapeutic regimens. These include removal of metabolites proximal to the block, supplementation distally, and administration of pyridoxine.

Abnormal levels of methionine (see Fig. 7) can inhibit normal growth and development and can interfere with the intestinal absorption and transport of histidine in animals. Most therapeutic diets decrease the methionine content, however some patients never manifest any hypermethioninemia, and removal of methionine in these patients could be detrimental.

A moderate abatement of clinical manifestations occurs when supplemental cystine is added to the diet. This may be explained on the basis that the enzymic block lowers the tissue level of cystine, making it an essential amino acid. Cystine also has a sparing effect on methionine, diminishing the body's total requirements for it. The removal of homocystine is unnecessary since its renal clearance is high and large amounts have never been found in the blood. Whether cystathionine should also be supplemented is unknown, as it is very expensive and fairly difficult to obtain in large enough quantities for continual use. It should be tested, however, since it has been found in the brain of homocystinurics, and its presence may be vital for normal brain function.

Two recent studies obtained good results from large doses of pyridoxine similar to those in cystathioninuria and vitamin B_6 dependency. The biochemical abnormalities and clinical manifestations were corrected. However, more cases are needed to confirm this.

C. Leucine-Induced Hypoglycemia

In 1956, a case of hypoglycemia was found to be related to the amino acid leucine. Leucine-induced hypoglycemia has not been conclusively designated as an inborn error of metabolism. The mode of inheritance is uncertain, and although a specific enzyme block has not been discovered, it undoubtedly exists. A thorough discussion of this disease is considered necessary, as the approach to therapy and biochemical investigation diverges greatly from the other nutritionally influenced diseases.

Manifestations of the disease may occur soon after birth or as late as 8 months, and particularly after a high-protein meal. A general neurological instability, occular problems, and convulsions leading to irreversible mental retardation constitute the primary symptoms.

1. Biochemistry and Pathogenesis

It was previously shown (Fig. 3) that leucine is reversibly transaminated to α-ketoisocaproic acid and later irreversibly decarboxylated to isovaleric acid.

Early investigations showed that L-leucine, and to a lesser extent isoleucine, were potent hypoglycemic agents and that other D or L amino acids, including valine, were not. Hypoglycosemia after the administration of α-ketoisocaproic acid was attributed to reverse transamination to leucine, and thus the resulting hypoglycemia was leucine specific.

Further biochemical knowledge was afforded when means were found for producing the disease experimentally, by pretreatment of individuals with sulfonylurea or lente-insulin. This caused a sharp drop in blood glucose after leucine ingestion, similar to the normally occurring sensitivity occasionally associated with pancreatic islet cell tumors. Other studies showed that both the experimental and natural sensitivities were associated with hyperinsulinemia which responded to epinephrine and glucagon.

The insulin pathogenetic theory of hypoglycemia has been seriously questioned. Many other amino acids are able to effect an insulin release, but without a concomitant hypoglycemia. Furthermore, leucine can by itself cause a slight decrease in blood glucose. In mice, leucine, but no other amino acid, inhibited the incorporation of ^{14}C from labeled three-carbon precursors into glucose *in vitro.* This suggested a direct inhibition of hepatic gluconeogenesis independent of insulin.

2. Treatment

Current therapy combines a low-protein intake with postprandial carbohydrate supplementation. Low-protein and minimal leucine diets have been devised which are effective in controlling convulsions. However, maintenance is difficult, as most food contains large amounts of leucine, and further restriction may interfere with growth.

The postprandial carbohydrate supplementation counteracts any hypoglycemia which may occur secondary to leucine ingestion. Previous to this, euglycemia was maintained by the administration of steroids or ACTH, which in themselves can cause a release of endogenous leucine; consequently, this treatment has never been universally adopted. Pancreatectomy has been used, but only as an accessory therapy, for it does not seem to be effective by itself.

During the past few years a potent hyperglycemic agent, diazoxide, has been used with increasing frequency. Many centers use it as their only means of treatment, with promising results. The only major side effect appears to be a reversible generalized hirsutism. Control of symptoms is remarkable, despite normal leucine intake, although its effect on mental status is unknown. It seems to function as a suppressor of pancreatic insulin and as an effector of adrenal medullary-controlled gluconeogenesis. Normal mentality is an attainable goal because the therapy is specifically directed at euglycemia and the leucine sensitivity diminishes with age.

IV. Conditions Not Fully Evaluated

There are several other nutritionally influenced metabolic diseases which have not been dealt with here. These include Hunter-Hurler's syndrome, prolinemia, hydroxyprolinemia, and hydroxykynureninuria, methionine malabsorbtion syndrome, and the two forms of hyperglycinemia. The reason for their exclusion here is that there are too few cases or therapeutic effectiveness is unknown. The relationship of Hartnup's disease to mental retardation is greatly disputed, and nutritional treatment has not yet been attempted in Wilson's disease, Crigler-Najjar syndrome, hypermethioninemia, hypersarcosinemia, Lowe's syndrome, or the sphingolipidoses.

V. Conclusion

In the past two decades a number of inborn errors have been discovered and treatment begun by means of dietary management. As a result of this, a child previously relegated to an institutional life or early death may in many instances have a relatively normal existence except for dietary restrictions.

The lack of suitable experimental animal models has hampered progress in the correlative studies between brain function and biochemical errors. Screening programs in newborns have made the detection of phenylketonuria rather easy, and newer methods should make many of these diseases routinely discoverable.

Clinical and biochemical variants are relatively common, making a universal-type therapy untenable. Dietary management being the only method of treatment, we were rushed into universal therapy without adequate scientific study. It is now apparent that not all forms of these diseases need or should have dietary restrictions. With these reservations it is our belief that dietary therapy is of value in the classical forms of PKU, galactosemia, and may be lifesaving in pyridoxine dependency, MSUD, tyrosinosis, and the disorders of urea biosynthesis. It is not possible to evaluate the eventual mental capacity in the latter diseases as too few cases have been treated.

One consequence of a compulsory screening program has been the seeming necessity to immediately treat all children with abnormal biological values. These diseases need more careful study to determine which children will be benefited, and we agree with the American Academy of Pediatrics, which "favors neither the extension of current compulsory legislation nor passage of new legislation for the compulsory testing of newborn infants for the presence of congenital metabolic disease" [*Pediatrics* **39,** 623 (1967)].

For references and further reading see Appendices 1 and 2.

28

DRUGS, SENSORY AND PERCEPTUAL PROCESSES, AND VARIATIONS IN DRUG EFFECTS RELATED TO ENVIRONMENTS

Jay T. Shurley

I. Ecopharmacology—A Point of View

It has been apparent for some years now that variations in physical and social conditions in the environment, in the absence of drugs, produce numerous and complex effects upon the physiology and behavior of biological, including human, systems. It should not be surprising, then, that environmental variables, and how these are sensed and perceived by the organism, are coming to be important considerations in pharmacology, and particularly in psychopharmacology. Reliable and reproducible experimental results are unlikely to be obtained without strenuous and continuous efforts to define and control the factors responsible for variations within and between experiments. When using animals, and especially humans, as the population under study, this can be a very difficult task. Sources of variation to be coped with may be summarized as follows:

1. The genotype, the genetically controlled response pattern.
2. The phenotype, which is conceptualized as the product of genetic and environmental factors. The environmental factors can be further categorized as developmental and proximate. During the developmental period of growth, genotype interacts with environment to produce the phenotype, which can only be considered fully established at sexual maturity. Phenotypic variation is expressed as variation in relatively stable morphological and behavioral characteristics of the organism. In considering drug effects, one is less concerned with stable morphological and behavioral characteristics than with specific physiological and psychological responses of relatively short duration.
3. The *dramatype*, the product of the interaction between the phenotype and the proximate environment acting during the experimental period.

Environment can thus be seen to affect an organism's response pattern to a drug by influencing both those characteristics emerging during development from conception to maturity and by relatively short-term effects acting during the experimental period. The distinction between developmental and proximate environment is, unfortunately, infrequently made, and, indeed, is not always a clear-cut one. In adolescents, infants, and immature animals, both aspects of the environment can be said to influence drug-elicited responses. Lilly and Shurley (253), in experiments with humans, have insisted upon a clear and complete description of the proximate environment, including even subtle social environmental factors. Shurley (254) has emphasized the importance of distinguishing environmental effects in experiments, where sensory and/or perceptual *deprivation* (in the case of immature experimental animals or subjects) and sensory and/or perceptual *isolation* (in the case of mature ones) are involved. The science of *ecopharmacology* (from ecology + pharmacology)—the relationship between the environment and drug responses—may now be said to be emerging.

Numerous deafferentation experiments in animals have demonstrated the vital role of sensory input to the brain in mediating response to the environment; in fact, the nervous system may be said to be the primary organ of adaptation. The study of Sprague *et al.* (255) suggests strongly that specific, patterned, localized sensory information, carried by way of the lemnisci to the forebrain, is essential for both the development and the maintenance of attentive, affective, and adaptive behavior in the cat. This same study also helps to differentiate the specific role of sensory stimulation in guiding specific, adaptive responses or behaviors, from the nonspecific role of the same stimulation, acting through and upon the ascending reticular activating system, in adjusting levels of arousal, activation, and attention. Indeed, the reticular activating system may be viewed as a kind of homeostat, regulating and adjusting input-output relations and possessing certain optimal adaptation levels, reflected by suitably high or low attention levels or anticipatory set. No assessment of drug effects upon behavior in the intact higher vertebrate can be considered complete without some consideration of the foregoing.

In the case of man—and it is man that we are almost exclusively concerned with in psychopharmacology—it is not enough, however, to consider only the foregoing. Schueler (256), among others, has emphasized that the *information content* of a given entity is also an essential concept, using *information* in the information theory sense. He says; "When objects or situations are viewed from the standpoint of their information content, they embrace not only all physical, chemical, and biologic systems, but also in the same breath, psychologic and sociologic systems as well." Matter and energy, and their equivalence, as expressed in Einstein's equation $E = mc^2$, are the fundamental ideas of classical physical science. Information content is an equally fundamental concept in biology, and is partially relatable to, but not derivable from, the concepts of mass and energy. The physically definable quantity most closely related to information is entropy, which is, in a sense, an inverse measure of the implicit information content in any situation. *Communication* may be viewed as the exchange of information from one system to another, conveniently referred to as *sender* and *receiver*. It is important to realize that, when communication occurs between sender and receiver, no implication of consciousness is necessary. What is crucial is that some pattern, or design, is transmitted from one system to another, which specifically signals, or triggers, the receiving system or systems into some alteration or continuation of ongoing behavior. It is like the function of a hormone, and specificity of the signal in a hormone is precisely the same form that information content takes in drugs. Information content, as a concept, may therefore be appropriately illustrated by drugs as well as by the environmental set. Drugs do not, to any significant degree, supply either energy or materials for the physiologic processes they prompt. The metabolism of the cells and the cytologic structures which "dance to the tune" of the drug moiety are already present—a "given"—and the response process is termed *biotransformation*.

The ego of man, which mediates—and sometimes determines—the relationships (communication) between the proximate environment, the future expectations, the past history, and the present action tendencies of the individual, evolves and matures out of the interaction between the individual and his collective biologic heritage coded in the nucleic acids (DNA and RNA) within the chromosomal sets of genes within the nuclei of his cells, (a type of biologic informational storehouse) and his social heritage, communicated from generation to generation and individual to individual in written and spoken words and in a number of kinesic and structural cultural patterns as well. The level of complexity and the level of integration needed to be dealt with here are partially indicated by the foregoing statements. Ecopharmacology, then, can be defined as that facet of psychopharmacology which strives to deal dynamically with the interaction between the dramatype and the drug design.

In man, in considering the dramatypic aspects of drug response, i.e., that part which is the product of the phenotype and the proximate environment acting during the experimental period, it is useful to elaborate briefly on the psychodynamic processes known to be involved. It is timely, perhaps, to recall that Freud, in one of his last publications (257), wrote: "[F]or the time being, we have no other (than psychological) methods for mental therapy. The future may teach us how to exercise a direct influence, by means of particular chemical substances, upon . . . the mind." Lindemann (258) reminds us that psychoanalytic theory postulates a system of integrative processes which underlie behavior patterns in an individual who is attempting to maintain an equilibrium between inner drives, with their unconscious and preconscious aspects, and the environmental opportunities and demands in an everchanging continuum. Both normal and abnormal behavior are viewed as parts of a comprehensive action pattern of a goal-directed organism. The determining integrative instrument of such goal-directed patterns of behavior is the system called personality. The personality is active in relating inner experience to outer perceptual cues, past experience to future anticipated events, and emerges with a relatively safe, and/or satisfying plan of action. These action patterns may be profoundly influenced by patterns "learned" during an early developmental period, equally as much as by the attitudes, goals, and aspirations of the significant members of the individual's social group. It is the function of the ego to constantly strive to achieve a compromise between what is innate, past, and learned and what is real, actual, and present in a highly organized, continuous homeostatic adaptive process. In a sense, the ego functions in a continuous effort at problem solving by rehearsing anticipated situations, and making choices between alternatives. These symbolic models representing anticipated real situations—presumably the essence of what we term "thought"—form a map, or template, for future behavioral responses. It is a cardinal contribution of psychoanalytic theory to regard these phenomena as part and parcel of normal human adaptive behavior. The neurophysiological concomitants of these highly organized, delicate, integrative processes remain almost completely undemonstrated and unexplored, although a few beginnings have been recently established.

Elkes (259), among others, has pointed out that the underlying neurophysiological mechanisms would depend, in some measure, upon sensory input, since reduction of input, or of meaningfully patterned input, demonstrably alters levels of consciousness and awareness, and alters aspects of brain function as an information-processing organ. He comments:

> Drug effects, while having certain elements in common with non-pharmacological challenges, also differ from them in certain important aspects. It is . . . apparent that, although certain special features attach to special drugs, it may be gross over-simplification to speak of drug-specific reactivity patterns. . . . Experience suggests that the same drug, in the same dose, in the same subject may produce very different effects according to the precise interpersonal and motivational situation in which it is given. In the integrative functions with which it interferes, and the "set" which it alters, environment, both past, present, and anticipated, plays a dominant part. Such factors must be constantly taken into account in a study of the integration and disintegration of ego functions.

It is the purpose of the present chapter to draw the attention of the psychopharmacologist and of the drug therapist, in a compelling way if possible, to the ubiquitous role of this multiplicity of environmental factors, as a rule unnoticed or overlooked, in influencing responses which may be initiated by, but not necessarily limited or controlled by, drug administration. Admittedly, in the long roster of sources of error in assessment of drug effects, environmental influences constitute but one more or less discrete entity, but their significance is enhanced disproportionately because (a) they are ubiquitous, and likely to be erroneously overlooked or ignored, and (b) when behavior is the variable under scrutiny (as is necessarily the case with so-called psychotropic and/or neuroleptic drugs), the environment in which the experiment takes place is implicitly involved. No comprehensive or exhaustive review of drug agents, nor of demonstrated environmental effects, is attempted, since it is a broadened focus and point of view which is being here espoused.

II. Experimental Results

Experiments which demonstrate environmental effects on drug action are relatively recent in occurrence and quite limited in number. Gunn and Gurd (260) noticed that symptoms of excitement in mice given benzedrine and allied compounds were markedly augmented when several mice were grouped together for the experiment, and markedly diminished when the animals were kept isolated after drug administration. Greenblatt and Osterberg (261) confirmed the findings with *dl*-amphetamine in mice, noting that isolated mice receiving eight times the dose given to grouped mice remained unexcited and showed no hyperthermia. They found methamphetamine, *dl*-amphetamine, methylphenidate, phenylisopropylhydrazine, pipradol, amphenazole, caffeine, and picrotoxin all showed increased lethality, motor activity, and rectal temperature in grouped, but not in isolated mice, and that phenelzine, mescaline, ephedrine, pentylenetetrazol, and bemegride showed no differences.

Cohen and Edwards (262), noting that sensory deprivation (sensory and perceptual isolation) and LSD administration produced many similar subjective and objective phenomena, tested the interaction of LSD and sensory isolation under the assumption that the combination would produce a potentiation of effect. Instead, they found that, whereas subjects in normal sensory environments experienced perceptual and somatic effects within 30–60 minutes, naive LSD subjects were unaware of any LSD effect until they left the sensory isolation box at the end of 2 hours. These authors were of the opinion that this represented not a postponement of effect, but eradication of effect, as though sensory isolation were an antidote. However, they report that experienced LSD subjects responded with a considerable intensification of symptoms under sensory isolation conditions. Luby *et al.* (263) found that the manifest psychotomimetic effects produced by Sernyl (phencyclidine) were markedly reduced if the subject was also under sensory isolation.

It has been noted that subjective reactions to LSD and to psilocybin, respectively, were altered in a positive direction when these drugs were administered in a socially supportive and aesthetically pleasant environment, while "bad trips" were likely to result under the opposite conditions. The experiments above are referred to here primarily to indicate that both social and physical aspects of the environment may interact with drug effects of certain drugs to produce unanticipated, yet predictable, results.

III. Perception-Blocking Agents

Reference needs to be made here to the drug phencyclidine hydrochloride (Sernylan, formerly Sernyl), first of a new class of drugs with unique anesthetic and analgesic properties (264) in man and animals. Meyer *et al.* (265) used 1-(phencyclohexyl)piperidine monohydrochloride (Sernyl) as an anesthetic agent in a series of 80 patients, and were able to draw the conclusion that it produced an especially severe, and somewhat uneven, "sensory isolation syndrome," believed to be mediated by a central "uncoupling" of sensory pathways in the brain stem, thalamus, and sensory cortex. Motor function was unimpaired, and consciousness maintained, although some difficulty in thinking and concentration occurred in some, and marked delusional, hallucinatory, psychotic-like syndromes in others. Luby *et al.* (263) labeled the drug a "schizophrenomimetic" drug, based on their study. Shortly afterwards, the drug was withdrawn for human use by the manufacturer (Parke-Davis & Co.), and limited to veterinary use under the name Sernylan, where it is considered very effective in the capture and management of a wide spectrum of wild and zoo-living animals requiring veterinary intervention. Its action is that of a central sensory transmission blocking agent, potent enough to produce surgical anesthesia without effect upon the motor system, a kind of chemically induced deafferentation. Therefore, it may be said to alter the organism's normal response to the environment by blocking perception of the environment.

There is a hint of related activity on the part of many of the anesthetic and analgesic agents in use today, ranging from alcohol and morphine, through chloroform, ethyl ether, and procaine, to the motion-sickness preventives, such as meclyzine. All of these agents, to a greater or lesser extent, dull or block perception of the environment, as well as proprioception. They give evidence of this effect in the "excitement phase" of general anesthesia, body-image disturbances with procaine and other powerful local anesthetic agents, pleasant fantasies and affect-tone with morphine and its derivatives, and emotional lability with alcohol. By blocking the transmission of excessive environmental stimulation effects upon the inner ear components, the motion-sickness preventives also act in a positive way to alter organism-environment relationships. Sometimes these perception-blocking effects are the main and desirable ones; sometimes they constitute the undesirable side effects. All these agents deserve considerable further study from the standpoint of the indirect effects of altered relationship between the organism and its environment, as well as from their direct effects.

IV. Sensory and Perceptual Isolation in Psychopharmacologic Research

Finally, it seems appropriate here to point out that the techniques of artificially altering the environment in specific ways, as in sensory and perceptual isolation and deprivation, and in sensory and perceptual "overload," furnish new tools for psychopharmacology which have much apparent potential and have hardly begun to be used.

For further reading see Appendix 2.

PART VII

PSYCHOPHARMACOLOGIC DRUG STUDY DESIGN AND RESEARCH PROBLEMS WITH HUMANS

29

GENERAL PRINCIPLES OF CLINICAL PHARMACOLOGY AND PSYCHOPHARMACOLOGY AND EARLY CLINICAL DRUG EVALUATIONS

Ronald Okun

I. Definition of Clinical Pharmacology

Clinical pharmacology encompasses the examination and detection of drug actions in man and their correlation with animal pharmacology. In other words, clinical pharmacology is a distinct entity which is primarily concerned with pharmacologic effects of drugs in man, including therapeutic problems and human toxicology.

II. Relationship of Clinical Pharmacology to Pharmacology

There is a parallel relationship between clinical pharmacology, which is primarily concerned with the pharmacologic effects of drugs in man, and pharmacology, which is concerned with the effects of drugs in all species of animals.

The relationship of the pharmacologist to clinical investigators has passed through several stages. Early in this century pharmacologists were working in the clinic. They had few laboratories and did much of their work on patients. As they began to stress the basic aspects of pharmacology, as their relationships with chemistry improved, and as more drugs began to be synthesized, pharmacologists drew away from the clinic into the laboratory. Then, full-time clinical investigators were increasing in number, and they and their colleagues in the practice of medicine did most of the studies of drugs in humans. Finally, in the past few years, a new type of investigator appeared. This is the clinical pharmacologist, who combines knowledge of the principles of pharmacology with knowledge of clinical medicine.

III. Clinical Pharmacology

A. *Methodology of the Clinical Trial*

Prior to initiation of a trial or even before a decision has been made whether or not to investigate a certain drug, the astute clinical pharmacologist will carefully evaluate the preclinical animal data to determine if there is good and sufficient reason to carry out a human drug trial. Numerous difficulties are met in applying data obtained from animals to man. One of the most important of these is the factor of species differences in metabolism of drugs. Various species of animals react differently to the same drug. Some of these differences are qualitative; for instance, morphine depresses man, rats, and dogs, but appears to stimulate cats, goats, and horses. Not only do variations in the metabolism of a drug make it difficult to extrapolate results of animal experiments to man but they create a serious obstacle to the development of new therapeutic agents. A drug may be active in one or more species and yet be relatively ineffective clinically. Indeed, the converse is also possible: A drug only slightly active in animals may be effective in man.

Thus trying to infer the response to a drug by one species from data secured on another species is always a risky venture. It is especially risky for the behavioral pharmacologist and the clinical psychopharmacologist. Not only must he deal with all the species differences in drug response that disturb other pharmacologists—differences in absorption, distribution, metabolism, etc.—but with differences in behavior as well. One has only to look about to see that evolution has lavished perhaps its richest variety of adaptations on the mechanisms of behavior. If one adds the variation produced by genetic differences, the number of potential interactions becomes virtually unlimited. Undoubtedly this is why there is hardly any comparative pharmacology of drugs that affect behavior. There simply is not enough known to permit conclusive statements across a broad range of species about any drug. The type of animal models used to evaluate potential psychopharmacologic agents can be found in Chapter 16.

Clinical pharmacology frequently depends on the cooperation of volunteer subjects. Such volunteers are often utilized to provide data to serve as normal base lines or a standard of reference against which data from abnormal subjects may be measured. The use of volunteer subjects for psychopharmacologic studies is fraught with great danger to the validity of the data. It has been clearly shown that drug responses to a normal volunteer population, the psychologic makeup of the volunteers, and the reasons involved for the subjects volunteering may be all very abnormal in themselves. Furthermore, there are great problems in using the results obtained in terms of generalizations to the population at large. For example, some of the reasons for normal subjects to volunteer for drug studies include the possibility of monetary rewards, the hope of finding professional advice for their problems, a search for new experiences, a search for escape or release from personal problems, a search for sexual gratification, and an attempt to satisfy self-destructive urges. It is obvious that data derived from volunteers with such feelings might be distinctly abnormal.

What about patient cooperation? Obviously the sensitivity of clinical trials depends a great deal on whether or not a patient takes his medication, eats an appropriate diet, collects his urine accurately, etc. Several studies have now shown that a minority of individuals were obedient to instructions in all possible occasions in some clinical trials. How then can we generalize our data to a population which may be less or more prone to accepting orders from physicians? There is no answer. Hopefully, studies will be undertaken in an attempt to develop ways of checking on patient reliability. Certainly when several studies are carried out with the same design and the same drug, the pooling of data would tend to give a more accurate picture than one study alone. One of the significant advances in pharmacology in the past few years has been the field of pharmacogenetics. Lessons taught to clinical pharmacologists from pharmacogeneticists are accurately covered in Chapter 25.

Several authors have pointed out some of the problems involved in administering a drug to a patient who is concurrently receiving another medication. Although investigators attempt to have patients refrain from taking any of their medication during clinical trials, some drugs may be absolutely necessary for the patient's well-being. One drug may reduce the therapeutic efficacy of another drug, or the combination may result in toxicity. There are many examples in the literature today. In addition, the chronic administration of one drug may reduce the pharmacologic activity of another by stimulating its metabolic inactivation. This field, enzyme induction, may explain some unusual pharmacologic effects that occur when drugs are given in combination and may account for tolerance observed with prolonged treatment of certain drugs. While a further discussion of this topic is beyond the scope of this chapter, readers are encouraged to refer to the current literature and other appropriate chapters and appendices in this text for further details.

Particularly in psychopharmacology, the difficulty in obtaining enough patients for early drug trials has been widely recognized, but rarely studied in detail. Many studies in the literature point out that only a very small percent of patients admitted to hospitals with the necessary diagnostic identification meet the criteria for inclusion in trials. For example, many patients are unsuitable owing to age alone; exclusion of age extremes is customary, though convincing evidence in support of this procedure is lacking; furthermore, restriction of the sample in this way involves separate testing of the excluded group on another occasion. For example, exclusion of women of child-bearing age, which is quite common in view of the possible teratogenic potential of drugs, and in view of the preponderance of depressive illness among women, their absence seriously hampers applicability of early clinical pharmacologic trials.

In recent years, the Federal Food and Drug Administration (FDA) has become a partner in clinical drug investigation along with the investigator and pharmaceutical industry. Prior to the passage of the 1938 Food, Drug and Cosmetic Act, drugs could be marketed before clearance by the Federal Government. The clearance procedures established by the 1938 act were limited to tests for safety. The 1962 Kefauver-Harris amendments to the 1938 act added a second basic regulatory requirement of proof of efficacy as a condition precedent to government approval of new drug applications. Thus the current regulations place under much closer scrutiny the evaluation of chemical substances employed in the treatment of human disease. Under current FDA regulations, the clinical administration of a drug may be initiated at the time the investigational new drug application is first filed. It is the responsibility of the FDA to review the investigational new drug application promptly to ensure that the data contained therein are adequate to support the claim by the manufacturer that the drug may be safely administered to man, in what is described as phase I of clinical trials in man.

Studies of new drugs in man are divided into three phases, designated as Phase I, II, and III. Phase I is the first trial in normal man, Phase II (often subdivided into early and later periods) deals with more detailed observations of drug effects in normals and initial trials in disease states; Phase III consists of broad clinical trials designed to ascertain whether or not the drug is of clinical benefit in the various disease states or syndromes for which effectiveness is to be claimed. As can be seen, there is considerable overlap in the conduct of the three phases of clinical trials. The FDA has taken the point of view that the primary concern of Phase I studies is the determination of biologic activity in man, its effects on such target organ systems as the liver, kidney, and heart; and while dosage range studies may be initiated in a small number of subjects in the Phase I part of the trial, dosage range is determined in the Phase II part of the clinical trial. Clinical pharmacologists generally direct Phase I and early Phase II studies with an occasional hand in the development of late Phase II studies. Phase III studies which may overlap with late Phase II studies are directed by physicians for the pharmaceutical corporation who have training and experience in one of the specialties of medicine. The Phase III studies are, however, conducted in the field by a number of clinicians not employed by the pharmaceutical corporation; they are attached to university medical centers or teaching hospitals, or are in private practice, or some combination of these three.

Many clinical investigators and people in pharmaceutical corporations have taken the point of view that the FDA laws are too stringent and require too much paper work. With the passage of time since the new Federal regulations went into effect, it has become more apparent that the regulations, while they do involve a good deal of record keeping, involve only good scientific principles. The regulations required good record keeping, good tabulation of patient data, and good follow-up of patients. Certainly some investigators have curtailed their activities greatly in view of these new regulations, but most feel with time that the temporary inhibitory effect of the FDA proposals will fade and we will be all the better for this period of internal revolution.

As mentioned above, the clinical pharmacologist is primarily concerned with Phase I and early Phase II studies. In the design of Phase I studies, the importance of careful planning, detailed directions, careful definition of variables and criteria, and accurate and complete record keeping for appropriate data analysis cannot be overemphasized. In the well-planned clinical study, the protocol is an essential tool in realizing these requirements. It serves as a road map for the investigator at each point in the study, telling him where he is at any moment, keeping him aimed in the right direction at all times, and providing a record of where he has been when he comes to report on his trial. By continuing reference to a sound study protocol, an investigator insures that his methods, materials, treatments, etc., remain constant and that his definitions do not change.

If a carefully worked out study protocol is important to the conduct of a single investigator performing his own individual clinical study, it is a *sine qua non* for a cooperative clinical study. In such situations, which are becoming more frequent in the area of psychopharmacology, protocol is an agreement among the cooperating clinicians to carry out the trial in a prescribed manner. Assuming that after careful consideration, the animal toxicity is not threatening and good animal models have demonstrated good reasons for believing that the drug may be active as a psychopharmacologic agent, it is appropriate for the potential investigator to give consideration to the details of this protocol. The investigator should keep in mind that not only is he attempting to find definitive therapy for a particular clinical condition but in addition to find any area of usefulness for the drug under investigation. All studies should be carried out by investigators who are alert to unexpected side effects and amelioration of associated conditions, in addition to the disease being investigated. An astute clinical investigator with a thorough knowledge of disease, pathophysiology, and pharmacology, is the most essential item in any experimental design in clinical pharmacologic research.

The investigator's first consideration should be to make certain that all patient volunteers are fully informed about the potentials of the drug under study and that an informed consent, now preferably in writing, is given to the investigator by the volunteer patient. The investigator should seek out patients who are appropriate for his study with the guidelines mentioned above. He should not start the study until he has a reasonable number of patients based on the potential differences expected between the treatment study, as for example the drug under study and the placebo; using too few patients to begin with, will result in a high probability of failure of the study to show any statistical difference. He should pay close attention to the diet of the patients and be personally acquainted with their medical and psychiatric histories. This study can be designed in one of many ways, utilizing the principles of adequate randomization of patients, using double-blind procedure with concurrent drug or placebo comparison, devising what objective parameters measurement may be available (psychologic tests, etc.), and devising a scheme to quantitate observations by the physician, nurse, ward technicians, etc. A statistician or biostatistician can be most helpful at this point. He should be brought into the clinical study at the very inception since data handling and evaluation will be much easier with his cooperation. The patient questionnaire or the record sheet for the physician, nurse, or ward technician should include observations for known adverse effects, particularly those dependent upon a prior knowledge of adverse effects with similarly appearing agents. Every attempt should be made to remove bias of the investigators or observers in these studies. To a great extent the use of double-blind control techniques is sufficient, but there are certain cases where more thought needs to be given to this problem. It has become evident that an individual's response to a drug is not a simple reaction to the drug's purely pharmacological properties but rather is influenced by a variety of psychologic and social forces operating in a treatment setting. These psychosocial influences are particularly important in the drug treatment of alcoholism because of the unique attitudes and feelings held toward alcoholics by society. It appears that alcoholism evokes irrational attitudes and behaviors from professional people. Many treatment personnel carry these negative feelings into the hospital and clinic, where they prejudge the alcoholic patient as unworthy and undeserving. The prevailing negative treatment bias makes drug therapy with alcoholics increasingly difficult and complex. Patients are not treated in a vacuum, and they respond to a variety of subtle forces on them in addition to the specific therapeutic agent under investigation. Those social forces impinging upon the patient from the hospital and those psychologic attitudinal influences present in the various personnel with whom he comes in contact are the situation variables that must be considered in drug therapy in research.

In the design of psychopharmacologic trials, clinicians have become involved with therapeutic labels and classification, for example, antipsychotic drugs, antianxiety drugs, antidepressants, etc. The psychoactive drugs available for clinical trial and for clinical use do not appear selective and surely cannot distinguish between a neurosis and psychosis or between such symptoms as anxiety and depression. Such terms defy precise definitions. Patients with the same diagnosis may be quite heterogeneous, and their symptoms and their disabling features may require different therapy. Psychiatric nosology in its present state leaves much to be desired. Nevertheless, an adequate nosology of mental illness is important for clinical psychopharmacologic studies. Patients who respond differently to different forms of treatment are, in a very real sense, different kinds of patients, and it is important that these differences be represented in the nosology. One helpful approach in the evaluation of the effects of a psychotrophic drug is to relate these effects to particular psychopathologic states such as "abnormal drive" rather than to diagnostic entities which are quite variable from psychiatrist to psychiatrist. These target symptoms include anxiety, tension, depression, fear, suspicion, hostility, apathy, delusions, various mannerisms, hallucinations, level of behavioral arousals, etc. It is becoming apparent that by using these target symptoms instead of psychiatric diagnostic entities, we can have more valuable clinical investigation. Therefore, it is suggested that rather than label a patient as a paranoid schizophrenic, etc., additional classifications be set up according to the type of abnormal symptomatology expressed by the patient.

In other fields of clinical pharmacology, the preference technique for comparing drug efficacy may be useful. It is not clear whether or not it will be useful in the realm of psychopharmacologic drug evaluation. By this technique differences between drugs of apparently unequal potency have been consistently demonstrated by means of this experimental design. This experimental design has several advantages: First, it is simple to carry out and requires a minimum amount of personnel, time, and patient cooperation; second, the patient may be used as his own control; third, multiple doses of compounds may be compared with relative ease; fourth, all the variables that affect the patient's symptoms are assimilated into one yes-or-no-type answer; fifth, the data collected are ideal for analysis utilizing the sequential technique; sixth, results are usually clear-cut and unequivocal; and, finally, the data presented from other studies indicate that the results of a given comparison are reproducible. However, the design has a number of limitations: It cannot be used to evaluate acute or changing symptomatology; data obtained within a given study are more qualitative than quantitative; detailed information is generally not obtained; and comparisons are generally limited to two drugs in any given study.

However, it should be pointed out that in evaluation of psychopharmacologic agents crossover designs are rarely possible, partly because they take too long and partly because psychiatric status changes too rapidly. Drug-placebo and drug-drug designs are the rule. It has been the author's experience that it is useful to give at least a week of placebo medication to all patients before the beginning of the evaluation proper of the drug. This clearing period tends to remove patients from the study who have a self-limiting illness, and this tends to cut down the number of positive results on both the drug and placebo groups. Following this placebo period, the actual double-blind study will start with appropriate initial evaluations. The timing of further observation tabulation depends on the duration of the study and the type of results required. Too frequent evaluations tend to result in less sharp differentiation by the observers. No general rule can be proposed here. However, with a larger number of patients less frequent observations should be made and less frequent objective testing should be done unless a large number of observers are at hand.

Duration of the study should be guided by several principles. It is rare for a patient treated adequately with an active drug to fail to show some degree of improvement. Total improvement from psychoactive drugs follows an almost exponential curve. There is rapid change in the first few weeks, a slowing of improvement in the sixth to twelfth weeks of treatment, and very little change thereafter. Thus a 12-week study may show the true efficacy potential of a psychoactive drug, but may not show all the side effects which can occur with prolonged therapy. Also, in the author's experience, drug dose level must be modified from time to time depending on the needs of the patient. Accordingly, the protocol should be so designed that the number of tablets of medication can be raised or lowered according to the physician's evaluation of the situation. It should also be remembered that the antipsychotic drugs, though not curative, are the foundation for an effective total-treatment program of psychosis. One cannot, therefore, expect the cure of even a greatly benefited patient unless he is treated in a setting which is tuned to taking treatment promoted by drugs and multiplying this effect by other methods of working with the patient to improve his capacity to profit constructively from interview contacts and programmed activities.

Antidepressive drugs may be considered a special case because depressions are often episodic, tending toward spontaneous remissions and exacerbations. Here also assessment of treatment effectiveness is hampered by nosology of depressions which is not clear-cut. Also it is very common to treat depressions with a combination of drugs as compared with a single antidepressant. Some order has been brought to the chaos by the work of the Veterans Administration cooperative studies. Some of these studies have found that most hospitalized depressed patients can be classified into one of three clinical syndromes—anxious, hostile, or retarded depression. These classifications are meaningful on the basis of drug effect.

While there is too little data available at the time of this writing, it appears that there may be a reasonable alternative to the double-blind procedure. Some workers advocate the employment of an independent assessment team as alternative to the classical double-blind technique. They feel that this team serves as an additional control over therapist bias and permits the use of modified double-blind procedures in a variety of research situations. The alternative advocated here is one in which assessment is completely separated from treatment. The team would consist of a psychiatrist, psychologist, and social worker, each trained to rate specific treatment effects within the competency of his professional discipline. Lack of direct involvment in treatment reduces bias on the part of the independent assessment team and produces a more objective appraisal of outcome. Whether or not the promises put forth by this new approach will bear fruit remains to be seen.

B. Drug Metabolism

The questions posed to the clinical investigator planning a protocol for a psychopharmacologic drug study include usually unaswered questions of absorption of drug, elimination of drug, biotransformation, detoxification of drug, distribution of drug in the body, protein binding of drug, transport of drug in the body, mechanism of action of the drug, and what structure-activity relationships of similar drugs are known. With every bit of additional information known about these points, a more meaningful protocol can be planned. For example, if it is known that the elimination of a particular drug may take several weeks after cessation of therapy, then it would be wise to plan post-treatment observation periods to take into account the prolonged effect of the drug. If the drug is rapidly changed in the body to an inactive form, then administration of the drug would be necessary several times rather than once a day. All these factors have great importance to the pharmacologist, but all too often little is known about these points until long after the drug is past Phase I trials.

IV. Problems in Clinical Pharmacology

A. *Informed Consent*

Reference was made above to the necessity of an informed consent. An informed consent is designed to safeguard the rights of the individual subject. Broadly speaking, it requires the physician experimenter to obtain from the patient written or verbal consent showing that he understands the nature and possible risk of the experiment to be performed. Apparently this consent has never been defined by the courts, with the results that, as the law now stands, the physician experiments at his own peril. Some investigators are somewhat skeptical that any formulation can, at the same time, provide adequate safeguards for the rights of the individual and the rights of humanity to the benefits of such medical progress as depends on clinical experimentation. The basic premise here is that the voluntary consent of the human subject is absolutely essential. The duty and responsibility for ascertaining the quality of the consent rests upon each individual who initiates, directs, or engages in experiment. It is his personal duty and responsibility and may not be delegated to another without great care. In the area of psychopharmacologic research it may be impossible to communicate to a psychotic patient. There is no ideal way of obtaining an informed consent from such a patient. However, all attempts should be made, and next of kin should be adequately informed about the study. It has become common at most large teaching hospitals to have set up research committees or some such committee which rules on the validity of research protocols. In the area of psychopharmacologic research it is appropriate that these committees themselves rule on the validity of informed consent and lay down ground rules as to how an informed consent is to be derived from psychotic patients.

B. *Poor Patient Cooperation*

As mentioned above, many patients take their medication only sporadically. This is a continuing problem in all areas of clinical drug research. While inpatients can be observed more carefully than outpatients in terms of drug administration, investigators are surprised every day to find that their patient has not been taking medication at all. Good physician-patient rapport usually improves the number of patients closely adhering to physician orders. Besides that, the only presently available technique is an attempt to measure the presence of the drug in a body fluid such as urine to determine that the patient has at least taken some of the medication. It is at present impossible to quantitate the amount of drug taken by patients in an experimental setup. Certainly when several studies are carried out with the same design and the same drug, the pooling of data would tend to give a more accurate picture than one study alone.

While we have touched on some of the problems and details involved in clinical psychopharmacologic drug testing, perhaps the most important point has been left for last. With each succeeding drug study we gain more knowledge about how to improve on our experimental design and about the relationship between animal and human pharmacology.

For further reading and references see Appendices 1 and 2.

30

STRUCTURAL EQUATIONS FOR LINEAR STATISTICAL ESTIMATION IN PSYCHOPHARMACOLOGY

Edward F. Gocka

I. The Structural Equation Approach

A. Introduction

Broadly speaking, any question on which it is possible to collect data can be the basis of a research problem. One example of such a question is, "Do phenothiazine tranquilizers facilitate performance on tests of intellectual functioning?" Another could be, "Do sugar absorption rates in the intestine increase as a result of a drug-induced diabetic condition?" It is obvious, however, that before one can collect data, a good deal more specificity must be given to the questions. In the first case, one might phrase the question as: "Does chlorpromazine medication enable schizophrenic patients to attend better in a test setting thereby resulting in the facilitation of performance on the Wechsler Adult Intelligence Scale?" In the second case, one might say: "Are the rates of absorption in the jejunum for an actively transported sugar such as galactose significantly increased over normal conditions when white rats are made diabetic by the parenteral administration of alloxan?" Even here one is not totally ready to collect data until one specifies other conditions such as the specific nature of the target group to be sampled from, the method of sampling, the sample sizes of the experimental and control groups, the dosage level or levels of the drug and the mode of administration, the techniques for measuring the outcome, and a whole host of other conditions necessary to run a proper experiment. Obviously, such a long list of "do's and don'ts" makes discussion, notwithstanding actual data collection, seem rather prohibitive. Fortunately, at this initial stage, many of the key principles of research design and statistical estimation can be brought to a focus and summarized conveniently through a structural equation approach, hence making the task less onerous.

A structural equation is one that relates the desired outcome measures to the treatment conditions and other factors that are utilized in designing the study under question. We can symbolize these relationships in our structural equation by borrowing from mathematics the representation for a functional equation; this would be of the form $Y = f(X)$. Applying this notation in the simplest sense to our problems, we would write that outcome is equal to a function of the experimental conditions, or

$$\text{Outcome} = f(\text{experimental conditions}) \tag{1}$$

Upon careful scrutiny, however, we see that this relationship indicates that outcome or outcome measures are completely determined by a knowledge of the experimental conditions. Because this is rarely the case in experimental work, we must modify this simple equation to read:

$$\text{Outcome} = f(\text{experimental conditions and unspecified conditions}) \tag{2}$$

where the unspecified conditions are assumed to account for all of the unique variation in the individual outcome measures not due to the known experimental conditions. The components or terms (i.e., outcome, experimental conditions, or unspecified conditions) in the structural equation represent "variables" that tend to take on different values from individual to individual or from one experimental subgroup to another. Conditions which are held constant for all members in the study are called laboratory or environmental controls and do not enter into the structural equation. Conditions which cannot be standardized or controlled experimentally in the laboratory or environment but which enter into the structural equation are called control variables. For example, if we consider ambient room temperature important in influencing the magnitude of our outcome measures, then one way of handling the situation would be to conduct the experiment in a temperature-controlled environment wherein temperature would be held constant for each subject in the study. However, if temperature control were not possible, but a recording of the room temperature was kept for each case and later found to covary with the outcome measures, then these temperature values would enter the structural equation as a control variable or covariate so that some adjustment for the influence of temperature on the outcome measures could be made. A third alternative possible is to systematically vary different levels or gradations of temperature throughout the experiment so that a more exact indication of temperature influences can be made. These variations or levels of temperature also would enter the structural equation as a variable, only in this case we would have an experimentally manipulated variable.

This chapter elaborates and discusses each element indicated in the modified equation, as well as the equation itself, for its implication on a research question. We begin first by considering the outcome measures on the left-hand side of the equation and proceed to the right, taking each element of the equation in turn for discussion.

B. Outcome Measures

It is sometimes said, and rightly so, that any study is only as good as the method for measuring its outcome. Therefore, it is the specific measuring scheme which completely delineates the exact nature of the outcome variable (also called "dependent variable," "response," or "criterion"). Conventionally, we talk in broad terms about outcome variables such as treatment success, symptom alleviation, behavior change, improvement, etc.; operationally, however, each variable must at some point be represented by an outcome measure. Problems often occur at this hiatus. For example, we may speak clinically about anxiety alleviation as an outcome, yet the method for measuring this anxiety alleviation or change is crucial to the scientific endeavor since we might choose one measuring scheme from among such measuring devices as self-report check lists, observer ratings, physiological instruments, biochemical indices, etc., in an attempt to quantify this outcome concept. On close scrutiny, there is no reason to believe that these different methods of measurement represent the concept of anxiety in the same way. Indeed, there is some evidence to indicate that there is wide divergence between the measurements obtained by some of these different methods. Other related problems persist. To measure any aspect of change such as that indicated by the words "anxiety alleviation," we need to obtain measures on at least two occasions. Such measures should be *reliable,* yet they must reflect the ability to be modified or changed by the treatment conditions. These requirements in a measure, however, are not always easily achieved since the concept of reliability is somewhat reciprocal to that of change. On the one hand, reliability implies a consistency of responding to the same experimental and environmental conditions; this consistency is desirable over two or more different occasions if we can assume no intervening disruption to the response pattern. Change measures, on the other hand, reflect not only that which is due to the experimental and environmental conditions but also any unreliability that exists in the measuring scheme. Frequently, one finds that some criterion variables having good reliability prove insensitive to change, while those sensitive to change plague research workers with negative results due largely to the unreliability inherent in the measures. Obviously, one way to avoid the above limitations is to do a sufficient amount of pretesting of the operational measuring devices that represent the outcome or criterion variable, thereby assuring a sufficient amount of sensitivity, standardization, and reliability. Furthermore, we can use several operational measures in different modalities, e.g., self-reports, observer ratings, or physiological responses, to represent the criterion variable. Although this makes the problem multivariate in nature, and hence more complex, the added complexity is usually worth the knowledge that the criterion variable has been characterized more adequately.

C. The Functional Equation

The letter f implies a functional equation relating the outcome scores to the experimental and unspecified conditions. Generally, such equations are divided into two classes, linear and nonlinear. Analytically, an equation is constructed from the known outcome measures and the known experimental antecedents. Given these, one is able to solve for the unknowns or coefficients in the full numerical expression of such an equation. By definition, for the linear case, the unknown or coefficients cannot be taken to any power in the numerical solution, nor can some transcendental function (any function which is not algebraic such as a cosine or tangent) be taken of the unknowns. Complex relationships, when needed, can often be handled by a linearizing process such as taking the logarithms of both sides of the equation. In fact, linearizing enables one to handle a very large portion of potential research situations by linear equations. Although purely nonlinear equations do appear in research, the complexities inherent in solving for their coefficients have made their utilization less frequent than in the case of linear or linearized models. It should be understood that when one "decides" to do an analysis on some data, such as an "analysis of variance," the nature of the equation is largely stipulated by this choice. Therefore, it is better scientifically to look at each problem and to specify explicitly the nature of the functional relationship. Unfortunately, much of research work is exploratory, and one usually begins by using the simplest and most common hypothesis for stipulating the equation. Yet it is doubly unfortunate if one assumes automatically that the right choice is made initially and that there is no need for follow-up efforts. The choice of the "wrong" or "inadequate" equation introduces "equation error" into the research system. The removal of such error requires very often some painstaking and thorough sleuthing on both the statistical characteristics of the data and on the characteristics of the specific research question under study.

D. Experimental Conditions

The experimental conditions characterize the independent variables or predictors of the system. These experimental conditions are generally of three types, although absolute distinctions are not always apparent; the first type is composed of variables which are designated as "treatment conditions," the second type is composed of variables which are designated as "ancillary predictors," while the third type is composed of variables which are designated as "controls" or "control variables." As mentioned before, conditions held constant for all members in the study are called laboratory or environmental controls and these do not enter into the structural equation.

1. Treatment Variables

Treatment variables are under the control of the investigator; he may either choose the levels of treatment directly (fixed model) or he may use random sampling (random model) in order to select a limited number of treatment levels to use in the study. In statistics, the word "treatment" is sometimes used as a general designation for those variables or factors we wish to predict from; here we will use the term to designate some pharmacological treatment. Levels of such a treatment could be: (1) the placebo level, (2) the minimum dose level, (3) the moderate dose level, and (4) the high dose level.

2. Ancillary Predictor Variables

Variables such as sex, age, diagnostic subgroup, etc., are frequently part of the experimental conditions under study. Although these may be called treatment variables in a statistical sense, it is better to call them ancillary predictor variables; their inclusion in the structural equation serves to give a broader picture of the effective role of the main predictor variable—the drug treatment. It should be noted that although one can randomly select subjects from a population and then randomly assign them to drug treatments, it is not possible to randomize subjects into sex groups, age groups, diagnostic subgroups, etc. These are natural rather than experimental variables, and each subject comes with a fixed set of natural characteristics. It is possible, however, to balance the number of subjects for each natural grouping within each treatment level using random selection and a modified random assignment. Attempting to match subjects first on a set of natural variables, although often tried, is difficult and can lead to statistical abuses rather than a good research design.

3. Control Variables

The remaining type or class of variable which is part of the experimental conditions is the "control variable." In a drug study, control variables might be variables such as body weight, ambient room temperature, prior exposure to the drug, etc. The experimenter is not so much interested in these variables as predictors as he is in controlling or standardizing them for all subjects. For these variables, it is assumed that it is impractical or uneconomical to control or standardize them in the laboratory or experimental environment. In certain instances, moreover, one of these conditions may become evident after the data have already been collected. If measurements on the condition are taken during the experiment, then it is often possible to use the values as a control variable. In the formulation and analysis of a structural equation, control variables are handled primarily through two procedures, one called *blocking* and the other called *covariance*.

E. Unspecified Conditions

This component of the structural equation contains the unstructured portion of the system under study. It is the residual or unpredicted portion of an outcome score. As such, it contains any equation error and any measurement error in the system. Equation error occurs if the wrong functional relationship f is hypothesized at the outset and if the appropriate set of predictors, control variables, and their combination is not used. Measurement error is pervasive throughout all research systems and reflects the lack of reliability inherent in the process of obtaining numerical values for the outcome variable. In many simple structural models, the predictor variables are *assumed* to be without measurement error. At a vague theoretical level one could speculate that if the appropriate predictor and control variables were studied, then one could predict an outcome exactly. Since this is not the case in practical situations, one selects what one considers to be the essential predictors and the essential control variables to place in the structural equation. If random selection and assignment to treatment groups is made, then one anticipates that the measures for the *unselected* variables will act like random elements and balance each other. Hence, in the most common models, we let one variable called the error variable ϵ stand for our unspecified conditions. Systematic effects obtained through the inadvertent use of the wrong functional relationship f or through improper sampling must be guarded against and checked for in each analysis. This is done in part by looking at the distribution of the error variable.

F. The Symbolic Structural Equation

If we augment our structural model to include the comments raised in the above sections describing the equation components, we would write

$$\text{Outcome} = f(\text{drug treatment, ancillary predictors, control variables, and unspecified conditions}) \quad (3)$$

Since this expression is a bit lengthy to write, we could shorten it by using first letters in the manner

$$\text{O} = f(\text{DT, AP, CV, and UC}) \quad (4)$$

This expression could be made even more general by using some conventional letter symbols found in most statistical texts, such as

$$Y = f(X_i, X_j, X_k, \text{ and } \epsilon) \quad (5)$$

Here we let the letter Y stand for any outcome or criterion measure. The subscripted letters X_i, X_j, and X_k stand for the drug treatment, ancillary predictors, and control variables, respectively, where the subscripts indicate that more than one variable is allowed in that particular structural component. For example, X_j indicates that there is more than one ancillary predictor in our system, etc. As a specific research example, we take the condition where we have a single drug to evaluate at two levels, two ancillary predictors, sex and age, and one control variable, and we assume that our functional relationship is best fitted by a linear equation. Our structural equation under these specification is

$$Y = B_0 + B_1X_1 + B_2X_2 + B_3X_3 + B_4X_4 + \epsilon \quad (6)$$

where the B_i values are the unknown coefficients, X_1 is our drug treatment or main predictor variable, X_2 and X_3 are the ancillary predictors, and X_4 the control variable. It should be emphasized that in addition to the overall assumption of a linear relationship, a full statistical analysis requires that each component of this structural equation have an associated set of initial conditions or assumptions. Once these assumptions are met or accepted as tenable, one collects the necessary measures or data called *knowns* (the Y and X's) and obtains a solution for the unknowns of the equation (B_i values). Knowledge concerning these unknowns plus the initial conditions and the method of analysis enables one to make statistical inferences about the data.

In our example, B_0 is the measurement scaling factor often called the origin or Y-intercept; differences in measurement units for the Y and X variables are absorbed by this component. Although usually not interpretable because of the arbitrary nature of the measurement units, it is possible in certain statistical designs to have this component take on specific meaning relative to the research problem, e.g., the grand mean of all the data, the estimated value of the outcome at time zero, the predicted outcome for the ideal or modal subject, the overall average measure of change, etc. In these instances, the numerical value of B_0 obtained through solution can be given substantive interpretation. The B_1 coefficient upon solution contains information on the drug treatment effects. Evaluation of this coefficient for our example is the main interest of the study—i.e., the evaluation of a single drug administered at two levels. The solutions for the B_2 and B_3 coefficients enable us to interpret the role of the ancillary predictors, sex and age, relative to the drug treatment. Similarly, the solution of the B_4 coefficient enables us to interpret the importance of the control variable X_4 in the system.

G. Basic Dimensions of Measurement

Each research situation contains three basic dimensions: entities, attributes, and occasions. Entities are the basic units under study and can be almost any set of denotable things such as human subjects, animals, tissues, cells, etc., while attributes are the conceptual variables assigned to the entities under study. Some attributes are strictly experimental or *instrumental* in that they are created by the experimenter and administered to the subjects. A drug treatment is an example of an instrumental variable. A subject either gets a particular level of a drug administered to him or he does not. Other attributes are natural in that they represent some existing traits or characteristics of the entity. Nevertheless, in a study each entity has a set of attribute measures associated with it, natural or instrumental. Of course, these attribute measures must be taken either at some point in time (occasion) or taken continually or intermittently over a period of time (over occasions). The structural equation model is not restricted to entities and attributes taken at one time point, but can be exended to several unique combinations of these basic dimensions. Some of these unique combinations have taken on status as special models.

H. Special Linear Models

Although linear statistical estimation through the structural equation approach is quite general, a number of specific linear models common in the statistical literature are worth noting as special cases. These among others are: Student's t-test, analysis of variance, analysis of covariance, bioassay, factorial designs, latin square designs, discriminant function analysis, multiple regression, and polynomial regression. If the reader already has some familiarity with these special models, then the wide applicability of the structural equation approach will be apparent.

A distinction between experimental studies and correlational or survey studies should be made for these special models. Some experimental studies require the random allocation of entities into the treatment groups of concern; e.g., if we are studying one drug, then we would randomly assign subjects to the different levels of the drug. Other experimental studies require a random presentation or balancing in the order in which two or more drugs are presented to the same individual. In any case, each subject is randomly allocated to a particular level of a drug or to a particular order of treatment. Correlational or survey studies, however, are those where random assignment is impossible and the predictors are either natural groupings or natural variables such as sex groups and age. These studies are usually associated with the exploratory phases of a research program. Statistical inferences depend strongly on whether the study is experimental or correlational. Correlational or survey studies generally lack the power and concise logic found in well-designed experimental studies.

II. Linear Statistical Estimation

A. *Initial Conditions*

Initial conditions or assumptions must be set for every experiment so that we can "go beyond our data" and make comparisons or inferences appropriate to a population. This can be done by relying on the principles of statistical estimation. Since statistical estimation is based on models related to the behavior of random events where chance alone determines the outcome, certain procedures must be followed if comparisons against chance are to be made. Certain games of chance such as the coin toss, dice throw, lottery, and card play served as our early intuitive notions of random models; however, these have been extended to "ideal" games and generated random number sequences. The initial conditions for our data demand random selection and assignments if we are to use the usual statistical tables for making evaluations. Because independence between events is a crucial condition of randomness, a sample of entities to be studied must be drawn in such a way that each entity in the sample is drawn independently of every other entity and each must have an equal likelihood or chance of appearing in the sample drawn. Taken singly, a random event is not predictable, but taken collectively, such as in the repetition of a coin toss or the repetition in a toss of a set of coins, the relative frequencies of certain collective events such as the "number of heads" appearing becomes highly predictable. Such collections of randomly based events may be described by mathematical equations and such expressions may be used to obtain theoretical relative frequencies or probabilities for each unique collective event. One may, for example, determine the expected or theoretical frequency of getting exactly eight "heads" in a toss of 10 coins. Hence, in many cases, the knowledge that we have randomly based events of a particular type assures us of the ability to formulate a mathematical expression of the distribution of such events, which then enables us to state probabilities for unique outcomes.

B. Tests of Significance

A structural equation is a hypothesis or statement on the nature of the relationship between outcome and experimental conditions. To test the hypothesis and its components, measures need to be obtained from which we can determine if the relationship is of the nature stated. We would proceed first by expressing the outcome values in terms of B_i coefficients obtained in the solution, as well as in a limited number of other appropriate summarizing statistics, e.g., means, variances, standard deviations, standard errors, correlation coefficients, etc. These B_i coefficients and summarizing statistics are then "tested" by comparing them with expected hypothetical results from some theoretical outcome. In statistics, a number of theoretical distributions based on possible outcomes, if chance only were operating, are available. We can, therefore, compare an actual outcome with what would be expected by chance. The expectation of certain results from a chance or theoretical position is often called a *null* hypothesis, and it is this null hypothesis that is compared with the experimental results.

Many of the theoretical tables called distributions are available in standard texts. Some of the most common tables are the unit normal distribution, Student's t-distribution, the F-distribution, and the chi-square distribution. Again, these tables allow us to compare an actual outcome against a theoretically estimated outcome. We first compute either a Z-value, t-value, F-value, or chi-square value from our data and then enter the respective theoretically based table to evaluate it. Evaluation is made by a probability value; if the probability value is small (e.g., equal to or less than 0.05) and our obtained value is greater than the tabled theoretical value at this probability level, then we conclude that the actual outcome statistic is different from the theoretical outcome. Since we compare against a "chance" hypothesis, we conclude that our results are statistically different from chance. If the probability value is large (e.g., greater than 0.05), we conclude that our results are not significantly different from chance.

C. Power, Precision, and Sample Size

In the planning of any experiment requiring a fixed sample size, a major concern centers around the number of subjects or entities to be used. One generally wants to get by with as few subjects as possible. Unfortunately, there are no simple answers here, and one must search for some guidelines in the purpose, cost, method of analysis, and operational procedures of the experiment. In the simplest sense, one needs to know as much as possible about the various kinds of "risks" taken at each choice point of an experiment such that the risk taken of making an incorrect decision at the final outcome is minimal. Statistically, one is concerned with two major kinds of errors that an investigator can make with respect to the outcome of his research. On the one hand, he may decide that his hunch or hypothesis is confirmed when in fact this may not be the case, thereby leading both him and possibly other investigators on a wild goose chase after a false theory. In psychopharmacology, this type of error occurs when one inadvertently concludes that a truly useless drug is effective. On the other hand, the investigator may decide on the basis of some analysis that the results are negative, whereas in reality a real difference or effect exists; this may cause him to abandon his theory or may cause him to identify an effective drug as of no value. Statistical decision procedures have made it possible for the investigator to choose either to increase or decrease the risk of making one of these errors relative to the other. Logically, one would desire to minimize the risk of both errors, but unfortunately they work in a somewhat reciprocal fashion. The second error listed is called type 2 error and has a direct relationship to what is called the power of a statistical test, that is, the sensitivity of the test to distinguish a real experimental effect of a certain magnitude when it indeed exists. Now the power of a test depends, among other things, upon the level or risk set for the first type of error, the precision of the measurements or its converse—experimental error—and the sample size. Sample size is often the easiest to regulate since the level of risk for the first type of error is preset by the nature of the study and since it is often difficult to increase the precision of the measurements once an efficient design has been established. A great difficulty here is that exact measurements of precision or its converse—experimental error—are frequently not available before the onset of an experiment (however, even rough estimates are better than none). Also, in considering the power of a statistical test, we deal with its ability to distinguish effects of various magnitudes; hence, we must have the magnitude of the experimental effect in mind before we can calculate a specific power value. If this magnitude cannot be preset at some exact value, all is not lost since it can be expressed as a proportion of the experimental error.

D. *Testmanship*

A statistically significant result is tantamount to the assertion that the treatment given does have some association with the outcome measures. Even though such evidence does not prove that there is a causal relationship, it nevertheless is useful. There is a fallacy, however, in evaluating the goodness of a result in terms of statistical significance alone; an association may be demonstrated to exist, but in no sense does this mean that this association is of any important degree. Very small degrees of association often can be declared significant because of a very large sample size which increases the power of our testing situation. Hence, besides a test of significance, one should always report the magnitude of the association. This can be done through the calculation of some correlational type of index. For example, t and F values obtained from the linear structural equation solutions can be readily converted to correlations that indicate a magnitude of association. Another procedure recommended when testing between treatment groups is to preset the minimal mean group differences that are important. If these differences are not exceeded, one can then have a negative conclusion about the experiment even if a test showed "significance."

E. Bias and Miscalculation

Bias and miscalculation can enter the results on which we base our conclusion for many reasons. In some cases, our results are confounded in that alternative explanations for the nature of the outcome can be postulated; these alternative explanations compete with the statement that it is our treatments which led to the unique results. In other cases, bias completely invalidates our results. Good experimental design procedures are just those which are established to eliminate bias and miscalculation. The establishment of an appropriate structural equation is one major step in the design of a study. Another feature of design requires a careful consideration of all the steps taken that might influence the solution for the unknown coefficients in this structural equation and that might influence the test of significance and the correlational measure of association. Let us consider a few examples of the pervasive and diverse nature of bias.

1. Sampling Bias

There is much evidence to show that hospital populations often have diseases in relative proportions different from those found in the general population of sick people. This is because different diseases and sicknesses differ in their rates of hospital admission. In this sense, hospital populations are biased samples from the general sick population. Measures of association found on such biased samples may be completely erroneous when generalized. Another instance of this type of bias occurs when one uses volunteer subjects or patients in a study instead of adequately sampling from the population of interest.

2. Regression Effect Bias

This is a special case of a sampling bias, but deserves its own unique name due to its frequent occurrence. Regression bias appears in those instances where we select two groups that are quite extreme on some measure. Being "quite extreme" on some measure is not always a stable characteristic because of the possibility of temporary or chance conditions being in operation. This instability tends to give some strange results when we attempt to measure change over time due to treatment. It has been found, for example, that even in the absence of any treatment, the group with the most severe symptoms can, in many cases, improve somewhat (regress toward the middle), while the group with the least severe symptoms will get more severe symptoms (regress toward the middle). There are enough studies which find, *as the regression effect would predict,* that mildly diseased groups tend to get worse under treatment, while severely diseased groups tend to improve under the same treatment to warrant paying attention to this phenomenon. Such an effect has long been noted in education where the group getting 100% on the first exam will almost invariably have a lower average score on the second exam, while the group getting 60% will on many occasions get a higher average score on the second exam. In such instances, can we conclude that bright students do not benefit by instruction, while dull students do?

3. Administrative Bias

Many biases arise because insufficient attention is paid to the scheduling or administration of the experiment. In some instances, the experimental mortality is very high due to failures by subjects to complete the experiment. Some studies note that subject loss is somewhat greater for the placebo group than for the psychoactive drug-treated group; clearly this loss could be anticipated and administrative efforts made to minimize it.

Another administrative problem concerns the location of sufficient subjects for a proper study. If shortcuts are taken, then obvious biases will arise. Kramer and Greenhouse (266) show that if one wants to test a drug on a group already having a 50% natural release rate and, if one wants to detect a minimum change from 50% to 60% in the drug treated group, keeping the significance level at 5% and the power for detecting such a difference at 90%, then 924 cases are required to carry out the experiment. If we are interested in some unique diagnostic groups, then it is most likely that no one hospital or institution would have this number of patients available for study.

4. Response Bias in Inventories

Many psychological and other self-report inventories require a subject to answer questions about himself or herself. Different results can be obtained for the same person depending on the instructions given, the nature of the items, and the "set" of the subject. Items tend to be answered in a socially desirable direction in most cases, although not necessarily so. The response can depend on what a person wants to communicate. For example, some neuropsychiatric patients coming into a hospital want to indicate that they are "sick" in which case they "complain" about a multitude of ailments and social ills; in other instances when leaving the hospital, items are answered in a socially desirable or "healthy" direction. How much of these answers are simply due to a "hello-goodby" effect rather than treatment is a matter of concern in many studies.

5. Other Biases

The list of biases is long and depends to a large extent on the area studied. One hears about experimenter bias, bias from publication practices, statistical bias, instrument bias, observer bias, doctor bias, and many others. There are obviously no limitations on the number of ways that an experiment can go wrong—what does one do about it? In the concluding remarks I discuss the virtues of a systematic dialogue between statistician and researcher calculated toward explicating and minimizing these difficulties.

III. Concluding Remarks

The obvious advice of having each and every research investigator become thoroughly conversant with research design principles and statistical analysis has not been followed in practice. It is frequently said, and rightly so, that interaction with a statistician on a research problem can prove rewarding as far as statistical efficiency is concerned if this interaction is begun early in the formulation of the problem. However, informal conversations with investigators generally indicate that a language barrier existing between the substantive areas of their research and the requirements of the statistical domain is a most significant deterrent to early interaction. This barrier must be broken if one is to take advantage of a statistician's advice on all of the difficulties to be considered. I have found that one of the most convenient ways of breaking the language barrier between statistician and researcher is by having the problem formulated in terms of a structural equation. Each component of the structural equation as well as the entire equation can be given careful scrutiny for its implication on the scientific question. The language surrounding most of the discussion can be in the domain or field of the research investigator with the elements of the equation serving as a check list on the many things to consider. Even those sophisticated in statistical design and analysis will find that they can explain their strategy more concisely by this method and thereby reap the benefits of rapid communication.

For those fortunate enough to be near a university center which offers statistical consultation, this method could offer a means of a standardized approach to consultation. It is a procedure which has been extensively tried and found to be successful at the Western Research Support Center in its regional consulting role with Veterans Administration and medical school investigators.

For further reading and references see Appendices 1 and 2.

31

EXPERIMENTAL DESIGN AND ASSESSMENT TECHNIQUES IN THE CLINICAL EVALUATION OF PSYCHOTROPIC DRUGS

Harry M. Grayson

I. The Experimental Design

A. Psychotropic Drugs as Tools and As Treatment Agents

Psychotropic drugs may be used either as investigative tools for exploring the processes of drug-induced changes in psychic or somatic functions or as treatment agents for altering psychological and behavioral processes, improving psychiatric disorders, and ameliorating disturbing symptoms. This chapter deals with the use of psychotropic drugs as treatment agents and is concerned with experimental design and assessment procedures for evaluating their clinical effectiveness.

B. Exploratory and Confirmatory Research Approaches

It is usually well to begin the clinical screening of new drugs by using an exploratory or uncontrolled research approach. Such an approach may be helpful in establishing dosage limits and optimal levels, disclosing toxicity, side reactions and contraindications, and observing the kinds of patients, symptoms, or syndromes which appear to respond favorably to treatment. If the exploratory clinical trials suggest that the drug appears to offer some promise as a useful therapeutic agent, then rigorously controlled, confirmatory studies should be undertaken (267). It is, unfortunately, the case that many apparently promising drugs fail to stand up under more rigorous scientific scrutiny. "Preliminary" studies are characteristically over optimistic.

C. Double-Blind Studies

An example of more rigorous control in clinical drug evaluation is furnished by the double-blind study, wherein neither the patients nor the observers know which patients are on active drug and which patients are on placebo. In practice, efforts are usually made to keep all participants, including the principal investigator, unaware of who is receiving what medication. This can be accomplished by precoding the various drugs under study, including the placebo, and then assigning them strictly at random to the study patients.

D. Statistical and Practical Significance

Statistical considerations should enter in at the very early stages of planning an experiment and should be part and parcel of the experimental design. Statistical analysis "after the fact" may not be able to salvage an experiment in which the design is faulty or the data inadequate and may, in fact, lead to misleading interpretations. Having a statistician present during the formulation of the experimental design is a sound investment.

References to the "significance" of findings typically appear in research reports. It should be noted that this term customarily is used in a statistical rather than in a practical sense and is a statement of probability that the obtained results could have happened simply by chance. The use of the term "significant at the 0.05 level" in a research report means that the obtained result could have happened by chance in 5 out of 100 trials; "significant at the 0.01 level" means that the obtained result could have happened by chance in only 1 out of 100 trials. By convention, significance at the 0.05 level is accepted as representing a true and not a chance difference, one attributable to the experimental factor, i.e., the drug under study. Practical significance, however, refers to the magnitude of the obtained findings, i.e., whether they are of sufficient size to "make a difference." Many experimenters fail to differentiate between the two concepts and erroneously tend to treat them as synonymous.

E. Extraneous Influencing Factors

In evaluating the efficacy of psychotropic drugs, or indeed of any experimental agent, the research design and the assessment instruments constitute the warp and the woof of the investigational fabric. To the extent that either one is faulty the end result will be faulty. The interplay of many obvious and subtle factors extraneous to the action of the drug per se may influence the experimental findings. These factors must be dealt with in such a way as to neutralize or at least to account for their effects. Some of the factors are described below.

1. The Experimenter

Numerous sociological, psychological, and technical traps beset the path of the investigator (268). One of these, which usually operates at a relatively conscious level, is that of *semantic bias.* It involves the use of classificatory labels which convey more favorable or less favorable connotations, e.g., tranquilizer vs. sedative; antidepressant vs. energizing vs. euphoriant; hallucinogenic vs. psychotomimetic vs. psychotropic; consciousness-expanding vs. mind-distorting, etc. Another is *unconscious experimenter bias,* which involves innocently stacking the cards in such a way that desired or expected outcomes emerge. Studies by Rosenthal and his co-workers at Harvard (269) demonstrate dramatically the powerful impact of this subtle factor. For example, in one study, ten experimenters were given the task of obtaining from the subjects rating of magazine photographs. The subjects were instructed to rate each photograph on a 20-point scale ranging from -10 to $+10$. Half of the experimenters were told that they would probably obtain mean ratings of $+5$ from their subjects, and half mean ratings of -5. All experimenters read identical instructions to their subjects and were told to say nothing other than what was on the instruction sheet. Despite this, the lowest mean rating obtained by *any* experimenter expecting high ratings was higher than the highest mean rating obtained by *any* experimenter expecting low ratings, i.e., there was no overlap in the mean ratings for the two groups. Similarly, in two studies using animals, some of the experimenters were told that the rats they would be using had been specially bred for brightness, while the remaining experimenters were told that the rats had been specially bred for dullness. In both studies, those experimenters who believed that their rats had been bred for brightness obtained significantly better learning performance from their rats that did those who believed their rats had been bred for dullness. The experimenters were, of course, unaware of the erroneous nature of their findings.

In order to avoid the operation of unconscious bias in drug research, the investigator must carefully set up conditions to insure that he will not know which patients are receiving the drug under investigation and which are receiving placebo.

2. The Physician

There is considerable evidence which documents the relationship between physicians' attitudes and the responsiveness of their patients to treatment. Studies have revealed that patients are much more likely to improve if their physicians have confidence in the use of drugs and are less likely to improve if their physicians lack such confidence. In a particularly comprehensive study reported by Honigfeld (270), 312 chronic schizophrenic, hospitalized VA* patients, were treated by 24 physicians for 20 weeks in a controlled double-blind study. The

* Veterans Administration.

patients in the study comprised a hard-core group of chronic schizophrenics whose previous response to chemotherapy had not been satisfactory. It is for just such a group that one might feel least optimistic about the potentiating effects of physician attitudes. However, even with this group of hard-core patients, physicians' attitudes (measured before treatment) correlated significantly with changes in patient behavior.

3. The Treatment Team

The members of the treatment team, especially the nurses, may influence drugs effects. For example, in their eagerness to help the doctor, they may display an attitude of enthusiastic confidence in the medication which they dispense to the patient; or, if they believe in psychotherapy rather than in drugs, they may convey a derogatory attitude regarding drugs to the patient.

Keeping the members of the treatment team "blind" as to the identity of the medication being dispensed, (i.e., whether it is an active drug or an inert placebo) is one way of cancelling out the effect of attitude of the treatment team since their attitude, whether positive or negative, would apply to patients receiving placebo as well as to those receiving the experimental drug.

4. The Patient

It is increasingly being recognized that administration of a drug involves a *transaction* between the giver and the receiver. The therapist's attitudes and expectancies about the medication and about the patient, the patient's attitudes and expectancies, the personality of each—all of these variables and many more influence the effects of the drug. Therefore, the attitudes, expectations, and cooperation of the patient are fully as important as the attitudes of the physician and the treatment team.

Other characteristics of the patients may also complicate the assessment of drug effectiveness unless they are equally distributed among the patients receiving drug and those receiving placebo. These include such things as diagnosis, prognosis, severity of illness, drug responsiveness, individual idiosyncrasy, fluctuation in condition, etc. For example, Hollister (271) classified patients into computer-derived diagnostic models and found that the experimental drug was highly effective in treating schizophrenic and depressive patients but much less so in treating paranoid patients, suggesting that specific areas of usefulness of a particular drug may depend on initial symptom profile of the patient. (Note: If analysis of subtypes within broad psychiatric categories is contemplated, a sufficient number of patients in each subcategory should be included to permit separate analyses.)

If a group has preponderately more patients with favorable prognoses, such as "good premorbid" rather than "poor premorbid" schizophrenic patients, favorable results may occur because of the nature of the group rather than because of the treatment drug. If, however, the placebo-treated group has a preponderance of "good premorbid patients," the apparent effectiveness of the drug may be significantly less than is really the case.

Naturally, the more nearly comparable the experimental and control groups are, the less likelihood there is of the results being contaminated by uneven distribution of drug-sensitive patient characteristics.

If the groups are sufficiently large, and if the patients are randomly assigned to drug or placebo, then differences among the patients may reasonably be expected to cancel out; or patients randomly assigned to the experimental and control groups may further be equated by matching them on selected relevant variables through the use of appropriate measuring devices. If the groups are so matched, then special formulas must be used to test for the statistical significance of obtained differences.

5. The Treatment Setting

It has long been recognized that the psychosocial environment in which the patient receives treatment exerts an influence on his behavior. Several studies have demonstrated, with particular reference to drug therapy, the important influence of hospital and treatment milieu. For example, Godfrey (272) administered lysergic acid diethylamide (LSD) to 120 alcoholic patients at the Winter VA Hospital under a variety of treatment conditions. In a complex factorial design, the setting was systematically varied from a formal "testing" one to an informal "homelike" one, while at the same time the therapeutic atmosphere was varied along an "experimental-impersonal" to "treatment-personal" continuum. Remarkably consistent differences were found in the alcoholics' response to LSD as a function of both the setting and atmosphere, with dosage held constant. Nearly all patients achieved a psychedelic experience in the "homelike" setting under "treatment-personal" atmosphere, whereas few patients reached psychedelic experiences in the formal "testing" setting under an "experimental-impersonal" atmosphere.

In another study of LSD, the effects of group vs. individual administration of the drug were investigated, with 24 subjects receiving the drug while alone and 48 receiving the drug in groups of two or more. Analysis of the data showed significant differences. The group subjects tended to have manifold schizoaffective reactions, while the subjects given the drug alone showed turmoil, anxiety, and perceptual pathology. The group influences did not counteract the impact of LSD, but they did modify considerably the nature of the behavioral response.

The effects of isolated vs. group drug administration has also been studied in animals. Brown (273), for example, has given phenobarbital to mice in these two situations. She found that phenobarbital sedated the mice which were in isolation but excited those that were in a group setting.

In reporting the results of drug studies, therefore, it is clearly important that the treatment setting or situation be described, since different results may occur in different settings.

6. The Drug

Most psychopharmacological researchers today recognize that one ought not to talk about a drug's effects without specifying dosage and the time after drug administration at which subjects are tested. For this reason, studies are frequently conducted which yield dose-response and time-response curves.

a. Fixed Dosage Schedule. In terms of dosage, it is desirable when evaluating the efficacy of any drug to use that dosage which approaches the optimum. A dosage that is too high may introduce such complicating toxic factors as to render the drug unsatisfactory. A dosage that is too low, however, may completely obscure any real effects the drug might have. Exploratory studies are often useful to determine the optimum range for a given drug. Where there is a body of knowledge about a drug's effects at different dosages, or where an investigator obtains information about effects of different dosages on the basis of preliminary exploratory trials, it may be reasonable to study the drug at the one dosage level at which the hypothesized effects are expected to occur. Although the use of a fixed dosage schedule may appear more "clean" scientifically, it suffers from two disadvantages: (1) generalization of the findings must be restricted to the particular dosage level used in the study; and (2) there is the possibility that one drug may be used at or near its optimal level, whereas a comparison drug may be used at far from its optimal level in which case misleading results may occur.

b. Flexible Dosage Schedule. In utilizing a flexible dosage schedule, in research evaluation, the treating physician usually begins at an agreed-upon level for all patients using a set number of capsules; after 1 week, he varies the dosage upward or downward (within fixed increment or decrement limits) for each patient, depending upon the response, until he reaches the optimal dosage level, which is then maintained so long as it remains that way. Advantages of using a flexible dosage schedule are: (1) wider dosage generalization of the finding and (2) greater similarity to actual clinical practice.

In a cooperative VA study (274) involving many hospitals and utilizing a double-blind experimental design, a number of phenothiazines were compared simultaneously. The schizophrenic patients were randomly assigned to one of several phenothiazines or to phenobarbital, which was used as a disguised placebo, producing otherwise giveaway cues such as drowsiness, yawning, etc. In this study, it was found that patients on phenobarbital were receiving ever-increasing dosages because the physicians were not achieving the desired effect; however, patients on phenothiazine compounds received increasing dosages up to a point, at which the dosage leveled off. The leveling-off point differed, of course, for different patients. In addition to yielding graphs which vividly contrasted the rise in dosage levels between the drug and placebo groups, statistically significant differences in comparative effectiveness were obtained. (One ineffective phenothiazine drug gave results remarkably similar to phenobarbital.)

c. Placebo Effect. Every drug has a built-in placebo effect which must be discounted in order to assess the drug's true effectiveness. Through the use of a control group which receives an inert placebo perceptually indistinguishable from the active drug, the true drug effect can be determined. This is done by subtracting out the changes in the placebo group (nonpharmacological) from the changes in the drug group (pharmacological plus nonpharmacological).

d. Disguised Placebo. In the case of drugs which produce side reactions typically associated with their use, these may become giveaway cues as to which patients are on active drug. The use of disguised placebos which produce similar side reactions may help to preserve anonymity.

e. Side Reactions. Side effects, in the form of organic or behavioral toxicity or less serious unfavorable symptoms, should of course be noted. Perhaps as much attention should be paid to the detection, measurement, and interpretation of side reactions as is traditionally devoted to clinical change. In order to assess the personal cost to the patient of taking the medication, intensity data indicating degree to which any side effects are present should be reported, rather than simple presence or absence of such side effects. Of course, not all of these necessarily result from the drug per se. A wide variety of side reactions, including rather devastating ones, have been attributed, in the research literature, to placebo.

F. Practical Problems

Note: Numerous practical problems are bound to occur during the course of conducting the experiment. Although not all of them can be anticipated, it is desirable to forestall or to be prepared to cope with those which experience suggests are likely to arise. Among such problems are the following:

1. Service vs. Research Attitudes

Investigators may expect to encounter staff who look upon research with a jaundiced eye. To minimize resistance and consciously or unconsciously motivated sabotage, it is desirable to read all staff participants into the study and to attempt to elicit their full cooperation through such measures as discussing the importance of the project, providing suitable recognition for them, etc.

2. Lines of Authority

Inadvertent bypassing of authority can create serious problems since lines of authority are jealously guarded. It is wise to procure the consent and approval of the ward psychiatrist and nurse before undertaking an experiment on their ward. The ward psychiatrist is in a position to screen out patients who, for medical or psychiatric reasons unknown to the investigator, may not be suitable subjects for the experiment; and the nurse may provide needed space in which to do the necessary interviewing, testing, etc. In addition, it is wise to procure cooperation from all other departments and laboratories which will necessarily be involved in the study. In some instances, the service load may be excessive, so that the added research chores will not be possible without providing funds for additional personnel.

3. Dry-out Period

Some staff may object to removing patients from drugs which they have been receiving. It is advisable to explain fully the importance of doing this in order to arrive at a proper base line against which to evaluate patient change. A convenient way to wash out existing drug effects is to put all patients on the study placebo for a few weeks before changing to the experimental drugs.

4. Loss of Patients

Almost invariably some patients who enter the study do not complete it. In some instances, patient loss may be considerable, and may be much more for some drugs than for others in the study. Appropriate records should be kept on each patient, giving the reasons for their leaving the study (e.g., elopement from the hospital, transfer to another ward because of physical illness, discharge from the hospital because of improvement, etc.). Such information enters into the interpretation of the experimental data. Anticipatory efforts should be made to minimize loss of patients.

5. Coding the Drug

The various drugs and placebo come in large bottles, properly identified, and must then be put into smaller bottles which are specifically assigned to each patient. In order to conceal the information regarding which patients are receiving the same medication, each patient's bottle should be assigned a different code number. In a hospital setting, the pharmacist can be of great assistance by sending individually coded bottles for the patients to the wards. These are identified for the investigator at the end of the study period (or for the treatment physician immediately in case of emergency). The medication code for each patient should be kept in a separate sealed envelope so that, in case of emergency requiring knowledge of the drug administered, the codes for the other patients remain unbroken.

6. Cracking the Code

Patients and nurses may sometimes discern the nature of the drug or placebo by biting and tasting the pill or capsule. Breaking the blind allows for the emergence of attitudes which may influence drug effects on patients and drug evaluations by staff. Perceptual identity of drug and placebo should be sought.

7. Known Drug Comparisons

To prevent prior attitudes regarding particular drugs from influencing the results, all drugs used in a study should be made to appear identical. For this, the cooperation of the different drug manufacturers may be required.

8. Randomization of Patients

To insure unbiased patient samples, all consecutive patients who meet the explicit or implied study criteria must be included and randomly assigned to drug or placebo. Physicians should be forewarned against holding out particular patients for reasons not relevant to the study.

9. Randomization of Drugs

Assigning certain experimental medications to particular wards, e.g., drug A to Ward 1, drug B to Ward 2, etc., is very poor procedure, subject to the confounding effects of ward climate, treatment attitudes, composition of patients, and evaluation standards of staff. Instead, all patients in the study, regardless of their ward location, should be assigned to the experimental drugs and placebo on a strictly random basis, preferably through the use of a table of random numbers.

10. Laboratory Tests

It should go without saying that, in using potent new drugs on human subjects, laboratory tests, e.g., tests of blood, liver function, kidney function, etc., are a wise precautionary measure.

11. Multiple Medications

Especially in a large hospital, care must be exercised to exclude the possibility of a patient serving simultaneously as a subject in more than one drug experiment, unknown to the respective investigators.

12. Contaminated Data

Some patients "pouch" their medication and later spit it out. Others give their drugs to patients who may be on placebo. For example, in a corollary study involving urinalysis of phenothiazine compounds which were being used in an experimental drug study, some patients who were presumably getting rather heavy dosages of the drug showed nothing whatsoever in the urine, whereas other patients, who were presumably receiving placebo, showed the presence of phenothiazine compounds in the urine. It was also discovered that some patients urinated into the bottles of other patients. (One fastidious nursing assistant added liquid deodorant to the bottles to clean up the smell.)

The nurses must be alerted to observe that the patients do swallow their assigned medications. In the study referred to, fully 20% of the patients were apparently receiving the wrong medication! Of course, the net effect is to reduce any true differences that may exist between drug and placebo and thus may lead to the discarding of a possibly useful drug.

13. Selective Biases

One of the major problem areas in drug research for many investigators concerns the biasing factors involved in the difficulties of removing patients from the drug regimen they have been on prior to the experimental study, and in possible pressures to remove from experimental conditions those subjects who become disturbed. The investigator should recognize the importance of such selective biases and be aware of the importance of attempting to offset them by gaining excellent prior understanding and cooperation of ward personnel.

14. Knowledge of the Literature

In their eagerness to do research, inexperienced investigators may undertake a study without adequate background preparation. Especially with regard to the selection of dependent variables, drug researchers should prepare themselves by becoming fully aware of the kinds of disturbance that clinical experience and the research literature have emphasized as of central relevance to the type of psychopathology of the patient population. For example, from the time of Bleuler to the present, associative interference and cue utilization have been emphasized as of central importance in schizophrenia, and many good measures that tap these variables are presented in the research literature. However, only a small fraction of the drug research on schizophrenics have used good measures of such dependent variables.

15. Dissemination of Findings

Upon completion of the experiment, the findings of the experiment should be fed back to staff, if only to insure their cooperation in future studies.

II. The Assessment Measures

A. *Criteria*

A crucial issue in clinical drug evaluation pertains to the selection of appropriate criteria. This issue is a philosophic one and centers around the basic question: What is a desirable change? If the goal of treatment is to ameliorate excessive tension, then anxiety reduction is a desirable change; if it is to minimize ward management problems, then reduction of acting out behavior is a desirable change. If, however, the goal of treatment is to make the patient more amenable to insight psychotherapy, then anxiety reduction may be an undesirable change since anxiety provides leverage for psychotherapy; and if the goal is emotional reeducation, then aggression-suppression may be an undesirable change since aggression control, not suppression of aggressive impulses, is the treatment objective.

B. *Some Measurement Concepts*

Once the evaluative criteria have been clearly specified and the goals of a particular treatment procedure carefully delineated, the problem becomes one of utilizing appropriate assessment procedures for measuring the extent to which the selected criteria and treatment goals will have been accomplished.

The measuring instruments, which, in essence, represent the evaluative criteria, are the Achilles' heel of psychopharmacological research. Even the best-designed, most carefully controlled study may stand or fall on the basis of the measuring instruments selected; yet, selection of the right instrument is not an easy task. Consideration must be given to such matters as the instrument's validity, reliability, sensitivity, and relevance.

1. Validity

This indicates the fidelity of a test or of any measuring instrument; it refers to the degree to which it measures what it purports to measure. Since the criteria or standards used in mental measurement for determining test validity are themselves imprecise, the validity of a test is also necessarily imprecise.

Theoretically, validity coefficients may vary from zero, indicating complete absence of validity to plus one, representing "perfect" validity. Naturally, the higher the validity coefficient of a test, the better. However, because of the complex, intangible nature of the phenomena dealt with in the psychological-psychiatric area, very high validity coefficients are difficult to achieve. Furthermore, validity coefficients reported in test manuals do not necessarily apply equally well to other populations differing in significant respects from the ones on which they were derived. Although these considerations necessarily impose a limit or validity ceiling on tests, validity coefficients should, of course, be reasonably high for a test to be used meaningfully.

2. Reliability

This refers to the consistency with which an instrument measures whatever it is measuring. Reliability coefficients, like validity coefficients, theoretically may vary from zero through one. Since the reliability of an instrument sets a ceiling for its validity, it is important that test reliability be quite high.

3. Jingle-Jangle Fallacy

This term has been coined to describe a semantic error. The "jingle fallacy" occurs when it is assumed that because tests have the same name (e.g., "intelligence test"), they are therefore measuring the same thing; conversely, the "jangle fallacy" occurs when it is assumed that because tests go by different names, they are therefore measuring different things.

4. Sensitivity

This refers to the extent to which a measuring instrument is capable of measuring fine or subtle differences in patient status or patient change. The units of measurement of a test, rating scales, or other instruments may be too coarse to measure certain differences. When such differences are important, test sensitivity may be a critical consideration.

5. Relevance

This refers to the appropriateness of the measure being taken in relation to the purpose intended. Where suitable instruments are not readily available, an experiment may be diverted from its intended objective through utilization of measures which are quite precise but not especially relevant in terms of the goals of the experiment.

6. False Positives and Negatives

These terms are used in the literature with reference to the ability of a test to differentiate groups that are known to be different. "False positive" means identifying a patient as having a condition which he does not in fact have; conversely, "false negative" means identifying a patient as not having a condition which he does in fact have. Of course, a good diagnostic test is one which yields relatively few "false positives" and "false negatives."

C. Examples of Assessment Instruments for Measuring Dependent Variables

The experimental agent, e.g., a new drug, is called the independent variable. The effects produced by the drug are called dependent variables. Evaluation of a drug is concerned primarily with measuring its effects; consequently, instruments are utilized for measuring dependent variables. For example, if we were interested in ascertaining the effects of a given drug on depression, then depression would be the dependent variable and we would need some means of judging or measuring presence or degree of depression. Ideally, of course, the measuring instrument should be as free from subjectivity as possible and should possess to a reasonably satisfactory degree the characteristics of validity, reliability, and sensitivity. By all means, of course, it should be relevant to the effect being sought. Examples of different types of more or less commonly used instruments or techniques for the clinical evaluation of psychotropic drugs include: psychiatric and behavioral rating scales, self-rating scales or check lists, psychological tests, and psychophysical techniques.

1. Psychiatric Rating Scales

*a. The Inpatient Multidimensional Psychiatric Scale.** The Inpatient Multidimensional Psychiatric Scale (IMPS), developed by Maurice Lorr *et al.*, is an excellent example of this type instrument (275). The scale consists of seventy-five items on which the patient is rated following a 30- to 60-minute psychiatric interview "whose focus is on discernible behavior and self-reports of feelings, attitudes and beliefs." The ratings require about 10 minutes and are entered on a special answer sheet. The rater is cautioned to make his ratings solely on observations made or information elicited during the interview, uninfluenced by previous knowledge about the patient. Ratings are to be made on observable behavior, not on psychodynamic inferences. Fifty-eight items are rated on a nine-point scale ranging from "extremely" through "moderately" to "not at all"; 17 items are rated as "yes" or "no." Sample items are: COMPARED TO THE NORMAL PERSON TO WHAT DEGREE DOES HE . . . Manifest irritability, grouchiness, annoyance or anger? (Cues: tone of voice; sharpness of response; explosiveness of retorts; use of profane or obscene language resulting from irritation.) TO WHAT EXTENT DOES HE APPEAR PREOCCUPIED WITH . . . Compulsive acts which he regards as irrational? (Touching, counting, etc.). HOW OFTEN DURING THE INTERVIEW DID HE . . . Grimace peculiarly or otherwise exhibit unusual or bizarre frowns or other facial expressions? HOW OFTEN DID HE . . . Hear voices that threatened punishment, torture, or death? DOES HE BELIEVE THAT . . . Certain people are trying to or now do control his actions or thinking? DOES HE KNOW . . . That he is in a hospital? In addition to yielding a "total morbidity score" for the patient, the IMPS profiles his scores on ten syndromes: excitement, hostile belligerence, paranoid projection, grandiose expansiveness, perceptual distortion, anxious intropunitiveness, retardation and apathy, disorientation, motor distur-

* Test used in the VA Cooperative Chemotherapy Studies in Psychiatry, Central NP Research Laboratory, VA Hospital, Perry Point, Maryland.

bances, and conceptual disorganization. By utilizing the IMPS with the experimental and control groups before and after treatment, it is possible to tell whether the patients have improved, remained unchanged, or gotten worse, in general and on each of the ten syndromes.

b. The Brief Psychiatric Rating Scale. The Brief Psychiatric Rating Scale (BPRS) was developed by J. E. Overall and D. R. Gorham (276) and is really a condensed IMPS. Instead of using all seventy-five items, clusters of items have been combined in the form of more generalized dimensions. Sample items are: SOMATIC CONCERN—degree of concern over present bodily health. The patient is rated for the degree to which physical health is perceived by him as a problem, regardless of whether complaints have a realistic basis or not. CONCEPTUAL DISORGANIZATION—degree to which the thought processes are confused, disconnected, or disorganized. The patient is rated on the basis of integration of his verbal productions, not on the basis of the patient's subjective impression of his own level of functioning. The 16 items on the BPRS cover the following relatively independent symptom areas: somatic concern, anxiety, emotional withdrawal, conceptual disorganization, guilt feelings, tension, mannerisms and posturing, grandiosity, depressive mood, hostility, suspiciousness, hallucinatory behavior, motor retardation, uncooperativeness, unusual thought content, and blunted affect. Each of these is rated on a seven-point scale ranging from "not present" through "moderate" to "extremely severe." The BPRS requires a relatively skilled psychiatric diagnostician capable of integrating the interview responses in the symptom areas into global ratings.

*c. The Global Rating of Patient Status.** Global rating provides an overall rating of severity of psychological disturbance on a single four-point scale: not present, mild, moderate, severe. A major limitation is its narrow range of three points (4 minus 1). Because of its extreme brevity, however, it can be easily used to obtain frequent ratings during treatment and is a quick supplementary measure to accompany more refined rating scales. It might also prove useful in preequating experimental and control groups.

*d. The Target Symptoms Rating Scale.** The Target Symptoms Rating Scale is an eight-point scale for rating twenty target symptoms as follows: not at all, very slightly, a little, moderately, quite a bit, distinctly, markedly, extremely. The symptoms rated are: anxiety, apathy, blunted affect, conceptual disorganization, depressive mood, emotional withdrawal, irritability, grandiosity, guilt feelings, hallucinatory behavior, hostility, mannerisms and posturing, motor retardation, poor concentration, somatic concern, suspiciousness, tension, uncommunicativeness, uncooperativeness, and unusual thought content. Each target symptom is clearly defined, e.g., ANXIETY—worry, fear, or overconcern for present or future. Rate solely on the basis of verbal report of patient's own subjective experiences. Do not infer anxiety from physical signs or from neurotic defense mechanisms. APATHY—absence of interest in surrounding activities. Lethargy, indifference, lack of drive or motivation.

* See footnote to p. 416.

*e. The Side Effects Rating Form.** The Side Effects Rating Form, devised for studying tranquilizing drug side effects on schizophrenic patients, provides for weekly ratings on a four-point scale: not present, mild, moderate, severe. The side effects rated are: agitation, akathisia, anxiety, ataxia, blurred vision, constipation, depression, dermatitis, dizziness, drowsiness, dry mouth, throat, fainting, nausea, vomiting, seizures, weakness, and others.

2. BEHAVIORAL RATING SCALES

a. The MACC Behavioral Adjustment Scale.† Developed by R. B. Ellsworth, the MACC Behavioral Adjustment Scale is a fourteen-item, five-point scale that yields scores in the following areas of activity: motility, affect, cooperation, communication. The sum of the last three areas yields a total adjustment score. Two forms are available. Sample items are: MOTILITY. How fast does he move, does he pace restlessly, seem agitated and tense in his movements? AFFECT. Is he pleasant, never seems to be irritable or grouchy? COOPERATION. Does he generally cooperate, "go along" with things asked of him? COMMUNICATION. Does he take part in sensible "back and forth" conversations, listening as well as talking to you, not just short answers to your questions, but a "give and take" conversation? Each item is rated in terms of behavior that has been most characteristic or typical of the patient for the last month.

*b. The Nurse's Observation Scale of Inpatient Evaluation.** The Nurse's Observation Scale of Inpatient Evaluation (NOSIE), developed by G. Honigfeld and J. Klett, is an eighty-item, five-point scale providing very brief behavioral descriptions. Sample items are: Is sloppy . . . Is excited, noisy and hilarious . . . Plays cards with others . . . Refuses to speak. Each item of behavior is rated as: always, usually, often, sometimes, never. The scoring system provides measures on seven factors: social competence, social interests, cooperation, personal neatness, irritability, manifest psychosis, and paranoid depression. The total score provides a global measure of ward behavior.

c. The Short Nursing Appraisal of Patients (277). The Short Nursing Appraisal of Patients (SNAP), developed by P. Keith-Lee and D. E. Spiegel, is a seven-point abbreviated scale consisting of only seven generalized or composite items representing the seven NOSIE factors described above. Sample items are: This patient is able to care for his own personal needs (for example, shaves self, makes own bed, combs hair, washes and dresses self, generally follows hospital routine). This patient shows a social interest in others (for example, talks freely with people, shows interest in activities around him, is generally cheerful, talks about ward events, tries to be friendly, laughs and smiles at funny comments).

d. The Psychotic Reaction Profile.‡ Developed by M. Lorr, J. P. O'Connor, and J. W. Stafford, the Psychotic Reaction Profile (PRP) contains eighty-five

* See footnote to p. 416.

† Distributed by Western Psychological Services, 12035 Wilshire Boulevard, Los Angeles, California 90025.

‡ Test used in the VA Cooperative Chemotherapy Studies in Psychiatry, Central NP Research Laboratory, VA Hospital, Perry Point, Maryland. Distributed by Western Psychological Services, 12035 Wilshire Boulevard, Los Angeles, California 90025.

simple behavioral statements which can be used to describe patients who are difficult or impossible to interview. Sample items are: Usually stays by himself. Tells the other patients what to do. Shows real sadness. Occasionally talks to himself. Ignores the activities around him. The rater (usually a nurse, psychiatric aide, or hospital therapist) indicates whether each statement is "true or mostly true" or "false or mostly false" about the patient, based upon a 3-day period of observation. Scores for withdrawal, thinking disorganization, paranoid belligerence, and agitated depression are obtained.

*e. The Hospital Adjustment Scale.** Developed by J. T. Ferguson, P. McReynolds, and E. L. Ballachey for evaluating patients' behavior in a psychiatric hospital, the Hospital Adjustment Scale consists of ninety statements which describe some of the ways patients act in different places in a psychiatric hospital. The statements were taken from descriptions of patients made by psychiatric aides in a large psychiatric hospital. Each statement is marked as true, not true, or doesn't apply. Sample items are: The patient never talks about sports with the aide. The patient is a good worker in shop. The patient doesn't take part in ward games.

3. Self-Rating Scales or Check Lists

a. The Clyde Mood Scale.† The Clyde Mood Scale contains 133 words or phrases, each printed on a prepunched IBM card. Sample words or phrases are: friendly, worthless, resentful, able to concentrate, sad, warmhearted, able to work hard, etc. The patient is asked to sort these cards into four piles to show the degree to which they describe his feelings: not at all, a little, quite a bit, extremely. The cards can then be fed into an electronic computer for automatic scoring and item analysis. Scores are computed for six factors: friendly, aggressive, clear-thinking, sleepy, unhappy, dizzy.

b. The Hildreth Feeling and Attitude Scale (278). The Hildreth Feeling and Attitude Scale consists of four scales of feelings and four scales of attitudes, each scale being made up of a series of statements which had been ranked by expert judges in descending order of degree of well-being. The statements were taken from statements actually made by patients about themselves at one time or another. One feeling scale contains the following statements: on top of the world; swell; cheerful most of the time; on the whole, feel all right; about like the average person; just fair; kind of low; pretty lousy; down and out; wish I were dead. One attitude scale contains the following statements: I get along fine with everybody. I like most everyone I meet. On the whole I feel friendly towards others. Some people I like, some I don't. I feel indifferent to most people. I don't get along with others very well. Most people irritate me. I can't stand people. I hate everybody and everything. The patient checks the single statement on each scale which best describes how he feels at the time. The scale values assigned to each checked statement are added to yield a feeling score, an attitude score, and a total score.

* Copyright 1953 by the Board of Trustees of the Leland Stanford Junior University.

† Distributed by Biometric Laboratory, University of Miami, Coral Gables, Florida.

c. The Adjective Check List (278). In the Adjective Check List there are a number of varieties, consisting of a list of adjectives printed on a sheet. The patient checks off those adjectives which reflect the way he feels at the time, or he may be asked to respond on a yes-no basis to each one. Sample adjectives from one of the check lists are: amused, annoyed, bashful, carefree, tense, unhappy, weak, worried. A mood score may be derived from the number of favorable-type adjectives to which the patient responds "yes" plus the number of unfavorable-type adjectives to which he responds "no."

d. The Grayson Personality Identification Scale (278). The Grayson Personality Identification Scale measures a number of variables, including self-esteem. It contains sixty statements describing various characteristics of people. Sample items are: loves animals and pets; has strong sense of humor; is easily bored; frequently worries about health. After responding yes or no to each item in terms of self-description, the patient responds to each item in terms of its desirability (D) or undesirability (U) as a personality characteristic. A self-esteem score is derived from the number of "yes" items about himself which he considers desirable plus the number of "no" items about himself which he considers undesirable. The possible range of scores is from plus 60 to minus 60.

e. The Zung Self-Rating Depression Scale (279). The Zung Self-Rating Depression Scale consists of twenty statements, each reflecting a common characteristic of depressive disorders, which are rated on a four-point scale: a little of the time, some of the time, good part of the time, most of the time. Sample items are: I feel downhearted and blue. Morning is when I feel the best. I have crying spells or feel like it. The scale yields a weighted raw score which converts to a Depression Index.

4. Psychological Tests

The number and variety of psychological tests which may be used in drug assessment studies are many, indeed, covering cognitive, conative, and affective spheres, tapping different levels of consciousness-unconsciousness, and utilizing subjective, objective, and projective techniques. For brevity, only a few examples are presented here.

*a. The Holtzman Inkblot Technique.** The Holtzman Inkblot Technique is a variation of the original ten-card Rorschach projective test. It consists of two comparable forms, each containing forty-five black or colored inkblot cards. The subject gives only one response as to what he "sees" in each blot. The test is scored for twenty-two response variables. Although not directly comparable to the Rorschach test in terms of clinical interpretations, it is better adapted for evaluative research studies.

*b. The Minnesota Multiphasic Personality Inventory.** The Minnesota Multiphasic Personality Inventory (MMPI) is the most widely used instrument for objective personality assessment. It contains 550 statements on cards which are

* Distributed by The Psychological Corporation, 304 East 45th Street, New York, New York, 10017.

sorted into three piles: true, false, cannot say; or 566 statements in the booklet form which are answered as "true or mostly true" or "false or not usually true." It provides scores on ten clinical scales: hypochondriasis, depression, hysteria, psychopathic deviate, masculinity-femininity, paranoia, psychasthenia, schizophrenia, hypomania, social introversion. The randomly distributed items run the gamut from subtle through obvious to blatant expressions of psychopathology. Because of its length, the MMPI is not especially suitable as a drug-evaluation instrument. However, many shorter scales, such as the Taylor Manifest Anxiety Scale, have been derived from it and these do lend themselves more readily to pre-post testing. Several different computer-based systems for scoring and interpreting the MMPI are now available for a service charge.

c. Psychomotor Tests. These measure speed of conceptual, perceptual, and motor performance. Examples of such tests are briefly presented.

1. The Word-Naming Test (278) requires the subject to name as many different words as he can in a given time, usually 3 minutes. Serial numbers, names, or colors are not permitted.
2. The Color Naming Test (278) consists of five different color squares (blue, red, green, black, yellow) printed in random order on a single page. There are five lines with ten colors on each line. The subject is instructed to name the colors as quickly as possible working from left to right in each line. Time and errors are recorded.
3. The Color Reading Test (278) is the same as the Color Naming Test except that the words representing the colors are printed in place of the actual colors.
4. The Figure-8 Test (278) requires the subject to write as many lines of 8's as he can across the page from left to right in 1 minute. Score is the number of 8's produced. In addition, the figures can be examined for size, placement, and motor coordination.
5. The Grayson Perceptualization Test* is a test of conceptual-motor speed. It consists of two simple reading passages in which the letters within and between words are equally spaced. The subject is required to separate the words by making vertical lines so as to restore the original meaningful passage. The performance is scored for speed, errors, and omissions.

5. Psychophysical Techniques

An adaptation of the method of paired comparisons applied to global clinical judgments has been used successfully as a rapid screening procedure for evaluating the clinical effectiveness of new psychotropic drugs. In this procedure, patients are paired off on the basis of global clinical judgment and then randomly assigned, one to the experimental drug and the other to placebo. One way of doing this is by ranking the patients on a ward from "most sick" to "least sick," randomly assigning the top two patients to the drug and placebo groups, respectively, and continuing this procedure for each successive pair of patients.

* Distributed by Western Psychological Services, 12035 Wilshire Boulevard, Los Angeles, California, 90025.

At the end of the treatment period, the initially paired patients are interviewed together and a decision reached as to which is the sicker patient. Only a fraction of the usual psychiatric interview time is required to make this comparative judgment. In the report describing this procedure, end-of-study comparative judgments were made "at first sight" in 2 out of 17 pairs; median time was 4 minutes; maximum time was 12 minutes (280). If the placebo group shows a significant preponderance of judged "sicker" patients, the superiority of the experimental drug has been demonstrated since the patients in both groups were equally sick at the beginning. By reference to a binomial probability table the statistical significance of the findings is quickly determined.

D. Examples of Assessment Instruments for Measuring Influencing Variables

The introductory section of this chapter discusses a number of factors which influenced drug effects, e.g., attitudes of the physician, the treatment team, and the patient; the patient's diagnosis and prognosis; the treatment setting; etc. It may be advisable, therefore, to utilize instruments for measuring these variables so that their effects may be accounted for or possibly removed by the use of appropriate statistical procedures, thereby allowing the true drug effect to emerge.

Various types of instruments, including attitudinal scales and treatment-prognosis scales, have been used in original, adapted, or revised form for measuring particular treatment-influencing variables in drug evaluation studies. For illustrative purposes, examples of such instruments are presented below.

1. Attitudinal Scales

a. The Patient Opinionnaire (Form B).* Modified from the *F*-scale of R. N. Sanford *et al.*, the Patient Opinionaire has been used for measuring authoritarian attitude of staff since such an attitude is associated with a custodial rather than a humanistic approach toward patients. It consists of twenty statements which are rated on a six-point scale as follows: agree very much, pretty much, a little; disagree very much, pretty much, a little. Sample statements are: People can be divided into two classes: the weak and the strong. Obedience and respect for authority are the most important virtues children should learn. No weakness or difficulty can hold us back if we have enough will power. The answers are keyed to yield an authoritarianism score.

b. The Hospital Setting Measure I (Form F).* The Hospital Setting Measure I, slightly revised from a scale developed by D. C. Gilbert, has been used for measuring staff attitudes about mental illness. The scale consists of twenty-one statements which are rated on a six-point scale ranging from "agree very much" to "disagree very much." Sample statements are: Close association with mentally ill people is liable to make even a normal person break down. Patients benefit as much from a warm personal relationship with a nurse or nursing

* Test used in the VA Corporate Chemotherapy Studies in Psychiatry, Central NP Research Laboratory, VA Hospital, Perry Point, Md.

assistant as they do from specific treatment methods. Once a schizophrenic, always a schizophrenic.

c. The Hospital Setting Measure II (Form G).* A scale slightly revised from one developed by J. M. Sacks, D. P. Halfner, and A. S. Mason of VA Hospital, Brockton, Massachusetts, the Hospital Setting Measure II measures staff attitudes toward medication. It consists of thirty statements which are rated on a five-point scale as follows: strongly agree, agree, undecided, disagree, strongly disagree. Sample items are: Produces behavioral improvement in most cases. Makes patients more confused than without it. Avoids dealing with patients' real problems.

*d. The Medication Attitudes Scale.** Adapted from a scale developed by Lewis J. Sherman, VA Hospital, Brockton, Massachusetts, the Medication Attitudes Scale is a scale for measuring patients' attitudes toward medication. It consists of fourteen incomplete statements, each followed by four choices reflecting positive, negative, or neutral attitudes. The total score measures essentially a single factor characterizing the patient's belief in the efficacy of medication for treating mental illness. Sample items are: I FEEL THAT MEDICATION (1) gives me a desire to get well; (2) is a part of hospital treatment; (3) does me no good; (4) makes me tired. I TAKE MEDICINE BECAUSE (1) I am forced to take it; (2) I want to get well; (3) I want to increase weight; (4) this is a hospital.

*e. The Ward Evaluation Scale.** The Ward Evaluation Scale contains sixty-nine statements about a hospital ward. Patients are asked to indicate whether each statement is true or false about their ward. Sample statements are: It's noisy on your ward. The beds on your ward are not comfortable. There's too much loud talking on the ward. Your ward is painted a cheerful color. The discipline on the ward is too strict. The patients on your ward help to make ward rules. Since attitudes influence perceptions, it is likely that this instrument is largely a measure of patients' attitudes.

2. Prognostic Scales

a. The Phillips Prognostic Scale (281). The Phillips Prognostic Scale was developed from the case histories of schizophrenic patients who improved or failed to improve after receiving some form of shock treatment. It covers three broad categories of case history data: premorbid history, possible precipitating factors, and signs of the disorder. The premorbid history items are the most discriminating ones and deal with the following areas: recent sexual adjustment, social aspects of sexual life during adolescence and immediately beyond, social aspects of recent sexual life, personal relations history, and recent premorbid adjustment in personal relations. Within each area appears a series of statements reflecting a descending order of adjustment. The single statement that most accurately describes the patient's adjustment in that area is checked. A score ranging from zero (representing best adjustment), to 6 (representing poorest adjustment) has been preassigned to each statement. The scores corresponding to the checked statements are added to yield a prognostic score. The higher the

* See footnote to p. 422.

score, the poorer is the prognosis. Sample items in the area of recent sexual adjustment are: stable heterosexual relation and marriage; casual but continued heterosexual relations, i.e., "affairs," but nothing more; occasional casual heterosexual or homosexual experience with no deep emotional bond; no sexual interest in either men or women. Sample items under personal relations history are: always had a number of close friends but did not habitually play a leading role; no intimate friends after childhood; no desire to be with boys and girls.

b. The Elgin Prognostic Scale (282). Developed by P. Wittman and modified in 1959 following a factor analysis by W. C. Becker, University of Illinois, the Elgin Prognostic Scale covers the following areas: defects of interest vs. definite display of interest; insidious vs. acute onset of illness; shut-in personality; heterosexual contact; careless indifference vs. worrying, self-conscious type; exclusive stubborn traits vs. insecurity and inferiority feelings; precipitating conditions; duration of psychosis since first onset; hebephrenic symptoms; and physical interpretation of delusions. Sample statements in the area are: keen ambitious interest in some of the following: home, family, friends, work, sports, arts, pets, gardening, social activities, music, dramatics; moderate degree of interest in several activities, e.g., social gatherings, sports, music, opposite sex, etc.; withdrawn and indifferent toward life interests of average individual, no deep interests of any sort. Sample statements in the area dealing with onset of illness are: development over a period of 0–1 months with sudden, dramatic divorcement from more or less commonplace living; changes have taken place over a period of 8–12 months, with noticeable personality modifications, but primarily an accenting of existing trends; very slow development of symptoms so that final disorder appears as an exaggeration of already strongly accentuated personality traits, indications even prior to adolescence.

III. Summary Statements

This chapter has dealt with experimental design and assessment procedures in the clinical evaluation of psychotropic drugs. The role of various subtle factors in influencing experimental findings was discussed, and methods for controlling or accounting for their effects indicated. Practical problems frequently encountered in experimental drug research were mentioned, and procedures for forestalling or coping with them described. Some important characteristics of measurement instruments were defined, and examples of various types of instruments presented.

For further references see Appendix 2 and other chapters, this Section and Section 9.

32

PLACEBO

Joseph del Giudice

I. Introduction

Among the many variables to be evaluated in judging the effectiveness of any drug are the group of nonspecific factors included under the term of placebo effect. It is probable that to some extent every substance or method used in the broad setting of medical therapy can exert an effect on symptoms, and the subjective feelings related to symptoms and can therefore at some time or another be considered a placebo. Traditionally, placebo has meant the deliberate use or giving of a pharmacologically inert substance. Actually, many chemical substances with quite active pharmacological properties have been used as placebos for centuries unknowingly to both the recipient and giver; they still are. The use of pharmacologically active compounds for specific illnesses where the drug effect has no relation to the illness is not limited to psychiatry. However, at least in psychiatry we have become sophisticated enough to call such compounds "active placebos."

It should be pointed out that the *concept* "active placebo" is a contradiction in terms, and the consequences of its continued use will be difficult to unravel. For the moment, in the methodology of drug study designs, an active placebo is a term used to designate a compound which may be active pharmacologically, such as phenobarbital, but which has not been shown to effect a significant positive change in relation to the specific illness in which it is being used as a placebo. Introduction of a pharmacologically active compound into a comparative drug study design is an attempt to disguise the placebo from both patient and evaluator (deliberate use of pharmacologic suggestion).

Evaluation of placebo effect is of utmost importance in psychiatric drug research since subjective changes are implicit in mental illness, and measures of these changes are to some extent used to determine a drug effect. Changes in behavior, symptoms, or signs that may occur need not have any relation to the therapeutic agent used. These factors present a considerable problem, and unless taken into account in the initial experimental design for the clinical trial of new agents, can result in misleading conclusions.

Broadly defined, placebo effect is a term used to denote reactions to a given treatment which are usually not related to the specific mechanical or pharmacologic action of the treatment agent. These effects, therefore, depend upon the state of being "treated" and, what is more important, they are also dependent upon the conscious awareness of being treated, or the conscious knowledge (whether true or not) that "treatment" has been given. This rather important point has been implicitly considered, but generally ignored, in most studies of placebo phenomena.

Experimental animals have been made to respond to chemically inert substances. This has occurred, however, only after preconditioning with active medication. To suggest from this that human placebo reactions are, therefore, conditioned responses is rather simplistic. The human response differs in that the subject can be completely naïve to the stimulus, the class of response is not predictable, the response to a second or subsequent stimuli is not predictable, and with constant reinforcement the response most frequently disappears. Also implicit or explicit to human placebo response is suggestion. There are no reported instances of it occurring otherwise.

II. Placebo Reactors

In drug experiments it has been frequently found that changes in patients' symptoms and an evaluator's judgment of drug effect are closely related not only to the evaluator's attitude in respect to the particular drug but also his knowledge of whether or not the subject is actually receiving active drug. Invariably this produces some bias. It should therefore not be surprising that a patient's response to what he perceives as active medication may actually be improvement in his symptoms or vice versa. The existence of a special group of individuals designated "placebo reactors" is quite unlikely, since any patient within the context of the proper variables for that particular individual can react in this manner. A search for a special group of personality factors necessary to a placebo response in a universal sense will inevitably prove fruitless.

The negative or positive response to a nondrug can be said to be related to: (a) the patient's ability to reality test and discriminate; (b) his conscious and unconscious wishes for health; (c) his perception of the therapist's evaluation of therapy; (d) the setting under which the medication is given; (e) the patient's needs related to denial of illness. Therefore, human placebo response can only occur in respect to the patient's feelings and perceptions and his reality concept in relation to his environment, his illness, and the therapeutic regimen. This includes his total evaluation, verbalized or not, conscious or not, of the physician and the medical regimen prescribed. Because some form of "therapeutic" transaction must be presented to the consciously aware patient, placebo response cannot occur in the absence of "social-psychological factors" at some time during the "treatment" period.

With the presence of serious organic illness or trauma a positive placebo response (improvement in symptoms) is related only to direct or indirect effects of the autonomic nervous system and the changes it is able to produce, and not the reality of the pathology. For example, the positive placebo response of a patient in acute congestive heart failure will not be very significant, since the reality of the organic illness has only small relation to cortical control of autonomic function able to affect a positive change.

III. Placebo in Drug Study Design

Because the phenomenon of placebo effect exists and its presence can significantly alter experimental findings if not considered, it is necessary, particularly in the study of new psychoactive compounds, at times to include a placebo parallel study group, to be compared with groups receiving one or more active drugs. As it were, the patient's bias toward health or illness, as well as the effect of the research milieu setting, must be canceled out in order to determine the true drug effect. The more subtle the pharmacologic effects of a compound, the more difficult the problem of separating them from placebo effects. Compounding the problem is the fact that the natural history of what is seemingly the same psychiatric illness can vary from patient to patient. In addition, the measuring instruments for determining change have been designed by using large numbers of patients who are assumed to represent a homogeneous section of a particular psychiatric illness. Although this approach has yielded unquestionable benefits in relation to methodology, its deficiencies should be obvious. In fact, a well-designed single case study may yield more reliable information as to a particular drug effect since the error of assuming homogeneity which is not present, or the attempts to match groups which are truly unmatchable, does not occur.

One of the most difficult and important aspects of a clinical drug trial, particularly in psychiatry, is in the initial design wherein those factors to be measured as indices of change or improvement are determined (cf. Grayson, Chapter 31). By choosing wrong parameters to measure, significant pharmacologic drug effects may not be detected, or detected at less than significant levels. This can easily lead to errors in which an efficacious compound is abandoned as worthless or vice versa (cf. Gocka, Chapter 30).

IV. Summary

The use of the double-blind clinical trial along with the placebo have become standard tools in clinical drug investigation. Although useful in determining efficacy, these methods are far from being the end-all of drug study and design. When the drug effect is strong, the "blind" aspects of the clinical trial are suspect. In addition, although symptomatic improvement as well as side effects can occur with patients on placebo, these effects almost invariably diminish or disappear with time, and the use of placebo in long-term drug studies is probably of limited value. In comparative drug trials the use of placebo is not necessary when a new drug can be compared with another compound of known efficacy. It should also be remembered that all observed effects, symptom changes, or complaints reported by patients on placebo may have no relation to the placebo itself, but merely reflect manifestations of the natural history of that particular illness, or symptoms which may have occurred with concomitant minor illnesses such as colds and other minor discomforts incident to a normal population, and which are erroneously attributed to placebo because of their occurrence coincidentally with its administration.

For references and further reading see Appendices 1 and 2.

33

VETERANS ADMINISTRATION (VA) COOPERATIVE STUDIES IN PSYCHIATRY

Eugene M. Caffey, Jr., Leo E. Hollister, C. James Klett, and Samuel C. Kaim

I. Introduction

Cooperative studies are not unique to clinical psychopharmacology. Indeed the first major VA cooperative study was a joint evaluation with the Armed Forces of the chemotherapy of pulmonary tuberculosis. With this experience and that of a 6-hospital study of prefrontal lobotomy to draw upon, the Veterans Administration Cooperative Studies of Chemotherapy in Psychiatry were started in 1956, setting the pattern for similar efforts. For example, a number of collaborative evaluation programs have been established under the auspices of the Psychopharmacology Research Branch of the National Institute of Mental Health. Smaller cooperative programs have been conducted by the Clinical Psychiatry Committee of the British Medical Research Council. Perhaps other such systems will be established, though because of the great expense and long training required to organize such groups, it is not likely that their number will increase rapidly. This chapter provides a general review of our experience in cooperative research. The detailed results of the studies have supplied part of the general information about drugs contained in this volume.

II. Advantages and Disadvantages of Cooperative Studies

The primary advantage of a cooperative trial is that a large sample of patients can be obtained far more rapidly than by any single unit. This is particularly important when the patient type is relatively rare, as is the case with manics and some varieties of depressed patients, or when the goal is to obtain a subgroup of patients that is homogeneous in respect to certain defining characteristics such as age, chronicity, or level of pathology. The sample can be drawn from a population of patients so large and diverse as to distribute biases based on geographic locale, a skewed distribution of age, sex, or ethnic composition of patients, varying supportive treatment programs, or local prejudices concerning drug therapy. The availability of large, carefully defined samples and the use of such techniques as blind controls, random assignment of treatments, objective assessment of patient changes, and statistical analysis of data provide a definitive evaluation of drugs.

The disadvantages of such studies are their expense, which can often be considerable, the difficulties which arise in training so many participants in the routine and special procedures to be followed in the experimental protocols, and the unlikelihood that really new drugs or new hypotheses about drug action will be tested on such a large scale. The organization and implementation often consume an inordinate amount of time and effort compared to the more flexible single hospital studies. Methodologically, a price must be paid for the rapid accumulation of large numbers of patients from many hospitals. Control of the study has to be delegated to principal investigators, and the research team must be duplicated at each participating hospital. Even with the most carefully written protocol and with the highest level of motivation and competence on the part of these individuals, there is an inevitable accumulation of small deviations in procedure across hospitals simply as a function of the number of people involved. There are a number of factors associated with hospitals that might introduce unwanted variability in results. Some are better staffed than others. Admission and discharge policies differ. Some get patients with better prognoses. Some tend to keep patients longer or may not treat as intensively. Even differences in climate could conceivably produce between-hospital variability. These differences are difficult to interpret and can only partially be corrected for statistically. In general, they decrease the sensitivity of the experiment and reduce the advantage of the large trial. We have found it useful in some instances to follow the cooperative study pattern, but on a more limited scale with a stable group of trained investigators who can move promptly to make systematic clinical investigations of new drugs often of a preliminary or pilot nature.

III. Methodological Principles of Cooperative Studies

Almost all cooperative studies evaluate several treatments using blind controls. The VA studies have included as many as six treatments of schizophrenic reactions in a single study, but generally fewer treatments are included, despite the obvious temptation to make the most of the control group and to obtain a maximum of comparable data using randomly assigned patients. The techniques of blind controls are by now well known. One word of caution should be introduced: No blind controlled studies should be undertaken until the indications, dose range, and side effects of a drug are reasonably well known. Although one usually thinks of placebo medication as the control, in some situations it may be more appropriate to use a standard therapeutic agent. However, it should be recognized that if an active therapeutic agent is used for comparison rather than placebo, a different research question is being answered and perhaps the only meaningful outcome would be if the new drug were better than the standard. Any other outcome is uninterpretable or has little direct bearing on the effectiveness, i.e., the new drug may be less effective than the standard and still be an effective, useful agent, but there is no way of knowing it if a placebo control has not been included in the trial. It is quite appropriate to omit the placebo group if the research question deals with relative effectiveness of two or more active agents and, of course, all trials generate safety data and offer the opportunity for serendipitous findings.

Sampling procedures vary depending upon the stage of the patient's illness. The goal is to achieve a representative sample of the patient domain, which in our case has been the population of VA patients. Sampling of acute patients is often done by taking all consecutive new admissions which meet the other criteria for inclusion in a study. For long hospitalized patients, the pool of eligible patients can be determined and a random sample drawn. It is particularly important in cooperative studies to specify with precision the sample of patients being studied. With widely spread hospitals and investigators, the criteria of eligibility must be objectively and clearly stated to avoid unwanted variability from this source and to be able to define the population to which results can be generalized. Usually it is wise to limit the sample to one major diagnostic category, such as schizophrenia or depression. The type of sample will often determine the drugs chosen for study, or vice versa. Dosage of drugs in VA studies has usually followed a partially fixed, partially flexible scheme. Initially, all patients are treated alike, so as to provide the safest possible beginning of treatment as well as assuring that all patients reach some middle range of therapeutic dosage. After this point has been reached, the clinician is given the opportunity to use the optimal treatment for individual patients. Duration of treatment depends on the kind of patient and drug. Three weeks is enough to demonstrate antidepressant effects in newly admitted depressed patients; 6 weeks will demonstrate antipsychotic effects in newly admitted schizophrenics; 12 to 16 weeks or even longer may be required in treating chronic schizophrenic patients.

A number of rating scales have been developed to standardize and quantify clinical observations. These scales may tap all the usual sources of data about psychiatric patients: what they say about themselves, what their family says about them, or observations of behavior in interview or on the ward. The rating scales which have been most widely employed in the VA studies include the Inpatient Multidimensional Psychiatric Scale (IMPS), the Psychotic Reaction Profile (PRP), the Brief Psychiatric Rating Scale (BPRS), and the Nurse's Observation Scale for Inpatient Evaluation (NOSIE). After one obtains numeric values for the various symptoms and signs of illness, a variety of statistical procedures can be applied to the data obtained from members of separate treatment groups. The VA studies have relied mostly on such standard techniques as analysis of variance and covariance, but the large samples available have also allowed the application of multivariate statistics. Obviously, the choice of rating scales and statistical techniques is highly dependent upon the types of patients being studied and the questions being posed (see Chapter 31).

IV. Studies of Antipsychotic Drugs

The first VA study was an enormous one involving 805 men with schizophrenic reactions hospitalized in 37 VA hospitals (283). The relative effectiveness of chlorpromazine, promazine, phenobarbital, and placebo was tested in both newly admitted and long hospitalized patients over a 24-week period. Chlorpromazine and promazine were administered in daily doses of 400 mg and phenobarbital in doses of 200 mg. After 12 weeks of this initial treatment, some patients continued for 12 more weeks on the same drug and some were switched to one of the other medications or placebos.

The value of the phenothiazines in treating schizophrenics, which was then still in doubt, was confirmed by this study. Using the original Lorr scale, Multidimensional Scale for Rating Psychiatric Patients (MSRPP) as the principal criterion, chlorpromazine was generally superior to promazine and the control substances were not effective. Further, we had evidence that our techniques were sensitive enough to distinguish between active drugs of different levels of potency as well as between these drugs and placebos or ineffective drugs. We were on our way.

Two additional "monolithic" studies, both restricted to newly admitted schizophrenics, followed the first. In one, 640 newly admitted schizophrenic men in 35 hospitals were assigned to chlorpromazine, triflupromazine, mepazine, prochlorperazine, perphenazine, and phenobarbital groups (284). Treatment followed a double-blind procedure for 12 weeks. Patients were started on low "equivalent" doses of each drug which were gradually increased in a predetermined manner during the first 4 weeks. During the final 8 weeks, each prescribing physician adjusted the dose for each of his patients in order to evoke an optimal therapeutic response. Average daily doses during the flexible period were: chlorpromazine, 635 mg; triflupromazine, 175 mg; mepazine, 190 mg; prochlorperazine, 90 mg; and perphenazine, 50 mg. The MSRPP again provided the major criteria. In general, the results indicated that all five phenothiazine derivatives were therapeutically more effective than phenobarbital, though mepazine was less effective than the other four phenothiazines. No significant differences in therapeutic efficacy were noted between chlorpromazine, triflupromazine, prochlorperazine, and perphenazine.

When the VA master records of these patients were reviewed three years later, the results indicated a rather successful hospitalization pattern (285). Ninety percent left the hospital at one time or another and one-third were not readmitted to a VA hospital after discharge.

The second study of this type also addressed itself to the question: "Is any new drug better than those we already have?" Although the consensus had already been reached that reserpine was less effective than the phenothiazines, we thought that this should be documented. On the basis of early reports, chlorprothixene appeared to be both safe and effective. Early published reports on fluphenazine and thioridazine were encouraging, but few studies had been well controlled or of large scope.

The drugs were introduced according to a fixed dosage schedule for 4 weeks and then individualized for the remaining 20 weeks of the study within specified limits. The average daily dosages used were: chlorpromazine, 746 mg; thioridazine, 845 mg; chlorprothixene, 224 mg; triflupromazine, 208 mg: fluphenazine, 10 mg; reserpine, 6 mg. The findings of this 32-hospital study involving 512 newly admitted schizophrenic men were in general agreement with clinical opinion and the few comparative studies (286). By our most comprehensive measure of improvement derived from the IMPS and PRP, chlorpromazine and thioridazine appeared nearly equal in clinical effectiveness. Fluphenazine was a close third, followed by chlorprothixene and triflupromazine. None of the differences among these five drugs was significant. Only reserpine, as expected, emerged as a distinctly less effective drug compared to the three leaders.

The data of this study were also used in several attempts to establish a reliable methodology for determining "the right drug for the right patient." We assumed that drugs have selective action, i.e., one drug is more effective with one kind of patient while another drug is effective with a different kind of patient. The problem is to identify the patient characteristics or, for some investigators, the patient type that is associated with a good response to particular drugs. There then could be a rational basis for differential drug therapy. As it is not realistic or practical to solve this problem by giving many drugs to each of a large number of patients and forming subgroups of specific drug responders, we used a different strategy. In the data of the previous study, favorable response to chlorpromazine was associated with, in a correlational sense, certain patterns of pretreatment symptomatology on the IMPS. Favorable response to thioridazine, fluphenazine, and the other drugs was associated with different pretreatment symptom patterns. Using these different patterns, we could predict how well a patient would respond to a given drug. To use a familiar computer concept, we could simulate treatment with a variety of drugs for a particular patient and then choose for him the one to which he would respond best, his drug of choice. Cross validation to an independent NIMH sample was successful enough to encourage further efforts (287), so another 20-hospital cooperative study was organized to provide a definitive test (288). Sampling and treatment of the 310 patients were identical to the previous study except that only chlorpromazine, fluphenazine, and thioridazine were used. Contrary to expectation, the predictive patterns (multiple regression equations) did not hold up in this second cross validation and persistent efforts to determine why they were unsuccessful. It is still believed that our approach is promising and that the question is an important one. Other groups are continuing to explore this area.

Many hospitalized schizophrenics are treated with group psychotherapy, in addition to their drugs. A study was undertaken to determine the comparative utility of each treatment alone and how the two interact (289). A total of 150 schizophrenic patients in 9 hospitals was assigned to (a) group psychotherapy alone, (b) thioridazine therapy alone, and (c) combined therapy for a 12-week treatment period. Five separate global measures from five independent sources indicated consistent findings: Chemotherapy alone or in combination with psychotherapy was superior to psychotherapy alone in reducing symptoms commonly associated with schizophrenia.

Another study of acute schizophrenic patients was concerned less with the comparative evaluation of drugs than it was with what could be accomplished by brief and intensive treatment using whatever resources the hospital staff had at its disposal in an effort to achieve discharge in a limited time and subsequently to maintain the patient in the community through an intensified aftercare program including maintenance drugs, outpatient contacts, and social work home visits (290). The results appeared to justify the following tentative conclusions in support of the trends in modern psychiatric management toward briefer hospitalization combined with intensive drug and social therapies: Intensive time-limited treatment is feasible and results in modest but quantitatively greater reduction in the floridity of symptoms when compared with routine hospital treatment. Despite their shorter stay, patients show no greater incidence of remission, nor is their mean time out of the hospital different; an intensive aftercare program appears to play an important role in reducing or preventing readmissions.

Chronic schizophrenics were not forgotten. With the advent of the so-called energizers, we decided to see if a combination of these with antipsychotics would improve the lot of such patients (291). Five-hundred-and-twenty chronic, withdrawn, and apathetic schizophrenic men were treated for 20 weeks with combined drug therapy. All had been on maintenance doses of chlorpromazine (200–600 mg) for two or more months. These doses were continued. "Activating" drugs were added in the following maximum daily dosage (or less): dextroamphetamine, 60 mg; isocarboxazid, 30 mg; trifluoperazine, 30 mg; imipramine, 225 mg; and placebo. Changes on the IMPS and PRP after 4 weeks of combined drugs were not impressive, but at the end of 20 weeks, every treatment group except dextroamphetamine had improved. In fact, adding dextroamphetamine led to a worsening of the psychotic state. It appeared, therefore, that little could be gained by such combination treatment.

A special kind of chronic patient is the elderly schizophrenic. Our studies were generally confined to patients under 55 or 60 years of age. A sizeable proportion of the VA inpatient population was beyond these limits. A study was focused on this group, evaluating acetophenazine, imipramine, trifluoperazine, and placebo with a sample of 308 schizophrenics aged 54 to 74 drawn from 13 hospitals (292). In addition to medication, half of the patients were assigned to a social group therapy condition. Symptomatic change was measured by the IMPS and NOSIE. The effectiveness of the two phenothiazines over a 24-week period was apparent, but imipramine was relatively ineffective. For all three drugs the incidence of side effects among these older patients (median age 66) was low. There was also evidence that social therapies, even as diffuse as that used in this study, could produce significant improvement despite the age and chronicity of these patients.

A somewhat different approach was taken to find the right drug for the chronic schizophrenic patient than that previously described for the newly admitted patient. In planning a comparative evaluation of carphenazine, chlorpromazine, and trifluoperazine, we learned of a subclassification of chronic schizophrenic patients that was alleged to be related to drug response. Our 330 patients from 11 hospitals were divided into hyperdynamic and hypodynamic subtypes, as described by Sainz, and treated with the study drugs for 24 weeks (293). No differences among the drugs nor between the subtypes was observed on the IMPS, NOSIE, or other scales used in the study.

The efficacy of a drug can be shown by treating new patients with it or, conversely, by removing from treatment patients who have improved on drug therapy and comparing them with those continuing treatment. A study of this type conclusively confirmed the effectiveness of antipsychotic drugs. Three-hundred-forty-eight chronic schizophrenic men from 16 hospitals who had been on maintenance dosages of chlorpromazine or thioridazine were continued on that dosage or assigned to a placebo or a reduced-intermittent treatment group for a 16-week study period (294). By the end of that time, 45% of the placebo patients, 15% of the reduced intermittent, and 5% of the continued treatment group had relapsed. Many patients who were not considered to have relapsed showed symptomatic worsening on the IMPS and PRP after drugs had been discontinued or reduced. The probability that schizophrenic patients will relapse if drugs are discontinued appears to be too high to commend it as a treatment policy. The results with the reduced-intermittent group suggests that some other variations in reduced dosage and/or intermittent administration could be profitably examined.

In addition to the phenothiazines and other drugs mentioned thus far, the VA cooperative program has examined almost all classes of antipsychotic drugs in an early drug screening series of studies partially supported by a grant from NIMH. These explorations were carried out in serial fashion using a small number of cooperating hospitals. Haloperidol and trifluperidol, as well as butyrophenone derivatives, were found to be effective antipsychotics. So were oxypertine, a phenylpiperazine, and benzquinamide, a benzoquinolazine derivative. Some drugs useful in other types of emotional disorders, such as diazepam, had relatively little antipsychotic activity, as expected. The antidepressant, imipramine, also fell into this category, although it was not, as commonly believed, absolutely harmful. A drug combination was also evaluated. The addition of an antidepressant, amitriptyline, offered no advantage in treating psychoses over a single active drug, such as perphenazine.

The smaller drug-screening studies have also examined the differences in responses to drugs by some types of patients. Using a prototypical model of functional psychotic disorders, it was possible to classify schizophrenic patients into three major groups: paranoid schizophrenics, nonparanoid schizophrenics, and "depressives," based on initial ratings of presenting symptoms and signs. It appeared that paranoid patients responded better to antipsychotic drug therapy than nonparanoid patients. This difference in response to drugs suggests that a dichotomy exists between these forms of schizophrenia and that this subclassification should be considered in experimental work dealing with the psychoses.

V. Studies of Antidepressant Drugs

Evaluation of antidepressants is difficult. The existence of a very effective somatic treatment, electroconvulsive therapy, and the ever-present danger of suicide makes investigators reluctant to include the seriously depressed patient in a controlled trial or to retain him in a study if there is not a rapid response. There is great resistance to the use of placebos with this group. The tendency of depressed patients toward spontaneous remissions and exacerbations presents additional design problems. The characterization of the depressed states is also not as well stabilized as that of some other psychiatric conditions. With all of these obscuring factors, it is generally agreed that the antidepressant drugs are of value.

Our first study in this area compared a commonly used combination of stimulant and sedative (dextroamphetamine-amobarbital), a representative of the tricyclic (imipramine) and of the MAO inhibitor (isocarboxazide) antidepressants, and a placebo control in 204 men with depressive reactions newly admitted to 32 hospitals (295). Each treatment group showed significant improvement over a 3-week period on special scales from the IMPS, PRP, and MMPI. Only imipramine was significantly better than any other treatment. Patients with neurotic depression fared better than those with psychotic symptoms, regardless of the treatment being given.

The drug-screening group has worked extensively in this area. One study compared amitriptyline, imipramine, and an atropine control in 93 newly admitted patients. Differences between antidepressant drugs were small and inconsistent, but both were clearly superior to the control in relieving the symptoms of thinking disturbance. In another study, there was some slight advantage, in total clinical improvement, from tricyclic drugs as compared with controls, but the single MAO inhibitor studied was relatively ineffective.

Since the demethylated analogs of the tricyclic drugs were said to be faster acting and more potent than the parent compounds, desipramine was compared with a placebo in 69 patients. Desipramine was no better than placebo.

Our most controversial study compared the antipsychotic drug, thioridazine, with the antidepressant, imipramine, in 77 depressed patients, all newly admitted to the hospital. Somewhat surprisingly, those depressed patients treated with thioridazine did about as well as a group as those treated with imipramine.

Along with these studies there has been a continuing attempt to identify the drug of choice for specific patient groups. A classification of patients with depression on the basis of their initial profile of symptoms and signs on the BPRS was developed analogous to a classification previously applied to schizophrenic patients. Three distinct clusters of depressed patients were found in our population: anxious, hostile, and retarded. Reexamination of the data from the study of imipramine and thioridazine in depressions, after subgrouping patients according to the above classification, revealed a remarkable difference in responses obtained. Thioridazine was much superior for anxious depressions, while imipramine was as superior for retarded depressions. Both treatments were equally effective in the hostile depressions. As the anxious depression group was the largest single group, this helped explain why thioridazine appeared so effective in the original analysis. Three other studies have strengthened the hypothesis that various types of depressed patients respond selectively to drugs. Tricyclic antidepressants, such as imipramine and amitriptyline, seem to be specific for retarded depressions, but are not much different from, or even less effective than, other drugs in other types of depression.

VI. Studies of Antianxiety Drugs

Anxiety is a symptom which is ubiquitous and often treated with drugs. Yet, evaluation of such treatment is exceedingly difficult. First, anxiety is often episodic and highly dependent upon environmental situations. Second, it is largely subjective and not easily measured. Third, anxious patients are seldom so disabled as to require hospitalization, which means that they are treated as outpatients; in such circumstances, even their faithful adherence to a treatment program is often in doubt. Finally, chronically anxious patients often have many confounding situations which may affect their mental state: alcoholism, unemployment, and family problems.

In the first VA outpatient study, 23 mental hygiene clinics collaborated in a 12-week double-blind study of the effects of drugs for control of anxiety on 180 male psychiatric outpatients (296). The major hypothesis was that individual psychotherapy with a new antianxiety agent added would be more effective in reducing anxiety and hostility than psychotherapy alone, or psychotherapy with either of two control substances. All patients received individual psychotherapy for 12 weeks. In addition, for the first 8 weeks, one group received chlorpromazine, one group received meprobamate, one group received phenobarbital, and one group was given a placebo. A fifth group received no medication. Chlorpromazine and meprobamate were administered at fixed dosage strengths. The 8-week findings from the standpoint of the patient were that neither of the new agents, used adjunctively, had an advantage over either of the control substances in reducing anxiety and hostility. Likewise, from the viewpoint of the therapist, anxiety was reduced about equally in all groups. However, therapists saw all active drug group patients as exhibiting more verbalized hostility than the psychotherapy only or placebo patients, a result contrary to hypothesis. The 12-week patient measures showed no advantage for any treatment over another. The major differences observed by therapists pointed chiefly to the disadvantage of phenobarbital.

This discouraging initial study was followed by one with somewhat similar results (297). A 4-week double-blind study was made of the effects of chlordiazepoxide on a group of 150 men newly accepted for individual outpatient psychotherapy. Three major hypotheses were tested: There would be a greater reduction in anxiety and tension (1) in groups receiving psychotherapy than those without psychotherapy; (2) in groups receiving chlordiazepoxide than those receiving placebo; (3) in groups receiving some medication than in groups receiving no medication. At specified intervals, the patients rated themselves and were rated by their therapists on various indices. The findings with respect to patient criteria were: (1) Patients receiving the drug reported themselves no better than placebo patients on nearly all criteria; (2) patients receiving either capsule (chlordiazepoxide or placebo) reported a greater reduction in tension, anxiety, and depression, greater overall improvement, and more social changes than patients not receiving capsules; (3) treatment groups receiving psychotherapy combined with drug or placebo reported themselves no differently from patients not receiving psychotherapy. It would appear that the addition of a capsule, whether drug or placebo, can add to the total management of anxious patients.

VII. Side Effects and Other Complications

Data relating to the incidence of side effects, deviant laboratory findings, and other untoward effects accompanying treatment with tranquilizing and antidepressant drugs have been collected in each of the Cooperative Studies in Psychiatry. As a general conclusion, our experience has been that complications of any kind have been neither excessive in frequency nor of great degree. For example, of 2687 patients included in the first six studies and treated with a variety of drugs, there were no deaths, and no cases of agranulocytosis or jaundice, attributable to the drugs. The failure to encounter any instance of frank jaundice or agranulocytosis suggests that these complications may have been more feared in the past than was warranted. The lack of serious complications is in part due to the conservative manner in which these studies have been planned and executed. Safe maximum dosages have been carefully set, laboratory tests have been routinely done for the protection of the patient, and the physician was always free to remove a patient from the study if he felt it was in the patient's best interest. Dosages have been slowly built up to a therapeutic level, a practice which some experts believe minimizes the incidence of side effects. Moreover, a large percentage of patients had received tranquilizers previously and may have become "desensitized" to some of the side effects of these agents.

Because we have handled large volumes of data on side effects, we have become aware of a number of methodological problems in the collection and interpretation of such information. The following questions point up the need to standardize the observing and reporting of side effects to the same extent as has been devoted to observing and reporting psychotic symptomatology.

When is a side effect a side effect?

Side effect or symptom of the illness? It is commonplace for patients suffering from depressive reactions to have frequent somatic complaints and also demonstrate physiologic disturbances of function. Ayd lists the following as physical symptoms of depression: fatigue, sleep disturbances, appetite disturbances, digestive disturbances, weight changes, constipation, urinary frequency, menstrual changes, sexual disturbances, cardiovascular disturbances, dyspnea, headaches, dryness of the mouth, dizziness, blurred vision, auditory sensations, numbness and tingling, feelings of unreality, hot flushes, dermatologic disturbances. Most of these symptoms which are said to be intrinsic to the depressive reaction have appeared on our side effects check lists. The best example from our studies of phenothiazines with schizophrenic patients has been akathisia. We are sure that the number reported as side effects included many instances of generalized restlessness related to tension or anxiety, symptoms of the disorder rather than a side reaction.

Side effect or normal base rate of the symptom? Some symptoms may occur in nondrug treated patients for reasons unrelated to mental condition or treatment. For example, our figures on itching or constipation may be simply approximating the normal base rate of occurrence of these symptoms. Nearly all of the side effects we have observed have also been recorded as occurring in our control groups or have been reported as present during the week prior to the administration of active medication.

Side effect of study drug or residual of earlier treatment? There are symptoms such as photosensitivity which are thought to be pretty well established as drug related and have a very low rate of occurrence for other reasons. In one study of depressed patients 11 cases of photosensitivity were reported before treatment and 3 cases subsequently developed in the placebo group. For this symptom and some others like it, it is possible that what is being observed is a result of drugs taken before admission to the hospital and the study. We have estimated that 60% or more of the newly admitted patients included in our studies have received drugs previously, many of them just prior to admission. A related question particularly in drug combination studies might be: "Side effect of what drug?"

Side effect or artifact? In several of our studies, a high proportion of the cases of extrapyramidal syndrome were reported by one investigator who happened to be particularly interested in this syndrome. Was it because he was an unusually sensitive observer and saw valid cases that others missed? Did he see cases that others would not have reported because the involvement was so minimal? Was it because he favored the use of higher dosages than most investigators?

Side effect or suggestion? Many symptoms are directly observable when they occur. Examples are seizures, dermatitis, dystonia, edema, and jaundice. To establish the presence of others requires either a spontaneous or elicited self-report by the patient. Undoubtedly, some side effects figures are inflated because the patient has been asked, "Are you having trouble sleeping?" or "Do you ever feel dizzy?" Another kind of suggestion is imposed when the clinician is provided with a check list of potential side reactions. He may tend to report items on his list with greater frequency than he otherwise would, and tend not to report symptoms not included. In a sense, his list tells him what to find. The manner in which the data are gathered in part determines the reported frequency of occurrence of some side effects. Even the language used on the check list can affect the reporting.

What is the true cost to the patient who takes drugs?

Therapeutic efficacy and cost. Nearly all drugs have side effects. This is part of the price the patient pays when he takes drugs. For this reason, it is best to evaluate side effects within the context of effectiveness. A drug that is very effective might be used despite its side effects. A less effective agent with fewer side effects might be preferred in older or debilitated patients.

Major side effects and minor side effects. Some side reactions are more serious threats to the well-being of the patient than others. Sheer numbers of side effects do not tell the story; there is a need for some differential weighting of side effects. Three cases of agranulocytosis out of a thousand might render a drug inappropriate regardless of its effectiveness, but if 50% of patients experienced some dry mouth or drowsiness, this need not interfere with its use.

A matter of degree. Some symptoms when they occur at all are always serious. Other symptoms can be ignored by patient and clinician when mild. The indication of mere presence or absence of a side effect may be misleading. Severity of side effect should be assessed as well as presence. However, a particular pattern of side effects, all in mild degree, might be the first sign of serious difficulty.

Reversibility. Nearly all the side reactions we have observed are reversible. Stop the drug or reduce the dose and the side effect disappears. For this reason it is often justified to continue a drug that is therapeutically effective even though the patient is temporarily inconvenienced or uncomfortable.

The individual case. Certain side reactions can be tolerated by the young but not the old, by hospitalized patients but not outpatients, by the strong but not the weak. A public speaker is distressed by slurred speech or dry mouth, and an airlines pilot would be alarmed by blurred vision. A patient with doubts about his masculinity would be threatened by drug-induced temporary impotence. To other individuals these same symptoms might be trivial.

Some of these and other problems can be exemplified by a brief mention of weight change during drug treatment. This is such a commonly observed phenomenon that it is curious that the exact nature of the relationship to drug therapy has not been determined. We have documented the changes that take place using rather gross measures of body weight, often without specifying under what conditions weight should be taken or considering height or body build. The changes, however, are often so pronounced that they could probably have been established by rating size of abdomen on a five-point scale, using waist measurements of trousers, or some other equally crude device. We have had patients gain as much as 84 pounds over a 5-month study. Should weight change be considered a side effect?

VIII. Program Notes

Conducting research on so large a scale over a period of so many years has led to other kinds of research products than those discussed above. First, working with so many patients and so many investigators from hospitals all around the country has forced us to consider problems of organizing and implementing research, the need to be specific in instructions and procedures, the training of research personnel, and other tactics of research. Many of these are not unique to cooperative research, but we have experienced them in a more intense form than would generally be true in a single-hospital study. We have commented on some of these experiences, and much of the early history and initial problem solving activity is described in the transactions of the cooperative study conferences. There is no question that this has been an important research by-product which through informal communication has influenced the efforts of others.

The capacity for generating large quantities of data quickly through an existing cooperative study structure and the accumulation of data over the years has resulted in related programs of research or supporting studies that would have been difficult to execute in any other way. Rating scale development which has already been mentioned is a case in point. The Inpatient Multidimensional Psychiatric Scale was developed to satisfy a specific need in the cooperative studies. It went through several stages of refinement in successive studies and is currently supported by a normative base of over 2000 patients. A related effort, the search for basic parameters of psychotic behavior, and for psychotic subtypes, might not have been possible in any other context. The same kind of factors led us to introduce a number of statistical techniques in studies of clinical psychopharmacology. Our very first study used an analysis of multiple covariance, quite an advanced technique for those early days. We explored the usefulness of Sequential Analysis, Factor Space D^2 Analysis, Canonical Correlation, Multiple Discriminant Analysis, and a variety of other multivariate statistics. Factor analysis has been used extensively, and some of the issues involved in its use have been studied. Like scale development these techniques demand great quantities of data (see Chapter 30).

Partially because we had multiple investigators, we were drawn to the question of whether the attitudes of the physician or patient about drug therapy were related to response. This led to a series of studies culminating in a review of nonspecific factors in treatment. Similarly, there has been a series of papers on side effects and related issues such as phenothiazine excretion. We have even touched on the field of psycholinguistics. Comments on methodologic issues have been included in most of our project reports or have been the subject of separate papers. The wealth of data and experience has also led to two VA medical bulletins for the guidance of physicians in the use of psychopharmacologic agents.

Finally, a word about the present and the future of the VA program. We have just undertaken, in collaboration with the Psychopharmacology Service Branch of the National Institute of Mental Health, a 5-year study of lithium carbonate in the affective disorders, which involves 15 VA hospitals and 6 private or state institutions. The VA program has completed its first study in alcoholism and hopes to initiate another dealing with the treatment of delirium tremens in the near future. A 3-year follow-up study of functional psychotics, now underway in 11 hospitals, may provide information on the natural history of these disorders as well as contributing to the validity of the psychotic subtypes that have been established by our earlier research. We have also been considering a cooperative study of the anti-Parkinson drugs.

For further references see Appendices 1 and 2.

34

BRIEF RESUME OF THE NATIONAL INSTITUTE OF MENTAL HEALTH STUDY IN ACUTE SCHIZOPHRENIA

Solomon C. Goldberg

I. Historical Introduction

Most people find it interesting to note that the discovery of most of the tranquilizers was an accidental matter. This would hold for reserpine, chlorpromazine (CPZ), and meprobamate. Since their discovery was fortuitous, it seemed to many that it would then be only a matter of time before the chemists would be able to make variations on the basic nucleus and synthesize compounds which were even more efficacious and less toxic than the ones which were merely stumbled upon. Indeed, there was such a proliferation of phenothiazines from the pharmaceutical industry that it was difficult to imagine how each of them could be tested by clinical trial.

It is of further interest that a by-product of this proliferation of antipsychotic agents resulted in the accidental discovery of imipramine as an antidepressant. Imipramine was being developed as an antipsychotic agent in order to compete commercially with the earlier discovered CPZ. Its accidental discovery as an antidepressant should be a clear indication of the dangers in inferring behavioral activity from similarity in chemical structure. To the scientific and clinical community it was clear through historical perspective that one really couldn't say what the behavioral effects of a drug would be without trying it out in the field experiment of a clinical trial, nor could one necessarily make any inferences from drug effects on animals or on normals. For example, CPZ in normals very clearly slows reaction time; in acute schizophrenics it appears to speed their reaction time. Thus, there would appear to be no real substitute for the conduct of a clinical trial to determine the effects of a drug in question on a patient population in question.

Congressional hearings in the mid-1950's led to the establishment under Dr. J. O. Cole of the Psychopharmacology Service Center, whose major task was to foster scientific research on psychotropic drugs. Actually the real pioneers in organizing nationwide research activities in psychopharmacology were the staff at the Veterans Administration (VA) (see Chapter 33).

The earliest trials of antipsychotic agents were typically done with chronically hospitalized schizophrenic patients for a number of reasons. Not only did they constitute an important public health problem, but since they were a "captive" population, the logistics of using these patients were much simpler than comparable trials on patients who were newly admitted to the hospital where the flow of intake was not so predictable. After the antipsychotic drugs had been in use for several years, they were said to have made a large dent in the number of chronically hospitalized schizophrenic patients. However, even though the discharge rate of such patients had risen considerably, there was a concomitant rise in the readmission rate of patients from the community. Informed speculation had it that drugs were certainly responsible for moving patients out of the hospital, and failure to maintain medication in the community was responsible for the increased readmission rate among those patients who required medication to maintain their remission. Thus, there was a change in the focus of attention from chronic schizophrenics to newly admitted acute schizophrenics, since the latter were a group for which there might be greater hope for social restoration.

II. Study Design and Research Questions

In 1959 Dr. Gerald Klerman began to organize a highly complex multihospital study of the effects of three phenothiazines and a placebo on the symptoms and behavior of newly admitted acutely ill schizophrenic patients. The present author assumed responsibility for the study when Dr. Klerman departed in 1961. Nine rather varied hospitals were to participate in the study because one of the main purposes of conducting a multihospital study is to test whether the results apply equally to all kinds of hospitals. The hospitals involved in this study included state mental hospitals, psychiatric units within general hospitals, private hospitals serving patients of somewhat high socioeconomic status, and university teaching hospitals. There was every possibility that the outcome of the study could differ from one clinical setting to the next, either because patients of different prognostic value are not served equally by all hospitals, or because hospitals differ in the strength and quality of their treatment programs.

A study of this size was not to be limited to a single research question and was, therefore, somewhat complex. A few of the questions that were asked of the data are listed as follows: (1) Were two relatively new (at that time in 1959) phenothiazines, thioridazine and fluphenazine, as good as the standard CPZ in the reduction of schizophrenic symptoms and behaviors? (2) Were the two relatively new compounds more effective than placebo? (3) Did the treatment differences apply equally to males and to females, to Negroes and to whites? (4) Did the treatment differences apply equally to the nine participating hospitals in the study? (5) Which schizophrenic symptoms respond most and least under the placebo condition, and on which symptoms do we observe the greatest change because of drug treatment? (6) Can we identify patients by means of symptom profiles and life history profiles who respond differentially to one or another active medication? If this could be done, patients could be assigned to that particular drug on which they were most likely to improve.

III. Early Results Showing Equal Efficacy of Phenothiazines as Antipsychotics

Our most striking results were that the three active medications were equally more efficacious than placebo. In no case could we find any difference *on the average* among the three phenothiazines, thus leading us to the conclusion that the two relatively new phenothiazines were just as good as the one which was then in standard use, CPZ. Moreover, the active drugs as compared with placebo seemed to reduce virtually every kind of schizophrenic symptom: auditory hallucinations, apathy and retardation, ideas of persecution, and incoherent thought, among a number of others. The active drugs not only appeared to have tranquilizing properties in reducing excitement and hostility but also appeared to have normalizing properties in that patients who were slow and apathetic now appeared to be energized. The term "tranquilizer" seemed to be a premature misnomer, and the term "antipsychotic" appeared to be more appropriate.

IV. Generalizability of Results across Varied Clinics

A test was made to determine whether the size of the drug-placebo difference varied from one hospital to the next, and since it did not, we concluded that the efficacy of drugs over placebo could be generalized to a wide variety of hospitals.

V. Failure to Generalize across Sex and Race

We examined the results for sex and race differences and found that the size of the drug-placebo difference was greater for females than for males, and greater for whites than for Negroes. However, the main reason for these differences is that females show less of a placebo response than males, and whites less than Negroes. The actual amount of improvement on drug treatment appeared to be the same for all. It was the amount of improvement due to drug (after placebo had been subtracted out) that made for the sex and race differences.

VI. Symptom Change under Drug and Placebo

We also found that the amount of improvement shown by patients on drug and placebo depended, of course, on the symptom which was being examined. Among placebo-treated patients, some symptoms showed no change at all, while other symptoms changed markedly. The amount of change due to drug treatment (defined as the size of the drug-placebo difference) also varied from one symptom to the next. To some extent, the group of symptoms on which there was no improvement on placebo, and the group on which there was the most improvement on placebo, corresponded, respectively, to Bleuler's distinction between "fundamental" and "accessory" symptoms. Among the fundamental symptoms Bleuler included bizarre associations, blunted and inappropriate affect, and autistic thinking. Among the accessory symptoms were hallucinations, ideas of persecution, grandiose delusions, defects of memory, and feelings of unreality. He contended that while the fundamental symptoms were present throughout the course of the disorder, the accessory symptoms occurred during acute exacerbations and were more subject to remission. Thus our results are consistent with Bleuler's observations in that we, too, find greater remission in accessory symptoms under the placebo condition. It is of interest that the major effects of the drugs are on the fundamental symptoms, which Bleuler maintained did not remit and which our results indicate made no change under placebo. It thus appeared that the introduction of phenothiazine treatment was having its main impact on a group of symptoms, the fundamental ones, which formerly were not being touched by any available treatment. We felt that the effects of drugs, therefore, were not only quantitatively different from placebo but also had a qualitatively different effect.

VII. Drug Effects in Averting the Development of Symptoms

Even though the usual textbook of psychiatry may list a lengthy array of symptoms manifested by the schizophrenic patient, it goes without saying that not every schizophrenic patient has every schizophrenic symptom. As long as we were giving drugs, one of the things we wanted to find out was what effects there were on the symptoms a patient did not have when he began the study. Was drug treatment responsible for producing somnolence and drowsiness so that some patients would appear to be more apathetic? Not only was this not the case but it appeared that drug treatment averted the development of symptoms which patients did not have at the beginning of the study. These were:

auditory hallucinations, poor self-care, incoherent speech, hebephrenic symptoms, slowed speech and movements, and indifference to environment. These symptoms developed in placebo-treated patients who did not manifest them at the time of admission, but did not appear among patients treated with phenothiazines. It is of further interest to note in the preceding list the heavy representation of "fundamental" symptoms and the conspicuous absence of "accessory" symptoms. Again, here was an indication of effects of phenothiazines primarily on fundamental, hard-core schizophrenic symptoms.

VIII. Identifying Drug of Choice—Study 2

In the course of using a variety of phenothiazines in the treatment of schizophrenia since the mid-1950's, a fairly consistent folklore developed concerning the appropriate phenothiazine to administer, depending on the symptom profile and life history of the particular patient. So, for example, patients who were hostile, belligerent, and obstreperous and in need of tranquilizing were said to do best on CPZ, while other schizophrenic patients who were apathetic and retarded and in need of energizing were said to do best on one of the piperazine phenothiazines such as fluphenazine and trifluoperazine. In spite of this folklore, large-scale studies such as ours or that of the VA had failed to show any significant differences among the major phenothiazines on any clinical measure of relevance. However, those findings were based on data analysis which did not subdivide patients into more homogeneous subgroups. Everyone had always given lip service to the idea that there was probably more than one type of schizophrenia, but no one seemed to have any penetrating thoughts on how a meaningful subdivision might be achieved. The first bit of evidence for drug specificity among the phenothiazines was provided by Overall and Hollister in the VA. They first categorized their schizophrenic patients according to similarity of symptom profile and then compared the patients with different symptom profiles in their response to various phenothiazines. Their results indicated that a so-called paranoid subtype responded better to acetophenazine than to perphenazine, and a so-called "core" schizophrenic subtype responded better to perphenazine. Here finally was evidence to support what the clinicians had been telling us all along; these results were responsible for a surge in research activity focused directly on this question. One part of that surge was the work of Klett and Moseley, also in the VA, who were able to predict, according to pretreatment symptom profiles, the response of their patients to various phenothiazines. As a test of their prediction equations, they attempted to apply them to the patients in our study. For each of our patients they made a predictive statement whether he should respond better to CPZ or to fluphenazine. Since our patients were actually assigned at random to those two drugs, it was possible to compare, for example, the patients that Klett and Moseley said should do best on CPZ, and who actually got CPZ, with those they said should do best on CPZ but who actually got the other drug. Of course the same kind of comparison could be made, but in the opposite direction, for those patients that they predicted would respond best to fluphenazine. The verification of their predictions was greeted by us with a mixture of astonishment and excitement and was partly responsible for our undertaking a second study in acute schizophrenia, where the major focus was to be on the prediction of drug response. It is worth noting that the implication of these results is that one would be able to identify the right drug for the right patient and greatly increase the effectiveness of drug treatment. Our second study was begun in 1963 and employed three major phenothiazines, acetophenazine, CPZ, and fluphenazine. Since two of these, CPZ and fluphenazine, had also been a part of our first study, it would be possible to compare the results of both studies for consistency, at least with regard to these two drugs. Essentially, our approach was to note the pretreatment profile of symptoms for the improvers on each of the drugs and then to determine whether or not these profiles were different. We did find that the symptom profiles, associated with each drug, were different. In comparing the two studies, we found no difference, for example, between the first and second study for the profile associated with improvement on CPZ or on fluphenazine, thus indicating some consistency in the findings. We also extended this analysis to the placebo-treated patients and had some modest success in predicting response under placebo conditions. Although most drug-treated patients improved more than most placebo-treated patients, there is a small subgroup of schizophrenic patients who apparently will improve more if given placebo than if given drug. Again, we seem to have verified, or at least documented, what the clinicians had known all along, that not every schizophrenic patient should be treated with drugs. The problem, however, was in identifying who should be and who should not be. Our own results indicate that the patient who has been done a disservice by drug treatment is a male who recognizes that he is mentally ill, has arrived voluntarily at the hospital for admission for the first time, and has no family history of mental illness. It seems to make sense that such a patient would tend to remit almost spontaneously, but it is still a puzzle why he would do poorly if given drugs.

IX. Clinical vs. Statistical Significance

We wondered about how much we were increasing our efficiency in drug treatment by assigning patients to their "drug of choice" as opposed to the drug on which they were predicted to improve least. We plotted the frequency distributions of patients who happen to have received the drug on which they were predicted to do best, and a similar distribution for patients who happened to receive the drug on which they were predicted to improve least. The difference in improvement between these two groups is approximately the same size as the difference between drug-treated patients in general and placebo-treated patients in general. This latter difference between drug and placebo has been considered by observers of the historical scene as "revolutionary" in size. Thus, the difference between the "best" drug group and the "worst" drug group is in answer to the question of how much can be gained over assigning the patient to the "worst" one for him. We concluded that it was worth the effort to make the predictive determination.

X. Future Trends

It is obvious that these results raise more questions than they answer. We would like to know about possible predictors of drug response other than symptom profiles; for example, psychological performance tests, psychophysiological measures, metabolite excretion, among others. We would also like to know what the prediction profiles are for all the major phenothiazines in use that we didn't have in our study, not to mention some of the newer antipsychotic drugs such as the butyrophenones and the thioxanthenes. The same question can also be raised with regard to the more prominent nonphysiologic treatments that such patients receive in the form of individual and group psychotherapy. The next few years should be exciting.

For references see Caffey, Jr. *et al.*, Chapter 33, and Appendix 2.

35

REGULATIONS OF THE U.S. FOOD AND DRUG ADMINISTRATION (FDA)

James L. Goddard and Frank N. Allan

I. Introduction

Progress in psychopharmacology in recent years has equaled, and often exceeded, the advances in other fields of medicinal therapy. This progress is all the more gratifying since this field seemed to offer rather barren prospects in the past.

Among some of the claims made for an increasing number of drugs are amelioration of morbid anxiety, elevation of depressed spirits, restoration of a natural sleeping cycle, alleviation of pains, aches and discomforts, relief of fatigue, facilitation of the capacity to bear stress. It is the responsibility of the Food and Drug Administration (FDA) to evaluate these claims and others, to recognize drugs that are effective, to identify undesirable or harmful adverse reactions, and to make an appraisal of the relative favorable and unfavorable responses. In short, the FDA exercises governmental responsibility for protection of the public and the prescribing physician through regulation of the testing, manufacture and distribution of drugs, and through the review of authentic information regarding their uses, properties, benefits, and hazards.

II. History of Federal Regulation of Drugs

The original Federal Food and Drug Act was passed in 1906 and became effective on January 1, 1907. At that time, its main emphasis was placed on measures to insure purity of foods. Drugs were placed under federal control, but to a limited extent. In later years, amendments were enacted to strengthen the law as specific needs were recognized.

In earlier days, much of the medication prescribed by physicians as well as self-prescribed home remedies, had little actual therapeutic benefit, and likewise had few undesirable side effects except for the unpleasant taste. Now, potent drugs have become available in growing numbers, but along with the increased potential benefit, one also finds greater potential for distressing and even dangerous effects. This situation has made government regulation essential in several important areas. Since 1938, manufacturers of drugs have been required to carry out tests to insure safety in advance of marketing. In 1962, additional amendments made it obligatory for the sponsor of a new drug to submit substantial evidence of efficacy as well. Legislation to control drug abuse became effective in 1966.

III. Current Responsibilities and Authority

The present law and regulations give the FDA comprehensive responsibilities in the interest of both the patient and the physician (298). It is the prime responsibility of the FDA to see that physicians can depend on the efficacy and stability of the drugs available for the treatment or diagnosis of disease in human beings. To make sure that their patients receive good drugs, the FDA monitors manufacturing standards and quality control procedures.

Information regarding undesirable and hazardous side effects is collected by the FDA. Essential details of such information are required to be presented in the labeling of every medication. It should be pointed out that the term labeling includes all written, printed, or graphic matter accompanying a drug. The law requires that new drugs must be given adequate trial before marketing. The FDA must have substantial evidence to support claims that the drugs will have the effect it purports or is represented to have under the conditions of use prescribed, recommended, or suggested in the labeling or proposed labeling.

Surveillance of new and old drugs is carried on systematically. Adverse effects not previously recognized may come to light with more extensive use among a larger population. The FDA regulates journal advertising and promotion of prescription drugs to assure that it is truthful, accurate, and appropriate. The FDA also maintains close liaison with the Federal Trade Commission, which has the regulatory responsibility for the advertising of over-the-counter drugs. The responsibilities formerly carried by the FDA in the prevention of abuse of stimulant, depressant, and hallucinogenic drugs were defined and extended through amendments to the Food, Drug, and Cosmetic Act that became effective in 1966. Two years later the Bureau of Drug Abuse Control along with the Bureau of Narcotics in the Treasury Department was transferred to the Department of Justice.

IV. Investigation of a New Drug (299)

It is reasonable and proper, as well as legally necessary, that every new drug should have appropriate trial and appraisal of its effects before it is marketed. According to law, a new drug cannot be distributed interstate for use in man without approval by the FDA. In practice, this applies to all new drugs developed commercially. Unless a drug is generally recognized by qualified experts as being safe and effective for the use proposed, it must be regarded as a "new drug." An old, accepted medication prepared in a new form or used for a new purpose also is considered a new drug. Distribution of a new drug for clinical investigation must comply with FDA regulations. Such investigation is usually carried out in three phases. As the first step, the sponsor is required to submit to the FDA information specified as a "notice of claimed investigational exemption for a new drug," generally known as an "IND." An IND usually includes the following information:

1. Details concerning the composition of the drug, its source, and sufficient data concerning the manufacturing process to show that appropriate standards exist to insure safety.
2. The results of all preclinical investigations of the drug, including studies of its effects on animals. The data must demonstrate that there will not be unreasonable hazard in initiating studies in human beings.
3. The FDA, as a rule, requires that acute toxicity should be determined in at least two species of animals, and that results of administration of the drug for 2 to 4 weeks be observed in at least two species using the same route of administration to be used in the human trials. Additional animal studies may be needed in the case of use under special conditions such as pregnancy and infancy.
4. A description of the investigation that will be undertaken.
5. Information regarding the training and experience of the investigators.
6. Copies of all informational materials supplied to each investigator.
7. An agreement from the sponsor to notify the FDA and all investigators if adverse effects arise during the testing procedure.
8. Certification that "informed consent" will be obtained from the subjects or patients to whom the drug will be given.
9. Agreement to submit annual progress reports.

The first phase of the investigation of the new drug requires the study of its pharmacologic effects in a small number of volunteers. As a rule, these are healthy individuals. The purpose of administration is to observe pharmacologic action, to evaluate toxic effects if they appear, and to secure an approximation of appropriate dosage. When Phase 1 studies indicate encouraging results, Phase 2 is begun. Here the new drug is administered to evaluate its effect in the treatment or prevention of the disease for which the drug is intended. A small number of carefully studied patients participate in this trial. Finally, if the studies made in Phases 1 and 2 show reasonable assurance of safety and effectiveness, or if the potential value outweighs any undesirable effects, Phase 3 begins. The new drug is given to a large group of patients by a number of investigators working under conditions that would correspond to the use of the drug in usual practice.

The patient must be informed about the experimental use of the drug unless the physician determines that such discussion might affect the patient unfavorably. The consent of the patient, when given, must be confirmed by his signature in the early stages of investigation—Phases 1 and 2. In Phase 3, the physician can decide whether it is preferable or essential to secure the patient's consent in writing or orally. In the latter case, the physician must make a note on the patient's record to show that use of the investigational drug has been explained and that consent has been given.

It is recognized that there are many situations in which the physician employing psychopharmaceutical agents may find it impossible to secure informed consent from his patients because of a disturbed mental state or because efforts to explain experimentation might have undesirable psychological effects.

V. Techniques of Drug Evaluation

The methods of drug evaluation must be adapted to the nature of the condition to be treated and the action of the agent. Observations of the results must be reported accurately and completely. The number of patients will vary, depending on the response. Under some circumstances a small number of cases may be adequate to give convincing evidence of beneficial effect.

Special criteria are needed in the evaluation of drugs relating to psychopharmacology. The involvement of psychological factors and the predominance of subjective data create difficulties. Observations comparing the effect of a placebo with that of the drug to be tested may be essential. Controlled double-blind studies are usually needed (see Chapter 32).

The FDA is authorized to direct the sponsor to terminate an investigation at any stage under stated conditions. These include evidence of significant hazard, convincing evidence that the drug is ineffective, submission of false data or the omission of material information, unsatisfactory manufacturing practices, failure to conduct the investigation in accordance with plans submitted by the sponsor, and premature commercialization of the drug. The IND regulations are not intended to provide a way of marketing a drug for profit without approval of a new drug application and the required evidence of effectiveness and safety.

Failure to submit progress reports at intervals not exceeding one year, failure to give an immediate report of serious or potentially serious adverse reactions, or failure to meet the requirements for consent of patients treated also are grounds for action. The Commissioner may notify the sponsor of any of the above conditions and invite correction. If steps to initiate correction are not undertaken within 10 days, the Commissioner can require the sponsor to terminate the investigation and recall unused supplies of the drug.

VI. A New Drug Application

When the manufacturer believes he has substantial evidence of efficacy and safety on the basis of human pharmacological and clinical studies, he can submit a new drug application (NDA), including all the supporting data not previously filed and proposed labeling. The FDA is required to act on this application within 180 days. An individual sponsoring a new drug can make a submission in the same manner.

VII. Surveillance of Drugs on the Market

After a drug is marketed, the manufacturer is required to send reports on the product to the FDA every three months during the first year, every six months for the second year, and annually thereafter. Reports must include information concerning clinical studies, the quantity of the drug distributed, and copies of advertising and other promotional material. Prompt reports are required of unexpected side effects or toxic manifestations.

VIII. Evaluation of Old Drugs

Prior to 1938, there was little governmental control of drugs placed on the market. Then, largely because of fatalities resulting from the sale of an untested medicinal preparation, the Food, Drug, and Cosmetic Act was amended to require that evidence for safety of new drugs must be submitted to the FDA prior to marketing. Drugs already in use which were generally recognized as safe by experts were not affected. In 1962, a further amendment to the act required substantial evidence of efficacy as well as safety. A broad review of the efficacy of drugs introduced between 1938 and 1962 (accepted on the basis of safety alone) was begun in 1966 by the National Academy of Sciences–National Research Council. The magnitude and importance of this task is indicated by the fact that more than 3000 new drugs were introduced in this period, approximately four-fifths of them prescription drugs.

IX. Abuse of Psychopharmacologic Drugs

The improper use of drugs affecting the mind and emotions has become an important problem in recent years. Medication is often self-administered, not to combat illness or alleviate distress but to give pleasure, achieve thrills, and "expand consciousness (300,301)." (Also see Cohen, Chapter 39.) The serious personal and social consequences have been widely recognized. Acute effects include impairment of judgment, loss of emotional control, and defective physical performance. Repeated use may lead to drug dependence. With some drugs such as narcotics and barbiturates the eventual result is physical dependence or addiction. With others such as amphetamines and presumably hallucinogenic agents the result is psychologic dependence. In either case the outcome may be physical and mental deterioration, loss of motivation, and withdrawal from normal life. The illicit traffic in narcotic drugs and other dangerous drugs subject to abusive use plus the crime associated with them led to amendment to the Food, Drug, and Cosmetic Act establishing the Bureau of Drug Abuse Control in February, 1966. The amendments impose tighter controls on the production and distribution of certain stimulant, depressant, and hallucinogenic drugs, giving broader authority for the fight against illegal traffic (302,303). However, not all authorities agree with this legalistic approach to the problem. (See Bloomquist, Chapter 38.)

Arrangements were made for close cooperation with the Bureau of Narcotics of the Treasury Department and in 1968, as noted above, both bureaus were transferred to the Department of Justice.

X. Conclusion

Physicians and patients can have confidence in the drugs available in the United States. Therapeutic advances depend on cooperation of scientific investigators, pharmaceutical manufacturers, the medical profession, and the FDA.

Noteworthy advances in the field of psychopharmacology in recent years have taken place under the scrutiny of the FDA, providing stronger assurance of the safety and efficacy of drug products. Governmental laws and regulations have raised no barriers to progress.

(See Chapters 29 and 36.)

36

ETHICAL DESIGN AND CLINICAL PSYCHOPHARMACOLOGIC RESEARCH

Joseph del Giudice

I. Introduction

Ethics weigh values rather than facts, and opinions in this chapter do not necessarily reflect those of the co-editor, fellow contributors, or publishers. It was included because the issues are current and important enough to be considered by anyone sufficiently interested in behavioral drugs to read this text.

Although clinical psychopharmacologic research as a scientific discipline is relatively new, the issues herein are quite old and are necessarily reformulated each generation. The content cannot really be divorced from individual judgment or fail to be influenced by current social milieu. Ethics are and should be personal; however, the reason for ethical considerations is to protect each of us from each of us. To that end, we must at times disdain valuable social goals, immediacy, and private wish fantasies.

It should be self-evident that ethical principles are imperative to a society, since law does and can only embrace the minimal standards of behavioral discourse. Legal standards are at times subject to erratic interpretation and very much influenced by political pressures. The law can only tell us in general what we may not do at a given time in social history. Our individual moral code tells us specifically what we should not do, regardless of law.

In the past twenty years, a new enthusiasm has entered into psychiatric research, engendered by feelings and some evidence that mental illness may have neurophysiological and neuropharmacological bases which are susceptible to disciplined scientific exploration. It can no longer be denied that behavioral changes are effected by drugs, and there is substantial evidence, consistent with our best means of mensuration, that some of these changes are for the benefit of the patient. A future with more effective psychic-acting compounds is not doubted. This thought is a beacon and a challenge. It also brings an anticipatory shiver of anxiety. It is no exaggeration to say that the potential for good for the individual and for society and the potential for harm are both very great indeed. The responsibility for direction falls upon the investigator as well as society, and this must be a legacy and admonition passed on by those of us who ignored the reality and dismissed the responsibility after Alamagordo.

II. Behavioral Research under Totalitarianism: A Warning

The premise of every dictatorship in history, whether one of the people or of a single despot, has been that society has rights above, rather than coequal with, those of the individual. Adolph Hitler considered the state as a means to an end, and he felt that its end was the preservation and promotion of a community of physically and psychically equal living beings. He also wrote that the state had to appear as the guardian of the future, and, because of this, the wishes and egoism of the individual were meaningless and had to submit. The state had to put the most modern medical means at the service of this knowledge.

It is easy for us at times to dismiss the dangers inherent in this statist philosophy, that the ends justify the means, and carelessly to endorse many things which after reflection might produce considerable uneasiness. There is evidence in the scientific literature today that the social desirability of an answer to a scientific question has taken precedence over the potential injury to an individual involved in an experiment. When the "greater good" becomes the "*sine qua non*" of a society, the logical corollary is that the individual does not exist.

It should be remembered that most of the experimental medical crimes committed by the Nazis involved a search for the answer to a *worthy* medical question. The behavioral scientist must heed these lessons of history, and be ever alert to the possibility of being used as an instrument of social or political power as were the scientists in Germany. It should also be remembered that *psychiatrists* from key universities formed the majority in the committees who determined which individuals should be used for experimentation, or killed. This was so, at least partially, because psychiatrists, as distinct from other scientists, have always been assigned the role of custodian of chronically ill individuals, and were answerable to institutions rather than to individual patients. It is not difficult to see why they were the first in Nazi Germany to succumb to the dictum that there are no rights which exist above those of society.

III. Controversial Issues in Psychiatric and Behavioral Research

A. *The Food and Drug Administration and the Clinical Investigator*

The Food and Drug Administration (FDA) regulations, under U.S. Public Law 87, have caused controversy in scientific circles because of alleged stringency in testing of drugs, particularly the phases involving human trials. The intrusion of a government agency into medical research, and the growth of the FDA from a mere testing bureau to a regulatory agency, should come as no more of a surprise than the increasing regulation of medical practice in general by the federal government. Whether a federal regulatory agency is needed to govern, control, or supervise medical research is no longer an issue. It is a fact from now on to be considered by all investigators. The present regulations regarding investigation of new drugs are still, for the most part, an extension of the natural law for the protection of the individual on which our Constitution is based, and also embody good scientific principles. There is nothing in them which should cause researchers to discontinue research with humans.

The aspect which may not be beneficial is the concept that scientifically disputable pronouncements of this agency will be accepted as fact by a court of law. One important issue is the supposed dictation by the FDA of dosage levels of drugs. Actually, the manufacturer is required by law to present in the labeling (package insert) the dosage recommended on the basis of all available evidence. This information is a safeguard for both the patient and the prescribing physician. If the physician chooses to experiment with a potent drug in a dosage larger than that demonstrated to be safe, he will be prudent to seek approval of his confreres (e.g., the committee on research of his hospital) and submit to the FDA a Notice of Claimed Investigational Exemption (an IND*). There is no question that the physician or researcher who uses dosages levels not appearing in the insert places himself in jeopardy and risks a charge of malpractice even if there are no adverse reactions.

Another issue is the regulation requiring written consent with patients involved in clinical drug trials. There will be other regulatory pronouncements in the future, and whether scientists like it or not, statements by this agency *will* have weight in a court of law, they *will* influence other government agencies, pharmaceutical companies, insurance companies underwriting malpractice, granting agencies, the public, and most certainly investigators. A more important concern is that these pronouncements will have the *effect* of law until constitutionally interpreted, such as now occurs with the National Labor Relations Board, the Internal Revenue Service, the Federal Communications Commission, and some other government agencies, leaving the burden of proving unconstitutionality to the pharmaceutical company, institution or individual.

It is hoped that the intent of this agency in extending future rules will be the protection of the individual first and foremost, and that interference with research with respect to rigid codified rules will be kept to a minimum in keeping

* Investigational New Drug.

with that purpose. The use of consultants outside of the Agency, such as the National Academy of Science, is a step in the right direction, as long as the recommendations of these consultants are weighed carefully, and it is remembered that what seems to be factual today may not be so tomorrow.

B. Normal Experimental Subjects

Much behavioral research is performed with volunteers with or without formal consent. Normal volunteers (individuals presumed disease free) are often used in experiments involving observations of behavior under conditions which may require psychologic or physical stress. There is usually not immediate, or perhaps not even future, benefit to the subject, while there may be various degrees of physical or psychic risk. Many experiments in sensory isolation, conditioning, sleep deprivation, and other forms of stress fall in this category. They are generally designed quite scientifically, but many times without adequate safeguards for the protection of the individual subjects involved.

The ethical problems of this kind of research are numerous, and many of these experiments are performed by investigators apparently not bound by a professional ethical code of any variety. There may be subtle coercion to induce subjects to volunteer. The coercion may be overt or covert, and the relation between the subjects and the investigator may be influential, as with psychology or medical students and their instructors. Even in harmless experiments, the ethic of this form of obtaining "volunteers" is dubious. It might be wiser to reject subjects who before an experiment have an official or nonofficial relationship to the investigators, and to exclude this bias for both ethical and scientific reasons.

It is wondered whether drug studies solely to determine toxicity are truly ethical unless the subject volunteers are as fully understanding of the dangers as are the investigators. It may be that the only ethical way to perform these experiments is if the investigators are willing to share the risks with the subjects. The same may be said of researches in toxicity of food chemicals and perservatives. Consent is not meaningful in these instances simply because a nonscientist volunteer has at best only a vague understanding of the risks, and the reason for volunteering is not for his own possible benefit, but for generally abnormal ideas of altruism. For a volunteer to take risks for a positive value is one thing, but the individual who risks himself for vague notions of social good would be considered by most psychiatrists to be at the very least neurotic. To take knowing advantage of this, or to pretend that it does not exist, would be immoral. Some experiments in toxicity involve little risk, and the investigator would have no qualms about self-participation. However, some involve considerable danger, and not many investigators would be willing to dose themselves with the same compounds they casually give to "volunteers."

Deception in psychological and sociological experimentation continues to be widely used under the premise that the conditions of the experiment are not valid if the subjects are aware of the true purposes. Many of these experiments are essentially harmless from a practical aspect. At what point are they no longer harmless in terms of painful or embarrassing experiences? Is infiltration into a group for the purposes of studying them, while pretending to be one of them, ethical? One wonders if condoning this kind of research design is essentially to negate validity of consent, to deny any rights of privacy, and to leave the door open for the logical extension of its use for studying any group of the population, without their consent or knowledge, and with knowledge of the results in the hands of special groups. These groups may not have ethical reasons for not using the information garnered for their own purposes.

A subject may volunteer for an experiment, but he does not volunteer to be made a fool of, or to disclose confidences without adequate and reasonable assurances of privacy. Neither does he volunteer to have the information obtained used against what he may consider his own interest. The use of normal volunteers in experimentation is most necessary, but ethical design of the experiment should take precedence over other considerations if we are to continue to value the worth of the individual.

It has also been pointed out that the volunteer subject is an entity unto himself, and extrapolation of findings in experiments with volunteers to the general population is, at the very least, scientifically risky. The use of monetary or other rewards with volunteer subjects is ethical if the reward is proportional to the effort expended by the subject, and as long as the reward is not used as bait for risks which are not spelled out to the volunteer.

Prisoners and other captive subjects cannot be considered normal volunteers, since they probably would not participate in an experiment if they were leading normal lives in the community. The motivation for volunteering and the way the prisoner subject views the possible rewards for his volunteering should be strongly considered in the ethical research design, as well as the fact that he is in a special group from which limited conclusions can be drawn.

C. Patients and Behavioral Research

Stress studies with psychiatric patients have little ethical validity and ought not be considered unless there is at least a plausible theoretic concept that might benefit the patient, and the risks can be predicted with fair certainty and are minimal. In drug research with psychotic patients, it is wondered if there may not now be overuse of crossover designs, particularly when a patient is obviously responding to a drug and then is withdrawn. In some studies a patient's symptoms have gotten worse, and when placed again on the drug from which he had previously benefited, he did not again respond, or responded poorly. Crossover was necessary and valuable when there were no proven effective drugs for relief of a patient's symptoms, and may be still considered ethical in the same kind of circumstances. It would now seem preferable, however, to reserve its use for studying patients who respond poorly to present antipsychotic medication. If there is predictable danger to the patient, it definitely should not be used.

One wonders if use of a placebo can continue to be justified with studies of new antipsychotic drugs, since we have known effective medication, regardless of its deficiencies. It would seem ethically preferable to compare the new compounds with the old, and not include placebo groups in these instances. Blind research designs also have ethical pitfalls, and have limited or no use with seriously ill patients. It must be remembered that in experimentation with patient subjects, there is a primary obligation to an individual which should not be immolated to demands of science or society, and the premise of the physician-researcher should continue to be that if he can do no good, he should do no harm.

It might be pointed out that although the term "controlled" is used for designs with blind and crossover technique, from the strictly scientific viewpoint these are not controlled, but parallel, studies. A scientific control is something exactly measurable and reproducible, to which an unknown may be compared. The use of the term in psychiatric drug studies is not correct, and has the tendency to give it an importance which is not warranted.

D. Control of Behavior

The philosophic issue underlying all behavioral research and potentially the most harmful to society's future is contained in this highly charged word, control. Will new mind drugs have the ability to control normal behavior, as well as abnormal? Will what we now think of as normal behavior become abnormal relative to some segment of society's values, or the government's? There is no question that if the tools exist to control behavior, they will be used. Who will use them? For what purpose? Who will define those values which are desirable? Undesirable? Is the quest for an anxiety-free existence self-defeating? Are current mind-drug experiences inherently regressive, and inherently antireality?

There is no evidence from a scientific basis that present psychopharmacologic agents enhance consciousness in any way, but quite the contrary. Many scientists become quite uncomfortable when confronted with the terms of consciousness and volition. Since consciousness is not measurable, it is treated as though it does not exist. There are also some who feel that consciousness is not a desirable state and needs assistance from drugs of one variety or another, that is, full consciousness, with the consequent anxieties related to making decisions of everyday living.

Some behaviorists would have everyone content, and see no harm in control of behavior as long as it is effectively to that purpose. The values of what should make one content are to be applied by control of one variety or another. It should be noted that the values to be pursued by control are the essential issue. Whose values? Certainly not the individual's, or control is not needed. Volition (free choice) to the behaviorist has no meaning since it would require a concept of consciousness. As long as man is viewed as essentially a conditioned animal, albeit a complex one, there may be increasing emphasis on group rather than individual welfare. To think that these concepts will not be applied in relation to behavioral control, drug induced or not, may indeed be wishful thinking.

E. Consent

The issue of consent is the nucleus around which the total philosophic question related to research with humans revolves. A very long time ago, Aristotle conceived that true agreement to an act presupposed understanding the possible consequences. He pointed out that it is possible to do many things willingly without choice, for we do many things willingly, suddenly. However, no one deliberately chooses anything suddenly, as this is a contradiction in terms. A choice is not arrived at by intuition, insight, hunch, or conscience, but rather by reasoning. It would seem, therefore, that choice is something that can be objectively determinable and is not the result of subjective preference. Consent therefore, implies consciousness and volition, and is meaningful only if the individual is aware of the alternatives and consequences of his decision. Whether the consent is in writing or not is a legal, not a moral, issue.

The investigator's responsibility should be with the subject's awareness of possible consequences as he (the investigator) honestly sees them, because he can never be assured of the patient's awareness of the alternatives. If at any time during an experiment the investigator feels by any cue that the subject seems not to be really aware of the consequences of his decision, the investigator's responsibility is to exclude the subject from the experiment, the importance, significance, and social good of the investigation notwithstanding.

The temptation to avoid the issue by rationalization or self-persuasion must be guarded against. The integrity of the investigation is based on the experimenter's ability to deal as honestly with this as he tries to deal with the experimental data and design. The investigator must never act on an immoral or political principle. He has no right of persuasion, but the duty of delineating the reality as he sees it. To deliberately distort the reality invalidates the patient's consent.

It should be noted that this right of informed consent is not something just given to Americans by the FDA. It is embodied in our Constitution, and has been upheld many times by our courts. By attempting to regulate protection, the FDA may have weakened it. In spelling out an informed consent requirement in writing, Public Law 87 also states that it may be ignored. The exact wording is "except where this [consent] is not feasible or, in the investigator's professional judgment, is contrary to the best interests of the subjects." It has been pointed out that this loophole actually is contrary to all universal codes of medical ethics, which insist on consent without exception. The constitutionality is also in question because it allows the investigator to decide on the criteria used in making a decision that obtaining consent is not in the patient's interest, or is not feasible.

Consent in relation to mentally incompetent individuals has raised other issues which have not been satisfactorially decided because the epistemologic clarification of the terms involved has been ignored. By definition, consent is meaningless with a mentally incompetent subject, whether he is declared so by a court or not. It should be noted that his legal incompetency may be by virtue of poor judgment in relation to funds, for example, but he still may be capable of deciding whether or not the risks outweigh the benefits to him of any clinical experiment. The evidence is that many psychotic patients are quite aware and capable of acting intelligently on issues outside their delusional system, and can give meaningful consent.

However, because a patient is not *legally* incompetent does not mean that he is capable of the understanding necessary to a decision of agreeing to be a subject in a study. It is the investigator's responsibility not to ignore this possibility. If the patient is truly incompetent to decide, the decision of including him in the study should not be left solely to the investigator, and should be based on what benefit the patient, not society, can derive from the experiment. Because the individual involved cannot give true consent, the term has no moral validity in this instance and the fact should not be disguised by attempts for legal protection in obtaining someone else's consent. The "someone else" may or may not represent the patient's best interest.

IV. Ethical Guidelines

In discussing a framework in which behavioral research can ethically occur, the author is fully aware of his bias for the strongest protection possible for the individual subject involved. He cannot agree that either science or society represent man's highest values, although science and society do reflect men's highest individual achievements. He agrees with those who feel there are definite limitations in research with human subjects and the potential good to humanity is not relevant, nor can it ever be a consideration in a truly free society. He would also agree that a research design with humans is ethical or not from its inception and not because of possible valuable data produced.

If an experiment with humans cannot be done ethically, it must be discarded, not because of scientific unworthiness but, it is hoped, because of a higher value: the worth of each and every individual human being. Because restrictive legislation can never embody all that is concerned with the protection of an experimental subject, the ethical responsibility cannot be delegated by the investigator to any other individual, a committee, or society.

A. Overview of Ethical Design in Behavioral Experiments

In evolving a research plan the investigator should ask the following questions: (1) Has the study already been done? (2) If it has, is there a definite value in reproducing it? (3) Does the potential importance of proving the hypothesis materially outweigh any risk of adverse effects, physical or psychic? (4) Have I examined my own motives for choosing the study and feel I can devote adequate supervision to its completion, or is this one of many studies which I am doing and therefore risks sloppy design, and poor theoretical justification and supervision. In short, am I overextended?

B. Research Committees

All proposals for studies with humans should be submitted to a committee composed of experienced researchers, clinicians, and at least one individual whose sole concern would be to evaluate the ethical considerations. A nonresearch psychiatrist should be a member, to examine the committee interaction and to see that the committee is not used for the purpose of sharing the guilt and responsibility of an unethical study. He could also help the committee avoid the tendency not to look too closely when protocols of colleagues (who may be on the committee next year) are involved.

C. *The Clinician/Researcher Team*

Many studies would benefit from a team in which the patient care and doctor-patient relation is assumed by an individual not responsible for the design and seeing through of the research protocol. The physician in charge of the patient would be able to obtain meaningful consent more objectively without an unconscious need to "sell" the patient. His duty would also be to stop the experiment whenever he felt it harmful to a given patient. This plan could also be readily adopted for use in studies with nonpatient normals, where an objective view to possible dangers is desperately needed, without burdening the investigator with a dual role which may end in harm to an individual, in spite of good intentions.

D. *Deception and Privacy*

A study which incorporates deliberate deception in its design is unethical except when the subject is aware that he may be deceived, and agrees. There is no doubt that this would prohibit many social-psychological experiments of potentially great social value. In the author's opinion, the risks far outweigh any possible benefit which may ensue for "the benefit of society." The use of deception in experimental design, particularly in psychosocial studies, has become a standard procedure. Many of these studies are unquestionably unethical, since the subject has not agreed to be deceived and would not participate if he knew of the deception. It is wondered whether these kinds of studies can ever be considered ethical except with informed consent, not to the purposes or aims of the study, as long as no danger is involved, but informed as to the fact that the subject knows he will not be aware of the aims.

Invasion of privacy cannot be explored fully here, but it should be noted that the values related to what constitutes privacy are changing, and what was once an individual's "own business" is no longer so. With psychiatric patients, invasion of privacy without permission cannot be considered ethical, nor can disclosure of confidential material without knowledge and consent. In addition, the subject has the right of anonymity in publication of research results.

E. *Normal Volunteer Subjects*

In behavioral research involving varieties of stress, the motivation of the subjects should be evaluated, and those subjects rejected who volunteer for psychopathologic reasons. In obviously dangerous experiments, the investigators should themselves share the risks. If they are unwilling, then the experiment should be abandoned regardless of how many volunteers are willing to undergo the perils.

In drug research with volunteers, the theoretic basis for trying a drug should be adequate, as well as sufficient data on animal toxicity, to exclude excess risk. The essentially empirical trial of drugs, without adequate theoretical justification, without knowledge of possible serious consequences, and without even a theoretically reasonable therapeutic potential has been widespread. The consequences of this rather casual research approach are becoming apparent with the hallucinogens.

F. Prisoners

All safeguards required of research with other segments of the human population should apply to prisoners. Extra precautions are required in evaluating the motivation for volunteering, since even when emphatically denied by the experimenter or prison authority, the fantasy wish of a reward in terms of a lessened sentence or other fantasies are present, and should be discussed with the subject. As long as the reality is presented, and the subject bias will not invalidate the design, the prison volunteer may be ethically used. Exceptions are in experiments which are hazardous, since a prison subject may volunteer for a hazardous experiment because of depression, or desperation, and would not ordinarily volunteer if he were out of prison. The experimenter has no right to take advantage of the unconscious wish of a human being to expiate guilt feelings.

G. Mental Patients

The particular situation of mental patients in our society makes them a captive and vulnerable subject group, especially when institutionalized. The need for ethical safeguards is increased rather than the opposite. This is so, at least partially, because of chaos relative to meanings of various psychiatric, psychologic, and legal terms, such as competency and incompetency, and the interpretation of criteria for diagnostic classification in behavioral abnormality.

Numerous factors point to the actuality of the mental institution population being a good deal less homogeneous than is inferred by many studies. Some of these factors are: the use of commitment for punishment after a family interaction (especially with individuals who have been committed previously), the tendency sometimes to hostilely and without sufficient cause designate behavior abnormal, or psychotic, and the casual way in which at times an individual can be labeled schizophrenic. Other factors are: the use of the hospital/institution to obtain or reinstate pensions, its use as a haven for board and meals for those who have no funds, for those whose family will no longer care for them, and for those who cannot or at times will not obtain gainful employment. Factually, many in this diverse group of individuals have actually been psychotic, but are not currently; have been labeled psychotic, but are not; are psychotic, but have not been designated as such. With this heterogeneous group, it is no wonder that the efficacy of drugs took so long to be shown as significant in relation to behavior.

Because of some notable contributions in which more objective data than diagnostic labels are substituted as criteria for including patients and recording changes in psychoactive drug studies, better experimental, as well as ethical, design has been possible, and individuals who cannot possibly benefit are excluded from studies. This knowledge, however, continues to be ignored, and patients are subjected to multiple trial medications from which there is no conceivable hope of benefit. Additionally, the experimental findings are of dubious value.

One wonders also, whether it is morally justifiable to discontinue a medication which is unquestionably benefiting the patient to substitute one whose efficacy is not known. It would seem more fitting to "wash out" those patients who are not responding to their current drug, or use new patients who are drug free. To use an untried drug while an efficacious drug is available is unethical if the risk to the patient is such as to cause irreversible injury or worse. Where the best drugs we have leave much room for improvement, and where there is no essential danger to the patient, it is not unethical to leave him drug free or to use a placebo or crossover design. The qualification in the preceding is the contigency of an informed consent.

The patient who is actually incompetent, whether by court declaration or not, cannot comprehend the alternatives or risks and must have the protection of being excluded unless the criteria are met that (1) his noninvestigator physician agrees that no essential harm will result. (2) The family members or guardian legally responsible are ascertained as the best possible, to be actually concerned with his welfare, and are not using the hospitalization and inclusion in an experiment as punishment for the patient, under the guise of some social good which may arise. This information, and the consent, should be obtained by the patient's physician and not the investigator. (3) The drug involved has good theoretical potential, and is not just a reworked molecule of another compound already tested.

In drug studies with psychotic patients, the moral validity of using a placebo in outpatient treatment is dubious, since the close supervision of the hospital setting is not possible. The ethical aspects of the blind design depend on the other factors mentioned, and also its necessity for a particular study, since it is pointless to subject patients to even trivial discomfort or danger when it is not necessary. Psychotic patients, even in remission, should not be used for potentially dangerous studies of any variety. Stress studies are particularly suspect.

H. Children

Inclusion of children in psychiatric drug studies produces special ethical problems. They cannot give informed consent. Parents or guardians may or may not have their best interest at heart. To use parents' discomfiture, concern, or guilt, or to sacrifice a child to unknown potentially serious risks, is immoral. Some of the criteria for involvement should be: (1) Sufficient animal toxicity studies are available, and the indications are that the possible hypothetical value strongly overshadows any potential risk; (2) the child's condition is such that even a small benefit would be of value; (3) the physician responsible for the patient agrees; (4) the parents or guardian have no pathologic motives for agreeing to involve the child.

I. *Publication of Data*

As ethical problems in research become more of a public issue, editorial boards of scientific journals may be required to recognize a responsibility on their part. Their contribution could be made in various ways such as designating an individual or committee to evaluate the ethical design of studies submitted, as well as the scientific design and findings. When the ethical design is questionable, they may find it necessary to reject the manuscript regardless of its scientific value. This approach without doubt would shortly curtail poor ethical research design, and cause investigators to reflect considerably on the ethical aspects of their next protocol. Rejection of a study under these conditions would not necessarily reflect on the particular investigator since he is fallible and subject to all of the frailties of the rest of humanity. When the values are ill-defined, he cannot be expected to become champion of what might be against his scientific interest.

V. Conclusion

Many other issues are not touched upon in this chapter. There is unquestionably a great need for a coherent and consistent approach to ethical design in research with humans. Although the investigator's responsibility is paramount, he cannot alone be expected to think of all the issues in a particular case, or to be aware continually of his own, perhaps unconscious, bias. Investigators in the area of behavioral research represent a diverse group of academic disciplines whose concepts of what may or may not be important in the area of ethical design of a research protocol will vary considerably. The various ethical codes of medical experimentation which have been promulgated, especially since World War II, represent a good beginning in relation to conceptualization of ethical design in research with humans. There remains a need for further clarification and extension of these codes for protection of individuals, and inclusion of some formal guidelines to which nonmedical researchers can adhere in areas of behavioral studies not having to do with drugs, such as the code of the American Psychological Association.

The responsible professions have a duty to outline for their own members the limits within which research with humans may be acceptably undertaken. If the behavioral scientists do not themselves develop these codes and standards, there is no doubt that restrictive legislation, in the long run more inimical to research, will ensue.

Most scientists have ignored normative ethics, since concepts of good or bad must be dealt with, and have limited themselves to metaethics, which is concerned only with questions of meanings and justification of normative judgments. If scientists continue to refuse to deal with these issues of relative value, even to exclusion of operational definitions, the vigilant public will define them, and not always reasonably or rationally.

For references and general reading see Appendices 1 and 2.

PART VIII

DRUG ABUSE AND RELATED PROBLEMS

37

PSYCHOLOGY OF ADDICTION

Alfred Lindesmith

I. Psychology of Addiction

A. Addicting and Nonaddicting Drugs

Drugs designated as addicting are those which produce physical dependence after a period of regular use so that when ingestion is abruptly terminated, a characteristic unpleasant or painful bodily reaction occurs. These withdrawal symptoms may be banished by another dose of the drug. This pattern of effects is clearly evident in the case of drugs of the morphine type, but it also occurs in alcoholics and the chronic heavy user of barbiturates.

The drugs designated as nonaddicting are sometimes used regularly and to a degree compulsively by some persons, but most often they are used irregularly, depending upon availability, social circumstances, and individual mood. Drugs of the nonaddicting type are generally classified as stimulants, whereas those of the addicting type are characterized as sedatives or depressants. These characterizations are misleading and oversimplified because the psychological effects of a drug may vary considerably with different sized doses, and with the user's attitudes and circumstances. In the case of addicting drugs, the perceived subjective effects change drastically during the initial period of regular use when physical dependence is being established. This will become evident in the subsequent discussion.

B. Positive and Negative Reinforcement

The psychological mechanisms involved in forming a habit of using the nonaddicting drugs such as cocaine, marihuana, LSD, and the amphetamines may be characterized as that of positive reinforcement. The person who uses drugs of this type notes that they produce pleasurable subjective effects which are distinctly different from his ordinary state of mind. The use of the drug is repeated on a regular or irregular basis in order to repeat the pleasurable experience, or sometimes, in the case of those who become psychologically dependent on it, to perpetuate the "high" as the constant state. Thus, persons who use marihuana or LSD expect that when the drug takes hold they will for a certain period of time have unusual subjective experiences which they regard as euphoric or desirable.

In the case of the addicting drugs the psychological mechanisms are different and more complex and may be described as those of negative reinforcement. The latter expression refers to the repetition of an act not because it is in itself pleasurable, but because it enables one to escape from or avoid pain or unpleasantness. Thus, in the case of the morphine or heroin addict, each injection that is taken either relieves or staves off the withdrawal distress that invariably occurs when the next dose is postponed too long. The point may be clarified by giving closer attention to opiate addiction.

During the initial period of regular use or administration of a drug such as morphine, the drug ordinarily produces in most persons a relatively mild and characteristic euphoric effect. When the beginner is administering the drug to himself, he is strongly impelled by the development of tolerance to augment his dosage. As he does so, he at first experiences increased euphoric effects both at the moment of impact and during the interval between injections. However, when physical dependence is fully established, the euphoric or "coasting" effect between injections diminishes close to the vanishing point and can only be temporarily restored by increasing the dose. The impact effects of an intravenous shot last only a few minutes after the injection and should be sharply differentiated from those that persist during the entire time interval between injections, which we may take to be 4 hours for illustrative purposes. Impact effects are maximal with the intravenous method of use and are less noticeable with intramuscular injection and when the drug is given by other methods such as orally or by suppositories. Impact effects also become more striking in direct proportion to the time that the shot is delayed and to the consequent severity of the withdrawal symptoms being experienced when the injection is made.

The morphine or heroin addict on a fairly stable regular dosage usually reports that he feels "normal" during the period between shots. At the same time, he paradoxically bestows extravagant praise on the drug's effects and even learns to evaluate positively some of the effects which beginners and nonusers find disagreeable, such as vertigo and nausea. To the confirmed addict such symptoms become desirable as indicators of good quality drugs. Impact effects come to have the same significance, and when addicts in the hospital setting are given drugs by routes other than the intravenous one, they commonly complain they cannot "feel" the shots.

The addict's claim that he feels normal between shots is sometimes disputed by investigators, who feel that this claim does not make sense in view of the opiate addict's notoriously powerful attachment to his drug and the enormous risks and sacrifices that he makes to obtain it. However, there is considerable evidence from a variety of sources which supports the claim. It is well known, for example, that the regular user of opiates is, from the organic point of view, not markedly different from the normal person and that if usage is controlled and other factors are held constant, he may escape detection from casual observation and successfully carry out complex occupational obligations for many years.

Other evidence tending to support the addict's claim of normality is that he can be deceived under certain circumstances about whether or not he is actually under the influence of the drug. This may be accomplished, for example, by changing the method of administration from the intravenous to the oral route when the user is put in a hospital and then progressively reducing the amount of the drug while continuing the injections. The changed method of ingestion in itself creates uncertainty in the addict's mind. The gradual elimination of the drug reduces the severity of withdrawal and spreads it out over a period of time so that when the last of the drug is taken away the user may not realize it and continue to believe that he is receiving it as long as the injections are continued. This method was used extensively during the nineteenth century in "curing" addiction—that is, in separating addicts from their drug. Obviously, it could not have been used if there were no validity in the addict's claim of normality or if the effects of morphine were remotely comparable to those of LSD or even of marihuana.

To take account of the above it may be suggested that the "hook" in opiate addiction arises not from the positive euphoria which is produced only in the initial period of use, but rather from the relief of withdrawal distress which occurs invariably and automatically after physical dependence has been built up—that is, from negative rather than positive reinforcement. It is of interest that drug habits established by negative reinforcement generally appear to be much more powerful and compulsive than those based simply on positive reinforcement. It is not clear why this should be so.

It should be noted that the responses of persons to drugs are powerfully influenced by what they know or believe and what they expect from the drug. Thus it has been noted by physicians that it is a wise policy to keep patients in ignorance of the drug being given them. It is claimed that this tactic prevents addiction even in neurotics who especially enjoy the effects and might seem predisposed to become addicted. Patients who are thus kept in ignorance may become physically dependent on morphine without ever becoming psychologically addicted to it. This points up the fact that psychological addiction is not identical with physical dependence and that each of these two conditions may be present while the other is absent. Two examples make the point: (1) an infant born of an addicted mother is physically dependent at birth, but if the drug is later successfully withdrawn no addiction in the usual sense ensues; (2) an addict serving a long sentence in a prison in which he is unable to secure drugs may continue to crave them and arrange to resume his habit as quickly as possible after release.

Since the powerful tendency of addicts to relapse after they have been taken off drugs is an essential aspect of addiction, it challenges attempts at theoretical explanation. From the standpoint that addiction is established in a process of conditioning by negative reinforcement, it is argued that the repeated experience of relief of withdrawal distress sets up a high-level conceptually controlled response system that becomes independent of the initial physiological or pharmacological events which are essential in its origins. The beginner, who starts by using the drug to *escape* the pains of withdrawal, progresses to using it to *avoid* anticipated withdrawal. Finally, by a process of generalization, he ends up using it to escape from or avoid virtually all traumatic or unpleasant experiences, including anxiety concerning anticipated events as well as anxiety arising from the very fact of his addiction. When the drug is removed, the user continues to think of all unhappy occurrences as occasions for another "fix." As with abstaining alcoholics or cigarette smokers, a single lapse is not in itself fatal, but, because it is usually followed by others, it tends very strongly to lead to readdiction.

C. Theories of Addiction

Theories concerning the psychological mechanisms involved in drug addiction fall into two broad classes. One of these, like the preceding account, assumes that virtually anyone can become addicted if he takes drugs or has them administered to him over a period of time sufficient to establish physical dependence and provided that he has some knowledge of what is happening to him. The other type of theory assumes that only individuals of a certain personality type, or persons subjected to various kinds of environmental or social pressures, become addicts. From the latter viewpoint it is commonly argued that most if not all addicts have personality problems needing psychiatric attention which antedate and lead to the use of drugs. Research on human subjects conducted by psychiatrists and clinicians tends to take the second position, while those who do experimental work with lower animals (usually monkeys and rats) tend to take the first. Since rats and monkeys do not voluntarily begin taking drugs of their own accord except under highly contrived laboratory conditions, and because it makes little sense to talk of personality or psychiatric problems in these animals, the experimenters who study the responses of subhuman species to morphine are strongly impelled to adopt theories of the first type that emphasize conditioning mechanisms.

Current controversies that arise from experimental work with lower animals have to do with the applicability of findings to human users. Some of the experimentalists argue that the rat or monkey may sometimes legitimately be called an addict and that the experimental findings may consequently be extended to humans. Others concede that while there appear to be substantial similarities between the responses of humans and lower animals to morphine, there are also very considerable differences, and that the extension of experimental findings to human subjects is premature and of dubious validity or value.

In view of existing current controversies concerning the psychological mechanisms involved in addiction and the absence of agreement concerning an addiction prone personality type, the prudent practical assumption of the physician who prescribes addicting drugs such as morphine clearly should be that anyone may become addicted. Whatever error may be embodied in this assumption will be on the side of caution. In the case of drugs classified as stimulants, which do not produce physical dependence, such as the amphetamines, marihuana, LSD, and others, personality factors are probably of central significance when chronic abuse occurs.

The theories advanced to explain alcoholism and barbiturate addiction are generally much the same as those applied to heroin or opiate addiction, and the theoretical problems are much the same. As in the case of opiate addiction, the discussion of these forms of addiction is characterized by a wide range of conflicting theories and a shortage of decisive evidence.

For further reading see other chapters this Section, and Appendices 1 and 2.

II. Drugs and the Law (see also Chapter 45)

A. *The Criminalization of the User*

Under U.S. federal law possession of LSD or other dangerous drugs is a criminal offense. In the case of heroin, morphine, and other opiates and opiate equivalents, as well as of marihuana and cocaine, the situation is the same. Mere possession of any of these drugs, provided they are illicit, as they invariably are, is itself heavily punishable, regardless of whether the possession is for personal use or for sale. A first possession offense involving heroin carries a possible prison sentence of from two to ten years, but the convicted offender may be placed on probation or, if sent to prison, released on parole. A second offense involves a sentence of from five to twenty and a third from ten to forty years in prison with probation and parole excluded. These penalties are among the most severe provided for any kind of crime.

Since the heroin or morphine addict is generally unable to secure legal drugs and hence patronizes the illicit trade, he willy-nilly becomes a criminal by the sheer fact that he is addicted. The marihuana user is in the same position since possession of this drug is subject to penalties that are virtually identical with those connected with heroin.

In recent years, the policy of subjecting to criminal prosecution persons who have what are judged to be undesirable or harmful personal habits has come to be seriously questioned, largely because of the rising popularity of marihuana smoking in the middle and upper classes and among college students. Most bad habits, such as overeating, overdrinking, and a host of others are not punishable offenses, but are regarded as matters of personal judgment or morality. In legal theory the apparatus of the criminal law is viewed as a means of controlling behavior that is harmful, dangerous, or obnoxious to others, not as a means of controlling or suppressing personal habits that harm primarily the person who has them. Thus, it is not an offense to drink alcoholic beverages in private, but it is an offense to drive an automobile when intoxicated, to be intoxicated in public, or to engage in rowdy or disorderly public behavior while drunk. Indeed, more than half of the offenses listed annually in the Uniform Crime Reports of the Federal Bureau of Investigation are connected with the abuse of alcohol. Nevertheless, the private consumption of alcohol as such, no matter how excessive or destructive to the person concerned, is not illegal, and most citizens would object violently if the government were to try to suppress it through the police power or try to make alcohol unavailable.

Obviously, if such habits as drinking and smoking were to be made illegal by punishing those found to be in possession of tobacco or alcohol, a very large portion of the population would be transformed into criminals by a stroke of the legislative pen. In addition one would expect, from the history of the Volstead Act and the prohibition era, that enormous black markets in tobacco and alcohol would come into being under the guidance of racketeering entrepreneurs of the criminal underworld. Even moderately strict enforcement would be impossible without a vast additional army of policemen and the wholesale invasion of privacy. Public hostility would rise and the law itself would be discredited and corrupted.

What is suggested by the foregoing is that if the drug addictions and the use of nonaddicting drugs are viewed as personal habits, the attempt to control them should probably be focused on reducing availability and on educational and preventive measures rather than on punishing the users. That the criminal law is not an effective instrument for the control of such practices is indicated by the fact that marihuana smoking has been spreading rapidly at the same time that the penalties for possessing the weed were being greatly increased. It is also indicated by the magnitude of the opiate addiction problem in the United States and by the large number of crimes committed by heroin addicts in order to pay inflated black market prices. The fiasco of the prohibition era is another case in point.

For references and further reading see Appendices 1 and 2, and other chapters, Part VIII.

38

THE USE AND ABUSE OF STIMULANTS

Edward R. Bloomquist

I. Introduction

The introduction of stimulants into the pharmacological armamentarium of medicine has given physicians a valuable weapon against disease. If the drugs could have remained in the hands of clinicians and researchers, the world would have been significantly better off. Unfortunately, as is currently true of almost all drugs that have any significant effect on the human mind, stimulants have been taken over as a "special" feature of the mind-altering cult. Since then, the drugs have assumed a significant role as a major item of abuse.

The number of currently available or potentially available stimulants (see Biel, Chapter 24) is steadily increasing. As researchers discover new compounds, drug abusers find new ways of introducing them into their subculture. Each of these stimulants has its own abuse pattern, its own cult of admirers, its aberrant as well as salutory reactions, and negative as well as positive effects on both the individual and society, depending upon how it is used.

Generally the pattern of use and abuse is about the same. The drug is discovered, produced, placed under experimental study, and, if approved, given to clinicians for trial and application. At this point a wave of enthusiasm occurs with much prescribing, some indicated, some not. At the same time the curiosity of the drug abuser is piqued and experimentation commences among self-medicators, drug cultists, and others intent on saturating their sensoriums with medicinals. The supply of legitimate drugs is usually inadequate to meet the new demand, thus black marketing both in production and sale begins. Soon it becomes apparent that the new drug is capable of being abused, and the scientific community begins issuing warnings. Generally these are ignored by the drug abusers. In many instances such warnings may merely increase their determination to become psychologically and/or physically dependent upon the new drug. The problem escalates until enforcement is brought into the picture. In desperation society then turns what has heretofore been a medical and social problem into a felony, with the abusers being incarcerated for their offense.

Since the pattern of stimulant drug abuse is generally the same, differing in minor detail from one drug to another, this chapter will concern itself with what is now the major stimulant drug abuse problem. The substances in point: amphetamines. Amphetamines were first prepared by Edeleano in 1887. The initial drug was the volatile amine, phenylisopropylamine. In 1910 Barger and Dale noted the amphetamines were related to epinephrine and were sympathomimetic in activity.

Nine years later Ogata developed desoxyephedrine (methamphetamine). A lull in interest in the amphetamines then occurred because of the current interest now in ephedrine, which Nagai had isolated from the Chinese herb Ma Huang in 1887. As it became increasingly difficult to obtain ephedrine from natural sources, researchers began to search once more for a comparable substitute. In 1927 amphetamine sulfate was synthesized by Gordon Alles and work began to determine if this new drug would be useful for clinical use. This same year synthetic ephedrine was prepared and marketed under the name Ephetonin. Its introduction, however, did not quell the revived interest in the amphetamines.

In 1930 Piness introduced amphetamine clinically as a vasoconstrictor, noting that while its effect was only about 1/100th that of epinephrine, it had the advantage of producing a longer duration of cardiovascular effects. It was also shown the drug had bronchodilator, analeptic, and respiratory stimulant properties. Effects of the drug included: an increased verbal and motor activity, an elevated mood response, and a decrease in drowsiness or sleep. In the same year Tainter found that the pressor response to amphetamine was diminished by repeated injections of the drug and by cocaine and that ergotamine did not reverse the rise in blood pressure elicited by its use. In these respects the amphetamines resembled ephedrine.

II. Classification of Amphetamines

Amphetamines are part of a group of drugs termed amines. Amines produce effects characteristic of those of the sympathetic nervous system. The effects may be succinctly described by using the old mnemonic "Fight, fright, or flight."

The principal components of the amine group include: epinephrine, ephedrine, norepinephrine, desoxyephedrine (methamphetamine), phenmetrazine, amphetamine, and its isomer (which is twice as potent) dextroamphetamine. These compounds are all closely related chemically, having benzene ring structures with side chains that vary in length from four to six members.

Amphetamines, when ingested, inhaled, or injected, act directly on the central nervous system. Here the site of action is apparently the reticular activating system. Once the drugs are taken they are rapidly assimilated into the bloodstream. The drugs are metabolized slowly; thus it may take from 2 to 3 days for the body to eliminate 10–20 mg of material. Additionally, large amounts of the drugs are excreted unchanged in the urine, a feature that is valuable as a diagnostic tool in cases of chronic or acute toxicity.

III. Addiction Potential

The question of whether or not amphetamines are addictive or habituating is a matter of semantics. The body builds up a tolerance to the drugs, with habitual users taking daily doses of such incredible quantity that a comparable amount given to a nonuser could easily be lethal. Habitual users develop a marked psychological dependence on the drugs and evidence definite withdrawal symptoms, including tenseness, anxiety, tremor and nervousness which may be of such degree as to incapacitate the user during his period of withdrawal. With this picture in mind it is difficult to understand why some authorities prefer to classify amphetamines as habituating rather than addicting.

IV. Clinical Application

The list of therapeutic applications of the amphetamines began for the most part with the discovery by Prinzmetal and Bloomberg that amphetamine could be utilized in the treatment of narcolepsy. In 1946 Bett published a monograph listing some thirty-six diseases which had responded in varying degrees to treatment with amphetamines. Since then, the field of investigation has widened, although it has tended to be more selective than at first.

Amphetamines have been useful in controlling certain forms of epilepsy. They have been utilized in treating hypotension which occurs during surgical procedures. They have been effective in lightening the sleep of nonorganically complicated enuretics so they can respond to the sensation of a full bladder and thus avoid nocturnal in-bed urination.

One of the unexpected uses of amphetamines centers around the drugs' ability to alter the electroencephalograms of certain types of brain-damaged children. They are also effective in calming hyperexcitable children, making the youngsters more amenable to treatment. This therapeutic paradox of giving stimulants to an already hyperactive child in an effort to calm him was introduced in 1937 by Charles Bradley. His findings have been corroborated by other investigators since then (cf. Eveloff, Chapter 54).

Amphetamines have been used successfully in reducing or eliminating stuttering in severely afflicted patients. They have been used, though more recently replaced by other methods, in counteracting the depression caused by barbiturate poisoning. The drugs have also found a place in the treatment of neurasthenic and depressive syndromes and in therapy of post-encephalitic Parkinsonism (but see page 509).

The most publicized uses of amphetamines, however, fall in the areas of interest where more people are involved. Though it can hardly be called a therapeutic application, some have been intrigued by the fact that amphetamines taken before a drinking bout may postpone or minimize alcoholic intoxication. They also seem to minimize to some extent the effects of heavy indulgence in alcohol. The drugs seem to hasten the metabolism of alcohol in the body and, additionally, act as a counterstimulant to the depressant effects of the alcohol.

Athletes have become fascinated by the promise of increased energy, prolonged endurance, and seemingly desirable alertness produced by the drugs. Again, while this is not a therapeutic use per se, the application has caught the interest of some to the detriment of others. Unethical managers have been known to drug both humans and animals in their desire to excel and win. Unfortunately, some athletes have died from the overstimulation resulting from the intake of the drug. "Amphetamines," the American Medical Association has warned, "are not a magic source of extra mental or physical energy: they serve only to push the user to a greater expenditure of his own resources, sometimes to a hazardous point of fatigue that is often not recognized."

There is little question that while some of the amphetamines are prescribed for problems such as those mentioned above, a high percentage are administered in an attempt to control weight and to produce weight reduction. They exert their effect in this area by acting directly on the brain to control the appetite center. Additionally, any depression which may cause the eater to seek refuge in food is temporarily assuaged.

V. Symptoms of Overuse

While amphetamines are reasonably safe drugs when used in proper quantity for appropriate conditions, undesirable symptoms may occur with continued and uncontrolled use. Various problems have been reported by different observers which may occur singly or in combination with amphetamine abuse. Included are: severe headaches, vomiting, inefficiency, tenseness, anxiety, memory loss, poor concentration, restlessness, glossitis, nasal congestion, dryness of the nasal passages, dizziness, hyperacuity, staggering, tachycardia, palpitation, undesirable weight loss, cold sweating extremities, pyrexia, and, ultimately, hallucinations, paranoia, and toxic psychosis.

Where these latter three complications are concerned, the outcome can be individually and socially dangerous. Ayache in 1960, noted that in certain prepsychotic personalties amphetamines act similarly to lysergic acid diethylamide in their ability to produce hallucinations. These hallucinations are very striking and may appear with almost any significant dosage. The variable is not due so much to the total dose, although this is significant, but the response to the drug of each individual user.

Hallucinations may be visual, auditory, olfactory, or may appear in combination. The user frequently recognizes the hallucinatory nature of his impressions, but even so, and this remains true even after detoxification, he remains impressed by the reality feeling of the drug experience. Some individuals are sufficiently unusual in their appreciation of bizarre experiences that they enjoy this sensation. Most, however, find the occurrence unpleasant and disturbing.

Before we accumulated our current experience with the true hallucinogens, McCormick made a statement which might now be equally applicable to lysergic acid diethylamide or other potent psychotoxins. "No other group of drugs," he said, "can affect or change character and personality traits to a greater degree than the amphetamines. It is not possible to predict which patients may react adversely to the amphetamines. . . . The reaction appears to be based on personality traits and organic predisposition rather than upon any pharmacological action of the drug."

VI. Amphetamine Abuse

Because amphetamines help prevent sleep and increase the user's alertness and activity, they have been referred to by the lay public as "pep pills." The drugs do produce stimulation in varying degree, depending upon the response of the user. Fatigue is temporarily reduced, although it usually returns in increased intensity once the effects of the drug has worn off. In addition, users experience a feeling of well-being and increased physical strength, confidence, and decisiveness. Unfortunately, if the user takes enough of the drug, he may lose all concept of reality.

With the coining of the term "pep pills" an entire lexicon of synonyms have appeared to plague the student who is trying to understand the riddle of amphetamine abuse. Synonyms include: purple hearts, dexies, speed, meth, splash, eye-openers, wake-ups, footballs, bennies, lid-proppers, and bombitas. "Pep pills" have a certain appeal for special types of occupations and personalities. Night workers, truck drivers, students cramming for exams, the overweight, the fatigued—all these and more have found a seeming answer to their problems in the very available amphetamine tablet. In addition the drug has been improperly and inadvisably prescribed.

People begin taking amphetamines for a variety of reasons. One of the more common is being exposed by prescription, finding that life can seem a bit more cheerful, asking for more and more drugs for nonmedical reasons, and having their physicians comply with their request. Others begin their habit by acquiring drugs from the surplus supply of friends, then continuing their drug abuse by obtaining black-market tablets. Youngsters often initially acquire amphetamine supplies from the medicine cabinet, where parents keep them to fight off various unwanted symptoms.

A. The Drug Subculture

Almost all major drugs of abuse have been adopted by groups which in turn nurture their use. Most inhabitants of this culture are youths who turn to abuse of the drugs, in this case the amphetamines, because of boredom, curiosity, rebelliousness, or an inability to cope with reality. Peer group pressure can tease some into trying the drugs. Some continue their use because they find the effects most desirable. Antisocial attitudes, rebellion against school and parents, and easy availability plus the "kicky" effects obtained constitute other reasons for abusing the drug.

A large number of youths have been exposed to the effects of amphetamines because of their wartime use by governments. In such cases the drugs were employed to keep soldiers awake during critical maneuvers. As an example, two years after German scientists discovered the CNS effects of desoxyephedrine the German armies began using the drugs to drive its soldiers on under conditions that otherwise would have overwhelmed them.

The Allies also used pep pills during World War II. It is estimated that during this period some 72,000,000 "energy tablets" were given to British soldiers with a similar amount being utilized by the American troops. In Japan desoxyephedrine was consumed in quantities close to toxic levels by kamikaze pilots. Once the war was over, huge quantities of unused amphetamines found their way into the civilian market in both Europe and Japan. Pills that were once used to promote wartime alertness were now taken in large quantities by bored, still hostile youths who were accustomed to living on raw nerve.

In 1954 the Pharmacists Association of Japan estimated one-and-a-half-million of their eighty-eight million people were misusing amphetamines, principally methedrine. In one regional investigation some 5% of the age 16–25 group were abusing the drug. Examination of the cases showed that abuse of the drug had produced auditory hallucinations and paranoid delusions. Schizophrenic reactions were also noted. Most of the cases required 30 days of treatment to attain successful withdrawal, although some needed twice this period of time to recover. The abuse pattern thus became established, and from this time has progressed to the current moment where amphetamine abuse now constitutes one of the more serious drug abuse problems, internationally and, in particular, in the United States.

Remarkably, with all this evidence of contemporary, abuse the British Ministry of Health released a report in the same year that Japan was experiencing its postwar amphetamine crisis that "amphetamines have the advantage of being relatively non-toxic, addiction to them rare and there are no serious ill effects; they may therefore be given to patients without undue risk."

With this official assurance British doctors began doling out excessively large quantities of amphetamines. In 1960, 2.5% of all prescriptions in Newcastle-on-Tyne, England were for amphetamines. When Kiloh and Brandon investigated prescription habits among doctors in that city, they found that of a population of 269,000 inhabitants, 2600 persons were receiving the drug, and consumed some 200,000 tablets of amphetamine each month.

Local doctors estimated that at least 20% of these 2600 users were habituated or addicted to the drugs, depending on how one classified the problem. Eight-five percent of these amphetamine abusers were women in the age 36-45 group, usually housewives with growing families. These women created real problems both at home and for society in general. They stole, deceived their doctors, and deprived their families in order to supply their growing habits until, for some at least, the cycle was interrupted by enforcement. The significant thing about this study was that the authors expressed the opinion that their town was not unique in its problem.

VII. Amphetamine Abuse in America

In 1954–1956, Connell reported observing toxic psychoses from the use of amphetamines in England.

The problems associated with amphetamine abuse in America have been similar to those experienced with any drug with a high abuse potential. If the material is available and there exists a ready market, difficulty will arise. One of the early problems began with the introduction in 1932 of the Benzedrine inhaler as an "over the counter" item. These inhalers contained 325 mg of amphetamine base, which was equivalent to 561 mg of amphetamine sulfate.

In a brief time those who found that they responded psychologically to the effects of amphetamine began to abuse this newly available source of drug. They broke the container, removed the wick, boiled it to obtain the active ingredient, then either swallowed or injected the solution. This activity was short-lived, however, for as soon as the manufacturer learned of this activity, the product was removed from the market and replaced with a new type of inhaler which contained propylhexadrine instead of amphetamine. This experience served as an introduction to a fact which many American physicians seemingly have not as yet accepted—that amphetamines possess a negative appeal for certain emotionally disturbed individuals who will use the drug if they can obtain it to the point of inducing toxic psychoses.

In 1937 the Council on Pharmacy and Chemistry of the American Medical Association accepted Benzedrine sulfate. Three years later methedrine was made available in Great Britain as a prescription item. With the drugs now more available it was axiomatic that in a short time significant drug abuse activity would begin. Soon, reports of abuse of the drugs appeared in the medical literature. In 1938 cases of paranoid psychoses caused by amphetamine abuse were reported by Young and Scoville. By 1952 the World Health Organization felt it necessary to warn that amphetamine was being abused by morphine addicts. They also noted that amphetamines possessed the potential of producing addiction on their own.

A. *Amphetamine Intoxication*

Amphetamine intoxication can be divided into three primary catagories. The first is chronic toxicity. This is caused by long-term, usually lower dosage intake of amphetamines. The second is acute in origin and is caused by accidental ingestion of the drug. The third type is also acute in origin, but is precipitated by intentional drug ingestion or injection. Each of these problems differs somewhat from the others.

B. *Chronic Toxicity*

The psychosis precipitated by prolonged abuse of amphetamines is an unpredictable entity as far as its relationship to total drug intake is concerned. It usually occurs after prolonged consumption of 100–500 mg per day, but it may appear in patients who have taken prolonged doses of as little as 20 mg per day. A patient may take as much as 1700 mg per day, as has occurred in one reported instance, before exhibiting toxicity, or he may have an idiosyncrasy to the drug and develop toxic symptoms after a single 50 mg dose.

Amphetamine psychosis is more common in men than in women. Males who develop it apparently have frankly sociopathic personalities. Women, however, are more often chronically neurotic, lacking in confidence, neurasthenic, or prone to react to stress with bouts of depression. When unstable behavior patterns exist, excess ingestion of amphetamines seems to aggravate this negative personality trait.

Chronic amphetamine intoxication is an insidious problem in the majority of cases. Symptoms usually take a long time to appear, although there are exceptions to this rule. The daily intake of drugs by chronic abusers can become incredibly high before significant trouble appears. Eventually, however, the drug abuser suffers personality changes, weight loss, and marked impairment of his cardiovascular, central nervous, and gastrointestinal systems.

C. *Acute Intoxication Caused by Accidental Ingestion*

Symptoms occurring in this group are similiar to those which will be described in the following section. They will occur in varying degree, depending on the susceptibility of the patient, the amount of drug intake, and the rapidity with which treatment is instituted. Almost all of the cases in this group involve children who have inadvertently acquired amphetamines from an adult source. Prevention of these crises must lie in the hands of adults who maintain supplies of amphetamines for various medicinal purposes. Such supplies should be kept in locked containers and, preferably, in locked cabinets.

Acute amphetamine poisoning is a sudden catastrophic event, particularly since children are the principal victims. The fatal dose for most youngsters is about 5 mg/kg of body weight. For adults it ranges from 20-25 mg/kg, provided the patient has no accumulated tolerance.

D. Acute Amphetamine Intoxication Caused by Intentional Ingestion

Although numerous drugs are currently available, it is generally agreed, even by the drug subculture itself, that the most dangerous drug now frequently being abused is methamphetamine. There was a time when heroin was considered the "bad" drug by the abuser set. Today heroin, although it is still abused and is still considered bad, has been replaced in frequency of use by intravenous amphetamines. How long this will continue to be true will be determined by the capricious interest of drug abusers of this particular pharmaceutical.

Within the drug world various medications have been categorized by the abusers and accepted as "the" drug to use for specific effects. Thus, if one wishes to socialize, the preferred drug adjunct to the situation is usually cannabis. If one wishes to "explore his mind" or indulge in various forms of internal psychological investigation, one of the stronger hallucinogenic substances such as lysergic acid diethylamide is preferred. If one wishes to abuse a drug (i.e., "really trip out"), he may resort to the intravenous injection of methamphetamine. The picture of drug abuse in America, therefore, has greatly changed since the time when the choice seemed limited to cannabis or heroin.

In our contemporary society there are a number of personality types which contribute to the growing number of cases of acute amphetamine toxicity which appear in emergency clinics or police stations. The most significant of these are the "heads." "Heads" are individuals who are attracted to the chronic abuse of a personally preferred drug. In street jargon they are classified in connection with their particular drug of abuse. Thus one speaks of potheads (cannabis users), acidheads (those who abuse lysergic acid diethylamide), hopheads (abusers of opiates, particularly heroin), and methheads (also known as speed freaks). This latter group prefers to abuse methamphetamine. Amphetamine droppers (individuals who prefer oral ingestion of the drug in contrast to "hypes," who utilize the intravenous route) are also referred to as "pill heads," although this latter term is a general one which can be applied to any person who drops (swallows) any variety of pill. Heads usually respond to the chronic abuse of various medications by experiencing a psychological "blast" (experience) that is so overwhelmingly pleasant to them they will "trip" (repeat the drug abuse event for the psychological effects) whenever possible.

Individuals who choose amphetamines as their choice of drug to abuse usually begin by taking the drugs orally. After experiencing an effect which they interpret as being desirable, they may continue their indulgence as an oral habit or may progress to the intravenous use of methamphetamine. Those who indulge in this latter method of drug intake refer to the process as "mainlining," just as heroin users refer to the term. Along the same line, methamphetamine users are frequently referred to as "hypes." The intravenous method of drug intake is preferred by those who wish a quick, intense, effect from the use of the drug. The effect is prolonged, not so much because of the effect of an individual dose of drug, as it is by the fact that most users will inject the drug repetitively at intervals of 3 to 4 hours for several days.

Individuals who abuse amphetamines, particularly those who inject methamphetamine may relate their experience in terms heavily cloaked in sexual overtones. The physical reaction obtained by the injection of methamphetamine is frequently referred to as an orgasm. Jargon of the amphetamine world (of the whole drug world or subculture, in fact) is quite similar to that used in the so-called sexual underworld or subculture. The association between the sexual response and the drug experience will vary from user to user, but frequently, among young male users in particular, injection of the drug is associated with a physical response similar to orgasm.

As with some heroin users, those who abuse methamphetamine may develop a "needle habit." Users who acquire this problem are capable of eliciting a psychological and sometimes physical response by merely playing with their intravenous injection equipment (kit). They do this by utilizing their eyedropper-needle improvised syringes, or by employing 1 or 2 cc medical syringes if available, sticking the needle in their vein, and flushing the blood and water solution back and forth in a monotonous repetitive action. This activity is often referred to in terms frequently employed to designate masturbatory activity.

Those who employ the intravenous method of injecting methamphetamine may prefer to use the eyedropper-needle technique because they find it easier to manipulate the equipment and to find their veins. Further, the eyedropper and the size 24 or 26 half-inch needle are less difficult to acquire from local sources. It is interesting to note, along this line, that campaigns on the part of some to destroy syringes to "keep them out of the hands of addicts" are not as apropos as they might seem. The main champions of the used syringe seem to be high school youngsters, who have found they can inject vodka into their oranges, which they suck from time to time during the day to relieve the tedium of the classroom. This does not imply, however, that certain users will not employ regular syringes if they are available.

Those who choose to utilize methamphetamine as their drug of abuse usually go on "runs" which last for several days. While they are "up" (under the influence of the drug), they may talk incessantly and may seem to acquire an immense feeling of power and personal importance. There is no simple reason why an individual will indulge in this type of behavior, but the most universal excuse is that drugs seem to help certain persons feel they belong to and are a part of a group in which they can be accepted and with which they at least feel they can cope. Obviously this sensation is short-lived and disappears once the user is separated from his drug. This feature may explain why some drug abusers indulge in repetitive use of a drug which to date many insist does not cause physical dependence.

The drug-induced attitude of intense power and personal capability is not a sociologically acceptable feature for several reasons. First, it is synthetic and brief. When it disappears, the user is in a less desirable condition than he was before he first used the drug in that he is often disappointed, and disillusioned. Because of this he may grow increasingly hostile. Second, as the users already are in a marginally adjusted emotional balance, they may become more disturbed, and aggressive, destructive behavior may occur. Within the sexual sphere this is important since users of intravenous amphetamine often indicate that, as they emerge from their drug experience which has lasted for several days, they have an intense interest in expressing themselves sexually. At such times the expression is intensely physical but is usually nonobject directed. Thus anyone or, possibly, anything animate that is in the vicinity that appeals to the drug-distorted mind may serve as the object of sexual aggression. The social implications of this feature are obvious.

Additionally, when the user of intravenous amphetamines has been "up" for several days, he often begins to experience paranoid delusions. Frequently he will direct his resulting hostility toward friends. If he does not direct his energies in this direction or express them in physical sexuality, he begins the final phase of his current drug experience by "crashing" or "coming down," words utilized in drug jargon to designate the beginning of a period of intense fatigue which may end in a coma for a day or more.

Surprisingly, deaths from metamphetamine abuse are apparently rare. Undoubtedly this is due to the fact that most users are otherwise healthy, young adults whose bodies can withstand this intense stress for some time before they finally collapse. If they emerge from the experience with minimal physical effects, and most seem to do so, the question still remains as to how much if any damage has been done to their central nervous or cardiovascular system. Most users report memory impairment of varying degree and note, for varying periods of time after the drug experience, that they have difficulty in concentrating.

This statement is not meant to imply that death is not a concomitant feature of intravenous amphetamine abuse. If the drug does not produce lethal effects through overstimulation, complications such as tetanus, hepatitis, bacteremia, and septicemia, and comparable problems arising from the use of contaminated intravenous equipment, may cause death.

VIII. Conclusion

A number of solutions have been offered from time to time in an effort to control or, hopefully, eliminate the problems and complications associated with the abuse of dangerous drugs. Some schools of thought feel that if we permit drug abusers to obtain controlled amounts of the drugs of their choice and administer them under medical supervision, the problem would be less important. The argument favoring this approach is based on the philosophy that many drug abusers, particularly the opiate users, are forced into a life of crime in order to maintain their habit.

Those who resist this approach feel the problems of tolerance and psychological dependence compounded by a preexisting antisocial trend within the patient's personality are ignored in this attempt to "do something" about the problem. This group feels that it is wrong to perpetuate a drug dependence, particularly where it is recognized that this dependence is sociologically and individually harmful.

Drug dependence is not an easy problem to solve. Yet it seems more practical to the conservatives who work with this situation to remove the drug as far as is possible, detoxify the patient, give him adequate psychiatric care, and try to arrange a place for him in society where the pressures of living are not so great that the abuser or potential abuser is driven to escape reality through the use of psychotoxic drugs.

Certainly, in cases of amphetamine abuse, good psychiatric care is necessary. Many patients who have been subjected to high blood levels of stimulants for long periods of time develop marked depression which seems even greater when the patient compares his depressed state with the abnormal period of elation he experienced while "high" on his drug. For many this comparison is frustrating and intolerable. In such instances the patient may well exhibit self-destructive tendencies.

Amphetamine drugs unquestionably have a place in the physician's pharmaceutical armamentarium. On the positive side these drugs possess a relatively low toxicity and exhibit minimal untoward reactions if they are used properly with adequate supervision. If one prescribes the drug with respect, it will usually provide beneficial effects. If the interest and motivation in taking these drugs is based on a desire for "kicks," unwarranted psychological support, or bizarre experiences, however, the drugs may produce physical problems and psychiatric illnesses which can destroy.

For further reading and references see Appendices 1 and 2.

39

THE HALLUCINOGENS*†

Sidney Cohen

I. Introduction

The hallucinogens (psychedelics, psychotomimetics, mysticomimetics, fantastica, psychodysleptics) have become not only valuable research aids but also a current sociological problem. This brief review is therefore timely, despite the fact that our knowledge of the mechanism of their action remains fragmentary.

The hallucinogens are principally of plant origin, although whole series of synthetic chemicals have also been developed. In man, they are capable of producing marked changes in perception, emotion, ego function, and thought. They are differentiated from the deliriants in that, ordinarily, little clouding of consciousness occurs. That some overlap exists is demonstrated by the anticholinergic psychotomimetics, which seem to occupy an intermediate position between the two categories of drugs.

The hallucinatory agents can be classified according to their chemical structure. Only the more common ones will be dealt with here.

* The survey of the literature pertaining to this review was concluded in January, 1968.

† Preparation of this review was supported in part by the Los Angeles Medical Research Foundation.

II. Substituted Indolealkylamines

A. D-*Lysergic Acid Diethylamide* (*LSD*)

Synthesized from lysergic acid in the fungus ergot (*Claviceps purpurea*), a series of lysergic acid compounds are known, some of which are hallucinogenic, for example, D,L-acetyl LSD (ALD) and D,L-methyl LSD (MLD).

This review will focus on LSD since it has been the hallucinogen most extensively investigated, and since its mechanisms of action seem to be similar to the other indole and phenylalkylamines.

In 1938 Hofmann synthesized D-lysergic acid diethylamide tartarate, and in 1943 he accidentally discovered its psychotomimetic effects. The compound was prepared in the hope that it might be an analeptic because of the close structural relationship between nikethamide and the D ring of LSD. Of all the stereoisomers and the substitutions in the ring and amide system that have been prepared, LSD remains the most potent from a psychotogenic point of reference. L-LSD and D-iso-LSD have no psychic activity whatsoever.

1. Metabolism

LSD is readily absorbed from the gastrointestinal tract and diffuses into all tissues. The brain does not achieve higher concentrations than other organs. Approximately 1% of the total dose is found in the central nervous system. It is detectable in the cerebrospinal fluid shortly after its appearance in the central nervous system. Very small amounts, less than 3 ng/ml, in the brain produce intense psychic changes. Earlier radioactive studies in mice demonstrated that labeled LSD disappeared from the brain and blood within an hour. The half-life for mice was less than ten minutes. This led to a theory that it acted as a trigger for a sequence of aberrant neurochemical reactions. The mouse data cannot be extrapolated to human excretion of the substance because of its rapid excretion in that animal. In monkeys LSD has a half-life of 100 minutes and in cats, 130 minutes. Recent spectrophotofluorometric measurements on samples of human plasma resulted in a calculated half-life of 175 minutes. One-half hour after the intravenous injection of 2 μg/kg, plasma levels reach 7 ng/ml. For the next 8 hours plasma levels decline, paralleling the improvement in performance test scores. At the end of this time 2 ng/ml were still detectable in the plasma. It seems unnecessary to invoke the trigger mechanism to explain the action of LSD in view of the recent reports. Bromine-labeled (Brom-LSD, BOL), a nonhallucinatory analog, accumulates in the liver and lower abdomen, and over 90% is eventually excreted by the kidneys over many days. LSD was also concentrated in the liver and intestines in mouse scan studies.

Depending on the dosage and the sensitivity of the individual, oral administration will produce effects in 20–80 minutes. The intramuscular route results in a delay in the onset of symptoms of about ten minutes. Intravenous administration decreases the delay to a few minutes, and intraspinal injection is followed by an almost instantaneous effect. As little as 0.3 μg/kg of LSD is subjectively detectable in man, and 1–12 μg/kg evoke a maximally intense depersonalization and derealization experience lasting 24 hours or more. Even higher individual doses have been claimed (5000–10,000 μg), but this was questionable material obtained from black-market sources. Tolerance is also lost within days. Tolerance is phasic with partial escape varying according to the species. In goats the rhythm seems to be about 4 days, in man about 9 days. No withdrawal syndrome following abrupt discontinuance of the drug has been described.

Cross tolerance between LSD and its hallucinogenic congeners, mescaline, psilocin, and bufotenine has been demonstrated. BOL, which has no psychotomimetic activity, blocks the LSD state if administered in sufficient amounts prior to LSD ingestion. The anticholinergic hallucinogens, Ditran, for example, do not show a cross tolerance to LSD, indicating that they may act over different pathways. The LSD state can be aborted by parenteral barbiturates or chlorpromazine. Succinate, nicotinic acid, and glucose have also been reported to reverse the LSD condition. Amphetamines and other stimulants will prolong or intensify the effect of the drug.

Schizophrenic patients are generally less reponsive to LSD than normal subjects. Whether this represents an enhanced capacity to metabolize the drug, or whether it is a part of the schizophrenic's overall refractory state to most chemicals, is unknown.

The rabbit is sensitive to LSD, the lethal dose for 50% of a population (LD_{50}) being 0.3 mg/kg intravenously. It also develops tolerance to the drug; the rat does not. For the rat and mouse the LD_{50} is 16 and 46 mg/kg, respectively. Rat brains examined after the animals had received 1 mg/kg showed no changes in acute experiments. When 25 mg/kg was given, the cerebral cortical neurons revealed vacuolization of nuclei, depletion and fragmentation of Nissl substance, rarefaction, and degeneration.

A dose of 297 mg (0.1 mg/kg) was placed intramuscularly into a male elephant. This was done to determine whether the LSD effects would resemble musth, a periodic form of deranged behavior, which is accompanied by temporal gland secretion. The animal died within 2 hours from laryngospasm and status epilepticus. Hoffer estimated an LD_{50} for man at 14 mg. A student survived an accidental dose of 10 mg or more without permanent ill effects. He was amnesic and hallucinated for 7 hours after which he quickly recovered.

Recent cytogenetic investigations *in vitro* and *in vivo* with human white blood cells have demonstrated a significant increase in chromosomal fragmentations, deletions, and exchanges. These alterations in chromosomal structure resemble those due to certain viruses. prolonged irradiation, and the use of antineoplastic chemicals. The percentages of chromatid or isochromatid breaks, exchange figures, and acentric fragments are 3 times that found in nondrug controls. Apparently, transplacental diffusion of LSD is possible since the offspring of mothers who had taken the drug during pregnancy demonstrated increased chromosomal changes. Although a few congenital malformations in infants from LSD-using parents are known, the possible phenotypic damage remains obscure. In one instance aplasia of one fibula with associated malformations resulted in a shortened and deformed extremity. The mother had taken LSD during the seventh week of pregnancy, the period when the extremity structures are being formed. In pregnant rats given LSD in amounts comparable to current human usage, miscarriages and the runting of some litters were seen. An attempt to duplicate these findings in a second study was unsuccessful.

A number of important questions remain to be answered. How long do the chromosomal anomalies persist? Are the sperm and egg cells affected? Do these alterations indicate that brain cell changes may be involved? What is the dose-effect relationship? What may be the long-term effects upon the heavy user of LSD alone or in combination with other drugs? Until some of these answers have been obtained, extreme prudence in the use of LSD seems warranted.

Axelrod found that guinea pig liver microsomes produced 2-oxy-LSD, an inactive metabolite. Szara extracted a 13-hydroxy-LSD as well as its glucuronides from rat liver microsomes.

A differential concentration within the brain of the squirrel monkey was noted by Snyder and Revich. Twenty minutes after intravenous injection, the blood, the cerebral cortex, the cerebellum, the white matter, and the brain stem all had approximately similar concentrations. The extrapyramidal system and the thalamus had 1.5 times as much, the limbic system and the hypothalamus 2 to 3 times as much, the auditory and visual reflex areas 2 to 5 times as much, the posterior pituitary and pineal gland 5 to 7 times as much, and the anterior pituitary 10 times as much. These spectrofluorophotometric results were approximately comparable to those obtained with ^{14}C-labeled LSD using an autoradiographic technique. The findings of a variable concentration within the brain substance may help explain some of the psychological phenomena. Inhibition of synaptic transmission in the lateral geniculate body (a visual reflex area) is known to occur. In human subjects with subcortically implanted electrodes, LSD induced paroxysmal EEG activation of the limbic system, particularly the hippocampus. Subcortical visual centers are presumably involved in visual misperceptions, the limbic system with emotionality, the hypothalamus with the autonomic elaboration of emotion, and the anterior pituitary with the stress response.

The original proposal of Woolley and Shaw that the hallucinogenic action of LSD was due to its serotonin antagonism was refuted by the demonstration that the nonhallucinogenic BOL is an even stronger serotonin antagonist and crosses the blood-brain barrier. Marchbanks has pointed out that LSD enhances the binding of serotonin to neuronal macromolecules and that BOL does not. Freedman reported that LSD increases serotonin levels, and the increase was in the bound fraction. At the same time, brain levels of norepinephrine were decreased. The alterations coincide with the electroencephalographic, autonomic, and behavioral effects in the rat. After serotonin depletion with reserpine, LSD stimulated repletion.

Andén and his co-workers found that LSD decreases the rate of biogenic amine depletion at serotonin nerve terminals after serotonin inhibition occurred. Thus a decrease in the activity of central serotonin neurons can be postulated. LSD and serotonin appear to have similar CNS actions. LSD directly stimulates serotonin receptors. The direct stimulation of serotonin receptors may induce a negative feedback on presynaptic serotonin neurons, and it would result in a decrease in the neuronal activity. Nonhallucinogenic compounds of the lysergic acid series do not produce these effects. In large amounts LSD produces similar effects on norepinephrine levels and receptors.

LSD inhibits pseudocholinesterase, brain acetylcholinesterase, and amine oxidase. Pretreatment with an amine oxidase inhibitor which elevates biogenic amine levels will attenuate the LSD state in human beings. Elevating serotonin levels by administering the precursor, 5-hydroxytryptophan, will also reduce the effect of LSD. Pretreatment with reserpine which depletes the brain of biogenic amines, including serotonin, was found to intensify LSD symptomatology. Some of the LSD-serotonin interactions seem conflicting. It must be remembered that the relative concentration and the location of these substances determines the final response. The well-established antagonism between LSD and serotonin on uterine muscle can be changed to facilitation by lowering the concentration of LSD.

The impact of LSD on enzyme systems varies according to the dose, the animal, and the part of the brain to be measured. Siva Sankar and Bender state that LSD increases oxidation of glucose in cerebral homogenates but reduces it in cerebellar tissues. Glutamic acid decarboxylase is activated by LSD in the cerebrum but inhibited in the cerebellum. Citrate, succinate, and γ-aminobutyric acid oxidation are increased in both brain fractions. Glycogen phosphorylase levels of rat brain treated with LSD and other hallucinogens tended to be depressed. BOL and tranquilizers increased the concentration of the enzyme.

2. Physiological and Behavioral Effects

LSD induces pupillary dilation, piloerection, salivation, lacrimation, tachycardia, and hyperglycemia in most species. Of these, mydriasis is most prominent and constant. Most animals will also manifest a rise in body temperature. The rabbit is particularly sensitive; doses of LSD as low as 0.5–1.0 μg/kg will produce hyperpyrexia. Hyperreflexia, restlessness, and some degree of peripheral vasoconstriction may develop. The head-shaking movements of mice can persist for many weeks after a single LSD exposure. Rats ordinarily demonstrate head shaking, motor hyperactivity, crawling movements, and, later, inactivity. Rats trained in rope climbing have a dose-related prolongation of the time required to accomplish the task. Monkeys manifest ataxia, spatial disorientation, and tameness. Sympathomimetic effects predominate in the LSD-treated animal.

Much evidence of nonspecific stress can be encountered in the LSD-treated organism. Leukocytosis, eosinopenia, slight elevation of 17-ketosteroids, and a moderate elevation of 17-hydroxycorticoids have been recorded. It is well confirmed that urinary phosphate excretion is diminished. Plasma free fatty acids are increased. This rather good evidence that adrenal cortical function is increased is accompanied by suggestive evidence of diminished thyroid and gonadal activity.

In man the most obvious autonomic effect is dilation of the pupils up to 6 mm. They react weakly to light. Hyperreflexia, nausea, rarely vomiting, tremor, gooseflesh, numbness, muscular weakness, and hyperthermia may be detected. In ordinary amounts, vasoconstriction and uterine contraction is minimal. There is no evident change in cerebral blood flow, cerebrovascular resistance or cerebral oxygen, and glucose utilization.

Beernink confirmed the increase in rhythmical activity of the liver fluke in an LSD solution. In addition, he demonstrated a good correlation between hallucinogenic activity and liver fluke motility in a series of LSD derivatives. Under LSD, the green sunfish is more aggressive than in the control state. Siamese fighting fish assume a nose up, tail down position in solutions of LSD. Goats given LSD showed stereotyped, fixed walking patterns.

In an electrographic study of LSD and nine of its analogs in rabbits, sustained arousal patterns were obtained in those that had an hallucinogenic effect. The locus of EEG action for LSD, as demonstrated by transections, was the lower brain stem level. This site corresponds to the reticular formation.

Transcallosal synaptic inhibition by LSD and other psychotogens has been demonstrated in cats, dogs, and monkeys by Marrazzi. He also noted an inhibition release effect on visual tract nerves. Pretreatment with chlorpromazine abolished the inhibition. The depression of photic-evoked responses has been demonstrated in rats.

LSD generally interfered with sleep in cats and reduced the EEG signs of dreaming sleep. On the days following drug administration, a marked increase in dream sleep occurred. In man, small amounts of LSD produced an increase of dreaming sleep, especially during the first dream periods of the sleep cycle. Using a dose of 300 μg, Green also found an increase in dream time during the two nights following LSD after an initial delay in the onset of dreaming.

During the LSD state, the surface EEG in human beings is diminished in amplitude and is of the low voltage, fast type. Desynchrony is noted. Energy content decreases, as does variability. Alpha rhythm tends to disappear. The rhythmic afterdischarge of photic-evoked potentials is also lost. The quantified EEG's of schizophrenics and of controls given LSD both show a state of sustained excitation. Whereas LSD decreases the variability of the record in normal subjects, it increases the variability of schizophrenic tracings. These are known to be less variable under nondrug conditions. Quiescent schizophrenics with implanted deep electrodes sustained both an exacerbation of their psychosis and paroxysmal hippocampal, amygdaloid, and septal activity under LSD.

LSD and other hallucinogens given to trained, hungry rats blocked the conditioned response to food but not to shock. This finding is opposite to the approach-avoidance behavior in animals given antipsychotic agents. In a similarly designed situation, varying the dose of LSD revealed that small doses increased bar pressing for food, while large amounts decreased it. Bar pressing to avoid shock was decreased at the lowest dosages but increased in higher doses. In general, the experimental animal under a psychotogen will require a longer time to extinguish a conditioned reflex.

A partial cycloplegia is produced by average amounts of LSD. This may be a function of the sympathetic dominance. The ciliary muscles and iris were found to contain much higher than average concentrations of the drug. When given to blind subjects, the congenitally blind did not report color or formed visual hallucinatory experiences. Of 20 subjects who once had sight, 13 reported visual phenomena under the drug. Hallucinatory, auditory, tactile, and gustatory experiences were reported more frequently in this group than in other studies when nonblind subjects were tested. The physiologic micronystagmus is increased by most hallucinogens. The 2/sec saccadic flicks are increased more than fivefold.

All types of reaction time were prolonged by 125 μg given normal subjects. Visual, auditory, and heat thresholds were elevated. Two-point discrimination was performed more poorly under the LSD conditions.

Kast found that 100 μg of LSD gave more prolonged and complete relief of pain than 100 mg of meperidine or 2 mg of hydromorphone in terminal cancer patients. Holliday, using D-lysergic acid morpholide, found that her subjects could tolerate more intense heat focused on the forehead than they could under placebo conditions.

Performance tests are almost invariably impaired under LSD. Psychomotor skills, learning, perceptual function, verbal fluency, abstracting capacity, and measures of intelligence are routinely worsened. Whether these results are due to an attenuation of attention and motivation, or whether the sensory-cognitive alterations interfere with performance is not clear. It is likely that the impairment involves a variety of contributing factors.

3. Psychic and Psychotherapeutic Effects

The psychological effects in man are numerous and diverse. They depend not only upon the dose and the personality of the subject but upon many other variables as well. All psychotropic drugs vary in their activity according to nonspecific factors, but the psychotomimetics are particularly influenced by them. The setting in which LSD is given has a potent influence. It is for this reason that the earlier investigators invariably elicited a "model psychosis." The subject was brought into a strange laboratory setting where unexplained procedures were periodically performed. Furthermore, the investigators expected him to become psychotic. This points up a second variable, the set, or expectation of the observer and of the subject. If the drug is taken with the implied or explicit idea that a transcendental state will ensue, a fair likelihood exists that it will. The LSD state is an hypersuggestible one, the rational, critical function of the ego is set aside and one's own "programming" or the investigator's can influence the nature of the response enormously. That LSD and mescaline in average amounts enhance primary suggestibility comparable to the induction of hypnosis has been demonstrated by Sjöberg and Hollister. These authors also confirmed the increase in trance phenomena while the drugs were acting. It is on the basis of increased susceptibility to environmental cues that setting and set effects can be explained.

The perceptual alterations are most notable. The first subjective effect may be a colorful mobile display of patterns slanting past one's closed eyes. Later, distinct and complex forms may be fantasied. With eyes open, the color of objects becomes more intense and saturated. The afterimage is noticeably prolonged. Flat surfaces assume a depth, fixed objects undulate and flow. Illusions are common, e.g., a spot on a wall may be mistaken for a face. Pseudo-hallucinations, images seen for which no external cue is evident, are apprehended as "not really there" by the subject. True hallucinations are infrequent at ordinary dosages. These are images projected onto the environment which are actually believed to be real. Auditory hallucinations are rare, however, the amplification of background noise is often described, and some subjects seem to have hyperacusis. Touch may be more sensitive, and alterations of taste and odor are known, but these are minimal in comparison to the visual changes. Synesthesia, the overflow from one sense modality to another, is a common manifestation of the state. Colors are heard, or music becomes palpable. A crossing over of what is emotionally felt with what is perceived or thought can be detected so that a fusion of percept, concept, and affect becomes apparent. Subjective time is seriously altered. Internal time may "stand still." Subjects are almost invariably astounded at how slowly clock time passes.

The emotional responses vary markedly both during any single session, between a series of exposures in the same individual, and between individuals. Initial apprehension is not uncommon, and sustained anxiety may pervade the period of LSD activity. Infrequently, the tension may become maximal and culminate in panic. What is more common is an euphoric feeling tone. Elation, bliss, and ecstasy have been described. The mood may be labile, shifting from depression to gaiety and back again. At times, prolonged laughter or tears seem inappropriate to the situation. Rarely, a catatonic withdrawal or a paranoid rage reaction will be encountered.

The thinking process is substantially altered under the influence of psychotomimetic drugs. A loosening of associations, unusual in content, is regularly noted. Thought sequences are nonlogical, fantasy-laden, and eidetic. A few patients, instead of describing a flood of thoughts, report an absence of thought. Intelligence testing is worsened, but this may be due to inattention to the task or preoccupation with the fast-moving sensory and mental alterations. Attempts to communicate may be accompanied by blocking. Orientation is ordinarily not impaired, but judgment is by no means dependable. Paranoid grandiosity or ideas of persecution might be elicited.

Changes of ego function may be imperceptible at the lowest dosages or completely disrupted in the higher ranges. At first, the usual ego defense mechanisms come into play to cope with the peculiar mental changes. Eventually, they may be demolished. The ego boundaries may dissolve partially or completely to the point that dedifferentiation of the self from the outer world, and separation of internal experience from sensory input, is lost. The body image is also distorted with parts of the body becoming larger or smaller or finally disappearing. Depersonalization of all degrees has been described, and derealization of some sort is invariable. One's evaluation and concept of onself undergoes considerable alterations, usually in the direction of self-enhancement, but the opposite may occur. Drives are ordinarily diminished.

Behavioral patterns are often more predictable than the other facets of human functioning. Under a moderate or large amount of a psychotomimetic agent, the subject is inclined to be passive, quiet, sitting or lying with closed eyes, attempting to cope with or integrate the unusual state. He may withdraw completely or respond minimally. Task orientation is grossly impaired. Of course, other behavior is possible. Attempts to control the state by talking about it incessantly are known. Hostile acting out has occurred in instances where a release of conscious controls unleashes underlying strong aggressive impulses. Disrobing is mentioned from time to time. When panic or a disorganizing loss of insight into the situation develops, the subsequent behavior reflects these affects.

The psychedelic state, in contrast to the psychotomimetic state, may be considered equivalent to a chemically induced transcendental event. The neurophysiological implications of a psychic condition similar to those achieved only through strenuous spiritual exercises, prolonged meditation, or spontaneously, are intriguing. At any rate, such phenomena are far from uncommon and form the basis of the use of these drugs within the context of religious ceremonies. The peyote cactus, for example, is a central item in the rituals of the Native American Church of the American Indian.

Leuner, Sandison, and other psychiatrists in Europe use LSD in multiple small doses (50–200 μg) as an adjunct to conventional psychotherapy. This is called psycholytic psychotherapy. It depends upon the disinhibiting effects of the drug on the emotions producing abreaction, upon impaired ego defenses producing lessened resistance to recall of repressed memories, and upon primary process thinking producing hallucinatory images which may have symbolic value for interpretation. The drug sessions are interspersed with nondrug interviews to deal with the material retrieved under LSD.

Psychedelic psychotherapy has been particularly used in North America, where Hoffer and Osmond and others employed one or a few high-dose (300–1000 μg) experiences primarily in the treatment of chronic alcoholics. The rationale is the induction of a psychological death-rebirth experience, allowing the patient a new start with a new value system and without the burden of the old guilt and self-hate. In addition, the loss of ego boundaries permits the alienated patient a transcendental feeling of belonging.

Attempts to employ LSD in psychotherapy ordinarily exclude psychotics, except for autistic children. Recently, confirmatory evidence of an increase in visual contacts and positive affects by autistic children under the drug as compared to a placebo was presented. Its value in infantile autism may depend more on its central sympathetic action than on its psychedelic effects. Bender believes that methysergide is as active as LSD in autism and the former agent has negligible psychedelic activity.

4. Complications

Complications during the controlled use of LSD remain infrequent. In the past 4 years increasing nonmedical use has produced increasing numbers of adverse reactions. A classification of the side effects that have been encountered is available. Death directly caused by the toxicity of LSD is unknown. Neurological sequelae are rare; isolated grand mal type convulsions have been reported.

The psychiatric complications are more frequent, although their incidence remains unknown. Chronic anxiety and depressive states, somatization reactions, and acute panic or paranoid reactions have all been seen. Recurrences of an LSD-like state days to months after the drug has been taken are well known. Suicide or accidental deaths are more apt to occur than homicide. The psychotic complications consist of schizophrenic decompensations or a prolonged hallucinosis. Quick recovery may ensue, but some patients have required hospitalization for years. No conclusive reports of permanent damage in human beings have yet appeared. Methods for the detection of LSD in body fluids are available.

B. *Lysergic Acid Amide and Isolysergic Acid Amide [Weak Hallucinogens Found in Species of the American Tropical Morning Glory (Ipomoea violacea, Rivea corymbosa)]*

The alkaloids of the seeds of *ololiuqui,* at least four species of the wild American morning glory, have been determined by Hofmann, who had also previously succeeded in synthesizing LSD, psilocybin, and psilocin. They proved to be ergot alkaloids, a surprising finding since these chemical structures had only been found in the lower fungi of the genus *Claviceps.* Now they were encountered in a higher plant of the *Convolvulaceae* family. That fungi contamination is not the source of the hallucinogenic material has been confirmed. D-Lysergic acid amide and D-isolysergic acid amide are the more active psychotomimetic ingredients. Elymoclavine, chanoclavine, lysergol, and ergometrine have been extracted. Their pharmacological properties have not yet been completely clarified. In mice, the alkaloidal fraction induces ataxia, ptosis, piloerection, and hypersensitivity to stimuli. Convulsions and respiratory arrest occur at lethal doses.

Human subjects report a definite sedative quality to morning glory seed intoxication not noted with LSD. D-Lysergic acid amide has previously been found to induce a dreamy, tired, somewhat clouded state. Nausea and vomiting are not uncommon. The potency of the seeds varies from batch to batch, even when *Ipomoea violacea* and *Rivea corymbosa* have been positively identified. Isbell and Gorodetzky reported that former narcotic addicts did not respond to the alkaloidal fraction of *ololiuqui* as they did to LSD. Other observers indicate that when enough seeds are pulverized and taken, the two states are similar. Hoffer suspects that ergotism may follow substantial morning glory seed ingestion.

C. *Dimethyltryptamine (DMT) (Found in Cohoba Snuff from the Seeds of Piptadenia peregrina)*

D. *Diethyltryptamine (DET) (Synthetic)*

E. *Hydroxydimethyltryptamine (May Be the Active Form of DMT in Vivo)*

A whole series of alkylated tryptamines exist which are known to be hallucinogenic. In addition to α-methyltryptamine, DMT, DET, and dipropyltryptamine, their 6-hydroxylation products are even more active than the parent compounds.

Szara has investigated this group. He points out that the 6-hydroxylated members can be produced in rat liver microsomes, and they may account for the perceptual and emotional changes. Human beings convert DMT into its 6-hydroxylated congener, and if a fluorine atom is placed on the 6-position, 6-hydroxylation is prevented. Under this condition, only the autonomic manifestations of DMT are evident, making it useful as an active placebo. Amine oxidation, not 6-hydroxylation, is the major metabolic pathway in man. Most of the tryptamine is converted to 3-indoleacetic acid and most of the serotonin to 5-hydroxyindole acetic acid.

Pretreatment with the monoamine oxidase inhibitor, iproniazid, reduces the effects of DMT. This is analogous to similar work cited with LSD. Apparently, the increase in brain serotonin levels prevents DMT activity. Pretreatment with the strong serotonin antagonist, the nonhallucinogenic 1-methyl-D-lysergic acid butanolamide (UML), accentuates the DMT effect. DMT is inactive by mouth; oral doses of 350 mg are without effect. It must be injected, sniffed, or smoked to produce its psychotomimetic effect. Intramuscular injections of 50 mg will induce autonomic and hallucinogenic symptoms.

F. *Bufotenine* (*Dimethyl-5-hydroxytryptamine*) [*Found in Cohoba Snuff, the Skin and Parotid Gland of the Toad* (Bufo marinus), *and in Small Amounts in the Fly Agaric Mushroom* (Amanita muscarina)]

The *N*-dimethylated analog of serotonin is bufotenine. It provokes marked autonomic activity, including a cyanotic flush, nystagmus, mydriasis, tachycardia, and hypertension. This is a remarkably uncomfortable drug to take. Very small amounts have been identified in human urine. Fisher and Heller report its presence in acute schizophrenics. Fewer chronic schizophrenics excreted it, and none of the controls did. When chronic schizophrenics were given an amine oxidase inhibitor, bufotenine was found in their urine, and their psychosis was often reactivated.

G. *Psilocybin* (*dimethyl-4-phosphoryltrytamine*) (*Found in* Psilocybe mexicana *Heim and Related Mushrooms*)

H. *Psilocin* (*dimethyl-4-hyroxytryptamine*) (*Found in* Psilocybe mexicana *Heim and other psilocybe species*)

Psilocybin and psilocin are the active alkaloids in the Mexican magic mushroom. The former is the 4-O-phosphorylated, and the latter is the 4-hydroxylated ester of DMT. The phosphoric acid radical is readily removed *in vivo* by alkaline phosphatase. Hollister estimates that LSD is approximately 130 times more potent than psilocybin. Psilocybin is 1.5 times weaker than psilocin. Apart from a shorter period of activity (2 to 6 hours), it is impossible for subjects acquainted with the LSD state to differentiate between the two drugs.

I. *Ibogaine* (*Found in the Bean and Root of* Tabernanthe iboga)

Ibogaine, one of many alkaloids in the Congolese plant, is a mind-altering agent with a number of unpleasant autonomic effects. In addition to visions, very excited states and epileptic seizures have been described. Unconsciousness has occurred as part of the native ritual taking of the crude drug. It is called "ordeal bean" by them, an evidence of the strenous nature of the experience.

J. Harmine (One of the Harmala Alkaloids from Banisteriopsis caapi)

The South American plant variously called caapi, yagé, and ayahuasca is a vine which Amazonian natives employ as an intoxicating drink. From it a series of indole alkaloids can be extracted. Some significance is attached to the close chemical relationship between harmine and harmaline, on one hand, and, on the other, melatonin and 6-methoxytetrahydroharman, which have been isolated from the pineal gland.

Somatic sensations are more likely to occur with harmine ingestion than with a drug like LSD. These consist of numbness, pressure sensations in the chest or head, and nausea or vomiting. Imagery is particularly vivid under caapi, and it, like iboga, is used by shamans as a divinatory drug.

II. Substituted Phenylalkylamines

A. Mescaline (3,4,5-Trimethoxyphenylethylamine)

Mescaline, one of the dozen-and-a-half alkaloids in the peyote cactus, was the first of the hallucinogenic alkaloids to be extracted and synthesized. It has already gone through one cycle of scientific, psychotherapeutic, and popular interest. Its close chemical similarity to norepinephrine has made it a subject of interest to those who assume an aberrant catecholamine metabolism hypothesis of psychosis.

The psychotomimetic equivalent dose of mescaline is 4000 times larger than that of LSD. Neff studied the distribution of mescaline in cat brains using ^{14}C-labeled material given intravenously. The cortical and subcortical gray matter showed relatively high concentrations. The biological half-life was 90–120 minutes. Maximum concentrations in the brain were achieved in 30–120 minutes, corresponding to the period of maximal intoxication. The only radioactive products identified were mescaline itself and 3,4,5-trimethoxyphenylacetic acid (TMPA), an inert metabolite. They were both detectable in brain tissue, cerebrospinal fluid, plasma, and urine.

Speck obtained an LD_{50} of 370 mg/kg for rats when mescaline was given intraperitoneally. Death was preceded by flexor convulsions and respiratory arrest. The EEG records showed fast wave, low voltage activity. Bradycardia at the intermediate dose ranges was evident. Mescaline prevented barbiturate hypnosis. The outstanding pathologic finding when 50 mg/kg of mescaline was injected into rats for a month was adrenal cortical hyperplasia.

In man, Charalampous found a biologic half-life of 6 hours. In the first 24 hours, 87% of the orally administered radioactive mescaline was excreted in urine; in 48 hours, a 92% recovery was obtained. Mescaline and TMPA were the principal metabolites found. Measurable quantities remained in the brain for $9\frac{1}{2}$ hours.

B. STP (2,5-Dimethoxy-4-methylamphetamine)

STP (also DOM) is 2,5-dimethoxy-4-methylamphetamine. It is approximately equipotent to psilocybin. The symptoms produced duplicate those of other phenylalkylamines and indolealkylamines which are hallucinogens. Animal work is available; the human study by Snyder *et al.* indicates that systolic hypertension, hyperpyrexia, pupillary dilation, and an increase in blood free fatty acids occur. About 20% of an ingested dose will appear in the urine unchanged, with peak excretion evident between 3–6 hours afterwards.

STP is apparently the first synthetic hallucinogen which has gone directly from the animal pharmacology laboratory to the street user. In so doing, larger than ordinary amounts have been swallowed, and the period of drug activity has been claimed to be 24–48 hours. This is undoubtedly a high-dose effect. The impression that an increased number of adverse effects are caused by STP may also be due to the inordinately high doses taken.

III. Miscellaneous

A. Tetrahydrocannabinol

The resin from the flowering tops of the female Indian hemp plant has been used in Asia for over 5000 years. The pharmacology of hashish was described in 3000 B.C. by Shen Nung. Although opium eventually displaced it in China, it later became a part of Indian religious and secular life. It has variously been used as an aid to meditation (by the Yogins), as a thought-control agent (by the Assassins), and as a disinhibiting drug (by the Thugs). Its modern use is predominantly as an euphoriant and social relaxant. The drug may be smoked, chewed, or drunk as a beverage.

Marihuana has about a sixth the potency of hashish and consists of the leaves and tops of the plant. Tetrahydrocannabinol has been extracted, and a large number of analogs have been synthesized. They are unusual structurally in that they do not contain a nitrogen atom. Marihuana is an hallucinogen rather than a narcotic, as it is classified legally. Many of the descriptions of low dosage LSD experiences resemble those of marihuana narrations.

In animals ataxia and tremors, an intensification of the scratch reflex and corneal areflexia are noted on administration of the oil, which contains the active ingredients of cannabis.

The LD_{50} in humans is unknown. Very few deaths directly due to cannabis toxicity are recorded. Tachycardia, tremor, and conjunctivitis are the more frequent physical signs. Hyperglycemia, dryness of the mouth, and urinary frequency have been mentioned. If the preparation is potent, the pupils are dilated.

Within minutes of inhaling a cigarette, a feeling of release of tensions and inhibitions, a dreamy "high," and of passivity occurs. Synesthesias, alterations of time sense, and changes in auditory and visual perceptions are described. The duration of the state does not exceed 4 hours, but may be prolonged by smoking additional "reefers." Only a partial tolerance develops, and this is rapidly lost. The major differences from the symptoms produced by other psychotomimetics are the drowsiness, which may culminate in sleep, and the craving for sweets or other food that often accompanies indulgence in marihuana. In the neophyte user hypoglycemia occurs to account for the hunger. The chronic user loses this symptom.

In this country, the usage of marihuana (also called grass, weed, and pot) has increased in recent years among underprivileged and intellectual groups. An occasional psychotic reaction, particularly in the unstable personality, has been seen. Chopra described both acute and chronic toxic psychosis. Two cases of acute panic and disorganization of thought lasting several weeks after smoking one or two cigarettes are the basis of a recent report. These patients had been seen by a physician prior to their marihuana-smoking episode and were neither psychotic nor seriously disturbed. Whether escalation to the hard narcotics evolves from marihuana smoking is doubtful. Crimes of violence following marihuana usage are in police files. This is not surprising since it has a disinhibiting effect. One undesirable use of marihuana consists of its consumption by juveniles, who employ it to evade or escape all frustrating or anxiety-provoking experiences.

A bibliography of 1860 references on all aspects of cannabis was issued in 1965 by the United Nations Economic and Social Council. Recent pharmacologic research with this drug in the United States has been negligible.

B. *Ditran and Its Analogs*

A number of 3-*N*-substituted piperidyl benzilates are psychotomimetic. JB-329 (Ditran) is a combination of two isomers: *N*-ethyl-2-pyrrolidylmethylphenylcyclopentyl glycolate and *N*-ethyl-3-piperidylphenylcyclopentyl glycolate. Ditran and the rest of the series are central anticholinergics, but according to Abood, their cholinergic blocking and hallucinatory properties do not correlate well. However, Giarman and Pepeu found a good relationship between brain acetylcholine levels following Ditran and the behavioral changes in rats. Ditran does not exert an effect on the chromatophores of minnows, it does not produce hyperthermia in rabbits, nor does it reverse reserpine-induced depressions. These are in contrast to the properties of LSD and psilocybin.

Ditran is rapidly excreted via the kidneys. The brain does not preferentially concentrate the drug, only the amount expected by the brain weight/body weight rates is found in the central nervous system. Within the brain itself, the caudate nucleus and the hypothalamus had the highest concentrations. Most of the drug was bound to mitochondria.

Tetrahydroaminocrine, an anticholinesterase, is presumably antidotal to the central and peripheral effects of Ditran. This provides additional support for the hypothesis that its hallucinogenic properties are the result of central cholinolytic activity. Tetrahydroaminocrine is ineffective in blocking the symptoms of LSD, mescaline, or psilocybin intoxication. Tachyphylaxis to Ditran occurs rapidly. Cross tolerance between members of the Ditran series is likely, cross tolerance between Ditran and LSD, mescaline, or psilocybin does not exist.

The general impression is that Ditran induces a toxic psychosis resembling other anticholinergics like atropine and scopolamine.

The oral dosage range is from 2–20 mg in adult males. The autonomic effects of Ditran exceed those of LSD. Mydriasis, flushing, nausea, vomiting, dryness of the mouth, tachycardia, hyperreflexia, and ataxia are encountered. More mental confusion, speech disturbances, and disorientation are seen than with other hallucinogens. Blocking, amnesias, thought disorganization, and feelings of strangeness are often mentioned. All contact with reality and insight into the cause of the mental disruptions may be lost. Alcoholics have likened it to a prior bout of delirium tremens. Ditran has been used in the treatment of severe depressive states after electroconvulsive therapy and antidepressants have failed. Some success has been claimed. Its mechanism of action in the treatment of depression is unknown. One suggested use is in the estimation of individual delirium thresholds.

C. Sernyl and Its Analogs

Phencyclidine (Sernyl) is an anesthetic which induces psychotic-like symptoms in some patients. The disorganization of thought and derealization are greater than with LSD. A complete loss of insight into the situation can be observed. Some sedative action is described. Sernyl is supposed to mimic symptoms of early schizophrenia better than other hallucinogens. Lawes found that sensory deprivation lessened the effects of the drug. He made the assumption that it acted on the coding mechanism of sensory data input. When the sensory input is reduced, the miscoding process is not active. The chronic miscoding of information may be one of the mechanisms of the schizophrenic reaction.

V. Summary

It is interesting that some drugs which have either central sympathomimetic or anticholinergic activity are psychotomimetic. The close relationship between neurohumors like norepinephrine and serotonin, on one hand, and hallucinogens like mescaline and bufotenine, on the other, is fascinating. That the hallucinogens may compete with the normally occurring cerebral amines and block the transmission of inhibitor neuronal activity is a speculation which could explain many of their manifestations on a neurophysiological level. A good part of brain function consists of quenching much of the sensory input and inhibiting fantasy-type mentation. If the inhibitors are depressed, a state similar to the one called psychotomimetic could emerge. When more is understood about the mode of action of biogenic amines in the brain, the neuropharmacology of the psychotomimetics will become clearer.

For further reading and references see Appendices 1 and 2, and Chapter 3.

40

ALCOHOL*

Jack H. Mendelson

I. Introduction

As with such natural phenomena as fire and water, the discovery of alcoholic beverages cannot be assigned a date or a patent number, nor credited to any man or place. Only a few basic ingredients, sugar, water, yeast, and a mild degree of warmth, are required for alcohol production. Where these occur together, it is virtually impossible for alcohol *not* to be produced. According to paleontologists, all four were present on earth in Paleozoic times, at least 200 million years ago.

It seems obvious, therefore, that alcohol preceded man and that he began to use it long before the beginnings of written history. Since the earliest civilizations, alcoholic beverages have been viewed as nutritious foods, valuable medicines, and sacred liquids for religious ceremonies.

Alcoholic beverages were probably known in the New World long before Columbus. They were certainly brought to America in 1607 with the settling of the Virginia Colony. Twelve years later, their excessive use was such that

* Portions of this manuscript are derived from *Alcohol and Alcoholism,* published by the National Institute of Mental Health, National Center for Prevention and Control of Alcoholism.

a law decreed that any person found drunk for the first time was to be reproved privately by the minister; the second time publicly; the third time to "lye in halter" for 12 hours and pay a fine. Yet in the same year, the Virginia Assembly passed other legislation encouraging the production of wines and distilled spirits in the colony. As one modern historian has noted, "It was not the custom of drinking that was unacceptable in early Virginia, but drinking to excess."

In the Massachusetts Bay Colony, brewing came to rank next in importance to milling and baking. There, as in Virginia, occasional drunkenness was punished by whipping, fines, and confinement in the stocks, but, as Norbert Kelly writes, "The Puritans neither disdained nor prohibited the use of beverage alcohol. They were emphatic, however, in urging moderation in drinking."

The temperance movement, which sprang in considerable measure from the alcoholic excesses of the Industrial Revolution in England, was not long in coming to America. It began with the goal of temperance in its literal sense: *moderation.* At the peak of this early campaign, in the 1830's, temperance leaders, many of whom themselves drank beer and wine, maintained that the remedy for intemperance was abstinence from distilled spirits only.

However, the next decades brought a significant change. The meaning of temperance was gradually altered from moderation to total abstinence. All alcoholic beverages were attacked as unnecessary, harmful to health, and inherently poisonous. The demand arose for total prohibition.

This demand culminated in the United States in the passage of the 18th Amendment, which prohibited the manufacture and sale of all alcoholic beverages. Beginning in 1920, national prohibition lasted until 1933. Even now, nearly 35 years later, Prohibition remains a controversial subject. Its defenders claim that it brought substantial reduction in drinking, a decrease in drunkenness, and marked economic improvement to the country. Those who oppose the concept say that the experiment curbed only the moderate drinker and brought new and dangerous glamour to drinking and intoxication. They claim that it destroyed public respect for law-enforcement officers and bred the crime, violence, and general corruption that marked the bootlegging of illicit liquor.

Whatever the validity of these views, one fact seemed fairly well established by the end of the Prohibition era: many Americans liked to drink and would insist with considerable vehemence on their right to drink. There were no signs that their views had changed to any extent by the 1960's.

II. The Chemical Composition of Alcoholic Beverages

In all major alcoholic beverages (beers, table wines, cocktail or dessert wines, liqueurs or cordials, and distilled spirits) the chief ingredient is identical: ethyl alcohol, known also as ethanol or simply as alcohol. The concentration is usually about 4% by volume in beers, 12% in table wines, 20% in cocktail or dessert wines, 22–50% in liqueurs, and 40–50% (80 to 100 proof) in distilled spirits.

In addition, these beverages contain a variety of other chemical constituents. Some come from the original grains, grapes, or other fruits. Others are produced during the chemical processes of fermentation or during distillation or storage. Others may be added as flavoring or coloring.

Many of these nonalcoholic substances do more than contribute to color, flavor, aroma, or palatability. Some may have a direct effect on the body in themselves. Others apparently affect the rate at which alcohol is absorbed into the blood and the rate at which it is oxidized or metabolized in the tissues.

The critical factor in analyzing the effects of drinking is not the amount of alcohol which is drunk or which reaches the stomach, but the amount which enters the bloodstream and the speed at which it is metabolized. Only after the alcohol has been absorbed from the digestive tract into the blood and carried to the brain and other tissues do its most important physiological and psychological effects become apparent.

Numerous studies have demonstrated that beers, wines, and distilled spirits may vary markedly in the rate at which the alcohol they contain is absorbed into the blood. In general, the higher the concentration of the alcohol, the more rapid is its absorption, and the higher the concentration of nonalcoholic components, the slower its absorption.

The use of the term "congeners," at one time the name for the various nonethyl alcohol substances in alcoholic beverages, has often been misleading. Strictly defined, "congener" means "of the same kind" and thus would seem to apply only to such other alcohols as methyl, propyl, and isopropyl. However, such beverages as beers and wines also contain many organic acids, aldehydes, ketones, esters, minerals, salts, sugars, amino acids, and vitamins, which are clearly not alcohols but are nonetheless often called congeners.

The notion that all "congeners" are toxic, unhealthy, or otherwise undesirable is invalid since some of the nonalcoholic substances such as the salts, sugars, amino acids, and vitamins are nutritionally useful.

However, certain components of alcoholic beverages, especially some of the higher alcohols known as fusel oils, are relatively more toxic than ethyl alcohol. However, these usually occur in such low concentrations that they pose no clinically significant hazard.

Contrary to the popular belief that fusel oils occur primarily in new, raw, or unaged whiskey, and similar spirits, and cause most of the objectionable taste and aroma of such beverages, chemical analysis has shown that their concentration actually increases with aging.

III. Effects of Alcoholic Beverages on the Body

It was long believed that the actions of beer, wine, and distilled spirits on the body and the mind could be measured simply in terms of the quantity of alcohol consumed. As a result, much of the classical laboratory research in this field was conducted with pure alcohol. It has now been demonstrated that the situation is far more complex and that many of the findings made with plain alcohol solutions do not necessarily apply to alcoholic beverages.

Further, it has been shown that the effects produced by alcohol taken on an empty stomach are far different from those produced by the same amount of alcohol taken with food. The effects on a light drinker are usually different from those on a heavy drinker. Also, the effects produced by the same amount of alcohol may differ from individual to individual, and even in the same individual from month to month or from day to day.

A. *Absorption*

Under ordinary conditions, the alcohol in any beverage is absorbed relatively quickly, some through the stomach, but most through the small intestine, and then distributed generally throughout the body. The absorption can be markedly influenced by a number of factors.

1. Alcohol Concentration

The greater the alcohol concentration of the beverage, up to a maximum of about 40% (80 proof), the more rapidly the alcohol is absorbed and the higher are the resulting peak blood-alcohol concentrations. With identical amounts of alcohol swallowed, the highest blood-alcohol levels are produced by undiluted distilled spirits and the lowest by beers.

2. Other Chemicals in the Beverage

The greater the amount of nonalcoholic chemicals in the beverage, the more slowly the alcohol is absorbed. For this reason, too, the alcohol in distilled spirits, especially vodka and gin, is absorbed most rapidly, and that in table wines and beers most slowly.

3. Presence of Food in the Stomach

Eating with drinking has a notable effect on the absorption of alcohol, especially when alcohol is consumed in the form of distilled spirits or wine. When alcoholic beverages are taken with a substantial meal, peak blood-alcohol concentrations may be reduced by as much as 50%.

4. Speed of Drinking

The more rapidly the beverage is ingested, the higher will be the peak blood-alcohol concentrations. Thus, these levels are lower when the beverage is sipped or taken in divided amounts than when it is gulped or taken in a single dose.

5. Emptying Time of the Stomach

In a number of clinical conditions, such as that marked by the "dumping syndrome," the stomach empties more rapidly than is normal, and alcohol seems to be absorbed more quickly. Emptying time may be either slowed or speeded by fear, anger, stress, nausea, and the condition of the stomach tissues.

6. Body Weight

The greater the body weight of an individual, the lower will be the blood-alcohol concentration resulting from ingestion of a standard amount of alcohol.

The blood-alcohol level produced in a 180-pound man consuming 4 ounces of distilled spirits, for example, will generally be substantially lower than that occurring when the same amount is taken by a 130-pound man in the same length of time.

B. Metabolism

Once absorbed and distributed by the blood, the alcohol undergoes metabolic or oxidative changes. A major part of these processes occurs in the liver. The alcohol is changed first into acetaldehyde, but this rarely accumulates and is oxidized quickly to acetate.

Acetate, the same as that produced as an intermediate in carbohydrate metabolism, is condensed with coenzyme A and subsequently oxidized to carbon dioxide and water via the Krebs cycle. The total metabolic process yields approximately seven calories of energy for each gram of alcohol.

The rate of alcohol metabolism, like that of alcohol absorption, may be influenced by a number of factors. It has been shown that both alcoholic and nonalcoholic subjects maintained on good diets can moderately increase their rate of alcohol metabolism if they consume substantial amounts of ethanol over a long period of time. In general, it appears that the rate of alcohol metabolism may have a small influence on behavioral tolerance to alcohol, but that no significant differences in ability to oxidize alcohol differentiate the alcoholic from the nonalcoholic. It has been reported that normal drinkers can metabolize on the average approximately seven grams per hour of pure alcohol; eight grams in the form of whiskey; nine grams in the form of dessert wine; twelve grams in the form of table wines; and nine to eleven grams in the form of beer.

Considerable effort has been devoted to a search for some method which could effectively speed the rate of alcohol metabolism and thus be useful in the treatment of intoxication. Particular interest has been expressed in the administration of insulin, triiodothyronine, and other agents, although none has yet been found to make any clinically significant difference in the rate of alcohol metabolism.

C. Excretion

Although most of the ingested alcohol is metabolized, from 2 to 5% is excreted chemically unchanged, mostly in urine, breath, and sweat.

D. Stimulant or Depressant?

As with most other biologically active chemicals, the general physiological effects of alcohol depend on the amount or concentration in the specific cells, tissues, or organs affected. In most organisms, from the simplest bacteria to the most complex mammals, the very lowest concentrations of alcohol in the cells may stimulate the activity of those cells. In higher concentrations, it can depress functions, seriously injure cells, or even kill them.

It is impossible to state the specific amounts of alcoholic beverages that will give specific concentrations of alcohol in the blood. In general, it has been found that a 155-pound moderate drinker rapidly consuming 90-proof whiskey on an empty stomach will probably have a peak blood-alcohol level of 0.05% (0.05 gm per 100 cc of blood) with 3 oz, 0.10 with 6 oz, 0.20 with 12 oz, and 0.30 with 15 oz.

The blood-alcohol level may be slightly higher if the drink is gin or vodka rather than whiskey, or if the drinker weighs much less than 155 pounds. The level will be lower if the beverage is beer or wine, if the drinking is spaced over a prolonged period, if the drinker weighs more than 155 pounds, or if solid foods are eaten at the same time.

These levels have important legal implications. In most parts of the United States and in some countries of Europe, an individual is legally presumed to be sober and in condition to operate a motor vehicle with a blood-alcohol level of 0.05% or less, while one with a level of 0.15% or more is legally intoxicated or "under the influence."

E. Effects on the Brain

The most notable and dramatic effects of alcohol are those on behavior attributed to the action of alcohol on the brain. These are related not necessarily to the amount of alcohol drunk but to the concentration in the blood. Very low blood-alcohol levels usually produce mild sedation, relaxation, or tranquility. Slightly higher levels, at least in some people, may produce behavioral changes which seem to suggest stimulation of the brain: garrulousness, aggressiveness, and excessive activity, but which may result from depression of neural function which normally inhibits or restrains such behavior. At still higher levels, greater depression may occur, producing incoordination, confusion, disorientation, stupor, anesthesia, coma, or death.

Due to variations among individuals, it is not possible to give the exact concentrations at which these various changes occur. For most people, however, it is usually accepted that blood-alcohol levels up to 0.05% will induce some sedation or tranquility; 0.05–0.15% may produce lack of coordination; at about 0.15–0.20%, intoxication is obvious; 0.30 or 0.40% may produce unconsciousness; and levels of 0.50% or more may be fatal.

Earlier investigators proposed that these actions of alcohol were due to direct effects on relevant parts of the brain—first, the cerebral cortex, depressing critical faculties and reasoning powers, and producing the behavior pattern characteristic of drunkenness. With larger doses, it was believed, alcohol would directly depress successively lower levels of the central nervous system, eventually impairing vital centers in the medulla.

Newer observations, however, have led investigators to suggest that alcohol may act from the start upon regulatory structures which in turn modify the activity of the cortex and other parts of the central nervous system. Even under the influence of low blood-alcohol concentrations, it has been found, the reticular formation not only affects brain function but also serves as an intermediary in producing the sensation of warmth, flushing of the skin, relaxation of muscles, reduction of blood pressure in peripheral vessels, stimulation of gastric secretion, and increased peristalsis, all typical reactions to alcohol.

F. Effects on Skilled Performance

It has not been clearly established whether there is a threshold below which alcohol has no detectable influence on reflex responses, reaction time, and various complex skills. When the blood level reaches 0.03 or 0.04%, it is generally agreed that changes are evident.

At very low blood-alcohol levels, such simple reflex responses as the knee jerk seem to be more rapid. At levels above 0.03 or 0.04%, reflex responses, reaction-time responses, and performances in such activities as automobile driving and many kinds of athletics generally change for the worse. Significantly, as a driver's performance is impaired, his judgment often deteriorates, and he believes he is driving better. A British investigator has found that for motorists the added risk is small and probably not significant up to about 0.05%. Above that level, the risk rises sharply.

G. Effects on the Liver

Cirrhosis of the liver occurs about eight times as frequently among alcoholics as among nonalcoholics. It also occurs in nondrinkers. Its cause is the subject of continuing investigation. Cirrhosis has been reported to be caused not only by alcohol but also by filterable viruses, parasites, overexposure to carbon tetrachloride and other chemicals, excessive ingestion of sugar and soft drinks, and a deficiency of essential nutrients, especially proteins and certain vitamins.

Whether cirrhosis can be produced in man by excessive quantities of alcohol in combination with an adequate diet remains uncertain. Many investigators seem convinced that adequate nutrition provides an effective protection against cirrhosis. Some recent investigations, however, have shown that large amounts of alcohol may cause liver damage even in well-fed subjects.

H. Effects on Other Organs and Tissues

In moderate quantities, alcoholic beverages slightly increase the heart rate, slightly dilate blood vessels in arms, legs and skin, moderately lower blood pressure, stimulate appetite, increase the production of gastric secretion, and markedly stimulate urine output. Diuresis induced by ingestion of alcohol is due to suppression of synthesis or release of the antidiuretic hormone from the pituitary. Prolonged and heavy ingestion of alcoholic beverages does not produce a sustained diuresis. Diuresis appears to occur only when blood alcohol levels are rising during the initial phase of drinking.

It has been found that prolonged ingestion of large quantities of alcohol may produce derangements in a variety of organ systems. An increase in serum triglyceride levels and concomitant fatty infiltration of the liver may occur when large quantities of ethanol are consumed even though other dietary intake is adequate. Alcohol consumption produces a rise in serum uric acid levels, probably as a result of the change of hepatic NADH/NAD ratio on alcohol oxidation producing increased hepatic lactate formation and elevated blood lactate levels. High blood lactate, in turn, decreases urinary uric acid excretion, leading to a new variety of secondary hyperuricemia: alcoholic hyperuricemia.

The hyperlipemia observed in intoxicated alcoholics involves glycerides, cholesterol, and phospholipids, and, conversely, alcohol administration has been found to affect each of these major lipid fractions.

The pathogenesis of alcoholic fatty liver has not yet been fully clarified. Fatty livers can be produced by alcohol despite concomitant adequate dietary intake and before any decreased hepatic lipid release or excessive peripheral fat mobilization. This supports the concept that the alcoholic fatty liver may result from a direct effect of alcohol on lipid metabolism in the liver, resulting from a change in the ratio of NADH*/NAD† produced by the oxidation of alcohol in the liver.

Thus, both the effects of alcohol on uric acid and on lipid metabolism appear to result from the rise in NADH/NAD ratio in the cytoplasm of the hepatic cell.

Chronic ethanol ingestion has been shown to impair red blood cell formation, probably through induced derangement in folate absorption and metabolism. Acute ingestion of large quantities of ethanol associated with fasting may induce a state of hypoglycemia which may be severe enough to result in a comatose condition. Increased urinary excretion of magnesium has been reported following acute ethanol ingestion. However, increased excretion of magnesium does not appear to be sustained during chronic alcohol intake.

The lowered resistance of alcoholics to pneumonia and other infectious diseases has long been known, and is usually attributed to malnutrition. Recent research has shown that lowered resistance may also occur in well-nourished heavy drinkers, and appears to result from a direct interference with immunity mechanisms. With blood-alcohol levels of 0.15–0.25%, produced by intravenous administration of alcohol, the inhibition of white blood cell mobilization was found to be as intense as that found in states of severe shock.

A variety of intercurrent illness and deficiency diseases are frequently seen in individuals who consume large quantities of alcohol and have associated poor dietary and general health standards. Since these disorders are not directly induced by ethanol, they are not discussed in this chapter.

I. The Hangover

The hangover is a common, unpleasant, but rarely dangerous aftereffect of overindulgence occurring in the moderate drinker who occasionally takes too much, as well as in the excessive drinker after a prolonged drinking bout. The exact mechanism is unknown. The symptoms are usually most severe many hours after the peak of the drinking bout, when little or no alcohol can be detected in the body. Although hangover has been blamed on mixing drinks,

* Reduced nicotinamide adenine dinucleotide phosphate.

† Oxidized.

it can be produced by any alcoholic beverage alone, or by pure alcohol. There is inadequate evidence to support beliefs that it is caused by vitamin deficiencies, dehydration, fusel oils, or any other nonalcoholic components.

No satisfactory specific treatment for hangover is known, and there is no scientific evidence to support such popular remedies as coffee, raw egg, oysters, chili peppers, steak sauce, "alkalizers," vitamin preparations, or such drugs as barbiturates, thyroid, amphetamine, or insulin. For general treatment, most physicians usually prescribe aspirin, bed rest, and ingestion of solid foods as soon as possible.

J. Effects on Longevity

There is little evidence to demonstrate whether or not drinking has an appreciable effect on longevity. Frequently cited are the findings of Raymond Pearl, who reported the shortest life expectancy for heavy drinkers, a somewhat higher expectancy for abstainers, and the highest for moderate drinkers.

IV. The Causes of Alcoholism

A. Alcoholism: Definition

There is at present no formal definition of alcoholism or of an alcoholic which is universally or even widely accepted. Perhaps the one most widely considered as authoritative is that by Mark Keller of the Center of Alcohol Studies at Rutgers University, which follows closely that of the World Health Organization:

> Alcoholism is a chronic disease, or disorder of behavior, characterized by the repeated drinking of alcoholic beverages to an extent that exceeds customary dietary use or ordinary compliance with the social drinking customs of the community, and which interferes with the drinker's health, inter-personal relations or economic functioning.

Other important facets of alcoholism include the following: (1) There is loss of control of alcohol intake; the victim finds himself drinking when he intends not to drink, or drinking more than he has planned. (2) There is functional or structural damage: physiological, psychological, domestic, economic, or social. (3) Alcohol is used as a kind of universal therapy, as a psychopharmacological substance through which the problem drinker attempts to keep his life from disintegrating.

These definitions and others that differ from them only in minor degree do not specify any habitat of the alcoholic; they do not mention any factors of poverty or degradation; they do not mention any particular beverage; and they do not involve the quantity of beverage consumed in any given period. All refer in common to a destructive dependency on alcohol.

Modern concepts of alcoholism no longer attempt to set rigid boundaries between the moderate drinker and the alcoholic. Most professionals concerned now agree that there is no exact point applicable to everyone, below which one can accurately state: "This man is not an alcoholic and can continue to drink safely," nor above which one can state: "This man is now an alcoholic and can never control his drinking."

Over the past decades many different factors have been suggested as the cause of alcoholism. None has yet been accepted as the single causative agent.

B. Physiological Factors

Much effort has been exerted to find chemicals in specific beverages which might be responsible for alcohol addiction, or physiological, nutritional, metabolic or genetic defects which could explain excessive drinking. To date, these attempts have not succeeded. So far, it has been impossible to produce clear-cut alcohol addiction by any practical means in experimental animals.

Although alcoholism occurs frequently in the children of alcoholics, and thus may seem to have some hereditary basis, it also occurs in the children of devout abstainers. Anne Roe and others have observed that children of alcoholics can be protected if they are reared away from their parents. This has added to the belief that alcoholism is related more to environment than to genetic factors.

It has been suggested that alcoholism is caused by vitamin deficiencies or hormone imbalances. For example, much research by Dr. Roger Williams and his associates at the University of Texas has demonstrated that increased alcohol intake in experimental animals may be induced by such deficiencies, but his findings have not been found applicable in human beings. Most of the nutritional and hormonal deficiencies observed in far-advanced alcoholics appear to be results rather than causes of excessive drinking.

Allergy has been blamed for some cases of alcoholism, but there is no proof that alcoholics are generally allergic to alcohol itself or to other components of alcoholic beverages.

Although it is frequently said that alcoholics are unable to metabolize alcohol as rapidly as normal individuals, recent research has indicated that many actually metabolize it more rapidly when they are drinking heavily. Whether alcoholics metabolize alcohol in a different manner, perhaps through different enzymic processes, is not known.

It has been suggested periodically that addiction may be due to certain nonalcoholic components present in beer, wine, whiskey, rum, and brandy. Investigations have shown, however, that alcoholism also occurs in users of alcoholic beverages very low in these components, such as brännvin in Sweden and Finland, and vodka in Russia, Poland, and the United States.

Although alcoholism would be impossible without alcohol, alcohol can no more be considered its sole cause than marriage can be considered the sole cause of divorce, or the tubercle bacillus the sole cause of tuberculosis.

If addiction were caused entirely or even largely by overexposure to alcohol, the highest rates of alcoholism might logically be expected among groups with the highest per capita intake of alcohol. No such general relationship can be found. Although a high alcohol intake with a high rate of alcoholism has been reported in France, a high intake but a low rate of alcoholism has been reported in Italy and Greece, and a relatively low intake but a high alcoholism rate in the United States and Sweden.

Even though research to date has not indicated any chemical, physiological, or genetic factor as a cause of alcoholism, the possibility that such a physical factor exists cannot be ruled out, and further investigations are essential.

C. Psychological Factors

It is believed by some people that alcoholics are psychologically "different," that they possess a number of traits which in common make up the "alcoholic personality." There is, however, no agreement on the identity of these traits, nor on whether they may be the causes or the results of excessive drinking.

Psychologists and psychiatrists have described alcoholics as neurotic, maladjusted, unable to relate effectively to others, sexually and emotionally immature, isolated, dependent, unable to withstand frustration or tension, poorly integrated, and marked by deep feelings of sinfulness and unworthiness. Some have suggested that alcoholism is a disastrous attempt at the self-cure of an unseen inner conflict, and might well be called "suicide by inches."

Freud and others proposed that excessive drinking may represent attempts to repress unconscious homosexual instincts, and thus the "two-fisted, he-man" drinker is in reality drinking heavily to cover his underlying homosexual drives. Still others have attributed alcoholism to an unconscious need to dominate, or an attempt to escape from guilt feelings, or an inability to give or accept tenderness or love. Many researchers have accumulated data to demonstrate that alcoholics often come from broken or unhappy homes and underwent serious emotional deprivation during their childhood. However, many of these same qualities and experiences have been observed in men and women who are not alcoholics, but who may be suffering from bizarre phobias or a wide assortment of mental ailments from mild neuroses to severe psychoses, or who may even be leading reasonably normal lives.

If there is an actual "alcoholic personality," or a "prealcoholic personality," its specifications are poorly defined and often contradictory, and seem to apply broadly to all mental illness. Knowledge of the role played by psychological factors in alcoholism also awaits further research.

D. Sociological Factors

Although intensive research has so far failed to identify a simple chemical, physiological, or emotional cause of alcoholism, studies in a different area are now yielding new findings regarded by many scientists as particularly illuminating and potentially practical. Largely in the field of sociology, but also involving physiology, psychology, nutrition, cultural anthropology, and epidemiology, these new studies have been aimed at determining why alcoholism is widespread in some national and cultural groups but rare in others.

Those with the highest reported rates of alcoholism are classed as high-incidence groups. They include particularly the northern French, the Americans—especially the Irish-Americans (but not the Irish in Ireland), the Swedes, the Swiss, the Poles, and the northern Russians.

By contrast, the relatively low-incidence groups include the Italians, some

Chinese groups, Orthodox Jews, Greeks, Portuguese, Spaniards, and the southern French.

Differences among some of these cultural groups are reflected in the composition of groups of alcoholics studied in the United States. In one group analyzed in New York City, where available figures indicate that roughly 10% of the total population is Irish, 15% is Italian, and 25% is Jewish, 40% of the alcoholics were Irish, 1% Italian, and none Jewish. In an extensive California study, in an area with large proportions of Irish, Italian, and Jewish inhabitants, 21% of the alcoholics were Irish, 2% Italian, and 0.6% Jewish.

It does not seem likely that genetics can adequately explain these variations. Various investigators have reported that alcoholism is decreasing among Irish-Americans and Swedish-Americans but rising among second- and third-generation Italian-Americans. Some workers claim that the rate may be rising among Italians in Italy, especially in Rome and other major cities, apparently paralleling the rise in personal income. A slight but distinct rise has been noted among Jews, particularly as they tend to change from Orthodox to Reform attitudes.

Similar studies have shown that the low rates of alcoholism exhibited by some groups cannot all be attributed to abstinence. Most Mormons and Moslems, for example, do not drink because of religious beliefs, and their alcoholism rates are low. However, other groups, especially the Italians, Greeks, Chinese, and Jews, contain very high percentages of drinkers, and many of them use alcohol abundantly. For example, the per capita alcohol consumption in Italy is rated second only to that in France, but the rate of alcoholism among Italians is relatively low.

For further reading and references see Appendices 1 and 2, and Chapters 3 and 41.

41

PSYCHOTROPIC DRUGS IN ALCOHOLISM

Max Hayman and Joseph del Giudice

I. Introduction

Because of the many-faceted aspects of alcoholism, its treatment by drugs is essentially symptomatic, and ranges from efforts to relieve the toxic and debilitating effects of periods of excess ethanol ingestion to treatment of the psychological dependence in the abstinent patient. Drug therapy also attempts to relieve anxiety and depression and represents a continual search for something less harmful which can substitute for the psychic pain relieving and pleasurable effects of the alcohol itself.

The expectation that a single drug will remedy all aspects of this pervasive problem is rather futile, and such a concept leads to much of the disappointment in the use of psychotropic drugs in the treatment of alcoholism. It is more a belief in magic, unfortunately possessed not solely by the patient, but often by physicians and researchers as well.

The use of psychotropic drugs must be regarded as an *adjunct* to other therapies in the long-range treatment plans, and at best offers some help in rehabilitation. With the abstinent alcoholic, this help must be intermittent, and limited to the periods of marked depression, phobic reactions, agitation, panic, intense anxiety, or severe insomnia. Drugs should always be used with concurrent regular therapeutic contact and emotional support.

It is a matter of common knowledge and is frequently reported that the alcoholic may easily become dependent on other drugs as well as alcohol; sometimes as a substitute, sometimes in addition. This impression is questionable scientifically for the total spectrum of alcoholism, but it is preferable to be cautious rather than contribute to additional addictions or dependencies in a particular patient. Strong dependency needs are observable in many patients; however, the relationship of such needs to a prealcoholic personality defect has not been definitely established for alcoholics or drug addicts. Some patients have multiple drug dependencies such as heroin, barbiturates, paraldehyde, or amphetamine addiction as well as alcoholism. These patients represent only a very small percentage, and may not be typical since it has been shown that thousands of patients have been treated, with relatively rare indications of the misuse of drugs apparent.

Although most would agree that drugs have a definite place in treatment of alcoholism, the efficacy of their use, in spite of hundreds of studies, cannot be stated without equivocation. This is at least partly due to the lack of any concerted effort to formulate operational definitions in respect to exact patient signs and symptoms at any given time in his illness, and to uncertainty as to what is meant by "improvement." There is, in addition, the impossibility of correlating data in reports of studies which at best vaguely describe the methodologic process and the statistical significance of the results of comparative drug regimens. Drug use in treatment of acute and chronic ethanolism remains realistically quite empirical, and is still based on impression and anecdotal reports rather than scientific evidence. (Cooperative hospital studies in an attempt to resolve some of these problems have been instituted within the Veterans Administration.) The treatment regimens suggested herein, therefore, cannot for the most part be considered scientifically supportable and may not even represent a consensus of sectional or national preferences.

II. Acute Ethanolism and Withdrawal Syndrome

The essential aim of any treatment regimen in ethanol withdrawal syndromes is to control psychomotor exhaustion, agitation, tremulousness, hallucinations, and anxiety. There is also the need to permit sleep and reestablish fluid and electrolyte balance, in addition to treating and preventing complications, trauma, or incidental concomitant illnesses.

It has been stated that the antipsychotic medications, primarily chlorpromazine and thioridazine, are of definite benefit in decreasing agitation and rendering the patient more able to cooperate with the remainder of the treatment regimen. This may be especially so in the patient with milder withdrawal states. Medication should be given orally rather than parenterally whenever possible. Thioridazine may be helpful as a routine measure in doses of 50–100 mg orally every

4–6 hours. A consideration in its use may be the reported lowering of the convulsive threshold, as well as cardiac conduction irregularities. In epileptics, the brain damaged, and in cardiac patients these risks although slight, must be properly weighed.

Chlorpromazine may be substituted for thioridazine in the same oral doses, or used in conjunction with thioridazine as the intramuscular preparation for agitation and restlessness. It should be remembered that the dosages suggested can be varied considerably, depending upon the circumstances of the individual case, and the number of other drugs being given simultaneously.

Other phenothiazines have been reported successful in treatment of symptoms of acute alcohol withdrawal syndromes, although the preponderance of evidence, and our own experience, indicates that they are not as useful or as effective as chlorpromazine and thioridazine, and may have more side effects. Clinical studies of thiothixene and haloperidol in alcohol withdrawal have not yet been reported.

In a well-designed VA cooperative hospital study comparing four drugs and placebo in the treatment of the acute alcoholic withdrawal state, chlordiazepoxide, which is cross-dependent with alcohol, was found to be significantly more effective in prevention of delirium tremens and withdrawal seizures than chlorpromazine, hydroxyzine, or thiamine. Chlorpromazine was associated with the worst outcome in respect to both seizures and delirium tremens. Chlordiazepoxide may be given orally 25–50 mg three to four times a day, or intramuscularly 50–100 mg every 4–6 hours, but not to exceed 300 mg within a 24-hour period.

Other drugs which are cross-dependent with alcohol such as paraldehyde, barbiturates, and chloral hydrate may be helpful in selected cases. Except for the milder cases of alcohol withdrawal syndrome, chlordiazepoxide would seem the drug of choice at this time.

Meprobamate may be helpful for some patients, particularly as bedtime sedation; 400–800 mg is generally sufficient for this use. Diazepam, due to its muscle-relaxant properties, may assist in decreasing daytime agitation, and can be given orally 5–10 mg at 4- to 6-hour intervals. It may also be substituted for meprobamate or barbiturates as a bedtime hypnotic. For this use, more than 20 mg is rarely indicated. The reported marked anticonvulsive properties of this drug may influence the physician to substitute it for chlordiazepoxide. It has been used as an anticonvulsant in doses up to 60 mg daily. However, it is more likely to produce the side effect of drowsiness. Diphenylhydantoin may be given prophylactically if there is a history of convulsions or epilepsy.

III. Chronic Alcoholism

Phenothiazines have little place in the treatment of the chronic alcoholic, and except for the psychotic or borderline schizophrenic patient, should be used sparingly if at all. There is no evidence that continued use of these drugs in the abstinent patient is helpful. In addition they have been used in suicidal gestures or attempts. For the occasional patient, in periods of sobriety, who is severely agitated, anxious or phobic, moderately depressed, or has insomnia, thioridazine or chlorpromazine may be useful for short periods. Doses should rarely exceed 200–400 mg per day, and are preferably given at bedtime and on arising. Prescriptions for large amounts of drugs should not be given, and they should be discontinued when the crisis has passed or the symptoms subside. It is good practice to collect excess pills from the patient should there be sufficient to represent a danger.

Although routinely prescribed, antianxiety agents and the antidepressants have a limited use in the treatment of chronic alcoholism. They should not be used except for specific reasons, and then concurrently with frequent contacts with the physician or therapist. Most careful studies have shown that their long-term use is not effective in promoting abstinence. Neither do they seem to have any significant effects in reducing the psychological compulsion to drink. For some patients, in crisis situation, they may be helpful for short periods. Chlordiazepoxide or diazepam seem to help acute anxiety attacks. Meprobamate may be useful for periodic insomnia. For depression amitriptyline, imipramine, or desipramine are possibly of use, although the evidence is still equivocal for their efficacy. Monamine oxidase inhibitors should be used in alcoholic patients only under the strictest supervision.

Reports of results with LSD in alcoholism have gradually changed from glowing and enthusiastic to cautious and disappointing. The drug does not have a place in routine treatment, and the best that can be said for it in alcoholism is that it may still have a use in well-designed comparative treatment studies. Whether it is effective in selected patients in significantly changing drinking patterns cannot as yet be stated. Better designed, and more recent investigations have not substantiated the earlier anecdotal reports.

Disulfiram and citrated calcium carbimide are not psychotropic drugs. Any psychic effect with their use is related to the deterrent memory of the unpleasant reaction they produce when combined with alcohol; or the fantasy fear of such a reaction if not previously experienced. Because of their potentially serious complications when combined with alcohol, they should be used under relatively strict supervision. As little as 0.5 gm of disulfiram given twice weekly can still produce a significant reaction.

More recently, metronidazole has been reported to produce a disulfiram-like reaction when combined with alcohol, although not as severe. Interestingly, it has been claimed that the compulsion or desire to drink is also reduced or obliterated. These early reports have not been confirmed by adequate or well-designed studies, so that the place of this drug in the treatment of acute and chronic alcoholism is not as yet established.

Amphetamines and barbiturates have very little place in the treatment of chronic alcoholism. The potential for abuse of these drugs is always present, and combinations of alcohol and barbiturates are often lethal. The intravenous use of amphetamines is dangerous. Besides the insult to the cardiovascular and central nervous systems, the potential addicting qualities represent a constant risk.

IV. Summary

Psychotropic drugs have a useful but limited place in the treatment of alcoholism. In chronic alcoholics the results will be uniformly disappointing if the therapist relies solely on drugs to achieve increased sobriety, or reduction of symptoms of depression and anxiety. Drug treatment must be accompanied by frequent, sometimes prolonged therapeutic contact for psychological support and assistance with the numerous problems with which the patient must deal.

In the overall evaluation of the treatment of alcoholism with antipsychotic, antidepressant, and antianxiety agents it should be noted, as a final, if pessimistic, note, that studies with animals, from dogs through rabbits and rats, have shown that not only is the effect of ethanol potentiated (increased blood levels) if taken in combination with some of these drugs, but in addition the toxicity of the drugs is enhanced. This may not be directly extrapolated to the same degree in humans, but must be given consideration in their use.

For references and suggested further reading see Appendices 1 and 2.

42

DRUGS, DEATHS, AND SUICIDES—PROBLEMS OF THE CORONER

Theodore J. Curphey, Edwin S. Shneidman, and Norman L. Farberow

I. Introduction

From time immemorial man has sought relief from his tensions by the taking of drugs, the results of which have been documented in poetry, prose, and scientific articles. In earlier times, the drugs were derived from botanicals and their derivatives and it is only since the latter part of the past century with the development of modern chemistry leading to the increasing production of the synthetic agents that the botanicals have been largely replaced by the manufacture of sedative agents.

The rapid development of knowledge relating to the specific pharmacological action of these various agents has led to the birth and growth of a relatively new field, namely, that of psychopharmacology, and a great deal of this newer knowledge is documented by the various contributors to this volume.

Along with the advancing knowledge in this field, there has been in the world at large a concomitant increase in the tensions of living. This has led to the development of a vicious circle where newer and more potent drugs have been associated with their rapidly increasing use as sedatives, which in turn has led in many instances to the abuse of these agents, followed frequently by death in the drug user.

The extent of the problem in this country in the use of a single group of drugs, namely, the barbiturates, is measured by a recent report (Committee on Alcoholism and Addiction and Council on Mental Health, 1965), mentioning a survey made in 1962 by the Food and Drug Administration, wherein it states that approximately one-million pounds of barbituric acid derivatives were available—enough to supply approximately twenty-four 100-mg ($1\frac{1}{2}$ grain) doses to every man, woman, and child in the country.

This figure represents the amount of drugs prescribed through legitimate medical channels. In many parts of the country, especially in areas such as Los Angeles, because of its geographic location, there is a large illicit traffic in the sedative and mood-expanding drugs, hence, it goes without saying that the total national consumption of these drugs is considerably greater, and because of this illicit factor, it can never be estimated accurately.

A word might be said about the prescribing of these drugs by physicians. The experience of the Medical Examiner's Office in Los Angeles is that many physicians contribute to the misuse of these drugs by prescribing them willy-nilly, often purely on a symptomatic basis, without either a justifiable clinical diagnosis or recent direct contact, and often also without seeking knowledge as to the drug habits of the patient relative to his dependence.

The problem is further compounded by the patient, who successfully shops around for prescriptions to support his dependence, with the result that he is able to hoard large quantities of the drug and frequently commits suicide by taking an overdose during a period of depression.

II. Drug Deaths

From the medical examiner's or coroner's point of view, this increasingly widespread use and availability of the various sedative drugs has in the past twenty years led to a corresponding increase in the number of deaths from overdosage, which has accelerated in the past decade. For example, in the fiscal year 1953–1954, the Los Angeles County Medical Examiner's Office handled 188 suicidal deaths from barbiturates out of a total of 723 suicides (26%), while in the fiscal year 1962–1963 there were 440 barbiturate deaths out of a total of 1136 suicides (38.8%).

The problem of the drug death is presently at a point in time where the medical examiner or coroner can, if he chooses, make a major contribution to the overall study if he is prepared to handle the suspected case of drug intoxication with the same degree of interest and responsibility he now applies to the case of homicide. For example, he must be able, first, to determine not by inference, but rather by means of precise qualitative and quantitative laboratory study, that the death is in fact due to a drug, present at a lethal level.

Furthermore, lacking a suicide note, he must have evidence provided him by autopsy study which he must then evaluate in the light of the toxicological findings, coupled with other pertinent information, especially the history of the drug habits of the individual and his psychological state immediately prior to his death.

The importance of the autopsy in a suspected drug death cannot be too strongly emphasized because of the necessity to distinguish it, for instance, from a natural death due to cardiovascular disease in an older person who might be addicted to a drug, the knowledge of which is unknown to the pathologist. Without an autopsy to demonstrate the fatal pathological changes in the heart, the height of the drug level might lead to the interpretation of drug intoxication as the cause of death. At present, drug levels in the known addict cannot be interpreted in the same light as in the nonaddicted individual by either the pathologist or toxicologist, and without an autopsy, an erroneous certification of suicide from drug intoxication would be issued.

To further insure the accuracy of certification, the drug death should be subject to further investigation by another scientific discipline, namely, that represented by the behavioral scientist. This investigation obtained through the services of psychologists, psychiatrists, or psychiatric social workers provides the medical examiner or coroner with an accurate history of the life style of the deceased as it relates to possible suicidal motivation or ideation, prior attempts at suicide, etc.

III. Total Approach

For the past nine years, many of the drug deaths studied in the Los Angeles Medical Examiner's Office have been subjected to such a psychological study, so that the total approach to the study of the drug death is now as follows:

Initially, a written report of the death is prepared by an "on the scene" investigation by a nonmedical investigator attached to the Medical Examiner's Office. A Deputy Medical Examiner with training in pathology then reviews both the lay investigator's report and that of the police department (the police are involved in such cases as unattended deaths in motels, rooming houses, etc.) and, if there is no suicide note, he performs an autopsy which will include, if necessary, a microscopic study of all or certain key organs in the case as well as a toxicological study. The cause of death is determined and the mode is suggested by the pathologist. If a suicidal note is found, the handwriting expert is asked for an opinion, and if the note is authentic, the case is certified without consultation with the Death Investigation Team, as the group of behavioral scientists is known.

If, however, no note is found, and the facts suggest a probable suicide but the evidence on file is not clear-cut, or the pathologist from the documentary evidence is unable to determine whether the death be accidental, suicidal, or even natural (as in cases suspected of being addicted to the drug found at autopsy), then the file is submitted to the special team (304). Their study in turn consists of interviewing persons who knew the deceased, e.g., the spouse, grown children, neighbors, employers, physicians, etc., in an attempt to reconstruct the life style of the deceased. In their investigation, they try to obtain information about any psychiatric idiosyncrasies or the presence of any prodromal clues to suicide that the victim may have communicated verbally and/or behaviorally, and then they make a scientific extrapolation of the victim's behavior over the days preceding his death, using all the information they have obtained. To emphasize the nature of their study, they have coined the descriptive term "psychological autopsy" as a connotation of its post mortem nature, its retrospective reconstruction, and its scientific content.

IV. Types of Information

The types of information gathered by the Death Investigation Team falls under the following headings:

A. Anamestic or life history details: history of previous suicide attempts.

B. Psychiatric and psychological data: indices of depression and agitation; for example, recent loss of appetite, loss of interest, or changes in habit patterns.

C. Communication information: indications of morbid content of thought as exemplified in such statements as "I can't go on," "Life isn't worth much," or "I'm a worthless person."

D. Other nonpsychiatric information: information which appears in the course of certain investigations where the scene of the death is personally viewed by a member of the team, and where material evidence found at the scene throws additional light on the mode of death, e.g., discovery of a small mophead stuffed in the drain of a bathtub, indicating that the victim had made careful preparation for death by ensuring sufficient water in the bathtub in which to drown.

V. Case Conferences

Following the gathering of all this information, the case is discussed in conference among the members of the team, after which a written report with their final recommendation is prepared. This is in the nature of a confidential communication to the Medical Examiner and is subsequently discussed in detail in personal conference with him. Subsequent to this, a certificate as to the cause and mode of death is issued, based upon all the evidence gathered by the pathologist, toxicologist, behavioral scientist, and the police investigator.

In the case of suicide, in our culture and our times, the certification of suicide often leaves behind in the survivors a trenchant feeling of shame or embarrassment. If for no other reason then, the investigation of any case in which suicide is a possibility deserves to be as complete as possible, so that sources of error might be eliminated. The behavioral scientists' investigations add in this area the most significant information. Suicide, by law designated as an act performed by an individual in which he consciously destroys himself, obviously is determined on the basis of information about the motivation of the individual. Motivation is psychological and knowledge of this is most readily established by the behavioral scientists in whose area of skills this evaluation lies. Oftentimes, the awareness by the survivors that the Medical Examiner's Office, in arriving at its certification, has employed scientists from many disciplines, serves to allay doubts and to forestall emotionally based feelings of anger. The completeness of the investigation may help in the cases involving insurance (although the presence of an insurance policy is generally not known and not sought after by the investigating team). In the investigations to date, the results have shown that many cases originally thought to be suicide were subsequently recommended as accident and vice versa.

It is important to recognize that in their expression of opinion, the team confines itself to the special field of competence, and by the very nature of the cases submitted to them for study, they are only called on to say whether they think the mode of death is suicide. If there is psychological evidence to support this, they so state in their written opinion.

VI. Equivocal Cases

If, however, the available investigative and medical evidence, coupled with their special study, leads to an equivocal opinion, then the mode is listed as undetermined. In this latter group, the difficulty most often arises in resolving the question as to whether the mode be either accidental or suicidal, in which case the mode is certified as "Accident-Suicide-Undetermined." Incidentally, the majority of these indeterminate cases are instances in which barbiturate intoxication is the cause of death and in which alcohol is found in sufficient amounts in the blood as to raise the question whether the victim was under the influence and might have accidentally taken an overdose or an unforeseen synergistic effect from the drug and alcohol might have occurred.

In this connection, we sometimes encounter a case where there is a documented history of addiction to barbiturates and where, as a consequence, not only the mode but also the cause of death is in question. Because of our present insecure knowledge relative to the interpretation of blood levels in barbiturate-dependent individuals, we are reluctant to accept as *prima facie* evidence of lethal intoxication in an addict those blood levels that we now associate with deaths from barbiturate intoxication in the nonaddicted individual.

Further, a real problem develops when one is confronted by a case which shows a high concentration of barbiturates in the blood, with no documented history of addiction, and which, with no autopsy, has been certified as due to barbiturate intoxication on the basis of blood level only. The members of the family frequently protest the certification and produce medical evidence to show that the deceased was dependent on the drug, thus raising the question of whether the death might be from natural causes. The problem is further complicated when psychological investigation of the life style of the deceased in such a case fails to yield any evidence that favors the probability of suicide. Under these circumstances, one is forced to certify that both the cause and the mode of death is undetermined, because of the failure to perform an autopsy to rule out a possible natural death. Fortunately, this type of case is rarely encountered. However, this rarity might be more fancied than real, for the simple reason that in so many of these drug deaths, the on-the-scene interrogation frequently fails to explore the possible presence and the extent of an addiction.

VII. On-the-Scene Interview

A passing comment on the matter of on-the-scene interviews in general might be made. It matters not whether the investigator be a medical examiner or a law enforcement officer; experience has shown that the index of his investigative interest and effort varies directly with the nature of the case. If the case be a homicide, it invariably gets a detailed study; if an accident, it is more likely that the matters of major importance will be sought after and documented. However, if it be a suspected suicide, or what on the surface appears to be a routine natural death (and many drug deaths initially present themselves as such), the degree of interest, interrogation, and documentation falls off precipitously. The result is that the subsequent steps of the investigation involving the pathologist and the toxicologist frequently raises many questions, the answers for which resided in the on-the-scene interrogation, but which are subsequently lost forever. This is more often noticeable in deaths from drugs, where the investigator might fail to search for and impound those drugs that could be associated with fatal overdose, e.g., the barbiturates, psychotropic agents, etc. The most serious error occurs when the investigator fails to notify the toxicologist of the nature of the drugs or to deliver them to his laboratory so that he can direct his preliminary studies to those particular drugs.

As is true in so many problems involving sudden and unexpected death, there can be no substitute for information obtained at the initial stages of the on-the-scene investigation, information which is frequently lost or becomes unavailable with the passage of time and the physical disruption of the scene. This principle is just as applicable to the study of cases of natural death or suicide as it is to homicidal or accidental deaths.

VIII. Multidisciplined Study

This role now being played by the behavioral scientist in the multidisciplined study of suspected suicidal deaths is entirely new in its application to the work of a medical examiner's office which is charged with the investigation of sudden and unexpected deaths. Reflection on the involvement of this discipline indicates it is a most logical development, perhaps even a long overdue responsibility. At the same time, it would appear to be an inescapable commitment if viewed from the perspective of the history of scientific progress in the medicolegal field. For example, during the past fifty years, there has been an evolutionary change in this field, leading to a gradual shift of responsibility away from the elected politically oriented lay coroner, possessing no knowledge of either medical or legal problems, to the medical profession, which does. This started with autopsies which were performed almost exclusively and infrequently by the general practitioner of the coroner's jurisdiction. With the growth of specialization in medical practice, the general practitioner was soon replaced by the pathologist trained in hospital practice whose autopsy experience had been largely related to problems of natural deaths. While this was a major advance, it soon became evident that the problems involving sudden and unexpected death, for example, from criminal means, from trauma of a noncriminal nature, and from other circumstances outside the field of natural deaths, called for additional training and experience. This led to the development of the subspecialty of forensic pathology, a discipline which in turn has contributed its fair share in raising the general level of scientific investigation in this field.

The passage of time and the development of pharmacology, however, has created a distinctly changing pattern and a widening of the spectrum of the case material, formerly handled by the forensic pathologist through the medium of the autopsy, to include deaths resulting from a great variety of chemical agents. This has necessitated the involvement of another scientific discipline, namely, that of toxicology, which is asked to determine the nature of the agent and, in the case of death from a drug, to determine quantitatively the amount present, providing the basis for evaluation in respect to its lethality.

Initially, with a limited number of drugs available for therapeutic use, as well as those used in industry and the home such as caustics, cyanide, arsenic, the heavy metals, etc., the toxicologist was invariably able to provide the required information. During the past two decades, however, his task has become considerably more difficult because of the marked increase in the number of drugs, the majority of them of a synthetic nature and some of them defying both recognition and quantitation in the tissues of the human being, even with the marked advances made in his field through the use of sophisticated technical methods and instrumentation. The best example currently is LSD. Thus, with the joint efforts of the pathologist and the toxicologist, greater precision has been achieved in determining the causes of death in this field, even though it has not been possible to keep abreast of all the demands currently made on the toxicologist.

However, the problem of sudden and unexpected death has another dimension. In this area, one seeks answers to the question: What is the mode of death? Is it natural, suicidal, accidental, or homicidal? It is here that the need arose for the involvement of practitioners of yet another scientific discipline, namely, the behavioral scientists, to assist in finding answers related to the mode of death. The particular group of cases to which their skills have contributed most has been in deaths resulting from drugs, as will be seen from the following data (Table I). It has been possible to increase the accuracy of certification of suicides from barbiturates from 74 to 90%, and to reduce that of accidents from 11 to 1%, and of undetermined modes from 15 to 9%.

This significant contribution brings to mind views dealing with the recognition of suicidal risks through the psychological examination in which the investigator sees the problem in the same light as any other disease process with its specific pathological changes, and which should be investigated by the techniques peculiar to the behavioral scientist, but within the same general ideological framework as any disease of somatic origin. Havens (305) recommends that the investigation begin with the initial symptoms and signs, corresponding to the history and physical examination of a somatic case, the elicitation of which leads to a "knowledge of the pathological psychic life from within." This he describes as the phenomenology of the psychic disease. He also advocates the application of the diagnostic method beyond the patient into the investigation of the social, institutional, and family contributions to the disturbed mental state, namely, the interaction between the patient and the extrinsic forces to which he is exposed. This he regards as the sociological factor, the conditions

Table I

A Comparison of Barbiturate Deaths "Before" and "After" the Pyschological Autopsy Study

1953–1954 Barbiturate deaths		1962–1963 Barbiturate deaths	
Total cases	8539	Total cases	12,516
Total suicides	723	Total suicides	1136
Before psychological autopsy study		After psychological autopsy study	
Suicides		Suicides	
Barbiturates	75	Barbiturates	395 (90%)
Other barbiturates	64		
	139 (74%)		
Accidents		Accidents	
Barbiturates	17	Barbiturates	4 (1%)
Alcohol plus barbiturates	3		
	20 (11%)		
Undetermined		Undetermined	
Barbiturates	29 (15%)	Barbiturates	41 (9%)
Total deaths	188	Total deaths	440

and interactions of which shape the individual's reactions from without. He makes this pertinent statement: "The modern psychiatrist is as obliged to understand his patient's family class and social experience as a modern internist is to know his patient's dietary habits and environmental hazards."

To the pathologist, this examination "of a specimen of his (the patient's) social interactions" has its counterpart in the obtaining of a biopsy specimen in the case of a somatic disease, such as cancer. Applying the comparison further, to the case where the somatic disease ends fatally, it is standard procedure for the pathologist to perform an autopsy so as to study and verify the nature and extent of the disease or to determine whether an error in diagnosis has been made.

It might be said that while the psychiatrist in his practice currently conforms to the standard medical pattern by performing "psychological biopsies" with his live patients, he has not yet followed the somatic disease pattern with the performance of a "psychological autopsy" in the fatal case, with the result that until very recently, no attempt has been made to utilize his special skill in the study of the case of completed suicide.

It is this signal contribution that the behavioral scientists from the Suicide Prevention Center of Los Angeles have made, and their efforts have blazed a trail for the specialists in this field to follow. From the coroner or medical examiner's point of view, the contribution that this discipline is now making, when coupled with that of the pathologist and the toxicologist, presages a substantial advancement of knowledge in this field, the importance of which grows with the increased incidence of drug deaths from the indiscriminate use and abuse of the modern mood-influencing drugs.

IX. Case Reports

The following case reports are illustrative of the benefits of the "psychological autopsy" as performed by this group of behavioral scientists.

A. *Case 1*

A 78-year-old female found dead in bed with a revolver clutched in both hands with her right index finger on the trigger and pointed to her head. Examination showed no wound of entrance; the revolver had not been fired and contained five live bullets. The police report stated: "Apparently the deceased died a natural death from fright contemplating suicide."

A routine postmortem toxicological study of the blood revealed 4.8 mg/ml of barbiturates (phenobarbital absent*), and the cause of death was certified as acute barbiturate intoxication and the mode probable suicide.

Investigation by the Suicide Team elicited from the deceased's physician, who was also a personal friend, that she was a brilliant, independent self-sufficient woman, suffering from a mild cardiac condition and from arthritis. He had not seen her within five months prior to her death and had never prescribed any barbiturates for her and was not aware of any depression or suicidal preoccupation on her part.

The final report submitted by the Suicide Team concurred in the certification of the cause and mode of death and made this comment: "This is the kind of case that might easily be misleading because the obvious cause of death would seem to be heart failure whereas only a toxicological examination would reveal the actual cause of death."

Comment. This case primarily illustrates the importance of a routine toxicological study in the case of sudden death, as emphasized by the comment of the Suicide Team.

* The quantitative blood levels here reported refer either to the short-acting or medium-acting barbiturates. A qualitative, and, where indicated, a quantitative, test for phenobarbital is, however, routinely performed on each case.

B. Case 2

A 48-year-old female whose death was reported as a possible natural with a history of alcoholism. The police report originally listed the case as an attempted suicide and stated that the deceased was last seen at 1 A.M. watching a TV program at which time she appeared sober and normal. At 1:15 A.M., her husband found her lying on the floor of the den. The local physician was called at 2 A.M. and pronounced her dead from a possible overdose (drugs), alcohol, or from a bump on the head when she fell in the den. The police officer also reported finding a paper bag of miscellaneous pills in the pocket of her housecoat.

The toxicologist's report on the blood revealed 1.8 mg/ml barbiturates (phenobarbital absent), with 0.26% alcohol. No autopsy was performed and the case was certified as death from acute barbiturate and alcohol intoxication with an undetermined mode, i.e., either accident or suicide.

The case was referred to the Suicide Team for study, which elicited the fact that the deceased was married for 20 years and her married life reflected an absence of sexual relations and an almost total breakdown of meaningful communication between husband and wife. They were both social drinkers, but the wife had become an excessive drinker and was described by her husband as an alcoholic who imbibed freely from midafternoon through to evening and would frequently pass out at the dinner table or even before dinner. She had a regular habit of watching the late shows on TV while under the influence of alcohol.

The couple employed a housekeeper who had become a surrogate mother to the children. The housekeeper had the responsibility of hiding the sleeping pills, as the wife would forget how many pills she had taken and at times would take an overdose, although never to the point of endangering her life. Both husband and wife had had periods when they both would depend greatly upon barbiturates. This seemed to appease the strong underlying feelings of hostility due to their strained family and marital relationships.

The psychological study showed further that the housekeeper had assumed full responsibility for the children and the family finances as both husband and wife gradually abdicated their positions as authority figures within the family. The ill effects of this negative environment were reflected in the children, and the eldest was under psychiatric care. The housekeeper in the course of her interview stated that she felt trapped in a very trying and difficult situation as she had to treat both the parents as children, catering to their emotional needs, as well as fulfilling the demands of the children.

Despite the negative psychological picture, the investigation failed to show any extraneous incidents or elements of change in the deceased's emotional state which could have precipitated a pronounced despondency. She had shown no unusual depression and had given no overt signs of wanting to destroy herself. On the strength of their study, the Suicide Team rendered the opinion that this was probably an accidental death even though definite subintentional self-destructive behavior was present in the deceased.

Comment. By the conventional method of study or without a "psychological autopsy," this case would very likely have been certified as a suicide of an undetermined mode.

C. Case 3

A 50-year-old female was found dead in bed. According to the police report, the husband stated that she was going through the menopause, had been very nervous and unable to sleep, and that she took large amounts of sleeping pills. He stated that he had found her unconscious on numerous occasions as a result of her overdosage. A search by the police for pills showed six empty pill bottles under the mattress of the bed.

A routine postmortem toxicological examination of the blood showed an alcohol level of 0.37%, and the presence of 2 mg/ml of ethchlorvynol with absence of any barbiturate. The cause of death was certified as acute ethchlorvynol and alcohol intoxication and the mode was left undetermined as to whether it was accidental or suicidal, following which the case was referred for consultation to the Suicide Team.

Their investigation reported that the husband, when interviewed, was at first extremely guarded and tended to withhold or deny much information. For example, he denied that she drank, even though a neighbor who was present at the scene of death revealed on questioning that four empty liquor bottles were found in the closet, a fact that did not appear in the police report. About four years prior to her death, she had taken to bed following an operation for cancer of the uterus and remained there for about a year except to go out to doctors to ask for sleeping pills. Although she was told that she was cured, she continued to feel that she still had cancer.

During the past four years, her husband had made many attempts to rehabilitate her, such as taking her on extended trips, purchasing land in another state where she said she wanted to live, and purchasing a small business in which they could work together. About eighteen months before her death, she had converted to the Roman Catholic faith.

Her husband described her as a very disturbed woman, unable to tolerate her feelings and always trying to calm herself with alcohol and pills. The most significant fact concerned her extensive use of sleeping pills which she obtained by prescriptions from different physicians. In the six months preceding her death, he had found twenty-two pill vials, many of which were empty. He often had found her unconscious from overdoses of these pills.

At one time, the deceased had been seen by a psychiatrist and hospitalized as a case of depressive reaction without psychosis. She objected to treatment and would not cooperate with her psychiatrist. At this time, her husband felt he had reached the end of his rope and that he could not continue their stormy marriage. Of all the people interviewed, no one could recall any prior suicide attempt or overt comments about committing suicide.

On the basis of their investigation, it was the feeling of the consultants that she took pills, not caring whether she lived or not, but that it was not possible to determine that she had made a deliberate attempt to end her life at this time. Accordingly, their recommendation was that the certified mode of accident-suicide-undetermined should stand.

Comment. This case illustrates a familiar problem where a known drug addict with an alcoholic history dies from an overdose and where even with a detailed psychological autopsy, it is not always possible to determine with certainty whether the death is accidental or suicidal. This type of case offers a fertile field for clinical research in those cases which are admitted to hospital in coma, and following recovery are subjected to a retrospective psychiatric study involving their addiction and their precomatose mental state in regard to suicidal ideation. To our knowledge, no such study has yet been made in this particular area of the problem of drug intoxication and is long overdue.

The association of fatal overdosage with alcohol and a depressant drug in an addicted or nonaddicted individual, in contrast to this case, presents another facet, namely, the theory of automatism, where the death is considered to be accidental on the grounds that because the individual is under the influence of alcohol, he loses count of the number of pills taken, thus dying accidentally from an overdose. The current view based on the study of the "psychological autopsy" is that this is probably a rare event and that usually when the individual takes an overdose of the drug while under the influence of alcohol, he is aware of the nature and consequence of his act.

The following two cases are examples:

D. Case 4

A 46-year-old female was chronically ill for the past twenty-five years. She had a history of five major operations for gastric ulcer and intestinal obstruction, as well as suffering from chronic arthritis. She relied on alcohol and barbiturates for relief of her constant pain and was known to have taken excessive medication if relief did not occur promptly after regular dose. On the day of death, after taking an overdose, she phoned for assistance but "passed out" before completing the call.

Toxicology report

Blood: 0.30% alcohol; 3.2 mg/ml barbiturate, of which 1.1 mg/ml is phenobarbital.

The case was certified as an accidental death.

Comment

1. Police report failed to state that patient was addicted to alcohol and barbiturates.

2. History of addiction was obtained through psychological autopsy.

3. Without the psychological autopsy, the case would have been certified as suicide rather than accident.

4. Mode certified as accident (a) provided next of kin with basis for accident claim in insurance settlement, (neither the Medical Examiner's Office nor the Suicide Team was aware of the presence of an insurance policy); (b) avoided the social stigma of a suicidal death.

E. Case 5

A 52-year-old female called the telephone operator to say she had taken thirty sleeping pills and to ask for help. During the call, the phone went dead, but the line remained connected. The operator traced the call and dispatched an ambulance to the address. The patient was dead on arrival. There was a prior history of recent suicidal attempt (police report); no history of addiction was obtained.

Toxicology report

Blood: 0.38% alcohol; 2.6 mg/ml barbiturates (phenobarbital absent).

The case was certified as a suicidal death.

Comment. Persons with high blood-alcohol and barbiturate levels have been found to be lucid enough to know the nature and quality of their actions, thus creating serious doubt as to the current theory of drug automatism and repetition of prescribed drug dosages.

X. Conclusion

From the foregoing evidence outlining the current problem concerning the investigation of deaths associated with the presence of the psychotropic and depressant drugs recovered at autopsy and quantitated by toxicological study, it can be seen that the coroner or medical examiner whose task it is to certify the cause and mode of these deaths is faced with a responsibility which in some respects is as great or at times even greater than that in the case of homicide or the result of traumatic injury. For example, in the investigation of such a homicide, the forensic pathologist is called upon to determine the extent and nature of the changes found at autopsy and inflicted by the injuring agent, be it gunshot, cutting, or stabbing. The majority of these cases frequently offer less of a problem to the pathologist than to the criminal investigator and the District Attorney, whose task it is to produce a competent and convincing body of evidence on which the prosecutor can base a criminal trial of an individual suspected of having caused the death.

In the case of the drug death, however, the problem is more involved. In the first place, unlike the homicide, by far the majority of these deaths are unwitnessed, and because of the lack of circumstantial evidence at the scene and, often too, because of incomplete on-the-scene investigation by the police officer, the coroner, or the medical examiner, and with the presence of certain evidence such as the age of the deceased or a history of previous organic disease, the drug death is frequently certified as a natural death from organic disease without either an autopsy or a toxicological study. This is especially true in coroners' offices operating in the smaller jurisdictions having fewer cases and having a limited budget to provide for pathological and toxicological studies. For these reasons then, it is a fair inference in the light of the marked increase in the current use and abuse, especially of the sedative drugs, that because of the current limitations placed on the scientific investigation of sudden and unexpected deaths in general in the medicolegal offices of the nation, that the current statistics as to the frequency of drug deaths, irrespective of the mode of death, do not reflect the true situation. This underreporting of the drug death has its statistical counterpart in the certification of suicidal deaths from whatever cause.

There is evidence to show that in the case of deaths from barbiturate drug intoxication, a large majority of the medicolegal offices are underreporting suicidal deaths, certifying them instead as accidents or as of undetermined modes.

These two facts where drug deaths are frequently unrecognized as such in the course of medicolegal investigation, and where recognized cases are being underreported as suicides, illustrate the need for greater emphasis on the problem of the drug death by the coroner or the medical examiner, not only in the interest of the accuracy of vital statistics but also, more importantly, because of the social, economic, and criminal implications evolving from a more comprehensive study at the hands of the pathologist and the toxicologist than is now performed.

With greater focus on the problem, there is reason to believe that the present interdisciplinary study of the drug death that now involves the pathologist and the toxicologist will of necessity have to include the behavioral scientist. Just as the contribution of the toxicologist has led to a greater refinement in determining the cause of death in the spectrum that comprises the range of sudden and unexpected death, so will that of the behavioral scientist contribute to the refinement of determining the mode of death, thus helping to distinguish the accidental from the suicidal death.

With the advances now being made in the field of psychopharmacology and the current research centering on the biochemical changes in relation to certain psychiatric and psychological states, and in order to complete the investigative approach to problems of mental health which involve the use and abuse of drugs which often leads to either suicidal or accidental death, the medical examiner or coroner must be prepared to accurately document these instances by not only utilizing the knowledge of the pathologist and the toxicologist but also by including the behavioral scientist as a member of his investigative team.

For suggested reading and references, see Appendices 1 and 2.

43

TOXICOLOGY OF PSYCHOTHERAPEUTIC DRUGS

Leo E. Hollister

Widespread use of the newer CNS depressants and stimulants has resulted in many instances of overdoses, either accidentally by children or purposely by adults. While many of the general principles of treatment of poisoning with these drugs are the same as for older sedatives and stimulants, some problems are different.

I. Epidemiological Considerations

Despite their easy availability, psychotherapeutic drugs are involved in only a relatively small proportion of poisonings and an even smaller proportion of fatalities. During the years 1959 and 1960, 968 cases of poisonings of all types were reported to the National Clearinghouse for Poison Control Centers, of which only 2.4% were due to psychotherapeutic drugs. Among the latter, phenothiazines were the most frequent single class of drugs, being involved in 39% of cases, followed by substituted diols (such as meprobamate) in 28.5%, rauwolfia alkaloids in 15.6%, and drugs of miscellaneous structure, such as chlordiazepoxide, in 11%. It is likely that more recent figures would show a sharp decline in the cases involving rauwolfia alkaloids and a proportionate increase in drugs of the antianxiety category. The rather high number of reports of cases involving phenothiazines may be an artifact, reflecting a greater degree of uncertainty on the part of the treating physician about the management of such intoxications. Ingestion of these drugs was intentional in 35% of cases, almost exclusively in the young adult or adult group of patients, while conversely almost all ingestions by children were accidental (306).

The prominent role still played by barbiturates is emphasized by a survey of 522 admissions to the Edinburgh Royal Infirmary during 1962–1963. Barbiturates accounted for 55% of drug poisonings, as compared with 23% from the psychotherapeutic drugs and 12% from aspirin (307). Among 44 fatal drug intoxications encountered during a 3-year survey of a Copenhagen intoxication center, barbiturates accounted for 23 deaths, as compared with only 8 from psychotherapeutic drugs (308). A similar situation applies in this country, where barbiturates or older sedatives still far outnumber the newer psychotherapeutic drugs as causes of intoxications.

II. Prevention and Diagnosis

A good way to prevent a fatal overdose of drugs is to limit the amounts prescribed to a total amount which, if taken all at once, would still be sublethal. While such a procedure creates some inconvenience and is still no absolute guarantee of safety, potential benefits are many. In the subsequent discussion, lethal doses of drugs will be translated into the actual numbers of commonly prescribed units of each drug to provide a guide for estimating sublethal quantities.

Treatment of drug intoxication is immeasurably helped if the identity of the drug is known right off. As there is usually some container about, it would be handy to have it labeled with the generic or trade name of the drug and the unit size; a pharmacy prescription number from an out-of-state pharmacy or one closed for the night can make direct identification most difficult. Many physicians now instruct pharmacists to label their prescriptions, a trend which should be encouraged (309). Clinical signs of CNS involvement are not entirely reliable clues concerning the nature of the drug, as many drugs ordinarily not considered CNS depressants or stimulants may produce prominent signs when taken in overdoses. Aspirin, methyl salicylate, petroleum products, and organic phosphorus insecticides are examples of drugs or poisons which may evoke CNS symptoms and signs in toxic doses; usually, other distinguishing aspects of the intoxication point to their identity.

III. General Principles of Treatment

Just as with the management of overdoses of other drugs, some general principles apply to handling intoxications with psychotherapeutic drugs.

A. *Rid the Patient of the Drug*

Initially, this is done by emptying the stomach, either by induced vomiting with mechanical or chemical means, or by gastric lavage. Although emptying the stomach might not seem to be worthwhile several hours after ingestion of the drug, the possible gains outweigh the risks. Aspiration is the greatest risk in a comatose patient, making lavage generally preferable to induced emesis. If possible, intubation with a cuffed endotracheal tube should precede lavage and provide protection against tracheal aspiration. The return from the stomach should be saved to confirm identification of the drug. Charcoal absorbs many of these drugs quite well and should be administered in a dose of 30 gm in 250 ml of water as soon as emptying of the stomach has been completed.

Excretion of drug is promoted by forced diuresis, usually involving the rapid intravenous injection of several liters of 5 or 10% dextrose in water solution. The addition of two or three 0.5-gm doses of aminophylline to the fluid at four hourly intervals may hasten diuresis, as well as stimulate depressed respiration. Urea and mannitol have been used as osmotic diuretics, and furosemide, ethacrynic acid, or chlorothiazide employed as naturetic diuretics, but simple fluid loading may be entirely satisfactory. Catharsis with 30 gm of sodium sulfate has been used to increase the passage of retained drug through the bowel; the cathartic should be administered some time after the charcoal. Later measures to rid the patient of the drug include either peritoneal dialysis or hemodialysis, or in the case of children, exchange transfusions.

B. *Frequently Observe the Patient*

The vital signs, state of consciousness, pupillary size and reactivity, and deep tendon reflexes should be recorded at the first examination and at frequent intervals throughout the course. Such observations may provide the earliest indication of an impending worsening of the clinical state.

During forced diuresis, the patient's intake and output of fluids should be carefully recorded. A urine flow of 350–500 ml or more per hour is the goal of such treatment, but a brisk urine flow may be slow to appear until an initial state of dehydration has been rectified. Serum electrolytes should be closely monitored, along with levels of the drug, if these can be measured. One must be careful not to drown the patient or produce cerebral edema; limitation of electrolyte-containing solutions should prevent these unhappy consequences.

C. *Support Respiration and Blood Pressure*

A clear airway is essential; if not clear, suction and placement of an oral airway are imperative; should these not suffice, intubation with a cuffed endotracheal tube should be carried out. Central respiratory depression may be combated by artificial respiration, preferably using the mouth-to-mouth or mouth-to-tube method, until mechanical ventilators are available; intermittent positive pressure oxygen should then be administered.

Decision on tracheotomy may be deferred for 24 to 48 hours, while other problems are being taken care of; then it may be scheduled as an elective procedure with much less risk. Use of respiratory stimulant drugs is highly controversial. Their gravest danger is that they may decrease assiduous measures of the type mentioned above. Aminophylline has the virtue of being both a respiratory stimulant and a water diuretic. Its use has been mentioned above. Although at times the use of other respiratory stimulants, such as intravenous methylphenidate, has been believed to be of special benefit, the recent trend has been to avoid these agents.

Shock is managed in part by support of respiration, as well as by the same procedures used to force diuresis. Large volumes of fluid alone often suffice to alleviate shock, although in refractory cases, plasma expanders or plasma may be used with benefit. At least 1 liter of intravenous fluid should be administered on admission, and as much as 4 or 5 liters in 24 hours may be required. Pressor agents are seldom needed in drug-induced shock and, in the opinion of some, are contraindicated.

IV. Special Problem with Specific Classes of Drugs

A. Antipsychotic Agents

These drugs consist of the large group of phenothiazine derivatives, exemplified by chlorpromazine (CPZ); a kindred thioxanthine derivative, chlorprothixine; the rauwolfia alkaloids, exemplified by reserpine; and the butyrophenones, exemplified by haloperidol. As mentioned above, poisonings with phenothiazine derivatives are probably fairly common in clinical practice, yet reports in the literature are scarce. Perhaps this rarity of case reports is due to the almost uniformly favorably outcome. The few fatal cases of ingestion of CPZ have all been in children (310). The minimal lethal dose in a 4-year-old child was 350 mg (fourteen 25-mg tablets). However, adults have survived doses of 9.75 gm (195 fifty-mg tablets). Apparently, no deaths have been reported from overdoses of chlorprothixine, the largest doses taken with survival being 1.075 gm (forty-three 25-mg tablets) in a 1-year-old child and 8 gm (eighty 100-mg tablets) in an adult. Neither reserpine nor haloperidol has been associated with death following overdoses. A child who took an amount of crystalline reserpine in excess of 1 gm (four thousand 0.25-mg tablets) survived with little apparent difficulty.

Progressive impairment of consciousness is the rule, leading from drowsiness to coma. Initially, patients may become agitated or delirious with confusion and disorientation. Twitching, dystonic movements, and convulsions are other prominent neurological signs. Convulsions may be tonic, clonic, or startle seizures. Pupils are miotic and deep tendon reflexes decreased. EEG's show diffuse slowing and low voltage. Tachycardia and marked hypotension are the principal cardiovascular manifestations, although an occasional patient may have a cardiac arrhythmia. The strong alpha-adrenergic blocking action of phenothiazines may make alleviation of hypotension difficult. Hypothermia is the rule, initially due to disturbance of temperature regulation; later, with increased activity, fever may appear, although rarely true hyperpyrexia; the usual ranges of temperature are between 31° and 40°C. Late respiratory failure, often sudden, has been the distinguishing features in fatal cases; vigilance must be careful and prolonged, so long as severe CNS depression persists. Prolonged shock and cardiac arrest have also been causes of death.

As most phenothiazines are readily water-soluble, removal by gastric lavage is feasible; as they delay gastric motility, lavage may be successful in removing considerable amounts of drug hours after ingestion. Once absorbed, phenothiazines are tightly bound to protein and become rapidly fixed in tissues. Experimental attempts to hemodialyze ^{35}S-labeled CPZ indicated little transfer across the cellophane membranes. Thus, it is unlikely that any dialysis procedure will be useful in ridding the body of absorbed drug; the same is very likely the case with exchange transfusions.

Besides the general principles of management mentioned above, the special problems of phenothiazine intoxication must be met as they arise. Convulsions are best treated by intravenous injections of diazepam or sodium diphenylhydantoin. The possibility of increasing central respiratory depression with further doses of a central depressant drug should be balanced against the anticonvulsant effect, and only minimally effective doses used. Acute hypotension, not responsive to forced fluids, may require the use of a pressor agent; norepinephrine is the logical drug for treatment, being primarily an alpha-adrenergic stimulant; other pressor agents which have been tried with success are intravenous dextroamphetamine and phenylephrine. Warm blankets and heat cradles may reverse the trend toward hypothermia, but, if one overshoots the mark, fever will ensue; the latter should not be immediately ascribed to some infectious complication in the absence of other evidence.

An unusual presentation of a case of presumed thioridazine overdose caused the diagnosis to be missed. Lateralizing neurological signs of sudden onset in a 47-year-old woman led to the diagnosis of a cerebrovascular accident, but post-mortem toxicological studies suggested an overdose of 8 gm or more of thioridazine. Lacking adequate treatment, the patient died in 12 hours. A single instance of permanent brain damage following recovery from a presumed overdose of a phenothiazine derivative was reported in a 5-year-old who showed residuals 2 years later. Brain damage was bilateral and diffuse, with prominent signs of basal ganglia and pyramidal tract involvement.

B. Antidepressants

These drugs consist of two separate pharmacological classes. One, termed the tricyclic antidepressants, consists of imipramine and amitriptyline, as well as the newly introduced analogs, desipramine and nortriptyline. Another class, the monoamine oxidase (MAO) inhibitors, is exemplified by tranylcypromine, phenelzine, isocarboxazid, and nialamide. It would be quite fitting if drugs used for treating depressed patients, where suicide is an ever-present danger, were as safe as the antipsychotics. Unfortunately, this is not the case. The problems from overdoses of the two separate classes of antidepressants are different and will, therefore, be considered separately.

1. Tricyclic Antidepressants

Doses of imipramine in excess of 1.2 gm are seriously toxic, with fatalities in adults fairly common after ingestion of 2.5 gm (100 25-mg tablets). The time of death following ingestion of such large doses varies between 3 and 72 hours (311). As much as 5.375 gm has been taken by an adult with survival. A $2\frac{1}{2}$-year-old child who ingested 2.5 gm of imipramine died within 90 minutes, but a dose of 75 mg per kilogram was survived by another child. Amitriptyline may be a bit more potent than imipramine in regard to toxity. A dose of 1.0 gm (forty 25-mg tablets) was fatal in a 15-month-old child, while a dose of as little as 950 mg was fatal in a 70-year-old woman. However, desipramine may be less potent. A 58-year-old woman who ingested 1.15 gm became semicomatose and hypotensive within 30 minutes, but responded quickly to infusion of norepinephrine and was conscious 3 hours later; the course might have been expected to be longer and more complicated with a similar dose of imipramine. Reports of overdoses of nortriptyline are not available, but this drug might be expected to produce less serious reactions than similar doses of amitriptyline.

The tricyclic antidepressants are more like the phenothiazines in their pharmacological actions than they are different. Consequently, they share many of the same clinical effects when given in toxic doses. A decreasing level of consciousness leading to coma is regularly observed; early, the patient may become temporarily agitated or delirious. Cardiorespiratory depression is frequent, although hypotension is less predictable than with the phenothiazines. The mechanism of hypotension is assumed to be a blockade of pressor receptors. Pupils are dilated and sluggish, a reflection of the potent anticholinergic actions of these drugs. The same problems in maintaining body temperature arise, although hyperthermia is likely to be a greater problem than hypothermia. Myoclonic seizures, twitches, increased deep tendon reflexes, and even plantar extensor responses are frequent concomitants of toxic doses. The major distinguishing feature of intoxication with these drugs is a number of disturbances of cardiac rhythm and conduction. These include ventricular flutter or runs of tachycardia, atrial fibrillation or tachycardia, and varying degrees of atrioventricular or intraventricular block. These arrhythmias may be due to combined vagal block and a negative chronotropic effect.

The cardiac problems are uniquely difficult to manage. One is faced with controlling arrhythmias in the face of impaired cardiac conduction; as most commonly used drugs for control of arrhythmias would aggravate the conduction disturbances, it is probably better to avoid their use. The anticholinesterases, especially pyridostigmine have been effective in diminishing toxicity in animals treated with toxic doses of amitriptyline. It is possible that this drug might ameliorate some of the arrhythmias, as well as other symptoms; doses of 0.5–1.0 mg intramuscularly have been recommended, with a repetition in 10 minutes if the pulse rate is not slowed. Electric cardioversion is a technique to be considered in the face of persistent arrhythmias. Because of the possibility of rapid changes in cardiac rhythm or cardiac arrest, continual EKG monitoring is desirable, with provisions at hand for defibrillation and resuscitation.

Treatment is in most respects similar to that outlined for the phenothiazines. In the most severely intoxicated patient to recover, mannitol was used as an osmotic diuretic to hasten excretion of drug, and dialysis was used to manage hyperpyrexia (312). More than with the phenothiazines, the tricyclic antidepressants tend to induce bladder and bowel paralysis due to their strong anticholinergic effects. Just as with phenothiazines, the potentiation of sedative effects of barbiturates makes these drugs less preferable than others for managing seizures. It should be remembered that one of the pharmacological tests for compounds of this type is the potentiation of pressor responses to norepinephrine or tyramine; use of pressor amines should be considered only if plasma expanders and fluid replacement fail to alleviate shock.

Just as with phenothiazines, removal of these drugs prior to absorption is easy but extremely difficult after they have been bound to protein. There is little evidence that these drugs are dialyzable, so the excretory route of choice is by forced diuresis.

2. Monoamine Oxidase Inhibitors

A 500-mg dose (fifty 10-mg tablets) of tranylcypromine proved fatal for a 17-year-old girl who exhibited agitation, delirium, tremors, sweating coma, shock, heart block, and profound hyperthermia (110°) for 8 hours before she died. Barbiturates were used, but were ineffective; a slight fall in body temperature was achieved by tubbing. A 15-year-old girl who ingested 350 mg of tranylcypromine was subjected to hemodialysis and made a rapid recovery; presumably the drug can be dialyzed readily (313). Ingestion of a dose of 750 (fifty 15-mg tablets) of phenelzine was not fatal in a patient weighing 54 kg, but ataxia, weakness, drowsiness, delirium, seizures, muscle fasciculations, and hyperthermia were encountered (314). Administration of CPZ appeared to be an effective antagonist. That the latter drug was effective seems reasonable, for most of the toxic effects of the MAO inhibitors are attributable to excessive adrenergic stimulation. In this regard, toxicity of these drugs resembles that from amphetamines. Reports of overdoses of these drugs are still infrequent; one would hope that this is due to their declining use. Many of us believe that the lack of convincing evidence for efficacy of these drugs in controlled trials in depressed patients, as well as their hazards, contraindicate their use.

C. Antianxiety Agents

The most widely used of these drugs are meprobamate and its congeners, chlordiazepoxide or its closely related analog, diazepam, and the so-called nonbarbiturate sedative-hypnotic, glutethimide.

Meprobamate has been fatal when taken in doses as small as 20 gm (fifty 400-mg tablets), though recoveries have occurred after doses of 40 gm. As sedatives are often taken in combination with other drugs or with alcohol, it is difficult to be certain about the contributing factors to mortality from overdoses of these drugs. The clinical picture of this intoxication resembles that of barbiturates and the management is the same. The relatively small amount of meprobamate excreted by the kidney as compared to the hepatic metabolism suggests that forced diuresis may be of limited value in these cases, but no doubt it should still be part of a generally supportive treatment program (315). Despite the popularity of this drug, it is still a relatively infrequent cause of suicide as compared with barbiturates. Perhaps the large size and the high price of the tablets act as a deterrent. A chemical congener, tybamate, has a very short biological half-life and should be free of suicidal potential.

It is probably impossible to commit suicide with chlordiazepoxide or diazepam. No deaths were encountered in 22 instances of overdosage of the former drug, even with doses of up to 2.25 gm (ninety 25-mg capsules) (316). After observing 121 cases of poisoning with chlordiazepoxide in patients from 15 months to 63 years of age, the conclusion was reached that when the drug was used alone, symptoms were quite mild, consisting only of drowsiness or stupor. When the drug was used in combination with others, the effects of the second drug always predominated (317). Two instances of diazepam overdosage in children have been relatively mild. Toxic effects of overdosage are deep stupor and coma, marked muscle relaxation, but little fall in blood pressure or respiratory depression. Supportive treatment is usually enough. As the drugs have a rather long half-life in plasma, dialysis may be used to hasten elimination and reduce the period of morbidity. The new analogs, such as oxazepam, should prove to be equally innocuous and briefer in their effects. As anxious patients are often issued large supplies of drugs between visits to the physician, it is easy to order an amount which could be lethal. The availability of such safe and effective sedatives as drugs of this type is a definite advantage.

Glutethimide is almost unique among CNS depressants in that it must be completely metabolized, none of the drug being excreted unchanged. Most of the excretion of drug is in bile; even comparatively small doses produce profound and lasting effects, coma and respiratory depression predominating. A fatal outcome occurred in a 27-year-old woman who took only 5 gm (20 250-mg tablets), despite the use of peritoneal dialysis. Death may very well have been hastened by a 1200-ml loss of dialysis fluid into the thorax 3 hours preterminally. However, doses as high as 35 gm have been taken with recovery, reemphasizing that the dose of drug taken is less a determinant of the outcome than the way the poisoning is managed.

Besides the slow metabolic disposition of glutethimide, its high lipid solubility allows it to be stored in fat depots; both make for a very long clinical course of any intoxication, some lasting for 5 days. Although not easily soluble, some drug may be removed by hemodialysis, which should be undertaken in any case with severe clinical signs. Dialysis may have to be repeated, as blood levels rise after an initial decline due to release of drug from fat stores. Removal of the drug by dialysis can be facilitated if a lipid dialysate is used; however, such treatment is largely experimental. Chemical determinations of blood levels of the drug are not too difficult and may provide a means for monitoring the effects of treatment. Hypoxia has always seemed to be greater than can be accounted for by respiratory depression; the occurrence of methemoglobinemia in conjunction with these intoxications has been reported. The special problems associated with poisonings due to this drug should be recognized if treatment is to be as effective as possible.

D. Combination of Drugs

Frequently, drugs are sold in fixed combinations or may be taken in mixtures because of their availability. The interactions between toxic doses of two or more drugs may create special problems.

The combination of tranylcypromine and trifluoperazine, marketed in Canada and Europe but not in the United States, proved fatal in a 27-year-old man who took 30 tablets containing 10 mg and 1 mg, respectively, of the drugs. Over a 24-hour period, he became restless, sweated profusely, showed signs of anxiety, and then became drowsy. Thirty hours after ingestion, he suddenly developed coma, hypotension, and intense muscle rigidity. The latter was severe enough to impair respiration; death occurred 36 hours after ingestion. The slow onset and the marked muscle rigidity were unusual features in this case; the authors suggest that future cases showing such symptoms be treated by muscle relaxants to the point of paralysis and maintained on positive pressure respiration. A milder version of the same clinical picture was seen in a 20-month-old girl who swallowed 4 or 5 tablets of this combination. Initially, she appeared to be normal, then vomited, became restless, and finally drowsy to the point of semicoma. Twenty hours after ingestion, she showed athetoid movements of the extremities and neck spasms. Generally increased muscle tonus, brisk reflexes, and nystagmus were also noted. Blood pressure was elevated to 130/90. The patient was treated with promazine and recovered, although it is not certain that the latter drug had any special effect. It was postulated that antihistaminic drugs might have been of benefit in alleviating the Parkinson-like symptoms.

A dose of 900 mg of phenelzine and 1.0 gm of phenobarbital was fatal in a 30-year-old man who had been taking the former drug for two years. He developed coma and severe hyperpyrexia with death 45 hours after ingestion. The clinical signs were mainly those of the phenelzine overdose. A similar dose of phenelzine (180 mg) combined with 800 mg of amitriptyline led to somnolence, disorientation, labile blood pressure, and plantar extensor responses in a 38-year-old woman. Late in her course, she developed bladder paralysis, presumably due to the anticholinergic action of the amitriptyline. Recovery was uneventful. The patient had been on chronic therapeutic doses of amitriptyline prior to taking the combination; the clinical symptoms in this instance were quite different from those of intense central sympathetic stimulation (coma, seizures, and hyperpyrexia), which have occurred in patients who have taken therapeutic or toxic doses of tricyclic antidepressants following prolonged treatment with MAO inhibitors.

Sublethal individual doses of three drugs (imipramine, 600 mg; tranylcypromine, 130 mg; and trifluoperazine, 13 mg) were lethal for a 26-year-old man who took them in combination. Initial symptoms were tremors, nystagmus, and carpopedal spasms; later he became semicomatose, developed fever, and died.

It seems always worth emphasizing the potential lethality of combining sedative drugs and alcohol. Many unwitting suicides by patients or homicides by physicians have followed the injudicious use of barbiturates to treat acute alcoholic states, as the two drugs have additive respiratory depressent effects. Sudden and unexpected deaths have followed paraldehyde therapy for alcoholism. Such deaths occurred from one-half to 4 hours following doses of 30 to 60 ml of paraldehyde in nine acute alcoholics; autopsy revealed no morphologic cause of death (318). Chlordiazepoxide, diazepam, and phenothiazines are widely used for treating alcohol intoxication, and thus far, at least, no deaths have been reported from their combination with alcohol. Hydroxyzine has also been used, but the danger of evoking seizures by overdoses is great. Lacking definite knowledge of possible interactions between many sedatives and alcohol, their employment in patients with high levels of blood alcohol should be most cautious.

V. Summary

In general, the management of overdoses of the newer psychotherapeutic drugs is similar to that for older sedatives and stimulants, although some special problems are associated with specific drugs. Further, it is comforting that at least some of the newer agents are remarkably safe, with the possibility of a lethal outcome quite rare. All the drugs have a very large margin between therapeutic doses and severely toxic doses. Still, it is well to remember that patients can use these drugs for suicidal purposes or that they may inadvertently fall into innocent hands with tragic results. Ordering only small quantities in single prescriptions, identifying the prescribed drug, and treating the patient in the most expeditious and specific fashion are ways to reduce mortality.

For suggested reading and references see Appendices 1 and 2.

44

TREATMENT OF DRUG ABUSERS

Jerome H. Jaffe

I. Introduction and Definitions

The definition of drug abuse is largely social and, therefore, the behavior defined as *abuse* with respect to any given pharmacological agent varies from culture to culture and from time to time within the same culture. From a pharmacological point of view, the social attitudes toward a particular drug are often inconsistent or irrational. Some drugs may be totally proscribed, while others with similar pharmacological actions are made generally available and may be self-administered with social approval. Such shifts and inconsistencies have caused so much semantic confusion that each writer must define his terms explicitly.

Drug abuse will be used here to mean the use of a drug, regardless of the legality of its use, that deviates from the patterns deemed acceptable by the society in which the individual is living. Since the laws may not always correspond to the attitudes of the majority of citizens, (e.g., the use of alcohol in the United States during the 1920's), there may be times when an occasional user of an illegal drug is not considered to be a drug abuser. The effects of some drugs are such that they are unlikely to be used outside of socially approved situations. For example, chlorpromazine is virtually never self-administered unless it is medically prescribed.

The term *psychological dependence* will be used to mean that as a result of repeated use the effects of a drug or the conditions associated with its use are necessary to maintain an optimal state of well-being. The intensity of the dependence may vary from a mildly felt desire to a "craving" or "compulsion" to use the drug. Under certain conditions, this *sense of need* (psychological dependence) may result in behavior characterized by a preoccupation with the use and procurement of the drug—i.e., *compulsive drug use.* This behavior may reach an extreme form which has the characteristics of a chronic relapsing disorder. Generally, intense reliance on the effects of a self-administered drug is a deviation from the expected and socially approved pattern of use. Thus, the terms *compulsive drug use* and *compulsive drug abuse* are usually interchangeable. However, there are exceptions. Currently, in Western societies the attitude toward the use of tobacco is so permissive that even chronic, heavy, compulsive use, damaging to the user's health, and over which he may have little control, is rarely thought of as compulsive abuse. This attitude may be changing. Usually, compulsive drug use is detrimental to the user or to society, but as the example of tobacco illustrates, attitudes are not entirely consistent.

Addiction is used here to describe a behavioral pattern of compulsive drug use, characterized by overwhelming involvement with the use of a drug, the securing of its supply, and a high tendency to relpase after withdrawal. Addiction is, therefore, an extreme on a continuum of involvement with drug use. Since it has a quantitative rather than a qualitative connotation, it is not possible to state with precision at what point compulsive drug use has sufficiently pervaded the total life activity of a user to warrant the term *addiction.*

II. Pharmacological Classification and Generalizations

It is clear that certain classes of drugs used for their subjective effects are more likely to be used compulsively than others. It is also clear that certain pharmacological phenomena such as tolerance and physical dependence are associated with some classes and not with others; but the relationship between the pharmacological and the behavioral phenomena is not entirely clear. In Table I the drugs used for their subjective effects have been put into four major categories: (1) hallucinogenic agents; (2) CNS stimulants; (3) CNS depressants; (4) narcotic analgesics (morphine-like drugs).

The narcotic analgesics include heroin, morphine, meperidine (Demerol), and methadone (Dolophine). The drugs specifically shown should be viewed only as representative. There are actually more than fifteen narcotic analgesics which are clinically available in the United States and more than a score are available in other parts of the world. The CNS depressants include substances with a wide variety of chemical structures: the barbiturates, alcohol, chloral hydrate, paraldehyde, the so-called nonbarbiturate sedatives, such as glutethimide (Doriden), ethchlorvynol (Placidyl), methyprylon (Noludar), and certain antianxiety agents such as meprobamate (Miltown), chlordiazepoxide (Librium), and diazepam (Valium). This group also includes anesthetic gases, such as chloroform and ether. Again, the drugs listed are merely suggestive of the diversity of agents that must be included in this category.

A more precise heading for the second group, the CNS stimulants, would be CNS sympathomimetics. There are many kinds of CNS stimulants, such as pentylenetetrazol (Metrazol) or strychnine, that are never abused. Those that are seem to exert their effects either by releasing norepinephrine from nerve endings or by potentiating its action once it is released.

TABLE I

Drugs Self-Administered for Subjective Effects

<table>
<tr><td colspan="3">1. Hallucinogenic agents:
marijuana, mescaline, LSD, psilocybin, DMT, DOM (STP), etc.</td><td rowspan="5">Subject to abuse

III</td></tr>
<tr><td>2. Central Nervous System stimulants:
cocaine, amphetamines, methylphenidate, phenmetrazine, etc.</td><td>?</td><td rowspan="4">Abuse of addictive proportions

II</td></tr>
<tr><td>3. Central Nervous System depressants:
barbiturates, alcohol, paraldehyde, chloral hydrate, meprobamate, chlordiazepoxide, diazepam, glutethimide, ethchlorvynol, methyprylon, anesthetic gases and vapors, etc.</td><td rowspan="3">Chronic use produces physical dependence

I</td></tr>
<tr><td>NO cross-dependence</td></tr>
<tr><td>4. Narcotic analgesics:
morphine, heroin, meperidine, methadone, codeine, hydromorphone, etc.</td></tr>
</table>

Included as hallucinogenics are such chemically diverse agents as lysergic acid diethylamide (LSD), mescaline, dimethyl tryptamine (DMT), psilocybin, and 2,5-dimethoxy-4-methyl amphetamine (STP). Again, the drugs shown are only illustrative of many with comparable actions. Marijuana is included here since, like the other hallucinogenics, at low doses it produces mood changes and alterations in sensory and time perception, and at high doses it can induce toxic psychoses.

Table I also illustrates several pharmacological generalizations that may be useful in the treatment of compulsive drug users. The column to the extreme right of the chart indicates that all of the drugs listed can be abused, in the sense that people have used them in socially unsanctioned ways. Column II indicates that it is only the drugs in the last three groups which are involved in that extreme form of drug-using behavior that we call *addiction.* Generally speaking, even those who use hallucinogenics with considerable regularity do not permit drug use to become so dominant a theme in their lives that we would view them as compulsive users overwhelmingly involved with the use and procuring of hallucinogenics. Column I indicates that the last two groups (the narcotic analgesics and the CNS general depressants) produce *physical dependence.* This term is neither synonymous nor interchangeable with the term *addiction.* It is possible to be physically dependent on a drug but not addicted to it; one can also be addicted to a drug, in the behavioral sense, without being physically dependent on it. *Physical dependence* is a general term used to refer to an altered state of physiology produced by the repeated administration of certain classes of drugs, such that a characteristic pattern of signs and symptoms appears when the drug is withdrawn and disappears when it is again administered. So defined, physical dependence can be produced by a wide variety of drugs, and each class of drugs seems to produce its own particular pattern of withdrawal phenomena. Some of these, chlorpromazine, imipramine, scopolamine, have never been known to be associated with the extreme form of compulsive drug-using behavior referred to as addiction.

As indicated in the chart, both the narcotic analgesics and the CNS general depressants produce physical dependence, but the character of the physical dependence produced by the narcotic analgesics is quite different from that produced by the CNS general depressants. For example, the withdrawal of barbiturates produces a syndrome characterized by anxiety, restlessness, tremors, and insomnia. If the degree of physical dependence is at all severe, the syndrome may also include grand mal convulsions and a delirium with disorientation and hallucinations. Meprobamate, glutethimide, or paraldehyde withdrawal syndromes are also characterized by anxiety, insomnia, tremors, convulsions, and delirium. The syndromes are clinically indistinguishable. When the drug being withdrawn is alcohol, we call the severe form of the withdrawal syndrome *delirium tremens* or D.T.'s, but when it is a barbiturate or meprobamate, we call it the barbiturate or meprobamate withdrawal syndrome.

The similarity of syndromes produced when any of these agents is withdrawn is a major reason for placing these heterogeneous chemicals into a single category (CNS general depressants). Another reason for considering these agents together has significant implications for the management of the withdrawal syndromes. All of the agents within each of classes 3 and 4 exhibit a considerable degree of cross-dependence; i.e., one agent can partially, if not totally, suppress the abstinence phenomena caused by withdrawal of another. For example, pentobarbital can suppress the abstinence phenomena seen after withdrawal of other barbiturates, meprobamate, glutethimide, and even alcohol. As a teaching exercise, we have treated D.T.'s with high doses of pentobarbital (it often required between 800 to 1000 mg per day), and found it quite satisfactory. Of course, once a patient is stabilized on such doses of pentobarbital, it is then necessary to withdraw the barbiturate over a period of 6–10 days in order to avoid the barbiturate withdrawal symptomatology.

Cross-dependence among the narcotic analgesics is even more apparent. In treating a heroin withdrawal syndrome it is not necessary to give heroin, but one can give morphine, methadone, or any number of potent narcotics.

There is little or no cross-dependence between the narcotics and CNS general depressants. Thus, patients physically dependent on barbiturates can be given rather high doses of narcotic analgesics, but will still show barbiturate withdrawal symptoms. Conversely, patients dependent on opiates can be given any of the sedative-like agents in the CNS general depressants group, but short of inducing general anesthesia, opiate withdrawal phenomena will still occur.

One other pharmacological generalization that is extremely useful in understanding and managing withdrawal syndromes is the inverse relationship between the rate at which a drug is metabolized or eliminated and the intensity of the withdrawal syndrome when the drug is abruptly withdrawn. For example, after abrupt withdrawal of shorter acting narcotics, such as heroin or hydromorphone (Dilaudid), the withdrawal syndrome begins sooner (8–12 hours) and is more intense, but is relatively brief, with obvious signs and symptoms lasting only a few days. In contrast, a drug like methadone seems to leave the body slowly; withdrawal symptoms may not occur until 36 hours after the last dose, and peak withdrawal symptoms usually occur on the fourth to sixth days. Although the signs and symptoms of methadone withdrawal are less dramatic (vomiting, diarrhea, and kicking movements are uncommon), the lassitude, general discomfort, restlessness, and insomnia may persist for more than 2 weeks. Similarly, after withdrawal of the shorter acting barbiturates (e.g., pentobarbital, secobarbital), and sedative hypnotics (glutethimide, meprobamate, chloral hydrate), the onset of signs and symptoms is relatively prompt—tremulousness, anxiety, and insomnia are prominent within the first 12–36 hours, and convulsions, when they occur, usually do so within the first 48 hours. Delirium commonly follows the convulsions. After withdrawal of drugs with longer biological half-lives (e.g., barbital, chlordiazepoxide), the withdrawal syndrome is slower in onset (seizures may not occur for 6–8 days), milder, and somewhat more prolonged. Wulff (319), in his review of the barbiturate withdrawal syndrome, concluded that if the rate of elimination is slower than 20% per day, EEG changes and withdrawal symptoms will not occur.

The physiological alterations associated with the compulsive use of the drugs in classes 1 and 2 are covered in other chapters.

In a very general way, these are the pharmacological principles on which the management of the physiological aspects of compulsive drug use is based. In the more detailed descriptions of the management of various types of drug abusers, some of these principles are illustrated further.

III. The Approach to Treatment: Assessment and Formulation of Goals

The role the physician or psychiatrist plays in the complex problem of drug abuse depends on what is asked of him and the social and legal context in which the problem is presented.

Over the past few years it has become increasingly clear that there is no single reason for beginning to use psychoactive drugs, no single pattern of drug abuse, nor any one inevitable outcome. In developing a rational program for an individual the physician must try to weigh the relative importance of the many possible contributory factors: These may include persistent characterological problems that antedated drug use; psychological or physiological disturbances (pain, anxiety, depression) for which the drugs were originally prescribed and for which they continue to act as therapeutic agents; highly reinforced patterns of drug-using behavior (320); the significance of the patient's drug use in maintaining the psychosocial equilibrium of his interpersonal relationships; and sociocultural factors, such as economic status, ethnic origin, housing, vocational possibilities, and previous antisocial patterns, all of which may limit the range of alternative nondrug-using behaviors.

Obviously, as brief a consideration of the problem as this one cannot discuss each of the relevant factors in detail; but the therapist must consider all of them in evolving a set of goals for a particular patient. As an ideal we would want every patient to become emotionally stable, law abiding, and productive. In most cases the goals we can realistically set are more limited, and often we must choose between some degree of continued drug use accompanied by productive and generally acceptable social behavior or periodic institutionalization followed by a return to drug use and reinstitutionalization.

A. The Urban Heroin User

1. Initial Management

A typical urban heroin user is a male in his middle twenties or early thirties. He probably belongs to an ethnic or racial minority, lives with his family or with his spouse, has been arrested more than once, has used drugs other than opiates (e.g., amphetamines and barbiturates), but only opiates consistently. His work record is irregular, and he usually has one or more sources of illegal income in addition to any job he may be holding.

Withdrawal of narcotics has been the first step in all of the traditional treatment approaches, and, with the exception of the methadone maintenance approach, complete withdrawal and eventual total abstinence from narcotics is one of the goals of treatment. In many parts of the country, physicians have become more willing to provide some form of medication while the patient is awaiting hospitalization for withdrawal. For example, the patient may claim to be working at the time he seeks treatment, and, while he is willing to be withdrawn from narcotics in a hospital, he requests a few days to get his affairs in order and to arrange for time off from work. Under these conditions it is always ethical, and perfectly legal in most of the United States (California is an exception), to prescribe medication to prevent withdrawal symptoms if the patient is physically dependent. The ethical status of this approach is clearly put forth in the most recent statement of the American Medical Association-National Academy of Science/National Research Council Committee on Drug Addiction and Narcotics (321).

The most satisfactory drug for this purpose is methadone. Many patients will attempt to persuade the physician to prescribe a narcotic that can be used intravenously, such as hydromorphone, meperidine, or morphine. This is generally unwise and not in the best interest of the community or the patient. Oral drugs are preferable for several reasons. There are significant differences between the effects of a drug given intravenously and the same drug given orally. The oral route produces no "rush," and the duration of action in preventing withdrawal symptoms is considerably longer. In addition, parenteral drugs prescribed for self-administration are more likely to be used before the prescribed period or to be illicitly diverted. When told firmly that oral methadone is the only drug that will be prescribed, most patients will accept this condition. One way to assure that the methadone is not illicitly redistributed and that the patient consumes only one day's supply at a time is for the physician to arrange for the patient to ingest the day's dose under the supervision of a nurse or the pharmacist. This is greatly facilitated by dissolving the methadone in 3 or 4 oz of fruit juice. The use of fruit juice also prevents parenteral use on those occasions when the patient is permitted to have more than one day's supply. (In many areas an elixir of methadone is available.) In a series of more than fifty urban heroin users so treated while awaiting hospitalization the daily dose of methadone required to permit them to discontinue illicit drugs entirely was between 25 and 60 mg, but only rarely was more than 50 mg required.

When treated with methadone, the heroin user can be expected to reduce or to discontinue entirely the use of illicit drugs, and to avoid antisocial behavior. If the period prior to hospitalization is to be more than a week or two, the patient can also be expected to become involved in productive behavior. It is usually possible to determine if a patient is working or looking for work, and in many parts of the country there are laboratories that can test urine for opiates and other commonly abused drugs. In contrast to this temporary procedure of using medication to prevent withdrawal, the narcotic regulations of most states view the prescription of a narcotic drug over a prolonged period (months or years) as permissible only in the context of carefully controlled medical research. Therefore, the patients for whom methadone is prescribed should be prepared for the withdrawal of this drug. However, many narcotics users provided with moderate doses of oral methadone once daily seem able to work and to reduce or discontinue illicit drug use. Some function so well on this daily schedule of oral methadone that there is now considerable interest in redefining the legal status of prolonged methadone maintenance treatment.

2. Narcotic Withdrawal Techniques

Sometimes oral methadone can be reduced gradually enough (e.g., 5 mg/week over a period of 4–6 weeks) so that hospitalization is unnecessary, but with most urban heroin users who are in daily contact with other active users such ambulatory withdrawal cannot be accomplished. If immediate relapse to use of illicit narcotics is to be avoided, patients must be housed in an environment where they have no access to such drugs for at least 7–14 days after all narcotics are withdrawn, and a period of several weeks is preferable.

The management of the narcotic withdrawal syndrome is now well standardized. It is based on two general principles previously described: (1) cross-dependence between morphine-like drugs, and (2) the inverse relationship between duration of drug action and intensity of the signs and symptoms of the withdrawal. Thus, regardless of the specific narcotic which has caused the physical dependence, the withdrawal syndrome can be suppressed by stabilizing the patient on oral methadone for 24 hours prior to beginning gradual reduction of methadone dosage. Very commonly, the urban heroin user tends to exaggerate the amount of heroin used in order to induce the physician to prescribe large amounts of methadone during withdrawal; however, more than 20 mg of methadone twice daily is rarely needed during the first 24 hours. Thereafter, it can be reduced by 5 mg/day and the patient should not experience more than mild discomfort and some difficulty in sleeping during the week following withdrawal. Oral methadone need not be given more than twice daily. The signs and symptoms of abrupt opiate withdrawal are clearly described by Isbell and White (322). However, the properly managed withdrawal syndrome seen with rapid reduction of substituted methadone produces few, if any, detectable signs or symptoms, and patients are able to eat and sleep reasonably well over the entire period.

3. Postwithdrawal Treatment

With the urban heroin user, the efforts of physicians using individual and group psychotherapeutic techniques to prevent relapse have been spectacularly unsuccessful. This does not mean, however, that detoxified narcotics users always relapse. It is more accurate to state that success in preventing relapse requires aftercare systems and techniques that are often unavailable to the individual physician. Among the rehabilitative systems that seem to have promise, and which are available in some areas, are therapeutic communities such as Synanon in California, Daytop Village, Phoenix Houses, and Odyssey House in New York, and Gateway House in Chicago. These organizations, run almost entirely by rehabilitated ex-addicts, are complex social systems in which status, prestige, and sometimes material goods and high salaries are bestowed on those members of the group who behave in a mature and constructive manner. Since participation requires an expression of interest and motivation on the part of those seeking admission, only well-motivated patients should be referred. Referral before narcotic withdrawal is often possible, because these organizations are able to create an environment in which healthy adults with only a moderate degree of physical dependence can be withdrawn without medical supervision or medication. Patients with medical problems or with physical dependence on barbiturates should be withdrawn prior to referral. [For a more detailed description of these therapeutic communities see Casriel (323), and Volkman (324).]

Some states have initiated civil commitment programs for narcotics users. These programs may offer group therapy during a period of involuntary institutionalization; but, in general, such programs are essentially *supervisory-deterrent* systems. Following relapse patients are tested with nalorphine, or their urine is tested frequently to determine if they are using narcotics. If they are found to be using such drugs, they are returned to the institution for further treatment. The efficacy of such systems for inducing long-term improvement is not fully established.

At present there are two pharmacological approaches to the compulsive opiate user available to the physician, or which will be available in the near future. These are the use of *narcotic antagonists* in the prevention of relapse, and *methadone maintenance*—a technique of using high daily doses of oral methadone with an implied commitment to continue such treatment for an indefinite period.

4. Narcotic Antagonists

Narcotic antagonists are most conveniently viewed as competitive antagonists of morphine-like drugs with a high affinity for the hypothetical morphine receptor sites in the nervous system, but with little or no activity at these sites. If a narcotic antagonist is given before the administration of a morphine-like drug, the antagonist, by occupying the receptors, prevents the narcotic from producing an effect. If it is given after a narcotic drug, the antagonist will displace the narcotic from the receptors and terminate the narcotic action. When as a result of repeated administration of a morphine-like drug physical dependence has developed (detectable physical dependence begins in man with the equivalent of 15 mg of morphine four times per day for 3 or more days), administration of a narcotic antagonist will not only terminate narcotic effects but will also precipitate withdrawal symptoms. For the purpose of treatment, however, the most important implication of the agonist-antagonist relationship is that when a narcotic antagonist is given daily in a way that keeps the receptors continually occupied, not only will drugs like morphine or heroin fail to produce effects each time they are taken but even their repeated use will not cause physical dependence (presumably since they never reach the receptors).

On this basis, Martin *et al.* (325) have suggested a new use for narcotic antagonists. Working with cyclazocine, a long-acting orally effective antagonist, they demonstrated that patients given this drug daily (2 mg orally every 12 hours) felt the effects of a 60-mg dose of morphine as equivalent to 10 mg and perceived a 120-mg dose as being less than the equivalent of a 30-mg dose. Even on this very modest dose schedule, 60 mg of morphine given four times each day for several weeks produced only a very mild morphine-type physical dependence. They therefore suggested that the regular administration of drugs like cyclazocine (after withdrawal of narcotics) might be useful in preventing relapse to narcotics once patients are released into the community.

a. Rationale for the Use of Narcotic Antagonists. Continued administration of narcotic antagonists might prove useful for several reasons. It has been proposed that in addition to whatever underlying personality problems might predispose to the initial abuse of narcotics, the compulsive user has acquired a complex set of instrumentally and classically conditioned responses—a set of responses that tend to perpetuate the use of opiates and to predispose to relapse after detoxification. Within this context opiate use may be viewed as an emitted response, and the relief of "tension" (pain, anxiety, depression, guilt, or anger) or the production of euphoria, produces a progressively stronger tendency to seek out the drug each time the tension reduction or euphoria reinforces the preceding drug-using behavior. With repeated regular use physical dependence develops. This causes still another tension (opiate withdrawal distress) that regularly appears when an opiate is not used, and that is dramatically and specifically relieved each time an opiate is used. It has been proposed that the repeated relief of this withdrawal distress is the major factor that generates the highly reinforced patterns of drug-using behavior (320). Recent research in which animals inject themselves with drugs suggests that opiates are reinforcers even if they do not reduce withdrawal distress. Thus, animals will inject themselves with amphetamines and cocaine which do not produce opiate-like physical dependence, and they will inject themselves with morphine under conditions where they are not physically dependent and where they do not seem to be under any tension. However, regardless of the mechanism by which a drug reinforces drug-seeking behavior, within the conditioning framework the elimination of such behavior could best be accomplished by having the addict (animal or man) use narcotics under conditions similar or identical to those in which the original reinforcement occurred, but without getting any drug effect. Theoretically, this situation could be brought about if the addict could be made to take a large enough dose of a narcotic antagonist to prevent the narcotic from reaching the receptor sites in the nervous system. In other words, the narcotic might still be put into the bloodstream, but it would not get to its site of action.

The conditioning hypothesis also implies that withdrawal symptoms may become conditioned to the internal and external stimuli that are present when withdrawal occurs. Thus, even after long hospitalization, an ex-addict may experience both craving and actual withdrawal symptoms on returning to a situation in which withdrawal was experienced previously. In response to these conditioned withdrawal symptoms he will probably use drugs, thereby reinitiating the cycle. Presumably, if the conditioned stimuli are presented repeatedly without the unconditioned stimulus (withdrawal distress), they will eventually lose their capacity to evoke withdrawal symptoms. The unconditioned stimuli require the development of physical dependence, and this can be prevented by the regular administration of antagonists like cyclazocine. There are many researchers who do not feel that conditioning and pharmacological factors play a major role in the genesis or perpetuation of narcotic addiction. Conceivably, the availability of antagonists such as cyclazocine will make it possible to test the hypothesis. In any case, the use of narcotic antagonists will prevent physical dependence, and the value of preventing physical dependence is quite independent of the validity of the conditioning hypothesis.

Although there are certain similarities, the use of narcotic antagonists in the treatment of narcotics abusers should be distinguished from the use of disulfiram (Antabuse) in alcoholics. The patients taking disulfiram must carefully avoid effects. The patient taking a narcotic antagonist is not injured if he uses a narcotic; he simply experiences no effect, and such ineffective use is one way in which the antagonist might help extinguish narcotics using behavior.

b. Cyclazocine Stabilization. Cyclazocine is the narcotic antagonist with which there is the most extensive clinical experience. Although it is still considered an investigational drug, the pharmacological techniques for using it are relatively straightforward. Patients who volunteer for treatment are, if necessary, withdrawn from narcotics using the methadone substitution technique. About forty-eight to seventy-two hours after the last dose of methadone, patients are tested with nalorphine, 3 mg subcutaneously. If this dose produces no discomfort it is followed 10 minutes later by 4 mg. If there is no marked increase in pupillary size, gooseflesh, or discomfort, the test is considered negative and the administration of cyclazocine is begun about 24 hours later with a starting dose of 0.10–0.25 mg. Patients are specifically told that 48 hours after the last dose of methadone the narcotic withdrawal process is not yet completed, that restlessness and insomnia may sometimes occur for an additional 7–10 days, and that a negative nalorphine test merely indicates that starting cyclazocine at this time will not make them feel worse. The staff is instructed to help patients distinguish cyclazocine effects from the residual abstinence symptoms. Patients frequently experience considerable restlessness and insomnia during this period and may require more than 200 mg of pentobarbital for adequate sedation. The rate at which the dose of cyclazocine is increased must be individualized. We have varied it from 0.10 mg every third day to 0.5 mg per day, but most commonly we have increased it by 0.25 mg/day. The purpose of increasing the dose gradually is to minimize unpleasant side effects. Therefore the rate employed depends on these side effects and on the patient's reaction to them. Some patients find the mild hallucinogenic effect quite distressing, while others seem to enjoy it; for the former it is necessary to raise the dose very slowly. Patients are permitted to leave the hospital on pass when the daily dose reaches 1.5 mg, and they can be discharged when it reaches 2.0 mg. However, they are instructed that they are not yet on full blocking doses in order to minimize the possibility that experimentation will lead either to toxicity or to disappointment with the efficacy of cyclazocine. During the time patients are hospitalized the staff must establish sufficient rapport to insure that they will continue their contact after discharge. The dosage is gradually increased over a period of several weeks to 6–8 mg/day. Unlike methadone, cyclazocine does not significantly reduce the residual hunger for narcotics which some patients seem to experience. Once the patient is discharged from the hospital there are a number of ways in which cyclazocine can be used. Thus far investigators have found it important to combine its use with group psychotherapy at least several times weekly. Since it is essential that the patient continue to take cyclazocine regularly, it is usually helpful to insist that he ingest 3 or 4 mg (or half the daily stabilization dose) in liquid form under direct observation at least twice weekly. (Patients who are omitting daily doses of cyclazocine begin to lose their tolerance for its psychotomimetic effects and are unable to tolerate the 3 to 4 mg as a single dose without mild discomfort.) Combining the supervision of cyclazocine, group therapy, and regular urine testing is perhaps the most effective way to use this pharmacological approach and quickly brings to the therapist's attention those patients who require more intensive care. Cyclazocine (6–8 mg/day) has been administered safely to several patients for periods of 18–24 months (326).

c. Precautions and Side Effects with Cyclazocine. Although the fairly rapid cyclazocine stabilization schedule just described keeps the period of hospitalization to a minimum, it also requires the greatest degree of individualization to minimize unpleasant side effects. Wherever possible it is preferable to extend the period between the end of the withdrawal syndrome and beginning the use of cyclazocine and to increase the dose of cyclazocine more slowly. A slower rate of building up to the full blocking doses of 6–8 mg/day will help to minimize side effects. Cyclazocine, like nalorphine, has mild analgesic effects and can produce mental clouding, sensory distortions, weird thoughts, and hallucinations. Other reported side effects include constipation, anxiety, dizziness, headaches, restlessness, increased libido, periods of depression, lethargy, muscular twitches, difficulty in focusing the eyes, skin sensitivity, and slowing of thought processes.

These effects of cyclazocine are apparently not due to its antagonistic actions, but rather to residual agonistic effects; therefore they are more properly thought of as dose-related side actions rather than side effects. Agonistic actions can be separated from the antagonistic actions. For example, Naloxone, the *n*-allyl derivative of oxymorphone, appears to be a relatively pure narcotic antagonist and is devoid of both analgesic and psychotomimetic effects. Fortunately, tolerance develops quickly to the agonistic actions of drugs such as cyclazocine, but not to their antagonistic effects. Therefore, if the dose is gradually increased (over a period of 3–6 weeks), most patients can be brought to full daily doses of 6–8 mg without experiencing any unpleasant side actions.

In common with nalorphine, cyclazocine produces a variety of physical dependence that is in many ways distinct from that produced by any other drugs. The most striking withdrawal symptom is repetitive episodes of brief periods of weakness and loss of environmental contact lasting less than a second and described by the patients as fainting spells or "electric shocks." When patients have been stabilized on 6–8 mg of cyclazocine per day, these withdrawal shocks appear sometime between 24 and 48 hours after the last dose. In spite of the withdrawal symptoms, there is no craving for cyclazocine and patients do not seem unduly distressed by their symptoms. In this sense cyclazocine produces physical dependence, but not addiction. Whenever it seems appropriate to discontinue cyclazocine, the withdrawal symptoms can be minimized by reducing the dosage by 0.5 mg/day.

5. Methadone Maintenance and the Notion of Narcotics Hunger

The other pharmacological approach to compulsive narcotics use involves the administration of oral methadone on a daily basis. It has been proposed that a major factor in the perpetuation of compulsive opiate use and in relapse after withdrawal is a persistent "craving" or "hunger" for narcotics—a hunger due to a "metabolic lesion" or disturbance caused by the repeated use of narcotics (320,327). The notion of a lesion-induced narcotics hunger is not incompatible with the conditioning model. Both phenomena may occur. The notion of narcotics hunger does imply, however, that to the extent that (independently of any highly reinforced drug-using behaviors) it is the hunger that motivates the continued drug use, narcotics use is best reduced by measures that reduce or eliminate the hunger. It is helpful to distinguish at least two possible varieties of such hunger. One variety is the user's verbalized urge to reexperience one or more of the initial narcotic effects—for example, the "rush" that follows intravenous use, the euphoria (the "high"), or perhaps the relief of anxiety, pain, or depression. Another entirely distinct variety consists of a prolonged or persistent "emptiness" experienced by many users after withdrawal, and that is seemingly corrected only by narcotics. This variety of narcotics hunger is not the urge to reexperience the "rush" or euphoria, but rather to reestablish a state of normality. Martin *et al.* (328) have presented findings that suggest that some physiological deviations from an individual's base-line normal state may persist for months after withdrawal of narcotics, a finding not inconsistent with a postulated metabolic disturbance.

With more than one phenomenologically distinct variety of narcotics hunger (the desire to obtain a particular drug effect and the desire to achieve physiological normality), we can conceive of agents that would satisfy one hunger without affecting the other.

The opiates and their synthetic surrogates are capable of allaying all varieties of narcotics hunger, but, depending on the dose, route of administration, and the specific agent, an opiate may affect one variety considerably more than another. For example, in the user who has been withdrawn from narcotics, a short-acting narcotic given intravenously at well-spaced intervals will produce a "rush," but between these periods the feeling of physiological abnormality will persist.

Methadone maintenance is an approach that evolved out of an attempt to find a medication that would allay narcotics hunger (329). As mentioned before, small doses of methadone given orally prevent the appearance of the opiate withdrawal syndrome in patients physically dependent on any morphine-like drug, and it is used routinely in the management of opiate withdrawal. Dole and Nyswander were the first to point out that patients maintained on a high daily dose function well and do not demand increases in dose over long periods. The methadone in such doses apparently relieves any persistent drug hunger, and patients usually report that they have lost all interest in illicit narcotics. In addition, the regular administration of methadone at high doses (100–180 mg/day) induces marked tolerance to all opiate-like drugs, including methadone itself. As a result of this tolerance, those treated with methadone cannot feel the effects of ordinary doses of other narcotics, such as heroin or morphine. Dole *et al.* (327) have referred to this high degree of tolerance as "narcotic blockade."

a. Techniques and Side Effects. As described by Dole and Nyswander, patients who volunteer for methadone maintenance are hospitalized for a period of 6 weeks, during which they are given methadone in gradually increased doses. The starting dose depends on the extent of narcotics use immediately preceding admission. Most patients are started on 15–20 mg twice daily. All medication is dissolved in fruit juice. Total daily dosage can be increased by 10–15 mg/week until "blocking doses" of 80–120 mg are reached. During the period of hospitalization patients are helped with vocational and social problems by the appropriate staff and are "oriented" to the kind of behavior that is expected of participants in the treatment program; prior to discharge they begin to take their medication in a single daily dose.

Medication is taken under direct observation, and each patient leaves a urine specimen which is analyzed for common drugs of abuse. After a variable period in the outpatient phase they are given the opportunity to come into the clinic less frequently (and to take their medication home) as their social behavior and urine tests demonstrate continued progress to a non-heroin-using and productive adaptation. Most program participants require no change of dosage once a stabilization level has been reached, and hundreds of patients have been kept on the same dose for periods of more than two years. Very often requests for increases in dose are manifestations of anxiety rather than of inadequate doses of methadone.

The most common side effects of the methadone maintenance treatment are constipation, sedation, sweating, and decreased libido. Tolerance develops to the sedative effects within a matter of days or weeks; it develops to the constipating effects only slowly, but the routine use of a stool softener is usually the only corrective measure required. Complaints about decreased libido also decrease with time, but many patients continue to complain of excessive perspiration even after months on the same dose.

Recently it has been shown that for many patients the 6 week period of hospitalization is unnecessary and that equally satisfactory results (in terms of decreased use of illicit drugs and increased social productivity) can be achieved using an ambulatory methadone stabilization technique.

b. Current Status and Critiques of the Methadone Maintenance Approach. Methadone maintenance has been criticized as substituting one euphoria-producing agent (methadone) for another (heroin). If this criticism were accurate, it would represent only a moralistic objection to a useful treatment technique. However, the tolerance to methadone is such that patients given the inactive isomer *d*-methadone cannot distinguish it from the active *l*-isomer until the onset of withdrawal symptoms several hours later (327), and it is virtually impossible for a clinician to distinguish the behavior of a person stabilized on methadone from a nontreated control.

Current reports indicate that more than two-thirds of the more than 700 former chronic heroin users now in treatment are either working or going to school or both. Furthermore, the amount of known antisocial behavior among treated patients is remarkably low when one considers that the patients selected were largely those who had failed to achieve abstinence after many years of drug use, repeated withdrawal treatments, and multiple jail sentences. The most dramatic effect of treatment is the decrease in the frequency of the use of illicit narcotics, verified objectively by means of thin layer chromatography of urine specimens taken each time the patient comes for medication. It is not clear whether the decrease in heroin use is a result of the "blockade" or the alleviation of "narcotics hunger," but at the present time the results obtained with patients treated with cyclazocine are considerably less dramatic. This suggests that the relief of "hunger" may be more important than "blockade" or that blockade may be unnecessary.

The methadone maintenance approach as described here must not be confused with the current British practice of prescribing narcotics to addicts for self-administration. For the younger heroin addict self-administration invariably means intravenous administration. It is now clear that even though the British heroin addict uses pure drugs in known amounts, he suffers from many of the same problems which in the American heroin addict were thought to be the result of contaminated drugs of widely fluctuating potency. Thus, hepatitis and endocarditis are quite common among British heroin users; and deaths from overdoses, infection, and suicide are many times higher than for comparable age groups. Social productivity is low, perhaps related to the behavioral ups and downs inherent in intravenous use of short-acting drugs (330,331).

An equally difficult problem inherent in prescribing short-acting drugs for self-administration is the impossibility of preventing illicit redistribution. If physicians prescribe considerably less than the addict states he needs, the addict will buy what he feels he needs; and if the physician prescribes more than is required, the addict may use the surplus to initiate new users. In either case, the soil is prepared for illicit drug traffic. With methadone the route of administration is exclusively oral, the dose is determined solely by the physician, and since the effects usually last at least 24 hours, it becomes feasible to observe the ingestion of each dose, thus making it possible to eliminate illicit diversion. More importantly, there is no sudden drug-induced "high" that is followed within a few hours by the development of withdrawal symptoms. While it is quite accurate to state that patients are physically dependent on oral methadone, it is pharmacologically naïve to imply that this state is equivalent to a dependence on intravenous heroin. The *differences* between the *psychologically* and *physiologically* disruptive effects of intravenous heroin with its periods of being "high" and being "sick" and the barely perceptible effects of oral methadone may be more significant than the fact that pharmacologically they are both narcotic drugs. Within the context of the conditioning model, the theoretical significance of this functional difference is obvious.

B. The Barbiturate-Sedative Abuser

The compulsive use of sedatives and antianxiety agents with barbiturate-like effects has not been studied as thoroughly as opiate use or alcoholism. There is little reason to assume that it will prove to be a less complex problem. Thus, we can expect that studies will eventually show that there is no single personality type which manifests the problem, and that there are different patterns of abuse causing varying degrees of impairment of social function and general health. The same kinds of factors must be considered in formulating treatment goals as were considered for the narcotics user. Medicolegally, the problem of barbiturate abuse is usually less complex than that of narcotics abuse since, until recently, there was no systematic attempt by law enforcement agencies to detect, arrest, and prosecute the individual drug abuser.

1. Diagnosis

Sometimes patients who use excessive amounts of barbiturates or related drugs will seek treatment directly. More commonly, the diagnosis is made in spite of the patient's attempt to conceal the facts. Dependence on CNS general depressants should be suspected if the family reports that the patient is frequently confused, ataxic, or alternatingly sedated and irritable. When questioned, the patient may admit to taking such medication, but will often grossly understate the amount.

Intoxication with barbiturates, glutethimide, meprobamate, and related agents resembles intoxication with ethyl alcohol. Depending on the degree of intoxication, there may be impairment of judgment, confusion, decreased emotional control, euphoria, or depression. Neurological signs include slurred speech, ataxic gait, muscular incoordination, and nystagmus. Sometimes patients are first seen in a deep stupor after accidental ingestion of amounts exceeding the current level of tolerance; sometimes they are admitted in coma as a result of a deliberate suicidal attempt. Since such patients may progress from coma through a stage of apparent normality into a barbiturate withdrawal syndrome, the possibility of dependence on barbiturate-like drugs should be considered in all cases of acute barbiturate-sedative overdosage.

Not infrequently patients are first seen and the diagnosis of dependence is made when withdrawal symptoms occur. There may be one or more convulsions or a state of tremulous anxiety which progresses into confusion and disorientation accompanied by hallucinations, weakness, and tremors. In the absence of evidence of heavy alcohol ingestion these signs and symptoms are strongly suggestive of physical dependence on barbiturates or barbiturate-like agents.

2. Initial Management

If the patient is ambulatory, the physician may elect to continue to prescribe the drug of dependence when arranging for hospitalization. Since there are very serious hazards to abrupt withdrawal of CNS general depressants, the ethics of refusing to prescribe such medications to one's own patient are questionable.

Eventually the patient should be hospitalized for withdrawal. As previously described, the abrupt withdrawal of any one of a wide variety of CNS general depressants results in a withdrawal syndrome that is characteristic for the entire group. As was the case with the opiate withdrawal syndrome, the time course of the CNS general depressant withdrawal syndrome is closely related to the biological half-life of the particular drug. With short-acting drugs (e.g., pentobarbital, glutethimide) the withdrawal syndrome begins within 8 hours after the last dose, seizures may occur within 24–48 hours, and delirium within 36–72 hours. With longer-acting drugs (e.g., barbital, chlordiazepoxide, ethchlorvynol) the onset of withdrawal will be slower and seizures may not occur until several days after abrupt withdrawal.

The general principles used to manage the opiate withdrawal syndrome are also applicable here. If no treatment is given, the syndrome is self-limited and unless death occurs, clinical recovery without sequelae occurs within 5–10 days, although normal sleep may not return for several weeks. However, since deaths have occurred during abrupt withdrawal of barbiturates, only a controlled gradual withdrawal is considered to be medically appropriate, at least in the United States.

The management of physical dependence depends on the stage of withdrawal. If the patient is hospitalized before the withdrawal syndrome begins, or while still slightly intoxicated, then the treatment is relatively straightforward. The two general principles are (1) that mild intoxication and withdrawal manifestations cannot coexist; and (2) that a significant degree of cross-dependence exists within the CNS general depressant group. This makes it possible to substitute one or two standard drugs (e.g., pentobarbital or chlordiazepoxide) for any of the more than twenty CNS depressants commonly abused. Therefore during the first 24–48 hours, regardless of which specific drug they were abusing, patients are kept just slightly intoxicated by administering pentobarbital every 4–6 hours. The dose of pentobarbital will depend on the degree of tolerance and physical dependence that is present. One should not depend on the information supplied by the patient. Some patients exaggerate the amounts they have been using, while others with multiple sources of drugs may minimize the actual amount. A very useful strategy is to wait until the patient no longer exhibits sedation, slurred speech or nystagmus, and then administer 200 mg of pentobarbital elixir. The patient is examined 45–90 minutes later. Signs of gross intoxication suggest either no significant physical dependence or a degree that is equivalent to less than that induced by 800 mg of pentobarbital per day. Such patients can be stabilized initially on 150–200 mg of pentobarbital every 6 hours. If examination does not show signs of intoxication, then it is necessary to infer that the degree of physical dependence is equal to or greater than that which occurs with 800 mg of pentobarbital per day. In these cases, if there are no signs of withdrawal, it is usually safe to wait an additional 3 hours and then to administer 300 mg of pentobarbital elixir and reexamine the patient an hour later. The absence of intoxication suggests that the degree of dependence exceeds that which would occur with 1200 mg of pentobarbital, and the presence of intoxication suggests that it would be safe to stabilize the patient on 1000–1200 mg of pentobarbital per day. In any event, the dosage over the first 48 hours should always be subject to modification, i.e., increased if there is tremulousness, weakness or insomnia, or decreased if there is gross intoxication. After the stabilization dose has been determined the daily dose can be reduced by 100 mg of pentobarbital per day. If signs of withdrawal appear during reduction, it is usually sufficient to maintain the previous dose level for an additional day.

The problem is more difficult if, when first seen, the patient is already having severe withdrawal symptoms. The principles are the same, but it is difficult to gauge mild intoxication in a patient who is weak, grossly tremulous, disoriented, and hallucinating. In spite of the difficulty this is still the most rational approach. However, unlike the opiate withdrawal syndrome, where the administration of an opiate quickly suppresses the signs and symptoms of withdrawal no matter how severe, the administration of intoxicating amounts of pentobarbital promptly suppresses the CNS general depressant withdrawal syndrome only in its early stages. Once a withdrawal delirium has developed it may require 24–72 hours of adequate dosage before the condition clears.

3. Aftercare

Withdrawal of the drug is only the first step in treatment. Unfortunately, at present, it is the only step where efficacy has been demonstrated. Although referral for psychiatric treatment following withdrawal is a common practice, there is little or no information on how many patients accept such referrals or how they fare when they do. So little is known about effective aftercare for the compulsive user of barbiturate-like drugs that almost anything can be tried with equal claim to rationality. For the antisocial or alienated barbiturate abuser the therapeutic community seems to be a logical approach, but the period of residence which such treatment implies is not likely to be acceptable to the businessman or the housewife with family responsibilities.

C. The Amphetamine and Hallucinogen Abuser

Separate chapters in this book are devoted to discussions of the patterns of amphetamine abuse and of the use and abuse of hallucinogens (cf. Bloomquist, Chapter 38, and Cohen, Chapter 39). The patterns of the use of both of these classes of drugs differ considerably from each other and from the patterns seen with the opiates and barbiturates. The overall treatment of the compulsive user is included in the individual chapters, and the way in which compulsive use of amphetamines may complicate the withdrawal of opiates and barbiturates is mentioned in the discussion of mixed abuses which follows.

D. Mixed Abuse

The simultaneous use of more than one class of drugs is common. For example, some heroin users also use barbiturates, amphetamines, and alcohol. Physical dependence may occur with any one or more of the drugs being used, depending on dose and frequency of use. The general principles which govern the management of withdrawal have already been stated; it is necessary to remember that there is little cross-dependence between the morphine-like drugs and the CNS general depressants. Therefore even large amounts of methadone will not prevent barbiturate withdrawal, and gross intoxication with pentobarbital will not fully alleviate opiate withdrawal. It is also important to remember that within classes the drugs are roughly additive. Thus, taken alone, 120 mg of codeine or 45 mg of morphine or 4 mg of hydromorphone or 15 mg of methadone per day will not cause significant physical dependence, but all of them combined will do so unquestionably. Similarly, 200 mg of pentobarbital 1200 mg of meprobamate, 1500 mg of glutethimide, or 8 oz of whiskey alone will not produce physical dependence, but all taken together regularly will certainly do so.

It is prudent to suspect mixed types of abuse in any drug user, and it is relatively easy to rule out a significant degree of CNS general depressant-type physical dependence by administering a test dose of pentobarbital. The management of withdrawal in mixed dependencies (i.e., opiates and barbiturates), is not much more difficult than managing a patient with only one type of physical dependence. A useful strategy is to stabilize the patient on methadone when he is first admitted, at a level 20–30% higher than might ordinarily be used. Maintaining this level for the first 48 hours insures that any difficulty during withdrawal will be due to CNS general depressants, and not to opiates. At the same time, the patient is stabilized on pentobarbital using the technique previously described. A level of mild intoxication is maintained for the first 24–48 hours, after which the pentobarbital can be reduced by approximately 100 mg/day. The methadone is simultaneously reduced each day by 5–10 mg. If weakness, loss of appetite, or insomnia develop, no further reductions of either drug should be made until the condition stabilizes, after which reductions of either or both drugs can be resumed. Mixed-drug abusers are usually ambivalent and often openly resistant to being withdrawn. Since they know that the physician will not proceed with reduction of dosage when there are manifestations of withdrawal, there is a tendency to exaggerate or simulate withdrawal distress.

It is not unusual to encounter patients who have used large amounts of amphetamine in addition to opiates, hallucinogens, and CNS depressants. The initial management of such patients does not differ from that of patients who have not used amphetamines. However, it is important to recognize that after a period of chronic use the abrupt withdrawal of amphetamine is not without adverse effects. Most patients experience a profound sense of weakness and fatigue; in some there is a severe depression. It is not yet clear whether fatigue and depression are a result of amphetamine withdrawal or merely an unmasking of conditions that were covered up by the drug use. For purposes of managing the withdrawal period, knowing the exact etiology is not as important as appreciating that the depression can occur, and has, on occasion, led to suicide. There would seem to be no reason why low doses of amphetamine should not be given during the first few days if profound weakness or depression develop. In any event, the withdrawal of opiates or barbiturates usually requires at least 10 days, and there is ample time to withdraw amphetamines entirely.

Occasionally, one encounters a patient who, in addition to all of the above, has used considerable amounts of LSD and related hallucinogenics. At the present time little is known about how such hallucinogenic use affects the course of withdrawal of other agents, and we can only proceed on the assumption that it has no effect.

There is no firm basis for recommending any specific form of postwithdrawal care for the multidrug user. The pharmacological approaches previously described for the opiate user may prove useful for that aspect of the problem, but the effect this would have on the pattern of nonopiate use is not clear at present. It is possible, of course, to combine disulfiram with either methadone or cyclazocine, but the efficacy of this procedure is not yet documented. Now under study are drugs that block or attenuate the effects of amphetamines. These agents are compatible with disulfiram and with methadone or cyclazocine; but the likely outcome of such a multiblockade is hard to predict.

E. The "Medical" Drug Abuser

Not infrequently the psychiatrist is called on to advise on the management of patients with complex or obscure medical problems who have also been using prescribed medications in excessive amounts or at inappropriate times. The medications may be narcotic analgesics, sedative-hypnotics (barbiturates, glutethimide, meprobamate, chlordiazepoxide, etc.), amphetamines and related agents, or combinations of these groups.

In evaluating such cases serious consideration must be given to the overall functioning of the patients and not just to the drug-use problem. Often, except for the anxieties and strains in the doctor-patient relationship engendered by the patient's self-medication, they are functioning reasonably well in their respective family and social roles. Sometimes, all of the pressure to discontinue the self-medication comes from the attending physician or the family and can be traced to the myths and stereotypes about drug abuse that are now deeply rooted in the American culture.

The consultant should keep in mind that much of the pressure for physicians to avoid prescribing habit-forming medication to patients with drug-abuse problems may have stemmed from fears that this would result in some illicit redistribution of the medication in question, thereby increasing the numbers of people who might become drug-dependent. Such illicit redistribution of opiates, barbiturates, and amphetamines undoubtedly does occur when physicians prescribe these agents for members of drug-using subcultures without adequate precautions, but it now seems clear that at the present time the "medical" drug-dependent individual is almost always isolated from a drug-using subculture and, therefore, rarely, if ever, participates in the illicit drug distribution system. The only valid reason for insisting that patients immediately discontinue the overuse of psychoactive drugs is the belief that the drug use is damaging to the patient's health or social adjustment, and that there are alternative modes of adjustment that will permit him to function better.

Most persons who are dependent on opiates as a result of painful medical problems can be withdrawn without difficulty. As with the heroin user, methadone substitution is a convenient procedure, but the period of withdrawal is sometimes lengthened to 1 or 2 weeks. During withdrawal such patients will commonly complain with renewed urgency of the kinds of pain or discomfort for which the drug was originally prescribed. It is often impossible to tell if these complaints are perceived as "real" by the patient or are conscious devices to perpetuate the administration of the narcotic drug. With emotional support and firm management such patients can almost always be withdrawn. Aftercare is often a major problem since they will frequently return to a pattern of medical complaints, diagnostic tests, and "doctor shopping" until the family is exasperated and some physician is found who will prescribe strong analgesics, and the cycle begins anew.

It may be that such patients have an abnormally low tolerance for pain, and perhaps a significant number of them will function better when provided with some strong analgesic. However, as long as the current attitudes toward narcotic analgesics persist, this class of drugs should be avoided when possible. Conceivably most of these patients will experience satisfactory relief with methotrimeprazine (Levoprome), a phenothiazine derivative with analgesic activity, or with pentazocine (Talwin).

The major disadvantage of methotrimeprazine is that when used in dosages that give analgesia comparable to 10 mg of morphine, it produces considerably more sedation and postural hypotension than does morphine and is, therefore, not well suited for use with ambulatory patients. Considering its relationship to the antiemetic phenothiazines, it is not surprising that it produces very little nausea and vomiting.

It has been known since the early 1950's that nalorphine had no abuse potential, but did have some analgesic properties. It was also clear, however, that many of the narcotic antagonists produced dysphoria and hallucinations at doses close to those which produce analgesia. By synthesizing and screening many narcotic antagonists, several useful agents have been developed. One such agent is pentazocine, an analgesic in the benzomorphan series, with weak narcotic antagonist actions. Pentazocine seems to be somewhat intermediate in its effects between the narcotics and the narcotic antagonists. In doses of 30–45 mg intramuscularly it can produce analgesia comparable to 10 mg of morphine or 75 mg of meperidine. At these doses, dysphoria and hallucinations are rarely seen. However, because of its weak antagonist action, patients receiving substantial amounts of narcotic analgesics on a daily basis may experience some withdrawal symptoms if given pentazocine without discontinuing the narcotics for a few days.

Pentazocine does have agonistic actions, so that with repeated administration of very high doses followed by abrupt withdrawal there is a withdrawal syndrome which can be minimized by gradual reduction. The physical dependence seems to differ somewhat from that seen after withdrawal of morphine, and pentazocine does not suppress the morphine withdrawal syndrome. It is claimed that very little tolerance develops when it is given repeatedly over long periods, but the absence of tolerance is not well documented. It is available for both parenteral and oral use. When dealing with the problem of pain in the high-risk patients (those with previous histories of drug abuse), or the patient with chronic pain, the use of pentazocine may be a valuable alternative to the use of opiates. However, pentazocine intravenously was identified by postaddicts as a morphine-like drug, and while the former opiate users who volunteered to test the pentazocine did not care to continue receiving it, and it is not currently classified as a narcotic, the possibility of abuse does exist. A few such cases have been reported—all with the parenteral form of the drug. Furthermore, pentazocine is a potent analgesic and the repeated relief of distress, especially when the drug is used parenterally, is a situation in which it is difficult to avoid developing highly reinforced drug-use patterns. It must not be assumed that because the drug does not suppress morphine withdrawal, it can be given for parenteral self-administration without careful supervision. Theoretically, the risk of perpetuating drug use beyond the period when pain relief is required can be reduced by instructing patients to use the drug only for pain relief (escape behavior) and not for the prevention of anticipated pain (avoidance behavior).

Most, but not all, cases of pentazocine abuse were in patients with previous histories of narcotics abuse. From the pharmacological point of view there may be little advantage to using pentazocine in preference to narcotics for such patients. Under appropriate conditions both types of drug will permit a reasonably normal level of social performance. In the United States, however, the legal and psychological implications of pentazocine dependence are qualitatively different from those of compulsive narcotics use, and as long as pentazocine is not subjected to rigid regulations that generate guilt and anxiety in both patient and physician, it will continue to have significant advantages.

The problems of treating the narcotics-dependent medical patient, after withdrawal has been completed, are many, and there is no concensus as to what approaches are most likely to be successful. The use of cyclazocine or methadone maintenance on an individualized basis has proven useful, but controlled studies of these techniques with these types of drugs are lacking. The peer-operated therapeutic community may be helpful in special cases, but older middle-class patients are often reluctant to leave family and vocation to enter such a situation. In addition, these patients run the risk of learning antisocial patterns which were previously not part of their behavioral repertoire.

The same lack of concensus exists with respect to the drug dependent "medical" patient who is using nonnarcotic drugs; i.e., barbiturates, sedatives, or amphetamines. In most hospital settings withdrawal of the drug can be accomplished with relative ease, but it is the postwithdrawal management that causes much professional perplexity. In the face of these uncertainties, physicians would do well to consider just how well such patients might function socially and vocationally if they continued to prescribe limited amounts of drugs. They should then weigh this level of functioning against an estimate of what locally available treatment facilities could produce. Certainly, there is no concensus concerning the postwithdrawal management of the middle-class "medical addict," or the barbiturate, tranquilizer, or amphetamine abuser. A period of individual psychotherapy may be helpful in permitting a full assessment of the individual situation; but, in general, *group* rather than *individual* treatment seems more effective for all of the addictive behaviors.

Until demonstrably effective postwithdrawal treatments are evolved, the physician should attempt to remain tolerant of the chronic, relapsing nature of the illness, and to be available to help the withdrawal should the patient again require such treatment.

IV. Population Heterogeneity and a Value System-Cost Effectiveness Approach to Treatment

In approaching the drug-dependent patient the physician must not set up goals that are unrealistic. Optimally, we should want to see all compulsive narcotics users become emotionally mature, law-abiding, productive, nondrug-using members of society, who require no additional medical or social support to maintain this status. This is obviously an ideal set of goals, equally applicable to any medical-psychiatric problem, and rarely are all of them reached in the treatment of any chronic medical or psychiatric disorder. For example, we do not expect people with mild congestive heart failure to abstain from diuretics and digitalis. We encourage them to continue to obtain medical supervision of their disorder and do not take the need for such continued care as evidence of the inefficiency of treatment. The elements in this set of goals may vary independently. For example some heroin users may stop using narcotics, but fail to become productive or even law abiding; others may become abstinent and productive, but continue to engage in antisocial activity; still others may become or remain productive and law abiding in spite of continued drug use. Because of their independence, it often becomes necessary to arrange these goals hierarchically. Such an arrangement can only be arbitrary and will vary with the situation. Thus a large-scale program directed at urban heroin users, most of whom have histories of antisocial activity, might well reject the concept that abstinence from narcotics must be the sole, or even the most important, criterion of successful treatment. Instead, the absence of antisocial activity might be considered the minimum criterion by which the outcome of treatment should be judged. Decreases in antisocial behavior accompanied by increased productivity and decreased use of illicit drugs would constitute an even more acceptable response to treatment. To set up an identical hierarchy for the financially successful physician-narcotics user, the barbiturate-dependent housewife, and the amphetamine-using college drop-out would be inappropriate. The goals and the approach must be designed for the individual and his situation. Obviously, how the hierarchy of goals is ordered will depend in part upon the values held in a given society at a given time. With respect to narcotics, there are still some states in the United States which place emphasis almost exclusively upon prolonged, continuous, and absolute abstinence from narcotics. Such states may expend large sums on civil commitment programs which employ monitoring systems designed to detect early relapse to narcotics use and bring about the enforced reinstitutionalization of the supervised subject. Other states are experimenting with the use of methadone in programs where the emphasis is primarily on the achievement of socially acceptable behavior rather than on abstinence. The use of methadone is considerably less expensive and more reliable in achieving its explicit goal than the civil commitment programs are in achieving their explicit goal of permanent abstinence. It would seem that, at present, the value of achieving abstinence from narcotics is given more weight than the high cost and relative inefficiency of the procedures now available to achieve that end.

Fortunately, this inordinate preoccupation with abstinence has not yet permeated the approaches to those dependent on alcohol, sedatives, and related drugs, and a flexibility of approach and cost-effect considerations are still utilized.

Perhaps it will require more time before the general public will accept the notion that drug users are a heterogeneous group, a group which uses different drugs for different reasons with widely differing social, psychological, and physical consequences. The medical and allied health professions are already grappling with the implications of this heterogeneity of motivation and of pattern of drug use. It is hoped that other segments of society will avoid passing legislation or establishing programs that prevent the development of flexible approaches to this heterogeneous population. We must also continue our efforts to fill in the huge gaps in our knowledge about which treatment approaches are best suited to achieve which goals for our ever more varied and expanding drug-using populations.

For suggested reading and references see Appendices 1 and 2.

45

DRUGS, ADDICTION, AND LEGAL PSYCHIATRY

John M. Suarez and Randall B. Spencer

I. Introduction

The behavioral sciences in general and psychiatry in particular have two basic tasks regarding the problems of drug abuse and addiction. First, they are responsible for the therapy of such conditions and for the related development of new treatment techniques. Second, they have the responsibility of influencing social and legal change in keeping up with new knowledge gained from research and experience.

The legal or punitive approach has clearly proved a partial failure in dealing with the problems of drug traffic, consumption, and addiction. This is so despite, or perhaps because of, very severe penalties for those who break the law in any way. It is likely that criminal sanctions will continue to be imposed on those who, in breaking the law, further support and foster problems associated with drugs. However, many feel that in the long run the legal approach will never deal successfully with the problem, and thus propose greater stress on the combination of public education, advances in medical services, and the delivery of such services to drug addicts.

With a few well-known exceptions, psychiatry has not concerned itself very seriously with the problem of addiction. There are a number of factors, many of them legal, that contribute to this situation, but the primary responsibility for noninvolvement must be shared directly by all psychiatrists who have failed to tackle the problem directly. Recent developments, such as the Robinson decision and radical changes in the laws of three states (California, New York, and Massachusetts), are still too new to assess their influence in terms of fostering psychiatric involvement.

II. Federal Statutes

Contemporary drug laws begin with the Harrison Narcotic Act, passed in 1914. This is a taxing law, part of the Internal Revenue Act, and it was aimed at the regulation of production and sale of narcotic drugs in the hope of limiting their use to professional and scientific purposes. The Harrison Act states that narcotic drugs may be prescribed and handled legally by a physician in the course of "his professional practice," but the definition and interpretation of this prase has become the controversial issue. Historically, the definition of "practice" became unusually narrow, and the federal government assumed the right to prosecute physicians who seemed to be stepping outside such limits.

In the 1919 case of Webb and Goldbaum, the Supreme Court ruled that the prescribing of drugs to an addict to keep him comfortable by maintaining his customary use was not proper practice within the limits of the law and did not fall within the exception available to medical practice. Thus, the Treasury Department could prevent the physician from providing narcotics to a user to keep him comfortable and maintain his customary use. It is theorized by some that this one ruling was critical to the events that followed, viz. the turning by addicts to nonmedical and illegal sources to maintain their habits. In 1922, the Behrman case ruled that medical prescriptions for drugs for addicts were illegal despite the fact, agreed to by the prosecution, that such dispensing was for the purpose of treatment and cure.

In 1925, the Supreme Court reversed the conviction of Dr. Charles O. Linder, which apparently somewhat modified earlier very strict decisions regarding doctors and their handling of drugs. Dr. Linder had dispensed four tablets to a woman who turned out to be a police informer. He was subsequently arrested and convicted under the Harrison Act. In reversing this decision, the Supreme Court introduced two important features. One was the explicit statement that addiction was a disease, and the other that physicians can legally, if in good faith, prescribe and dispense to addicts small dosages to relieve withdrawal symptoms. Thus, a physician may regularly administer drugs to known or suspected addicts only for the sake of acute withdrawal, and also to those people who are so aged and infirm that withdrawal may cause death, and to those people afflicted with painful and incurable diseases.

In 1937 a special Marihuana Tax Act was passed regulating the production and traffic of marihuana much in the way the Harrison Act regulates the transfer of opiates. As marihuana has little if any legitimate use in medicine, the registration and taxation features of this act rarely are used to control legitimate transfers, but the penalty features are available for the prosecution of illegitimate marihuana sales.

The 1950's saw further reactions and attempts at control because of the increasing problem with narcotics. Congress passed the Boggs Act in 1951. This law prescribed a definite sentence, fixed by the court within a 2- to 5-year range, for possession of narcotics on first conviction. Second conviction carried with it a sentence of 5 to 10 years, and third conviction came to 20 years. In addition, this new law denied the possibility of parole to those convicted under it. In 1956, following a review of narcotic legislation by the Senate Judiciary Committee, Congress passed the Federal Narcotic Control Act, which maintained the penalties prescribed in the previous act, but increased the maximum possible sentence on a third conviction to 40 years.

The Drug Abuse Control Amendments of 1965 were signed by the President and became law early in 1966. These amendments were designated as "an Act to protect the public health and safety by amending the Federal Food, Drug and Cosmetic Act to establish special controls for depressant and stimulant drugs and counterfeit drugs and for other purposes." These amendments provide for stronger regulations of the manufacture, distribution, delivery, and possession of depressant and stimulant drugs, including barbiturates, amphetamines, and other psychotoxic drugs which have a potential for abuse because of their depressant or stimulant effect on the central nervous system or because of their hallucinogenic effect. The passage of this act clearly recognized the growing problems with drugs besides the hard narcotics previously covered by the Harrison Act and its subsequent amendments.

The medical rather than criminal approach to the problem of addiction was given some support in a decision by the U.S. Supreme Court in 1962 in the case of Robinson vs. California. In this case, the Supreme Court struck down a section of a California statute which imposed a criminal status and a penal sanction on one who is addicted to the use of narcotics. The critical point in the decision is that California had interpreted their law as making unlawful the "status" or "condition" of addiction without proof of actual use of narcotics or other accompanying misconduct. The Court found this law to be cruel and unusual punishment, but made it clear that while the condition of addiction itself cannot be subject to criminal prosecution, the state can continue to prosecute for the many actions incident to addiction. Therefore, penal sanctions directed toward these incidental actions have continued to cause many drug addicts to be sentenced to prison.

III. State Laws

The Bureau of Narcotics drafted a model for state laws called the Uniform Narcotics Drug Act, which has been adopted by most states, the District of Columbia, and Puerto Rico. In most states the penalties are similar to those of the federal act, though often more detailed. Illinois offers a typical situation and thus will be looked at in some detail. Penalties for soliciting or encouraging a minor to violate the Drug Act include indeterminate sentences with minimum and maximum fixed within a range of 2–5 years. The range is 1–10 years for agreeing to sell narcotics, and increases with a second offense to a 10 year minimum and no maximum. The Illinois penalty for illegal purchase or possession is an indeterminate sentence, with 2- to 10-years limits for the first offense and 5 years to life for subsequent offenses. Probation or suspension are forbidden for the subsequent offender. For selling or dispensing, the penalty range is from 10 years to life for the first offense, and mandatory life for subsequent offenses, with no suspension or probation even on first offense. In addition, Illinois provides a jail sentence for a definite term ranging from 90 days to a year for unlawfully using or being addicted to narcotics. Needle scars are defined as *prima facie* evidence of use. Probation is permitted for this offense only if part of the probation is served in jail.

Many states authorize synthetic opiate (Nalline) tests for any person arrested on a drug charge, but only with his written consent, and permit such consent to be a condition of probation or parole for anyone with a record of a drug offense. The arrested addict, who can be convicted for one of the several separate offenses distinguished in the narcotics legislation, generally can be convicted for other ones also, so the prosecutor can threaten to indict on the charge with the most severe penalty in order to induce a plea of guilty to a lesser charge.

State laws in the area of control relating to hallucinogens are less uniform than those that apply to opiates and marihuana and in some instances are nonexistent. For example, the Massachusetts legislature has seen fit to label LSD and the other hallucinogens as narcotics, and to bring the LSD user into the same class as the heroin addict, subjecting him to the same legal sanctions. New Hampshire, at the other extreme, has no legislation to control the illicit use of LSD, and state officials are at the moment powerless to deal at all with the problem. A few states cover peyote under their narcotic laws, although exemptions are made for the use of it in *bona fide* religious ceremonies of the Native American Church. Because hallucinogens are rarely administered by physicians, and then only in a carefully controlled setting, their possession by a person for his own use would almost always be associated with abuse.

Most states have civil commitment laws for addicts. These resemble equivalent laws for the commitment of the mentally ill, and in most cases the legal channels and practices are the same. As with the commitment for the mentally ill, these laws, unfortunately, typically do not provide for any aftercare program beyond the period of institutionalization of the patient.

Apparent success in rehabilitating drug addicts in a community setting encouraged legal, medical, and correctional authorities in three states thus far to pass new legislation to set up rehabilitation programs. California led the way, and its law went into effect in 1961. This was followed closely by New York, which passed the Metcalf-Volker Act in 1962. In addition to establishing commitment procedures and aftercare programs for the addicts, these laws provide a radical breakthrough in the criminal area as well. For certain addicts, those with less serious prior criminal records, their being channeled through commitment and rehabilitation into this program can substitute entirely for a criminal sentence which would keep the addict under arrest and try him for a crime. Massachusetts became the third state to adopt such legislation.

The program in California includes not only addicts but also people "in imminent danger of becoming addicted." Because of the difficulty of defining and interpreting such wording, the other two states rejected this category. The New York and Massachusetts programs are more flexible in operation. Decisions remain in the hands of those administering the program. The commitment in New York is for a maximum of 3 years and in Massachusetts for a maximum of 2 years, with a court allowed extension of one more year. Neither state requires a minimum inpatient period.

IV. The British Approach

The British approach to the resolution of the narcotics problem is very old and was essentially unchanged since its conception until very recently. While certain people may even deny the existence of a "British system," there is no doubt that there exists in Great Britain a distinctly different approach to the problem of addiction than in the United States. A difficulty encountered in evaluating this system arises from looking at the statistics on the number of drug addicts. There has been a sharp increase in the number of addicts since 1960, so much so that Great Britain has deemed it necessary to alter its laws. Does this increase in the number of addicts and change in the law reflect failure of the old system or a new innovation? This section reviews the British approach, some arguments for and against it, and the recent changes and their possible implications.

The Dangerous Drug Law was adopted in 1920, and several minor regulations have followed with no essential changes. It was not defined adequately until 1924, when a group of medical men, called the Rolleston Committee, codified it in a formal report. Their interpretations have since guided the enforcement of the law and put the problem of drug addiction in the hands of the medical practitioner, who has to deal with it under the guidance of the law. Stringent control is placed on opium, heroin, morphine, meperidine, methadone, and cocaine in regard to their possession and supply, the dose or use being left to the doctor. Marihuana or cannabis is also included in this list, except it is not addicting and has no real medical use and, therefore, is not prescribed by doctors and has to be obtained on the black market, the user being subject to the penalties of illegal drug use. Therefore, in practice, Great Britain deals with marihuana as does the United States, through legal penalties where the user is a criminal and not a patient.

The principles set forth by the Departmental Committee on Morphine and Heroin Addiction in 1926 are contained in the following:

> Morphine or heroin may properly be administered to addicts in the following circumstances, namely: (a) where patients are under treatment by the gradual withdrawal method with a view to cure; (b) where it has been demonstrated, after a prolonged

> attempt at cure, that the use of the drug cannot be safely discontinued entirely, on account of the severity of the withdrawal symptoms produced; and (c) where it has been similarly demonstrated that the patient, while capable of leading a useful and relatively normal life when a certain dose is regularly administered, becomes incapable of this when the drug is entirely discontinued.

Other recommendations include the following: The gradual withdrawal method should be undertaken in an institution, there should be a reliable and capable nurse; a second medical opinion should be obtained before placing a patient on a maintenance dose; a new patient should have a general physical exam before prescription of drugs; and records should be kept regarding quantity of drugs prescribed.

The treatment of the addict is a medical problem and is in the hands of the doctor, as compared to the United States, where the addict is a criminal. The drug addict is a criminal in Great Britain if he obtains his drugs on the black market without a prescription, goes to more than one doctor for greater quantity of drugs to supply a larger habit, changes the prescription, or sells the drugs.

The system seems to be working in practice as well as in theory. In reviewing the nature and number of convictions for offenses against the Drug Act there can be determined no indications of a large group of unknown addicts who rely on the black market. It is the opinion of officials that the addict cannot rely on the black market for his supply of drugs, and will eventually come to a physician. The drugs are inexpensive, and the addict's name appears on the prescription and the doctor's register, making him a known addict.

In 1935 it was estimated that there were 700 addicts in Great Britain, while in 1951 the number fell to 301. There has been a steady rise since 1951 to 317 in 1954, 335 in 1955, 359 in 1957, 454 in 1959, 635 in 1963, 753 in 1964, and 927 in 1965. These figures come from the registers of doctors and pharmacists and represent the drugs included in the Drug Act and not such things as the hallucinogens or marihuana. This is still not a great number in a country of 55 million.

The arguments in favor of the system have already been stated indirectly The readily available drugs through a physician's care, the low cost of the drugs, and the specific laws which prosecute the violator of the system or the drug user who does not get drugs through a physician, all combine to deter the making of a large black market where drugs would be expensive and the addict would have to turn to crime in order to pay for his habit, profits going to organized crime. The addicts would also become pushers to pay for the drugs, thus increasing their numbers. These activities build an entire subculture with its own mores and rules, which breed more addicts and is very difficult to control.

In Great Britain the drug addict has traditionally been an individual over 30 years of age who is in either the middle or upper class. There is a relatively large proportion of medically related people addicted to drugs. In the United States the drug addict is viewed as a young man of the lower class or racial minorities who lives by crime and subterfuge in the back alleys of a large city's drug subculture.

The criticism against the British approach arises mainly in the United States when an official proposes such a system. Not too much can be said against the approach in Great Britain because it seems to work, at least until recently. It has been said that Britain's and the United States' cultural history differ enough as to make it an unworkable plan here. Britain has not experienced mass immigration, or migration of greatly underprivileged people. The British Interdepartmental Committee on Drug Addiction in 1960 said that the cause of the almost negligible traffic in illicit drugs "seems to lie largely in social attitudes to the observance of the law in general and to the taking of dangerous drugs in particular." Harney has also said that the British system would not work in the United States because the British are basically more law abiding. In Hong Kong, where there were 100 times more drug addicts per population than in the United States, it was tried without success.

Much criticism has come from the drug addicts themselves. They state that the system has been at fault for maintaining their addiction because once they went to a doctor they were addicted forever. The desire to attempt a cure was dissolved because the drugs were so easy to get, and some even claimed that a few doctors placed them on maintenance drugs right away without encouraging a cure while their habits were still relatively small.

The United States has waged a battle against Great Britain because of the feeling that the country offers a haven for dope addicts and an arsenal for possible illegal spread of such drugs as heroin or cocaine. They have attempted through the World Health Organization to get Britain to outlaw the use and sale of certain narcotics, especially heroin.

Recently, it appears that the number of addicts has greatly increased, and that drugs are being sold to initiates by addicts, and the profits used to get more drugs from other physicians. Very few physicians seem to be interested in working closely with drug addicts to attempt a cure. Too many doctors are content to dole out pills. Most people blame the physicians for their laxity in handling prescriptions, saying that they are unwittingly overprescribing and being manipulated by the addicts. The new laws which will be in effect this year reflect this viewpoint.

Narcotic addicts must now report to special narcotic treatment clinics to obtain their drugs. General practitioners will not be able to prescribe drugs, and most of the treatment centers will be attached to psychiatric units of general hospitals. The emphasis will be on treatment and cure through encouraged, but not forced, hospitalization. The tightening of control on prescriptions is another change which will hopefully do away with the narcotics resale at a profit. The prescription will be mailed to the pharmacist instead of being brought to him by the drug user, allowing for alteration of the written dose or amount. The pharmacist will dispense only *one* day's supply at a time, although the prescription may be written for a week. It is hoped and thought that the addict will not bother selling the small daily allotment.

From one point of view this new legislation seems to indicate a failure of the old system in that it was a response to the abuse of the old system. The British Government insists that the changes represent progress in that this field of therapeutics has become specialized, as have other fields of medicine, and that direct care by psychiatric facilities is the result of this trend. The addict may find himself complaining, as do other patients under the care of a multitude of specialists, that the personal contact with one doctor who "knows you" is gone and is replaced by an impersonal institution. Whether or not the addict will feel that this is too much an impersonal, government institution with legal connotations and decide to turn to the black market for his supply remains to be seen.

V. The International Scene

In discussing the drug laws of countries around the world, it is impossible to review each one in detail. Only general trends and approaches will be covered with appropriate illustrations.

Most of the laws involving control of drug addiction are related to either the treatment of mental patients or to the traffic in narcotic drugs. In some countries where drug addiction is an endemic problem, e.g., Burma, Viet Nam, Iran, etc., there are special laws which plan for progressively tighter control of drugs and the elimination of drug addiction. In Greece, by way of contrast, the mere use of drugs is a crime.

There are few definitions of the addict in legislation, but common to countries which do attempt definition are the terms "habitual" and "narcotics" and the phrase "danger to himself and/or others." Certain countries, e.g., Finland and Norway, make the offense more specific by stating that the law is only broken when the addict does certain things, such as becoming a charge on his relatives or other persons, maltreating his spouse or children, or exposing his children to moral danger or neglect. The 1957 World Health Organization study group on treatment and care of drug addiction defined the addict as a person "who habitually and compulsively uses any narcotic drug so as directly to endanger his own or other's health, safety, or welfare."

The only countries which have compulsory registration of drug addicts are Australia, Argentina, Brazil, the Dominican Republic, Ecuador, Italy, Korea, Panama, and Venezuela. In Finland, Switzerland, and the United Kingdom, practitioners are asked to report drug addiction. In Burma and Iran, drug addicts must apply for ration cards for their supply of narcotics.

Drug legislation relating to treatment of mental patients generally contains provisions for commitment, either voluntary or ex officio, to hospitals as an alternative for incarceration. Western Australia, Brazil, Canada, Finland, Switzerland, and the United States have voluntary treatment. Two alternative commitment procedures are through the judicial and administrative powers. In France, any magistrate may order compulsory treatment for any addict violating the Public Health Code. Similar powers are entrusted to the magistrates in Greece, Italy, and Norway. In the Dominican Republic, Ecuador, Finland, Guatemala, Korea, and Panama commitment powers lie with the administrators.

Treatment without hospitalization is specifically prohibited in certain countries and authorized in others. In Argentina this is controlled by the medical officer effecting the detoxication cure. In Spain, a special book is issued to addicts for obtaining specified amounts of narcotics. Detoxication is recommended in a health institute, but physicians may follow an approved course of gradual withdrawal plus psychotherapy in the treatment of an outpatient.

The use of narcotics in the treatment of incurable disease is generally unlimited in most countries. Canada, Ecuador, the Dominican Republic, and Panama specify that the authorities must be notified of the treatment of incurable disease for permission of extended dosages of narcotics.

In France there is no legal definition of drug addiction, and medical practitioners have no obligation to report cases of addiction to authorities, but it is recognized that addicts may violate the Public Health Code and thus be subject to punishment; therefore, legislation provides for compulsory medical treatment of addicts in such cases by the examining magistrate.

In Germany the detention of an addict in a psychiatric institution is considered a deprivation of personal liberty, forbidden by federal constitutional law. In order to commit an addict, the decision must be made by the judicial authority or the addict himself. There are two ways that a judicial decision may be made. One is that whenever an addict has broken the law which is related to traffic and procurement of narcotics, the magistrate may then choose to dictate medical treatment rather than incarceration. The other method of judicial decision for commitment differs with the laws of each land, but all govern the detention of persons of unsound mind, drug addicts, and alcoholics.

VI. The Psychiatrist's Role

The Harrison Act seems to have placed the treating physician in a bind. It seems clear that the administration of a drug for the sake of dealing solely with the problems of withdrawal is not permitted by the law. Further, even treatment of the addiction problem as a whole seems to be limited to custodial, drug-free environment, since ambulatory and outpatient treatments are not acceptable to law enforcement officials.

Some authorities have gone as far as saying that any prescribing of drugs to an addict, regardless of the intent, is a violation of the Act. The dispensing doctor seems to run the risk of being adjudicated as having merely fostered and encouraged the habit, and not as part of an overall scheme to treat the addiction. As a consequence, most physicians have discontinued prescribing narcotics, regardless of the acuteness of the situation that the addict or user may present.

To be sure, there have been other rulings and decisions by federal circuit courts and the Supreme Court itself that suggest that prescriptions for and even self-administration by the addict are permissible if done in good faith and according to medical standards. In spite of these, most doctors stay as far away from addicts as possible, and one reason may be that the interpretation of "good faith" and "adherence to fair medical practice" may hinge on a judicial determination.

However, it is likely that fear of the law keeps addicts away from available treatment, at least in some cases. This has not changed, despite recent trends that have enlarged the rights of patients, psychiatric ones particularly, to confidentiality and privilege of communication. This supports the notion that has been entertained all along, namely, that failure to seek and continue therapy has little to do with the existing sociolegal structure. Instead, it likely reflects the typical addict's high degree of denial and inability to tolerate the necessary stresses of therapy.

VII. Comments

The failure of communication between medical personnel and law enforcement officials stems from a basic philosophical difference. The behavioral scientist views the addiction as a symptom of a pathological condition. The physiological need for the drug that results merely compounds the problem and establishes a vicious circle. The extreme medical position supports the ready availability of addicting drugs for those who need it, thus fostering healthy and law-abiding individuals who would have no need for a black market, peddling, or violence.

Law enforcement tends to view the addict as basically criminal and the addiction as proof of his weak will and antisocial tendencies. Related to this is the criminality that results directly from the effects of the drug. In the most narrow view, the critical task becomes the identification and punishment of those who are too lazy and degenerate to work and abide by the laws, and who go around committing crimes.

As stated, much of the disagreement rests on moral and philosophical grounds. The medical treatment approach regards addiction as a private matter and thus cannot understand its being handled as a crime, particularly if the user does not spread the problem to others and conforms to existing regulations as to obtaining drugs. In this way, the addict resembles the diabetic whose proper functioning is dependent on the regular administration of insulin. Critics of this position view the addict as morally evil and as a source of moral degeneracy to others.

The relationship between addiction and crime is an interesting one, and one that has elicited a great deal of controversy. With the exception of law enforcement officers, most observers believe that the evidence is very poor in terms of a cause-and-effect relationship. Actually, most addicting drugs are CNS depressants and so the user is rendered lethargic and less motivated, and thus less likely to engage in antisocial conduct. The American Bar Association and the American Medical Association stated in the final report of their Joint Committee (1957):

> Some responsible authorities state that the dependence on drugs, the compulsion to obtain them and their high price are primarily responsible for crimes committed by addicts. Others claim that the drug itself is responsible for criminal behavior. The weight of evidence is so heavily in favor of the former viewpoint that the question can hardly be called controversial. . . . Crimes of violence are rarely, and sexual crimes are almost never committed by addicts.

A number of arguments have been voiced recently challenging the constitutionality of existing drug laws. First, they are considered as irrational, arbitrary, and discriminatory. Second, when compared to alcohol, they are thought to violate an equal protection under the law. Third, the Robinson decision is emphasized, thus underscoring that addiction is not a crime. Fourth, existing statutes, which often result in lifelong ruination, are considered cruel and unusual punishment. Finally, the issue is raised as to the validity of the notion of criminality without a victim.

To date, Western society has relied primarily on the legal and punitive approach with results that are far short of ideal. We may be coming around to the time when the second and perhaps more critical approach may be instituted, namely, the expansion of medical research, the greater availability of medical and rehabilitative services for addicts, and the more successful education of the people at large.

For further reading and references see Appendices 1 and 2.

PART IX

CLINICAL USE OF PSYCHOTHERAPEUTIC DRUGS

46

MECHANISMS OF EXTRAPYRAMIDAL SIDE EFFECTS OF THERAPEUTIC AGENTS

Oleh Hornykiewicz and Charles H. Markham,
William G. Clark, and Robert M. Fleming

I. Introduction

This chapter on the extrapyramidal actions of drugs will be limited to two aspects: (a) the behavioral and neuropathological effects of such disturbances which one can relate to extrapyramidal centers such as the striatum (caudate nucleus and putamen), globus pallidus, substantia nigra, and nucleus subthalamicus; and (b) the side effects of the antipsychotic agents (i.e., the phenothiazines, butyrophenones, and reserpine), monoamine oxidase inhibitors and tricyclic antidepressants (dibenzoazepines and related compounds). We shall confine ourselves to substances which are actually used clinically and disregard compounds of experimental interest only, such as tremorine and bulbocapnine.

II. Pathophysiological Substrates

The characteristic syndromes which these drugs produce, probably by acting on higher extrapyramidal centers, are as follows: *Hypokinesia,* associated with rigidity and tremor, as seen in the classical Parkinsonian syndrome; *Hyperkinesias* of different kinds; choreiform, athetoid, and ballistic movement disorders; *Dystonia* and other *dyskinetic* states similar to those found in dystonia musculorum deformans (torsion dystonia), and *Myoclonus.*

In order to understand the drug-induced extrapyramidal effects, the diseases with known neuropathological changes should be considered first.

A. *Hypokinesia*

The main symptoms in paralysis agitans (classical Parkinson's disease) and post-encephalitic Parkinson's disease are tremor, rigidity, and akinesia. The principal neuropathological substrate in both types is degeneration of the melanin-bearing cells in the substantia nigra, particularly in the zona compacta. The loss is especially severe in the post-encephalitic variety. The deficiency in the regulating ability of the substantia nigra on other extrapyramidal centers, especially the striatum and the globus pallidus, may lead to rigidity and akinesia. Tremor, not an invariable feature of Parkinsonism, may be due to a disturbed relationship between the diseased substantia nigra and other parts of the midbrain.

B. *Hyperkinesia*

There is general agreement that the usual origin of hemiballismus is destruction and functional deficit of the nucleus subthalamicus (corpus Luysi). Huntington's chorea, the most common hyperkinetic disease, is characterized by a progressive degeneration of the nerve cells of the striatum. The striatal disease may lead to the release of neuronal inhibition by a more primitive motor center, possibly the globus pallidus. In athetosis of the type often following severe anoxia at birth, there is hypermyelination, gliosis, and nerve cell loss in the striatum, and occasionally the globus pallidus.

C. *Dystonia and Related Dyskinesias*

So far as is known, injury to different extrapyramidal centers can cause these symptoms. In dystonia musculorum deformans one not infrequently finds isolated injury to the putamen (both small and large cells) or of the centrum medianum projections to the putamen. Occasionally, there is accompanying damage to the pallidum, the nucleus subthalamicus, or the substantia nigra. Spasmotic torticollis, often a localized form of dystonia, has no identifiable pathological substrate, although midbrain head-turning mechanisms may be implicated physiologically.

D. Myoclonus

Another motor disturbance of note consists of sudden brief muscular contractions in different parts of the body. Sometimes this is part of a seizure disorder. It has no regularly occurring pathological substrate, although cell loss in the dentate nucleus or the inferior olive is sometimes seen.

III. Biochemistry of Extrapyramidal Centers

For some time it has been known that the striatum has elevated concentrations of acetylcholine (ACh) and of the enzymes which synthesize and inactivate ACh (27). ACh must have an important role in the function of these extrapyramidal centers, but this has not yet been clearly established. For example, Parkinsonian tremor and rigidity, symptoms clearly of basal ganglia origin, are favorably influenced by anticholinergic drugs. Furthermore, the hyperkinetic manifestations of Huntington's chorea are exacerbated by the same drugs. It has been experimentally shown that the injection of ACh or carbachol in the caudate nucleus or globus pallidus can lead to tremor.

In contrast to the paucity of results with ACh, recent investigations have shown that dopamine (DA) may play an important role in extrapyramidal function. In 1957, the existence of DA in the brain of animals and man was established. It was next shown that this catecholamine is predominantly in the striatum, in the substantia nigra, and to a lesser degree in the globus pallidus. The demonstration in idiopathic Parkinson's disease of a deficiency of DA in the caudate nucleus, putamen, pallidum, and substantia nigra made it even more probable that DA has a significant function in the extrapyramidal system. The concentration of the DA metabolite homovanillic acid (HVA) is reduced in the striatum in patients with Parkinson's disease as compared to normal controls (332). HVA levels have been reported to be decreased in the cerebrospinal fluid of Parkinsonian patients. However, low levels also have been found in various inflammatory diseases of the central nervous system and in epilepsy; hence this is not specific for Parkinson's disease.

A correlation between the degree of destruction of the substantia nigra and the DA deficiency in the striatum can be shown. In higher primates, coagulation of the substantia nigra leads to a loss of DA in the striatum. By the use of fluorescent microscopic techniques, a dopaminergic pathway has been shown to exist between the substantia nigra and the striatum. The connection between DA and the function of the extrapyramidal system is supported by the observation that L-3,4-dihydroxyphenylalanine (L-dopa), the amino acid precursor of DA, leads to an improvement of Parkinsonian akinesia and rigidity (333). Finally the production of a Parkinsonian syndrome by centrally acting drugs which disturb DA metabolism and storage, such as reserpine and α-methyltyrosine, further sustains a role of DA in the functioning of the extrapyramidal system.

IV. Extrapyramidal Actions of Drugs

A. *Drug-Induced Parkinsonism*

Ten years ago, there were practically no drugs known which could produce a Parkinsonian syndrome. Today more than a dozen are known, and their number probably will increase in the future. Included in this group are antipsychotic agents such as the phenothiazines, butyrophenone derivatives, and reserpine and its analogs.

1. Chemical Aspects

a. Reserpine and Substances with Reserpine-like Activity. The occurrence of extrapyramidal symptoms following administration of rauwolfia alkaloids is an old observation (cf. Laborit and Sanseigne, Chapter 18). Reserpine and its analogs such as deserpidine, rescinnamine, and syrosingopine, which have central effects like reserpine, cause a Parkinsonian syndrome in man. The same is true for synthetic substances with a central reserpine-like action such as the benzoquinolizines (for example tetrabenazine). Other substances such as α-methyltyrosine do not resemble reserpine chemically, but can produce a Parkinsonian state. These chemically heterogeneous substances are biochemically related in the way they influence the precursors and levels of the brain amines.

b. Phenothiazine and Butyrophenone Derivatives. Nearly all these antipsychotic agents can produce a Parkinsonian state, the severity of which varies for the different preparations. Compared to chlorpromazine (CPZ), which occupies a middle position in this regard, the phenothiazines with a piperidyl side chain in the 10-position (for example thioridazine) have a much weaker effect, while those with a piperazine side chain (for example, prochlorperazine, trifluroperazine, and perphenazine) cause stronger reactions. An additional substitution in the 2-position plays a role. Those drugs with an unsubstituted molecule (for example promazine or perazine) have a weak effect. Substitution of a chlor- or trifluomethyl group (for example CPZ, trifluopromazine, prochlorperazine, or trifluoperazine), increases the extrapyramidal side effects considerably. It should also be noted that the piperazinylalkylphenothiazine derivatives (for example perphenazine, thioperazine, fluphenazine, or thiopropazate) not only produce less sedation but considerably more dystonic and hyperkinetic reactions as well.

The butyrophenones (for example haloperidol or triperidol) in small doses can produce a Parkinsonian syndrome as well as hyperkinetic or dystonic states. In this regard they are most like the more potent phenothiazines with a piperazine side chain.

2. Clinical Observations

The Parkinsonian syndromes induced by reserpine and the phenothiazines are similar to each other and differ little from post-encephalitic Parkinson's disease. The cardinal symptoms of Parkinson's disease, namely, tremor, rigidity, and akinesia, are present in the syndromes induced by the phenothiazines and reserpine, with akinesia especially severe on occasion. α-Methyldopa infrequently induces a very mild Parkinsonian state, while α-methyltyrosine (which blocks the enzymic conversion of dopa to DA) does so to a greater extent. However, in patients who have Parkinsonism secondary to reserpine, α-methyldopa can aggravate the symptoms. α-Methyldopa can also increase the tremor and rigidity of patients with Parkinson's disease.

The occurrence of drug-induced Parkinsonism seems to be dependent upon many factors. It must be mentioned that some patients do not develop extrapyramidal symptoms even on chronic high dosages of antipsychotic drugs. The fact that patients who easily react to phenothiazines with a Parkinsonian syndrome also do so to reserpine, and vice versa, suggests that there may be an individual predisposition. In Ayd's 1961 survey comprised of 3775 patients treated with phenothiazines, 38.9% had drug-induced extrapyramidal reactions (371). The Parkinsonian state, which consisted of 15.4% of the total number, was found to occur in 90% of these cases in the first 72 treatment days. There is also an age and sex predisposition: Females and patients over fifty are especially prone. The age distribution of phenothiazine-induced Parkinsonism corresponds to that of paralysis agitans.

It is of interest that drug-induced Parkinsonism is relieved by conventional anti-Parkinson drugs, as is the genuine syndrome. Parkinsonism induced by reserpine also is benefited by dopa (332).

3. Findings in Experimental Animals

Reserpine, reserpine-like drugs, and the phenothiazines, produce in most laboratory animals a state (sometimes called cataplexy) which is characterized by akinesia (loss or decrease in mobility) and rigidity. For example, the animals remain motionless for long periods after being placed in unnatural positions. There is a fair correlation between the ability of a phenothiazine derivative to produce the cataleptic effect in animals and the Parkinsonian state in humans. Tremor, also a characteristic side effect of the antipsychotic agents, should not be confused with shivering, for the same drugs are often used to prevent shivering in therapeutic hypothermia.

Some recent investigations of drug-induced extrapyramidal effects are important because objective measurements were carried out. Simultaneous recordings were made from segmental alpha and gamma efferents in the rat tail during reserpine and CPZ administration. Gamma firings almost entirely stopped, while alpha motor activity and monosynaptic spinal reflexes were enhanced. This suggests that the site of action of reserpine and CPZ is supraspinal, since the rigidity, tremor, and accompanying electrophysiological effects are completely abolished by cutting the spinal cord. CPZ also abolishes gamma activity in the intracollicular decerebrate cat. The possible relationship between human Parkinson's disease and the reserpine-induced extrapyramidal disorder in animals is strengthened by the fact that dopa significantly improves the rigidity and akinesia in both conditions.

It is noteworthy that the reserpine- and phenothiazine-induced extrapyramidal states are temporarily abolished by amphetamine, methylphenidate, and other centrally acting stimulants. Drugs with atropine-like effects, as well as pretreatment with a monoamine oxidase inhibitor (MAOI) impede development of the extrapyramidal syndrome.

Most of the phenothiazines have atropine-like activity which antagonizes the cataplexy-Parkinsonism effect in proportion to their atropine-like potency.

B. Drug-Induced Hyperkinesias

The hyperkinesias can be produced by nearly all groups of the strong antipsychotic agents. In contrast to drug-induced Parkinsonism, the side reactions of chorea, athetosis, and hemiballismus have little counterpart in the experimental animal. In most instances the motor effect resembles the genuine syndrome only in certain respects.

1. Chemical Aspects

There is little apparent chemical relationship between the drugs which produce the hyperkinetic states. These include the hydrazine MAOI's, amphetamine-like amines, tranylcypromine, harmine derivatives, and the tricyclic antidepressants (dibenzoazepine and its derivatives), as well as phenothiazine and butyrophenone derivatives. As mentioned above, phenothiazines with a piperazine side chain often produce bizarre hyperkinesias.

2. Clinical Observations

MAOI's and the tricyclic antidepressants frequently produce a choreiform syndrome, and they occasionally worsen the abnormal movements of preexisting Huntington's chorea. This finding suggests that these substances have an "extrapyramidal" site of action. Tremor, hyperreflexia, and muscular twitching are also frequent side effects of these drugs. Animal investigations on harmine-induced tremor support this view.

However, antipsychotic agents such as phenothiazines, butyrophenone derivatives, and reserpine may produce hyperkinetic phenomena which usually subside upon discontinuation or reduction in dosage. These are the reversible hyperkinesias and include akathisia, acute dystonia, and, very seldom, a choreiform syndrome. In some instances, the regression of symptoms is slow, particularly of akathisia. This has been attributed to the fact that the excretion of a phenothiazine may continue for months before it is eliminated from the body. Women and middle-aged patients are especially likely to show such symptoms for weeks or months after drugs are discontinued. In addition to rapidly or slowly subsiding hyperkinesias, persistent neurological disorders may occur in patients who have been treated with antipsychotic agents for long periods of time. Such manifestations are the so-called tardive dyskinesias (Faurbye) or "terminal extrapyramidal insufficiency syndrome (Haddenbrock) (334)." These are neurological manifestations characterized by complex movements of the tongue (the flycatcher's tongue) and also by athetoid or choreiform movements which may involve practically every muscle of the body. These symptoms plus a protrusion of the pelvis are part of a syndrome which resembles Huntington's chorea. There is also a drug-induced myoclonic component with rhythmical twitchings of individual or symmetrical muscle groups (cf. Davis, Chapter 47). A literature review on dyskinesia and an extensive survey of chronic hospital populations did not indicate any sex difference with respect to the incidence of this syndrome (334). There is general agreement that the frequency of this disorder increases with age. Individuals with organic brain conditions seem to be more predisposed to dyskinesia, although no diagnostic group is immune to it. As to the frequency of this disorder, data from the literature are somewhat contradictory, but all systematic studies indicate that the number of patients exhibiting dyskinetic symptoms is large in chronic state hospital populations, approximately 22%, according to a 1967 study. Since this complication of treatment with antipsychotic agents was practically unknown until a few years ago, there is little information as to the onset or evolution of dyskinetic symptoms in subjects so afflicted. In most instances, symptoms develop after two or three years of continuous treatment with antipsychotic agents. A regression of dyskinesia may occur over a period of months and years, but in a high percentage of cases (possibly 50%), the syndrome remains practically unchanged. There is also some evidence that tardive dyskinesia becomes apparent or increases in severity after the withdrawal of the drug. In many cases this has been attributed to a lessening of muscular rigidity following discontinuation of drugs, or to increased psychomotor activity of the patient. However, further studies will be needed to shed more light on this problem.

3. Findings in Experimental Animals

MAOI's seldom produce a motor effect in acute experiments, except those (such as tranylcypromine) having a central amphetamine-like action. Most of the MAOI's cause heightened motor activity, usually of stereotyped character, when the trial is continued over several days. Tremor and ataxia are also observed. The tremor secondary to harmine administration seems to need the striatum for its manifestation, since it is abolished by destruction of this region.

Tricyclic antidepressants rarely lead to motor hyperactivity, but desipramine in high doses causes heightened motor activity in mice. Following imipramine, a definite increase in motor activity has been observed in higher primates. In most instances tricyclic antidepressants, like the phenothiazines, cause sedation. In spite of the relative ineffectiveness of antidepressants on the motor system, it is significant that these substances strongly antagonize reserpine and phenothiazine-induced cataplexy. In addition, the hyperactivity produced by L-dopa or amphetamine is significantly potentiated by MAOI's and other antidepressants.

Reserpine and the phenothiazines rarely cause hyperkinesia in animals. In rats a hyperkinetic state has been observed following sudden cessation of chronic CPZ administration. Pretreatment with MAOI's and other antidepressants before reserpine administration may convert the reserpine-induced cataplexy and akinesia into hyperactivity and overexcitement. CPZ in very small doses (1.5 mg/kg) significantly enhances the central stimulating action of amphetamine. The antidepressants also have this action.

C. *Drug-Induced Dystonia and Related Dyskinesias*

Dystonic movement disorders occur predominantly following treatment with strong antipsychotic agents such as fluorinated phenothiazines, especially those with a piperazine side chain. The clinical symptoms include oculogyric crises, spasms of the mouth and pharyngeal musculature, forceful protrusions of the tongue, torsion spasms of the trunk, and opistotonus. Many of these symptoms resemble those in dystonia musculorum deformans. The drug-induced dystonia occurs more often in men than in women, and usually in those under forty. It is striking that in contrast to practically all the other drug-induced movement disorders, dystonia almost always occurs in the first few days of treatment.

There are no reports of dystonic effects of the antipsychotic agents (reserpine and the phenothiazines) in animals.

V. Functional Mechanisms of Drug-Induced Extrapyramidal Side Effects

A. *Biochemical Pharmacology*

1. Drug-Induced Parkinsonism

It has been postulated that drug-induced Parkinsonism produced by reserpine, the phenothiazines, and butyrophenones is due primarily to the effect of these drugs on DA metabolism or transport in the extrapyramidal centers. This is especially likely for reserpine-induced Parkinsonism. Reserpine, similarly acting substances, and α-methyldopa displace catecholamines and 5-hydroxytryptamine (5HT, serotonin) from storage sites in the brain and in the periphery, leading to a DA and 5HT deficiency in the extrapyramidal centers. As mentioned earlier, elevation of the lowered DA levels by administration of its precursor L-dopa, correspondingly improves the extrapyramidal symptoms in idiopathic Parkinson's disease and in reserpine-induced Parkinsonism, and also counteracts the cataplexy in animals due to reserpine. Anti-Parkinson drug therapy is also beneficial in reversing drug-induced extrapyramidal symptoms. The alkaloid harmine has been reported to be effective only in reserpine-induced Parkinsonism, with variable results. Diphenhydramine, an antihistamine, is beneficial in reversing reserpine and phenothiazine (CPZ, trifluoperazine, and thioproperazine) symptoms.

With regard to the effects of reserpine in man and animals, it should be pointed out that this drug acts not only on the extrapyramidal centers but also on other brain areas. Since α-methyldopa displaces the brain amines, it is at first surprising that it has only a weak Parkinsonism-producing effect. The amine α-methylnorepinephrine which is formed from α-methyldopa, can assume the function of the endogenous catecholamines to a very slight degree.

The phenothiazines and the butyrophenones do not alter the concentration of DA, norepinephrine (NE), and 5HT as does reserpine. They are, however, central adrenergic blocking agents at the receptor sites and thus bring about effects comparable to amine depletion. Recently, it has been shown that CPZ causes a small, but significant reduction of DA in the caudate of cats. More significant is the observation that a series of phenothiazine derivatives (CPZ, thioridazine, trifluoperazine, thioproperazine) and the butyrophenone haloperidol cause an elevation of the DA metabolite HVA in the caudate nuclei in several species of experimental animals. In man, these compounds have been reported to cause alterations in cerebrospinal fluid proteins. However, these latter findings have been disputed.

It has been suggested that phenothiazines and butyrophenones block central catecholamine receptors in the same way as they do peripheral catecholamine receptors. They would thus cause a functional DA deficit at the synapse. The elevation of HVA has been interpreted as being due to a compensatory feedback activation of tyrosine hydroxylase, the enzyme which converts tyrosine to dopa, and a subsequent increase of DA release in order to overcome the receptor blockade. This interference of extrapyramidal center DA metabolism relates to Barbeau's (cf. 335) formalized and modified version of the biogenic amine equilibrium hypothesis of McGeer *et al.* (336), by linking DA to ACh. A disequilibrium in this DA–ACh system favoring cholinergic dominance might result in production of rigidity and akinesia. The second system comprising 5HT and histamine was postulated to be involved with tremor and akathisia. Many aspects of the hypothesis are still incomplete, especially with regard to the 5HT-histamine system.

On the basis of EEG investigations, Himwich and Rinaldi postulated in 1956 (337), that phenothiazines produce Parkinsonian tremor and rigidity by stimulating ascending and descending mechanisms of the reticular system. Very high doses of a phenothiazine caused a stimulating effect on the EEG recorded from the reticular formation, while small amounts caused a synchronizing effect. However, the Parkinsonian-producing effect of reserpine cannot be explained by this assumption since reserpine has been shown to produce, after an initial excitation, a long-lasting depression of reticular activity.

2. Hyperkinesias

Elevation of brain levels of DA and NE, and of 5HT, by administration of dopa and 5-hydroxytryptophan (5HTP), in animals, often is associated with symptoms of pronounced central hyperactivity. Further, giving 5HTP to patients with Huntington's chorea causes a prompt increase in the choreiform movements (and also worsens the preexisting organic dementia). This suggests that 5HT plays a role in this disease with predominant striatal destruction, possibly by acting directly on the pallidum, which has been released from normal striatal influences (338). Intravenous dopa caused a prompt exacerbation of the choreiform symptoms in two cases of Huntington's chorea that had developed Parkinsonian symptoms on reserpine therapy. Dopa alone also worsens the abnormal movements in Huntington's chorea.

a. MAOI's and Other Antidepressants. These compounds have one common characteristic. They functionally influence the metabolism of the catecholamines and 5HT in the same direction. The MAOI's inhibit enzymic breakdown of the organic amines and lead to elevation of their total concentration. They also naturally amplify the pharmacological effects of certain exogenously introduced amines or their precursors (for example dopa and 5HTP). The tricyclic antidepressants do not influence the activity of the MAO in any way, but they do elevate the concentration of the active amine portion in the receptor area in that they block its absorption into the storage cells. They thus significantly increase the effects of the endogenously freed and the exogenously introduced amines. By this means the MAOI's and other antidepressants can significantly enhance the motor hyperactivity produced by dopa. The MAOI's definitely, and other antidepressants probably, cause the same changes in amines in humans. The accentuation by MAOI's of abnormal movements in Huntington's chorea probably also has the same mechanism, and should be compared to a similar worsening produced by 5HTP and dopa.

b. Antipsychotic Agents. In addition to their peripheral adrenolytic action, the phenothiazines have the paradoxical effect of blocking catecholamine uptake into their storage sites. However, this latter action is currently being questioned because of the hypothermic effect of the phenothiazines which was not controlled by maintaining the animals at normal body temperature. If the blocking effect were true, however, the phenothiazines thus could potentiate the effects of epinephrine and NE under certain conditions. It is well established that the tricyclic antidepressants have this effect. It is especially interesting that with chronic CPZ administration, the adrenolytic effect soon diminishes, while the catecholamine-potentiating effect remains unchanged or even increases. These results suggest that the phenothiazines, under certain conditions and in predisposed patients, cause an antidepressant-like hyperkinetic side effect (it has been known for some time that chronic CPZ administration has an antidepressant action). The similarity of action of the phenothiazines and the antidepressants is emphasized by the observation that small doses of CPZ potentiate the central excitatory effects of amphetamines.

As noted above, it is unlikely that the irreversible hyperkinesia following chronic antipsychotic agent therapy has an exclusively biochemical effect in the brain. It does produce definite lesions in certain extrapyramidal centers.

The atropine-like action of the antipsychotic agents and antidepressants may also play a role in the production of extrapyramidal side effects. In this regard, atropine itself can potentiate the central excitatory effect of amphetamine, and can strongly promote choreiform hyperkinesias.

3. Dystonia

We do not know of any biochemical or pharmacological studies clarifying the mechanism of drug-induced dystonia. The fact that these extrapyramidal effects occur in the first days of therapy with antipsychotic agents suggests that the drugs may act on specific brain structures. It is again probable that symptoms which follow chronic high-dosage therapy are due to definite brain lesions.

B. *Pathological and Anatomical Research*

In rabbits, intravenous administration of CPZ at 7.5 mg/kg for 6 days or reserpine at 0.6 mg/kg for 4 days produces the following morphological changes: The cells in the basal ganglia, the hypothalamus, the anterior and posterior horns of the spinal cord (and medullary nuclei with reserpine) show clumping of Nissl substance, disintegration of nuclear and cell membranes, migration of the nucleolus to the periphery of the nucleus, piknosis of the nucleus, and, in severe instances, cell destruction. The glial reaction is insignificant. In man, pathological cell changes have been seen in the inferior olive in a patient who developed irreversible dystonia of the face and neck on high doses of chlorperphenazine. In the dog, cell damage in the inferior olive also occurs after chronic high-dosage treatment with different MAOI's. Depigmentation in the substantia nigra, nerve cell degeneration, and neuronophagia have also been found, especially in the putamen. These few studies in man and dog clearly show that pathological changes in the brain may occur with psychotherapeutic drugs, especially with antipsychotic agents. It should also be noted that ^{35}S-tagged CPZ seems to concentrate in significant amounts within the basal ganglia.

VI. Clinical Therapeutic Aspects

It has often been stated that minimal extrapyramidal side effects are necessary for the antipsychotic action of drugs. A minority of psychiatrists feel they are necessary, but most reject this thesis. It is, nonetheless, interesting that the observation was made that schizophrenics showed an improvement if they later became sick with Parkinson's disease as a sequel to encephalitis lethargica. It is also noted that the extrapyramidal side effects of the phenothiazines with piperazine side chains apparently play a role in the therapeutic success of these compounds in inactive and catatonic schizophrenia. To date it has not been possible to make an effective antipsychotic drug without extrapyramidal side effects. One may conclude that the extrapyramidal effects, at least to a certain degree and in certain cases, may exert a useful therapeutic action.

Extrapyramidal disorders represent a complex of symptoms and possible etiologies. Obviously, insight into the problem will require the effort of many disciplines. Progress, however, is now being made.

For general reviews and further reading see Appendix 1.

47

CLINICAL USE OF PHENOTHIAZINES

John M. Davis

I. Clinical Use of Phenothiazines: Therapeutic Effects

A. Introduction

In the last fifteen years, since the discovery of the antipsychotic properties of chlorpromazine, a revolution has swept through the psychiatry world. Prior to this time, the number of hospitalized psychiatric patients was steadily increasing. Beginning with the widespread use of phenothiazines in the state hospitals and primarily because of the use of these drugs, this trend has been reversed, and the size of the inpatient population has decreased dramatically.

Those psychiatrists who first used the phenothiazine derivatives immediately noted that their effects were far superior to those of any drugs previously used in the treatment of schizophrenic illness. The use of chlorpromazine quickly spread throughout the world. There was some scepticism about the therapeutic efficacy of the phenothiazine derivatives, particularly by those scientists who had no experience in their use. This scepticism was well justified, since patients can benefit markedly from the so-called placebo effect, an effect related to the personal meaning to a patient of taking a pill (see del Giudice, Chapter 32). Furthermore, uncontrolled studies give consistently more positive results in the evaluation of new drugs than do controlled studies. The necessity for the accurate evaluation of psychopharmacological agents has led to the application of a complex methodology for carrying out drug trials, including such techniques as random allocation of patients, double-blind design, use of placebos, quantitative evaluation of psychiatric improvement, checks that patients are ingesting proper dosage, etc. (see Gocka, Chapter 30, and Grayson, Chapter 31). The most important of these factors is quantitative evaluation of therapeutic improvement and the random allocation of patients. It is also important to consider pharmacological criteria such as the accuracy of the dose, the skill of the clinical pharmacologist, and also, whether or not the patients do in fact take their medication. Even in inpatient studies, many patients will somehow manage not to take their pills.

Well-controlled clinical studies do provide a background of relatively hard information upon which to base clinical judgment. Questions that can be asked of clinical psychopharmacologists are as follows:

1. Is a drug or class of drugs superior to placebo? What is the qualitative nature of improvement?
2. Is one or are several drugs in this class superior to other drugs of the same class? Do subtypes of patients respond better to one rather than to another of the phenothiazines?
3. If a patient fails to respond to one drug of this class, will he respond to another drug of the same class or to another drug of a different class? How do these drugs interact, and are they best combined with other forms of treatment, such as the various forms of psychological and social therapies? Can a combination of drugs of a single or of several classes produce better improvement than a single drug?
4. How long should a patient be kept on a drug? Do patients relapse if a drug is discontinued, and, if so, when? Are there withdrawal effects?
5. What side effects occur with drugs of this class, and are there quantitative or qualitative differences in side effects which would favor one drug over another? Are there side effects consequent to long-term medication?

B. General Therapeutic Efficacy

An extensive review of studies (using random allocation of patients and double-blind design) testing the effects of phenothiazine derivatives on populations of acute or chronic schizophrenic patients shows clearly that the phenothiazine derivatives are markedly superior to placebo. In certain of the earlier and smaller studies, the phenothiazine tested was not found to be effective; however, in these early studies, the average dosage used was too low to show an effect. When adequate doses of chlorpromazine are administered, this drug has proved quite consistently to be superior to placebo. Almost without exception, most of the other phenothiazines have also been shown to be definitely superior to placebo in the treatment of acute and chronic schizophrenia. There is good evidence for antipsychotic activity with thioridazine, chlorpromazine, prochlorperazine, triflupromazine, trifluoperazine, perphenazine, fluphenazine, acetophenazine, thioproperazine, thiopropazate, and carphenazine. The common phenothiazines and their effective dose ranges are listed in Table I.

The therapeutic effects of the phenothiazine derivatives are clearly shown by the most carefully controlled double-blind studies, such as those carried out on a cooperative basis by the Veterans Administration and the National Institute of Mental Health (see Caffey *et al.*, Chapter 33, and Goldberg, Chapter 34). The quantitative extent of improvement provided by the phenothiazines can be illustrated by the finding that two-thirds of the acutely ill, hospitalized schizophrenics were very much improved following phenothiazine treatment, as opposed to 25% of the placebo group. In addition, only 10% of the patients receiving phenothiazines were rated as "no improvement" or "worse," while 50% of the patients in the placebo group were so rated.

Table I

MAJOR PHENOTHIAZINE DERIVATIVES AND THEIR EFFECTIVE DOSE RANGES[a]

Phenothiazine derivative	Dosage (mg/day)
Chlorpromazine	570 (100–1600)
Triflupromazine	160 (25–400)
Mepazine	160 (25–450)
Thioridazine[b]	675 (50–1600)
Prochlorperazine	60 (10–150)
Trifluoperazine	20 (5–50)
Perphenazine	40 (8–144)
Fluphenazine	8 (1–25)
Promazine	420 (150–1600)

[a] Dosage should be individualized for each patient, since many variables may influence the dose used (See text). The doses given above are average doses used in ten double-blind controlled studies which found the drugs to be effective. Dose ranges are given in parentheses. Higher doses may occasionally be indicated in certain patients. (Also see Usdin, Chapter 15).

[b] It is not recommended that thioridazine be used in doses over 1000 mg/day because of the danger of producing pigmentary retinopathy.

In a descriptive sense, the nature of the improvement produced with phenothiazines consists of an improvement in a wide variety of psychotic symptoms. In this sense, the action of these drugs can best be defined as antipsychotic or antischizophrenic. For the average patient, perhaps two-thirds to three-fourths of the maximal therapeutic gain occurs in the first 6 weeks of phenothiazine treatment. However, significant treatment gains are often made throughout the subsequent 12–18 weeks of therapy. Some patients may show a very rapid improvement on phenothiazine treatment over the course of a single day or a few weeks, while other patients may show a very gradual rate of improvement over several years. It would be important in future studies to gain more information about the rate of improvement in different types of patients, for there is a tremendous variation in rates of improvement.

It is obviously important to know not just that phenothiazines benefit patients but also the quality and type of benefit which they produce. The unraveling of the quality of the alterations may lead to a more rational basis for using these drugs; but this, of course, rests in part on a better understanding of the etiology and pathogenesis of schizophrenia. Conversely, incorrect speculation on the mechanism of action of the phenothiazines may lead to the use of these drugs in less than optimal fashion.

Following phenothiazine therapy, a cognitive restoration can occur. In a significant proportion of schizophrenic patients, where a marked decrease in psychotic thinking is observed, there is a lessening of the use of psychotic projection to attribute unusual personal symbolic significance to objects and gestures, as well as a reduction in suspiciousness, perplexity, ideas of reference, etc. (339). There is also a reduction in pathological psychomotor behavior, with both retarded and hyperactive patients tending to become more normally active. Improvement in agitated depression is also observed (339). In patients who are labeled as process schizophrenics, a decrease may occur in their fragmented, jumbling, fuzzy thinking process, and fearful self-presentation, this being replaced by a sort of schizoid compliance (339). Data from rating scales indicate that, following phenothiazine therapy, there is a reduction of both fundamental and accessory symptoms of schizophrenia, such as thought disorder, blunted affect–indifference, withdrawal–retardation, autistic behavior mannerisms, hallucinations, paranoid ideation, hostility–belligerence, and resistiveness–uncooperativeness. The symptoms which are reduced are typical of schizophrenia in particular, and of psychosis in general. Symptoms such as anxiety–tension, guilt–depression, disorientation, and somatization are not so typically affected by phenothiazines.

In chronic schizophrenics, chlorpromazine reduces the amount of overinclusive thinking measured by a categorizing task, reducing errors of excessive breadth of concepts (340). In a test of psychotic thinking, the Gorham Proverbs Test, phenothiazines reduce bizarre circumstantial and inappropriate responses (341). In general, phenothiazines normalize schizophrenic behavior. At the present state of our knowledge, it is more accurate to refer to the phenothiazines as antipsychotic drugs in this descriptive sense rather than by the name tranquilizing drugs, since they do not, in any real sense, produce a state of tranquility in normal or in psychotic individuals.

C. Comparative Efficacy of Different Phenothiazine Derivatives

In order to form a digest of the evidence relating to the differential therapeutic effectiveness of the standard phenothiazine derivatives, all double-blind studies using random allocation of patients and otherwise achieving a reasonable degree of scientific quality were reviewed. The results are summarized in a box score form in Table II. It can be seen that no phenothiazine is clearly superior to most of the other phenothiazines. Promazine and mepazine are somewhat inferior to the other phenothiazines, and, incidentally, may be slightly more dangerous in terms of side effects.

In any statistical analysis, findings will occasionally be statistically significant as the result of chance factors alone. On certain measures in certain situations, one phenothiazine occasionally does become statistically more effective than others; however, no phenothiazine has proved consistently superior to other phenothiazines (see Table II). In an attempt to demonstrate whether or not

Table II

EFFECTIVENESS OF OTHER PHENOTHIAZINE DERIVATIVES COMPARED TO CHLORPROMAZINE[a]

	Numbers of studies in which:		
Drug	Drug was more effective than chlorpromazine	Drug was equal to chlorpromazine	Chlorpromazine was more effective
Triflupromazine	0	10 (100%)	0
Perphenazine	0	6 (100%)	0
Prochlorperazine	0	10 (100%)	0
Trifluoperazine	0	8 (100%)	0
Thioridazine	0	12 (100%)	0
Fluphenazine	0	8 (100%)	0
Acetophenazine	0	1 (100%)	0
Thiopropazate	0	1 (100%)	0
Promazine	0	3 (37.5%)	5 (62.5%)
Mepazine	0	0	4 (100%)
Phenobarbital	0	0	6 (100%)

[a] The data in this table consider patient populations in their entirety. In some of the studies included in this table, specific phenothiazines were found to be more or less effective than chlorpromazine on single variables or in specific patient subgroups. Such single-variable or subgroup differences should not be considered as definitive until cross-validated in other studies. (See text).

a given drug is perhaps slightly, although nonsignificantly, superior to others, Table III was prepared, showing the results from a number of well-controlled studies, in which the rank orders of therapeutic effectiveness of the phenothiazines are listed. A given phenothiazine was categorized as being approximately equal to chlorpromazine, in an intermediate category, or equal to placebo, based on an examination of the quantitative data in the study. It can be seen that promazine and mepazine are slightly inferior to the other phenothiazines, but other than this, the phenothiazines are all approximately equal in therapeutic efficacy.

If most of the phenothiazines are about equally effective, the next problem involved in choosing the best drug for a given patient is that of predicting whether or not a given patient might do particularly well on a particular phenothiazine. It could be argued that, since all the phenothiazines have very similar

Table III

Rank Order Efficacy of the Penothiazines in Carefully Done Studies Using Rating Scales As a Measure of Reduction of Psychopathology[a]

Rating scale used	NIMH collab-orative study I (global rating scale)	NIMH collab-orative study II (global rating scale)	Schiele *et al.*[b] (manifest behavior scale)	Vestre *et al.*[b] (PRP)	Lasky *et al.*[b] (IMPS-PRP)	Casey *et al.*[b] (change on MSRPP)	Casey *et al.*[b] (MSRPP)	Hanlon *et. al.*[b] (high group) (MSRPP)	Hanlon *et al.*[b] (low group) (MSRPP)	Adelson and Epstein[b] (MSRPP mean differ-ence)	Kurland *et al.*[c] (MSRPP)
Drug approxi-mately equal to CPZ	FPZ TDZ CPZ	APZ FPZ CPZ	TFl*uo*PZ TDZ CPZ	TFl*u*PZ FPZ	CPZ TDZ FPZ CPT TFl*u*PZ	CPZ	TFl*u*PZ PPZ CPZ PCPZ	PCPZ FPZ PPZ CPZ TFl*u*PZ TFl*uo*PZ TDZ TPZ	TFl*uo*PZ TDZ TPZ FPZ CPZ PCPZ TFl*u*PZ PPZ	PPZ TFl*u*PZ PCPZ CPZ	PCPZ TFl*u*PZ CPZ PPZ PZ
Drug slightly better than PCB, but less effective than CPZ	–	–	–	–	RP	PZ	MZ	–	–	–	MZ
Drug equal to PCB	PCB	–	PCB	PBT	–	PCB PBT	PBT	–	–	Active PCB Inactive PCB	PCB PBT

[a] APZ = Acetophenazine; CPT = Chlorprothixene; CPZ = Chlorpromazine; FPZ = Fluphenazine; MZ = Mepazine; PBT = Phenobarbital; PCB = Placebo; PCPZ = Prochlorperazine; PPZ = Perphenazine; PZ = Promazine; RP = Reserpine; TDZ = Thioridazine; TFl*u*PZ = Triflupromazine; TFl*uo*PZ = Trifluoperazine; TPZ = Thiopropazate

[b] See Appendix 1.

[c] Reference cited in Master Bibliography (342).

structures, and the antipsychotic action of the drug is related to those aspects of the molecule shared by all the phenothiazines, there would be no reason to expect that a subtype of patients would respond better to a particular phenothiazine. Although this possibility is certainly a real one, the possibility also exists that subtypes of patients may indeed respond better to a certain phenothiazine rather than to others; this could relate to differential absorption, accumulation at receptor sites, or metabolism of one derivative vs. another. In addition, psychological effects such as sedation could also play a role. For example, certain subtypes of patients who use activity as a defense mechanism may be quite alarmed when they are sedated, while, in other patients, sedation, and consequent passivity, is quite egosyntonic. In any case, determining whether a subtype of patient responds differentially to a given drug is a research question of obvious clinical importance. A myth exists in psychiatry that hyperexcitable patients respond best to chlorpromazine because it is a sedating phenothiazine, while withdrawn patients respond best to an alerting phenothiazine such as fluphenazine or trifluoperazine. This has not been found to be true. There is evidence from the NIMH collaborative studies that the second-order factor labeled "apathetic and retarded" predicted a differentially good response to chlorpromazine (see Goldberg, Chapter 34).

It is particularly important in evaluating predictive studies to remember that when many predictors, many criterion variables, and different methods of statistical analysis are used, the multiplicity of variables makes possible some statistically significant predictions which are actually due to chance alone. Hence, it is particularly important that results be cross-validated before they be accepted as truth. Indeed, empirically speaking, many predictions in this field have dropped out upon attempts at cross-validation. Some of the most sophisticated work on prediction of drug response has been carried out in the NIMH and the VA collaborative studies. Although there has been considerable emphasis on symptomatology in prediction, the patient's past history of response to phenothiazines is an important factor which should not be overlooked.

One can ask whether a patient who has failed to respond to one phenothiazine can be helped by another. Some investigators have argued that because these drugs are structurally similar, and similar in their efficacy on a statistical basis, a patient who fails to respond to one phenothiazine must, therefore, not respond to a second phenothiazine. Clinically, psychiatrists have noticed that, in opposition to this theoretical position, patients who fail to respond to one phenothiazine occasionally *do* show a good response to another. It is unfortunate that there has been no well-controlled research to date on this question. Since phenothiazine improvement can continue, in some patients, long beyond the 6-week limit usually delineated in comparative studies as time for maximal improvement, an improvement attributed to a second phenothiazine may in fact be due simply to the continuation on medication and not necessarily involve a more optimal response to a second drug. Thus, until cross-validated, reliable information on prediction of which patient will do best on which drug is available, the choice of phenothiazines remains a matter of clinical judgment. Consideration of the differential risk of severe side effects is important here.

D. Drug Combinations

Another aspect to be considered is whether or not drug combinations have advantages which single drugs do not possess. The necessity for cross-validation of results also exists here. The VA has collected some excellent data on drug combinations, showing that the addition of trifluoperazine, imipramine, and monoamine oxidase (MAO) inhibitors to chlorpromazine did not benefit chronic VA schizophrenics more than chlorpromazine alone, and that the addition of amphetamine may have been harmful. This question has been studied in detail by Kurland and his collaborators and the reader is referred to their monograph and to the review of Freedman (342,343). There is little evidence that combining one phenothiazine derivative with another is beneficial. In such trials, dosage should be strictly controlled to insure that the single medication controls get an amount of antipsychotic medication equal to the combination. There is some evidence from drug studies, as well as from clinical observation, that some patients may benefit from the addition to phenothiazine derivatives of other drugs, such as tricyclic antidepressants (see Klerman and Paykel, Chapter 49), MAO inhibitors (see Crane, Chapter 50), or butyrophenones (see Lehmann and Ban, Chapter 48). Research is not able, at the present time, to predict which patients show these improvements or to prove that the improvement is uniquely related to the combination. The use of combinations at the present time thus rests only on an empirical basis. Indiscriminate polypharmacy is to be discouraged. Therapeutic trials of a few selected patients on combination therapy are indicated on a clinical basis until more research information is available (e.g., depressed schizophrenics on a phenothiazine–antidepressant combination, manic-like schizophrenics on a phenothiazine–haloperidol or phenothiazine–lithium combination).

Poor therapeutic results can occur with some patients taking chlorpromazine or any other phenothiazine. Although the most likely reason for poor results is that the patient is not taking his medication, other possibilities include poor oral absorption or rapid metabolism. These patients can be treated with intramuscular injections of the drug, with a different phenothiazine, or with the long-acting parenteral administration of fluphenazine decanoate or fluphenazine enanthate. With the latter drugs, depot injections can be given weekly, or biweekly, and this regime is approximately as effective as oral administration. These long-acting fluphenazine compounds are particularly indicated for patients who may not take their medications as directed, and for treatment-resistant patients in general.

The phenothiazines are most useful for the treatment of the schizophrenic patient, in both the inpatient and the outpatient setting. They have also been widely used in the treatment of neuroses and character disorders. There is evidence which indicates that the phenothiazines do have some antianxiety effect in many of these patients, although a definitive comparison of the phenothiazines with the various antianxiety agents has not been made. Outpatients with anxiety, phobias, neurotic depression, character disorders, or other conditions may respond to chlordiazepoxide (and related drugs of the same class), tybamate or meprobamate, tricyclic antidepressants, MAO inhibitors, or placebo. Treatment remains empirical, and it should be remembered that phenothiazines are associated with more diverse and more serious side effects than the antianxiety drugs such as chlordiazepoxide, meprobamate, or tybamate. Some psychoneurotic patients deserve an empirical trial of phenothiazines, particularly if other drugs fail to help them. Patients who may have an underlying schizophrenia clearly should be treated with phenothiazines since antianxiety drugs do not have marked antipsychotic properties in most patients. Delay or inappropriate treatment may allow an incipient psychosis to develop. It is particularly important that patients with an incipient psychosis be treated vigorously with adequate doses of phenothiazines to abort their psychosis and prevent hospitalization or self-destructive behavior.

E. Drugs and Other Therapies

Because of the great interest in psychological therapies such as psychoanalysis, psychotherapy, and group therapy, and the obvious importance of social and psychological factors in schizophrenic disease, it is of paramount importance to know how the pharmacological therapies, such as phenothiazine therapy, interact with psychological therapies. It has been said by some, in our view incorrectly, that chlorpromazine can dull the schizophrenic patient's emotional sensitivity and make him less accessible to psychotherapy. Most investigators are of the opinion that antipsychotic drugs facilitate rehabilitation efforts.

The efficacy of drug therapy in combination with or without psychotherapy or psychoanalysis has been studied by several workers. In controlled studies, the results of psychotherapy without drug therapy are not impressive. These studies indicated that the drugs, whether alone or with psychotherapy, do have antipsychotic properties. Psychotherapy alone (without drugs) did not produce a lessening of the psychosis above that observed with hospitalization alone, and in no sense substituted for the drugs. There was no evidence from these studies that drug therapy made patients unresponsive to interpersonal relationships. Indeed, the opposite was the case in that the schizophrenics seemed more involved with their ward, the psychiatrists, and psychoanalysts, and current events (such as President Kennedy's death) when on phenothiazines (344). A particularly important study in this regard comparing four variations of social therapies and pharmacotherapy, using 115 chronic schizophrenic patients, was made by Greenblatt *et al.* at the Massachusetts Mental Health Center (MMHC) (345). Patients who had been continuously hospitalized in state hospitals for five to ten years, were under fifty years of age, and showed no clinical evidence of mental deterioration or retardation were divided into four matched groups. Group A was transferred to MMHC and treated vigorously with social therapies. Group B was transferred to MMHC and treated with both social therapies and tranquilizing drugs (chlorpromazine–reserpine). Group C remained at state hospitals and received no special treatment, while group D remained at the state hospitals but received the same drug treatment as those transferred in Group B. It must be noted that MMHC has a large staff and provided a maximum of social therapies, while the state hospitals provided a minimum. After

6 months of treatment, improvement was assessed and comparisons made. A clear-cut drug effect was observed. Improvement with drugs was greater than without drugs, both at MMHC (33%) and at the state hospitals (25%) vs. that observed in the state hospital milieu-only group (10%) or the MMHC milieu-only group (0%). Patients receiving intensive social therapy and no drugs showed little improvement. Patients initially and continuously receiving both social and drug therapy are most likely to improve and leave the hospital. It seems that in terms of ultimate outcome, social therapy and drug therapy may potentiate each other. The social therapies make it possible for the patient to better utilize the gain produced by the drugs in reducing psychotic symptoms.

The group receiving no drugs but receiving high social therapies did receive drugs after 6 months and were also continued on the vigorous social therapies regime. Yet, in spite of this, they did not catch up with the group receiving drugs. Attention is called to the VA collaborative studies on the question of the interaction of drugs with group therapy.

Phenothiazine therapy has largely replaced the shock therapies as a treatment of schizophrenia, although some clinicians feel that a brief course of ECT is useful in the treatment of selected patients when given concurrently with phenothiazine therapy. However, there is no extensive evidence from controlled studies on this point, although one excellent study does suggest that ECT is helpful (346).

F. *Maintenance Therapy*

The decision of whether or not to keep a patient on his phenothiazine medication after improvement is clinically an important one. It is obviously very important in arriving at a rational decision to know how many patients relapse after discontinuation of phenothiazine medication, and at what times such relapses occur. At one time, it was felt by some physicians that many schizophrenic patients should be kept on phenothiazines for their entire lives. Unfortunately, long-term side effects such as corneal opacities and permanent extrapyramidal effects are being noted, raising the question of the dangers of long-term medication. Thus, there are a number of important questions to be asked: whether or not short-term treatment affects the patient's long-term clinical course; whether or not prophylactic phenothiazine treatment prevents relapse in remitted schizophrenics treated with maintenance therapy; whether or not patients with partial remission will relapse if their phenothiazine is discontinued; how long should the therapy be continued to minimize immediate or delayed relapse; and does long-term maintenance therapy lead to a qualitatively or quantitatively greater improvement?

As an overview, it is important to know that in properly controlled studies of maintenance chlorpromazine as compared with placebo, it is a consistent finding that a significantly greater percentage of patients relapse when they are switched to placebo rather than maintained on their original phenothiazine medication. This occurs in both outpatients and inpatients. The percentage of relapses varies from study to study. For example, a long-term investigation of patients maintained in the community on chlorpromazine and/or placebo showed that when the study was extended beyond 30 months, the hospitalization rate with chlorpromazine and the placebo groups were 19% and 30%, respectively, thus indicating that maintenance chlorpromazine treatment did prevent some hospitalizations (347). There have been many studies on the withdrawal of chlorpromazine in chronic schizophrenic patients maintained in the hospital. Again, consistent findings over many double-blind studies show that there is an increased proportion of relapses following discontinuation of chlorpromazine medication. Relapses occur gradually over many months after discontinuation of treatment, so a given relapse may occur at a few weeks to 6 months or more following discontinuation of the phenothiazine medication. We cannot now adequately predict which patients will or will not relapse. It is not surprising that one can find small groups of patients, particularly when studies are done for short periods of time, who do not manifest a clinically significant number of relapses when maintained in the sheltered environment of the state hospital. Nor is it surprising that some patients can successfully be managed through so-called drug holidays. Although it has not been documented in double-blind research, it has certainly been observed clinically that an occasional chronic schizophrenic patient does better when phenothiazines are withdrawn. Therefore, the question of maintenance phenothiazines depends very much on clinical judgment, and more research is needed. It would seem reasonable that, if a patient does not respond optimally to a given phenothiazine, such that he can leave the hospital and make a good adjustment on the outside, further therapeutic effort is necessary. Although the exact time taken to achieve maximal improvement in a given patient is highly variable, it is certainly clear that most patients achieve a fair amount of improvement by 6 weeks or 3 months, and, in the case of suboptimal improvement, treatment either with complete discontinuation of drug therapy, trial of a very high dosage schedule, or treatment with a different phenothiazine or an antipsychotic agent of a different class would be indicated.

In the hospital, it is relatively easy to discontinue medications in the chronic patient, since the patients are in a controlled situation, and if their behavior deteriorates, it can be handled appropriately. The situation is much more difficult with outpatients, where a patient's deterioration can be socially harmful to his family and to himself, and difficult to manage. The practicing psychiatrist must be cognizant of both the increased risk of relapse and the existence of long-term side effects, and make the choice on clinical grounds. It is most important that a good doctor-patient relationship exists and that the patient be followed so that if early signs of a relapse occur, phenothiazine medication in adequate dosage can be initiated quickly to abort the relapse. The natural history of the given patient's illness and his response to drugs can be helpful. If the necessary degrees of freedom in management exists, it is better to start or stop, or change medication at times different from major environmental changes so that one can clinically separate drug responses from other factors. For example, if drugs are started at the onset of hospitalization or discontinued on the day of discharge, one cannot separate the effects of drugs from those of hospitalization.

G. Practical Hints for Treating Schizophrenic Patients with Phenothiazine Derivatives

The pharmacotherapy of psychiatric patients is as much an art as any other form of psychiatric therapy, necessitating to a considerable degree adaptation of treatment to the individual patient. No firm universal rules can be made. For example, it may be useful to set behavioral limits on the patient's psychotic behavior by psychological means during the first few days of hospitalization so that a more careful and judicious evaluation of the patient can be made, rather than rushing precipitously into phenothiazine therapy. However, when treating as an outpatient a patient who may be undergoing a schizophrenic break, and for whom hospitalization would be a disaster, it may be wise to quickly and vigorously begin treatment with phenothiazines in order to prevent the psychosis.

In terms of sound pharmacotherapy, dosage is the most important variable. One should avoid routine dosage strategies, such as high doses for long periods of time for every patient, or minimal dosages necessary to temper severe symptomatology. Dosage should be adapted for the individual patient to achieve maximal benefit from the antipsychotic properties of the drug. Since the range between a therapeutically effective dose and a toxic overdose is very wide for the phenothiazines, it is generally safer to err in the direction of higher dosage, thus avoiding inadequate dosage. Many schizophrenics may require 600–800 mg of chlorpromazine (or an equivalent dose of another drug) per day for optimal improvement; others may need less drug, while still others may require as much as 1.5–2.0 gm/day.

The manic schizoaffective and the schizophrenic in catatonic excitment may require a rather large dose of phenothiazine medication. It is often best to start with intramuscular phenothiazine; for example, chlorpromazine 50–100 mg intramuscularly, three or four times per day, or an equivalent dose of another phenothiazine. Some psychiatrists prefer chlorpromazine because of its marked sedative property. Other physicians prefer more activating phenothiazines, such as perphenazine, which can control psychotic behavior just as quickly as chlorpromazine, but which do not produce excessive sedation. Intramuscular chlorpromazine should be given deeply into the buttocks, since it is irritating, and injection sites should be rotated. Oral medication should be administered at the same time, so that after 2 or 3 days it will be possible to switch from intramuscular to oral medication at levels of 1.0–1.5 gm/day of chlorpromazine, or equivalent amounts of another phenothiazine. During the period immediately after discontinuing intramuscular medication, the patient should be closely observed for exacerbation, which could be controlled by increasing oral dosage, or by reinstating intramuscular injections.

In the treatment of depressed schizoaffective or retarded schizophrenic patients, it is not generally necessary to begin with intramuscular medication; however, they often require large doses of phenothiazines for control of their psychotic symptoms, even though troublesome "target" symptoms, such as agitation, can be completely absent. The aim should be for maximal cognitive reorganization. If at 6 weeks a retarded schizophrenic does not respond to administration of phenothiazine medication, addition of an antidepressant drug or ECT should be considered.

Patients with incipient psychoses often require phenothiazine medication to abort the psychotic episode. If severe insomnia and consequent sleep loss play a role in the progression from incipient psychosis to a full-blown attack, control of sleep by adequate phenothiazine medication is important. Chlorpromazine is often useful for this purpose because of its sedative properties, and can be administered in a single large dose 2 hours before bedtime. Dosage must be individualized, but a typical dose schedule may begin with 200 mg on the first day, and increase over the next few days to 600 or even 800 mg/day. If this dose is not adequate to control psychotic symptomatology, the dose should be gradually raised to 1.0–1.5 gm/day. Once adequate control of sleep has been achieved, patients may be switched to a less sedating phenothiazine, such as trifluoperazine, perphenazine, fluphenazine, or acetophenazine, in order to avoid troublesome sedation, particularly if the sedative properties may interfere with cognitive function on the job.

Treatment of the so-called childhood asocial schizophrenia (also called process schizophrenia) involves using much the same dose schedule as for the treatment of an incipient psychosis. Resolution of the psychosis and cognitive restoration is not so marked in this group, but schizoid compliance occurs more commonly. The same dose considerations apply to the treatment of the paranoid schizophrenic patient, although here again, one should not hesitate to use high doses. If the patient's illness is not characterized by insomnia, initial treatment with fluphenazine, perphenazine, trifluoperazine, or another nonsedating phenothiazine can be initiated. Typical dose schedules of these drugs would be: fluphenazine, initially 2.5 mg/day, increasing over several days to 20 mg/day; perphenazine, initially 4 mg/day, increasing to 36 mg/day; and trifluoperazine, initially 5 mg/day, increasing to 30 mg/day (see Table I).

The process of recovery from an acute schizophrenic episode can be seen as progressing through three overlapping phases: (1) control of the acute break with reality; (2) gradual resocialization; and (3) remission of core psychotic symptoms and return of inner psychic normality. The first phase occurs over a period of several days to weeks after initiation of phenothiazine treatment. Clinically, it is characterized by lessening of withdrawal or hyperexcitability, reduction of hostility, irritability, anxiety, and suspiciousness, and the beginning of participation in ward activities, such as conversing, eating, playing games, watching television, and reading. The patient may experience considerable sedation for several days or weeks until he develops tolerance to this side effect. The second phase involves the consolidation of the gains so that the patient can begin to have more normal social behavior; however, close contact with the patient will reveal that residuals of thought disorder, such as delusional thinking, remain. The third phase of recovery involves the gradual lessening of these abnormalities, and may continue for several months (or years) after phenothiazine therapy has been initiated. The patient, of course, does not go through a rigidly defined series of stages in the process of therapeutic improvement. The use of the term "phase" is merely meant to indicate that there is some moderate regularity in the patient's response to treatment, and that different emphasis may be placed on what occurs in the patient at different time periods during treatment. Throughout the second and third phases, the dosage of the phenothiazine medication is adjusted, often lowered, on the basis of clinical judgment.

After complete remission of the psychotic symptomatology, dosage is lowered to maintenance level. Radical reduction of dosage on the day of discharge should be avoided. It is often wise to keep patients on maintenance phenothiazine for at least 6 months to one year following an acute psychotic episode. The necessity for maintenance phenothiazine medication should be individualized after that time. Psychotherapeutic and social intervention during the recovery phases, as well as during posthospital care, are of very great importance in aiding social adjustment and preventing relapse.

The most important single cause for lack of improvement in the schizophrenic patients treated with phenothiazines is failure to take the medication. It is important to emphasize to the patient the necessity of taking the medication, and to work in the hospital situation or with the family to insure that the medication is being taken regularly. It is very important to deal with the patient's fantasies about medication, and also with one's own expectations regarding psychopharmacological treatment. Transference and countertransference difficulties can be as destructive here as in any other aspect of the therapeutic relationship. Some psychiatrists do have countertransference difficulties which focus around medication, and these should not be exempt from analysis.

II. Clinical Use of Phenothiazines: Side Effects and Their Management

Since over 50 million patients have been treated with phenothiazines in the last decade (348), physicians are becoming increasingly aware of both short- and long-term side effects of this class of psychopharmacological agents. For the purpose of this review, we will classify these side effects in the following categories: allergic reactions, autonomic effects, central nervous system effects, long-term skin and eye effects, and endocrine and other side effects. We shall describe the side effects, provide data relevant to the differential incidence of the various side effects which may be useful in deciding which phenothiazine to prescribe for a particular patient, and discuss the management of these adverse reactions.

A. Allergic Reactions

Chlorpromazine-induced jaundice was one of the earliest noted and more dramatic of the phenothiazine-induced side effects, although it is seen in only a small percentage of patients on chlorpromazine. The jaundice generally occurs within 1–5 weeks after initiation of phenothiazine therapy. It is generally preceded for 1–7 days by a flu-like syndrome consisting of malaise, abdominal pain, anorexia, fever, nausea, vomiting, and diarrhea. These symptoms resemble gastroenteritis or infectious hepatitis, and, indeed, it is difficult to clinically differentiate chlorpromazine-induced jaundice from infectious hepatitis since the virus has not been isolated. In making the correct diagnosis, one notes the temporal association to the beginning of phenothiazine therapy, the clinical picture of lack of liver enlargement or tenderness, and chemical evidence of cholestasis with an increase in bilirubin (direct-reacting more than indirect-reacting), increase in alkaline phosphatase, reduction of esterified cholesterol, etc. SGOT* and SGPT* are also increased, but often these increases are less impressive than those of bilirubin and alkaline phosphatase. The jaundice is generally mild, with the plasma bilirubin rarely rising above 15 mg/100 ml. Peripheral blood smears demonstrate eosinophilia, and liver biopsy shows bile plugs in the canaliculi, with eosinophilic infiltration in the periportal space. The fact that the halogenated phenothiazine, chlorpromazine, is secreted by the liver may relate to the existence of chlorpromazine jaundice. The jaundice generally disappears within several weeks, although it can last as long as 6 months or a year. In order to arrive at a reasonable estimate of the incidence of chlorpromazine jaundice, an accurate measure of the number of cases of chlorpromazine jaundice must be compared with the number of patients placed on chlorpromazine. We have analyzed and combined data from a large number of studies using chlorpromazine in the treatment of schizophrenic patients. When these data are classified by year of report of the study, it can be seen that the incidence of chlorpromazine jaundice is decreasing. The reason for this drop in incidence is unclear. In the early years of chlorpromazine jaundice, the incidence varied from 0.5% to over 1%, while at present the incidence is probably well under 0.5%. Jaundice has been reported during treatment with promazine, thioridazine, and prochlorperazine; however, no accurate estimation of the incidence of jaundice with these phenothiazines is available. Most of the other phenothiazine derivatives, such as fluphenazine and triflupromazine, have produced jaundice in rare cases. There is no evidence that the incidence of chlorpromazine jaundice is related to a prior history of liver disease, although, of course, a patient with an impaired liver may have less liver reserve if he develops a case of chlorpromazine jaundice. Very rarely, a patient can develop xanthomatous biliary cirrhosis. The evidence that chlorpromazine jaundice may be an allergic phenomenon is that its onset occurs in the first few weeks of treatment, it is frequently associated with other allergic reactions or eosinophilia, and there is prolonged retention of sensitivity on challenge test. It has been claimed that chlorpromazine may produce some long-term effects on the liver, such as fatty infiltration; however, these effects might also occur as a result of chronic hospitalization.

Although it is useful to have base-line liver function tests in case the patient does develop chlorpromazine jaundice, the advisability of weekly or biweekly liver function tests on a routine basis has not been proved. Since the chlorpromazine jaundice is preceded by a prodromal syndrome of a flu-like nature, one is more likely to pick up the impending jaundice from the clinical picture than from abnormal values noted on routine liver function tests. A proper trial to prove the efficacy of routine liver function tests would have to demonstrate that it is possible to pick up chlorpromazine jaundice prior to the clinical syndromes so that the drug can be discontinued more quickly. It is generally felt that it is best to discontinue the chlorpromazine, although it has not been shown

* SGOT = serum glutamic-oxalacetic transaminase
SGPT = serum glutamic-pyruvic transaminase

experimentally that discontinuation of chlorpromazine actually does lessen the jaundice and leads more quickly to a return of normal liver function. Most cases of chlorpromazine jaundice are benign and complete return to normal liver function occurs. It has been suggested that forcing fluids decreases the incidence of chlorpromazine jaundice.

Agranulocytosis is a serious, though rare, side effect of phenothiazines. It is not dose-related, and generally occurs within the first 6–8 weeks of treatment. Its onset is extremely abrupt, consisting of the sudden appearance of a sore throat, ulcerations, and fever. The mortality rate is high (30%). Agranulocytosis can occur in the presence of other side effects, such as jaundice and skin rash. The phenothiazine medication should be immediately discontinued, and the patient should be transferred to a medical facility for reverse isolation precautions. Energetic treatment of infection can be instituted, although prophylactic antibiotic therapy is not indicated because of the danger of propagation of drug-resistant organisms. Adrenal cortical steroid therapy does not appear to hasten recovery.

Cross-sensitivity to other phenothiazines may occur with this side effect. The incidence of agranulocytosis is very low, probably less than 1 out of 10,000 patients. This side effect has been reported with chlorpromazine, promazine, mepazine, and thioridazine, but it is probable that it may, in rare cases, occur with almost any phenothiazine. Thrombocytopenic or nonthrombocytopenic purpura, hemolytic anemias, or pancytopenia may also occur on rare occasions, and these side effects may be controlled by stopping the drug or switching to another.

A variety of skin eruptions has been associated with chlorpromazine treatment, including urticarial, maculopapular, petechial, and edematous types. These often occur early in treatment, generally in the first 5 weeks. A contact dermatitis can occur in personnel who handle chlorpromazine. A photosensitivity reaction of the phototoxic type which resembles severe sunburn can also occur. When appropriate, patients should be warned of this side effect. Treatment consists of protecting the patient from sunlight. Long-term skin and eye effects will be discussed in a subsequent section.

B. Autonomic Side Effects

A variety of anticholinergic and antiadrenergic side effects occur in patients treated with phenothiazines, including dry mouth and throat, cutaneous flushing, diarrhea, blurred vision, nasal congestion, precipitation of glaucoma, constipation with fecal impaction, paralytic ileus, and mental confusion. Dry mouth, which is a fairly frequent side effect, may be helped by asking the patient to rinse his mouth out with water frequently. It is not advisable to ask the patient to chew gum or candy, since adding sugar to the mouth may provide a good culture media for fungal infections such as moniliasis, and, in addition, this practice may increase the incidence of dental caries. Inhibition of ejaculation can occur, particularly with thioridazine. This can be controlled by decreasing the phenothiazine dose. Miosis and, very rarely, mydriasis are other occasionally seen effects.

Postural (orthostatic) hypotension can occur during phenothiazine therapy, and if this side effect occurs, it usually does so in the first few days of treatment. This can generally be controlled by bedrest with the feet higher than the head, although vasopressor agents can be used in rare cases. Tolerance to this side effect generally develops quickly; however, it can be troublesome, particularly in the elderly and in cardiac patients. The patient's blood pressure should be taken on a reasonable schedule, lying and standing, during the first few weeks of phenothiazine therapy. If the patient becomes symptomatic, if pulse pressure falls to below 30 mm, or if systolic pressure falls below 90 mm, dosage reduction should be considered; the dose should then be built up more slowly to an optimal dose. Support hose may help ameliorate the hypotensive effect of the phenothiazines. Since the postural hypotension often occurs when a patient gets out of bed, the patient should be warned of this side effect, and instructed to arise from bed gradually, sitting at first, dangling his legs, waiting for 1 minute, etc. Occasionally, it may be necessary to keep the patient in bed for several days. It is important to keep a patient with postural hypotension from fainting and falling and hitting his head. In elderly or cardiac patients, a predrug electrocardiogram and routine drug electrocardiograms may be indicated. In patients with cardiac disease or a history of cardiac problems, dose should be increased slowly and blood pressure carefully monitored to avoid episodes of severe postural hypotension. Since the phenothiazines have alpha-adrenergic blocking effects, epinephrine is not indicated to correct phenothiazine-induced hypotension.

Also clinically important is the fact that anti-Parkinsonian drugs, and tricyclic antidepressants, as well as phenothiazines, possess anticholinergic side effects. In a combination involving two or three drugs, they may produce additive anticholinergic action, resulting in paralysis of the bowel or bladder which on rare occasions can lead to death.

C. CNS Side Effects

1. Extrapyramidal Side Effects

Extrapyramidal reactions are the most dramatic of the CNS side effects of the phenothiazines. These can be placed into three categories: dyskinesias, Parkinson's syndrome, and akathisia. The dyskinesias consist of such syndromes as bizarre movements of the tongue, face, or neck, torticollis, tics, and abnormal eye movements. These occur generally within the first week after institution of phenothiazine therapy, and have an acute, time-limited course, either responding to anti-Parkinsonian medication or disappearing spontaneously without treatment. Parkinsonian syndrome consists of motor retardation, masklike facies, tremor at rest, rigidity, and shuffling. If not treated, this syndrome tends to persist in a fairly constant state. Akathisia is a motor restlessness characterized by great difficulty in sitting still, and a strong urge to move about. Although often considered a single class of side effects with three subtypes, the extrapyramidal effects may actually be more properly regarded as a family of related but separate side effects.

a. Differential Incidence of Extrapyramidal Effects. Thioridazine, although it does produce some extrapyramidal effects, produces very few in comparison with the other drugs. Trifluoperazine and fluphenazine produce the most extrapyramidal effects. Chlorpromazine produces a moderate number of extrapyramidal effects, more than thioridazine, but considerably fewer than trifluoperazine or fluphenazine. Perphenazine occupies an intermediate position between chlorpromazine and trifluoperazine or fluphenazine. Since most authors, in addition to administering phenothiazines, also administer anti-Parkinsonian agents, and since the statistics on side effect incidence are usually based on the entire time period of the study, the differential incidence of extrapyramidal effects with different phenothiazines is clouded by the administration of anti-Parkinsonian drugs and quantitative measurements of the differential incidence of extrapyramidal effects is difficult. It is said that perphenazine and prochlorperazine often produce dystonia, while trifluoperazine, prochlorperazine, and fluphenazine often produce akathisia, but solid data on the point are lacking.

It is also said that the Parkinsonian syndrome and akathisia occur more frequently in women, whereas the dyskinesias are seen more frequently in men. The dyskinesias and akathisia are said to occur at earlier ages, whereas Parkinsonism per se occurs more frequently in the older age groups.

b. Diagnosis. Dyskinesias can often be confused with the bizarre mannerisms of a psychotic patient, and akathisia can be confused with agitation. Since the treatment of agitation or bizarre psychotic manifestations may involve increasing the phenothiazine dosage, and the treatment of dyskinesias or akathisia involves lowering the dosage or adding an anti-Parkinsonian medication, an accurate diagnosis is important. These extrapyramidal side effects often respond dramatically to intramuscular or intravenous treatment with either diphenhydramine or anti-Pakinsonian agents such as procyclidine or benztropine. This provides a fairly simple method of making such a differential diagnosis.

c. Treatment of Extrapyramidal Effects. It is worthy of note that as many as ten acute dyskinetic reactions may present within a single month to a busy emergency room, often occurring in patients treated for nausea with phenothiazine derivatives. Occasionally an acute dyskinetic reaction may be resistant to treatment with diphenhydramine or an anti-Parkinsonian medication. Some cases will respond to methylphenidate or to barbiturates.

On a chronic basis, Parkinsonian syndrome can be controlled by the addition of anti-Parkinsonian drugs (benztropine, procyclidine, diphenhydramine, trihexyphenidyl, orphenadrine, chlorphenoxamine, etc.). The minimal dose of extrapyramidal drugs sufficient to control the Parkinsonian syndrome should be used, and dosage adjustments may be required. Roughly speaking, one can prescribe 5 mg of procyclidine (or an equivalent amount of other anti-Parkinsonian medication) for every 400 mg of chlorpromazine or its equivalent. Procyclidine is a short-acting drug, and hence requires a three-times-daily regime. There is little necessity for increasing the dose above 15 mg daily.

Some physicians argue that one should not routinely administer prophylactic anti-Parkinsonian medication because (1) only a minority of patients develop troublesome extrapyramidal symptoms; (2) some toxicity is associated with high doses of the anti-Parkinsonian drugs, including mental confusion, dry mouth, blurred vision, and occasional paralysis of the bladder or bowel; and (3) the expense of treatment is increased. However, extrapyramidial side effects often are distressing to a patient, particularly in an outpatient situation, so other physicians advise prescribing prophylactic anti-Parkinsonian drugs. In the hospital situation, the author would not favor routine administration of prophylactic anti-Parkinsonian drugs, but would recommend their judicious use, particularly in the outpatient situation. Since the development of extrapyramidal effects can be alarming and quite troublesome, prevention by the administration of prophylactic anti-Parkinson medication is clinically indicated in many patients. Use should be individualized in consideration of the particular problem posed by the individual patient. Akathisia can be resistant to treatment with an anti-Parkinsonian drug, and thus is most often controlled by a reduction of dosage or by switching to a different phenothiazine.

It is important to remember that there may be subclinical manifestations of extrapyramidal effects. Observations of patients on phenothiazines alone indicate that they often show lack of spontaneity, inability to participate in social activities, lifelessness, and drowsiness. Introduction of anti-Parkinsonian medication often results in definite benefits in these areas.

It has been said that patients may develop tolerance to the extrapyramidal disorders so that, after several months of phenothiazine treatment, especially in a hospital situation where it is easy to observe the patient, a gradual reduction of anti-Parkinsonian medication can be attempted.

Because the anti-Parkinsonian drugs are excreted faster than the phenothiazines, if patients treated with both drugs have them both suddenly discontinued, withdrawal symptoms (nausea, vomiting, restlessness, etc.) can develop associated with the discontinuation of the anti-Parkinsonian medication, and a reemergence of extrapyramidal symptoms could conceivably occur because of the faster washout of anti-Parkinsonian drugs. Upon discontinuation of phenothiazines in a patient on high doses, it may be advisable to continue the anti-Parkinsonian drugs a day or two longer than the phenothiazines, and withdraw both drugs gradually over several days. Toxic psychoses do occur when anti-Parkinsonian drugs are given in high doses (e.g., 6–8 mg of benztropine). Anti-Parkinsonian medication should, of course, be given with caution in the presence of benign prostatic hypertrophy and glaucoma.

The fact that all antipsychotic compounds (phenothiazine derivatives, thioxanthene derivatives, butyrophenones, reserpine and reserpine-like drugs) produce extrapyramidal effects suggests that the qualitative presence of extrapyramidal effects may be associated with antipsychotic properties. Furthermore, it has been thought that the optimal therapeutic dose of phenothiazine has been reached at that point at which the onset of a certain special type of extrapyramidal effects, such as a subtle alteration in handwriting, occurs. Investigators have not produced solid evidence that this is true. Since extrapyramidal side effects and therapeutic effects are both dose-related, it is not surprising that there should be an apparent association between these two types of effects.

It is also significant that some people treated with phenothiazines do not seem to get extrapyramidal effects, although they are benefited by the antipsychotic properties of the phenothiazine derivatives.

d. Long-Term Extrapyramidal Effects: Tardive Dyskinesia. A somewhat controversial extrapyramidal syndrome which occurs late in the course of treatment with antipsychotic drugs has been called tardive dyskinesia or terminal extrapyramidal insufficiency syndrome and is characterized by its late occurrence in the course of treatment, sometimes appearing after the drugs have been discontinued, its persistence for years, its treatment-resistant quality, and its absence during sleep. Tardive dyskinesia is characterized by grimacing, by buccofaciomandibular or buccolingual movement, sucking and smacking movements of the lips, lateral jaw movements, or a rhythmical forward and backward (or lateral) movement of the tongue, which has been described as a "fly-catcher movement." Choreiform-like movements can occur with jerky, sometimes athetoid movements of the upper extremities, or of the fingers, ankles, and toes. Tonic contractions of the muscles of the neck and back are sometimes encountered.

Tardive dyskinesias often become intensified or make their initial appearance within 1–14 days after the cessation or reduction of dosage, although these symptoms may also appear when the patient is on drug therapy, and disappear when the drugs are discontinued. In many cases the symptoms of these tardive dyskinesias disappear within a month after the cessation of drug treatment, but in some cases they persist for years and appear to be permanent. Anti-Parkinsonian medication frequently does not control these symptoms and may even aggravate them. Paradoxically, the symptoms may sometimes be controlled by giving the patient large doses of phenothiazines or butyrophenones.

The fact that most cases of tardive dyskinesia have been reported after 1964, and that most of these cases occur in patients with long-term, high-dose therapy, suggests that the length of therapy is an important factor in the etiology of this condition. It should be remembered, however, that the drug etiology of this condition is supported only by circumstantial evidence, as this chronic population has a high incidence of organic brain damaged, elderly, and chronically ill patients. However, these symptoms were rare in chronic schizophrenics before the antipsychotic drug era. The importance of the tardive dyskinesias is somewhat controversial and the reader is referred to the reviews by Crane and Kline. (See Chapter 46.)

2. Nonextrapyramidal CNS Effects

One toxic effect on the central nervous system which is mentioned frequently is that of seizures. It is difficult, however, to prove a causal relationship between seizures and phenothiazines, since patients may have seizures for reasons unrelated to their phenothiazine therapy. Chlorpromazine does lower the seizure threshold, and patients do have seizures when treated with very high doses, or during a toxic overdose. The question then arises, can patients with epilepsy and schizophrenia be treated with phenothiazine derivatives? There have been no large controlled studies on the problem of seizures occurring in seizure-prone schizophrenics. However, clinical experience suggests that, generally speaking, patients who are seizure-prone show an improvement in their seizure problem when treated with phenothiazine derivatives, and rather than increasing the incidence of seizures, phenothiazines in a schizophrenic population decrease their incidence.

In normal subjects, high doses of the more sedative phenothiazines such as chlorpromazine may cause sedation. The mild or moderate drowsiness usually disappears after the first or second week, and patients should be cautioned about driving or operating machinery while taking phenothiazines. If this effect proves troublesome, it can be controlled by lowering the dosage or by having the patient drink coffee. Interference with mental function may occur. However, in schizophrenic patients mental performance is generally improved after phenothiazine therapy. This may be explained by assuming that the antipsychotic benefit derived from the phenothiazine more than cancels out the sedative effects. Disturbed body temperature, paroxysmal or focal electroencephalographic slowing, and respiratory depression are some additional CNS side effects which may be seen with phenothiazine therapy. The respiratory depression is often not seen unless the phenothiazine is combined with another causative factor such as meperidine. Dosage reduction is usually sufficient for management. In drug patients who are given EEGs the EEG reader should be informed of the patient's drug history because of the possibility of drug-induced EEG changes as mentioned above.

Behavioral complications of phenothiazine therapy have also been noted. These effects, such as insomnia, bizarre dreams, impaired psychomotor activity, sedation, aggravation of schizophrenic symptomatology, and a toxic-confusional state, can usually be controlled by reduction of dosage or switching to another drug. It is often difficult to separate a nondrug-related worsening of the schizophrenic state from drug-induced behavioral toxicity, but on occasion these effects could be drug-related and managed by an alteration in dose and/or addition and deletion of drugs. It is possible that some patients may metabolize the drugs more slowly than others, and hence high blood and tissue levels of phenothiazines accumulate, resulting in behavioral symptomatology. Mental confusion could result from phenothiazines, particularly when given in combination with antidepressants or anti-Parkinsonian agents; hence polypharmacy is not indicated unless clinically warranted, based on the clinician's judgment.

D. Long-Term Skin and Eye Effects

In the first few years of chlorpromazine use, it was thought not to produce any long-term side effects; unfortunately, however, in recent years it has become apparent that skin and eye changes do occur in patients treated with long-term high-dose chlorpromazine therapy. The skin changes consist of a blue-gray metallic discoloration of the skin over areas exposed to sunlight such as the face and nose, sometimes the neck and open collar area of the chest, and the dorsum of the hand. The skin changes often begin with a tan or golden brown color and progress to such colors as slate gray, metallic blue or purple, or even a marked purple color. Skin biopsies indicate an aggregation of golden-brown pigment granules, histochemically similar, but not identical, to melanin.

Eye changes have also been noted following long-term, high-dose chlorpromazine therapy. These are described as bilateral whitish-brown granular deposits concentrated in the anterior subcapsular area, which in more severe cases may also be found in the anterior lens cortex and in the posterior cornea at times. The lens changes begin with bilateral, fine dotlike particles in the anterior capsular and subcapsular portion of the pupillary area, generally only visible by slit-lamp examination. These progress to opaque white or yellow-brown granules, often stellate in shape. In some patients, the conjunctiva is discolored by a brown pigment. These lens changes are quite different from those of senile cataracts and are in no way related to them. These opacities tend to occur more frequently in patients with skin discolorations than in those patients without skin changes.

Retinal damage is not seen and, in general, vision is not impaired. The most significant factors affecting ocular deposits are duration and total dose of chlorpromazine received, with the majority of the patients showing deposits having ingested 1 to 3 kg of phenothiazines throughout their therapeutic course. There have been no severe eye deposits such as star formations reported below a total drug intake of 0.75 kg within the last 2 years of treatment.

Hospitals differ in their reported incidence figures of skin and eye effects from less than 1% in some to more than 30% in others. Until these discrepancies are resolved, the actual incidence figures for skin and eye effects must remain unknown. One possible reason for this difference in incidence figures may be that some hospitals may use high doses of chlorpromazine and expose their patients to a considerable amount of sunlight, while other hospitals may use lower doses and their patients may have less exposure to sun.

Treatment for these side effects has been formulated on the theory that blocking melanin synthesis would be helpful. This can be accomplished by giving the copper-chelating agent D-penicillamine (300 mg three times daily for 6 days with a mineral supplement on the seventh day) to depress tyrosinase activity. A second method is to increase melanotonin production by keeping the patients in darkness.

E. Endocrine and Other Side Effects

There are a number of metabolic or endocrine effects which may result from phenothiazine therapy. Some of these are weight gain, edema, impotence in males and increased libido in females, gynecomastia, lactation, and menstrual irregularities. Most of these are related to hypothalamic neuroendocrine stimulation. The reader is referred to the extensive review of chlorpromazine and endocrine function by de Wied (349).

Weight gain is a well-documented side effect with phenothiazines, particularly with chlorpromazine, often occurring rapidly when the drug is started. The etiology of this weight gain remains obscure. Phenothiazines can produce galactorrhea and gynecomastia, most commonly in premenopausal women, although it does occur in postmenopausal women and in men. It can occur as early as within the first or second week of phenothiazine therapy. This side effect was first described in patients being treated with chlorpromazine, but can also occur with other phenothiazines such as thioridazine, trifluoperazine, prochlorperazine, and fluphenazine.

It has been suggested that phenothiazines and their sulfoxide metabolites suppress the secretion of prolactin inhibitory factor from the hypothalamus, thus accounting for the observed frequency of galactorrhea. Amenorrhea, a frequent occurrence with psychiatric patients, has been reported to occur in a small percentage of schizophrenic patients under phenothiazine treatment, a finding which may relate in part to the endocrine effects of the phenothiazines and in part to the nature of the schizophrenic illness and its consequent psychological disturbances.

An electrocardiographic abnormality of uncertain significance, consisting of broadened, flattened, or cloven T-waves, has been described in patients treated with phenothiazines, particularly thioridazine. Although not associated with clinical electrolyte disturbance, it is said to be reversible by potassium supplements, discontinuation of the drug, isorbide dinitrate, and ergotamine tartrate. S-T segment depression has also been observed in patients treated with phenothiazines. The fact that they occur after commencement of phenothiazine therapy and disappear when the drug is stopped suggests that they are drug-induced. In addition, bradycardia, tachycardia, or palpitations may occur. A cardiomyopathy consisting of a thickening of cardiac vessels less than 0.1 mm in diameter has been described in patients treated with phenothiazines for long periods, including a fair percentage of patients who died suddenly and unexpectedly while on these drugs. It is unclear whether sudden death occurs more frequently in phenothiazine-treated patients than in nondrug patients, or if this phenomenon is related to the cardiomyopathy mentioned above, to seizures, to ventricular fibrillation, or to the extensive deposition of pigment which has been found in the lung, heart, and kidneys of patients who have died after long-term phenothiazine therapy. The role of the phenothiazines in aspiration deaths is uncertain since, although these deaths do occur, particularly in chronic mental patients with debilitated condition, neurological impairment, and poor dentition, they often occur in patients not receiving tranquilizing medication (350).

Thioridazine has produced a pigmentary retinopathy in patients who were receiving 1.6 gm or more per day, and this side effect can be produced by other phenothiazines in very rare instances. This effect is a different side effect from and not related to the anterior lens opacities.

Overdoses of phenothiazine derivatives are usually not fatal, and the few fatalities reported may be attributed to idiosyncrasies of drug reaction or to complications of coma rather than to the direct action of the drugs themselves.

For further reading and reference see Appendices 1 and 2.

48

CLINICAL USE OF OTHER ANTIPSYCHOTIC AGENTS

H. E. Lehmann and T. A. Ban

I. Introduction

Prior to Delay and Deniker's discovery of the new and strikingly unexpected therapeutic properties of chlorpromazine in 1952, there were no drugs which could beneficially influence psychotic symptoms such as hallucinations, delusions, autistic behavior, and dereistic thinking. Since that time, the situation has entirely changed.

At first by substitutions and replacements on the phenothiazine moiety, new therapeutically effective phenothiazine preparations were synthesized, and as time passed a considerable number of other structurally different antipsychotic drugs have been made available for clinical application. Today there are at least three major groups of nonphenothiazine antipsychotic drugs available for clinical use: (1) the rauwolfias and related benzoquinolizines, (2) the thioxanthenes, which are derived from the phenothiazines, and (3) the butyrophenones, an entirely new class of psychoactive agents.

A common characteristic of at least some of the members of all three of these groups is that they can effectively be used in the treatment of such specific symptoms as hallucinations, delusions, and thought disorder. This means that on the basis of precalculated dose equivalence, one therapeutically effective antipsychotic substance in many cases may be replaced by another without producing any essential alteration in the course of the treatment. However, there is sufficient evidence to indicate that there are some patients who are responsive to one and refractory to another group of antipsychotic drugs and others whose improvement can be facilitated and furthered by supplementing their therapeutic drug regime, e.g., of phenothiazines, with a butyrophenone preparation.

II. Rauwolfias and Benzoquinolizines

In the same year (1952) the unique antipsychotic properties of chlorpromazine were discovered, the active principle of the rauwolfia plant, which had been used for centuries in India as a treatment for a variety of mental and emotional disorders, was isolated in the form of reserpine by Mueller, Schleter, and Bein. This was soon followed by the first clinical reports with the newly isolated substance on the basis of which Kline was moved to study its usefulness in the treatment of psychotic and especially schizophrenic patients. It is interesting to note that the first two drugs which proved to be effective in the treatment of schizophrenia were discovered almost simultaneously, but independently, and neither were the result of a systematic search for such a treatment procedure.

Since the introduction of reserpine, numerous other antipsychotic rauwolfia derivatives have been introduced. Among them, the clinically most important are deserpidine and rescinnamine, both of which are used in the oral dosages of 8–15 mg three times per day for intensive treatment and 1–5 mg one or two times a day for maintenance therapy.

Furthermore, other heterocyclic compounds with pharmacological properties similar to reserpine have been synthesized and employed in therapeutic trials. Among them, the most important are benzquinamide (100–400 mg per day), a serotonin antagonist, and a psychotropic drug which was shown to exert antipsychotic action, and tetrabenazine (100–200 mg/day), a central parasympatholytic which has been primarily employed in the treatment of schizophrenic patients, but was later reported to be particularly useful in the management of manics.

Today all of these drugs are prescribed only infrequently in the treatment of psychotic patients. They are slower in their action than drugs from the other antipsychotic categories, and their side effects (e.g., depression) are often so disturbing that Barsa and Saunders claim, for example, that adverse reactions to benzquinamide outweigh its therapeutic value. The additional fact that drugs of this type cannot be used in combination with monamine oxidase inhibitor antidepressants or electroconvulsive therapy (ECT) further limits their clinical attractiveness. However, in a small number of cases which have been refractory to treatment with other antipsychotic agents, rauwolfia derivatives still remain therapeutically useful. This is in accordance with findings in controlled studies in which reserpine was shown to be inferior to chlorpromazine in its overall therapeutic effectiveness, but superior to an inactive placebo.

III. Phenothiazine Analog Thioxanthenes

Besides depression, other commonly occurring adverse effects encountered in the course of treatment with the antipsychotic phenothiazines and rauwolfia alkaloids are various extrapyramidal manifestations. However, some believe that at least minimal extrapyramidal signs are essential for successful treatment. In the course of systematic work Petersen *et al.* succeeded in synthesizing a series of compounds with preserved antipsychotic, but reduced toxic and adverse effects, by replacing the phenothiazine nucleus with a thioxanthene nucleus. To date there are at least three of these thioxanthene analogs available in one or another country for clinical use: (1) chlorprothixene, the chlorpromazine analog; (2) clopenthixol, the perphenazine analog; and (3) thiothixene, the thioproperazine analog.

In subsequent clinical studies the antipsychotic properties of the thioxanthenes were confirmed, as well as the relatively low incidence of adverse reactions in the course of treatment. Nevertheless, it was recognized that chlorprothixene—the parent substance of this group—is inferior to chlorpromazine and haloperidol in the treatment of acute schizophrenic patients and inferior to trifluoperazine in chronic cases. Because of this, the use of this substance is usually restricted to the treatment of certain schizo-affective conditions in contradistinction to thiothixene, which is gradually more extensively employed in the treatment of schizophrenics in the dosage of 30–60 mg/day.

The place of the third compound, clopenthixol, has not yet been fully established. It is already known, however, that in the dosage range of 100–200 mg/day it exerts a particularly beneficial effect on affective psychopathological manifestations differentiating it from perphenazine, its phenothiazine analog, which primarily improves mental integration.

IV. Antipsychotic Butyrophenones

Entirely different in their chemical structure from the rauwolfia alkaloids, phenothiazines and thioxanthenes are the antipsychotic butyrophenones, substances which in some way are reminiscent of the γ-aminobutyric acid structure. Haloperidol, the first member of this series was originally synthesized in 1956, clinically tested in 1958 and made available for therapeutic use in 1960. Today there is general agreement that it is a reasonably effective antipsychotic drug which may have some superiority in the treatment of hyperactive psychotic conditions, mania, and Gilles de la Tourette's syndrome.

Furthermore, there are indications that of the various butyrophenone preparations, haloperidol is therapeutically effective (or superior to chlorpromazine or chlorprothixene) in the treatment of acute schizophrenic patients, especially when excitement and perceptual psychopathology prevail in the clinical picture. Triperidol, another butyrophenone, is particularly useful in the treatment of chronic schizophrenic patients. It has been demonstrated that the optimal therapeutic dosage range for intensive treatment with haloperidol is 5–15 mg and for triperidol 5–10 mg/day, with a maintenance dosage of 2–8 mg for each. Above this dose range there is a significant increase in adverse effects and not infrequently also a decrement in the overall therapeutic efficacy.

V. Other Antipsychotic Groups

There are a number of new groups of drugs with possible antipsychotic effects, but none of them has yet reached clinical significance. Among them chronologically first are the benzothiazines (or azaphenothiazines) the outcome of the substitution of a pyridine ring for the chlorinated benzene ring. In spite of the promising animal data, however, no therapeutic effects could be demonstrated in schizophrenic patients with these drugs. However, findings with another group, the so-called acridanes, in which the sulfur atom of the phenothiazine ring is replaced by a nitrogen atom, are more promising.

The chlorpromazine analog of this group was shown to have potent antipsychotic effects. More recently, favorable therapeutic results in chronic schizophrenics were reported also with pinoxepin, a dibenzoxepine derivative originally considered to be an antidepressant drug.

VI. Treatment Procedures

Treatment of the *acute schizophrenic breakdown* follows similar patterns with antipsychotic rauwolfias, thioxanthenes, and butyrophenones. In the first therapeutic stage the primary aim is the reduction of excitement and tension in the shortest possible time. This can best be achieved by the regular administration of the antipsychotic drug at first parenterally (for the first 3–5 days), and then orally. In this way a state of drowsy and cooperative passivity can be produced within the first few days of treatment with a significant reduction of psychomotor excitement before the end of the first week.

If the treatment of the acutely psychotic patient is successful, the reduction of psychomotor excitement is followed after 2–3 weeks by an improvement in the sphere of emotional responsiveness and mood (second therapeutic stage) and after about six to eight weeks by the elimination of all or most psychotic pathology during the third therapeutic stage. That this chain of sequence in the therapeutic progress applies generally to any effective antipsychotic pharmacotherapy was demonstrated by Lehmann and Ban in a controlled study with three different classses of antipsychotic drugs: phenothiazines, thioxanthenes, and butyrophenones. In this study, reduction of excitement was observed with all drugs in the first week or two. From the second to the sixth week, improvement of behavior, appearance, affect, and social participation was seen, and only after 6 weeks was there any significant reduction of major psychotic symptoms involving perceptual and cognitive processes, e.g., hallucinations and delusions.

It is essential to continue treatment after the acute episode has been handled successfully. In this maintenance period the therapeutic dosage may be reduced to one-fourth or one-fifth of the original level, which then has to be administered over an extended period of time. After the first schizophrenic episode this period does not necessarily have to exceed 6–12 months, but, if it is the second episode, treatment has to be carried on for at least two to three years. In patients who have had more than two schizophrenic breakdowns maintenance treatment may have to be continued for an indefinite period of time.

Treatment of chronic schizophrenics follows lines similar to those guiding the therapy of an acute schizophrenic breakdown. Although chronic patients, too, will respond to a surprising extent to pharmocotherapy, the longer a schizophrenic condition has existed, the longer it will take for pharmacotherapy to become effective. In such cases the therapeutic action of pharmacotherapy may not become evident before 3–6 months, and its full effects not before a year.

VII. Practical Conclusions

After the introduction of phenothiazines several other groups of antipsychotic drugs were synthesized and clinically employed. Among them, rauwolfia alkaloids, thioxanthenes, and butyrophenones are the most important. While the psychiatric use of rauwolfia alkaloids, mainly because of their mood-depressant effects, has been almost entirely abandoned, drugs of the other two chemical groups are being clinically employed at an increasing rate. Butyrophenones seem to be especially useful when excitement, agitation, and perceptual disturbances prevail, and the thioxanthenes are often preferred when depressive elements are associated with the schizophrenic illness.

For further reading and references see Appendices 1 and 2.

49

THE TRICYCLIC ANTIDEPRESSANTS

Gerald L. Klerman and Eugene S. Paykel

I. Introduction

Imipramine and the related tricyclic drugs have emerged in the recent decade as the most effective compounds for the treatment of depression. This chapter reviews the general pharmacology and clinical effects of the tricyclic antidepressants, with major attention given to imipramine. Imipramine, the first of the tricyclic series shown to have clinical utility, serves as the prototype; its clinical pharmacology exemplifies important issues in the evaluation of the antidepressants. Moreover, pharmacological investigations of imipramine's mode of action have stimulated imaginative theories about the etiology and pathophysiology of depressions.

A. Definitions and Classification of Clinical Depressions

Before reviewing the individual drugs, it will be useful to summarize a number of clinical features of depression, emphasizing the variability of the clinical phenomena. This variability is an important consideration for clinicians faced with the question of whether or not to prescribe drug therapy for an individual patient who is depressed, and, if so, which drug to select. It is also important for the researcher confronted by discrepancies in the published reports.

Considerable confusion arises because "depression" has different meanings in neurophysiology, pharmacology, psychology, and psychiatry. For the neurophysiologist, depression refers to any decrease in electrophysiological function, such as "cortical depression." The pharmacologist uses depression for drug actions which induce decreases in the activity of the target organ. Thus, the "CNS depressants" include drugs like the barbiturates and the anesthetics, which are unrelated either clinically or pharmacologically to the antidepressant drugs. The psychologist uses the term for any decrement in optimal performance, including slowing of psychomotor activity or reduction of intellectual functioning. For the psychiatrist, however, depression covers a wide range of changes in affective state which may include normal mood swings at one extreme and states of severe psychosis at the other. The use of the same term in a number of fields has tempted many to believe that there is a common mechanism underlying these phenomena. As a result, various authors infer that clinical depression symptoms are the result of a depression of CNS functioning and can, therefore, be treated best with a stimulant drug. This view was plausible during the period when the amphetamines and ECT were the only available therapies. It cannot be maintained, however, in light of current knowledge.

When used by clinical psychiatrists, the term "depression" covers a broad span of human phenomena. As a mood, depression is part of normal living. Feelings of disappointment, frustration, and grief are vicissitudes of the normal human condition. As a symptom, pathological depression often occurs secondary to physical and emotional disturbances such as viral infections, nutritional deficiencies, or schizophrenia. In clinical practice, however, depression refers most frequently to one or more syndromes in which there are abnormal, persistent moods of sadness associated with feelings of worthlessness, guilt, helplessness and hopelessness, anxiety, crying, suicidal tendencies, loss of interest in work and other activities, impaired capacity to perform everyday social functions, and hypochondriasis accompanied by such physical alterations as anorexia, weight change, constipation, psychomotor retardation or agitation, headache, and other bodily complaints. Such states may be clearly seen as pathological even to the untrained observer by virtue of the intensity, pervasiveness, and persistence of these feelings, and the interference with normal social and physiological functioning.

Psychiatrists do not agree on the full range of phenomena to be diagnosed as depression. The line between a normal mood and an abnormal depresssion is unclear. In many episodes of depression the precipitating events are obvious, such as in bereavement, adolescent development, posttraumatic states, persistent social problems among minority groups, aging, and reactions to chronic illness. It is important to emphasize that there is not one clinical depression syndrome, but a wide variety of such syndromes. Some psychiatrists believe that among the various depressive states there is a distinct group which forms a unique disease entity, called, variously, "primary affective illness," "manic depressive illness," or "primary depression." In this illness, episodes occur without any immediate life stress. These individuals often experience recurrence, a small percentage of them alternating depression with episodes of euphoria and manic excitement. Somatic therapies, including the antidepressant drugs and electroconvulsive therapy (ECT), are most useful with these patients.

B. Clinical Course and Spontaneous Remission

Depressions have a high improvement rate; most depressive episodes are self-limiting. Among psychiatric conditions, depressions have a good prognosis even without specific treatment. Most acute depressions in the majority of hospitalized and outpatients will have remissions with almost complete symptomatic relief, often enabling the patient to return to his previous level of social, intellectual, and occupational functioning.

Various compilations have been made of the "spontaneous" remission rate. Alexander (351), in his extensive compilation of clinical studies of hospitalized patients in the 1920's and 1930's, reports recovery or social improvement in 44% of hospitalized patients within the first year, with up to 56% recovery over longer periods. These data were collected on hospitalized patients before the advent of ECT, which subsequently raised recovery rates. Outpatients, whose milder illness does not require hospitalization, have better improvement rates. Klerman and Cole (352) point out that these spontaneous improvement rates approximate the rates reported in uncontrolled drug studies where 65–75% of the patients are improved. There are, of course, differences in the rate at which patients recover, and many investigators believe that the role of somatic therapies is to decrease the intensity of the symptoms and hasten recovery, rather than "cure" the illness.

Social scientists and dynamically oriented psychiatrists have delineated a number of the processes which are involved in what has been called "spontaneous" improvement. From experience with controlled clinical trials, at least two components of "spontaneous" remission have been identified: placebo effects and milieu influences.

C. Placebo Effects

Placebo effects have become increasingly prominent in discussions of research design and clinical actions (cf. del Giudice, Chapter 32). Specific studies of placebo effect in depressed patients have been few, however, and their results inconclusive. In an analysis of placebo effects from a large Veterans Administration multihospital cooperative study, it was found that the predictors of placebo effect were different from that of response to drugs. In extensive studies of outpatients, many of whom had depressive symptoms, placebo response was found to vary with the type of drug, social background of the patient, educational level, and whether or not the patient was seen in a clinic setting or in the office of a private psychiatrist.

The important role of expectations and attitudes as mediators of the placebo effect has been greatly stimulated by the work of social psychologists. A number of studies of doctors' attitudes show that expectations seem to have little influence on the treatment of depressed patients with antidepressants. Two studies of doctors' attitudes failed to show any effects, although another study did show that optimistic doctors obtained better results. Investigations of patients' attitudes found no influence on outcome.

Research is necessary which undertakes a control for the placebo itself in order to determine whether or not there is a therapeutic effect from pill taking separate from the social–psychological influences of therapeutic zeal, attendance at clinics, and the relation between the patient, physician, and treatment. Such an experiment, now underway by the authors, involves a tripartite design, with a group of patients treated with amitriptyline being compared to a group taking placebo and another group receiving no pills at all, but all three groups participating in clinic.

D. Milieu Effects

Research on placebo effects has been paralleled by study of the social processes in the "milieu." Milieu research refers to studies of inpatient and day hospital settings where patients are influenced by other patients, nurses, attendants, family activities, and various groups and occupational therapies. The hypothesis states that, because the therapeutic effects of drugs varies with the nature of the setting, drug-placebo differences would be greatest under primarily custodial conditions, principally in large public mental hospitals. This hypothesis was first formulated during the studies of the phenothiazines, and has been applied recently to studies of depressed patients in Philadelphia and

Table I
ANTIDEPRESSANT DRUGS[a]

General group	Generic name	Daily dose range (mg)
1. Psychomotor stimulants		
A. Amphetamines	Amphetamine	5–15
	Dextroamphetamine	5–15
	Combinations with barbiturate	5–15 Dextroamphetamine and 30–100 amobarbital
B. Others	Methylphenidate	10–30
2. Monoamine oxidase inhibitors		
A. Hydrazines	Phenelzine	30–75
	Isocarboxazid	20–30
	Nialamide	50–200
B. Nonhydrazines	Tranylcypromine	10–30
	Pargyline	10–50
3. Tricyclic compounds		
A. Iminodibenzyls	Imipramine	75–300
	Desipramine	75–300
	Trimipramine	
B. Dibenzocycloheptenes	Amitriptyline	50–250
	Nortriptyline	20–100
	Protriptyline	15–40

[a] Also cf. Usdin, Chapter 15.

in Maryland. A relatively insignificant drug-placebo difference was found where imipramine was used in an active treatment hospital, which was interpreted to be the result of the beneficial influence of an active milieu. In the Maryland study, comparison was made of the treatment of depressed patients with isocarboxazid and placebo in two different settings: a research ward at one hospital and the admissions unit of a large state hospital. The patients in the research ward devoted specifically to depression did considerably better than those in the admission unit. This study indicates that there may even be deleterious milieu effects where the treatment setting does not provide special attention to the depressed patient.

These questions will be settled by further study. In addition to research, and of equal importance, there are the matters of further conceptualization and an increased sophistication about the social–psychological processes involved.

E. Classification of Antidepressant Drugs

Contemporary antidepressant treatment began in 1957, when the monoamine oxidase (MAO) inhibitors and imipramine were made available simultaneously. Over a dozen new compounds have been developed since then. Some drugs with antidepressant activity are listed in Table I and grouped by major category.

II. General Pharmacology

The clinical efficacy of imipramine was not predicted from routine pharmacological animal studies in the mid-1950's. At that time, clinical antidepressant activity was predicted from animal motor stimulant actions, a criterion derived from experience with the amphetamines. The pharmacological profile of imipramine resembled chlorpromazine and it was first used as a tranquilizer. The clinical observation of Kuhn (6) that imipramine had antidepressant actions stimulated extensive pharmacologic research to distinguish tricyclics from phenothiazines. From these efforts, considerable knowledge of imipramine's pharmacology has accumulated, and evidence has been generated that the mode of action of imipramine, amitriptyline, and other tricyclics involves adrenergic mechanisms.

A. Chemical Structural Considerations

The tricyclic derivatives are closely related to the phenothiazines, the difference being in the bridgings between the two benzyl rings.

Among the tricyclic derivatives, there is close similarity between the structural formula of the phenothiazines, thioxanthenes, and imipramine derivatives. Imipramine, the parent compound of the tricyclic antidepressants, is an iminodibenzyl derivative. Amitriptyline is a dibenzocycloheptene. The pharmacologic and clinical actions of these drugs are closely similar, although differing at a number of points. (The implications of these structural relationships are discussed in detail by Biel, Chapter 19).

The thioxanthenes are not usually listed among the antidepressant compounds in American and British studies. Their chemical structure and pharmacologic activity, however, are related to the phenothiazines and the tricyclics. In European studies, especially among French and German clinicians, antidepressant action of the thioxanthenes has been advocated. Two thioxanthenes are currently marketed in the United States, chlorprothixene and thiothixene.

B. Absorption and Distribution

The tricyclic compounds are readily absorbed parenterally or from the gastrointestinal tract. Measurable concentrations of imipramine may be found in the plasma within 30 minutes after intramuscular injection. Attempts have been made to develop clinical methods for determination of plasma levels. The hypothesis that variations in the rate of therapeutic response may be related to the rates at which the drug is removed from the plasma, bound to the tissues, and metabolized is still being studied.

Limited information is now available about the differential distribution of the drugs in various organs. In general, the highest concentrations occur in the liver, brain, and lungs, a distribution similar to that observed with the phenothiazines.

C. Metabolism

The metabolism of the imipramine series has received considerable attention because of the claims for clinical efficacy of the desmethyl derivatives. Goldenberg and Fishman review in this volume the urinary excretion and metabolism of imipramine. The main urinary metabolites excreted are the *n*-oxide and its free parent compound. Further research has identified other metabolites. The main degradation pathway seems to be hydroxylation at position 10. Goldenberg and Fishman list over a dozen compounds in addition to the glucuronides. The urine of patients treated with imipramine contains only small amounts of the drug in the parent form. It is likely that imipramine and related derivatives are metabolized by pathways which are very much like those in the metabolism of chlorpromazine.

Considerable attention was given to the possibility that the active form of the imipramine was the desmethyl compound. As a result, the desmethyl derivatives of imipramine and amitriptyline have been marketed clinically. The clinical trials have not substantiated the initial hypothesis that the desmethyl derivatives would be more rapid acting and more potent than the parent compound. Recent pharmacologic studies have demonstrated marked species and sex differences in the metabolism of imipramine, probably related to the speed of various enzymic transformations. The clinical significance of these transformations remains to be fully investigated.

D. Behavioral, EEG, and Autonomic Effects

The various tricyclic derivatives produce behavioral, electroencephalographic (EEG), and autonomic effects, on animals in the resting state, which are very much like those of the phenothiazines. The EEG's of animals such as rabbits and cats tend to be slowed, with occasional spindles. Similar effects are seen in man. The ability of amitriptyline, imipramine, and their related compounds to lower the convulsive threshold is reflected clinically in an increased incidence of seizures. Electrophysiological studies, other than those employing self-stimulation, have contributed little thus far to identifying sites of action, although the role of limbic and hippocampal structures seems to be a promising area of investigation.

Considerable attention has been devoted to exploring the autonomic effects of imipramine and other tricyclic compounds. Although these compounds do not produce changes in blood pressure, pulse, or EEG, they do have a number of autonomic actions, especially anticholinergic effects which produce an atropine-like pattern. More significantly, there are indirect effects on blood pressure based on interactions with many compounds. On the basis of these peripheral autonomic effects, it was proposed that the potentiation of adrenergic effects noted peripherally might also occur centrally, probably through sensitization of adrenergic receptors to norepinephrine. This hypothesis has stimulated considerable research in the CNS actions of the tricyclics, and has been a considerable spur to the catecholamine theory.

The atropine-like effects are manifested clinically by dry mouth, constipation, and blurring of vision. Indirect evidence for central atropine-like effects has been inferred from EEG studies, in which desynchronization and changes in theta rhythm have been noted.

Many of these investigations have involved potentiations and interactions of tricyclic antidepressants with monoamines or drugs which influence amine metabolism. These efforts have been directed toward delineating actions of imipramine and related compounds from structurally similar drugs, like the phenothiazines, lacking specific clinical antidepressant action. A number of such properties have been established including: (1) potentiation of peripheral effects of exogenous catecholamines; (2) potentiation of pre- and postganglionic sympathetic nerve stimulation adrenergic responses; (3) potentiation of central effects of amphetamine and related psychomotor stimulants; and (4) antagonisms of reserpine syndrome.

E. Effects on Monoamines

The possible role of the monoamines in CNS activity related to emotion and behavior has been extensively reviewed. Attention has been directed to both the catecholamines and the arylindolylamines. The current consensus favors the catecholamines as the more important substances implicated in the antidepressant activity of both tricyclics and MAO inhibitors (cf. Fuxe *et al.*, Chapter 6, and Synder, Chapter 9).

When the MAO inhibitors were first developed, the hypothesis was put forth that depressions were associated with a decrease in levels of brain monoamines. With the introduction of imipramine, it seemed logical to investigate whether or not imipramine had any direct influence on MAO enzyme. Numerous studies have shown that imipramine and the other tricyclics do not inhibit either the MAO or the catechol *o*-methyltransferase systems.

Based on the work upon peripheral activities, attention was turned to attempts to demonstrate effects of imipramine upon central adrenergic systems. Based upon this work, the neuron uptake blockage hypothesis has become widely accepted. Imipramine inhibits the reuptake of norepinephrine (NE), thus preventing the physiological inactivation on this enzyme at the synapse. Support for this concept derives from the effects of tricyclic drugs upon the brain metabolism of radioactive norepinephrine. Starting with Glowinski, the technique of injection of tritiated NE into the ventricular system was developed. In this preparation, imipramine, desipramine, and amitriptyline increase brain levels of normetanephrine, a major metabolite of NE. This effect can be interpreted as reflecting increased level of activity. It is of note that neuronal uptake of dopamine is not inhibited by the tricyclic antidepressants. Effects upon serotonin have been reported both in brain slices and peripherally.

The tricyclic antidepressants slow the disappearance of NE in the brain. They also appear to slow the turnover of NE by decreasing the storage permeability and slowing the rate of intraneuronal release. It may thus be possible that NE is more available for extraneuronal discharge.

F. Interactions with Drugs

As discussed previously, much of the evidence for the adrenergic actions of the tricyclics derives from studies involving interactions with other drugs which alter peripheral or central adrenergic processes (cf. Valzelli and Garattini, Chapter 17; Fuxe *et al.*, Chapter 6; and Snyder, Chapter 9).

1. Potentiation of Peripheral Actions of Catecholamines

Sigg first reported that imipramine enhanced and prolonged the effects of exogenous NE on cardiovascular and nictitating membranes of cats (353). Similar effects occur with all active tricyclics, as well as with cocaine, reserpine, and ganglionic blocking agents. Although the pressor effect of NE is potentiated by tricyclics, the pressor response to epinephrine is less affected. In contrast, the pressor effect of tyramine, amphetamine and phenethylamine, the indirectly acting vasopressor amines, is blocked. Since the tricyclics do not directly deplete catecholamines, these effects are inferred to be due to actions on membrane transfer at storage sites or receptors.

2. Reversal of Reserpine Syndrome

Numerous studies have established that the tricyclic antidepressants block or prevent a range of autonomic effects of reserpine such as ptosis, miosis, hypothermia, gastric ulcers, diarrhea, bradycardia, and salivation. Similar effects are also produced by antihistamines and a number of ganglionic blocking agents. However, imipramine and other tricyclics antagonize the behavioral changes produced by reserpine and other amine depletors, especially benzoquinolines (cf. Laborit and Sanseigne, Chapter 18). This pattern of actions has generated an animal pharmacological model for testing potential antidepressants. This model also has value for study of mechanism of action. For example, it is established that presence of central catecholamines is necessary for these effects of imipramine and other tricyclics.

3. Other Interactions

Experiments with amphetamines and methylphenidate indicate potentiation of central stimulant effects by imipramine and other tricyclics. Metaraminol, guanethidine, and other catecholamine blocking agents are antagonized by tricyclics, as are adrenergic neuron blocking agents such as guanethidine and bretylium.

Interpretation of these studies has supported emphasis on adrenergic mechanism as central mediators of tricyclic actions. However, the indoles and cholinergic systems still merit consideration.

These neuropharmacological actions, which are of considerable theoretical importance to our understanding of modes of action, have as yet not led to immediate clinical application. In the clinical domain, behavioral and symptomatic methods remain predominant.

III. Clinical Effects

A. Controlled Studies of Efficacy in Depression

Based on controlled studies, it would seem that the tricyclic antidepressants are the most effective drugs available for the treatment of depression. A substantial majority of controlled trials comparing the tricyclic compounds to placebo have demonstrated the effectiveness of the active agent. Of this group, imipramine has been the most widely studied. Among studies of amitriptyline, eight were positive and one negative. With desipramine, two studies were positive and two were negative. Studies of the newer tricyclic drugs are now accumulating. Nortriptyline has been reported to be superior to placebo in five trials with no published negative studies; protriptyline was superior to placebo in two studies; and trimipramine was more effective than placebo in one study, while one study was negative.

It is noteworthy that about one-quarter of these controlled studies have not shown drug-placebo differences. The trend appears to be that 50–70% of patients are moderately improved while on the tricyclic drug; 30–50% improve in placebo groups. As a consequence, many studies reach conventional statistical significance, but some do not, although similar trends are evident. While they represent an important advance compared to previous therapies, the overall efficacy of the drug is limited. Consequently, it has become important to identify those individuals among the heterogeneous depressive population who may be specifically responsive to the tricyclic antidepressants. This problem will be discussed further below.

B. Differences among the Tricyclic Antidepressants

Most comparisons of two or more tricyclic antidepressants use either imipramine or amitriptyline as the standard. Amitriptyline appears to be the most effective compound. There is no published controlled study in which another tricyclic antidepressant has been found to be more effective than amitriptyline, although another drug has appeared equal in several studies. There is little conclusive evidence available to distinguish among the others. Of the newer tricyclic drugs, trimipramine shows promise. Opipramol, which is not available commerically in the United States, appears less effective than the standard drugs.

As a group, the tricyclic antidepressants have a similar spectrum of clinical effects, although amitriptyline tends to have more hypnotic-sedative actions than imipramine, while protriptyline has more psychomotor stimulant actions. Desipramine and nortriptyline are the desmethyl derivatives of imipramine and amitriptyline. Desmethyl derivatives show strong NE-potentiating effects in animals. As pointed out earlier, it was postulated that they are the pharmacologically active compounds into which the methylated analogs are converted. The desmethyl derivatives do not appear any more clinically effective, however. When they were introduced, it was also hoped that they would act more rapidly than the parent compounds, but subsequent controlled studies did not show evidence of this. The question still remains open, however, and two recent studies, one of each drug, did show them to be acting more quickly.

These comparisons must be interpreted with caution. Most studies utilize fixed doses, but comparisons of milligram-per-milligram potency are important clinically. What is more important is the ratio of efficacy to adverse effects, the best drug being that which, even if large absolute doses are required, provides maximal efficacy with minimal adverse effects. Comparisons of the various drugs, administered at different levels of dosage, are needed to ascertain this optimal effectiveness.

C. Dosage and Route of Administration

The usual starting dose of imipramine for outpatients is 10–25 mg given orally three to four times daily. Inpatients are usually started at 25–50 mg orally three or four times daily. As a rule, older patients tolerate higher doses poorly, and should, therefore, be started on low doses to be increased cautiously. The dose may be increased over 1–2 weeks to a maximum of 225–250 mg daily, depending on clinical response and adverse effects. Dosages of up to 300 mg and even 400 mg daily have been used in hospitalized patients, but are likely to produce considerable adverse effects, particularly behavioral toxicity, atropine-like effects, and postural hypotension.

The usual dosage of desipramine is the same as for imipramine; for amitriptyline it is a little lower; for nortriptyline the recommended maximum is 100 mg daily; and for protriptyline it is 40–60 mg daily.

Parenteral preparations of imipramine and amitriptyline are available, but are little used in the United States or England. There is scanty evidence that their use offers any advantage, but in one nonblind, controlled study of amitriptyline a response was achieved twice as fast by intramuscular injection.

Studies are required to establish clinical response curves. Quite often in clinical practice, dose levels prescribed are probably too low. One group of investigators was unable to differentiate between placebo and imipramine given to hospitalized patients in a dosage of 150–200 mg daily, but showed the imipramine to be effective at a dose of 240 mg.

D. Onset and Speed of Clinical Response

The onset of initial response and the rate of improvement with the tricyclic antidepressants vary. Initial improvement may be noted in a few days, and is most likely to appear by the second to third week. In most controlled trials, drug-placebo differences appear at about two to three weeks after the initiation of treatment and become maximal at 4–6 weeks. Drug-placebo differences may diminish later, probably because the improvement of the placebo-treated group begins to catch up with the active treatment group. Most patients show some improvement fairly early, and if some clinical response has not occurred within 4 weeks and maximally tolerated dose is being taken, it is not worthwhile continuing.

The latency in the onset of improvement distinguishes the tricyclic antidepressants from the amphetamines and antianxiety agents, and is of major pharmacological importance. The reasons for this phenomenon are not understood. It is probably not due to a demethylation since this takes place within 16 hours after the administration of a single dose. Studies of blood levels in chronic administration show that they do build up to some extent over 2–3 weeks. This latency of clinical action is also in contrast to the relatively rapid onset of actions in animals. Systematic work in this area is long overdue.

E. Duration of Treatment

The optimum duration of treatment has not been determined conclusively. The recommended clinical practice is to begin reducing the drug dose approximately three months after symptomatic remission has occurred, keeping the patient under observation to ascertain if symptoms return. The dosage should be reduced gradually over a period of at least 2–4 weeks since withdrawal symptoms of nausea, vomiting, malaise, coryza, dizziness, and muscular pains occasionally occur.

There is some evidence suggesting that tricyclic antidepressants may be valuable as a long-term maintenance treatment in averting further depressive episodes. A follow-up of 93 patients, maintained for 6 months on either imipramine or amitriptyline after a controlled trial, revealed fewer relapses than in a retrospective control group treated a year before with ECT. In two other studies, patients who were maintained on imipramine after receiving ECT showed fewer subsequent relapses than patients maintained on placebo.

F. Factors Affecting Response

The definite, but limited, efficacy of the tricyclic antidepressants in the treatment of the heterogeneous groups of depressed patients has stimulated efforts to ascertain whether particular types of depressions are responsive to individual drugs. Research in this area is made difficult by the lack of agreement among psychiatrists on the criteria for diagnosis and the absence of a validated etiologic classification of depression. Few studies distinguish the factors predicting general improvement from those which predict the differential outcome between the placebo-treated and drug-treated patients.

Hospitalization status seems to be one important factor. In a review of controlled studies up to 1965 among patients treated with placebo, only about 20% of outpatients improved, whereas there was a 45% improvement among inpatients. In both cases, the proportion responding to tricyclic antidepressants appeared to be 60–70%. This is surprising in view of the generally higher improvement rate among outpatients. It may be that selected outpatients were included in early controlled trials. However, psychoneurotic depressives appear to respond particulary well to the effects of the hospital milieu and environmental change.

Increasing effort has been devoted to relating drug response to clinical classifications of depressives, particularly the distinction between endogenous, neurotic, or reactive depressions. A number of controlled trials have reported greater response to the tricyclic drugs among patients described as endogenous, psychotic, or retarded depressives. These patient groups, although overlapping, are not identical. Similar characteristics are also associated with response to ECT. These findings represent trends. Good results have also been reported in neurotic depressives and in anxious, phobic patients. Schizo-affective patients usually respond poorly.

G. Comparison with Other Treatments

1. Electroconvulsive Therapy

Electroconvulsive therapy (ECT) remains an important treatment against which drug treatments should be compared. For severe depression, ECT still appears to be the most effective treatment available. A number of controlled comparative trials have been published. None of them showed a tricyclic drug clearly superior to ECT, although ECT was more effective in three studies. In several other studies, the two treatments appeared equal. Patients with the characteristics of endogenous depression appear to respond well both to ECT and the tricyclic drugs. Whether the drugs or ECT act faster is disputed at present. The administration of ECT entails certain disadvantages. These include memory disturbance, the risk of anesthetic, and cardiovascular complications. Because of these considerations, the tricyclic drugs are preferable as the initial treatment.

2. MAO Inhibitors

In contrast with ECT, the MAO inhibitors seem less effective in general than the tricyclic drugs. The tricyclic drugs were found to be significantly superior in numerous controlled studies, while no study has shown the reverse. Again, a number of studies have shown no significant differences between the two treatments, but usually without clear evidence that either drug was superior to placebo in the patient groups studied.

Nevertheless, there is a sizable group of clinicians who report certain patients to be responsive to the MAO inhibitors and not other drugs (cf. Horita, Chapter 20; Crane, Chapter 50). It has been suggested that while endogenous depressives repond particularly to the tricyclic drugs, patients with neurotic and atypical depressions improve more with the MAO inhibitors. Controlled trials provide some support for the former proposition, but have so far produced little evidence of a specific response of neurotic groups to MAO inhibitors. There is evidence, however, suggesting familial, genetically based consistency of response to drugs of either class.

Two studies show slight, although not significant, tendencies of psychotic depressives to do worse on isocarboxazid than on placebo. In one trial, tranylcypromine was significantly better than placebo in the reactive, but not the endogenous group, while in another study MAO inhibitors appeared to be superior to tricyclic drugs only in endogenous depressions and not in the reactive ones. Most clinicians currently use MAO inhibitors only if the patient has shown a previous response to them or if treatment with a tricyclic antidepressant has failed.

3. Phenothiazines

Until recently, the phenothiazines were considered of little benefit in depression, and possibly capable of worsening the depressed mood. At least three controlled studies have demonstrated, however, that phenothiazines may be of considerable benefit to many depressed patients. Fink and associates (354) found both chlorpromazine and imipramine to be considerably better than placebo in hospitalized depressives, with only minor differences between them. Paykel and associates (355) found no significant differences between the two drugs in a similar population. In the first of a series of Veterans Administration studies (cf. Caffey *et al.*, Chapter 33), thioridazine was found to be generally as effective as imipramine in depressives. Grouping patients according to typology of depression based on Brief Psychiatric Rating Scale (BPRS) profiles showed differential effects among the subtypes. Imipramine was found to be superior in "retarded" depressives, thioridazine superior in "anxious" depressives, with no difference in "hostile" depressives. A subsequent study of amitriptyline and perphenazine by the same group of investigators produced similar findings. In these studies, the number of retarded patients was relatively small, being only one-fifth to one-seventh of the total sample. These findings may be clarified further when detailed results are reported from the recently completed large-scale National Institute of Mental Health collaborative trial of imipramine, chlorpromazine, and placebo.

4. Combinations of Tricyclic Antidepressants with Phenothiazines or Antianxiety Agents

In clinical practice, physicians frequently combine a tricyclic antidepressant with a phenothiazine or an antianxiety agent such as meprobamate or the diazepoxide derivatives. The combination of amitriptyline and perphenazine is marketed by two pharmaceutical firms and has gained moderate acceptance, as judged by prescription sales. Such combinations are based on a number of considerations: (1) Many depressed patients suffer from symptoms of anxiety, tension, restlessness, agitation, and insomnia, which respond to a phenothiazine or an antianxiety drug. (2) The combination counters the tendency of certain of the tricyclics to induce psychomotor stimulation, irritability, or even insomnia as adverse effects. (3) Patients with schizo-affective reactions, mixed involutional paranoid-depressive states, or with histories of previous psychotic episodes require phenothiazines. (4) The latency of onset of improvement with the tricyclics may cause discomfort for many patients; immediate relief of the agitation and tension often enables them to continue working or endure their depression until the tricyclic antidepressant takes effect.

Controlled studies have not always substantiated these clinical indications (cf. Caffey *et al.*, Chapter 33). Pending further controlled studies, the authors remain hesitant to recommend combination treatment. Nevertheless, we must acknowledge the rationale of combination of phenothiazines and tricyclics in schizo-affective and other psychotic states in view of the tendency of patients with these disorders to do poorly with antidepressant therapy alone.

H. Effects in Disorders Other Than Depressions

1. Schizophrenia

Experience has borne out the observations of early investigators that although schizophrenic patients treated with imipramine showed changes in their activity and mood, improvement was limited and infrequent. In one large controlled trial, schizo-affective patients treated with imipramine did worse than depressed patients given the same treatment. In two studies comparing imipramine and a phenothiazine, imipramine was found to be less effective for treatment of schizophrenics. Certain schizophrenics may even become worse when given imipramine.

Many clinicians have advocated the addition of a tricyclic drug to the more usual treatment with a phenothiazine as leading to greater improvement in schizophrenics. Controlled studies of amitriptyline and perphenazine have shown the combination to be superior both to placebo and to perphenazine alone in the treatment of chronic schizophrenics. The degree of improvement, however, was not striking.

2. Enuresis

The use of tricyclic drugs, chiefly imipramine and amitriptyline, in nocturnal enuresis is an interesting recent development (cf. Eveloff, Chapter 54). The early report by MacLean (356) was followed by a number of encouraging accounts from uncontrolled studies which were later supported by double-blind controlled trials. In children, five of the seven reported studies showed efficacy of the drug. For adults, the situation is less encouraging. The three reported controlled studies have been negative, although the dose of 50 mg which was employed may have been low (357,358). The efficacy of the tricyclics in comparison with other accepted treatments has not been established.

The usual starting dose has been 25 mg in the evening for children under twelve and 50 mg for patients over twelve. Suggested explanations of the mechanism for improvement have included relaxation of the detrusor muscle by anticholinergic or adrenergic actions, alteration of REM sleep, and antidepressant effects, enuresis being postulated as a "depressive equivalent." Physiologic measurements have shown an increase in bladder capacity and delayed desire to void.

3. Anxiety States

Neurotic patients whose clinical features involve a mixture of anxiety and depression do not respond as well to the tricyclic antidepressants as they do to the antianxiety agents and phenothiazines, although one study describes a group of anxious neurotic patients who were particularly responsive to imipramine. However, Sargant and associates (359) in London have advocated MAO inhibitors for depressions with atypical hysterical and anxiety symptoms. It is difficult to interpret these studies because of the variable meaning attached to "neurotic" by different research centers and clinical groups.

IV. Adverse Effects

Although a variety of adverse effects may occur, the tricyclic antidepressants are relatively safe drugs. The most common adverse effects are autonomic disturbances, manifested as dry mouth, increased sweating, constipation, difficulty in visual accommodation, and postural hypotension. The hypotension is usually experienced as dizziness or lightheadedness, often in the morning. These effects are dose-related, and can be alleviated by lowering the dose. They tend to become less troublesome after the initial weeks of treatment, as tolerance develops. Autonomic effects are especially frequent in the elderly, and require caution, since serious consequences may ensue. Hypotension may lead to congestive cardiac failure and myocardial infarction. Urinary retention may occur, particularly in men, and paralytic ileus has been reported, especially with amitriptyline and nortriptyline.

Allergic skin reactions and blood dyscrasias may develop, usually early in treatment, but are uncommon. A persistent fine tremor, particularly in the upper extremities, occurs in as many as 10% of patients on the drug. The tremor with tricyclic antidepressants differs from the extrapyramidal tremor induced by the phenothiazines. Tremor with tricyclic antidepressants does not respond well to anti-Parkinsonian medication. Convulsions occasionally occur, most frequently in patients with a previous history of epilepsy or EEG abnormality. Toxic confusional states may develop, especially in the elderly. They are often associated with visual hallucinations, which sometimes also occur in the absence of obvious confusional features such as defects of orientation, memory, and intellect. Schizophrenic symptoms may be precipitated or worsened. Manic episodes occur, but it is not clear at present if these are any more frequent in manic depressives treated with tricyclic drugs than they are in the absence of treatment. Some authors have, in fact, regarded these drugs as "mood normalizers," and have advocated their use to control or prevent mania as well as depression. This contention has not been tested so far in controlled trials. Withdrawal symptoms of nausea, vomiting, malaise, coryza, dizziness, and muscular pains occasionally occur following abrupt withdrawal.

Acute toxic states may follow suicidal attempts by ingestion of large amounts and accidental ingestion by children (cf. Hollister, Chapter 43).

It is potentially dangerous to combine a tricyclic antidepressant with a MAO inhibitor or to change from one type of drug to another without waiting at least a week. The interval is more important when a MAO inhibitor is to be followed by a tricyclic drug. Restlessness, tremor, dizziness, hyperpyrexia, collapse, and coma may occur. Some clinicians continue to advocate the use of the two types of drugs in combination, and have reported that if they are administered carefully in a hospital serious adverse effects can be avoided (360,361).

V. Conclusions

The introduction of effective antidepressant drugs has changed the treatment of depressions significantly. Ambulatory treatment is more effective, and maintenance drug therapy for the prevention of relapse and recurrences offer promise. Among the various antidepressant drugs, the tricyclic derivatives have emerged as the safest and most effective. Within the tricyclic series, imipramine, the prototypic drug, has been the most actively studied. Established as an effective and safe drug, it is widely prescribed. Other members of the series, especially amitriptyline, are used clinically. Within the tricyclic group, differences are mainly in dosage potency, frequency of adverse effects, and the relative balance of sedative-hypnotic and psychomotor stimulant actions. The tricyclics differ little as to their pattern of clinical action. Research indicates that patients with retardation and other clinical features resembling endogenous depressive patterns respond best to tricyclic derivatives. Although these trends are not exclusive, they provide a tentative guide to the clinician.

In addition to their clinical utility, the tricyclic drugs have greatly stimulated research on the modes of action of antidepressant therapies in general. Emphasis is currently placed upon interactions with various amines, particularly the catecholamines and the indolylalkylamines. Moreover, clinical concepts of depression have been greatly broadened, with an increased range of clinical phenomena considered under the diagnosis of depression. This expansion of the definition of depression has both theoretical and clinical implications for psychiatry.

While the tricyclic antidepressants represent a significant advance, their efficacy has limitations. Hopefully, new therapies will be developed with more extensive actions. In current practice, however, the tricyclics are the mainstay of antidepressant drug therapy.

For further reading and references see Appendices 1 and 2.

50

USE OF MONAMINE OXIDASE INHIBITING ANTIDEPRESSANTS

George E. Crane

I. The Monoamine Oxidase Inhibiting Antidepressants: General Characteristics

The clinical effects of the monoamine oxidase inhibitors (MAOI's) on patients are numerous and widespread as these drugs are active on the MAO, a ubiquitous enzyme in the organism, as well as on other biological substrates, but their main clinical use is for the treatment of depression. The MAO inhibitors which are currently used as antidepressant drugs in the United States are as follows: isocarboxazide, nialamide, phenelzine, and tranylcypromine. Pargyline, which is prescribed as an antihypertensive agent, is not included in this class of therapeutic agents despite its effectiveness on depression. Other MAO inhibitors (e.g., mebanazine) and combinations of a MAO inhibitor with other drugs are used as antidepressants in Europe or the United Kingdom, but are not available for prescription use in the United States.

MAOI's may vary in their chemical and biochemical properties, but a qualitative difference in their activity on depression has not been proven. Some clinicians think that iproniazid, the first MAOI to be used in psychiatry, was superior to its successors. This, however, was never established with certainty, as the drug was withdrawn from clinical use before more advanced methods of assessing drug effectiveness were developed. All MAO inhibitors are active on the autonomic nervous system, orthostatic hypotension being the most common reaction. As a rule, these side effects are not dangerous, but may cause considerable discomfort to the patient. Whether MAO inhibitors differ among themselves in this respect is also difficult to prove, as there are no standard methods of reporting adverse reactions. Furthermore, many side effects such as dry mouth, dizziness, anorexia, and constipation, are frequently encountered in neurotic and depressed patients for whom these drugs are prescribed. However, certain complications do occur with relative frequency with some MAO inhibitors and seldom with others. The most serious of all, acute degeneration of the liver, was first reported in patients treated with iproniazid; this condition has become rare since this drug was removed from the market. Pheniprazine seemed to cause damage to the optical nervous system in addition to liver disease, and etryptamine was held responsible for agranulocytosis. Hypertensive crises (the so-called cheese reactions) are definitely more frequent in patients receiving tranylcypromine than in those treated with other MAO inhibitors.

The reader will find in a brochure by Smith, Kline and French Laboratories (1967) a description of the contraindications, the most common side effects, incompatibilities with other drugs, and the methods recommended for the prevention and treatment of untoward reactions. Although this publication provides instructions for the use of tranylcypromine, the same precautionary measures are applicable to all MAO inhibitors.

II. Historical Background

Iproniazid was first introduced in therapy as a chemotherapeutic agent for the treatment of tuberculosis in 1951. Six years later the same drug was hailed as a therapeutic agent of unlimited possibilities for the treatment of depression and as one of the most valuable tools for research in the field of neurochemistry. This was due to an unusual set of circumstances: (1) The drug was first tried on patients who suffered from advanced tuberculosis as well as from mental depression; (2) iproniazid and isoniazid, similar in their antibiotic activities but different in their ability to inhibit MAO, were introduced simultaneously in therapy; and (3) reserpine, a drug having effects opposite to those of the MAO inhibitors, was the object of intensive studies both in humans and laboratory animals.

The physicians who first used iproniazid at the Seaview and Montefiore Hospitals, New York, may have had little training in psychiatry, but were quite familiar with the psychological makeup of their patients. For the specialist of chest diseases, symptoms such as continuous preoccupation with bodily ailments, dependence on the hospital, and apathy deserved as much attention as X-rays or temperature curves. An attitude of despair and a passive resignation to a hopeless future were in many cases the most serious obstacles to a successful rehabilitation. In other words most patients affected by chronic tuberculosis presented symptoms of a "reactive depression" with a serious physical illness and confinement to a hospital being plausible external causes for this syndrome. The physicians treating tuberculous patients were greatly impressed by the dramatic psychological changes produced by iproniazid, even in terminal cases where no improvement of tuberculosis could be demonstrated. A return of vitality, a desire to leave the hospital, and a general increase in social interests were particularly unexpected in subjects, who for years had shown little interest in life. Iproniazid also created new problems. Some patients developed an arrogant and careless attitude about routine hospital care and thus became serious management problems. A few individuals with previous histories of major psychiatric disorders became frankly psychotic. However, patients treated with isoniazid did not exhibit significant effects of a psychological nature.

Approximately one year after iproniazid was introduced in therapy, chemists discovered that this drug had the capacity to inhibit the MAO, both *in vitro* and *in vivo,* and also suggested that there was a relationship between inhibition of the MAO and elevation of mood in humans. Thus, by the end of 1952 the most important clinical effects of iproniazid were known and, moreover, the biochemists were able to provide a scientific explanation for the unusual and unexpected behavior displayed by the patients in the sanatoriums for tuberculosis.

Despite its remarkable effects on physical debilitation, iproniazid found little use in the treatment of pulmonary tuberculosis because the dosage required for antibiotic effectiveness invariably caused undesirable reactions of a psychiatric and physical nature; consequently chest specialists preferred the use of isoniazid. This difficulty, however, could be overcome by combining the two drugs; thus it was possible to carry out further studies on the psychotropic effects of the drug in a sanatorium for tuberculosis. Efforts were also made to find new indications for iproniazid in other fields of medicine. Not only were excellent results reported on widespread tuberculous lesions of the skeletal system but "miraculous" effects on the patient's general physical condition and morale were noted as well. Some patients, who for all intents and purposes were on their deathbeds, were able to leave the hospital. The hypotensive activity of the drug, which was particularly undesirable in debilitated patients was used to good advantage in the treatment of hypertension.

Up to this point, the MAO inhibitor was used mainly as an adjunct to the treatment of debilitated individuals. Even the first mental patients on whom iproniazid was tried were chosen from wards housing retarded, apathetic, and physically depleted individuals. Significantly, the term energizer was introduced at this stage of drug trials to describe the fundamental characteristics of the drug. The use of the drug for patients suffering from purely psychogenic depression was the next logical step. At the first symposium on iproniazid in 1957 eight studies were presented involving some 200–300 patients who had received the drug for mental conditions, mainly depression. The results reported ranged from encouraging to miraculous. Furthermore, the drug was found to have favorable effects on a variety of unrelated diseases such as anorexia and pain in advanced cancer, acne vulgaris, collagenous diseases and arthritis, autistic schizophrenia in children, ileocolitis, hypertension, and particularly angina pectoris. This versatility of action was attributed to the powerful and diverse pharmacological effects of the drug on the organism, but it was also conceded that mood elevation was a major contributing factor to the patient's improvement regardless of his illness. Despite some skepticism, one fact emerged from this symposium, namely, that iproniazid was no ordinary stimulant. The main feature that set iproniazid apart from other drugs was its ability to produce a reasonable amount of happiness and a positive attitude toward life in mentally and physically depleted patients.

After 1957, the number of patients treated with antidepressants increased to astronomical figures as more and more clinicians became acquainted with iproniazid and the newer MAO-inhibiting drugs. Major drug manufacturers endeavored to produce new agents capable of blocking the MAO and in this effort proved to be eminently successful. Chemists manufactured new analogs of iproniazid, and also synthesized compounds whose power to inhibit the MAO was much greater than that of the parent substance. The introduction in clinical practice of tranylcypromine, which acted as a stimulant and as an antidepressant, seemed to be the final triumph for the pharmaceutical industry as this dual action had been predicted from the chemical structure. The new MAO inhibitors appeared to be at least as effective as iproniazid with fewer side effects, nialamide being the first agent to fulfill these requirements. However, serious side reactions were observed also in patients treated with the new MAOI.

Practically all adverse reactions reported to date were already known prior to the large-scale introduction of MAOI in the treatment of depression and allied conditions. Hepatic toxicity with its high mortality and sudden onset created considerable alarm in the psychiatric community. Eventually, iproniazid was withdrawn from the market. Although this complication has become rare in patients treated with other MAO inhibitors, the fear of such a disastrous complication seems to have shaken permanently the physician's confidence in the whole class of compounds. Pheniprazine and etryptamine were quietly removed from prescription use without much opposition on the part of the medical profession. Tranylcypromine seemed to be doomed in the early part of 1964, when it was withdrawn from clinical use due to an increasing number of reports on hypertensive crises. The drug was reintroduced in the market for a number of reasons. First, reliable documentation as to the seriousness of paroxysmal hypertension and the rate of fatalities was made available to the clinician, which allowed him to weigh the risk of using the drug against its beneficial effects. Second, and most important, the etiological factor responsibile for hypertensive crises could be established with certainty and thus a means was provided for the prevention of disastrous effects in the great majority of cases.

Hypertension was described and attributed to iproniazid and other MAO inhibitors as far back as 1955, and the danger of wide fluctuations in the blood pressure, particularly in cardiovascular disorders, was emphasized by several authors. These, however, were isolated reports, and not until 1961 were the clinicians able to identify a syndrome characterized by throbbing headaches and a sudden rise in blood pressure, complicated in some cases by intracranial hemorrhage. Such crises occurred only in certain individuals and were not related to the duration of treatment. This, plus the observation that abnormal changes in blood pressure failed to recur despite continuation of the medication, suggested the possibility that some other factor in addition to tranylcypromine had to be incriminated. At first the precipitant was thought to be a sympathomimetic drug administered in conjunction with tranylcypromine. Later on attention was focused on alcohol, ingestion of heavy meals, and, finally, on certain cheeses, hence the name of "cheese reaction." It was discovered also that only cheese rich in tyramine was responsible for this complication. Subsequently, beans, chicken liver, chocolate, yeast, and products of prolonged bacterial fermentation such as wine and seasoned herring were found to have effects similar to those of cheese. According to several reports, it has been estimated that 8–10% of patients who do not adhere to dietary restrictions are likely to develop hypertension in response to tranylcypromine, whereas only 1.5% of those receiving phenelzine are subject to such a disorder. This is, indeed, a very common complication, but up to 1964 intracerebral hemorrhages were diagnosed only in 38 patients with 21 fatalities, a small percentage considering that an estimated one-and-a-half-million individuals had taken the drug. As in many retrospective epidemiological studies, these figures must be accepted with some skepticism. However, "cheese reactions" have become infrequent in hospitals since the physicians learned to eliminate foods rich in tyramine from the diet of patients on MAO inhibitors.

Many clinicians became reluctant to use MAOI in view of the variety of side effects and complications caused by these drugs. Another reason for the decline in the popularity of these drugs was a reappraisal of their therapeutic effectiveness.

After the first symposium on MAO inhibitors in 1957, other symposia followed and a large number of papers were published. Most studies were impressionistic, utilizing heterogeneous populations ranging in size from less than 10 to over 100 patients. A cursory survey of major clinical papers published between 1959 and 1960 reveals that the ratio of favorable to unfavorable reports is four to one, with the negative reports emphasizing side effects rather than a low efficacy on depression. Comparative and controlled studies, which began to appear in the 1960's, reported less favorable results than earlier uncontrolled investigations, and a substantial number of papers failed to show any difference in results between patients treated with the active agent and those receiving placebo. The conclusions, however, were far from being uniform. For instance, two well-controlled papers comparing iproniazid and placebo were published in the second half of 1960, one study reporting superiority of iproniazid over placebo, and the other showing no difference between the two agents. Four years later an extensive investigation involving a large number of patients from several British hospitals seemed to indicate that phenelzine, with only 26% improvement, was inferior to placebo, while according to another collaborative study conducted in the United States, phenelzine was effective in 50% of the cases. In both studies the percentage of placebo-improvement was approximately 45%. Papers published during this period at least proved that iproniazid or its analogs were not a panacea for all mental patients with manifestations of depression. In the late 1950's and early 1960's numerous clinical studies on imipramine and analogous tricyclic antidepressants appeared in the literature, and the consensus was that they were both efficacious and relatively safe drugs. Hence, it was logical to use them as standards against which other drugs could be compared. In most controlled studies utilizing both classes of drugs, the MAO inhibitors did not fare much better than in studies using placebo as a control substance.

Information derived from the majority of comparative and controlled studies provided only a rough estimate of the mental status for a sample of patients prior to and after a treatment. Depending on the number and the types of patients investigated, samples were then subdivided into subsamples according to sex, age, severity of illness, hospital status, etc. Interactions were found between types of drugs and some of these variables, but the conclusions based on such analyses were far from convincing. Most investigators, however, seemed to agree that the MAOI and imipramine or its analogs were equally effective in the nonhospitalized and less severe cases of depression.

In recent years the literature on antidepressant medication was reviewed by several investigators. By pooling data from a large number of studies these authors were able to conclude that tricyclic antidepressants are generally more effective than the MAOI, although the difference is not such as to be readily detected by the clinician. The imipramine derivatives are safer and, consequently, the treatment of choice for the majority of depressed patients. MAOI are indicated in cases where other therapeutic modalities prove unsatisfactory.

Despite these unfavorable reports, the prescription of the MAOI is by no means limited to exceptional cases. According to reports from the manufacturers of isocarboxazide, approximately 100,000 patients received this drug in 1966. Tranylcypromine was prescribed to more than 350,000 patients since the middle of 1964, when this compound was reintroduced in the market. Controlled and uncontrolled studies on antidepressant drugs which were published between 1959 and 1964 included approximately 5000 patients being treated with MAOI and a comparable number of subjects receiving the tricyclic antidepressants. These figures do not permit any comparison between the number of depressed patients being treated with MAO inhibitors and those receiving other types of drugs, but they seem to indicate a continued interest in the clinical value of drugs like phenelzine, isocarboxazide, and tranylcypromine.

III. An Appraisal of the Usefulness of the MAO Inhibitors in Medical Practice

The MAO inhibitors are antidepressant drugs for the following reasons: (a) They may effectively reduce symptoms of depression and restore a state of affective balance in the patient. (b) They may reverse depression and produce a state of euphoria, mania, or other psychoses of an expansive type. (Treatment cannot be considered a success when symptoms shift from under- to overactivity, but when this happens the patient is no longer depressed.) The fact that these drugs are also effective on symptoms which one associates with neuroses rather than with depression does not justify their inclusion in the class of sedative or anxiolytic agents. Neurotic symptoms are frequently observed in affective disorders, and a reduction of depression is usually accompanied by a decrease in the intensity of all other symptoms. MAOI may have other therapeutic effects. Iproniazid, for instance, was known as a powerful stimulant of appetite, particularly in debilitated individuals. Whether the new MAOI agents have similar activity is not known, as such compounds have not been tried extensively on patients with debilitating physical disorders.

The issue is whether or not the MAO inhibitors are useful therapeutic agents in psychiatry, safety and efficacy being major considerations.

A. *How Safe Are the Monoamine Oxidase Inhibitors?*

The medical community has learned to accept a certain amount of risk when potent pharmacological agents are used in therapy; hence the safety of a drug is relative and can be assessed only by making a comparison with other agents prescribed for similar diseases.

The number of serious complications have been greatly reduced, since the three most toxic MAO inhibitors have been removed from the market and attempts have been made to impose dietary restrictions on patients receiving such drugs. Whether the MAO inhibitors are safer or better tolerated than the tricyclic antidepressants or electric shock treatment cannot be answered with any degree of confidence. There is consensus among psychiatrists, however, that the administration of the MAO inhibitors requires greater vigilance than other treatments. Furthermore, certain physical conditions, such as advanced age, cardiovascular disorder, and diabetes, contraindicate their use in many patients.

B. *How Effective Are the MAO Inhibitors?*

The clinician using recent reviews as a guideline must conclude that there is little place for the MAO inhibitors in clinical practice. The question is, how much can one depend on the literature? In an attempt to answer this question it is necessary to deal with certain basic issues, fully recognizing that such issues will be handled in much greater detail in other parts of this textbook.

1. Is Depression a Serious Disease?

The cyclical nature of depressions has been known since antiquity, but only recent studies utilizing inert substances as controls have shown that a certain portion of depressed patients may recover within a few weeks without any active treatment. These observations have reinforced the impression that depression is a benign, self-limiting disorder. According to a recent review paper, 21% of outpatients and 27% of inpatients may improve markedly or recover, without receiving any type of physical or drug therapy. This is hardly an impressive percentage of spontaneous improvement. Moreover, a patient may be rated as improved at the end of a drug trial only to relapse a few weeks later. This is a common occurrence in subjects who deny their illness or develop subtle clinical changes in the direction of hypomania. Yet the absence of clear-cut depression is frequently interpreted as major improvement or recovery, even though the patient is still emotionally labile, often incapacitated, and potentially suicidal. In a follow-up study of war veterans, 80% of the patients admitted to hospitals for depressive disorders were discharged within a year, but a substantial number were incapable of holding gainful employment. This type of social impairment is consistent with the picture of chronic depression, a condition well known to psychiatrists using long-term psychotherapy in their practice. Depression may begin in adolescence, or even earlier, and continue unchanged for years, occasionally interrupted by improvements, hypomanic episodes, or periods of deep depression. Therefore, the average depression is not only a serious disease because of the risk of suicide but also because of its long-term incapacitating effects. Everybody will agree that the treatment of this disorder poses challenging problems for the psychiatrist.

2. What Constitutes Improvement?

Most rating instruments measure improvement in terms of symptom reduction, but cannot distinguish a restitution to norm from a condition only superficially resembling mental health. As was remarked earlier, a return to an asymptomatic base line may be interpreted as a total recovery when it is only a shift to a different type of symptomatology. It is true that more advanced measuring instruments which utilize self-rating techniques and complex analyses of data can distinguish real improvement from pseudoimprovement, but such methods are still in the experimental stage. Clinically, a treatment for depression is successful only when the patient experiences something positive about himself and others in addition to relief from psychological distress. In the first symposium on iproniazid several clinicians described this type of dramatic change at least in some of their cases. At first physicians and patients alike could not believe that a recovery from a life-long maladjustment was possible after a short term of drug therapy. As more experience was gathered, even the skeptics had to admit that in a matter of days the drug could relieve some patients from the heavy burden of a lengthy and crippling disease.

These early clinical impressions later received support from sophisticated studies comparing the effects of iproniazid, imipramine, and electric shock on depression. Iproniazid seemed to increase the patient's ability to utilize his resources and to interact more effectively with his environment. Performance in cognitive and perceptual tests also improved. Imipramine or electric shock did not seem to achieve these results, the latter treatment causing a general dulling of the patient's affectivity.

These studies are particularly important as they emphasize the positive and more subtle aspects of a patient's response to a drug. It is true that early clinical impressions as well as data obtained from advanced psychometric techniques are based on the effects of iproniazid, a drug no longer available for prescription use. The effectiveness of other MAO inhibitors may not be of the same order of magnitude. Patients responding so dramatically to a MAO inhibitor may be uncommon and the therapeutic effects may be transitory. Moreover, the superior performance of a drug in a small number of depressed patients may be nullified by mediocre or unfavorable effects on the majority of patients. Nevertheless, treatment with iproniazid, a MAO inhibitor, could, in a relatively short time, restore mental health to individuals who for years had known nothing but a dismal existence.

C. What Are the Clinical Indications for the MAOI?

The excellence of therapeutic effects on depression by one of the MAO inhibitors, plus the fact that selected individuals react rather well to all compounds of this class, provides an explanation for the continued use of the MAO inhibitor in psychiatry. The question is, what type of depression will respond favorably to a MAO? Experienced psychiatrists agree that it is extremely difficult to identify the patient who will respond particularly well to this class of drugs. However, well-documented studies of patients with recurrent depressions have shown that some subjects consistently improve with MAOI, while others react favorably only to tricyclic antidepressants, despite the similarity of presenting symptoms. Therefore, it is important to know the patient's reactions to previous drug trials. It has been found that family members of the responders to MAOI have a tendency to react favorably to such compounds, negatively to tricyclic antidepressants, and vice versa. Therefore, it has been suggested that a genetic factor is responsible for specific interactions with drugs even though patients cannot be differentiated on clinical grounds. At present the practitioner may expect little information from the clinical or pharmacological literature on antidepressants to guide him in the selection of subjects and the timing for the administration of such drugs. Thus the clinician is still largely dependent on his judgment, experience, and all available clinical data when he must choose the best therapeutic procedure for his patients.

For references and further reading see Appendices 1 and 2.

51

USE OF LITHIUM

Mogens Schou

I. Pharmacology

The pharmacology of lithium, as well as its use in the treatment of mental illness, was the subject of a recent review (362). This study may be consulted for details and documentation.

A. Chemistry

Lithium is a monovalent cation which belongs to the group of alkali metals together with sodium, potassium, rubidium, cesium, and francium. Due to the arrangement of its electrons and the high density of the positive charge on its nucleus, lithium is extremely reactive, and the metal never occurs free in nature; the term "lithium" in this chapter refers to lithium ions or lithium salts. Lithium shares a number of properties with the other alkali metal ions, but in certain respects it behaves more like magnesium or calcium. Lithium colors a flame red: Emission line is at 670.7 mμ. In nature it occurs in minerals and in trace amounts in mineral waters, sea water, plants and animal tissues. Nothing is known about a possible physiological role of the traces of lithium naturally present in the human organism.

B. Absorption

Lithium ions are readily absorbed when administered orally, the only route of administration used in man. Since the lithium ion itself is the active agent, any soluble lithium salt might in principle be used for treatment, but lithium chloride is too hygroscopic for incorporation into tablets. The most widely used lithium salt is the carbonate; lithium citrate and lithium acetate have also been employed. Experiments have shown that lithium is absorbed with equal ease after administration of the carbonate, the citrate, and the acetate, even by persons suffering from achlorhydria. None of the salts produce local irritation when given as tablets. The ready absorption of lithium may lead to side effects during the hours after intake, coinciding with a rise of the serum lithium concentration: gastrointestinal irritation, a dazed feeling, muscular weakness. Usually they occur only during the first week of lithium treatment; thereafter, the organism adapts itself. One method to avoid side effects is to start lithium administration with low dosage and increase gradually to maintenance level. Another possibility may be the use of slow-release lithium tablets; preliminary experiences with this type of preparation are promising.

C. Distribution

Lithium is not bound to plasma proteins. It passes from the bloodstream into the tissues, and an equilibrium is eventually established between serum and cells. The equilibrium is a dynamic one; serum lithium is an indicator of the lithium content of the organism and therefore may be used to monitor treatment.

Lithium is distributed in the organism differently from both sodium and potassium. Its apparent volume of distribution is about the same as that of total body water, but lithium is not distributed evenly throughout the water phase. At equilibrium the lithium concentration in some tissues is higher and in some lower than in serum; the concentration gradients across the cell wall are only in the order of 2–4 and never approach those found for either sodium or potassium.

D. Excretion

The main route of lithium excretion is through the kidneys, and lithium elimination in urine is of decisive importance for the safe use of the drug. Once the therapeutic and prophylactic level in the organism has been established, the kidneys must be able to excrete as much lithium as is being administered if accumulation and intoxication are to be avoided.

Renal lithium excretion is proportional to the plasma concentration within a wide concentration range, i.e., the renal lithium clearance is independent of the blood level. About four-fifths of the filtered lithium is reabsorbed in the tubules and one-fifth excreted in the urine; the site and mechanism of the tubular reabsorption have not been fully clarified. In normal adults under ordinary dietary conditions the renal lithium clearance is in the order of 15–25 ml/minute. Lithium clearance decreases with age, and clearances of 10–15 ml/minute are not unusual in old persons. In these patients a lowering of lithium dosage is often necessitated by side effects such as coarse tremor of the hands and a feeling of muscular weakness, and full effect is obtained from the lower dose. Young persons have a relatively high renal lithium clearance; they frequently require a lithium dosage higher than average to maintain therapeutic or prophylactic effect.

In any one person, the renal lithium clearance is remarkably constant. There is little day-to-day or month-to-month variation, and the clearance remains unaffected by a number of procedures which profoundly alter the excretion of sodium, potassium, and water. It has been noted, however, that lithium clearance and excretion fraction fall when the sodium intake is lowered. This became tragically apparent in 1949 when lithium chloride was given as a taste corrective to patients with cardiac or renal disease who were kept on salt-free diet. In some cases severe intoxications resulted, a few fatal; they were presumably caused by a combination of overdosage and lowered excretory capacity of the kidneys.

E. Side Effects and Complications

Two main types of unwanted lithium effects can be distinguished. One is represented by the side effects that may be seen at low serum lithium concentrations and which are inconvenient rather than dangerous. The other is the lithium intoxication or poisoning associated with accumulation of lithium to serum levels above ca. 2 meq/liter.

The side effects observed most frequently are: transient discomfort, nausea or abdominal pain, vomiting, diarrhea, thirst, a dazed feeling, muscular weakness, tremor of the hands, slight tiredness, and sleepiness. Some of these were mentioned in the section on absorption; they often coincide with serum lithium peaks, and preliminary experiments indicate that some of the side effects may be counteracted by the use of slow-release lithium tablets. It is usual that the side effects appear early in the treatment and fade away within a week or two. More persistent side effects which may be noted are a feeling of thirst, sometimes combined with polyuria, and fine hand tremor, which does not yield to anti-Parkinson drugs. Occasionally, they continue for months or years in patients given continuous lithium treatment, and in most cases the patients become accustomed to the slight inconvenience and consider it a small price for the benefit of the treatment.

Transient electroencephalographic and electrocardiographic changes may on occasion be observed in patients who are without clinical signs of intoxication. During maintenance treatment with lithium a small number of patients have developed diffuse, nontoxic goiters, but it is not known if lithium can be held responsible.

For any drug that may be given to fertile women the problem of possible teratogenic effects must be examined. The few lithium studies on mammals have not given clear-cut results, and further investigations seem desirable. At the present stage, one might request more weighty indication for lithium treatment than average in women of child-bearing potential, and also try to avoid giving lithium during the first trimester of pregnancy. However, the fact that conception has taken place while a woman was receiving lithium cannot be sufficient ground for induced abortion.

Lithium has been given as a maintenance treatment to many patients for years; some patients have been on lithium almost continuously for more than ten years. It is worth noting that not a single instance of altered tolerance to the drug has been observed; neither have patients become sensitized to the effects of lithium nor have they become less responsive. Lithium is not habit forming, and abstinence symptoms after discontinuation are unknown.

F. Poisoning

Lithium intoxications develop when more lithium is administered than can be excreted by the kidneys; lithium is thus accumulated in the organism and may eventually reach a level that produces severe toxic reactions.

Severe lithium intoxication in man primarily involves the central nervous system, while kidneys and heart are affected only moderately and reversibly. Consciousness is severely impaired and total coma may develop. The muscles are hypertonic or rigid with hyperactive deep reflexes, and universal muscle tremor or fasciculations can be seen. A further characteristic is the appearance of attacks of hyperextension of arms and legs, sometimes combined with gasping, grunts, and wide opening of the eyes. Epileptic seizures may be seen. Transitory neurological asymmetries may in some cases simulate cerebral hemorrhage, and electroencephalographic disturbances are frequent. Death may result from pulmonary complications.

Lithium poisoning is not an instantaneous occurrence. Prodromal symptoms can usually be observed for some days to a week: sluggishness, languidness, drowsiness, coarse tremor or muscle twitchings, dysarthria, loss of appetite, vomiting, and diarrhea. Treatment of poisoning consists in supportive therapy, prevention of complications, and removal of lithium from the organism. The symptomatic treatment is of the same type that is used in barbiturate poisoning: correction of abnormalities in fluid and electrolyte balance, regulation of kidney function, frequent determinations of blood pressure, regular X-ray photos of the lungs, preservation of free respiration, frequent change of the patient's position in bed, physiotherapy of the lungs, infection prophylaxis, etc. Severe lithium intoxications may last more than 2 weeks, but recent experiments indicate that it is possible to reduce the duration by forced diuresis (urea), alkalinization of the urine, and possibly administration of aminophylline. Lithium poisoning does not leave any permanent effects.

G. Preparations, Dosage, and Control

Lithium treatment must be started under careful clinical and laboratory control. A physical examination of the patient should be accompanied by determinations of serum creatinine or blood urea nitrogen, sedimentation rate, blood pressure, electrocardiogram, and analysis of the urine for protein and formed elements. These studies must be supplemented by others when the history or physical examination suggests somatic disorder.

Treatment may be instituted during mania, depression, or an interval between episodes. In order to obtain full therapeutic and prophylactic effect, the dosage must be sufficient to produce a serum lithium concentration of at least 0.8 meq/liter in a blood sample drawn before the patient has had his first lithium tablet of the day. Previously, 0.6 meq/liter was considered adequate, but later experience has shown that patients maintained on this level may suffer relapses which disappear when the concentration is raised.

A morning concentration of 0.8 meq/liter corresponds roughly to an average daily concentration of about 1.1 meq/liter. When slow-release lithium tablets are used, fluctuations in serum level are smaller, and the morning concentration should then be about 1.0 meq/liter. Outpatients usually come to the clinic in the afternoon. In order to avoid drawing blood samples during the absorptive serum lithium peak, one must instruct the patients to omit midday tablets on the day of the control visit. Serum lithium concentrations of 1.6 meq/liter or higher are often accompanied by side effects and may indicate impending intoxication; if serum lithium reaches this level, dosage should be reduced.

The flame photometric lithium determination is rapid, sensitive, and accurate; it can be carried out on blood samples that have been sent from a hospital in one part of the country to a laboratory in another, and even considerable hemolysis does not interfere with the analysis (363).

The dosage required to maintain a particular serum lithium concentration is determined by the ability of the kidneys to excrete lithium. Renal lithium clearance is remarkably constant in any one person, but may vary by as much as 100–200% from one person to another. *Dosage must, therefore, be adjusted individually.* During the first month of treatment serum lithium should be determined once a week; when a proper dosage level has been reached, lithium determinations may be performed at longer intervals. Serum lithium should always be checked in case of relapse; if it is too low, the dosage is inadequate or the patients are not taking their tablets.

As danger signals of impending intoxication, serum lithium determinations every 3 or 6 months are too infrequent to be of much value, but regular blood samples may serve to insure adequate clinical control. Patients come more willingly and take the prescribed medicine more carefully when they are under laboratory control. During prophylactic treatment, when no immediate symptoms serve to remind the patient or his relatives of the tablet intake, there is always danger of negligence, and it is important to give specific warning on this point. In some cases it might be advantageous to use mnemonic aids such as medicine boxes with a separate compartment for each day of the week.

During continuous lithium administration, clinical observation of the patient is essential. The patient, as well as members of his family, must be instructed about clinical signs and symptoms of impending intoxication: sluggishness, languidness, drowsiness, coarse tremor or muscle twitchings, dysarthria, loss of appetite, vomiting, and diarrhea. The appearance or reappearance of any one of these symptoms is an indication to obtain a serum lithium determination. The result of this analysis will show whether the suspicion of lithium intoxication is justified or if the malaise has a different cause. In the evaluation of serum lithium values one should take into consideration that it ordinarily falls by one-half every 1–2 days after discontinuation of lithium.

Given in equivalent dosage, lithium carbonate, lithium citrate, and lithium acetate are of equal therapeutic and prophylactic efficacy, but the carbonate has one practical advantage over the others: Its anion weighs about half as much. This means that relatively large amounts of lithium can be contained in one lithium-carbonate tablet or capsule of suitable size. It has been mentioned that slow-release lithium tablets may prove of benefit to the patients; their practical usefulness is at present being tested.

In adults with normal kidney function maintenance dosage may vary from 25 to 50 meq/day, corresponding to 900 and 1800 mg of lithium carbonate, respectively. Elderly persons, who often have low lithium clearances, may need only 15 meq/day or less (600 mg of lithium carbonate). In order to minimize initial side effects, it may be advisable to start treatment with lower doses and then increase gradually to the maintenance level.

In acute mania, rapid therapeutic action is desirable. This may be achieved by using high initial lithium dosage, but perhaps more effectively by giving ECT, haloperidol, or one of the phenothiazines. Maintenance treatment with lithium may be instituted simultaneously. Prophylactic lithium administration is often started while the patient is still depressed and may be given simultaneously with conventional antidepressant therapy. There is no indication of side effects due to interaction between lithium and either ECT or tricyclic antidepressants; a combination with monoamine oxidase inhibitors has rarely been tried. Lithium should not be given, or should be given with caution, to patients on a salt-free diet; but it is unnecessary to supplement ordinary diets with extra sodium chloride.

A number of authors have advocated giving lithium on 6 days of the week and omitting it on the seventh. In some hospitals, this procedure may offer administrative advantages; but it does not, as has been suggested, allow complete elimination of lithium. In 24 hours the lithium content of the organism falls by less than one-half. The lithium level is controlled more rationally by adjustment of the daily dosage than by the introduction of weekly days of purgation.

II. Use in Psychiatry

Lithium was introduced in psychiatry as a drug against psychotic excitement. Its specific effect against manic phases of manic-depressive disorder was demonstrated later, and during the past years evidence has been presented that lithium may prevent not only manic but also depressive relapses if given continuously to patients suffering from recurrent manic-depressive disorder or recurrent endogenous depressions.

A. Therapeutic Effect against Mania

Therapeutic effects of lithium against manic phases of manic-depressive disorder have been demonstrated in a limited number of controlled clinical trials and in many uncontrolled ones, but it is difficult to obtain an exact quantitative measure of its efficacy because factors other than pharmacological may have played a role in most of the trials, primarily spontaneous remission. Critical assessment of the literature indicates that while 20–30% of manic patients cannot be expected to respond satisfactorily to lithium, 70–80% show distinct improvement within 1–2 weeks. The therapeutic lithium effect is independent of age, sex, and duration of the disorder.

It may be questioned whether the figures for treatment response are better than those obtained by treating comparable manic patients with conventional neuroleptics; systematic comparative studies between lithium and, for example, chlorpromazine or haloperidol have not been carried out. However, clinical experience shows that lithium and the neuroleptics differ distinctly on three points in their effects on mania.

First, they have different time courses. The lithium action sets in relatively slowly, while chlorpromazine and, in particular, haloperidol usually act more rapidly; on the whole, the latter drugs seem preferable in acute and unusually violent cases of mania. Second, whereas the action of conventional neuroleptics is largely independent of the disease which caused the agitation, lithium acts more specifically against mania and has a higher efficiency in typical cases than in those with atypical features. Third, and perhaps most important, the effects of the two treatment procedures differ in kind. While neuroleptics at best produce an effective suppression of the manic overactivity and bring about a drug-produced state of quietude, lithium seems to remove the manic symptoms without sedation or production of lethargy. The patients are brought into a state which cannot be distinguished, subjectively or objectively, from their normal, premorbid condition.

As an antimanic drug, lithium seems to supplement rather than to replace the usual forms of therapy. An acute manic attack is managed as effectively and often more rapidly with chlorpromazine, haloperidol, or intensive ECT, but in cases of protracted mania, frequent manic relapse, or, last but not least, the hypomanic states that are so often socially detrimental, lithium seems superior to any other therapy. Maintenance treatment with lithium may be started simultaneously with the administration of ECT or any of the neuroleptics.

B. Therapeutic Effect against Depression

Lithium is therapeutically active against mania and may exert prophylactic action against both manic and depressive relapses. We do not yet know, however, whether it actually exerts a direct therapeutic action during a depression. Clinical trials have given varying results. While it appears that lithium is without value as a therapeutic agent against severe depression, some observations indicate that it may alleviate symptoms in depressions of slight to moderate intensity. The question awaits controlled clinical trials.

C. Prophylactic Effect against Manic and Depressive Relapses

The antimanic action of lithium has been known for a long time, but it is only during the last few years that its prophylactic properties against recurrent manic-depressive disorders have become known. Observations of individual cases or small groups of patients have been indicative. Not until recently were data presented for a large group of patients who had been observed and treated for a long period.

The main results of this study are summarized in Fig. 1. From among a larger group of manic-depressive patients, the authors selected 88 who (1) had two or more manic-depressive episodes during one year, or one or more episodes per year during at least two years, before being started on lithium; and (2) had been given lithium continuously for at least 12 months. No patient who fulfilled these criteria was excluded from the study. The patients were observed for six years and six months; lithium was administered prophylactically for periods of one to five years. For each patient the relapse frequency (average number of episode starts per year) was calculated for the periods without lithium and with lithium. Comparison revealed a statistically highly significant fall during lithium administration. Without lithium treatment relapses occurred, on the average, every 8 months; during lithium treatment only every 60–85 months. The few relapses that did occur during lithium treatment were of shorter duration than the psychotic episodes before lithium. For the group as a whole it was found that without lithium treatment the patients spent an average of 13 weeks a year in a psychotic state; during lithium treatment, less than 2 weeks.

Lithium prevented relapses with equal efficacy in patients having had both manias and depressions and in patients with a history of depressions only. A small group of atypical cases, characterized by delusions, especially of persecution, responded less well; the ideas of persecution often persisted, and there was considerable tendency to relapse. The prophylactic action of lithium was equally good in young, middle-aged, and old patients; it was also independent of the duration of the illness.

All the patients in the study had been treated extensively with drugs or ECT or both prior to lithium treatment. Antidepressant therapy was administered simultaneously with lithium when the latter was started during a depression and during severe depressive relapses. In all cases antidepressant therapy was discontinued within 2 weeks after the end of the depressive episode.

During the study 25 patients stopped taking lithium against the advice of the doctor. Side effects had not been troublesome, and there had been no relapses. On the contrary, the patients had been without relapse for an extended period and felt that their illness had ceased and that they would now be safe without medication. They could not be persuaded to continue. After discontinuation of lithium, relapses reappeared with the same frequency and duration as before lithium treatment had been started.

In 18 of the 88 patients relapses occurred in spite of continuous lithium treatment; 12 patients had one relapse and 6 more than one. As many as one-third of the patients who relapsed belonged to the group of atypical cases; atypical clinical features are obviously unfavorable for lithium prophylaxis.

Some of the relapses may have been due to inadequate lithium dosage; increased dosage was often followed by freedom from relapse. Relapses may also have occurred because the patients did not take their tablets or did not take them regularly.

A time factor often seemed to be involved. Relapses tended to occur within the first few months of treatment, while later relapses were rare. A gradual disappearance of subpsychotic mood swings was also noted; it might be months, in some cases a year, before full stability was attained.

Even when continued for years, the administration of lithium in prophylactic dosage did not affect normal mental function. Apart from occasional slight tiredness initially, mental side effects did not occur. The treatment did not impair consciousness or memory or interfere with intellectual productivity. Nor did it restrict the emotional range; patients in lithium treatment were able to feel happiness and sorrow to an entirely normal extent. Experiments on lithium administration to healthy subjects confirm that prophylactic lithium doses affect the normal mind slightly or not at all.

In the study under discussion, the patients served as their own controls in that relapse frequencies observed during the periods without lithium were used to calculate the relapse frequencies to be expected during the lithium periods. Such quantitative predictions are possible only when the group is sufficiently large, when the relapse frequency during the pretreatment periods is sufficiently high, and when the observation periods are sufficiently long. In this study the differences in relapse frequency between periods without lithium and with lithium were statistically highly significant ($p < 0.001$).

The study was carried out as an open experiment because the authors felt that the slight side effects of lithium administration (mainly fine tremor of the hands) would have given the game away in a double-blind prophylactic trial. Psychological factors may accordingly have been at work, but presumably did not play any major role. The patients in the study suffered from recurrent manic-depressive disorder that was sufficiently severe to necessitate regular supervision in the home or periodic admission to a mental hospital. This type of patient is not easily influenced by suggestion, certainly not to the extent that the entire course of the disease is altered. One might consider the possibility of psychotherapeutic effect from the regular control interviews during lithium administration, but it is difficult to see why brief interviews at intervals of 2 weeks to 3 months should stave off manic and depressive relapses so much more effectively than the almost incessant psychotherapy, drug treatment, and shock treatment to which these patients had been subjected, in and out of hospital, before they were put on lithium. Moreover, patients who stopped taking lithium but continued attending the interviews had relapses as before lithium. A pharmacological action of the treatment seems altogether the most likely explanation.

In addition to the effect against manias and depressions of psychotic intensity, the author noted that even between psychotic phases, lithium treatment led to emotional stabilization. Prior to lithium treatment, many of the patients had suffered from slight to moderate depressive or hypomanic symptoms during the intervals. Usually they were not hospitalized, but when suffering from slight depression, they were unable to work and usually spent a large part of the day in bed; when hypomanic, they had to be guarded against entering ill-considered commitments; when alternating frequently between slight depression and hypomania, they were the despair of their doctors, their spouses, and themselves. It was with these patients that some of the most gratifying lithium results

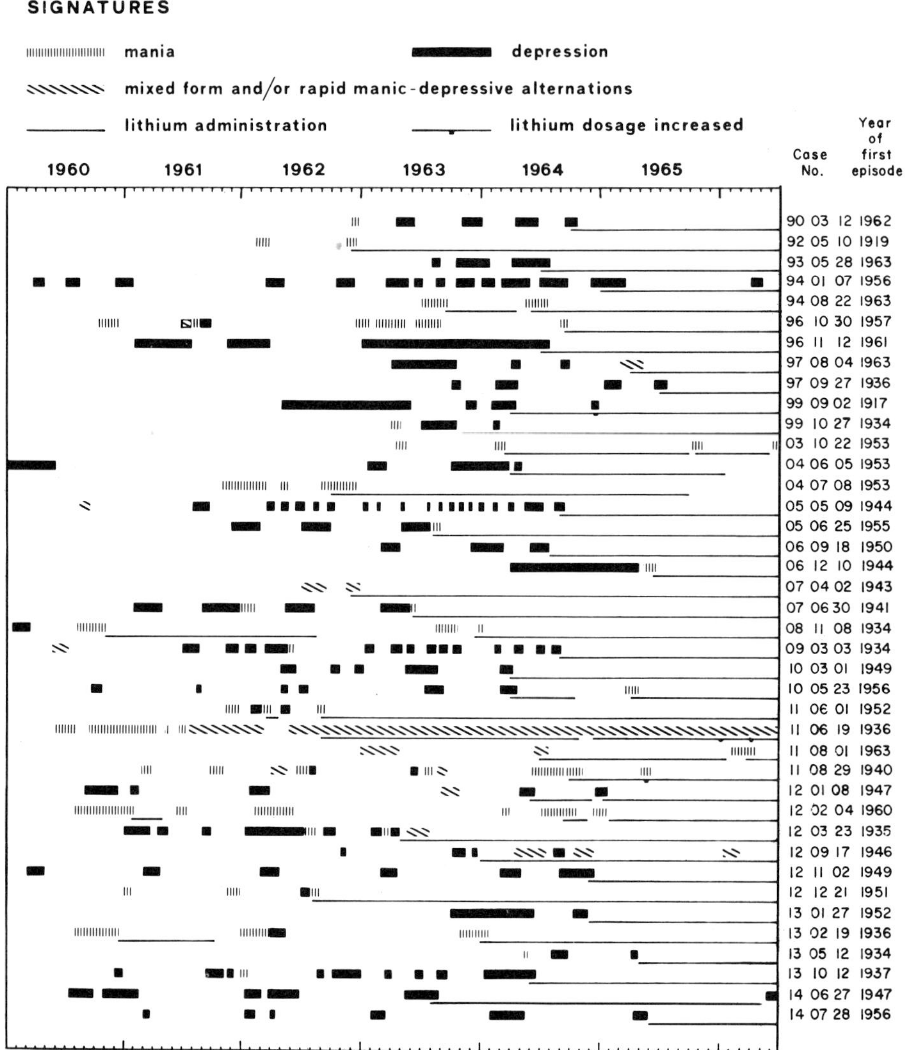

Fig. 1. Diagrammatic presentation of case histories from the study by Baastrup and Schou (364). The diagram shows, for each patient, all psychotic episodes that occurred between January 1, 1960, and July 1, 1966. The cases are arranged according to age; the first two digits of each case number indicate the year of birth. In the second column is shown the year when the first manic or depressive episode appeared.

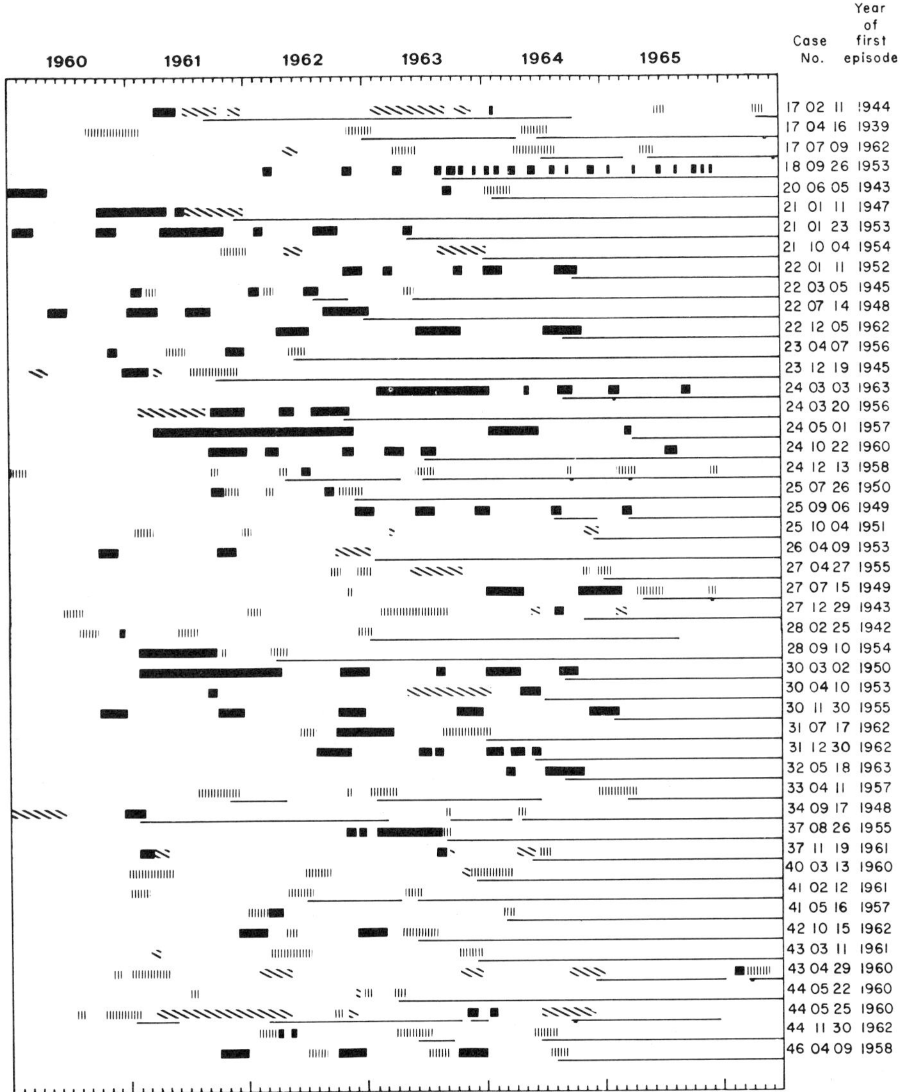

Fig. 1. Continued.

were obtained. Hypomanic overoptimism and hyperactivity disappeared, depressive periods with tiredness and lack of initiative were prevented, and capricious phase shifts no longer occurred. A regained feeling of security was the recurrent theme in reports from manic-depressive patients who had been on prophylactic lithium for a long time.

It was not in all cases, however, that the changes produced by lithium were received with gratitude, at least in the beginning. Patients who habitually or frequently were in a hypomanic state did not want the periods of extra inspiration and impetus removed because they were felt to be absolutely necessary for the patients' work and self-esteem. However, even the occasionally hypomanic patients would usually accept lithium treatment when they had experienced its capacity to prevent depressive episodes.

The discovery of lithium prophylaxis against manic-depressive disorder—including, in this context, recurrent endogenous depressions—is still young. As this chapter is being written, a number of prophylactic lithium studies against recurrent manic-depressive disorder are under way. Preliminary communications report shorter, less intense, and less frequent relapses during lithium treatment, as well as complete freedom from relapse. The coming years will show whether the conclusions drawn on the basis of observations at present available are confirmed or refuted.

D. Effects against Other Mental Disorders

Lithium treatment has been tried in mental disorders other than manic-depressive psychosis; the results have been variable. Lithium seems to be without any general sedative or neuroleptic properties and does not alter thought content or remove delusions, but in some cases it may ameliorate the affective overlay. There is no evidence that lithium prevents reactive or neurotic depressions. Observations of prophylactic action against the premenstrual syndrome await confirmation.

III. Mode of Action

The mechanism by which lithium exerts its psychiatric effects is not yet known. Many observations are available of metabolic and functional lithium effects *in vitro* and *in vivo,* but it is difficult to decide which ones are relevant since so little is known about the biological disturbance underlying manic-depressive disorder.

Much speculation has centered around the role of monoamines, and recent studies disclose an interference of lithium with norepinephrine and serotonin metabolism and neuron activity in the brain (365). The observations support the assumption that these amines may be involved in the regulation of mood and psychomotor activity, but further studies are required for an elucidation of the mechanism underlying the ability of lithium to counteract manic and depressive relapses.

Lithium is chemically related to sodium and potassium, both of which are of fundamental importance for almost all nervous activity. It would, therefore, seem likely that its mechanism of action should be sought in an interference with the metabolism and function of these ions. Furthermore, there is evidence of alterations of water and electrolyte balance or distribution in patients suffering from manic-depressive disorder.

A number of studies of sodium, potassium, water, and lithium balance and distribution have been carried out during lithium administration to patients and to normal subjects. They have led to interesting results and call for validation and extension, but they do not yield direct information about metabolic events in the central nevous system. *In vitro* studies on nerve tissue preparations have shown lithium effects on resting potential, impulse generation, impulse transmission, afterpotentials, etc.; similar or related phenomena might conceivably occur in the brain, mediated through interference with metabolism, or caused by direct action of the lithium ion on membrane transport or excitability or on other functions critically dependent on particular protein–electrolyte–water patterns. The presence of lithium in low concentration might hereby serve to correct cerebral abnormalities responsible for the tendency to recurrent manic and depressive relapses.

IV. Epilogue

Lithium treatment may appear cumbersome when compared with the use of traditional drugs which do not require such precise dosage and careful control. Other drawbacks must also be considered before a patient is placed on lithium treatment that may have to be continued for years, in some cases for the rest of the patient's life: the occurrence of side effects, the risk of intoxication if the control fails, etc. For each individual patient these debit items on the lithium account must be weighed against the personal and family tragedies associated with recurrent manic-depressive disorder and against the suicide risk. Patients suffering from affective disorder take their own lives ten to twenty times as often as the average population. The exact figure for patients with frequent manic-depressive relapses is not known, but must be higher, and this is the group that can derive particular benefit from prophylactic lithium treatment. We possess, of course, conventional antidepressants that are effective therapeutically, but these patients tend to commit suicide at such an early stage of a depressive relapse that there is no opportunity for antidepressant therapy. A decision to administer lithium should be made only from careful examination and evaluation; the decision *not* to give it to a patient with recurrent manic-depressive disorder must be based on the same scrupulous deliberation.

For further reading and references see Appendix 2.

52

ANTIANXIETY DRUGS

Joseph del Giudice

I. Introduction

The use of the term anxiety is pervasive to all aspects of the behavioral sciences; however, its exact meaning remains for the most part a function of the user, as are all terms related to feelings. The concept of anxiety holds an important position in the theories of personality and psychopathology and, therefore, requires careful definition as a psychiatrically characterized component of behavior.

Anxiety often is expressed via psychophysiological mechanisms produced through unconscious pathways seemingly triggered through subconscious neural or neurohumoral mechanisms. This is to be differentiated from stress or tension, which originate from consciously recognized mechanisms. Therefore, anxiety may be differentiated from fear and states of tension which exist as the consequence of failure to satisfy basic needs. Fear is the emotional reaction to perceived external threat, whereas anxiety may ensue without current direct perception of an external threat. In addition, it may persist inappropriately for prolonged periods after the perceived threat in reality no longer exists. It may also arise as the result of unresolved conflict between the expression of basic drives in confrontation with social or cultural proscriptions and internalized restrictions (superego) on their expression.

Anxiety states are best considered as a group of syndromes manifested by a diverse group of symptoms and signs. These states may be dominated by subjective feelings of apprehension, fear or panic associated with the physiological concomitants of fear such as restlessness, increased muscular tension, tightness of the chest, breathlessness, choking, palpitation, giddiness, trembling, sweating, and flushing. The individual subjective feeling of fear may be diffuse and unrelated to a direct object or it may have a topical content. The patient may identify the fear with a specific imagined impending event (heart disease, insanity, death, etc.). In chronic forms of anxiety the individual may experience days of restlessness, irritability, excitability, headache, fatigue and insomnia. It may occur in a relatively uncomplicated form such as an anxiety neurosis, or it may represent a large or small component of the symptom complexes of most psychiatric illnesses, including psychosis.

II. Antianxiety Drugs

The use of the term antianxiety drug is an operational one only and, of course, we should not expect one, or a group of psychotropic agents to be efficacious for all states where anxiety exists.

For the most part the group of medicinal compounds which we will consider are ineffective with psychotic target symptoms, but are capable to some extent of changing subjective feeling states and sometimes the behavior related to these states. They may be sedative but are not hypnotic in recommended doses. They may be skeletal muscle relaxants, weakly antihistaminic and, in addition, may have anticonvulsant qualities. Some are capable of producing tolerance in addition to psychological or physical dependence. Some are cross-dependent with ethanol, and in animals as well as man; the effects of CNS depressants and analgesics may be enhanced by combination with these drugs.

The use of antianxiety agents represents symptomatic treatment and their use will not change underlying psychopathologic factors in emotional illness, although they may modify to some extent tension and autonomic manifestations of central discomfiture. Their effects on cognition, memory, and perception has not been satisfactorily determined.

Because antianxiety drugs will not remove underlying neurotic patterns, nor change basic responses to prolonged environmental stress, they should be used with considerable discrimination with definite objectives and in adequate dosages. If they are considered in this light they will prove quite effective. However, when they are used as "shotgun" therapy for undefined symptomatic clusters over prolonged periods, the therapist and patient will invariably be disappointed in the results.

The patient often views the prescription of any drug as a definitive solution to his problem and may even be led to believe this by the therapist by either unspoken or verbalized, conscious or unconscious attitudes incidental to their prescription. It is most difficult for the relatively sophisticated physician to be truly aware of the extreme naivety of the patient in this respect, whose internalized concept of all drugs often is as a curative, e.g., etiological solution; much as penicillin vs. pneumococcal penumonia.

III. Antianxiety Agents in Treatment

A. Antipsychotic Drugs

The phenothiazines and other antipsychotic compounds are useful in ameliorating some manifestations of anxiety in schizophrenia, as well as other psychotic illnesses, drug and alcohol withdrawal syndromes, borderline psychotic states, acute neurotic anxiety attacks (cf. Davis, Chapter 47; Lehman and Ban, Chapter 48), and some can safely be used in transient anxiety-provoking situations, as preanesthetic and preparturition medications. For this purpose, they may be used alone or in combination with analgesics and/or sedatives.

B. Glycerol Derivatives (Carbamates)

In this group are meprobamates, oxanamide, phenaglycodol, and tybamate. These compounds are most useful with patients whose predominant symptoms are acute anxiety and tension. Proper selection of patients is essential and the key is a history of a previously stable personality. An unfavorable outcome can be expected with chronic neurosis and a labile or immature personality structure. Because of muscle-relaxant properties, they may be useful in general clinical practice in presurgical and postsurgical procedures, trauma (fractures and muscle injury), low back injuries, myalgias, and myositis. Meprobamate has been used for anxiety in pregnancy in all trimesters without apparent toxic effects and no evidence of teratogenicity. In premenstrual tension, these drugs can help relieve associated muscle tension, anxiety and secondary depression.

Other conditions where anxiety, tension and irritability are contributing factors, such as dermatoses and allergies, e.g., varieties of asthma where large psychosomatic components are present, relief can be partial or complete during acute episodes. Gastrointestinal disturbances with or without large functional components as in spastic colitis may be helped by carbamates alone or in combination with anticholinergics. These compounds have been useful in selected cases of recurrent headaches and in some instances of petit mal epilepsy and myoclonic seizures. However, they tend to make some patients with grand mal epilepsy worse.

C. Diphenylmethane Derivatives

The commonly used compounds of this group are benactyzine, hydroxyzine, and diphenhydramine. Pharmacologically, they are primarily antispasmodics and antihistaminics. Other compounds in this group are pipradol, a CNS stimulant and its optical isomer, azacyclonol. Azacyclonol was claimed to have been used with limited success to antagonize the effects of lysergic acid diethylamide and mescaline, however, more recent studies have not supported this claim.

Clinical experience with hydroxyzine has shown that it may be useful with mild emotional disorders, hyperkinetic brain-injured children, and geriatric patients. It seems to lessen tension and symptoms of autonomic dysfunction, and calms hyperkinetic behavior. It also may be useful in children facing stressful situations such as dental or surgical procedures. Since hydroxyzine will reduce anxiety without loss of alertness, it may be of use in obsessive patients who have phobic feelings toward loss of control. The efficacy of hydroxyzine in correction of supraventricular arrhythmias has not been established without question.

Benactyzine possesses strong anticholinergic activity, and its usefulness is primarily related to this effect, rather than antianxiety action per se. Diphenhydramine is quite useful as a calming agent particularly in older patients and may be used as bedtime sedation in lieu of barbiturates.

D. Benzodiazepines

This group of compounds as compared with the carbamates, seems to be more useful for the clinical management of anxiety and tension states. Currently used agents in this category are chlordiazepoxide, diazepam, and oxazepam. Chlordiazcpoxidc is the prototype of this group and, as with meprobamate, seems to benefit most patients who have a previous history of a fairly stable life style.

The antianxiety agents of this group may be used for similar indications as with the carbamates, and their muscle-relaxant properties are even more potent. Diazepam has been used successfully in treatment of epileptic seizures and the muscle spasms of tetanus. In addition, chlordiazepoxide, in a recent well-designed study of alcohol withdrawal syndromes, has been shown to be the drug of choice in preventing both delirium tremens and seizures when compared with chlorpromazine, thiamine, hydroxyzine and placebo (cf. Hayman and del Giudice, Chapter 41).

IV. Side Effects

With proper use, side effects can be nonexistant or minimal with the antianxiety drugs. Some "side-effects" can even be desired therapeutic goals, i.e., sedation with diphenhydramine, which is primarily antihistaminic. It must be mentioned that prolonged use of meprobamate and chlordiazepoxide with abrupt cessation has produced withdrawal syndromes, including seizures and death. Because their effects are potentiated by ethanol, this must be a consideration in their use with alcoholic patients, particularly those with suicidal tendencies. Additionally, all patients should be warned of the possible drowsiness which may accompany their use. This can be significant with the patient who must drive or whose employment necessarily is with dangerous machinery or on heights.

V. Summary

Antianxiety drugs, when properly used, have a definite place in the armamentarium of all clinicians. Although not curative, they can extend the range of symptomatic treatment. They should be used only with specific goals in mind, and dosages should be titrated to each patient. Changing from one drug to another should not be done until the therapist is satisfied that *adequate* doses have been used for a sufficient period of time. An ascending dosage schedule is generally most appropriate and will tend to minimize side effects until the optimum dosage is achieved, or side effects are not tolerable to the patient. The dose can then be decreased to comfortable levels while maintaining treatment goals. Frequent contact with the patient is desirable during this initial period.

Many of these compounds have been continuously used by patients for periods of years without apparent loss of efficacy or serious toxicity. If efficacy of one agent diminishes or significant tolerance occurs, the therapist can change to use of another antianxiety drug.

For references and further reading see Appendices 1 and 2.

53

IMPROVED CLINICAL PRACTICE AND RESEARCH IN THE TREATMENT OF PRIVATE AMBULATORY PATIENTS, INCLUDING THE USE OF THE COMPUTER WITH PRECODED DATA FORMS

Nathan S. Kline

I. Introduction

There are unique opportunities for research in private practice. The largest number of patients, the greatest amount of psychiatric manpower, and the most crucial understanding of certain types of success in therapy involves precisely these patients. Vast new possibilities have become available through the application of computers to this mass of data.

II. Special Qualifications of Private Patients as Research Subjects

A. Greater Variety

In certain countries (e.g., Denmark) it is customary to hospitalize at least initially all except the very mildest cases regardless of diagnosis. In other countries the vast majority of patients of all social classes are seen by preference at a university clinic since this is the place of superior diagnosis and therapy. In the United States, however, it is usually only the severe cases that are hospitalized, and attendance at a university clinic is usually quite stratified in respect to socioeconomic class. Yet, almost all private psychiatrists carry in their private practice a reasonable number of patients who either do not pay or make token payments. As a result, the private practitioner often sees an extremely wide spectrum of patients both in respect to diagnosis and socioeconomic and occupational backgrounds.

B. Observation of Special Groups

Since a substantial number of psychiatric patients are referred in tandem fashion by other patients, a psychiatrist often finds himself in the interesting position of becoming a "specialist" on a particular disease entity or for a particular occupational or social group. For instance, a psychiatrist who has successfully treated a homosexual with depression is likely to be referred other homosexuals with depression.

The same is true in respect to occupation, artists refer artists, electricians refer electricians, and advertising men refer each other. In my own practice, for example, I have a large population of mutually referred Greek-born Sephardic Jews whose customs differ sufficiently from the average population to make them an intriguing population to study.

In the process of identifying the subpopulations, very often some common factor of psychopathology or treatment response becomes evident which otherwise might have been completely missed. Such useful information as missed appointments, nonpayment of bills, and other items of practical interest might emerge.

III. Special Conditions of Observation

A. Field Behavior

Whereas patients in institutions can be controlled and observed more closely, the varieties of behavior open to them are obviously restricted. Ambulatory patients have a much broader spectrum of social, interpersonal, sexual, familial, and occupational areas in which to perform.

B. Self-Selection

Because the patients are self-selected (i.e., they chose to come to a particular psychiatrist), their motivation for continuing in treatment is usually far superior to that of clinic patients and consequently the dropout rate is probably only a quarter that of patients attending outpatient or follow-up clinics. In addition if treatment is successful, the patient will tend to return to the same physician if there is a subsequent episode. Often this is not the case with clinic or hospital patients.

IV. Techniques of Evaluation

A. Real Life Observation

Many evaluations done in a hospital setting try to approximate how the patient will function once he leaves. With the ambulatory patient, one has the opportunity of directly viewing the effect of treatment in a real-life setting which does not require transferral.

B. Job Performance and Family Adjustment

Instead of rating occupational therapy or recreational therapy performance, it is possible with the private patient to determine whether or not he is actually functioning on the job and with his hobbies and how well he is able to get along with his family and adjust to his community. In part this is determined by his own reporting, but also can be measured by whether he is working, attending social or civic functions, etc.

C. Reports from Interested Although Biased Observers

When desirable, it is often possible to obtain permission from the patient to discuss his condition with selected others. Even in those circumstances where the patient requests that no information be given *out,* there is no reason why reports concerning the patient's behavior cannot still be obtained from his employer, his spouse, close relatives, and friends. With particular biases taken into consideration, it is possible to judge how well the patient is performing from a variety of different points of view. In some respects the reports of these observers are no more or no less biased than those of hospital nurses, attendants, and doctors.

D. Superior Psychiatric Observation

As a rule, the private psychiatrist is intensely concerned about each of his patients since his living depends on them. He also has many fewer patients to care for than does his counterpart in the hospital and, hence, can devote much more time to individual patients. Also, as a rule, he alone has the responsibility and must make crucial interpretations and decisions.

V. Types of Projects

A. Drug Evaluations

There is a great need, particularly after the early phases of investigation have been completed, for good clinical observations (Phase 3 studies), usually under the auspices of one or another of the pharmaceutical companies. At times this will permit a clinician to have access to a drug before it is generally available on the market, which in a sense provides him with a therapeutic advantage over other psychiatrists. It is also possible, if an individual psychiatrist believes he has a treatment technique superior to those generally available, to apply for his own own IND (Investigational New Drug) from the Food and Drug Administration.

B. Social Factors in Response

Often in the hospital there is a paucity of information about the patient's social background, since to lighten the load such data are obtained by the social worker. In private practice the psychiatrist not only hears about but often sees other family members.

C. Hospitals

Many psychiatrists do not have a formal affiliation with a hospital or, if they do, limit themselves to a clinical affiliation. At the present time there is a good deal of biological investigation going on both in the university and nonuniversity settings. In most cases such university or institutional researchers are delighted to find assistance in the collaboration of psychiatrists in private practice. Such collaboration can range from the evaluation of psychological test instruments (and often the Chief Investigator is willing to supply personnel) to the evaluation of particular blood or urine factors in a variety of psychiatric disorders. In many cases such investigators are hesitant to contact practicing psychiatrists because they presuppose disinterest or, oddly enough, it may never have occurred to them that such collaboration was possible.

VI. Computer Analyses*

A. Recording Data

Resistance against using precoded forms often arises because such forms are poorly conceived, excessively lengthy, and are not flexible enough. Further, the

* Portions of the material dealing with computer analyses have appeared previously in an article entitled "The Use of Computers in Office Practice of Psychiatry" by Nathan S. Kline and George W. Logemann. *Comprehensive Psychiatry,* Vol. 8, No. 6, (December) 1967, pp. 544–551. Reproduction of this material is with permission of the Publishers Grune and Stratton, Inc., 381 Park Avenue South, New York, New York. Also see "Applications of Computers in Psychiatry and General Medicine" by Nathan S. Kline. *Southern Medical Bulletin* Vol. 57, No. 3 (September) 1969, pp. 53–57.

"feedback" produces no gratification and is more difficult to deal with than ordinary brief notes. However, when completion of the forms will produce an unusually complete and readable narrative case history, the matter is quite different. A great deal of the information obtained in initial histories can be recorded on precoded optical or mark sense scan sheets, and the carrying out of analyses of a particular psychiatrist's practice or a collaborative study becomes delightfully simple. This approach, moreover, by no means limits the recording of idiosyncratic data, but only insures that a core of necessary information is obtained. At the center data "bank" is a file which contains *all* of the information about a patient, i.e., clinical records, progress notes, medications, and records of every contact (phone, visit, letter) which the office has with or about the patient. This bulk of information would be unmanageable to record or retrieve were it not for the capacity of the computer to store data in such a way that it can be selectively recalled regardless of when recorded.

The file is created when the patient makes his first appointment or appears in person. Much of the information to be obtained is best elicited by asking a set of questions the content of which is decided upon in advance. By making certain that the individual questions are unambiguous, it is often possible to avoid misunderstandings that will interfere with competent diagnosis and therapy, i.e., by preparing the questions in advance there is greater assurance that important areas will not be overlooked and the number of questions will be fewer than would ordinarily be the case.

Similarly, the possible types of answers can usually be predicted with a high degree of probability. These can be set down in advance, and if a response does fall into one of the categories, a great deal of time and effort is saved by merely checking at the appropriate place. If the answer is not one of the precoded ones, space can be allowed for recording any unusual responses.

At times the contingencies are such that the usual format of the question or of the answer is unsuitable. One of the choices for answering should allow for this, i.e., "The question cannot be answered," and whenever possible another item should permit writing in of the appropriate response.

To insist that a patient answer specific questions in a specific order is apt to destroy the spontaneity of the interview. However, it is not difficult to encourage a patient to remain in a certain area of questioning until it has been clarified. This leads to a natural solution of the problem, i.e., a separate questionnaire for each major area of inquiry. In most psychiatric interviews this would mean one questionnaire dealing with actuarial-type information such as place and date of birth, years of education, number and age of siblings, type of occupation, and present job status. A second area of inquiry would be developmental history; a third would cover mental status; a fourth would deal with affect (if the patient is depressed or manic), and a fifth would possibly deal with prior treatment, including medications and hospitalization.

There is almost a fatal tendency when one is making out questionnaires to be both exhaustive and exhausting. This is also true in recording the ordinary case histories. We have all seen records which contained 40 and 50 page anamneses which have never been looked at by anyone, including their author. A question should be asked only if the answer is likely to prove useful at some future date.

B. Applications

1. Previous Treatment

Frequently, a patient seen for the first time will have a history of previous therapy with other psychiatrists or even a series of past hospitalizations. Once a release has been obtained from the patient, information such as the names of the doctors and hospitals can be stored in the computer memory together with the approximate dates and duration of hospitalization or treatment. Then a letter to each of the treating persons or agencies could automatically be printed out, together with envelope, so that the request for information could be sent within minutes of the time that the necessary information was provided. Note that the letters sent would then become part of the patient's file and the computer could be programmed to send a follow-up note if the record has not been received within a set time limit, e.g., 2 weeks. The computer could also be so programmed that when notation was made that a letter or record was received from one of the doctors or hospitals involved, it would automatically cancel the follow-up letter. The request for information itself might be on a precoded form sufficiently brief to make its completion simple and could be prepared in a manner that would permit rapid transfer to the computer memory. Idiosyncratic information could be noted separately.

2. Drug Evaluation

Similarly, if the patient is placed on medication, it may be of the greatest importance to notify the patient's family physician as rapidly as possible that this has been done. For instance, if the patient is to be given a monamine oxidase inhibitor, it would greatly influence the selection of medications by the family doctor. Once again, with the obtaining of the release the computer could be programmed to write a letter containing the necessary information so that it too would go out by the time the patient left the office. If it was the family doctor who referred the patient, the same letter should contain a brief resumé of the case and whatever information the psychiatrist was in the habit of supplying to the referring physician.

In those cases where the patient was already on medication, a phone call would be automatically placed to the prescribing doctor or the supplying pharmacy to make certain that there were no incompatabilities for the new medication prescribed. Limiting the questions to ten or twenty in each area, it becomes possible for the patient to relate his story in a relatively spontaneous manner, and it is relatively simple to fill in the answers to the asked or unasked questions as they occur rather than in a specific order. At the end of the patient's spontaneous dscussion, one can ask the neglected questions.

Inevitably, a great deal of idiosyncratic material may be lost, but at present the same information is equally if not more abandoned since it is deeply buried in a voluminous case history that never gets looked at. The important idosyncratic data of this sort tends to stick in the mind of a good physician, but often the nature of its telling is as important as the information itself. It obviously is often not transmittable by written records and so would be lost in any case if another physician were to take over the care of the patient. Further, it is likely that the meaningful and important material of this type would be different for each physician since it reflects his own personality and his own relationship to the patient.

3. Other Uses

In the previous section we discussed day-to-day applications of a centralized, integrated computer file. In this section we discuss some long-term applications. Moreover, the topics discussed in the previous section are realizable in terms of present technology: All that one need do is to expend the effort. In this section we indicate techniques which are still being developed.

We assumed in the previous discussion that the computer file was dynamic. We implied that information no longer needed could be erased from the computer's memory file. Suppose, however, the data were kept in an archive. In several years one could accumulate a storehouse of information which could be used, for example, to help validate the efficacy of drugs or methods in the treatment of specific disorders.

Moreover, one could discover trends in his patient population—the gradual changes in the numbers and percentages of patients with particular disorders, the efficacy of particular schedules of treatments, the need to expand or contract one's staff with personnel with particular talents and training. Shifts in geographical distribution of patients may dictate opening a branch office or moving the central office.

Based on overall studies of responses, the need for research in specific areas may become obvious. Further, questionnaires administered by one's staff could be periodically revised to include more detailed questions or to eliminate demonstrably useless information. The studies could indicate what information should be kept in the archive, and for how long.

Moreover, the doctor can evaluate the costs of his practice, which methods more effectively employ his resources—the funds allocated to drugs, the time and talents of his assistants, etc.

Such questions as briefly outlined above can only be answered if they are planned for, necessitating careful experimental design. The computer can help by generating simulated results. Conversely, it is of importance to allow the doctor to make quick studies of existing statistical data. Some questions the doctor may wish to ask can be answered in terms of simple counts and census taking about the class of patients. More involved questions require more advanced querying methods. The computer might draw conclusions from the data according to a technique which seems applicable at the moment: Having this suggestion at hand, the doctor can then propose alternative and possibly more correct solutions.

In the future we may expect the computer to take over some of the routines now necessarily handled by human assistants. The computer can ask the patient, either orally via programmed tape recorders (already in existence) or visually on a display screen, the basic facts of his past history. One must first establish the relative merits of a various combination of machine and personal contact. Certainly, these computer techniques in a public, multilingual clinic, may provide needed "contact" and obtain needed information when there is insufficient personnel. Even in private practice, the completely uniform impersonal approach may be most useful for obtaining certain types of information. It would be interesting to compare responses of a manipulative hysterical woman to (1) the computer and (2) a sympathetic psychiatrist.

The doctors may also benefit from automatic methods, particularly when they must obtain information about a patient's records when the patient calls, e.g., when the psychiatrist is at home. The doctor could call the computer, whose audial response unit could compose informative spoken sentences from the computer's written memory record; alternately the doctor's home typewriter could be driven by a mechanism connected to the telephone, or he could have his television set function as a visual display screen by linking it via telephone to his stored computer records.

Furthermore, prescriptions might be stored in the computer and the patient's pharmacy obtain this via a computer code. This would eliminate lost prescriptions, prevent alteration, and provide a permanent record. The computer could also be programmed to notify the doctor when the amount of medication called for has run out. If the patient still had any drug left, it would indicate that either he wasn't taking medication as prescribed or that something else was amiss.

Suppose information is needed concerning the latest accepted treatment for a condition seen only infrequently, e.g., Gilles de la Tourette's syndrome, or advice is needed concerning rapid diagnostic procedure for porphyria, or the question arises whether yogurt, since it is fermented, would be restricted if the patient is to be given a monamine oxidase inhibitor. Immediate computer inquiry could be made to a central file supported by the National Medical Library, the Food and Drug Administration, a pharmaceutical company, or even a private service established for such a purpose. More detailed information could be provided via an on-line typewriter which could type out a longer précis and institute an automatic request for reprints of articles or photocopies.

VI. The Future

A. Community Mental Health Centers

The implementation of the Community Mental Health Center Act will have far-reaching implications as to the future practice of psychiatry. It is quite likely that the psychiatrist will be more and more used as are specialists in other disciplines. The emphasis on the simpler treatment techniques will be shifted to the general practitioner. Except for the more difficult cases, the role of the psychiatrist will probably be to diagnose and recommend treatment for those patients about whom the general practitioner is uncertain. The locus of psychiatric activity is in part likely to be shifted from the hospital as well as the individual physician's office to the Community Mental Health Center itself.

B. Patient Activities and Job Placement

Undoubtedly the greatest gap which could presently be filled in psychiatric care is the way in which patients spend the vast vistas of their time when they are not being seen by the psychiatrist. In addition to the requirement that someone be employed, or a member of the family remain at home with them, the day even then is often not spent very constructively. The Community Mental Health Centers should provide work therapy, suitable recreation, educational opportunities, and all the other activities which would expedite patient improvement and convert many a failure to successful treatment. This should also include suitable job placement for those patients unable to return to their former occupations. Computer programs capable of storing and analyzing data of this type could help insure appropriate work or occupational therapy as well as suitable job placement (even though it be as a volunteer, etc.).

54

PEDIATRIC PSYCHOPHARMACOLOGY

H. H. Eveloff

I. Introduction

Although psychopharmacologic agents are commonly in use in the pediatric age range (0–16), there are disproportionately fewer reports concerning drug research with children than in the adult literature. This is especially so with respect to controlled studies. The reason for this paucity of studies is not clear, but it is unfortunate. The disparity between the mental health needs of children and the availability of services is well known. Yet the need for therapeutic intervention of all types, including psychotropic drugs, is even more acute with children, especially from a preventive point of view.

Although the state that pediatric psychopharmacology is in at present does not allow one to make recommendations to the reader with a full sense of gratifying assurance, it is hoped that this summary will provide some guidelines to those responsible for the health of their young patients in their crucial formative years.

This review is based on over 100 reports and encompasses the majority of articles appearing between 1960 and 1967.

A. Problems Peculiar to the Evaluation of Studies in Child Psychopharmacology

The factors which are peculiar to children in degree or kind are in addition to those usually found in adult psychopharmacology. They are:

1. Poor diagnostic terminology.
2. Lesser occurrence of certain significant dramatic indicators of improvement such as seen with adults; for instance, cessation of delusions and hallucinations, lifting of clearly defined depression, etc.
3. Problems of assessing environmental factors because of: (a) heightened suggestibility of children; (b) increased dependence of the child on his surroundings; (c) lack of awareness, or other factors which make accurate reporting difficult such as poor motivation, absence of speech, failure to comprehend, etc.
4. Difficulties arising out of evaluating a drug administered over a long period of time to an organism that is in a constant state of flux due to maturational processes. This increases the problem of obtaining truly matched groups for controlled research.
5. Problems arising out of uncertainty as to whether or not the child actually has ingested the medication. Parents and even school nurses will forget to give the medication and not report this. Often the child will forget to take the medication, particularly at the school lunch time, but say that he did when questioned.
6. Frequent negative attitude of a disturbed child toward the medication secondary to hostility directed at parents and authorities who are administering medication.

In general then, the problems of evaluation are those of assaying the ingestion of a medication by a pliable changing organism in transaction with a complex, largely unknown environment where the clinician or investigator has the further challenging task of describing this complex transaction with inaccurate diagnostic and descriptive terms.

II. Discussion of Medications

A. Antipsychotic Agents

1. Phenothiazines

As a group, the phenothiazines have received the widest acceptance as possessing psychoactivity when compared to all other chemicals used for the treatment of emotional disorders of children. This is especially so for psychotic symptomatology and agitated states. This acceptance has been fairly well substantiated by a number of controlled studies, although even with the phenothiazines the endorsements are not without qualifications and reservations. In general, these drugs are not recommended as those to be initially employed when treating neurotic behavior, mild to moderate behavior disorders, or mild hyperactivity. Minor tranquilizers (or stimulants in the latter case) appear to be equal or superior and are considered safer.

a. Sedating Phenothiazines (Dimethylaminopropyl Group). Chlorpromazine is the most frequently employed medication of this subgroup. It is effective in agitated states associated with illnesses such as psychoses, mental deficiency including children with very low IQ's, and several behavior disorders. Although phenothiazines do improve the thinking of psychotic children, this effect is not as marked as seen in similarly disturbed adults. Its major beneficial effect seems more related to its ability to reduce agitation, thereby allowing the child to benefit from his environment. This benefit is not always evident in reports evaluating phenothiazines, either because of a failure to include long-term follow-up or a failure to systematically and aggressively take advantage of the child's increased receptivity.

b. The Piperidine Phenothiazines. These are considered neither depressing nor stimulating. They allegedly cause fewer Parkinson-type side effects. The major representative of this group is thioridazine and is the only one of this subgroup reported on in the child literature. A number of studies indicate its usefulness in controlling aggressive, hyperactive behavior of psychological or organic origin. No papers have appeared to indicate that thioridazine has any proven advantage over other phenothiazines. However, evaluators of thioridazine tended to report fewer side effects by comparison. Unfortunately, the majority of studies reviewed were either poorly controlled or not controlled at all, thereby leaving such questions unanswered.

c. The Piperazine Ring Phenothiazines. These generally share the common therapeutic effect of stimulation, which is unfortunately accompanied by increased extrapyramidal involvement. Trifluoperazine is by far the most widely accepted stimulating phenothiazine. It is generally agreed to benefit withdrawn schizophrenics, although this is not its exclusive use. A few reports have included incidences of dramatic, though unpredictable, responses to this medication in a small number of autistic children.

Prochlorperazine has not been well received and the remainder mentioned in the child literature, perphenazine, fluphenazine, and acetophenazine, are not sufficiently represented to allow any conclusions to be drawn.

Drug combinations have not been reported on except for a combination of meprobamate (200 mg) and promazine hydrochlorize (25 mg). Several investigators suggest its use for mild to moderate behavior disorders. However, in my estimation, the value of this combination over other drugs taken singly remains to be proven.

As a group, the phenothiazines have received the broadest acceptance for the control of agitation. Though benefits have been reported in other areas of human psychopathologic response such as thought disorder, poor social contact, autistic withdrawal, and poor school performance, there is less unanimous agreement on the usefulness of these drugs for these symptom complexes. The three phenothiazines and principal representatives of their respective groups, chlorpromazine, thioridazine, and trifluoperazine, have received greatest endorsement. However, it cannot be ascertained whether or not this popularity is in part due to a lack of experimentation with other phenothiazines, especially those that have proven in some adult studies to be equally effective of the three mentioned.

Most of the mild side effects seen in adult use, drowsiness, constipation, skin reactions, etc., are seen, but less frequently, especially when one considers the higher milligrams of drug per kilogram of body weight usually utilized in children. This is also true for extrapyramidal symptoms, with one exception. Extrapyramidal dystonic reactions and agitation are frequently reported to be more common in children at lower milligrams-per-kilogram doses than in adults, especially when utilizing a stimulating (piperazine ring) phenothiazine. Dystonic reactions that often resemble tetanus or meningitis can be particularly frightening to both patient and physician. As a consequence, low milligrams-per-kilogram starting doses for piperazine ring phenothiazines are recommended. Treatment of these side effects does not differ from that reported for adults elsewhere in the text. Moderate side effects have been reported infrequently.

An increase of seizures has been noted. The chronic irreversible extrapyramidal symptoms, as well as ocular changes, that have recently been demonstrated in adults have just begun to be observed in children, thereby making it mandatory that the clinician keep his index of suspicion high and employ these powerful drugs only when there is clear indication for their use.

No serious life-threatening side effects such as bone marrow depression or liver involvement, have been reported. However, a 14-year-old schizophrenic girl treated with a phenothiazine (chlorpromazine) for two-and-one-half years by the author developed clinical signs and symptoms of pancytopenia which was confirmed by laboratory studies. An uneventful recovery was achieved by withdrawal and medical management.

2. Other Antipsychotic Agents

a. The Rauwolfia Alkaloids. The rauwolfia alkaloids are not used with any significant frequency for their antipsychotic properties. They are not as potent as the phenothiazines. Somatic and emotional side effects such as hypotension and depression limit their usefulness. However, it is well to remember the rauwolfia alkaloids when the use of an antipsychotic agent is crucial and phenothiazines cannot be utilized or prove ineffective.

b. Phenothiazine Analogs. The only drug representing the phenothiazine analogs reported on is chlorprothixene. Its usefulness as compared to better known phenothiazines is yet to be proven.

c. The Butyrophenones. The butyrophenones which have been used in adult psychiatry in Europe have not been tried in any adequate research study on children either in the United States or abroad.

B. Stimulants

1. Discussion of the Hyperactive Child with Minimal Cerebral Dysfunction

For over a quarter of a century stimulants have enjoyed wide application in child medicine. Their principal usage has been for the treatment of hyperactive children, mainly those who have been diagnosed as having minimal cerebral dysfunction. Before discussing the stimulants, it is worthwhile to digress here to discuss this clinical syndrome because of its ubiquity in clinical practice.

The syndrome of minimal cerebral dysfunction is essentially a descriptive one. There is a lack of agreement as to its definitive etiology and even some disagreement as to the exact criteria necessary for making a diagnosis. This ambiguity is almost certainly due to the fact that the "syndrome" probably includes several illnesses of various etiologies, much as has been presumed for schizophrenia. Most investigators in the field feel that there is a physical substrate for the clinical manifestations, but no one has been able to precisely describe the physical abnormality that allegedly exists. Is there some type of cellular or subcellular organic damage? Does some chemical abnormality exist? Is there some problem with transmission? Is it a matter of normal brain cells being patterned or "hooked up" in abnormal ways; i.e., is there a functional rather than a physical abnormality? The confusion in this field is reflected in the various names given to the syndrome: hyperactive child, minimally brain-damaged child, minimal cerebral dysfunction, hyperactivity-impulsivity syndrome, hyperkinetic child, etc. There are even some who are not willing to accept the idea that the hyperactive child need necessarily have any cerebral pathology at all to be included in the syndrome.

The brief description below should serve to orient the clinician for the purposes of a discussion of the stimulants, but by no means can it substitute for a thorough reading of the various monographs and texts concerning this vital subject.

The symptoms exhibited by the hyperactive child can be viewed as largely dependent upon one primary malfunction, namely, the relative inability of the organism to maintain an activity for an expected length of time. A common but not invariable finding is evidence of mild organicity, to be described later. Usually, the primary symptoms are compounded by a large number of secondary environmentally determined symptoms. The primary abnormality involves a variety of cerebral functions which, for purposes of discussion, I have arbitrarily grouped together. These are: *receptivity*, *selectivity*, *expressivity*, and *emotionality*.

Receptivity is defined as perception and preparation of input information for higher level decisions. The hyperactive child seems to collect less information than is necessary for adequate problem solving not because he lacks innate intellectual ability to organize this input into a meaningful whole but because he does not seem to engage in this activity for a sufficient period of time; that is, he suffers from a short attention span. In addition, many, if not most, of these children obtain incorrect information to begin with because of perceptual abnormalities.

Selectivity is defined as the ability to accentuate one pattern of sensory and cognitive activity while damping all others, coupled with the ability to maintain this "set" for a desired period of time. The hyperactive child has difficulty in deciding which group of stimuli are important and in maintaining a mental "set" long enough to realize the full potential of his cognitive ability to meaningfully organize, pattern, and compare stimuli with previously stored information. It is as if he projects an image of the external world (already distorted because of receptive defect) onto his "internal screen," but is not allowed sufficient time to view it. One of the important reasons for this appears to be that many external and internal impulses ordinarily not strong enough to reach sufficient threshold to command focal attention manage to gain supremacy over ongoing mental processes. The child is more or less "stimulus bound" in that he may perceptually respond to one aspect of the situation before appreciating the entire gestalt. Behaviorally, these difficulties are seen as impulsivity and poor judgment. The child seems not only unable to respond for an expected period of time but he also seems unable not to respond to spurious stimuli; that is, he is distractable.

Expressivity is defined as the ability to maintain an output of motor and intellectual activity until a predetermined goal is achieved. The afflicted child demonstrates the malfunction in this area by his restlessness, hyperactivity, and lack of motor and intellectual perseverance. In addition, such children often have diffuse mild abnormalities of their motor systems ("soft" signs) such as mild incoordination and abnormalities of muscle tonicity.

Emotionality is defined as the ability to exhibit appropriate emotions both in kind and degree. The hyperactive child does not usually suffer from inappropriate affect as seen with schizophrenics, but he does demonstrate abnormalities of degree. The emotions that a normal child learns to attenuate are apt to be expressed without control. This leads to emotional lability. There are often wide swings of emotional tone from frenetic, gleeful excitement to aggressive anger within brief periods of time. A ubiquitous concomitant of this emotional lability is reflected in a low tolerance for frustration.

Another common emotional phenomenon, and a highly significant one psychologically, is a relative inability of these children to form and maintain stable internal images. This complex abnormality has enormous consequences with respect to the psychological development of such children since satisfactory relations with parents and others (and even more significantly with himself!) are highly dependent on this capacity to develop permanently etched memory traces of nurturing adults. As a consequence of their inability to perform this important mental function (i.e., "cathect" internal objects), hyperactive children often have difficulty in forming deep, tender, loving relationships. Parents will often say "he doesn't seem to love us"; "he never lets us cuddle him"; etc. The consequences for both parents and child throughout the years are evident.

The early diagnosis and treatment of these children is vital. Their short attention span, hyperactivity, distractability, aggressiveness, low tolerance for frustration, impulsivity, primary emotional difficulties, and frequent perceptual motor problems not only interfere with their appraisal and integration of the world around them (including the constructive use of play and fantasy) but has many serious secondary sequelae as well. They try the patience of the most dedicated parent, antagonize teachers, and alienate peers. Conversely, the children cannot understand the hostile reception they get from the environment, especially in grammar school years. Everything they do seems to cause trouble and they soon internalize negative identities as bad children. In school, their problems preclude full use of their intelligence, and they frequently become class clowns to gain lost self-esteem. Since they are impulsive and lack judgment (or cannot apply what they may know), they appear fearless and can lead other children into dangerous antisocial activities such as fire setting. Those in the environment and indeed the children themselves are at a loss to understand or modify this behavior.

Each succeeding year they go untreated exponentially complicates the total problem. The importance of early diagnoses is further accentuated by the frequent observation that the basic primary abnormalities seem to spontaneously subside partially or totally in mid- or later adolescence leaving behind a scarred, distorted personality.

Diagnosis can be suspected in infancy by the observation of poor sleeping habits, frequent crying, irritability, and increased motor activity. Prenatal traumata are frequently but not always found. Failure to develop cerebral dominance and/or coordinated laterality (same eye-hand) is occasionally observed.

The hyperkinicity of these children becomes progressively apparent as they become more independent of their parents in the second and subsequent years. Toilet training, behavior, peer relations are all affected. Theoretically, the absence of any family or other psychological substrate for this disturbing behavior should help in the diagnosis. However, pathologic relationships are frequently present even in good families because of the intense entanglement between child and angry, guilt-ridden parents that develops as early as infancy. A history of severe excitement, even temporary psychosis, following the ingestion of a barbiturate or other sedative is highly suggestive.

A careful psychiatric and neurologic examination is in order at any age. Lab tests should include an EEG and skull films. Psychological examination in the school-aged child is helpful, particularly if a Bender Gestalt and/or the Frostig battery is employed. Not infrequently a stimulant is used to help establish a diagnosis, especially where the secondary problems mentioned above make it virtually impossible to distinguish the neurotic from the organically hyperactive child.

The etiology of this illness has been saved for the end of this discussion because it leads us into a resumption of a consideration of stimulants. Most investigators feel that the primary clinical manifestations are sequelae of an imbalance between cortical and subcortical areas. Some propose that this imbalance may be due to a maturational defect of the cortex which affects its suppressor activities, thereby leaving subcortical areas free of normal control. Others feel that the imbalance may be due to some diffuse damage to subcortical cells causing them to discharge abnormally. Finally, some consider that damage to cortical cells may be causing them to lose some of their attenuation potential.

Because of the ability of the amphetamines to increase cortical resistance to metrazol stimulation, it has been proposed that the stimulants either strengthen weak cortical control over subcortical areas or make the cortex more resistant to aberrant subcortical discharge.

2. Treatment

a. Amphetamines. The efficacy of the amphetamines (and other stimulants) in the treatment of the hyperactive child has received a degree of endorsement second only to the phenothiazines. Other salutary effects of the amphetamines have been reported, such as improvement in the behavior of delinquents in a residential setting and control of school phobias, other neurotic fears, sexual preoccupation, hypochondriasis, and even neurotic hyperactivity.

b. Methylphenidate. Methylphenidate has not been extensively reported on, but results similar to that obtained with amphetamines have been noted.

The most frequent side effects seen with the two above drugs, amphetamines and methylphenidate, are sleeplessness and weight loss. Both can often be controlled by a carefully tailored program of drug administration. Weight loss is the more serious of the two, and, in the author's experience, is less likely to occur with methylphenidate. The serious consequence of the chronic use of the drug seen with adults, namely, paranoid-like reactions, have not been reported in children below adolescent years.

Although after puberty the amphetamines and methylphenidate tend to affect hyperactive patients the same way as other patients; that is, stimulate instead of calm, the author has seen several hyperactive adolescents up to the age of 17 with histories consistent with a diagnosis of minimal cerebral dysfunction who have benefited.

c. Deanol Acetamidobenzoate. Deanol acetamidobenzonate is a postulated precursor of acetylcholine that has been advocated for the treatment of behavior disorders. The general consensus is clearly in the general direction of questioning the efficacy of this drug.

C. Antidepressants

1. Non-Monoamine Oxidase Inhibitors

a. Amitriptyline and Related Drugs. Since early 1965, amitriptyline, a drug commonly used for adult depressions, has been increasingly utilized for a variety of childhood disorders in addition to depression. These include behavior disorders, psychophysiologic disorders, school failure despite adequate intelligence, and hyperactivity. No improvement of thought disorders has been noted.

The side effects reported have been generally mild and only occasionally have necessitated cessation of either drug. There have been drowiness, tiredness, dry mouth, mydriasis, hyperhidrosis, tremulousness, weight gain, temper tantrums, and confusion.

b. Imipramine. This drug has enjoyed wide usage as an antidepressant in adult psychopharmacology and, to a lesser extent, in adolescent psychopharmacology. In recent years, the drug has proven of at least some use in the treatment of childhood enuresis, as revealed by many studies in the literature. Concurrent with its vigorous investigation as an antienuretic drug, imipramine has been the subject of a smaller number of studies to explore other treatment potentials, largely secondary to alleged tranquilizing and normalizing properties. Value has been claimed for this drug in a suspiciously large variety of symptoms, including hyperactivity, psychosomatic disorders, stammering, behavior problems, onanism, tics, trichotilomania, somnambulism, pavor nocturnus, compulsiveness, poor learning, encopresis, and depression. Unfortunately, none of the eight articles reviewed used controls. This fact leaves imipramine and its analog opipramol hydrochloride in the "usefulness as yet to be proven" category, except for enuresis in children and depression in adolescents.

There is some variation in suggested administration. The majority advise divided doses, but a single evening dose, as is often done in treating enuresis, has also been suggested. Side effects are usually not serious and only occasionally force cessation of the drug. The most common are atropine-like effects such as mydriasis, dry mouth and palpitations, vertigo, perspiration, somnambulance, and hypomania, and are not different from those reported elsewhere for adults with two uncommon exceptions, nightmares and cardiovascular collapse in preschool children on high doses.

2. Monamine Oxidase

The monamine oxidase inhibitors have been used very little in child psychopharmacology. Two reports on phenelzine demonstrated improvement for behavioral and depressive symptomology. The results concerning these and other drugs used for the treatment of adult depression make it imperative that all of the antidepressants be vigorously evaluated not only for potential antidepressive qualities but also for possible "normalizing" properties as well.

D. Antianxiety Drugs

Despite their wide usage, which is readily attested to by questioning one's colleagues, there is a paucity of studies concerning them, and just a few well-designed controlled studies. In general, they are recommended for nonpsychotic disorders where free anxiety, or its neurotic manifestations, are evident.

1. Chlordiazepoxide

Chlordiazepoxide has received endorsement for a broad range of neurotic symptomotology, including school phobias, anxiety, habit disturbances, and so forth. Although the incidence of serious side effects is low with the use of chlordiazepoxide, even this mild tranquilizer cannot be used indiscriminately and without caution. Several investigators have demonstrated a paradoxical reaction of stimulation in some children, including an increase of aggression, logorrhea, euphoria, and confusion. It has been suggested that chlordiazepoxide be used with caution or not at all in aggressive children, especially if they demonstrate so-called 14 and 6 EEG abnormality.

Otherwise, side effects are generally reported to be similar to those seen with adults and are usually of short duration. Addiction and convulsions on withdrawal have not been cited in the child literature.

The related drug diazepam, widely used and reported in the adult literature, has not, to my knowledge, been subjected to a controlled study on emotionally disturbed children.

2. Hydroxazine

Hydroxazine hydrochloride has been reported to be useful for neurotic and behavioral symptoms, but all of the studies suffer from lack of control or poor design.

3. Diphenhydramine

A few reports suggest this drug useful for the same range of symptomatology mentioned above. However, it has also been reported to be useful for hyperactive children under the age of 10. No favorable reports have appeared since 1961.

4. Meprobamate

Contrasted with the enormous adult literature concerning meprobamate, this compound has been sparsely mentioned in child and adolescent psychopharmacology. It has been recommended for mild neurotic disorders, but has not received wide endorsement. No controlled or well-designed studies could be found. Drowsiness has been noted with the drug, but as with chlordiazepoxide, withdrawal symptoms have not been reported.

E. Miscellaneous

1. LSD-25

Lysergic acid, so commonly the subject of investigation in adult and adolescent psychopharmacology, has received little attention in child psychopharmacology. The sparse attention it has received has been on small numbers of children with profound disorders such as early infantile autism and childhood schizophrenia. Some improvement has been noted in these severely, intractably ill children, although insufficient evidence exists for its use other than in an experimental investigative capacity.

2. Sedatives

Sedatives, such as the barbiturates, have no place in the treatment of the emotional disorders of children. They have no antipsychotic, antianxiety, or antidepressant qualities, and in several studies have been demonstrated to be worse than placebo.

III. Guidelines for the Administration of Psychoactive Compounds to Children

There are a few special concerns in administering drugs to children which are in addition to the suggestions mentioned elsewhere in the text. In taking a history of prior treatment, it is not uncommon, especially for psychiatrists, to find that the child has been on a variety of drugs, if not at least one representative of each group. The usual parental comment is that the drug did not help or helped for a very short time. Upon closer examination, the careful clinician will often find that the drug may have been given half-heartedly, without proper preparation, or in a homeopathic dose over too short a trial period. In addition, the parents might indicate they did not always give the medication and they were not sure that the child took the drug at school. The above composite example illustrates several important points which are in addition to adult administration. A detailed past drug history must be taken and verified by contacting the previous physicians. Parental fears, expectations, and motivation must be explored. The child's fantasies about the medication must be investigated. The parent-child relationship must be thoroughly familiar to the physician lest a distraught mother use the medication as a punishment or to put the child in a drug straitjacket. With older and more responsible children, it is often a good idea to deal directly with them after, of course, gaining the cooperation of the parents. Others who come in contact with the patient on occasion must be notified; for instance, a school teacher who might mistake a temporary drug lethargy as inattentiveness or boredom. The physician should offer the drug in a firm, encouraging manner to make the most of the increased suggestibility of children (positive placebo effect). Serious potentially harmful side effects are discussed with the parents. Nondangerous but annoying side effects are not usually discussed, but the parent or the child is advised to call if anything unusual at all occurs. The initial dose should be low.

In my experience, a dosage calculated on a weight basis for adults usually will be just below the minimum therapeutic level for children and is a good starting point. (As previously mentioned, the only exception might be the stimulating phenothiazines.) The parents and the child must be cautioned that this starting dose may not be effective because of the low drug levels. The low dose permits one to deal with side effects one at a time as they appear with gradually increasing dosages. Though children generally do not experience as severe side effects as adults, they do not have the emotional tolerance of adults and will resist the medication if made too uncomfortable. Further, a low starting dose conveys to the parent that the physician is cautious.

Dosages should be adjusted so as to minimally interefere with school. If a schedule can be worked out to avoid the noon dosage, this is desirable because children often forget to take the drug and will not admit to it. Occasionally, a dosage found to be adequate for school days will be an overdose on the weekends or on a vacation when stresses may be lower.

Above all, the physician must keep in close contact with the parents. When starting medications, adjusting dosages, and conducting trials of drugs, contact with the family no less than every third day either by phone or in person is recommended. This regimen gives increased assurance that the drug is being given in the prescribed manner and keeps motivation high. Beyond the above special considerations, all those listed elsewhere for adults should be observed.

IV. Summary and Recommendations

Although the emotional ills of children are treated with drugs at a frequency which probably approaches that for adults, relatively few studies have been published on child psychopharmacology. A small fraction of these papers report studies that were well controlled. The clinician will unfortunately have to keep this in mind when reviewing the recommendations made below based on my evaluation of the greater proportion of the world literature from 1960 to the present. Although the drugs listed here are those which seem to be the best available, the text of this report should be consulted for other drugs in the same group if the recommended medication fails.

RECOMMENDATIONS*

I. Schizophrenia
  A. With agitation or hyperactivity
    1. Chlorpromazine
    2. Thioridazine (less than 1200 mg)
  B. Withdrawn (including autistic states)
    1. Trifluoperazine
    2. Thioridazine
    3. Perphenazine (not reported on but effective with adults and worth a trial)

II. Organicity
  A. With severe hyperactivity (obvious organicity; chronic brain syndrome)
    1. Chlorpromazine
    2. Thioridazine
  B. With mild to moderate hyperactitivy (organicity not marked; so-called hyperkinetic child)
    1. Dextroamphetamine
    2. Methylphenidate
    3. Diphenhydramine (under 10 years)
    4. Chlorpromazine or Thioridazine
  C. With severe withdrawal
    1. Thrifluoperazine
    2. Thioridazine
    3. Perphenazine
  D. With minimal to moderate withdrawal
    1. Trifluoperazine
    2. Thioridazine
    3. Perphenazine

III. Nonorganic†
  A. Neurotic
    1. Chlordiazepoxide
    2. Hydroxazine
    3. Meprobamate
  B. Behavior problems and hyperactivity related to anxiety
    1. Chlordiazepoxide
    2. Hydroxazine
    3. Chlorpromazine or Thioridazine

It should be noted that drugs in general are recommended for use as an adjunctive measure subordinate to some other treatment program involving parents, physicians, teachers, ward personnel, and so forth. Although this or similar comments have been made frequently and is the best advice available, it should be noted that no paper appeared that systematically attempted to test this hypothesis.

For references and further reading see Appendices 1 and 2.

* These recommendations for drug treatment are made in order of preference. The recommendations take into account effectiveness, side effects, safety, and the nature of the illness.

† Nondrug approach (psychotherapy, family therapy, collaborative therapy, etc.) treatment of choice especially with neurotic children.

55

PSYCHOPHARMACOLOGY IN GERIATRICS

Kenneth Lifshitz and Nathan S. Kline

I. Introduction

Medical science is enabling an increasing percentage of individuals to avoid an early death. However, there has been only miniscule progress made in the retardation of aging and in healing of the degenerative diseases of the aged. The result of this is an enlarging population of the aged with their particular difficulties, some of which most appropriately become the problem of the psychiatrist. If we consider the geriatric population as those individuals over 65 years of age, then it consists of about 18-million persons (about 9% of the population).* Since 21% of all first admissions to state and county mental hospitals are over 65 years of age, there is a disproportionate amount of serious mental illness in these individuals. The usual psychiatric diagnostic group of these elderly patients is that of acute and/or chronic brain syndrome, due to cerebral arteriosclerosis or other circulatory disturbances, or senile brain disease. These diagnostic groups accounted for 20% of all first admissions to public mental hospitals in 1963. The schizophrenics are the only other diagnostic category, accounting for a similarly high percentage of first admission.

* In the United States.

All too frequently an attitude of hopelessness is adopted by the psychiatrist dealing with the elderly patient. This is clearly unwarranted in the case of the nonhospitalized patient. In private practice the remission rate for this type of patient is about 55%. For patients seen initially in a psychiatric clinic, 37% recovered or were sharply improved, with an additional 10% showing slight improvement (366). Even with severely impaired hospitalized patients, proper care can greatly diminish human discomfort and decrease the more onerous nursing requirements.

II. Organic Pathology

In a study conducted by Epstein and Simon (367) a thorough evaluation was made of 534 persons over 60 years of age who were admitted to a psychiatric screening ward of a metropolitan general hospital for the first time. In this group of patients the diagnostic categorization showed: 28% with chronic brain syndrome, 13% with acute brain syndrome, 33% with mixed (acute and chronic) brain syndrome, and 8% with chronic brain syndrome due to alcohol. The etiologic cause of most chronic brain syndrome is cerebral arteriosclerosis or senile brain disease; however, it is generally impossible to accurately evaluate the relative contribution of these factors on a premortum basis. The necessity for a total evaluation of the patient is emphasized by the finding that 80% of these patients had other physical impairments of either a moderate or severe nature. The following physical illnesses were found in descending order of frequency: malnutrition, congestive heart failure, stroke, severe respiratory infection, peripheral neuritis, cancer, cirrhosis, and diabetes. Straker (366), in an analysis of 100 psychiatric outpatients over the age of 60, found that only 24% had no clinically significant organic disease.

Since the physical state is a major factor in these patients, the psychiatrists' medical training is of particular importance in the psychiatric therapy of the elderly. These patients commonly have a borderline ability to maintain oxygenation of the brain, and thus the resolution of congestive failure or a respiratory infection can yield dramatic improvement of a brain syndrome. Improving the patient's nutritional status, including the maintenance utilization of vitamins, may also yield some improvement, though not generally of a dramatic nature.

Because cerebral arteriosclerosis is the most common cause of brain syndrome, the question frequently arises: Is there a possibility of effectively treating this condition? Pharmaceutical houses advertise substances said to be cerebral vasodilators and which are claimed to be of value in the treatment of cerebral arteriosclerosis. Most of these substances are not specific cerebral vasodilators and may even be detrimental in that they may shunt blood to less critical areas of the body. Even known potent cerebral vasodilators such as carbon dioxide do not appear to be beneficial in cerebral arteriosclerosis. Since the blood vessels and tissue in an ischemic area of the brain are subjected to elevated carbon dioxide tension, anoxia, and ionic alterations, they are probably already maximally dilated. An effective specific cerebral vasodilator may result in shunting of blood, even within the brain itself, to areas less in need. It is possible that cerebral vasodilators may be of use in a few selected patients who appear to have vasospastic phenomena as the underlying pathology. Neurological consultation is desirable since surgery may be indicated in selected patients with extracerebral atherosclerotic lesions which interfere with blood flow to the brain. Anticoagulant therapy may also be evaluated, though at present the possible benefits do not generally seem to warrant the difficulties and risks involved. Hypertension should be cautiously controlled, particularly since it appears to predispose to stroke; however, lowering of the blood pressure should not be taken to the point where increased difficulties arise because of a decrease in cerebral blood perfusion. In cases of hypotension an attempt should be made to elevate the blood pressure.

At the present time there is no direct therapy for senile brain disease. Claims have been made that mental activity and interest in the environment slows the progression of senile changes.

III. Psychodynamic Considerations

With the generally failing ego capabilities of the aged, there is a concomitant loss of facility in handling psychological stress. Things are made worse by the realistic recognition that functional capacity is diminished or threatened. This commonly leads to both conscious and unconscious feelings of insecurity, and an increase in hypochondriasis. There is a resultant narcissistic preoccupation, and frequently depression results from the perceived loss of self as well as from external object loss. Defenses may be increasingly ineffective unless there is an associated increase in divorcement from reality.

The psychodynamic factors in the intellectual and emotional malfunctioning of the elderly must always be kept in mind, for they are of considerable importance in determining the degree of potential response to medical ministrations. This is true even in those persons with cerebral damage. The importance of dynamic factors can be appreciated if thought is given to what might happen to a younger person, who has the advantage of normal cerebral function, if he were subjected to the same emotional stresses as are many of the aged. Under such circumstances, no one would be surprised if a younger person had a severe emotional reaction to such occurrences as: seeing loved ones and close associates die; an awareness of approaching death; recognition that many life-long goals are forever unattainable; and, in addition, some degree of physical incapacitation due to one or a combination of chronic diseases.

Despite the fact that it has been frequently demonstrated that many elderly patients respond to individual psychotherapy, group psychotherapy, and milieu therapy, use of these techniques in the geriatric population is commonly ignored. To some extent this is probably due to the personal threat experienced by many psychiatrists who are called upon to treat this population. It is important that the psychiatrist examine and attempt to deal with his own discomforts which arise when treating elderly patients. With or without drug treatment, a therapist who is interested and reassuring will greatly enhance the probability of a favorable patient response. The invalidity of a nihilist viewpoint in regard to psychotherapy is indicated by the report of Wolff (368) on the controlled group therapy of geriatric, psychiatric inpatients. In over 200 patients treated with group therapy 90% showed some improvement and 40% were able to make adjustments outside of the hospital after 1 year of therapy. Of a comparable group not receiving group therapy, only 15% could be released from the hospital.

Geriatric patients, more commonly than others, expect to receive a medication to ease their discomfort. When there is no indication for a specific psychopharmaceutical, medications with minimal side effects, such as a sodium glutamate preparation or pentylenetetrazol, may be prescribed. These are preferable to placebos since the physician may have some legitimate expectation of benefit, and the pharmacist who fills the prescription may also communicate a hopeful expectation to the patient or his family.

IV. Psychopharmaceuticals

The physiological and pathological changes which occur with aging accentuate the degree of variability found between individuals in their sensitivity to drug effects. Commonly, the side and toxic effects of a particular dose increase while the primary, or desired effect, remains the same or decreases. Briefly, changes which lead to this effect in the aged include: alterations in the absorption and elimination of medications, tissue distribution changes, tissue sensitivity alterations due to pathological changes, and a general loss of homeostatic ability. More detailed information may be found in the symposium reports edited by Freeman (369) and the review of Bender (370). Because of these factors, greater caution must be exercised in utilizing psychopharmaceuticals in the elderly than in the younger individual. Dosages should in general be started lower by about one-half than in the younger adult, and the dose level should be built up more gradually. Side effects that in a younger individual might result in a minor postural hypotension or constipation, in the elderly can result in a cerebral vascular accident or an acute intestinal obstruction.

Because of the elderly individual's generally reduced cerebral reserve, centrally active pharmaceuticals may accentuate or initiate the clinical picture of brain syndrome. This may insidiously build up when the rate of excretion of the substance drops below the rate of intake. Perhaps the commonest clinical example of this is seen in the elderly individual for whom phenobarbital has been prescribed because of minor anxiety, psychosomatic difficulty, or insomnia. The patient may have been taking the medication for months or years when he begins to show the picture of a gradually progressing chronic brain syndrome. This situation will be made worse by adding further psychopharmaceuticals; however, discontinuing the phenobarbital (or other centrally active medication) can yield appreciable improvement in the "chronic brain syndrome."

In this chapter we shall not repeat the detailed characterization of the various psychopharmaceuticals which can be found in other chapters. We will limit our comments to those aspects which have particular applicability to the elderly or to instances where there is specific knowledge in relation to the geriatric patient.

A. *Antipsychotics*

1. Rauwolfia Alkaloids

Although these alkaloids are antipsychotic to some extent, they are not as effective as the phenothiazines and other substances for this purpose. They are useful in the elderly for symptoms of anxiety, agitation, and inappropriate aggressiveness, but since the dosage range which can be used without definite side effects is narrow and there is a time lag of about two weeks before medication effect can be clearly seen, other medications are more commonly used. *They are of value when it is desirable to also lower the patient's blood pressure or pulse rate.* The difficulties encountered in the use of rauwolfia alkaloids include: depressive reactions, increased gastrointestinal motility, increased gastric hydrochloric acid, diarrhea (these gastrointestinal effects contraindicate use in the presence of peptic ulcer and ulcerative colitis), lowering of the convulsive threshold (the danger of ECT is increased; current and duration of application should be decreased), dangers of hypotensive effects, nausea, headache, nasal stuffiness, weight gain, fatigue, weakness, dizziness, exacerbation of asthma, dermatoses, and parkinsonism. Caution is indicated when used with digitalis, quinidine, guanethidine, or CNS depressants.

The commonly available rauwolfia alkaloids and their usual therapeutic range in the elderly are: alseroxylon fraction, 1–6 mg *o.d.* (= per day); deserpidine, 0.1–3 mg *o.d.;* reserpine, 0.1–3 mg *o.d.;* whole-root extracts, 50–300 mg *o.d.* There appears to be no particular advantage to any of the preparations, and so the cheaply available reserpine can be reasonably used.

2. Phenothiazines

The antipsychotic phenothiazines currently available for general use in the United States include: promazine, chlorpromazine, thioridazine, acetophenazine, triflupromazine, prochlorperazine, perphenazine, trifluoperazine, and fluphenazine. The listing is in order of increasing antipsychotic activity for an equal weight of drug. The order is approximately the same for increasing extrapyramidal system side effects at an equivalent therapeutic level. The long-acting, parenteral form of fluphenazine, fluphenazine enanthate, probably has the highest incidence of extrapyramidal system side effects. The question of extrapyramidal system side effects takes on particular importance in the elderly. Thus, in a study by Ayd (371) of a large number of patients it was found that this side effect occurred in approximately 50% of patients on phenothiazines in the 60- to 80-year age group. The extrapyramidal reaction most common in the over-50 age group was parkinsonism; this corresponds to the incidence of naturally occurring parkinsonism. Akathisia is the next most frequent extrapyramidal manifestation in this group. Early dyskinesias are rare. About 90% of the parkinson reactions occur by the end of 10 weeks of treatment. The same is true for patients with akathisia. The dyskinisias have a different onset, 90% occurring in the first four-and-one-half days of treatment. There have been occasional reports of extrapyramidal reactions persisting in elderly patients after discontinuance of the phenothiazine agent. However, in most instances this side effect is easily handled by reassurance, use of an anti-parkinsonism drug and/or reduction of dosage. Some patients who have been on phenothiazines for extended periods develop a dyskinesia which tends to involve principally the oral region. This "tardive" dyskinesia generally occurs after more than two years on medication and seems to have a higher incidence in the elderly. It is nonresponsive or poorly responsive to the usual anti-parkinsonian drugs, reduction of dosage or discontinuance of the phenothiazine may be necessary in order to eliminate the dyskinesia. It may take up to 6 months for the symptoms to disappear. In a few patients the symptom may persist, an occurrence apparently most frequent in elderly brain-damaged females.

Extrapyramidal side effects are of particular importance because of the possibility of misinterpreting them as an indication of a worsening of the patient's condition. For example, akathisia may be interpreted by both the patient and physician as an increase in agitation. The immobile facies of parkinsonism could be interpreted incorrectly as depression.

Other untoward side effects of particular consequence in the elderly are the hypotensive effects, and the parasympatholytic effects on the gastrointestinal system, genitourinary system, and the eye. Significant hypotensive difficulties may require a reduction in medication. Any question of increased intraocular tension, an event more common in the elderly, should be carefully evaluated. Queries should be made about constipation and action taken before fecal impaction results. In male patients the question of urinary retention should be borne in mind.

At the present time the phenothiazine of first choice in the geriatric patient appears to be thioridazine. For an equivalently effective dose, the incidence of extrapyramidal reactions is lower than with other phenothiazines. There is also some evidence that "dizziness" and falling are less common with thioridazine. In long-standing diabetes insulin requirements have been found to fluctuate as thioridazine therapy affects the degree of agitation. The incidence of nonspecific electrocardiographic abnormalities associated with phenothiazine-like drugs is disproportionately high for thioridazine; however, the effect is reversible and does not seem to be of pathological significance. Depending on the clinical state of the patient, dosage may be started as low as 10 mg twice a day and can commonly be taken to 100 mg three times a day without significant side effects. As an alternative, if psychotic symptomatology does not respond, or if difficulty is encountered with side effects such as sleepiness, perphenazine is a useful phenothiazine. It is clearly less hypnotic than thioridazine, but with less extrapyramidal difficulties than trifluoperazine or fluphenazine. The usual dosage would range from 2 mg twice a day to 8 mg three times a day. It is sometimes useful to combine these two phenothiazines so that the thioridazine is given at night, when hypnosis is desired, and the perphenazine is given in the morning.

3. Other Antipsychotics

Chlorprothixine is a nonphenothiazine, very similar in structure and potency to chlorpromazine. Thiothixene is another close relative of the phenothiazines. The principal question which arises here is: If a psychotic patient has failed to respond to a particular phenothiazine, is there a greater chance that he will respond if switched to a nonphenothiazine antipsychotic drug than if switched to another phenothiazine? To our knowledge this question has not, as yet, been answered.

Haloperidol is the first representative of the butyrophenones to be marketed in the United States. It appears to be equivalent to the more active phenothiazines in antipsychotic activity. Because of the high incidence of extrapyramidal reactions associated with its use, it would not seem to be particularly useful with geriatric patients.

B. Antianxiety Agents and Hypnotics

There are a very large number of substances which have been used as antianxiety agents (sedatives, minor tranquilizers) and as hypnotics (sleep-producing) agents. Most are to some extent interchangeable in that antianxiety agents are usually also hypnotic and hypnotics are also usually antianxiety agents. The rauwolfia alkaloids, some of the phenothiazines, and phenothiazine-related compounds also have an antianxiety effect and are frequently used for this purpose in lower than antipsychotic doses.

In popular use in the United States as antianxiety agents and having evidenced some value in the geriatric patients are: chlordiazepoxide, diazepam, oxazepam, meprobamate, tybamate, hydroxyzine, and ethanol (beer, wine, whiskey, etc.).

Anxiety is an extremely common symptom of the elderly. It is a concomitant of many of the real threats which exist and also occurs with the magnification of these threats, as in hypochondriasis. Agitation can be considered, to an appreciable extent, the motor expression of anxiety and frequently contains an element of hostile aggressiveness. Chronic anxiety also commonly contributes to depression, insomnia, and behavioral reactions. Anxiety may also intensify or accelerate many of the physical diseases present in the elderly. Therefore, if we can effectively decrease the intensity of anxiety, the effects can be globally beneficial. The most common use of psychopharmaceuticals in the elderly is as antianxiety agents.

All of the above-listed substances have been reported of value in geriatric patients over the past few years. The benzodiazepine derivatives (chlordiazepoxide, diazepam, oxazepam) all appear to be similar in use and activity. The usual initial geriatric dose of chlordiazepoxide is 5–10 mg three times a day and a high dose would be 20 mg four times a day. The equivalent dose of diazepam is perhaps slightly lower and that of oxazepam slightly higher. Meprobamate has a dosage range in the elderly ranging from about 200 mg three times a day to a maximum of 800 mg four times a day. We have found meprobamate of particular usefulness when "P.R.N." medication is prescribed, as the onset of effect of the medication can be more readily perceived by the patient (perhaps because of a more marked hypnotic effect) than is the case with many of the other antianxiety agents. Long-term use and intermittent use also appears to be relatively safe with a very low incidence of serious side or toxic effects. Meprobamate can frequently also be used as a mild nighttime hypnotic with little morning hangover. If a longer duration of action is desired, slowly absorbed forms are available. Meprobamate is relatively cheap since generically labeled preparations are available. Tybamate is used in an initial dose of about 250 mg three times a day and ranges to about 350 mg four times a day. Several recent "blind" investigations have found it useful as an antianxiety agent in elderly patients with a relatively low incidence of hypnosis; it may have a particularly short duration of action. Hydroxyzine may be classified with the antihistamines, the usual starting dose is about 25 mg three times a day ranging up to about 100 mg four times a day. It is relatively safe to use with a low incidence of side effects and has been used in geriatric patients with some success. It is worthwhile noting that it has been reported to benefit patients with intermittent claudication. Diazepam appears least likely to produce dependency. Tolerance may develop for any of these drugs, and rather than increase of dosage, it is often more desirable to switch to an alternate medication.

A very old antianxiety agent is ethanol (ethyl alcohol). It has the advantage of being familiar to the patient. In controlled doses it is effective, pleasant, and safe (in the absence of genitourinary or liver disease). Gastrointestinal irritation is reduced if it is taken in a relatively dilute form, such as beer or wine. The average dose would be about 12 oz of beer or 5 oz of wine two to three times daily. It can also be useful in the evening as a mild hypnotic. In a noncontrolled environment there is the danger of overmedication, perhaps because of the familiarity of patients with this substance. In a hospital environment ethanol may be of additional use in promoting socialization of patients at some such event as a daily beer hour.

Among the newer nonbarbiturate hypnotics commonly utilized in the United States are: ethchlorvynol, ethinamate, glutethimide, and methaqualone. Also in popular use are numerous barbiturates and chloral hydrate. All hypnotics, and in particular those with a longer duration of action, should be used in the elderly only with caution. There exists in particular the danger of producing a confusional state with increased anxiety, agitation, and aggressiveness. Doses should be small and should not be used daily. If chronic insomnia is a problem, it is preferable to first use appropriate continuous medication with an antianxiety agent in an effort to correct the problem and then, if necessary, a hypnotic. Most, or perhaps all, of the antianxiety agents (not including low doses of the antipsychotics) may result in addiction if misused; therefore, in prescriptions the permissible frequency of refilling should be indicated.

C. *Antidepressants*

Depression is the most common of all psychiatric symptoms. The incidence of this difficulty becomes particularly high in the aged. The typical psychiatric depressions are usually divided into: (1) primary (endogenous), and (2) secondary (reactive) depression. Primary depressions can be either single episodes or part of a pattern of a manic-depressive cycle. Some drugs and probably some viral infections may cause depressions. If a reactive depression is of appropriate dimensions and in response to a real situation, it is generally not treated with antidepressants; however, antianxiety agents may be of some use in some of these situations. In the elderly, the commonest early overt symptom of depression is hypochondriasis. At times the depression may be so severe as to be mistaken for arteriosclerotic or senile regression. If in doubt, a therapeutic trial of an antidepressant is indicated.

The antidepressant drugs entail in the elderly a higher risk of serious side effects than any of the other categories of psychopharmaceuticals. The toxic effects of these substances (discussed elsewhere) occur with a higher incidence in the elderly. Serious difficulties, e.g., cardiovascular deaths, agranulocytosis, and paralytic ileus requiring surgery, have been mainly in the elderly. It is thus important to be on the alert for such symptoms as syncope, tachycardia, edema, sores in the mouth or throat, constipation, and urinary retention. However, it is only in a very small number of patients that serious difficulty arises, and in view of the fact that the antidepressants have been shown in several instances to be as effective as electrical convulsive therapy, there remains many occasions when their use is warranted.

The commonly available monoamine oxidase inhibitors in the United States are: isocarboxazid, nialamide, phenelzine, and tranylcypromine. The commonly available tricyclic antidepressants are: amitriptyline, desipramine, imipramine, nortriptyline, and protriptyline.

It is inadvisable to use MAO inhibitors as the antidepressant of first choice in the elderly, since the risks associated with their use is greater than with the tricyclics and they do not appear to be any more effective. Aside from the dietary problems [re: tyramine (which rules out liver—chopped chicken liver included—aged cheeses, pickled herring, yeast, and wines)], individuals in this population are frequently taking other medications which may adversely interact with the MAO inhibitor. Potentially adverse reactions include those with rauwolfia alkaloids, tricyclic antidepressants, barbiturates, anesthetics, narcotics, amphetamines, alcohol, anticholinergic agents, diuretics, and vasoconstrictors (including those available in over-the-counter cold medications).

In terms of the elderly there is more information indicating effectiveness for amitriptyline and imipramine than for the other tricyclics. This may merely be because they are available longer. In the use of these substances it is advisable, unless there is reason for urgency, to start dosage low and build up in gradual increments. Thus, a usual dose for the tricyclics, except for protriptyline, would be 25 mg twice a day to start and, if no difficulty or clear improvement occurs in a week, increase to 25 mg three times a day for two weeks. Further increases, of 25 mg per day, might be at 2-week intervals to a maximum of 150–200 mg per day. Protriptyline is the most recently marketed antidepressant, its dosage is different from the above—about 5 mg three times a day to start, with a maximum of 10 mg three times a day. It is contraindicated in the presence of agitation or anxiety.

D. Psychomotor (CNS) Stimulants

There are many different substances which can be included in this grouping, and it may be that some substances whose mode of action is presently obscure (e.g., procaine) may be appropriately in this group. Caffeine, which is in common use, falls into this grouping. Among the more commonly used substances whose use has been reported in geriatric patients are amphetamine, *d*-amphetamine, methamphetamine, methylphenidate, pipradol, ethamivan, and pentylenetetrazol. In general these substances seem to have little usefulness. Effects of these substances tend to be transient, and though activity levels are increased, there appears to be little benefit in the senile confusional difficulties. A possible exception to this is pentylenetetrazol, which some investigators have found to be of use, while others have found to have no effects. In any event this appears to be a safe substance with only minor side effects, though it possibly lowers the convulsive threshold. The usual dosage is 100–200 mg three times a day.

E. Rejuvenants and Miscellaneous Substances

Many different substances have been utilized in an effort to slow down, halt, or reverse the progressive deterioration which occurs with time in the adult human organism. It is clear that no matter what form therapy takes in the treatment of diseases which are concomitants of aging, the battle will eventually be lost unless there is some means of directly altering the aging process, and not until this process is completely halted can an actual victory be achieved. Historically, efforts have been made to counteract aging by such things as "royal jelly," embryo preparations, "antireticular cytotoxic serum," yoghurt, monkey testicular implants, hormone preparations, and vitamins. It seems clear that none of these substances have exerted an *appreciable* effect since even a few subjects of such therapy living past the age of 100 years would have attracted sufficient attention to result in further evaluation.

The problems of evaluating possible smaller effects are considerable. The most recent substance to attract general attention has been procaine. In general the treatment consists of a 5-cc intramuscular injection of 2% procaine solution, once per day, three times per week, either continuously or with intervening rest periods every 4 weeks or so. There is some evidence that this form of treatment may be of value in improving the mental and physical status of the geriatric patient. Only minimal risk is taken if patients are first skin tested for sensitivity to procaine. However, any effect which exists is not marked, and the reason for the effect is not clear. Procaine or its metabolic products may exert a stimulant effect, and procaine has on at least one occasion been called a monoamine oxidase inhibitor. It is possible that this type of "stimulant" action may be responsible for the effects of procaine.

At various times different hormones or hormone combinations have been said to have a general rejuvenating effect; particularly popular have been the use of estrogenic substances in elderly females, androgenic substances in elderly males, and combinations of low dosages of each in males and females. There is no solid evidence that these substances are generally of value. It is clear that in certain individuals specific hormonal abnormalities, especially of thyroid and adrenal cortical hormones, may cause mental difficulties. However, these individuals must be separately identified, and the appropriate therapeutic measures taken on the basis of the particular case.

A number of pharmaceuticals have been directed at the central nervous system in an effort to rejuvenate or improve age related functional losses. One in current common usage is monosodium L-glutamate usually in combination with B vitamins and ferrous sulfate (L-Glutavite). The original rationale for the use of this substance—penetration into the brain, where it is utilized to remove toxic substances or as a substrate—appears to be in error since there seems to be no consistent elevation of glutamate blood level when it is taken orally, and it is doubtful if it passes the blood-brain barrier. However, it is safe to use, and there are some reports, of what appear to be reasonable experiments, which show some benefit. The usual dosage is one teaspoon or packet three times a day in tomato juice or soup. It is possible that any beneficial effect is due to an adrenergic effect or raising the blood glycogen level.

Recently, there have been a large number of investigations pertaining to the possible role of ribonucleic acid (RNA) in the storage of memories in the central nervous system. Cameron and co-workers reported that yeast RNA administered intravenously (with some difficulty due to systemic reactions) and orally to chronic brain syndrome patients led to an improvement of memory function. This result has been disputed by others. Additionally, there are a large number of animal experiments which suggest that RNA may play a role in memory and learning. These findings have led to the study of drugs which may stimulate the formation of brain RNA. Pemoline and magnesium hydroxide and tricyanoaminopropene are two such substances. Their status still remains vague; however, it is our impression that preliminary studies do not indicate any appreciable benefit.

For further references see Appendix 2.

MASTER BIBLIOGRAPHY*

1. Lindemann, E. (1932). *Am. J. Psychiat.* **88,** 1083.
2. Sakel, M. (1933). *Z. Ges. Neurol. Psychiat.* **143,** 506.
3. von Meduna, L. (1935). *Psychiat.-Neurol. Wochschr.* **37,** 317.
4. Delay, J. *et al.* (1952a). *Ann. Médico-Psychol.* **110,** No. 2, 112.
5. Selling, L. E. (1955). *J. Am. Med. Assoc.* **157,** 1594.
6. Kuhn, R. (1957). *Schweiz. Med. Wochschr.* **87,** 1135.
7. Brill, H., and Patton, R. E. (1962). *Am. J. Psychiat.* **119,** 20.
8. Berger, F. M. (1967). *Am. Scientist* **55,** 67.
9. Macht, D. I. *et al.* (1920). *J. Pharmacol. Exptl. Therap.* **15,** 149.
10. Feldman, P. T. (1965). *Bull. Menninger Clin.* **29,** 256.
11. Lewin, L. (1885). *Berlin Klin. Wochschr.* **22,** 321.
12. Guiraud, P., and David, C. (1950). *Compt. Rend. Congr. Alien.* **48,** 599.
13. Laborit, H. (1949). *Acta Chir. Belg.* **48,** 485.
14. Laborit, H. (1950). *Acta Chir. Belg.* **49,** 390.
15. Laborit, H. (1950). *Anésthesie Analgésie* **7,** 299.
16. Laborit, H. (1950). *Semaine Hôp. Paris* **26,** 3646.
17. Charpentier, P. *et al.* (1952). *Compt. Rend.* **235,** 59.
18. Laborit, H. *et al.* (1952). *Presse Méd.* **60,** 206.
19. Snezhnevsky, A. V. (1965). *Intern. J. Psychiat.* **1,** 219.
20. Hamon, J. *et al.* (1952). *Ann. Médico-Psychol.* **110,** No. 1, 331.
21. Delay, J. *et al.* (1952). *Ann. Médico-Psychol.* **110,** No. 2, 267.
22. Vogt, M. (1955). *Pharmacol. Rev.* **6,** 33.
23. Verney, E. B. (1947). *Proc. Roy. Soc.* **B135,** 25.
24. Karczmar, A. G. (1967). *Physiol. Pharmacol.* **3,** 163.
25. Karczmar, A. G. (ed.) (1969). *Federation Proc.* (Symp.) **28,** 89 and 147.
25a. Koketsu, K., and Nishi, S. (1968). Unpublished data.
26. Marczynski, T. J. (1967). *Ergeb. Physiol., Biol. Chem. Exptl. Pharmakol.* **59,** 86ff.
27. Koelle, G. B. (1963). *Handbuch Exptl. Pharmakol.* **15,** Springer, Berlin.
28. Shute, C. C. D., and Lewis, P. R. (1966). *Brit. Med. Bull.* **22,** 221.
29. Eccles, J. C. (1964). "The Physiology of Synapses." Springer, Berlin.
29a. Kim, K. C., and Karczmar, A. G. (1968). Unpublished data.
30. Dahlström, A., and Fuxe, K. (1964). *Acta Physiol. Scand.* **62,** Suppl. 232, 1.
31. Larramendi, L. M. H. *et al.* (1967). *Science* **156,** 967.
32. Gray, E. G., and Guillery, R. W. (1966). *Intern. Rev. Cytol.* **19,** 111.

* Numbered in-text references are listed in this section in numerical order.

33. Bloom, F. E., and Aghajanian, G. K. (1966). *Science* **154,** 1575.
34. Aghajanian, G. K., and Bloom, F. E. (1967). *Brain Res.* **6,** 716.
35. Whittaker, V. P. (1965). *Progr. Biophys. Mol. Biol.* **15,** 39.
36. De Robertis, E. (1966). *Pharmacol. Rev.* **18,** 413.
37. Wolfe, D. E. *et al.* (1962). *Science* **138,** 440.
38. Aghajanian, G. K., and Bloom, F. E. (1967). *J. Pharmacol. Exptl. Therap.* **156,** 23.
39. Aghajanian, G. K., and Bloom, F. E. (1967). *J. Pharmacol. Exptl. Therap.* **156,** 407.
40. Glowinski, J., and Baldessarini, R. J. (1966). *Pharmacol. Rev.* **18,** 1201.
41. Hökfelt, T. (1967). *Z. Zellforsch. Mikroskop. Anat.* **79,** 110.
42. De Robertis, E. (1967). *Science* **156,** 907.
43. Shute, C. C. D., and Lewis, P. R. (1966). *Z. Zellforsch. Mikroskop. Anat.* **69,** 334.
44. Bloom, F. E., and Barrnett, R. J. (1967). *Ann. N.Y. Acad. Sci.* **144,** 626.
45. McGeer, P. L. *et al.* (1965). *Life Sci.* **4,** 1859.
46. Udenfriend, S. (1966). *Pharmacol. Rev.* **18,** 43.
47. Davis, J. M. *et al.* (1967). *Pharmacologist* **9,** 184.
48. Hosie, R. (1965). *Biochem. J.* **96,** 404.
49. Torack, R. M., and Barrnett, R. J. (1963). *J. Histochem. Cytochem.* **11,** 763.
50. Paton, W. D. M. (1960). *Proc Roy. Soc. Med.* **53,** 815.
51. Carlsson, A. *et al.* (1965). *J. Pharm. Pharmacol.* **17,** 521.
52. Kretschmer, E. (1936). "Physique and Character," 2nd rev. ed. Miller, London.
53. Slater, E. (1938). *Z. Ges. Neurol. Psychiat.* **163,** 1.
54. Eiduson, S. *et al.* (1964). "Biochemistry and Behavior." Van Nostrand, Princeton, New Jersey.
55. Waal, H. J. (1967). *Brit. Med. J.* **II,** 50.
56. Bliss, E. L., and Zwaniger, J. (1966). *J. Psychiat. Res.* **4,** 189.
57. Shaw, D. M. (1966). *Brit. Med. J.* **II,** 262.
58. Dencker, S. J. *et al.* (1967). *Acta Physiol. Scand.* **69,** 140.
59. McAnderson, W., and Dawson, J. (1963). *Brit. J. Psychiat.* **109,** 225.
60. Coppen, A. (1965). *Brit. J. Psychiat.* **111,** 1133.
61. Schanberg, S. M. *et al.* (1967). *Biochem. Pharmacol.* **16,** 393.
62. Pryce, I. G. (1958). *J. Mental Sci.* **104,** 421 and 1079.
63. Hoffer, A. *et al.* (1954). *J. Mental Sci.* **100,** 29.
64. Axelrod, J., and Tomchick, R. (1958). *J. Biol. Chem.* **233,** 702.
65. Pollin, W. *et al.* (1961). *Science* **133,** 104.
66. Hoffer, A. *et al.* (1957). *J. Clin. Exptl. Psychopathol. and Quart. Rev. Psychiat. Neurol.* **18,** 181.
67. Haavaldsen, R. *et al.* (1958). *Confinia Neurol.* **18,** 270.
68. Heath, R. G., and Krupp. I. M. (1967). *Arch. Gen. Psychiat.* **16,** 1.
69. Heath, R. G., and Krupp, I. M. (1967). *Am. J. Psychiat.* **123,** 1499.
70. Heath, R. G., and Krupp. I. M. (1968). *Am. J. Psychiat.* **124,** 1019.

70a. Milhailovic, L., and Janekovic, B. D. (1965). *Neurosci. Res. Program Bull.* **3,** 8.

71. Winter, C. A., and Flataker, L. (1958). *Arch. Neurol.* **80,** 441.
72. Bergen, J. R. (1963). *J. Chem. Educ.* **41,** 168.
73. Frohman, C. E. *et al.* (1960). *Am. J. Psychiat.* **117,** 401.

73a. Ryan, J. W. *et al.* (1966). *Science* **171,** 1408.

73b. Ryan, J. W. *et al.* (1968). *J. Psychiat. Res.* **6,** 33.

73c. Kety, S. S. (1967). *New Engl. J. Med.* **276,** 325.

74. Krasnova, A. I. (1965). *Zh. Nevropatol. i Psikhiat.* **65,** 1206.
75. Bergen, J. R. *et al.* (1968). *Arch. Gen. Psychiat.* **18,** 471.
76. Frohman, C. E. (1968). *In* "Mind as a Tissue" (C. Rupp, ed.), p. 181. Harper (Hoeber), New York.
77. Gottlieb, J. S. (1967). *In* "Molecular Basis of Some Aspects of Mental Activity" (O. Wallaas, ed.), Vol. 2, p. 347. Academic Press, New York.
78. Sullivan, T. M. *et al.* (1967). *Am. J. Psychiat.* **123,** 947.
79. Kety, S. S. *et al.* (1958). *J. Clin. Invest.* **27,** 500.

80. McIlwain, H. (1953). *Biochem. J.* **53**, 403.
81. Ghosh, J. J., and Quastel, J. H. (1954). *Nature* **178**, 28.
82. Whittam, R., and Blond, D. M. (1964). *Biochem. J.* **92**, 147.
83. Nakazawa, S., and Quastel, J. H. (1968). *Can. J. Biochem.* **46**, 355.
84. Chance, B., and Schoener, B. (1962). *Nature* **195**, 956.
85. Chan, S. L., and Quastel, J. H. (1967). *Science* **156**, 1752.
86. Keesey, J. C. *et al.* (1965). *Biochem. J.* **95**, 289.
87. McGeer, E. G. *et al.* (1967). *Life Sci.* **6**, 2221.
88. Efron, D. H. *et al.* (eds.) (1967). "Ethnopharmacological Search for Psychoactive Drugs," U.S. Public Health Serv. Publ. No. 1645, Sup. Doc. U.S. Govt. Printing Office, Washington, D.C.
89. Schanker, L. S. (1962). *Pharmacol. Rev.* **14**, 501.
90. Hensch, C. (1968). *Proc. 3rd Intern. Pharmacol. Meeting, São Pãolo. 1966,* Vol. 7, pp. 141–168. Pergamon Press, Oxford.
91. Gill, E. W. (1965). *Progr. Med. Chem.* **4**, pp. 39–85.
92. Schlittler, E. (1966). *In* "CNS Drugs" (G. S. Sidhu *et al.,* eds.), p. 1ff. Council Ind. Res., New Delhi.
93. Jucker, F. (1963). *Angew. Chem., Intern. Engl. ed.* **2**, 493.
94. Sternbach, C. H. *et al.* (1964). *In* "Psychopharmacological Agents" (M. Gordon, ed.), Vol. 1, p. 137. Academic Press, New York.
95. Janssen, P. A. J. (1967). *In* "Psychopharmacological Agents" (M. Gordon, ed.), Vol. 2, pp. 199–248. Academic Press, New York.
96. Clare, N. T. *et al.* (1947). *Australian Vet. J.* **23**, 340 and 344.
97. Forrest, I. S., and Piette, L. H. (1962). *In* "International Congress of Neuropsychopharmacology. Proceedings of the 3rd Meeting of the Collegium Internationale Neuro-Psychopharmacologicum" (P. B. Bradley, ed.), p. 52. Elsevier, Amsterdam.
98. Forrest, F. M. *et al.* (1961). *Am. J. Psychiat.* **118**, 300.
99. Salzman, N. P., and Brodie, B. B. (1956). *J. Pharmacol. Exptl. Therap.* **118**, 46.
100. Ross, J. J. *et al.* (1958). *Science* **128**, 1279.
101. Walkenstein, S. S., and Seifter, J. (1959). *J. Pharmacol. Exptl. Therap.* **125**, 283.
102. Fishman, V., and Goldenberg, H. (1960). *Proc. Soc. Exptl. Biol. Med.* **104**, 99.
103. Goldenberg, H., and Fishman, V. (1961). *Proc. Soc. Exptl. Biol. Med.* **108**, 178.
104. Fishman, V. *et al.* (1962). *Proc. Soc. Exptl. Biol. Med.* **109**, 548.
105. Fishman, V., and Goldenberg, H. (1965). *J. Pharmacol. Exptl. Therap.* **150**, 122.
106. Johnson, D. E. *et al.* (1965). *Biochem. Pharmacol.* **14**, 1453.
107. Rodriguez, C. F., and Johnson, D. E. (1966). *Life Sci.* **5**, 1283.
108. Bolt, A. G. *et al.* (1966). *J. Pharm. Sci.* **55**, 1205.
109. Lin, T. H. *et al.* (1959). *Proc. Soc. Exptl. Biol. Med.* **102**, 602.
110. Posner, H. S. (1959). *Abstr. Am. Chem. Soc., 136th Meeting, Atlantic City,* p. 81C.
111. Beckett, A. H. *et al.* (1963). *Biochem. Pharmacol.* **12**, 779.
112. Fishman, V., and Goldenberg, H. (1963). *Proc. Soc. Exptl. Biol. Med.* **112**, 501.
113. Goldenberg, H., and Fishman, V. (1964). *Biochem. Biophys. Res. Commun.* **14**, 404.
113a. Goldenberg, H., and Fishman, V. (1964). *Proc. Soc. Exptl. Biol. Med.* **115**, 1044.
114. Coccia, P. F., and Westerfeld, W. W. (1967). *J. Pharmacol. Exptl. Therap.* **157**, 446.
115. Daly, J. W., and Manian, A. A. (1967). *Biochem. Pharmacol.* **16**, 2131.
116. Posner, H. S. *et al.* (1962). *J. Pharmacol. Exptl. Therap.* **137**, 84.
117. Manian, A. A. *et al.* (1965). *Life Sci.* **4**, 2425.
118. Bolt, A. G., and Forrest, I. S. (1967). *Proc. Western Pharmacol. Soc.* **10**, 11.
119. Perry, T. L. *et al.* (1964). *Science* **146**, 81.
120. Huang, C. L., and Ruskin, B. H. (1964). *J. Nervous Mental Disease* **139**, 381.
121. Wechsler, M. B. *et al.* (1967). *J. Psychiat. Res.* **5**, 327.
122. Curry, S. H., and Marshall, J. H. L. (1968). *Life Sci.* **7**, 9.
123. Hammar, C. G., and Holmstedt, B. (1968). *Experientia* **24**, 98.
124. Allgen, L. G. *et al.* (1963). *Acta Psychiat. Scand.* **39**, Suppl. 169, 1.
125. Huang, C. L., and Kurland, A. A. (1964). *Arch. Gen Psychiat.* **10**, 639.

126. Zehnder, K. *et al.* (1962). *Biochem. Pharmacol.* **11,** 535.
127. Eiduson, S., and Geller, E. (1963). *Biochem. Pharmacol.* **12,** 1429.
128. Allgen, L. G. *et al.* (1960). *Experientia* **16,** 325.
129. Huus, I., and Khan, A. R. (1967). *Acta Pharmacol. Toxicol.* **25,** 397.
130. Wallace, J. E. (1967). *J. Pharm. Sci.* **56,** 1437.
131. Maronde, R. F. *et al.* (1963). *J. Am. Med. Assoc.* **184,** 7.
132. Numerof, P. *et al.* (1958). *Psychiat. Res. Rept.* **9,** 139.
133. Herrmann, B. *et al.* (1959). *Med. Exptl.* **1,** 381.
134. Herrmann, B., and Pulver, R. (1960). *Arch. Intern. Pharmacodyn.* **126,** 454.
135. Herrmann, B. (1963). *Helv. Physiol. Pharmacol. Acta* **21,** 402.
136. Crammer, J. L., and Scott, B. (1966). *Psychopharmacologia* **8,** 461.
137. Christiansen, J. *et al.* (1967). *Psychopharmacologia* **11,** 255.
138. Koechlin, B. A. *et al.* (1962). *J. Pharmacol. Exptl. Therap.* **138,** 11.
139. Pöldinger, W. (1966). *Wien. Z. Nervenheilk. Grenzg.* **24,** 128.
140. Jacobson, E. (1959). *Bull. World Health Organ.* **21,** 411.
141. Usdin, E., and Efron, D. H. (1967). "Psychotropic Drugs and Related Compounds," U.S. Public Health Serv. Publ. No. 1589. U.S. Govt. Printing Office, Washington, D.C.
142. American Medical Association. (1966). "New Drugs; Evaluated by the A.M.A. Council on Drugs," 2nd ed. Am. Med. Assoc., Chicago, Illinois.
143. Miller, A. B. *et al.* (1965). "Physicians' Desk Reference to Pharmaceutical Specialities and Biologicals," 12th ed. Medical Economics, Inc., Oradell, New Jersey.
144. U.S. Pharmacopeial Convention. (1965). "Pharmacopeia of the United States of America," 17th rev. Board of Trustees, 46 Park Avenue, New York.
145. DeHaen, P. (1964). "De Haen Nonproprietary Name Index with Therapeutic Guide." Paul DeHaen, 11 West 42nd Street, New York.
146. Gavin, M., and Hutton, R. (1966). "Medindex; January-March 1967." Medindex Ltd., London.
147. Osol, A. *et al.* (1967). "United States Dispensatory and Physicians' Pharmacology," 26th ed. Lippincott, Philadelphia, Pennsylvania.
148. Pöldinger, W. (1967). "Compendium of Psychopharmacotherapy," F. Hoffman-La Roche & Co., Basle.
149. Efron, R. (1966). *Perspectives Biol. Med.* **9,** 488.
150. Cook, L., and Weidley, E. (1957). *Ann. N.Y. Acad. Sci.* **66,** 740.
151. Heise, G. A., and McConnell, H. J. (1961). *Proc. 3rd World Congr. Psychiat., Montreal, 1961* Vol. 2, p. 917. Univ. of Toronto Press, Toronto; quoted in *Current Therap. Res.* **7,** 606 (1961).
152. Sidman, M. (1953). *Science* **118,** 157.
153. Heise, G. A., and Boff, E. (1962). *Psychopharmacologia* **3,** 264.
154. Scheckel, C. L., and McConnell, H. J. (1963). *Bioscience* **16,** 692.
155. Scheckel, C. L. (1965). *J. Comp. Physiol. Psychol.* **59,** 415.
156. Kersta, L. G. (1962). *Nature* **196,** 1253.
157. Pletscher, A. *et al.* (1955). *Science* **122,** 374.
158. Holzbauer, V., and Vogt, M. (1956). *J. Neurochem.* **1,** 8.
159. Brodie, B. B. *et al.* (1957). *Science* **125,** 1293.
160. Carlsson, A. *et al.* (1957). *Nature* **180,** 1200.
161. Laborit, H. *et al.* (1957). *J. Physiol.* (*London*) **49,** 953.
162. Divry, P. *et al.* (1958). *Acta Neurol. Psychiat. Belg.* **58,** 878.
163. Biel, J. H. (1968). *In* "Drugs Affecting the Central Nervous System" (A. Burger, ed.), *Med. Chem. Res. Ser.,* Vol. 2, p. 86. Marcel Dekker, New York.
164. Brodie, B. B. *et al.* (1959). *Pharmacol. Rev.* **11,** No. 2, Part II, 548.
165. Hess, W. R. (1954). "Diencephalon. Autonomic & Extrapyramidal Functions; Monographs in Biology & Medicine," Vol. 3. Grune & Stratton, New York.
166. Schindler, W., and Häfliger, F. (1954). *Helv. Chim. Acta* **37,** 472.
167. Janssen, P. A. J. (1965). *Intern. Rev. Neurobiol.* **8,** 221ff.

168. Häfliger, F., and Burckhardt, V. (1964). *In* "Psychopharmacological Agents" (M. Gordon, ed.), Vol. 1, p. 35. Academic Press, New York.
169. Stach, K., and Pöldinger, W. (1966). *Progr. Drug Res.* **9**, 129ff.
170. Meduna, L. J. *et al.* (1961). *J. Neuropsychiat.* **2**, 232.
171. Sulser, F. *et al.* (1961). *Federation Proc.* **20**, 396.
172. Brodie, B. B. *et al.* (1961). *Psychopharmacologia* **2**, 467.
173. Murad, J. E., and Shore, P. A. (1966). *Intern. J. Neuropharmacol.* **5**, 299.
174. Glowinski, J. *et al.* (1966). *J. Pharmacol. Exptl. Therap.* **153**, 30.
175. Meisch, J. J. *et al.* (1967). *J. Pharm. Pharmacol.* **19**, 63.
176. Schildkraut, J. J. *et al.* (1967). *Am. J. Psychiat.* **124**, 5.
177. Biel, J. H. *et al.* (1962). *Ann. N.Y. Acad. Sci.* **96**, 231.
178. Biel, J. H. (1966). *In* "Annual Reports in Medicinal Chemistry, 1965" (C. K. Cain, ed.), Vol. 1, p. 12. Academic Press, New York.
179. Carlsson, A. *et al.* (1968). *J. Pharm. Pharmacol.* **20**, 150.
180. Blaschko, H. (1952). *Pharmacol. Rev.* **4**, 415.
181. Horita, A. (1961). *J. Neuropsychiat.* **2**, S141.
182. Mann, P. J. G., and Quastel, J. H. (1940). *Biochem. J.* **34**, 414.
183. Zeller, E. A. (1959). *Ann. N.Y. Acad. Sci.* **80**, 551ff.
184. Zeller, E. A. (1963). *Ann. N.Y. Acad. Sci.* **107**, 809ff.
185. Biel, J. H. *et al.* (1964). *In* "Psychopharmacological Agents" (M. Gordon, ed.), Vol. 1, p. 359. Academic Press, New York.
186. Cole, J. O. (1964). *J. Am. Med. Assoc.* **190**, 448.
187. Pscheidt, G. R. (1964). *Intern. Rev. Neurobiol.* **7**, 191.
188. Zirkle, C. L., and Kaiser, C. (1964). *In* "Psychopharmacological Agents" (M. Gordon, ed.), Vol. 1, p. 445. Academic Press, New York.
189. Pletscher, A. (1965). *In* "The Scientific Basis of Drug Therapy in Psychiatry" (J. Marks and C. M. B. Pare, eds.), pp. 115–126. Pergamon Press, Oxford.
190. Pletscher, A. *et al.* (1966). *Handbuch Exptl. Pharmakol.* **19**, 593–743. Springer, Berlin, New York.
191. Costa, E., and Neff, N. H. (1966). *In* "Biochemistry and Pharmacology of the Basal Ganglia" (E. Costa *et al.*, eds.), pp. 141–156. Raven Press, Hewlett, New York.
192. Goldberg, L. I. (1964). *J. Am. Med. Assoc.* **190**, 456.
193. Sjöqvist, F. (1965). *Proc. Roy. Soc. Med.* **58**, Part II, 967.
194. Selikoff, I. J., and Robitzek, E. H. (1952). *Diseases Chest* **21**, 385.
195. Zeller, E. A., and Barsky, J. (1952). *Proc. Soc. Exptl. Biol. Med.* **81**, 459.
196. Brodie, B. B. *et al.* (1956). *J. Pharmacol. Exptl. Therap.* **116**, 9.
197. Loomer, H. P. *et al.* (1957). *Psychiat. Res. Rept.* **8**, 129.
198. Horita, A. (1958). *J. Pharmacol. Exptl. Therap.* **122**, 176.
199. Pletscher, A. *et al.* (1960). *Progr. Drug Res.* **2**, 417.
200. Schuler, W., and Wyss, E. (1960). *Arch. Intern. Pharmacodyn.* **128**, 431.
201. Biel, J. H. *et al.* (1959). *Ann. N.Y. Acad. Sci.* **80**, 568.
202. Maxwell, M. M. *et al.* (1960). *Am. J. Cardiol.* **6**, 1146.
203. Horita, A., and McGrath, W. A. (1960). *Biochem. Pharmacol.* **3**, 206.
204. Burger, A., and Yost, W. L. (1948). *J. Am. Chem. Soc.* **70**, 198.
205. Biel, J. H. (1964). *Advan. Chem. Ser.* **45**, 114.
206. Swett, L. R. *et al.* (1963). *Ann. N.Y. Acad. Sci.* **107**, 891.
207. Heinzelman, R. V., and Smuszkovicz, J. (1963). *Progr. Drug Res.* **6**, 75.
208. Berger, F. M. (1963). *Clin. Pharmacol. Therap.* **4**, 209.
209. Berger, F. M., and Ludwig, B. J. (1964). *In* "Psychopharmacological Agents" (M. Gordon, ed.), Vol. 1, p. 103. Academic Press, New York.
210. Berger, F. M. (1966). *In* "Methods in Drug Evaluation" (P. Mantegazza and F. Piccinini, eds.), pp. 218–233. North-Holland Publ., Amsterdam.
211. Brown, B. B. *et al.* (1956). *J. Pharmacol. Exptl. Therap.* **118**, 153.
212. Domino, E. F. (1962). *Clin. Pharmacol. Therap.* **3**, 599.
213. Gluckman, M. I. (1965). *Current Therap. Res.* **7**, 721.

214. Heise, G. A. (1965). *In* "The Scientific Basis of Drug Therapy in Psychiatry" (J. Marks and C. M. B. Pare, eds.), pp. 165–178. Pergamon Press, Oxford.
215. Kletzkin, M. (1962). *Ann. N.Y. Acad Sci.* **96,** 263.
216. Levis, S. *et al.* (1957). *Arch. Intern. Pharmacodyn.* **109,** 127.
217. Randall, L. O. *et al.* (1961). *Current Therap. Res.* **3,** 405.
218. Randall, L. O. *et al.* (1965). *Current Therap. Res.* **7,** 590.
219. Zbinden, G., and Randall, L. O. (1967). *Advan. Pharmacol.* **5,** 213.
220. Stein, L. (1964). *Ciba Found. Symp., Animal Behaviour Drug Action,* p. 91.
221. Olds, J. (1962). *Physiol. Rev.* **42,** 554.
221a. Dews, P. B. (1958). *J. Pharmacol. Exptl. Therap.* **115,** 380.
222. Gollub, L. R., and Brady, J. V. (1965). *Ann. Rev. Pharmacol.* **5,** 235.
223. Sidman, M. (1956). *Ann. N.Y. Acad. Sci.* **65,** 282.
223a. Stein, L. (1964). *Fed. Proc.* **23,** 836.
223b. Wise, C. D., and Stein, L. (1969). *In* "International Symposium on Amphetamine and Related Compounds" (S. Garattini and E. Costa, eds.), p. 60. Raven Press, New York.
224. Hillarp, N. A. *et al.* (1966). *Pharmacol. Rev.* **18,** 727.
224a. Stein, L. (1969). In press.
225. Stein, L. (1964). *In* "The Role of Pleasure in Behavior" (R. G. Heath, ed.), p. 113. Harper, New York.
226. Hill, R. T. (1967). Ph.D. Thesis, Columbia University, New York.
227. Weissman, A. *et al.* (1966). *J. Pharmacol. Exptl. Therap.* **151,** 339.
228. Goodman, L. S., and Gilman, A. (1955). *In* "The Pharmacological Basis of Therapeutics" (L. S. Goodman and A. Gilman, eds.), 2nd ed., p. 324. Macmillan, New York.
229. Tripod, J. *et al.* (1954). *Experientia* **10,** 261.
230. Tripod, J. *et al.* (1954). *Arch. Intern. Pharmacodyn.* **96,** 406.
231. Barger, H. H., and Dale, G. (1906). *J. Physiol.* (*London*) **41,** 54.
232. Alles, G. (1927). *J. Pharmacol. Exptl. Therap.* **32,** 121.
233. Ingvarsson, C. G. (1965). *Arzneimittel-Forsch.* **15,** 849.
233a. Fischer, J. E. *et al.* (1968). *Am. J. Med. Sci.* **255,** 158.
234. Hertting, G. *et al.* (1961). *J. Pharmacol. Exptl. Therap.* **134,** 146.
235. Glowinski, J. *et al.* (1966). *J. Pharmacol. Exptl. Therap.* **151,** 385.
236. Committee on Alcoholism and Addiction and Council on Mental Health. (1966). *J. Am. Med. Assoc.* **197,** 1023.
237. Connell, P. H. (1966). *J. Am. Med. Assoc.* **196,** 718.
238. Greig, M. E. *et al.* (1959). *J. Pharmacol. Exptl. Therap.* **127,** 110.
238a. Azima, H. *et al.* (1962). *Am. J. Psychiat.* **119,** 573.
239. Murphree, H. B. *et al.* (1961). *Clin. Pharmacol. Therap.* **2,** 722.
240. Gershon, S. *et al.* (1966). *Clin. Pharmacol. Therap.* **7,** 223.
241. Kalow, W. (1962). "Pharmacogenetics: Heredity and the Response to Drugs," Saunders, Philadelphia, Pennsylvania.
242. Motulsky, A. G. (1965). *In* "Genetics Today" (S. J. Geerts, ed.), pp. 875–895. Pergamon Press, Oxford.
243. Evans, D. A. P., and Clarke, C. A. (1961). *Brit. Med. Bull.* **17,** 234.
244. La Du, B. N. (1965). *Federation Proc.* **24,** 1287.
245. Sawin, P. B., and Glick, D. (1943). *Proc. Natl. Acad. Sci. U.S.* **29,** 55.
246. Goldberg, S. C. *et al.* (1966). *Psychopharmacologia* **9,** 31.
247. Myrianthopoulos, N. C. *et al.* (1962). *Arch. Neurol.* **6,** 19.
248. Angst, J. (1964). *Arzneimittel-Forsch.* **14,** 496.
249. Pryor, G. T. *et al.* (1966). *Life Sci.* **5,** 2105.
250. Scudder, C. L. *et al.* (1966). *Intern. J. Neuropharmacol.* **5,** 343.
251. Meier, G. W. *et al.* (1963). *Psychopharmacologia* **4,** 81.
251a. Fuller, J. L. (1968). Unpublished data.
252. Fuller, J. L. (1966). *Psychopharmacologia* **8,** 408.
253. Lilly, J. C., and Shurley, J. T. (1931). *In* "Psychophysiological Aspects of Space Flight" (B. E. Flaherty, ed.), p. 238. Columbia Univ. Press, New York.

254. Shurley, J. T. (1968). *In* "Hypodynamics and Hypogravics" (M. McCally, ed.), p. 237. Academic Press, New York.
255. Sprague, J. M. *et al.* (1963). *Arch. Ital. Biol.* **101,** 225.
256. Schueler, F. W. (1960). "Chemobiodynamics and Drug Design." McGraw-Hill, New York.
257. Freud, S. (1949). "An Outline of Psychoanalysis." Norton, New York.
258. Lindemann, E. (1958). *World Health Organ., Tech. Rept. Ser.* **152,** Working Paper WHO APH 10 pp.
259. Elkes, J. C. (1961). *In* "Lectures on Experimental Psychiatry" (H. Brosin, ed.), p. 65. Univ. of Pittsburgh Press, Pittsburgh, Pennsylvania.
260. Gunn, J. A., and Gurd, M. R. (1940). *J. Physiol. (London)* **97,** 453.
261. Greenblatt, E. N., and Osterberg, A. C. (1961). *J. Pharmacol. Exptl. Therap.* **131,** 115.
262. Cohen, S., and Edwards, A. E. (1963). *In* "Recent Advances in Biological Psychiatry" (J. Wortis, ed.), Vol. 6, Chapter 14, p. 139. Plenum Press, New York.
263. Luby, E. D. *et al.* (1959). *A. M. A. Arch. Neurol. Psychiat.* **81,** 363.
264. Domino, E. F. (1964). *Intern. Rev. Neurobiol.* **6,** 303.
265. Meyer, J. S. *et al.* (1959). *J. Nervous Mental Disease* **129,** 54.
266. Kramer, M., and Greenhouse, S. W. (1959). *Natl. Acad. Sci.—Natl. Res. Council, Publ.* **583,** 356–371.
267. Group for the Advancement of Psychiatry. (1959). Rept. No. 42, p. 544.
268. Grayson, H. M. (1961). *Diseases Nervous System* **22,** Suppl., 52.
269. Rosenthal, R., and Fode, K. L. (1963). *Psychol. Rept.* **12,** Monogr. Suppl. No. 3, 491.
270. Honigfeld, G. (1962). *Psychol. Rept.* **11,** 683.
271. Hollister, L. E. *et al.* (1963). *J. New Drugs* 3, 26.
272. Godfrey, K. E. (1965). *Paper, 10th Ann. Conf., V. A. Coop. Studies Psychiat., New Orleans, 1964.*
273. Brown, B. (1960). *Arch. Intern. Pharmacodyn.* **128,** 391.
274. Lasky, J. J. *et al.* (1960). *Trans. 4th Res. Conf. Chemother. Psychiat. 1960,* pp. 7 and 269. Veterans Admin., Washington, D.C.
275. Lorr, M. *et al.* (1963). "Snydromes of Psychosis." Pergamon Press, Oxford.
276. Overall, J. E., and Gorham, D. R. (1962). *Psychol. Rept.* **10,** 799.
277. Keith-Lee, P., and Spiegel, D. E. (1965). "Newsletter for Research in Psychology," Vol. 7, No. 4, p. 43. Veterans Admin., Washington, D.C.
278. Rothman, T. *et al.* (1962). *J. Neuropsychiat.* **3,** 234.
279. Zung, W. W. K. (1965). *Arch. Gen. Psychiat.* **12,** 64.
280. Grayson, H. M. *et al.* (1960). *Trans. 4th Res. Conf. Chemother. Psychiat., 1960,* Vol. 4, p. 155. Veterans Admin., Washington, D.C.
281. Phillips, L. (1953). *J. Nervous Mental Disease* **117,** 515.
282. Wittman, P. (1941). *Elgin Papers* **4,** 20.
283. Casey, J. F. *et al.* (1960). *A.M.A. Arch. Gen. Psychiat.* **2,** 210.
284. Casey, J. F. *et al.* (1960). *Am. J. Psychiat.* **117,** 97.
285. Sherman, L. J. *et al.* (1964). *Arch. Gen. Psychiat.* **10,** 123.
286. Lasky, J. *et al.* (1962). *Diseases Nervous System* **23,** 698.
287. Klett, C. J., and Moseley, E. C. (1965). *J. Consult. Psychol.* **29,** 546.
288. Galbrecht, C. R., and Klett, C. J. (1968). *J. Nervous Mental Disease* **147,** 173.
289. Gorham, D. R., and Pokorny, A. D. (1964). *Diseases Nervous System* **25,** 77.
290. Caffey, E. M. *et al.* (1968). *Hosp. Community Psychiat.* **68,** 282.
291. Casey, J. F. *et al.* (1961). *Am. J. Psychiat.* **117,** 997.
292. Honigfeld, G. *et al.* (1965). *J. Am. Geriat. Soc.* **13,** 57.
293. Platz, A. *et al.* (1967). *Diseases Nervous System* **28,** 601.
294. Caffey, E. M. *et al.* (1964). *J. Chronic Disease* **17,** 347.
295. Overall, J. E. *et al.* (1962). *Clin. Pharmacol. Therap.* **3,** 16.
296. Lorr, M. *et al.* (1961). *A.M.A. Arch. Gen. Psychiat.* **4,** 381.
297. Lorr, M. *et al.* (1963). *J. Psychiat. Res.* **1,** 257.
298. Anonymous. (1967). *FDA (Food Drug Admin.) Papers* **1,** 21.

299. Hodges, R. (1967). *FDA (Food Drug Admin.) Papers* **1,** 27.
300. Smith, J. P. (1967). *FDA (Food Drug Admin.) Papers* **1,** 10.
301. Lasher, L. P. (1967). *FDA (Food Drug Admin.) Papers* **1,** 5.
302. Finlator, J. (1967). *FDA (Food Drug Admin.) Papers* **1,** 4.
303. Durren, K. A. (1967). *FDA (Food Drug Admin.) Papers* **1,** 23.
304. Farberow, N. L., and Shneidman, E. S. (1961). *In* "Cry for Help" (N. L. Farberow and E. S. Schneidman, eds.), p. 112. McGraw-Hill, New York.
305. Havens, L. L. (1967). *New Engl. J. Med.* **276,** 210.
306. McKown, C. H. *et al.* (1963). *J. Am. Med. Assoc.* **185,** 425.
307. Kessel, N. (1965). *Brit. Med. J.* **II,** 1265 and 1336.
308. Jacobsen, P. (1963). *Danish Med. Bull.* **10,** 115.
309. Brophy, J. J. (1967). *Arch. Gen. Psychiat.* **17,** 652.
310. Hollister, L. E. (1965). *Practitioner* **194,** 72.
311. Frejaville, M. L. *et al.* (1965). *Med. Soc. Paris Hosp.* **116,** 927.
312. Harthorne, J. W. *et al.* (1963). *New Engl. J. Med.* **268,** 33.
313. Matter, B. J. *et al.* (1965). *Arch. Internal Med.* **116,** 18.
314. Benbow, S. H., and Super, W. C. (1961). *Am. J. Psychiat.* **117,** 836.
315. Bloomer, H. A. (1966). *Clin. Res.* **14,** 186.
316. Zbinden, G. *et al.* (1961). *Toxicol. Appl. Pharmacol.* **3,** 619.
317. Gjerris, F. (1966). *Danish Med. Bull.* **13,** 170.
318. Kaye, S., and Haag, H. B. (1964). *Toxicol. Appl. Pharmacol.* **6,** 316.
319. Wulff, M. H. (1959). *Electroencephalog. Clin. Neurophysiol.* Suppl. 14, 1.
320. Lindesmith, A. R. (1968). "Addiction and Opiates." Aldine Press, Chicago, Illinois.
321. American Medical Association Council on Mental Health and the National Academy of Science, National Research Council Commitee on Problems of Drug Dependence: Narcotics and Medical Practice. (1967). *J. Am. Med. Assoc.* **202,** 137.
322. Isbell, H., and White, W. M. (1953). *Am. J. Med.* **14,** 558.
323. Casriel, D. (1963). "So Fair a House: The Story of Synanon." Prentice-Hall, Englewood Cliffs, New Jersey.
324. Volkman, R. (1965). *Brit. J. Addict.* **61,** 91.
325. Martin, W. R. *et al.* (1966). *Clin. Pharmacol. Therap.* **7,** 455.
326. Jaffe, J. H. (1967). *In* "Current Psychiatric Therapies" (J. Masserman, ed.), Vol. VII, p. 147. Grune & Stratton, New York.
327. Dole, V. P. *et al.* (1967). *Proc. 1st Natl. Conf. Methadone Treatment, 1967,* p. 11. Rockefeller Univ. Press, New York.
328. Martin, W. R. *et al.* (1968). *J. Pharmacol. Exptl. Therap.* **162,** 189.
329. Dole, V. P., and Nyswander, M. E. (1965). *J. Am. Med. Assoc.* **193,** 646.
330. Bewley, T. (1965). *Brit. Med. J.* **II,** 1284.
331. Gillespie, D. *et al.* (1967). *Brit. J. Addict.* **62,** 155.
332. Hornykiewicz, O. (1966). *Pharmacol. Rev.* **18,** 925.
333. Cotzias, G. C. *et al.* (1967). *New Engl. J. Med.* **276,** 374.
334. Crane, G. E. (1968). *Am. J. Psychiat.* **128,** 40.
335. Friedman, A. H., and Everett, G. (1964). *Advan. Pharmacol.* **3,** 83.
336. McGeer, P. L. *et al.* (1961). *J. Am. Med. Assoc.* **177,** 665.
337. Himwich, H. E., and Rinaldi, F. (1956). *Yale J. Biol. Med.* **28,** 308.
338. Barbeau, A., and Brunette, J. R. (eds.) (1969). "Progress in Neuro-Genetics. Proceedings 2nd International Congress of Neuro-Genetics and Neuroophthalmology." Excerpta Med. Found., Amsterdam.
339. Klein, D. F., and Davis, J. M. (1969). "Diagnosis and Drug Treatment of Psychiatric Disorders." Williams & Wilkins, Baltimore, Maryland.
340. Chapman, L. J., and Knowles, R. R. (1964). *J. Consult. Psychol.* **28,** 165.
341. Shimkunas, A. M. *et al.* (1966). *Arch. Gen. Psychiat.* **14,** 79.
342. Kurland, A. A. *et al.* (1961). *J. Nervous Mental Disease* **133,** 1.
343. Freeman, H. (1967). *Psychopharmacol. Bull.* **4,** 1.
344. Grinspoon, L. *et al.* (1967). *Intern. J. Psychiat.* **4,** 116.

345. Greenblatt, M. *et al.* (1965). "Drugs and Social Therapy in Chronic Schizophrenia." Thomas, Springfield, Illinois.
346. Smith, K. *et al.* (1967). *J. Nervous Mental Disease* **144**, 284.
347. Engelhardt, D. M. *et al.* (1967). *Arch. Gen. Psychiat.* **16**, 98.
348. Jarvik, M. E. (1965). *In* "The Pharmacological Basis of Therapeutics" (L. S. Goodman and A. Gilman, eds.), 3rd ed. p. 163. Macmillan, New York.
349. de Wied, D. (1967). *Pharmacol. Rev.* **19**, 251.
350. Leestma, J. E., and Koenig, K. L. (1968). *Arch. Gen. Psychiat.* **18**, 137.
351. Alexander, L. (1953). "Treatment of Mental Disorder." Saunders, Philadelphia, Pennsylvania.
352. Klerman, G. L., and Cole, J. O. (1965). *Pharmacol. Rev.* **17**, 101.
353. Sigg, E. B. (1959). *Can. Psychiat. Assoc. J.* **4**, Suppl. 1, 75.
354. Fink, M. *et al.* (1964). *Psychopharmacologia* **5**, 27.
355. Paykel, E. S. *et al.* (1968). *Brit. J. Psychiat.* **114**, 1281.
356. MacLean, R. E. G. (1960). *Am. J. Psychiat.* **117**, 551.
357. Hicks, W. R., and Barnes, E. H. (1964). *Am. J. Psychiat.* **120**, 812.
358. Dorison, E. E., and Blackman, S. (1962). *Am. J. Psychiat.* **119**, 474.
359. Sargant, W., and Dally, P. (1962). *Brit. Med. J.* **I**, 6; Sargant, W. (1961). *ibid.* p. 225.
360. Gander, D. R. (1965). *Lancet* **II**, 107.
361. Dally, P. (1965). *Brit. Med. J.* **I**, 384.
362. Schou, M. (1968). *J. Psychiat. Res.* **6**, 67.
363. Amdisen, A. (1967). *Scand. J. Clin. & Lab. Invest.* **20**, 104; Lehmann, V. (1968). *Clin. Chim. Acta* **20**, 253.
364. Baastrup, P. C., and Schou, M. (1967). *Arch. Gen. Psychiat.* **16**, 162.
365. Colburn, R. W. *et al.* (1967). *Nature* **215**, 1395; Corrodi, A., *et al.* (1967). *Psychopharmacologia* **11**, 345; Schildkraut, J. J. *et al.* (1967). *Am. J. Psychiat.* **124**, 600.
366. Straker, M. (1964). *J. Am. Geriat. Soc.* **12**, 473.
367. Epstein, L. J., and Simon, A. (1967). *Geriatrics* **22**, 145.
368. Wolff, K. (1967). *J. Am. Geriat. Soc.* **15**, 575.
369. Freeman, J. T. (ed.) (1963). "Clinical Principles and Drugs in the Aging." Thomas, Springfield, Illinois.
370. Bender, A. D. (1964). *J. Am. Geriat. Soc.* **12**, 114 and 1154.
371. Ayd, F. J. (1961). *J. Am. Med. Assoc.* **175**, 1054.

APPENDICES

This section has been included to assist the serious student of behavioral science in identifying important source material for in-depth reading on most of the basic and clinical subjects discussed in the text.

The appendices include references and suggested readings sent by authors but not cited in the text, key reviews, texts, and monographs, annals and serials, "core" journals pertaining to psychopharmacology, and bibliographic aids.

Many valuable publications in psychopharmacology and related fields are published by the National Institute of Health, the United States Public Health Service, and other United States Government agencies. These are generally obtainable from Superintendent of Documents, United States Government Printing Office, Washington, D.C. 20402.

APPENDIX

1

FURTHER SUGGESTED READING AND GENERAL REFERENCES

Chapter 2
A. Caldwell, History of Psychopharmacology

Caldwell, A. (1970). "Origins of Psychopharmacology from CPZ to LSD." Thomas, Springfield, Illinois.

Caldwell, A. E. (comp.) (1958). "Psychopharmaca. A Bibliography of Psychopharmacology. 1952–1957," Public Health Publ. No. 581 (Public Health Biblio. Ser. No. 19). Natl. Library Med., U.S. Dept. Health, Education and Welfare, Washington, D.C. 258 pp.

Holmstedt, B. (1967). *In* "Ethnopharmacologic Search for Psychoactive Drugs" (D. H. Efron *et al.*, eds.), Public Health Serv. Publ. No. 1645, p. 3. U.S. Dept. Health, Education and Welfare, Washington, D.C.

Hordern, A. (1968). *In* "Psychopharmacology; Dimensions and Perspectives" (C. R. B. Joyce, ed.), p. 95. Tavistock, London; Lippincott, Philadelphia and Toronto.

Chapter 3
M. Opler, Cross-Cultural Uses of Psychoactive Drugs

Blum, R. W. (1968). *In* "Psychopharmacology; Dimensions and Perspectives" (C. R. B. Joyce, ed.), p. 243. Tavistock, London; Lippincott, Philadelphia and Toronto.

Chen, A. I., and Chen, K. K. (1939). *Quart. J. Pharm. Pharmacol.* **12**, 30.

Efron, D. H. *et al.*, eds. (1967). "Ethnopharmacologic Search for Psychoactive Drugs," Public

Health Serv. Publ. No. 1645. U.S. Dept. Health, Education and Welfare, Washington, D.C. 468 pp.
Kennedy, J. G. (1963). *Am. Anthropologist* **65**, 620.
Larson, P. S. *et al.* (1961). "Tobacco. Experimental and Clinical Studies. A Comprehensive Account of the World Literature." Williams & Wilkins, Baltimore, Maryland. 932 pp.
Mandelbaum, D. G. (1965). *Current Anthropol.* **3**, 281.
O'Hara, M. J. *et al.* (1965). *J. Pharm. Sci.* **7**, 1021.
Opler, M. K. (1940). *Am. Anthropologist* **42**, 463.
Ribeiro do Valle, J. (1966). "Primordia Pharmacologiae in Brasilia," 3rd Intern. Congr. Pharmacol. Revista dos Tribunais, Inc., São Pãulo. 247 pp.
Schultes, R. E. (1941). "A Contribution to Our Knowledge of Rivia Corymbosa: The Narcotic Ololiuqui of the Aztecs." Botan. Museum of Harvard University, Cambridge, Massachusetts. 45 pp.
Schultes, R. E., and Holmstedt, B. (1968). *Rhodora* **70**, 113.
Uhr, L., and Miller, J. G., eds. (1964). "Drugs and Behavior." Wiley, New York. 676 pp.
UNESCO (1960). "Medicinal Plants of the Arid Zones." Arid Zone Research, No. 13. UNESCO, Paris. 96 pp.
Wasson, S. H., and Holmstedt, B. (1963). *Ethnos.* **1**, 5.
Wasson, R. G. (1963). "Notes on the Present Status of Ololiuqui and the Other Hallucinogens of Mexico," Botan. Museum Leaflets No. 2. Harvard University, Cambridge, Massachusetts. 45 pp.

Chapter 4
J. Hayward, Functional Neuroanatomy of the Hypothalamus

Bradley, P. B. (ed.) (1965). *Brit. Med. Bull.* **21**, 1.
Brown-Grant, K., and Cross, B. A. (eds.) *Brit. Med. Bull.* **22**, 195.
Dayan, A. D. (1968). *In* "Psychopharmacology; Dimensions and Perspectives" (C. R. B. Joyce, ed.), p. 319. Tavistock, London; Lippincott, Philadelphia and Toronto.
De Robertis, E. D. P. (1964). "Histophysiology of Synapses and Neurosecretion." Macmillan, New York. 256 pp.
Levine, R. (ed.) (1966). "Endocrines and the Central Nervous System," Res. Publ. Assoc. Res. Nerv. Ment. Dis., Vol. 43. Williams & Wilkins, Baltimore, Maryland. 467 pp.
Nalbandov, A. V. (ed.) (1963). "Advances in Neuroendocrinology." University of Illinois Press, Urbana. 525 pp.
Szentágothai, J. *et al* (1962). "Hypothalamic Control of Anterior Pituitary." Akadémiai Kiado, Budapest. 230 pp.
Yamamoto, W. S., and Brodbeck, J. R. (eds.) (1965). "Physiological Controls and Regulation." Saunders, Philadelphia, Pennsylvania. 362 pp.

Chapter 6
K. Fuxe, T. Hökfelt and U. Ungerstedt, Central Monaminergic Tracts

Andén, N. E. *et al.* (1966). *Acta Physiol. Scand.* **67**, 313.
Carlsson, A. *et al.* (1966). *Acta Physiol. Scand.* **67**, 481.
Corrodi, H., and Jonsson, G. (1967). *J. Histochem. Cytochem.* **15**, 65.
Fuxe, K. *et al.* (1968). *Advan. Pharmacol.* **6A**, 235.
Hillarp, N. A. *et al.* (1966). *In* "Mechanisms of Release of Biogenic Amines" (U. S. von Euler *et al.*, eds.), p. 31. Pergamon Press (Symp. Publ. Div.) Oxford.

Chapter 8
W. G. Dewhurst, The Blood-Brain Barrier and Other Membrane Phenomena in Psychopharmacology

Albert, A. (1968). "Selective Toxicity," 4th ed. Methuen, London. 531 pp.
Angel, C., and Roberts, A. J. (1966). *J. Nervous Mental Disease* **142**, 376.
Bertler, A. *et al.* (1966). *Pharmacol. Rev.* **18**, 369.
Bourke, R. S., and Tower, D. B. (1966). *J. Neurochem.* **13**, 1071.
Bulat, M., and Supek, Z. (1967). *J. Neurochem.* **14**, 265.
Davson, H. (1960). *In* "Handbook of Physiology" (Am. Physiol. Soc., J. Field, ed.), Vol. II, Sect. I, p. 1761. Williams & Wilkins, Baltimore, Maryland.
Davson, H. (1963). *Ergeb. Physiol., Biol. Chem. Exptl. Pharmakol.* **52**, 20.
Davson, H. (1966). *In* "The Scientific Basis of Medicine; Annual Reviews," p. 238. Oxford Univ. Press (Athlone), London and New York.
Davson, H. (1967). "Physiology of the Cerebrospinal Fluid." Churchill, London. 445 pp.
De Jaramillo, G. A. V., and Guth, R. S. (1963). *Biochem. Pharmacol.* **12**, 525.
Dencker, S. J. *et al.* (1966). *Med. Pharmacol. Exptl.* **15**, 291.
Dobbing, J. (1961). *Physiol. Rev.* **41**, 130.
Edström, R. (1964). *Intern. Rev. Neurobiol.* **7**, 153.
Glen, A. I. M. *et al.* (1968). *Lancet* **II**, 241.
Glynn, I. M. (1966). *In* "The Scientific Basis of Medicine; Annual Reviews," p. 217. Oxford Univ. Press (Athlone), London and New York.
Guth, P. S., and Amaro, J. (1965). *Biochem. Pharmacol.* **14**, 67.
Herz, A. *et al.* (1965). *Intern. J. Neuropharmacol.* **4**, 207.
Kaplan, H. A., and Ford, D. H. (1966). "The Brain Vascular System." Elsevier, Amsterdam. 230 pp.
Kety, S. S. (1960). *In* "Handbook of Physiology" (Am. Physiol. Soc., J. Field, ed.), Vol. **II**, Sect. I, p. 1751. Williams & Wilkins, Baltimore, Maryland.
Lajtha, A. (1961). *In* "Regional Neurochemistry (S. S. Kety and J. Elkes, eds.), p. 19. Pergamon Press, Oxford.
Lajtha, A. (1962). *In* "Neurochemistry" (K. A. C. Elliott *et al.*, eds.), 2nd ed., p. 399. Thomas, Springfield, Illinois.
Mayer, S. *et al.* (1959). *J. Pharmacol. Exptl. Therap.* **127**, 205.
Oldendorf, W. H., and Davson, H. (1967). *Arch. Neurol.* **17**, 196.
Paykel, E. S. *et al.* (1968). *Brit. J. Psychiat.* **114**, 1281.
Schanberg, S. M. *et al.* (1967). *J. Pharmacol. Exptl. Therap.* **157**, 311.
Schanker, L. S. (1962). *Pharmacol. Rev.* **14**, 501.
Schanker, L. S. (1964). *Advan. Drug Res.* **1**, 71.
Schmidt, C. F. (1960). *In* "Handbook of Physiology" (Am. Physiol. Soc., J. Field, ed.), Vol. III, Sect. I, p. 1745. Williams & Wilkins, Baltimore, Maryland.
Seeman, P. M. (1966). *Intern. Rev. Neurobiol.* **9**, 145.
Tschirgi, R. D. (1960). *In* "Handbook of Physiology" (Am. Physiol. Soc., J. Field, ed.), Vol. III, Sect. I, p. 1865. Williams and Wilkins, Baltimore, Maryland.
Van Harreveld, A. (1966). "Brain Tissue Electrolytes." Butterworth, London and Washington, D.C. 171 pp.

Chapter 9
S. Snyder, Catecholamines, Brain Function, and How Psychotropic Drugs Act

Axelrod, J. (1966a). *In* "Mechanisms of Release of Biogenic Amines" (U. S. von Euler *et al.*, eds.), p. 189. Pergamon Press (Symp. Publ. Div.), Oxford.

Axelrod, J. (1966b). *Pharmacol. Rev.* **18**, 95.
Bloom, F. E., and Giarman, N. L. (1968). *Pharmacol. Rev.* **8**, 229.
De Robertis, E. (1964). "Histophysiology of Synapses and Neurosecretion." Pergamon Press, Oxford. 256 pp.
Glowinski, J., and Baldessarini, R. J. (1966). *Pharmacol. Rev.* **18**, 1201.
Kopin, I. J. (1968). *Pharmacol. Rev.* **8**, 377.
Salmoiraghi, G. C. (1966). *Pharmacol. Rev.* **18**, 717.
Schildkraut, J. J. (1965). *Am. J. Psychiat.* **122**, 509.
Shore, P. A. (1962). *Pharmacol. Rev.* **14**, 531.

Chapter 10
H. Weil-Malherbe, The Biochemistry of Affective Disorders

Bunney, W. E., Jr., and Davis, J. M. (1965). *Arch. Gen. Psychiat.* **13**, 483.
Bunney, W. E., Jr. *et al.* (1967). *Arch. Gen. Psychiat.* **16**, 448.
Durell, J., and Schildkraut, J. J. (1966). *In* "American Handbook of Psychiatry" (S. Silvano, ed.), Vol. 3, p. 423. Basic Books, New York.
Eiduson, S. *et al.* (1964). "Biochemistry and Behavior." Van Nostrand, Princeton, New Jersey. 554 pp.
Himwich, H. E. *et al.*, eds. (1967). "Amines and Schizophrenia." Pergamon Press (Symp. Publ. Div.), Oxford. 290 pp.
Pletscher, A. (1964). *Arzneimittel-Forsch.* **14**, 479.
Schildkraut, J. J. (1965). *Am. J. Psychiat.* **122**, 509.
Schildkraut, J. J. *et al.* (1965). *J. Psychiat. Res.* **3**, 213.
Schildkraut, J. J., and Kety, S. S. (1967). *Science* **156**, 21.
Weil-Malherbe, H. (1967). *Advan. Enzymol.* **29**, 479.

Chapter 11
C. Frohman, Possible Biochemical Mechanisms of Schizophrenia

Leach, B. E. *et al.* (1963). *In* "Serological Fractions in Schizophrenia" (R. Heath, ed.), p. 7. Harper (Hoeber), New York.
Pennell, R. B. *et al.* (1963). *In* "Serological Fractions in Schizophrenia" (R. Heath, ed.), p. 23. Harper (Hoeber), New York.

Chapter 12
J. H. Quastel, Metabolic Effects of Some Biochemical Agents in Brain *in Vitro*

Axelrod, J. *et al.* (1961). *Science* **133**, 333.
Beer, C. T., and Quastel, J. H. (1958). *Can. J. Biochem. Physiol.* 36, **531**.
Elliott, K. A. C., and Wolfe, L. S. (1962). *In* "Neurochemistry" (K. A. C. Elliott et al., eds.), 2nd ed., p. 177. Thomas, Springfield, Illinois.
Himwich, H. E. (1962). *In* "Neurochemistry" (K. A. C. Elliott *et al.*, eds.), 2nd ed., p. 766. Thomas, Springfield, Illinois.
Hokin, L. E., and Hokin, D. R. (1958). *J. Biol. Chem.* **233**, 805.
Lovtrup, S. (1967). *In* "Molecular Basis of Some Aspects of Mental Activity" (O. Walaas, ed.), Vol. 2, p. 3. Academic Press, New York.
Magee, W. L., and Rosslter, R. J. (1963). *Can. J. Biochem. Physiol.* **41**, 1155.
Michaelis, M., and Quastel, J. H. (1941). *Biochem. J.* **35**, 518.
Quastel, J. H. (1965). *Proc. Roy. Soc.* **B163**, 169.

Quastel, J. H. (1967). *In* "Molecular Basis of Some Aspects of Mental Activity" (O. Walaas, ed.), Vol. 2, p. 19. Academic Press, New York; also *Brit. Med. Bull.* **21**, 49 (1965).
Schneider, M. (1957). *In* "Metabolism of the Nervous System" (D. Richter, ed.), p. 238. Pergamon Press, Oxford.
Wallgren, H., and Kulonan, E. (1960). *Biochem. J.* **75**, 150.
Zeller, E. A. (1963). *In* "Metabolic Inhibitors" (R. M. Hochster and J. H. Quastel, eds.), Vol. 2, p. 3. Academic Press, New York.

Chapter 14
H. Goldenberg and V. Fishman, Metabolism of Psychotropic Agents

Forrest, I. S. *et al.* (1968). *Biochem. Pharmacol.* **17**, 2061.
Goldenberg, H. *et al.* (1964). *Proc. Soc. Exptl. Biol. Med.* **115**, 1044.
Gordon, M., ed. (1964). "Psychopharmacological Agents," Vol. 1. Academic Press, New York. 678 pp.
Gordon, M., ed. (1967). "Psychopharmacological Agents," Vol. 2. Academic Press, New York. 622 pp.
Steinecker, G. *et al.* (1968). *Ann. Pharm. Franç.* **26**, 143.

Chapter 15
E. Usdin, Classification of Psychopharmaca

Kline, N. S. (1959). *Bull. World Health Organ.* **21**, 397.

Chapter 16
C. Scheckel, Preclinical Psychopharmacology

Boff, E., and Scheckel, C. L. (1964). *Pharmacologist* **6**, 179.
Chance, M. R. A. (1968). *In* "Psychopharmacology; Dimensions and Perspectives" (C. R. B. Joyce, ed.), p. 283. Tavistock, London; Lippincott, Philadelphia and Toronto.
Cook, L., and Kelleher, R. T. (1963). *Ann. Rev. Pharmacol.* **3**, 205.
Dews, P. B., and Morse, W. H. (1961). *Ann. Rev. Pharmacol.* **1**, 145.
Ferster, C. B., and Skinner, B. F. (1957). "Schedules of Reinforcement." Appleton, New York, 741 pp.
Maxwell, D. R. (1968). *In* "Psychopharmacology; Dimensions and Perspectives" (C. R. B. Joyce, ed.), p. 57. Tavistock, London; Lippincott, Philadelphia and Toronto.
Scheckel, C. L., and Boff, E. (1967). *In* "Neuro-Psycho-Pharmacology" (H. Brill *et al.*, eds.), Excerpta Med. Found., Intern. Congr. Ser. No. 129, p. 789. Excerpta Med. Found., Amsterdam.

Chapter 18
H. Laborit and A. Sanseigne, Pharmacology of Other Antipsychotic Drugs

Ahtee, L. (1966). *Ann. Med. Exptl. Biol. Fenniae (Helsinki)* **44**, 458.
Brodie, B. B., and Beaven, M. A. (1963). *Med. Exptl.* **8**, 320.
Chance, B., and Schoener, B. (1962). *Nature* **195**, 956.
Garry, J. W., and Leonard, I. J. (1962). *J. Mental* Sci. **108**, 105.
Janssen, P. A. J. *et al.* (1959). *J. Med. Pharm. Chem.* **1**, 281.
Laborit, H. (1964). *Agressologie* **5**, 99.
Laborit, H. (1966). *Ann. anesth. franç.* **7**, 191.
Laborit, H. *et al.* (1959). *Presse méd.* **67**, 927.

Laborit, H. *et al.* (1962). *Psychopharmacol. Bull.* **2**, 34.
Laborit, H. *et al.* (1965a). *Agressologie* **6**, 425.
Laborit, H. *et al.* (1965b). *Agressologie* **6**, 655.
Miller, N. E. (1956). *Ann. N.Y. Acad. Sci.* **65**, 318.
Sen, G., and Bose, K. C. (1931). *Indian Med. World* **2**, 194.
Sutherland, E. W., and Rall, T. W. (1961). *In* "Adrenergic Mechanisms" (G. E. W. Wolstenholme and M. O'Conner, eds.), p. 295. Churchill, London.

Chapter 21
J. Biel, Non-Monoamine Oxidase Inhibitor Antidepressants: Structure–Activity Relationships

Agin, H. V. (1959). *Ann. N.Y. Acad. Sci.* **80**, 705.
Azima, H. *et al.* (1962). *Am. J. Psychiat.* **119**, 573.
Biel, J. H. (1967). *In* "Annual Reports in Medicinal Chemistry, 1966" (C. K. Cain, ed.), Vol. 2, p. 11. Academic Press, New York.
Biel, J. H. *et al.* (1958). *J. Am. Chem. Soc.* **80**, 1519.
Gardner, T. S. *et al.* (1962). *J. Med. Pharm. Chem.* **5**, 503.
Huebner, C. F. *et al.* (1966). *J. Med. Chem.* **9**, 830.
Knoll, J. *et al.* (1965). *Arch. Intern. Pharmacodyn.* **155**, 154.
Perron, Y. G. *et al.* (1966). *J. Med. Chem.* **9**, 136.
Sigg, E. B. *et al.* (1964). *Arch. Intern. Pharmacodyn.* **149**, 164.
Tedeschi, R. E. *et al.* (1959). *Proc. Soc. Exptl. Biol. Med.* **103**, 380.
Tedeschi, D. H. *et al.* (1960). *Proc. Soc. Exptl Biol. Med.* **103**, 680.
Youngdale, G. A. *et al.* (1964). *J. Med. Chem.* **7**, 415.

Chapter 22
S. Margolin and M. Kletkzin, Pharmacological Properties of Antianxiety Drugs

Domino, E. F. (1962). *Ann. Rev. Pharmacol.* **2**, 215.

Chapter 23
L. Stein and C. D. Wise, Behavioral Pharmacology of Central Stimulants

Alles, G. A. (1959). *In* "Neuropharmacology" (H. A. Abramson, ed.), p. 181. Josiah Macy Jr. Found., New York.
Brodie, B. B. *et al.* (1960). *J. Pharmacol. Exptl. Therap.* **129**, 250.
Brutkowski, S. (1964). *In* "The Frontal Granular Cortex and Behavior" (J. M. Warren and K. Akert, eds.), p. 242. McGraw-Hill, New York.
Carlsson, A. *et al.* (1966). *Acta Physiol. Scand.* **67**, 481.
Carlton, P. L. (1963). *Psychol. Rev.* **70**, 19.
Clemente, C. D., and Sterman, M. B. (1967). *In* "Sleep and Altered States of Consciousness" (S. S. Kety *et al.*, eds.), p. 127. Williams & Wilkins, Baltimore, Maryland.
Dews, P. B., and Morse, W. H. (1961). *Ann. Rev. Pharmacol.* **1**, 145.
Glowinski, J., and Axelrod, J. (1965). *J. Pharmacol. Exptl. Therap.* **149**, 43.
Glowinski, J. *et al.* (1965). *J. Neurochem.* **12**, 25.
Hearst, E., and Whalen, R. E. (1963). *J. Comp. Physiol. Psychol.* **56**, 124.
Heller, A. *et al.* (1966). *Intern. J. Neuropharmacol.* **5**, 91.
Hernandez-Peon, R. *et al.* (1963). *Exptl. Neurol.* **8**, 93.
Horovitz, Z. P. *et al.* (1962). *Psychopharmacologia* **3**, 455.
Javoy, F. *et al.* (1968). *J. Comp. Behav. Biol.* **1**, 43.
Kelleher, R. T. *et al.* (1961). *J. Pharmacol. Exptl. Therap.* **133**, 271.

McLean, J. R., and McCartney, M. (1961). *Proc. Soc. Exptl. Biol. Med.* **107**, 77.
Margules, D. L., and Stein, L. (1966). *Proc. Am. Psychol. Assoc.* p. 113.
Moore, K. E. (1963). *J. Pharmacol. Exptl. Therap.* **142**, 6.
Sanan, S., and Vogt, M. (1962). *Brit. J. Pharmacol.* **18**, 109.
Sidman, M. J. (1953). *J. Comp. Physiol. Psychol.* **46**, 253.
Skinner, B. F., and Heron, W. T. (1937). *Psychol. Record* **1**, 340.
Smith, C. B. (1963). *J. Pharmacol. Exptl. Therap.* **142**, 343.
Stein, L. (1962a). *In* "Psychosomatic Medicine" (J. H. Nodine and J. H. Moyer, eds.), p. 297. Lea & Febiger, Philadelphia, Pennsylvania.
Stein, L. (1962b). *Recent Advan. Biol. Psychiat.* **4**, 288.
Stein, L. (1964). *Federation Proc.* **23**, 836. (Symp.)
Stein, L. (1965). *J. Comp. Physiol. Psychol.* **60**, 9.
Weiss, B., and Laties, V. G. (1963). *J. Pharmacol. Exptl. Therap.* **140**, 1.

Chapter 25
J. Fuller, Pharmacogenetics

Broadhurst, P. L. (1964). *In* "Animal Behaviour and Drug Action" (H. Steinberg *et al.*, eds.), p. 224. Churchill, London.
Huff, S. D. (1962). *Genetics* **47**, 962.
Jay, G. E. (1955). *Proc. Soc. Exptl. Biol. Med.* **90**, 378.
Kakihana, R. *et al.* (1966). *Science* **154**, 1574.
Kalow, W. (1962). "Pharmacogenetics." Saunders, Philadelphia, Pennsylvania. 231 pp.
Meier, H. (1963). "Experimental Pharmacogenetics. Physiopathology of Hereditary and Pharmacologic Responses." Academic Press, New York. 213 pp.
Peters, J. W. (1964). *Pharmacol. Rev.* **8**, 427.

Chapter 26
J. Werboff, Developmental Psychopharmacology

Hagerman, D. D., and Vilee, C. A. (1960). *Physiol. Rev.* **40**, 313.
Kalow, W. (1962). "Pharmacogenetics." Saunders, Philadelphia, Pennsylvania. 231 pp.
Lenz, W. (1966). *Am. J. Diseases Children* **112**, 99.
Levine, S., and Mullins, R. F., Jr. (166). *Science* **152**, 1585.
Meier, H. (1963). "Experimental Pharmacogenetics. Physiopathology of Hereditary and Pharmacologic Responses." Academic Press, New York. 213 pp.
Moya, F., and Smith, B. E. (1965). *Anesthesiology* **26**, 465.
Nair, V., and DuBois, K. P. (1968). *Chicago Med. School Quart.* **27**, 75.
Sereni, F., and Principi, N. (1968). *Pharmacol. Rev.* **8**, 453.
Vorster, D. W. (1965). *Brit. J. Psychiat.* **111**, 431.
Werboff, J., and Gottlieb, J. S. (1963). *Obstet. Gynecol.* **18**, 420.
Young, R. D. (1967). *Psychol. Bull.* **67**, 73.

Chapter 27
J. Berman and D. Hsia, Nutritional Psychopharmacology: Inherited Metabolic Disorders and Mental Retardation

American Academy of Pediatrics, Committee on Nutrition. (1967). *Pediatrics* **40**, 289.
Dobbing, J. (1968). *In* "Psychopharmacology; Dimensions and Perspectives" (C. R. B. Joyce, ed.), p. 345. Tavistock, London; Lippincott, Philadelphia and Toronto.
Frimpter, G. W. *et al.* (1963). *New Engl. J. Med.* **268**, 333.
Garattini, S., and Valzelli, L. (1965). "Serotonin." Elsevier, New York. 392 pp.

Garrod, A. E. (1908). *Lancet* **II**, 73, 142, and 214.
Ghadimih, H., and Partington, M. W. (1967). *Am. J. Diseases Children* **113**, 83.
Gjessing, L. R. (1966). "Symposium on Tyrosinosis." Universitetsforlägets Trykninqssentral, P. O. Box, 142, Boston Massachusetts 02133. 132 pp.
Green, O. C., and Berger, S. (1968). *Ann. N.Y. Acad. Sci.* **150**, 356.
Hsia, D. Y. Y. (1967a). *Am. J. Diseases Children* **113**, 1.
Hsia, D. Y. Y. (1967b). *Metab., Clin. Exptl.* **16**, 419.
Komrower, G. M. *et al.* (1966). *Arch. Disease Childhood* **41**, 666.
Lyman, F. L. (1963). "Phenylketonuria." Thomas, Springfield, Illinois. 318 pp.
Martin, G. J., and Kisch, B. (1966). "Enzymes in Mental Health." Lippincott, Philadelphia, Pennsylvania. 208 pp.
Menkes, J. H. (1967). *Pediatrics* **39**, 297.
Scriver, C. R. (1966). *Pediatrics* **37**, 553.
Stanbury, J. B. *et al.* (1966). "The Metabolic Basis of Inherited Disease," 2nd ed. McGraw-Hill, New York. 1434 pp.
Woolley, D. W. (1962). "Biochemical Bases of Psychoses." Wiley, New York. 331 pp.

Chapter 29
R. Okun, General Principles of Pharmacology and Psychopharmacology and Early Clinical Drug Evaluations

Burns, J. J. (1964). *Am. J. Med.* **37**, 327.
Chassan, J. B. (1967). "Research Design and Clinical Psychology and Psychiatry." Appleton, New York. 280 pp.
Greiner, T. (1962). *J. Am. Med. Assoc.* **181**, 120.
Handy, R. (1964). "Methodology of the Behavioral Sciences." Thomas, Springfield, Illinois. 182 pp.
Joyce, C. R. B. (1962). *J. Chronic Diseases* **15**, 1025.
Lasagna, L. (1955). *J. Chronic Diseases* **1**, 353.
Lasagna, L. (ed.) (1966). *In* "International Encyclopedia of Pharmacology and Therapeutics," Sect. 6, Vols. 1 and 2. Pergamon Press, Long Island City, N.Y.
Modell, W. (1962). *Clin. Pharmacol. Therap.* **3**, 235.
Nodine, J. H., and Siegler, P. E. (eds.) (1964). "Animal and Clinical Pharmacologic Techniques in Drug Evaluation." Year Book Publ., Chicago, Illinois. 325 pp.
Okun, R. (1965). *Proc. Western Pharmacol. Soc.* **8**, 23.
Parkhouse, J. (1964). *Proc. Roy. Soc. Med.* **57**, 67.
Reznikoff, M., and Toomey, L. C. (1959). "Evaluation of Changes Associated with Psychiatric Treatment." Thomas, Springfield, Illinois. 132 pp.
Rosenbloom, S. E. *et al.* (1961). *New Engl. J. Med.* **264**, 164.
Weatherall, M. (1968). *In* "Psychopharmacology; Dimensions and Perspectives" (C. R. B. Joyce, ed.), p. 1. Tavistock, London; Lippincott, Philadelphia and Toronto.
Wittenborn, J. R., and May, P. R. A. (eds.) (1966). "Prediction of Response to Pharmacotherapy." Thomas, Springfield, Illinois. 231 pp.
Wolf, S. (1950). *J. Clin. Invest.* **29**, 100.

Chapter 30
E. Gocka, Structural Equations for Linear Statistical Estimation in Psychopharmacology

Beebe, G. W. (1957). "Statistics and Clinical Investigation," Med. Bull. MB-2. Vet. Admin., Washington, D.C.

Benor, D., and Ditman, K. S. (1967). *Clin. Pharmacol.* **7**, 68.
Butler, D. C. (1968). "Design of Experiments," Tech. Doc., WRSC S-07-78. Western Res. Support Center, Vet. Admin. Hosp., Sepulveda, California 91343.
Chessick, R. D., and McFarland, R. L. (1963). *J. Am. Med. Assoc.* **185**, 237.
Cohen, J. (1964). *In* "Handbook of Clinical Psychology" (B. B. Wolman, ed.), p. 9. McGraw-Hill, New York.
Edwards, A. L. (1954). "Handbook of Social Psychology" (G. Lindzey, ed.), Vol. I, p. 259. Addison-Wesley, Boston, Massachusetts.
Feinstein, A. R. (1964). *Ann. Internal Med.* [N.S.] **61**, 564.
Gocka, E. F. (1967). "Theory and Application of Regression Models," Chapter I, Tech. Doc. Western Res. Support Center, Vet. Admin. Hosp., Sepulveda, California 91343.
Lasky, J. J. (1962). *J. Nervous Mental Disease* **135**, 332.
Mainland, D. (1968). "Notes on Biometry in Medical Research," Note 10, Vet. Admin. Monograph 10-1, Suppl. 2. U.S. Govt. Printing Office, Washington, D.C.
Overall, J. E., and Hollister, L. E. (1967). *Arch. Gen. Psychiat.* **16**, 152.

Chapter 32
J. del Giudice, Placebo

Baker, A. A., and Thorpe, J. G. (1957). *A.M.A. Arch. Neurol. Psychiat.* **78**, 57.
Dinnerstein, D. J. *et al.* (1966). *Perspectives Biol. Med.* **10**, 103.
Efron, R. (1967). *Perspectives Biol. Med.* **9**, 488; **11**, 9 resp.
Fisher, S. (1967). *Diseases Nervous System* **28**, 510.
Gelfand, S. *et al.* (1963). *J. Nervous Mental Disease* **136**, 379.
Goldberg, S. C., and Mattsson, N. B. (1968). *Diseases Nervous System* **29**, 153.
Hollister, L. E. (1960). *Current Therap. Res.* **2**, 477.
Honigfeld, G. (1964). *Diseases Nervous System* **25**, 145.
Liberman, R. (1962). *J. Chronic Diseases* **15**, 761.
Liberman, R. (1964). *J. Psychiat. Res.* **2**, 233.
Loranger, A. W. *et al.* (1961). *J. Am. Med. Assoc.* **176**, 920.
Park, L. C. *et al.* (1966). *J. Nervous Mental Disease* **143**, 199.
Parkhouse, J. (1963). *Nature* **199**, 308.
Penick, S. B., and Fisher, S. (1965). *Psychosomat. Med.* **27**, 177.
Pogge, R. C. (1963). *Med. Times* **8**, 773 and 778.
Pogge, R. C., and Coats, E. A. (1962). *Nebraska State Med. J.* **47**, 337.
Ross, S. *et al.* (1968). *J. Nervous Mental Disease* **146**, 328.
Rubin, W. (1963). *Arch. Otolaryngol.* **77**, 6.
Shapiro, A. K. (1964). *J. Am. Med. Assoc.*, **187**, 712.
Snell, P. (1956). *Current Res. in Anesthesia Analgesia* **35**, 495.
Trouton, D. S. (1957). *J. Mental Sci.* **103**, 344.
Wolf, S. (1959). *Pharmacol. Rev.* **2**, 689.

Chapter 33
E. Caffey, L. Hollister, C. J. Klett, and S. C. Kaim, Veterans Administration (VA) Cooperative Studies in Psychiatry

Anonymous. (1968). Vet. Admin. Cooperative Studies in Psychiatry. *In* "Highlights of the Thirteenth Annual Conference, Denver, April 4–6." Vet. Admin., Washington, D.C. 100 pp.
Galbrecht, C. R. *et al.* (1968). *Comp. Psychiat.* **9**, 482.

Chapter 36
J. del Giudice, Ethical Design and Clinical Psychopharmacologic Research

Alexander, L. (1948). *Am. J. Psychiat.* **105**, 170.
Alexander, L. (1949). *New Engl. J. Med.* **241**, 39.
Alexander, L. (1966). *Diseases Nervous System* **27**, 61.
Anonymous.(1964). *Science* **135**, 1024.
Anonymous Editorial. (1948). *J. Am. Med. Assoc.* **136**, 457.
Anonymous Editorial. (1962). *Brit. Med. J.* **II**, 1108.
Anonymous Editorial. (1964). *New Engl. J. Med.* **271**, 473.
Anonymous Editorial. (1966a). *Pediatrics* **38**, 373.
Anonymous Editorial. (1966b). *J. New Drugs* **6**, 366.
Ayd, F. J., Jr. (1965). *In* "International Psychiatry Clinics" (N. S. Kline and H. E. Lehman, eds.), Vol. II, p. 909. Little, Brown, Boston, Massachusetts.
Ayd, F. J., Jr. (ed.) (1968). Medical-Moral Newsletter. Baltimore, Maryland.
Bean, W. B. (1952). *J. Lab. Clin. Med.* **39**, 3.
Beecher, H. K. (1959). *J. Am. Med. Assoc.* **169**, 461.
Beecher, H. K. (1966a). *New Engl. J. Med.* **274**, 1354.
Beecher, H. K. (1966b). *J. Am. Med. Assoc.* **195**, 1135.
Beecher, H. K. (1966c). *J. Am. Med. Assoc.* **195**, 34.
Bressler, B. *et al.* (1959). *Am. J. Psychiat.* **116**, 522.
Efron, R. (1967). *Perspectives Biol. Med.* **11**, 9.
Freund, P. A. (1965). *New Engl. J. Med.* **273**, 687.
Greiner, T. (1962). *J. New Drugs* **2**, **7**.
Guttentag, O. E. (1953). *Science* **117**, 207.
Hamblen, J. W. (1966). *Science* **151**, 1174.
Hayman, M. (1964). *Calif. Med.* **101**, 266.
Hill, A. B. (1963). *Brit. Med. J.* **I**, 1043.
Hilmar, N. A. (1968). *Am. J. Public Health* **58**, 324.
Hinkle, L. E., and Wolff, H. G. (1956). *A.M.A. Arch. Neurol. Psychiat.* **76**, 115.
Ivy, A. C. (1948). *Science* **108**, 1.
Ivy, A. C. (1949). *J. Am. Med. Assoc.* **139**, 131.
Kelman, H. C. (1967). *Psychol. Bull.* **67**, 1.
Kidd, A. M. (1953). *Science* **117**, 211.
Ladimer, I. (1966). *J. New Drugs* **6**, 313.
Ladimer, I., and Newman, R. W. (eds.) (1963). "Clinical Investigation in Medicine; Legal Ethical and Moral Aspects." Law-Med. Res. Inst., Boston University Press. 517 pp.
Lasagna, L., and von Felsinger, J. M. (1954). *Science* **120**, 359.
Lesse, S. (1964). *Am. J. Psychotherapy* **18**, 373.
Lynch, J. J. (1960). *Clin. Pharmacol. Therap.* **1**, 396.
McDonald, J. C. (1967). *J. Am. Med. Assoc.* **202**, 511.
Minchew, B. H., and Gallogly, C. (1967). *FDA (Food and Drug Admin.) Papers* **1**, 8.
Moore, F. D. (1960). *Clin. Pharmacol. Therap.* **1**, 149.
Page, I. H. *et al.* (1967). *Am. J. Cardiol.* **19**, 892.
Pappworth, M. H. (1962). *Twentieth Century* **172**, 66.
Research and Education Service, Department of Medicine and Surgery, Veterans Administration. (1967). "Medical Ethics and Research," Vet. Admin. Monograph 10-2. U.S. Govt. Printing Office, Washington, D.C.
Rogers, C. R., and Skinner, B. F. (1956). *Science* **124**, 1057.
Rosenheim, M. (1967). *Brit. Med. J.* **III**, 429.
Ruebhausen, O. M., and Brim, O. G. (1963). *Columbia Law Rev.* **65**, 1184.
Shawver, J. R. (1967). *Diseases Nervous System* **28**, 187.

Shimkin, M. B. (1953). *Science* **117,** 205.
Westin, A. F. (1967). "Privacy and Freedom." Atheneum, New York. 487 pp.

Chapter 37
A. Lindesmith, Psychology of Addiction—Drugs and the Law

Anslinger, H. J., and Tompkins, W. F. (1953). "The Traffic in Narcotics." Funk & Wagnalls, New York. 345 pp.
Chein, I. *et al.* (1964). "The Road to H." Basic Books, New York. 428 pp.
Eldridge, W. B. (1967). "Narcotics and the Law," 2nd ed. American Bar Foundation. Univ. of Chicago Press, Chicago, Illinois. 264 pp.
Glaser, E. M. (1966). "Psychological Basis of Habituation." Oxford Univ. Press, London and New York. 102 pp.
Lindesmith, A. R. (1947). "Opiate Addiction." Principia, Bloomington, Indiana. 238 pp.
Lindesmith, A. R. (ed.) (1961). "Drug Addiction: Crime or Disease?" Joint Comm. Am. Bar Assoc. and Am. Med. Assoc. Indiana Univ. Press, Bloomington, Indiana. 173 pp.
Lindesmith, A. R. (1965). "The Addict and the Law." Indiana Univ. Press, Bloomington, Indiana. 337 pp.
Nichols, J. R. (1965). *Sci. Am.* **212,** 80.
Nichols, J. R. *et al.* (1955). *J. Am. Pharm. Assoc., Sci. Ed.* **44,** 229.
O'Donnell, J. A., and Ball, J. C. (eds.) (1966). "Narcotic Addiction." Harper, New York. 248 pp.
Schur, E. M. (1962). "Narcotic Addiction in Britain and America." Indiana Univ. Press, Bloomington, Indiana. 281 pp.
Terry, C. E., and Pellens, M. (1928). "The Opium Problem." Ballière, London. 1042 pp.
Weeks, J. R. (1964). *Sci. Am.* **210,** 46.
Wikler, A. (1953). "Opiate Addiction." Thomas, Springfield, Illinois. 72 pp.
Wikler, A. (1968). *Res. Publ., Assoc. Res. Nervous Mental Disease* **46,** 590.
Wilner, D. M., and Kassebaum, G. G. (eds.) (1965). "Narcotics." McGraw-Hill, New York, 302 pp.

Chapter 38
E. R. Bloomquist, The Use and Abuse of Stimulants

Bell, D. S., and Trethowan, W. H. (1961a). *Arch. Gen. Psychiat.* **4,** 474.
Bell, D. S., and Trethowan, W. H. (1961b). *J. Nervous Mental Disease* **133,** 489.
Connell, P. H. (1958). *Maudsley Monograph No. 5,* p. 57. Chapman and Hall, London.
Kiloh, L. B., and Brandon, S. (1962). *Brit. Med. J.* **II,** 40.
Leake, C. D. (1958). "The Amphetamines." Thomas, Springfield, Illinois. 167 pp.
McConnell, W. B. (1963). *Brit. J. Psychiat.* **109,** 218.
McCormick, J. C., Jr. (1962). *J. Diseases Nervous System* **23,** 219.
Seevers, M. H. (1965). *Postgrad. Med.* **37,** 1.

Chapter 39
S. Cohen, Hallucinogens

Allen, J. R., and West, L. J. (1968). *Am. J. Psychiat.* **125,** 364.
Alpert, R. *et al.* (1966). *In* "LSD" (C. S. Smith, ed.), p. 128. New American Library, New York.
Andén, N. E. *et al.* (1968). *Brit. J. Pharmacol.* **34,** 1.
Blacker, K. H. *et al.* (1968). *Am. J. Psychiat.* **125,** 341.
Bromberg, W. (1968). *Am. J. Psychiat.* **125,** 391.

Clark, L. D., and Nakashima, E. N. (1968). *Am. J. Psychiat.* **125**, 379.
Cohen, S. (1964). "The Beyond Within: The LSD Story." Atheneum, New York. 268 pp.
Cohen, S. (1966a). *Ann. Rev. Pharmacol.* **7**, 30.
Cohen, S. (1966b). *Psychosomatics* **7**, 182.
Cohen, S. (1968). *Am. J. Psychiat.* **125**, 393.
Freedman, D. X. (1967). *In* "Ethnopharmacologic Search for Psychoactive Drugs" (D. H. Efron *et al.*, eds.), Public Health Serv. Publ. No. 1645, p. 77. U.S. Dept. Health, Education and Welfare, Washington, D.C.
Giarman, H. J., and Freedman, D. X. (1965). *Pharmacol. Rev.* **17**, 1.
Hoffer, A. (1965). *Clin. Pharmacol. Therap.* **6**, 183.
Jacobsen, E. (1968). *In* "Psychopharmacology; Dimensions and Perspectives" (C. R. B. Joyce, ed.), p. 175. Tavistock, London; Lippincott, Philadelphia and Toronto.
Keeler, M. H. (1968). *Am. J. Psychiat.* **125**, 386.
Keeler, M. H. *et al.* (1968). *Am. J. Psychiat.* **125**, 384.
Kwan, V. H. Y., and Rajeswaran, P. M. C. (1968). *J. Forensic Sci.* **13**, 279.
McGlothlin, W. H., and West, L. J. (1968). *Am. J. Psychiat.* **125**, 370.
NLM Literature Search. (1964–1968). "Adverse Effects of LSD," L.S. No. 24–68. Natl. Library Med., Bethesda, Maryland.
Ungerleider, J. T. *et al.* (1968). *Am. J. Psychiat.* **125**, 352.

Chapter 40
J. Mendelson, Alcohol

"Alcohol and Alcoholism." (1967). Publ. No. 1640. Natl. Inst. Mental Health, Natl. Center for Prevention and Control of Alcoholism, Chevy Chase, Maryland. 73 pp.
Chafetz, M. E., and Demone, H. W., Jr. (1962). "Alcoholism and Society." Oxford Univ. Press, London and New York. 319 pp.
Isselbacher, K. J., and Greenberger, N. J. (1964). *New Engl. J. Med.* **270**, 351 and 402.
Jellinek, E. M. (1960). "The Disease Concept of Alcoholism." Hillhouse Press, New Haven, Connecticut. 246 pp.
Lolli, G. *et al.* (1959). "Alcohol in Italian Culture." Rutgers Center of Alcohol Studies, New Brunswick, New Jersey. 140 pp.
Lucia, S. P. (ed.) (1963). "Alcohol and Civilization." McGraw-Hill, New York, 416 pp.
McCord, W. J. (1960). "Origins of Alcoholism." Stanford Univ. Press, Stanford, California. 193 pp.
Mendelson, J. H. (ed.) (1964). *Quart. J. Studies Alc.* Suppl. 2, 226 and 235.
Mendelson, J. H. (ed.) (1966a). "Alcoholism." Little, Brown, Boston, Massachusetts. 260 pp.
Mendelson, J. H. (1966b). *Psychosomat. Med.* **28**, 1.
Pittman, D. J., and Snyder, C. R. (eds.) (1962). "Society, Culture, and Drinking Patterns." Wiley, New York. 616 pp.
Pittman, D. J., and Sterne, M. W. (1965). "Report on Alcoholism: Community Agency Attitudes and Their Impact on Treatment Services," Public Health Serv. Rept. No. 1273. 54 pp.
Roueche, B. (1960). "The Neutral Spirit: A Portrait of Alcohol." Little, Brown, Boston, Massachusetts. 151 pp.
Sadoun, R. *et al.* (1965). "Drinking in French Culture." Rutgers Center of Alcohol Studies, New Brunswick, New Jersey. 133 pp.

Chapter 41
M. Hayman and J. del Giudice, Psychotropic Drugs in Alcoholism

Acton, C. (1968). *Diseases Nervous System* **29**, 265.
Benor, D., and Ditman, K. S. (1966). *J. New Drugs* **6**, 319.

Benor, D., and Ditman, K. S. (1967). *J. Clin. Pharmacol.* **7**, 17.
Catanzaro, R. J. (1968). "Alcoholism, the Total Treatment Approach." Thomas, Springfield, Illinois. 528 pp.
Charnoff, S. *et al.* (1963). *Am. J. Med. Sci.* **246**, 89.
Ditman, K. S. (1961). *Quart. J. Studies Alc.* Suppl. 1, 107.
Ditman, K. S., and Cohen, S. (1959). *Quart. J. Studies Alc.* **20**, 573.
Eerola, R. (1963). *Acta Anaesthesiol. Scand.* **7**, 87.
Fox, R. (1967a). "Alcoholism: Behavioral Research, Therapeutic Approaches." Springer, Berlin. 340 pp.
Fox, R. (1967b). *Am. J. Psychother.* **21**, 585.
Goldberg, L. (1961). *Quart. J. Studies Alc.* Suppl. 1, 37.
Hayman, M. (1966). "Alcholism: Mechanism and Management." Thomas, Springfield, Illinois. 315 pp.
Hoff, E. C. (1961). *Quart. J. Studies Alc.* Suppl. 1, 138.
Johnson, R. B. (1961). *Quart. J. Studies Alc.* Suppl. 1, 66.
Rosenfeld, J. E., and Bizzoco, D. H. (1961). *Quart. J. Studies Alc.* Suppl. 1, 77.
Smith, M. E. *et al.* (1961). *Quart. J. Studies Alc.* **22**, 241.
Tipton, D. L. *et al.* (1961). *Am. J. Physiol.* **200**, 1007.

Chapter 42
T. Curphey, E. S. Shneidman, and N. L. Farberow, Drugs, Deaths, and Suicides—Problems of the Coroner

Committee on Alcoholism and Addiction and Council on Mental Health. (1965). *J. Am. Med. Assoc.* **193**, 673.
Shneidman, E. S., and Swenson, D. D. (eds.) (1968). "Bulletin of Suicidology," Natl. Inst. Mental Health, U.S. Public Health Serv., Chevy Chase, Maryland.

Chapter 43
L. E. Hollister, Toxicology of Psychotherapeutic Drugs

Davis, J. M., Bartlett, E., and Termini, B. A. (1968). *Diseases Nervous System* **29**, 157.
Hollister, L. E. (1968a). *Pharmacol. Rev.* **8**, 491.
Hollister, L. E. (1968b). "Chemical Psychoses: LSD and Related Drugs" (Am. Lect. Living Chem.). Thomas, Springfield, Illinois. 260 pp.
Turunen, S., and Salminen, J. (1968). *Diseases Nervous System* **29**, 474.
Turunen, S. *et al.* (1967). *Nord. Psykiat. Tidskr.* **21**, 228.

Chapter 44
J. H. Jaffe, Treatment of Drug Abusers

Jaffe, J. H. (1965). *In* "The Pharmacological Basis of Therapeutics" (L. S. Goodman and A. Gilman, eds.), 3rd ed., p. 285. Macmillan, New York.
Martin, W. R. (1967). *Pharmacol. Rev.* **19**, 463.
Wilker, A. (1965). *In* "Narcotics" (D. M. Wilner and G. G. Kassebaum, eds.), p. 302. McGraw-Hill, New York.

Chapter 45
J. M. Suarez and R. B. Spencer, Drugs, Addiction, and Legal Psychiatry

Brain, R. (1961). *Brit. J. Drug Addict.* **57**, 81.

Bureau of Narcotics. (1966). "Prescribing and Dispensing of Narcotics Under Harrison Narcotic Law," Pamphlet No. 56 (3-66), U.S. Treasury Dept., Washington, D.C. 21 pp.

Davidson, H. A. (1965). "Forensic Psychiatry," 2nd ed. Ronald Press, New York. 473 pp.

Fact Sheet—Drug Abuse Control Amendments of 1965. (1966). Public Law 89-74. U.S. Dept. Health, Education and Welfare, Food and Drug Admin., Washington, D.C. 32 pp.

Guttmacher, M. S. (1968). "The Role of Psychiatry in Law" (Salmon Lecture). Thomas, Springfield, Illinois. 184 pp.

Law-Medicine Notes. (1964). *New Engl. J. Med.* **271**, 309.

Lindesmith, A. R. (1957). *Law Contemp. Problems* **22**, 138.

Lindesmith, A. R. (1965). "The Addict and the Law." Indiana Univ. Press, Bloomington, Indiana. 337 pp.

"Narcotics and Medical Practice," Council on Mental Health. (1967). *J. Am. Med. Assoc.* **202**, 137.

Public Health Serv. Publ. No. 1021. (1963). "Narcotic Drug Addiction," Mental Health Monograph No. 2. U.S. Dept. of Health, Education and Welfare, Washington, D.C. 22 pp.

Robitscher, J. B. (1966). "Pursuit of Agreement—Psychiatry and the Law." Lippincott, Philadelphia, Pennsylvania. 270 pp.

Schur, E. (1961). *J. Criminal Law, Criminol. Police Sci.* **51**, 619.

U.S. Dept. of Health, Education and Welfare. (1966). "Parole Decision-Making; The Control and Treatment of Narcotic Use," JB-5005, Parole Ser. Welfare Admin., Office of Juvenile Delinquency and Youth Development.

White House Conference on Narcotics and Drug Abuse. (1963). 330 pp.

World Health Organization. (1962). "Treatment of Drug Addicts—A Survey of Existing Legislation." Geneva, Switzerland. 46 pp.

Chapter 46
O. Hornykiewicz, C. Markham, W. G. Clark, and R. Fleming, Mechanisms of Extrapyramidal Side Effects of Therapeutic Agents

Barbeau, A. *et al.* (1955). "Parkinson's Disease. Trends in Research and Treatment." Grune & Stratton, New York. 171 pp.

Bordeleau, J. M. (ed.) (1961). "Extrapyramidal System and Neuroleptics." Editions Psychiatriques, Montreal. 574 pp.

Costa, E. *et al.* (eds.) (1966). "Biochemistry and Pharmacology of the Basal Ganglia." Raven Press, Hewlett, New York. 238 pp.

Duvoisin, R. C. (1967). *Arch. Nerol.* **17**, 124.

Gebbink, T. B. (1967). "Structure and Connections of the Basal Ganglia in Man." Van Gorcum, Assen, The Netherlands. 159 pp.

Haase, H., and Janssen, P. A. (eds.) (1965). "The Action of Neuroleptic Drugs." North-Holland Publ., Amsterdam. 174 pp.

Jenden, D. J. (1968). *In* "Selected Pharmacological Testing Methods" (A. Burger, ed.), Vol. 3, p. 337. Marcel Dekker, New York.

Nashold, S. S., Jr., and Huber, W. V. (eds.) (1966). "The Second Symposium on Parkinson's Disease." *J. Neurosurg.* **24**, Suppl., Part II. 481 pp.

Chapter 47
J. Davis, Clinical Use of Phenothiazines

Adelson, D., and Esptein, L. (1962). *J. Nervous Mental Disease* **134,** 543.
Anonymous. (1966). "Stelazine Brand of Trifluoperazine in Psychiatry." Smith, Kline & French Laboratories, Philadelphia, Pennsylvania.
Anonymous. (1968a). "Thorazine Brand of Chlorporomazine Fundamental in Psychiatry." Smith, Kline & French Laboratories, Philadelphia, Pennsylvania. 68 pp.
Anonymous. (1968b). "The Clinical Uses of Compazine Brand of Prochlorperazine." Smith, Kline & French Laboratories, Philadelphia, Pennsylvania. 39 pp.
Casey, J. R. *et al.* (1960a). *Am. J. Psychiat.* **117,** 97.
Casey, J. F. *et al.* (1960b). *Arch. Gen. Psychiat.* **2,** 210.
Cole, J. O., and Davis, J. M. (1970). *In* "Schizophrenia" (L. Bellak, ed.). Grune & Stratton New York (in press).
Crane, G. E. (1968). *Am. J. Psychiat.* **124,** 40.
Davis, J. M. (1968). *Arch. Gen. Psychiat.* **13,** 552.
* Gittelman-Klein, R., and Klein, D. F. (1967). Long-term effects of 'antipsychotic' agents: A review. *Proc. Am. Coll. Neuropsychopharmaciol., San Juan, Puerto Rico, 1966,* p. 119. U.S. Govt. Printing Office, Washington, D.C.
Goldberg, S. C. (1967). Prediction of response to antipsychotic drugs. *Paper, Am. Coll. Neuropsychopharmacol., San Juan, Puerto Rico, 1966,* p. 1101. U.S. Govt. Printing Office, Washington, D.C.
Hanlon, T. E. *et al.* (1965). *Psychopharmacologia* **7,** 89.
Hollister, L. E. (1961). *New Engl. J. Med.* **264,** 291.
Hollister, L. E. (1965). *Practitioner* **194,** 72.
Hollister, L. E. (1966). *Clin. Pharmacol. Therap.* **7,** 142.
Klein, D. F. (1967). *Arch. Gen. Psychiat.* **16,** 118.
Kline, N. S. (1968). *Am. J. Psychiat.* **124,** Suppl. 48.
Kline, N. S., and Lehmann, E. E. (eds.) (1965). "Psychopharmacology." Little, Brown, Boston, Massachusetts. 321 pp.
Lasky, J. J. *et al.* (1962). *Diseases Nervous System* **23,** 698.
May, P. R. A., and Tuma, A. H. (1964). *J. Nervous Mental Disease* **139,** 362.
May, P. R. A., and Tuma, A. H. (1965). *Brit. J. Psychiat.* **111,** 503.
Michaux, M. H. *et al.* (1966). *Current Therap. Res.* **8,** Suppl. 117.
National Institute of Mental Health. Psychopharmacology Service Center Collaborative Study Group. (1964). *Arch. Gen. Psychiat.* **10,** 246.
National Institute of Mental Health. Psychopharmacology Service Center Collaborative Study Group (1966). Prepubl. Rept. No. 6, Bethesda, Maryland.
Passamanick, B. *et al.* (1967). "Schizophrenics in the Community. An Experimental Study in the Prevention of Hospitalization." Appleton, New York, 448 pp.
Schiele, B. C. *et al.* (1961). *J. Clin. Exptl. Psychopathol. & Quart. Rev. Psychiat. Neurol.* **22,** 151.
Vestre, N. D. *et al.* (1962). *J. Clin. Exptl. Psychopathol. & Quart. Rev. Psychiat. Neurol.* **23,** 149.

Chapter 48
H. Lehmann and T. Ban, Clinical Use of Other Antipsychotic Drugs

Cole, J. O. (1967). *Intern. J. Neuropsychiat.* **3,** Suppl. 1, S150.
Crane, G. E. (1967). *Intern. J. Neuropsychiat.* **3,** Suppl. 1, S111.

* Editorial footnote: Cf. Gittelman-Klein, R., and Klein, D. F. (1967). Follow-up of patients treated with antipsychotic drugs." *Paper, Am. Coll. Neuropsychopharmacol., San Juan, Puerto Rico, 1966,* p. 1119. U.S. Govt. Printing Office, Washington, D.C.

Gallant, D. M. *et al.* (1966). *Current Therap. Res.* **8**, 153.
Gordon, M. (ed.) (1964). "Psychopharmacological Agents," Vol. 1. Academic Press, New York. 678 pp.
Kurland, A. A., and Yazicioglu, E. (1961). *Diseases Nervous System* **22**, 11, 636.
Lehmann, H. E. (1961). *Can. Med. Assoc. J.* **85**, 1145.
Lehmann, H. E., and Ban, T. A. (eds.) (1964). "The Butyrophenones in Psychiatry." First North American Symposium Organized by Quebec Psychopharmacological Research Association, 6875 LaSalle Blvd., Verdun, Quebec. 164 pp.

Chapter 49
G. L. Klerman, and E. S. Paykel, The Tricyclic Antidepressants

Adams, B. O. (1968). *In* "Psychopharmacology; Dimensions and Perspectives" (C. R. B. Joyce, ed.), p. 149. Tavistock, London; Lippincott, Philadelphia and Toronto.
Angst, J. (1961). *Psychopharmacologia* **2**, 381.
Davis, J. *et al.* (1967). Drugs used in the treatment of depression. *Paper, Am. Coll. Neuropsychopharmacol., San Juan, Puerto Rico, 1966,* p. 719. U.S. Govt. Printing Office, Washington, D.C.
Efron, D. H., and Kety, S. S. (eds.) (1966). "Antidepressant Drugs of Monoamine Inhibitor Type," Workshop Ser. Pharmacol. Unit, Natl. Inst. Mental Health, Rept. No. 1. Public Health Serv., Bethesda, Maryland. 213 pp.
Friday, G. A., and Feldman, E. C. (1966). *Clin. Pediat. (Philadelphia)* **5**, 175.
Glowinski, J. *et al.* (1965). *J. Neurochem.* **12**, 25.
Greenblatt, M. *et al.* (1964). *Am. J. Psychiat.* **120**, 935.
Hollister, L. E. *et al.* (1967). *Arch. Gen. Psychiat.* **17**, 486.
Honigfeld, G. (1964). *Diseases Nervous System* **25**, 145.
Hordern, A. *et al.* (1964). *Brit. J. Psychiat.* **110**, 641.
Imlah, N. W. *et al.* (1965). *Neuropsychopharmacol.* **4**, 438.
Jensen, E., and Schulsinger, F. (1963). *Acta Psychiat. Scand.* **39**, Suppl., 244.
Klerman, G. L. (1966). *In* "Pharmacotherapy of Depression" (J. Cole and J. R. Wittenborn, eds.), p. 134. Thomas, Springfield, Illinois.
Neff, N. H., and Costa, E. (1967). *In* "Antidepressant Drugs" (S. Garattini and M. N. G. Dukes, eds.), p. 28. Excerpta Med. Found., Amsterdam.
Pare, C. M. B. *et al.* (1962). *Lancet* **II**, 1340.
Stark, J. E., and Bethune, D. W. (1965). *Lancet* **II**, 390.
Steel, C. M. *et al.* (1967). *Brit. Med. J.* **II**, 663.
Wilson, I. C. *et al.* (1964). *Psychosomatics* **5**, 88.

Chapter 50
G. E. Crane, Use of Monamine Oxidase Inhibiting Antidepressants

Atkinson, R. M., and Ditman, K. S. (1965). *Clin. Pharmacol. Therap.* **6**, 631.
Bennett, I. F. (1966a). *Proc. 2nd Intern. Congr Hormonal Steroids, Milan, 1965* Exerpta Med. Intern. Congr. Ser. No. 111, Abstr. 375, p. 215. Excerpta Med. Found., Amsterdam.
Bennett, I. F. (1966b). *In* "Prediction of Response to Pharmacotherapy" (J. R. Wittenborn and P. R. A. May, eds.), p. 102. Thomas, Springfield, Illinois.
British Medical Research Council. (1965). *Brit. Med. J.* **I**, 881.
Greenblatt, M. *et al.* (1964). *Am. J. Psychiat.* **120**, 935.
Kline, N. S. (1964). *J. Am. Med. Assoc.* **190**, 732.
Smith, Kline & French Laboratories. (1967). "Prescribing Information," Part 27, p. 1. Philadelphia, Pennsylvania.

Symposium on the Biochemical and Clinical Aspects of Marsilid and Other Monoamine Oxidase Inhibitors. (1958). *J. Clin. Exptl. Psychopathol. & Quart. Rev. Psychiat. Neurol.* **19**, 1.
Wechsler, H. *et. al.* (1965). *J. Nervous Mental Disease* **141**, 231.
Wittenborn, J. R. (1966). *In* "Prediction of Response to Pharmacotherapy" (J. R. Wittenborn and P. R. A. May, eds.), p. 125. Thomas, Springfield, Illinois.

Chapter 52
J. del Giudice, Antianxiety Drugs

Ayd, F. J., Jr. (1962). *J. Neuropsychiat.* **3**, 177.
Ayd, F. J., Jr. (1964). *Psychosomatics* **5**, 82.
Ayd, F. J., Jr. (1965). *Am. J. Nursing* **65**, 89.
Barrett, J. E., and DiMarcio, A. (1966). *Diseases Nervous System* **27**, 483.
Benson, W. M., and Schiele, B. C. (1962). "Tranquilizing and Antidepressant Drugs." Thomas, Springfield, Illinois. 89 pp.
Caffey, E. M. *et al.* (1966). "Antipsychotic, Antianxiety and Antidepressive Drugs." Med. Bull. MB-11. Vet. Admin., Washington, D.C. 28 pp.
Daneman, E. A. (1964). *J. Med. Assoc. Georgia* **53**, 55.
Dickel, H. A. *et al.* (1962). *Psychosomatics* 3, 129.
Ditman, K. S., and Gottlieb, L. (1964). *Am. J. Psychiat.* **120**, 910.
Gardos, B. *et al.* (1968). *Arch. Gen. Psychiat.* **18**, 757.
Halpern, M. M. (1968). *Clin. Med.* **75**, 42.
Hollister, L. E. (1964). *Clin. Pharmacol. Therap.* **5**, 322.
Hollister, L. E. (1965). *Practitioner* **194**, 72.
Hunt, H. F. (1957). *Ann. N.Y. Acad. Sci.* **67**, 712.
Korchin, S. J., and Heath, H. A. (1961). *J. Consult. Psychol.* **25**, 398.
Lear, E. *et al.* (1961). *Anesthesiology* **22**, 529.
Lear, E. (1966). "Chemistry and Applied Pharmacology of Tranquilizers." Thomas, Springfield, Illinois. 117 pp.
Malmo, R. B., and Shagoss, C. (1949). *Psychosomat. Med.* **2**, 9.
Margulis, D. L., and Stein, L. (1968). *Psychopharmacologia* **13**, 74.
O'Connor, J. P. *et al.* (1956). *J. Clin. Psychol.* **12**, 160.
Sadove, M. S., and Albrecht, R. F. (1968). *Med. Clin. N. Am.* **52**, 47.
Wittenborn, J. R. (1966). "The Clinical Psychopharmacology of Anxiety." Thomas, Springfield, Illinois. 228 pp.

Chapter 54
H. Eveloff, Pediatric Psychopharmacology

Alderton, H. R. *et al.* (1964). *Can. Psychiat. Assoc. J.* **9**, 239.
Allen, M. *et al.* (1963). *Am. J. Mental Deficiency* **68**, 63.
Baldwin, R. W., and Kenny, T. J. (1966). *Current Therap. Res.* **8**, 373.
Beaudry, P., and Gibson, D. (1960). *Am. J. Mental Deficiency* **64**, 823.
Bender, L., and Collington, F. (1942). *Am. J. Psychiat.* **99**, 116.
Bender, L., and Fareta, G. (1961). *Diseases Nervous System* **22**, Suppl. 4, 110.
Bradley, C., and Bowen, M. (1941). *Am. J. Orthopsychiat.* **11**, 92.
Conners, C. K. (1964). *J. Consult. Psychol.* **28**, 14.
Conners, C. K. *et al.* (1963). *Am. J. Psychiat.* **120**, 458.
Cytryn, L. *et al.* (1960). *Am. J. Orthopsychiat.* **30**, 113.
De Negri, M. *et al.* (1963). *Infanzia anormale* **54**, 419.
Eisenberg, L. *et al.* (1961). *Am. J. Psychiat.* **117**, 1088.

Fish, B. (1963). *Current Psychiat. Therap.* **3**, 82.
Geller, S. J. (1960). *J. Am. Med. Assoc.* **174**, 481.
Harman, C., and Winer, D. A. (1966). *Inter. J. Neuropsychiat.* **2**, 72.
Knobel, M. (1962). *Arch. Gen. Psychiat.* **6**, 198.
Kraft, I. A. *et al.* (1965). *Intern. J. Neuropsychiat.* **1**, 433.
Krakowski, A. J. (1965). *Psychosomatics* **6**, 355.
Laveck, G. D., and Buckley, P. (1961). *J. Chronic Diseases* **13**, 174.
Sereni, F., and Principi, N. (1968). *Pharmacol. Rev.* **8**, 453.
Shaw, C. R. *et al.* (1963). *J. Am. Acad. Child. Psychiat.* **2**, 725.
Zrull, J. P. *et al.* (1963). *Am. J. Psychiat.* **120**, 590.

APPENDIX

2

KEY REVIEWS, MONOGRAPHS, TEXTS, ETC.

I. History

Caldwell, A. (1970). "Origins of Psychopharmacology from CPZ to LSD." Thomas, Springfield, Illinois.

Holmstedt, B. (1967). Historical survey. *In* "Ethnopharmacologic Search for Psychoactive Drugs" (D. H. Efron *et al.*, eds.), Public Health Serv. Publ. No. 1645. U.S. Dept. Health, Education and Welfare, Washington, D.C. p. 3.

Holmstedt, B., and Liljestrand, G. (1963). "Readings in Pharmacology." Pergamon Press, Oxford. 408 pp.

Leake, C. D. (ed.) "International Encyclopedia of Pharmacology and Therapeutics." Sect. I, Vol. 1: History. Pergamon Press, Long Island City, New York (in press).

Lewin, L. (1964). Phantastica Narcotic and Stimulating Drugs," 2nd ed. Routledge & Kegan, London. 335 pp.

McKnight, W. K. (1958). Historical Landmarks in Research on Schizophrenia in the United States. *Am. J. Psychiat.* **114**, 873.

Wolestenholme, G. E. W., and Knight, J. (eds.) (1965). "Hashish—Its Chemistry and Pharmacology," Ciba Found. Study Group No. 21. Little, Brown. Boston, Massachusetts. 96 pp.

II. Chemistry (Organic, Pharmaceutical Chemistry, Pharmacy, Structure–Activity Relationships, Syntheses, Structures, Drug Name Lists, Nomenclature, etc.)

Aleksandrovsky, Y. A. *et al.* (1963). "Psychopharmacological Compounds," Rept. No. 63-41237. Clearing House for Scientific and Technical Information, U.S. Dept. Commerce, Washington, D.C. (transl.). 26 pp.

Ariëns, E. J. (1966). Molecular pharmacology, a basis for drug design. *Fortschr. Arzneimittelforsch.* **10**, 429.

Bovet, D., and Bovet-Nitti, F. (1948). "Médicaments du Système Nerveux Végétatif-structure et activite pharmacodynamique." Karger, Basel. 849 pp.

Bradley, P. B. (1963). Tranquilizers: Phenothiazine derivatives. *In* "Physiological Pharmacology. A Comprehensive Treatise" (W. S. Root and F. G. Hofmann, eds.), Vol. 1, p. 417. Academic Press, New York.

Brunings, K. J., and Lindgren, P. (eds.) (1962). Mode of Action of Drugs. Vol. 7, "Modern Concepts in the Relationship Between Structure and Pharmacological Activity." Macmillan, New York. 247 pp.

Burger, A. ed. (1968). "Drugs Affecting the Central Nervous System," Medicinal Research: Vol. 2. Marcel Dekker, New York. 437 pp.

Cain, C. K. *et al.* (1964). Benzoxazoles, benzothiazoles and benzimidazoles. *In* "Psychopharmacological Agents" (M. Gordon, ed.), Vol. 1, p. 325. Academic Press, New York.

Cerletti, A. von (1960). Über Vorkommen und Bedeutung der Indolstruktur in der Medizin und Biologie. *Progr. Drug Res.* **2**, 227.

Chi, Ju-yun. (1965). "Shen ching hsi t'ung yao wu hua hsueh" (Chemistry of drugs for nervous system disorders). K'o Hsueh ch'u pan she, Peking (in Chinese. Index in English). 268 pp.

Childress, S. J. (1967). Antipsychotic and anti-anxiety agents. *In* "Annual Reports in Medicinal Chemistry, 1966" (C. K. Cain, ed.), Vol. 2, p. 1. Academic Press, New York.

Domino, E. F. *et al.* (1968). Substituted phenothiazines: Pharmacology and chemical structure. *In* "Drugs Affecting the Nervous System" (A. Burger ed.), Medicinal Research: Vol. 2, p. 327. Marcel Dekker, New York.

Donahue, H. B., and Kimura, K. K. (1968). Synthetic centrally acting skeletal muscle relaxture. *In* "Drugs Affecting the Nervous System" (A. Burger ed.), Medicinal Research: Vol. 2, p. 265. Marcel Dekker, New York.

Foldes, F. F., and Foldes, V. M. (1962). The influence of chemical structure on the interaction of gamma-aminobutyryl-choline derivatives and human cholinesterases. *In* "Modern Concepts in the Relationship Between Structure and Pharmacological Activity" (B. Üvnas *et al.*, eds.), Mode of Action of Drugs: Vol. 7, p. 313 (Proc. 1st Intern. Pharmacol. Meeting, Stockholm, Sweden, 1961). Macmillan, New York.

Goldbaum, L. R., and Bomanski, T. J. (1965). An approach to the analysis of biological specimens for basic drugs. *Progr. Chem. Toxicol.* **2**, 221.

"International Encyclopedia of Pharmacology and Therapeutics." Sect. 5: Structure-Activity Relationships. Pergamon Press, Long Island City, New York (in press).

Janssen, P. A., and Van de Eycken, C. A. M. (1968). The chemical anatomy of potent morphine-like analgesics. *In* "Drugs Affecting the Nervous System" (A. Burger, ed.), Medicinal Research: Vol. 2, p. 25. Marcel Dekker, New York.

Jucker, E. (1963). Some new developments in the chemistry of psychotherapeutic agents. *Angew. Chem. Intern. Engl. ed.* **2**, 493; see also German ed. *Angew Chem.* **75**, 524 (1963).

Kelleher, R. T., and Morse, W. H. (1968). Determinants of the specificity of behavioral effects of drugs. *Ergeb. Physiol., Biol. Chem. Exptl. Pharmakol.* **60**, 1.

Korte, R., and Sieper, H. (1965). Recent results of Hashish analysis. *In* "Hashish—Its Chemistry and Pharmacology" (G. E. W. Wolstenholme and J. Knight, eds.), Ciba Found. Study Group No. 21, p. 51. Little, Brown, Boston, Massachusetts.

Lebeau, P. *et al.* (eds.) (1955–1956). "Traite de pharmacie chimique," 5 vols. Masson, Paris. 4140 pp.

Lewis, J. J. (1963). Tranquilizers: Rauwolfia derivatives. *In* "Physiological Pharmacology. A Comprehensive Treatise" (W. S. Root and F. G. Hofmann, eds.), Vol. 1, p. 479. Academic Press, New York.

Lucas, R. A., ed. (1963). The chemistry and pharmacology of the rauwolfia alkaloids. *Progr. Med. Chem.* **3**, 146.

Margolin, S. (1963). Effects on physiological systems: Non-barbiturates. *In* "Physiological

Pharmacology. A Comprehensive Treatise" (W. S. Root and F. G. Hofmann, eds.), Vol. 1, p. 23. Academic Press, New York.
Marler, E. E. J. (1967). "Pharmacological and Chemical Synonyms," 4th rev. ed. Excerpta Med. Found., Amsterdam. 349 pp.
Millichap, J. G. (1965). Anticonvulsant drugs. *In* "Physiological Pharmacology. A Comprehensive Treatise" (W. S. Root and F. G. Hofmann, eds.), Vol. 2, p. 97. Academic Press, New York.
Negwer, M. (1967). "Organisch Chemische Arzneimittel und ihre Synonyma," 3rd rev. and enlarged ed. Pergamon Press, Oxford. 1232 pp.
Patel, A. R., and Burger, A. (1966). 3,4-Dihydroxyphenylalanine and related compounds. *Progr. Drug Res.* **9**, 223.
Peterson, P. V., and Nielson, I. M. (1964) Thiaxanthene derivatives. *In* "Psychopharmacological Agents" (M. Gordon, ed.), Vol. 1, p. 301. Academic Press, New York.
Poser, C. M., and Osbourn, V. (1962). "International Dictionary of Drugs." Thomas, Springfield, Illinois. 157 pp.
Remmen, E. *et al.* (1962). "Psychochemotherapy. The Physician's Manual." Western Med. Publ., Los Angeles, California. 152 pp.
Schenker, E. von, and Herbst, H. (1963). Phenothiazine und Azaphenothazine als Arzneimittel. *Progr. Drug Res.* **5**, 269.
Schlittler, E., and Plummer, A. J. (1964). Tranquilizing drugs from rauwolfia. *In* "Psychopharmacological Agents" (M. Gordon, ed.), Vol. 1, p. 9. Academic Press, New York.
Spinks, A., and Young, E. H. P. (1962). The relation between structure and central nervous action of some hydrazine derivatives. *In* "Modern Concepts in the Relationship Between Structure and Pharmacological Activity" (B. Üvnas *et al.*, eds.), Vol. 7, p. 303. Macmillan, New York.
Sternbach, L. H. *et al.* (1968). Structure-activity relationships in the 1,4-benzodiazepine series. *In* "Drugs Affecting the Nervous System" (A. Burger, ed.), Medicinal Research: Vol. 2, p. 237. Marcel Dekker, New York.
Stolman, A. (1965). Thin layer chromatography application in toxicology. *Progr. Chem. Toxicol.* **2**, 321.
Usdin, E., and Efron, D. H. (1967). "Psychotropic Drugs and Related Compounds," Public Health Publ. No. 1589. U.S. Govt. Printing Office, Washington, D.C. 365 pp.
Üvnas, B. *et al.* (eds.) (1963). "Modern Concepts in the Relationship Between Structure and Pharmacological Activity," Mode of Action of Drugs: Vol. 7 (Proc. 1st Intern. Pharmacol. Meeting, Stockholm, Sweden, 1961). Macmillan, New York. 387 pp.
Yonkman, F. (ed.) (1954). Reserpine (Serpasil) and other alkaloids of *Rauwolfia serpentina* chemistry, pharmacology, and clinical application. *Ann. N.Y. Acad. Sci.* **59**, 1–140.

III. Neurophysiology and Psychophysiology (Preclinical and Basic Human)

Almajan, E., and Semen-Negrea, E. (1967). Probleme de specificitate in psikofarmacologic endocrina. *Studii cercetari Endocrinol.* **18**, 21.
Bekhtereva, N. R. *et al.* (eds.) (1966). "International Symposium on Human Deep Brain Structures in Normal and Pathological States." Nauke, Moscow. 288 pp. (in Russian).
Brazier, M. A. (1963). Effects upon physiological systems: The electrophysiological effects of barbiturates on the brain. *In* "Physiological Pharmacology. A Comprehensive Treatise" (W. S. Root and F. G. Hofmann, eds.), Vol. 1, p. 219. Academic Press, New York.
Brown, C. C. (ed.) (1968). "Methods in Psychophysiology." Williams & Wilkins, Baltimore, Maryland. 375 pp.
Brown, L. (1965). The Croonian Lecture, 1964. The fate and release of the transmitter liberated by adrenergic nerves. *Proc. Roy. Soc.* **B162**, 1.
Buchner, R., ed. (1966). "Neurovegetative Regulation." Springer, Berlin. 453 pp. ff.
Bureš, J. *et al.* (1967). "Electrophysiological Methods in Biological Research," 3rd rev. ed. Academic Press, New York. 824 pp.

Cameron, D. E., and Greenblatt, M. (eds) (1959). Recent advances in neurophysiological research. *Psychiat. Res. Rept.* **11**, 136.

Campbell, H. J. (1966). "Correlative Physiology of the Nervous System." Academic Press, New York. 313 pp.

Clemente, C. D., and Lindsley, D. B. (eds.) (1967). Brain function: Vol. 5. "Aggression and Defense. Neural Mechanisms and Social Patterns." Univ. of California Press, Los Angeles, California. 361 pp.

Cohen, R., and O'Leary, J. L. (1966). General neurophysiology. Bioelectric aspects. *Progr. Neurol. Psychiat.* **21**, 23.

Costa, E. *et al.* (eds.) (1966). "Biochemistry and Pharmacology of the Basal Ganglia." Raven Press, Hewlett, New York. 238 pp.

Eccles, J. C. (1961). The mechanism of synaptic transmission. *Ergeb. Physiol., biol. Chem. exptl. Pharmakol.* **51**, 229.

Eccles, J. C. (ed.) (1966). "Brain and Conscious Experience." Springer, Berlin. 590 pp.

Feldberg, W., and Fleischhauer, W. (1965). A new experimental approach to the physiology and pharmacology of the brain. *Brit. Med. Bull.* **21**, No. 1, 36.

Field, J. *et al.* (eds.) (1960). "Handbook of Physiology," Sect. 1: Neurophysiology, 3 vols. Williams & Wilkins, Baltimore, Maryland. 2013 pp.

Florey, E., ed. (1961). "Nervous Inhibition." Pergamon Press, Oxford. 475 pp.

Florey, E. (1967). Neurotransmitters and modulators in the animal kingdom. *Federation Proc.* **26**, 1164 (Symp).

Gaito, J. (1966). "Molecular Psychobiology." Thomas, Springfield, Illinois. 259 pp.

Glaser, G. H. (ed.) (1963). "EEG and Behavior." Basic Books, New York, 409 pp.

Glass, D. C. (ed.) (1967). "Neurophysiology and Emotions." Rockefeller Univ. Press and Russell Sage Found., New York. 234 pp.

Gorski, R. A., and Whalen, R. E. (1966). "Brain and Behavior," Vol. 3: The Brain and Gonadal Function. Univ. of California Press, Los Angeles, California, p. 289.

Grundfest, H. (1959). General physiology and pharmacology of synapses and some implications for the mammalian central nervous system. *J. Nervous Mental Disease* **128**, 473.

Himwich, H. E. (1965). Loci of actions of psychotropic drugs in the brain. *Folia Psychiat. Neurol. Japon.* **19**, 217.

Holtz, P., and Palm, D. (1966). Brenzkatechinamine und anderer sympathicomimetische Amine (Biosynthese und Inaktivierung, Freisetzung und Wirkung), *Ergeb. Physiol., biol. Chem. exptl. Pharmakol.* **58**, 592 pp.

"International Encyclopedia of Pharmacology and Therapeutics." Sect. 9: Physiology and Pharmacology of Synaptic Transmission. Pergamon Press, Long Island City, New York (in press).

Itil, T. M. (1964). "Elektroencephalographische Studien bei endogenen Psychosen und deren Behandlung mit psychotropen Medikamenten unter besonderer Berücksichtigung des Pentothal-elektroencephalograms." Ahmet Sait Mathaasi, Istanbul. 128 pp.

Itil, T. M. (1968). Electroencephalography and pharmacopsychiatry. *In* "Clinical Psychopharmacology, Modern Problems of Pharmacopsychiatry" (F. A. Freyhan *et al.,* eds.), Vol. 1, p. 163. Karger, Basel.

Kety, S. S. *et al.* (eds.) (1967). "Sleep and altered states of consciousness." *Res. Publ. Assoc. Res. Nervous Mental Disease.* 591 pp.

Leusen, I. (1962). Actions neurophysiologiques des mobilsateurs des monoamines et des inhibiteurs de la monoamines oxydase. *In* "Monoamines et système nerveux central" (J. de Ajuriaguerra, ed.), p. 119. Masson, Paris.

Longo, V. G. (1966). Behavioral and electroencephalographic effects of atropine and related compounds. *Pharmacol. Rev.* **18**, 965.

McDonald, D. G. (1965). Physiological correlates of mental disease. *Phychol. Rev.* **16**, 225.

McIlwain, H. (1963). Metabolic and electrical measurements with isolated cerebral tissues: Their contribution to study of the action of drugs on cortical excitability. In "Brain Function" (M. A. B. Brazier, ed.), Vol. 1, p. 49. Univ. of California Press, Los Angeles, California.

McLennan, H. (1965). Synaptic transmission in the central nervous system. *In* "Physiological Pharmacology. A Comprehensive Treatise" (W. S. Root and F. G. Hofmann, eds.), Vol. 2, p. 399. Academic Press, New York.
Malmo, R. B. (1957). Anxiety and behavioral arousal. *Psychol. Rev.* **64,** 276.
Marley, E. (1966). Behavioural and electrophysiological effects of catecholamines. *Pharmacol. Rev.* **18,** 753.
Marrazzi, A. S. (1963). The generality of cerebral synaptic drug response and its relation to psychosis. *Recent Advan. Biol. Psychiat.* **6,** 8.
Martini, L., and Ganong, W. F. (eds.) (1966, 1967). "Neuroendocrinology," Vols. 1 and 2. Academic Press, New York. 774 pp. and 777 pp. resp.
Nakajima, H., and Thullier, J. (1965). Contribution a l'étude des mecanismes d'action biochimique des drogues psychotropes, corrélation avec les effets pharmacologiques. *Encephale* **54,** 285.
Paton, W. D. M. (1968). The principles of drug action. *Proc. Roy. Soc. Med.* **33,** 815.
Roberts, E. *et al.* (eds.) (1960). "Inhibition in the Nervous System and Gamma-Aminobutyric Acid." Pergamon Press, Oxford. 591 pp.
Root, W. S., and Hofmann, F. G. (eds.) (1963, 1965, 1967). "Physiological Pharmacology. A Comprehensive Treatise," Vols. 1, 2, and 3. Academic Press, New York. 703 pp., 486 pp., and 519 pp. resp.
Sarkisov, S. A. (1966). "The Structure and Function of the Brain." Indiana Univ. Press, Bloomington, Indiana. 291 pp.
Stern, J. A., and McDonald, D. C. (1965). Physiological correlates of mental disease. *Ann. Rev. Psychol.* **16,** 225.
Stumpf, C. (1965). Drug action on the electrical activity of the hippocampus. *Rev. Neurobiol.* **8,** 77.
Volle, R. L. (1966). Modification by drugs of synaptic mechanisms in autonomic ganglia. *Pharmacol. Rev.* **18,** 839.
Welsh, J. H. (1955). Neurohormones. *In* "The Hormones: Physiology, Chemistry, and Applications" (G. Pincus and K. V. Thimann, eds.), Vol. 3, p. 97. Academic Press, New York.
Wolstenholme, G. E. W., and O'Connor, C. N. (eds.) (1958). "Neurological Basis of Behavior," Ciba Found. Symp. Little, Brown, Boston, Massachusetts. 400 pp.
Zimmer, H., and Krusberg, R. J. (1966). "Psychophysiological Components of Human Behavior. A Compendium." Univ. of Georgia Press, Athens, Georgia. 534 pp.

IV. Neuropharmacology, Pharmacology, Psychopharmacology (Preclinical and Basic Human)

Abramson, H. A. (ed.) (1955, 1956, 1957, 1959, 1960). "Neuropharmacology," Transactions of Five Conferences. Josiah Macy, Jr. Found., New York. 210 pp., 328 pp., 381 pp., 285 pp., and 251 pp. resp.
Anichkov, S. V. (1960). [Pharmacology of central cholinergic synapses.] *Farmakol. i Toksikol.* **23,** 194 (in Russian).
Ariëns, E. J. (ed.) (1964). "Molecular Pharmacology: The Mode of Action of Biologically Active Compounds," Part I, Vol. 1: Molecular Approach to General Pharmacology. Academic Press, New York. 503 pp.
Ariëns, E. J. (1966). Molecular pharmacology, a basis for drug design. *Fortschr. Arzneimittelforsch.* **10,** 429.
Baker, W. W. (1962). Pharmacology of the central nervous system. *Progr. Neurol. Psychiat.* **17,** 101.
Balestrieri, A. (1961). "Patologia Mentale e Farmacologia." Cedam, Padova. 258 pp.
Barry, H. *et al.* (1966). Drug effects on animal performance and the stress syndrome. *J. Pharm. Sci.* **55,** 1159.
Bickel, M. H. (1968). Untersuchungen zur Biochemie und Pharmakologie der Thymoleptika. *Progr. Drug Res.* **11,** 121.

Braceland, F. J., ed. (1959). The effect of pharmacologic agents on the nervous system. *Res. Publ., Assoc. Res. Nervous Mental Disease* **37**, 488 pp.

Bradley, P. B. (1963). Tranquilizers: Phenothiazine derivatives. *In* "Physiological Pharmacology. A Comprehensive Treatise" (W. S. Root and F. G. Hofmann, eds.), Vol. 1, p. 417. Academic Press, New York.

Bradley, P. B., and Fink, M. (eds.) (1968). Anticholinergic drugs and brain functions in animals and man. *Progr. Brain Res.* **28,** 184 pp.

Brazier, M. A. (1963). Effects upon physiological systems: The electrophysiological effects of barbiturates on the brain. *In* "Physiological Pharmacology. A Comprehensive Treatise" (W. S. Root and F. G. Hofmann, eds.), Vol. 1, p. 219. Academic Press, New York.

Brodie, B. B. (1964). Difficultes de transposer a l'homme les résultats experimentaux obtenus sur l'animal. *Actualites Pharmacol.* **17,** 1.

Brown, C. C. (ed.) (1968). "Methods in Psychophysiology." Williams & Wilkins, Baltimore, Maryland. 375 pp.

Brücke, F. T. von, and Hornykiewicz, O. (1966). "Pharmakologie der Psychopharmaka." Springer, Berlin. 136 pp.

Brunings, K. J., and Lindgren, P. (eds.) (1963). Mode of Action of Drugs. Vol. 7. "Modern Concepts in the Relationship Between Structure and Pharmacological Activity." Macmillan, New York. 247 pp.

Burger, A., ed. (1968). "Selected Pharmacological Testing Methods," Medicinal Research: Vol. 3. Marcel Dekker, New York. 515 pp.

Burn, J. H. (1965). Effect of psychopharmacological drugs on the circulation. *In* Handbook of Physiology" (Am. Physiol. Soc., J. Field, ed.), Sect. 2, Vol. III, p. 2441. Williams & Wilkins, Baltimore, Maryland.

Burn, J. H., and Rand, M. J. (1962). A new interpretation of the adrenergic nerve fiber. *Advan. Pharmacol.* **1,** 1.

Cain, C. K. (1967). Sedatives, hypnotics, anticonvulsants, muscle relaxants, general anesthetics. *In* "Annual Reports in Medicinal Chemistry, 1966" (C. K. Cain, ed.), Vol. 2, p. 24. Academic Press, New York.

Cain, C. K., and Roszowski, A. P. (1964). Benzoxazoles, benzothiazoles, and benzimidazoles. *In* "Psychopharmacological Agents" (M. Gordon, ed.), Vol. 1, p. 325. Academic Press, New York.

Caldwell, J. M. (ed.) (1967). Haloperidol. International psychopharmacology symposium. *Intern. J. Neuropsychiat.* **3,** Suppl. I, 6.

Campbell, P. N. (ed.) (1968). "The Interaction of Drugs and Subcellular Components in Animal Cells." Churchill, London. 355 pp.

Carlsson, A. (1966). Pharmacological depletion of catecholamine stores. *Pharmacol. Rev.* **18,** 541.

Carlsson, A. *et al.* (eds.) (1965). "Pharmacology of Cholinergic and Adrenergic Transmission," Vol. 3 Proc. 2nd Intern. Pharmacol. Meeting, Prague, 1963). Pergamon Press, Oxford. 370 pp.

Carr, E. A., Jr. (1967). Extrapolation of pharmacologic data: Lower animals to man. *Federation Proc.* **26,** 1089 (Symp.).

Chen, K. K. (1968). The philosophy of pharmacological testing. *In* "Selected Pharmacological Testing Methods" (A. Burger, ed.), Medicinal Research: Vol. 3, p. 1. Marcel Dekker, New York.

Cleghorn, R. A. (1957). Steroid hormones in relation to neuropsychiatric disorders. *In* "Hormones, Brain Function and Behavior" (H. Hoagland, ed.), p. 3. Academic Press, New York.

Cook, L., and Catania, A. C. (1964). Effects of drugs on avoidance and escape behavior. *In* "Types of Behavior on which Drugs Act. Pharmacology Symposium" (P. B. Dews, ed.), *Federation Proc.* **23,** 818 (Symp.)

Cook, L., and Kelleher, R. T. (1963). Effects of drugs on behavior. *Ann. Rev. Pharmacol.* **3,** 205.

Costa, E., and Sandler, M. (eds.) (1968). Biological role of indolealkylamine derivatives. *Advan. Pharmacol.* **6A**, 1; **6B**, 1.

Costa, E. *et al.* (eds.) (1966). "Biochemistry and Pharmacology of the Basal Ganglia." Raven Press, Hewlett, New York. 238 pp.

Crossland, J. (1967). Psychotropic drugs and neurohumoral substances in the central nervous system. *Progr. Med. Chem.* **5**, 251.

Crossman, C. A. (1966). Chlorpromazine and imipramine. Parallel studies in animals. *Psychopharmacol. Bull.* 3, 151 pp.

Decsi, L. (1965). Biochemical effects of drugs acting on the central nervous system. *Progr. Drug Res.* **8**, 53.

Deghwitz, R. (1967). "Leitfaden der Psychopharmakologie." Wiss. Verlag., Stuttgart. 512 pp.

Delafresnaye, J. R. (ed.) (1961). "Brain Mechanisms and Learning; A Symposium." Blackwell, Oxford. 701 pp.

Delay, J. (ed.) (1956). Colloque international sur la chlorpromazine et les médicaments neuroleptiques en thérapeutique psychiatrique, Paris, Oct. 20–22, 1955. *Encephale* **40**, 301.

Deniker, P. (1966). "La psychopharmacologie." Presses Univ. de France, Paris. 128 pp.

De Schaepdryvver, A. (1964). La psychopharmacologie. *Ars Medica* **19**, 1.

Dews, P. B., ed. (1956). Techniques for the study of behavioral effects of drugs. *Ann. N.Y. Acad. Sci.* **65**, 249.

Dews, P. B. (1962). Monoamines and conditioned behavior. *In* "Monoamines et système nerveux central" (J. de Ajuriaguerra, ed.), p. 143. Masson, Paris.

Dews, P. B., ed. (1964). "Types of Behavior on which Drugs Act." *Federation Proc.* **23**, 799. (Symp.)

Dews, P. B. (1966). Conditioned behavior as a substrate for behavioral effects of drugs. *In* "Psychiatric Drugs" (P. Solomon, ed.), p. 22. Grune & Stratton, New York.

DiPalma, J. R. (ed.) (1965). Drugs in epilepsy and hyperkinetic states. *In* "Drill's Pharmacology in Medicine" (J. R. DiPalma, ed.), 3rd ed., p. 232. McGraw-Hill, New York.

Domino, E. F. (1957). Pharmacology of the central nervous system. *Progr. Neurol. Psychiat.* **12**, 92.

Domino, E. F. (1965). Psychosedative drugs. I. Substituted phenothiazines, resperine and derivatives. II. Meprobamate, chlordiazepoxide, and miscellaneous agents. *In* "Drill's Pharmacology in Medicine" (J. R. DiPalma, ed.), 3rd ed., p. 337. McGraw-Hill, New York.

Domino, E. F. *et al.* (1968). Substituted phenothiazines: Pharmacology and chemical structure. *In* "Drugs Affecting the Nervous System" (A. Burger, ed.), Medicinal Research: Vol. 2, p. 327. Marcel Dekker, New York.

Donahue, H. B., and Kimura, K. K. (1968). Synthetic centrally acting skeletal muscle relaxants. *In* "Drugs Affecting the Nervous System" (A. Burger, ed.), Medicinal Research: Vol. 2, p. 265. Marcel Dekker, New York.

Dunnett, C. W. (1968). Biostatistics in pharmacological testing. *In* "Selected Pharmacological Testing Methods" (A. Burger, ed.), Medicinal Research: Vol. 3, p. 7, Marcel Dekker, New York.

Eccles, J. C. (1961). The mechanism of synaptic transmission. *Ergeb. Physiol., biol. Chem. exptl. Pharmakol.* **51**, 229.

Ehrenpreis, S. (ed.) (1967). Cholinergic mechanisms. *Ann. N.Y. Acad. Sci.* **144**, 383.

Erspamer, V. (1961). Recent research in the field of 5-hydroxytryptamine and related indolealkylamines. *Progr. Drug Res.* **3**, 151.

Euler, U. S. von (1965). Aufnahme, Speichergung und Freisetzung von Katecholaminen in Adrenergischen Neuronen. *Z. Vitamin-, Hormon- Fermentforsch.* **14**, 174.

Euler, U. S. von *et al.* (eds.) (1966). "Mechanisms of Release of Biogenic Amines." Pergamon Press, Oxford. 482 pp.

Feldberg, W., and Fleischhauer, W. (1965). A new experimental approach to the physiology and pharmacology of the brain. *Brit. Med. Bull.* **21**, No. 1, 36.

Ferry, C. B. (1967). The autonomic nervous system. *Ann. Rev. Pharmacol.* **7**, 185.

Fields, W. S. (ed.) (1957). "Brain Mechanism and Drug Action." Thomas, Springfield, Illinois. 147 pp.

Florey, E. (ed.) (1961). "Nervous Inhibition." Pergamon Press, Oxford. 475 pp.

Flügel, F. (ed.) (1960). Neuropsychopharmakologie. *Med. Exptl.* **2,** 170 pp.

Flügel, F. (ed.) (1961). Neuropsychopharmakologie. *Med. Exptl.* **5,** 299 pp.

Flügel, F. *et al.* (eds.) (1964). Wirkungsmodalitäten und qualitäten des antidepressiven effektes. *Arzneimittel-Forsch.* **14,** 479 (125 pp.)

Flügel, F. *et al.* (eds.) (1966). 4th Symposium der Deutschen Arbeitsgemeinschaft fur Neure-psychopharmakologie. *Arzneimittel-Forsch.* **16,** 106 pp.

Foo, J. W. *et al.* (1968). The effects of some β-adrenoreceptor blocking drugs on the uptake and release of noradrenaline by the heart. *Brit. J. Pharmacol.* **34,** 1.

Freedman, D. X. (1966). Aspects of the biochemical pharmacology of psychotropic drugs. *In* "Psychiatric Drugs" (P. Solomon, ed.), p. 32. Grune & Stratton, New York.

Friedman, A. H., and Everett, G. M. (1964). Pharmacological aspects of Parkinsonism. *Advan. Pharmacol.* **3,** 83.

Frommel, E. *et al.* (1966). Neuropharmacological study of central reactions to intense muscular exertion, sensorial fatigue, sexual excitation, hunger and thirst. *Med. Pharmacol. Exptl.* **14,** Suppl. 1, 1–56.

Fronkova, K., and Chrlich, V. (1963). The effect of psychopharmaca on higher nervous activity as revealed by autonomic reactions in dogs towards environmental stimuli. *In* "Psychopharmacological Methods" (Z. Votava, *et al.*, eds.), p. 186. Macmillan, New York.

Gaddum, J. H. (ed.) (1965). Pharmacology of the central nervous system. *Brit. Med. Bull.* **21,** 1.

Gaito, J. (1966). "Molecular Psychobiology." Thomas, Springfield, Illinois. 259 pp.

Garattini, S., and Dukes, M. N. G. (eds.) (1967). "Anti-depressant Drugs. Proceedings of the First International Symposium," Excerpta Med. Found., Intern. Congr. Ser. No. 122. Excerpta Med. Found., Amsterdam. 407 pp.

Gillette, J. R. (1965). Reversible binding as a complication in relating the *in vitro* effect of drugs to their *in vivo* activity. *In* "Drugs and Enzymes" (B. B. Brodie and J. R. Gillette, eds.), Vol. 4, p. 9 (Proc. 2nd Intern. Pharmacol. Meeting, Prague, 1963). Pergamon Press, Oxford.

Goldbaum, L. R., and Bomanski, T. J. (1965). An approach to the analysis of biological specimens for basic drugs. *Prog. Chem. Toxicol.* **2,** 221.

Grundfest, H. (1959). General physiology and pharmacology of synapses and some implications for the mammalian central nervous system. *J. Nervous Mental Disease* **128,** 473.

Gyermak, L. (1966). The pharmacology of imipramine and related anti-depressants. *Inter. Rev. Neurobiol.* **9,** 95.

Hamburg, D. A. (1966). Effects of progesterone on behavior. *Res. Publ., Assoc. Res. Nervous Mental Disease* **43,** 251.

Himwich, H. E. (1965). Loci of actions of psychotropic drugs in the brain. *Folia Psychiat. Neurol. Japon.* **19,** 217.

Holtz, P., and Westermann, E. (1965). Psychic energizers and antidepressants drugs. *In* "Physiological Pharmacology. A Comprehensive Teatise" (W. S. Root and F. G. Hofmann, eds.), Vol. 2, p. 201. Academic Press, New York.

Horvath, M. *et al.* (1963). Experimental studies of higher nervous system functions in pharmacology and toxicology. *In* "Psychopharmacological Methods" (Z. Votava *et al.*, eds.), p. 131. Macmillan, New York.

Hunt, H. F. (1961). Methods for studying the behavioral effects of drugs. *Ann. Rev. Pharmacol.* **1,** 125.

"International Encyclopedia of Pharmacology and Therapeutics." Sect. 7: Biostatistics in Pharmacology; Sect. 9: Physiology and Pharmacology of Synaptic Transmission; Sect. 10: Parasympathomimetic Agents; Sect. 11: Parasympathetic Blocking Agents; Sect. 13: Anticholinesterase Agents; Sect. 15: Sympathomimetic Agents; Sect. 18: Hypnotics and Sedatives; Sect. 19: Anticonvulsant Drugs; Sect. 20: Alcohols and Derivatives; Sect. 21:

Stimulants and Convulsants; Sect. 22: Analgesics; Sect. 23: Psychopharmacology; Sect. 24: Centrally Acting Skeletal Muscle Relaxants; Sect. 28: Effect of Autonomic Drugs on Central Nervous System; Sect. 33: Pharmacology of the Cerebral Circulation. Pergamon Press, Long Island City, New York (in press).

Itil, T. M. (1964). Elektroencephalographische Studien bei endogenen Pychosen und deren Behandlung mit psychotropen Medikamenten unter besonderer Berücksichtigung des Pentothal-elektroencephalograms." Ahmet Sait Mathaasi, Istanbul. 128 pp.

Itil, T. M. (1968). Electroencephalography and pharmacopsychiatry. *In* "Clinical Psychopharmacology, Modern Problems of Pharmacopsychiatry" (F. A. Freyhan *et al.*, eds.), Vol. 1, p. 163. Karger, Basel.

Iverson, L. L. (1965). The inhibition of noradrenaline uptake by drugs. *Advan. Drug Res.* **2,** 1.

Jenden, D. J. (1968). Testing of drugs for therapeutic potential in Parkinson's Disease. *In* "Selected Pharmacological Testing Methods" (A. Burger, ed.), Medicinal Research: Vol. 3, p. 337. Marcel Dekker, New York.

Kelleher, R. T., and Morse, W. H. (1964). Escape behavior and punished behavior. *In* "Types of Behavior on which Drugs Act" (P. B. Dews, ed.), *Federation Proc.* **23,** 808 (Symp.)

Kelleher, R. T., and Morse, W. H. (1968). Determinants of the specificity of behavioral effects of drugs. *Ergeb. Physiol. biol. Chem. exptl. Pharmakol.* **60,** 1.

Kety, S. S. (ed.) (1957). The pharmacology of psychotomimetic and psychotherapeutic drugs. *Ann. N.Y. Acad. Sci.* **66,** 417.

Killam, K. E. (1962). Drug action on the brain stem reticular formation. *Pharmacol. Rev.* **14,** 175.

Kinnard, W. J., Jr., and Watzman, N. (1966). Techniques utilized in the evaluation of psychotropic drugs in animal activity. *J. Pharm. Sci.* **55,** 995.

Kline, N. S. (ed.) (1956). "Psychopharmacology," Publ. No. 42. Am. Assoc. Advance. Sci., Washington, D.C. 164 pp.

Krakowski, A. J. (1966). Recent advances in psychopharmacology—a review. *Med. Times* **94,** 1209.

Lajtha, A., and Ford, D. H. (eds.) (1968). Brain-barrier systems. *Progr. Brain Res.* **29,** 552 pp.

Lapine, I. P. (1961). Charactéristiques pharmacologiques de l'imipramine. *Therapie* **19,** 1107.

Laurence, D. R., and Bacharach, A. L. (eds.) (1964). "Evaluation of Drug Activities. Pharmacometrics," Vols. 1 and 2. Academic Press, New York. 456 pp. and 444 pp. resp.

Leusen, I. (1962). Actions neuophysiologiques des mobilisateurs des monoamines et des inhibiteurs de la monoamine oxydase. *In* "Monoamines et système nerveux central" (J. de Ajuriagurerra, ed.), p. 119. Masson, Paris.

Lewis, J. J. (1963). Tranquilizers: Rauwolfia derivatives. *In* "Physiological Pharmacology. A Comprehensive Treatise" (W. S. Root and F. G. Hofmann, eds.), Vol. 1, p. 479. Academic Press, New York.

Lingjaerde, O. (1963). Tetrabenazine (Nitoman) in the treatment of psychoses. With a discussion on the central mode of action of tetrabenazine and reserpine. *Acta Psychiat. Scand.* Suppl. 170, 109 pp.

Longo, V. G. (1966). Behavioral and electroencephalographic effects of atropine and related compounds. *Pharmacol. Rev.* **18,** 965.

Lucas, R. A. (ed.) (1963). The chemistry and pharmacology of the rauwolfia alkaloids. *Progr. Med. Chem.* **3,** 146.

McGaugh, J. L., and Petrinovich, L. R. (1965). Effects of drugs on learning and memory. *Intern. Rev. Neurobiol.* **8,** 139.

McLennan, H. (1965). Synaptic transmission in the central nervous system. *In* "Physiological Pharmacology. A Comprehensive Treatise" (W. S. Root and F. G. Hofmann, eds.), Vol. 2, p. 399. Academic Press, New York.

Mannering, G. J. (1968). Significance of stimulation and inhibition of drug metabolism in pharmacological testing. *In* "Selected Pharmacological Testing Methods" (A. Burger, ed.), Medicinal Research: Vol. 3, p. 51. Marcel Dekker, New York.

Mantegazza, P., and Piccinini, F. (eds.) (1966). "Methods in Drug Evaluation." North-Holland Publ., Amsterdam, and Med. Exam. Publ. Co., Flushing, New York. 580 pp.

Margolin, S. (1963). Effects on physiological systems: Non-barbiturates. *In* "Physiological Pharmacology. A Comprehensive Treatise" (W. S. Root and F. G. Hofmann, eds.), Vol. 1, p. 23. Academic Press, New York.

Menshikov, V. V., and Matlina, E. S. (1965). [Effect of pharmacological agents in catecholamine metabolism. Review of the literature.] *Farmakol. i Toksikol.* **28,** 372 (in Russian).

Mikhelson, M. I. *et al.* (eds.) (1965). "Pharmacology of Conditioning, Learning and Retention," Vol. 1 (Proc. 2nd Intern. Pharmacol. Meeting, Prague, 1963). Pergamon Press, Oxford. 365 pp.

Miller, N. E., and Barry, H., 3rd. (1960). Motivational effects of drugs: Methods which illustrate some general problems in psychopharmacology. *Psychopharmacologia* **1,** 169.

Millichap, J. G. (1965). Anticonvulsant drugs. *In* "Physiological Pharmacology. A Comprehensive Treatise" (W. S. Root and F. G. Hofmann, eds.), Vol. 2. p. 97. Academic Press, New York.

Mongar, J. L., and deReuck, A. V. S. (eds.) (1962). "Enzymes and Drug Action," Ciba Found. Symp. jointly with Coordinating Committee for Symposia on Drug Action. Little, Brown, Boston, Massachusetts. 556 pp.

Nakajima, H., and Thullier, J. (1965). Contribution à l'étude des mécanismes d'action biochimique des drogues psychotropes, correlation effets pharmacologiques. *Encéphale* **54,** 285.

Neff, N. H., and Costa, E. (1967). Effect of tricyclic antidepressants and chlorpromazine on brain catacholamine synthesis. *In* "Antidepressant Drugs" (S. Garattini and M. N. G. Dukes, eds.), Excerpta Med. Found., Intern. Congr. Ser. No. 122, p. 28. Excerpta Med. Found., Amsterdam.

Nodine, J. H., and Siegler, P. E. (eds.) (1964). "Animal and Clinical Pharmacologic Techniques in Drug Evaluation." Year Book Publ., Chicago, Illinois. 659 pp.

Paton, W. D. M., and Lindgren, P. (eds.) (1962). Pharmacological analysis of central nervous action. *Proc. 1st Intern. Pharmacol. Meeting, Stockholm, 1961* Vol. 8. Macmillan, New York. 330 pp.

Pennes, H. (ed.) (1958). "Psychopharmacology. Pharmacologic Effects on Behavior." Cassell, London, and Harper (Hoeber), New York. 362 pp.

Pletscher, A. (1964). Biogene Amine und antidepressiver Effekt. *Arzneimittel-Forsch.* **14,** 479.

Pletscher, A. *et al.* (1960). Monoaminoxydasehemmer. *Progr. Drug Res.* **2,** 417.

Plotnikoff, N. *et al.* (1960). "Drug Enhancement of Performance." Stanford Res. Inst., Menlo Park, California. 192 pp.

Poldinger, W. (1967). "Compendium of Psychopharmacotherapy." Sci. Serv., F. Hoffman-LaRoche & Co., Ltd., Basel. 125 pp.

Poser, C. M., and Osbourn, V. (1962). "International Dictionary of Drugs." Thomas. Springfield, Illinois. 157 pp.

Raskova, H. (ed.) (1968). "Mechanisms of Drug Toxicity." Pergamon Press, Oxford. 104 pp.

Remmen, E. *et al.* (1962). "Psychochemotherapy. The Physician's Manual." Western Med. Publ., Los Angeles, California. 152 pp.

Roberts, E. *et al.* (eds.) (1960). "Inhibition in the Nervous System and Gamma-Aminobutyric Acid." Pergamon Press, Oxford. 591 pp.

Robson, J. M., and Stacey, R. S. (eds.) (1962). "Recent Advances in Pharmacology," 3rd ed., Churchill, London. 406 pp.

Root, W. S., and Hofmann, F. G. (eds.) (1963, 1965, 1967). "Physiological Pharmacology. A Comprehensive Treatise," Vols. 1, 2, and 3. Academic Press, New York. 703 pp., 486 pp., and 519 pp. resp.

Rosen, A. (1965). [Psychopharmacologic drugs: Mechanism of action.] *Lakartidningen* **62,** Suppl. 2, 27 (in Swedish).

Ross, S., and Cole, J. O. (1960). Psychopharmacology. *Ann. Rev. Psychol.* **11,** 415.
Rothlin, E. (ed.) (1959). "Neuropsychopharmacology," Vol. 2. Elsevier, Amsterdam, 521 pp.
Russell, R. W. (1964). Psychopharmacology. *Ann. Rev. Psychol.* **15,** 87.
Salmoiraghi, G. C. *et al.* (1965). Pharmacology of central synapses. *Ann. Rev. Pharmacol.* **5,** 213.
Sarkisov, S. A. (1966). "The Structure and Function of the Brain." Indiana Univ. Press, Bloomington, Indiana. 291 pp.
Schenker, E. von, and Herbst, H. (1963). Phenothiazine und Azaphenothiazine als Arzneimittel. *Progr. Drug Res.* **5,** 269.
Schlittler, E., and Plummer, A. J. (1964). Tranquilizing drugs from rauwolfia. *In* "Psychopharmacological Agents" (M. Gordon, ed.), Vol. 1, p. 9. Academic Press, New York.
Schneider, J. A., and Sigg, E. B. (1958). Pharmacologic analysis of tranquilizing and central stimulating effects. *Progr. Neurobiol.* **3,** 75.
Selbach, H., and Pletscher, A. (1960). Pharmaka mit Wirkung auf den Monoamin Stoffwechsel des Zentralnervensystems. *Psychiat. Neurol.* **140,** 1.
Shepherd, M., and Wing. L. (1962). Pharmacological aspects of psychiatry. *Advan. Pharmacol.* **1,** 227.
Shepherd, M. *et al.* (1967). "Clinical Psychopharmacology." English Univ. Press, London. 320 pp.
Shore, P. A. (1966). The mechanism of norepinephrine depletion by reserpine, metaraminol and related agents. The role of monoamine oxidase. *Pharmacol. Rev.* **18,** 561.
Sidman, M. (1959). Behavioral pharmacology. *Psychopharmacologia* **1,** 1.
Siegler, P. E., and Moyer, J. H. (eds.) (1967). "Animal and Clinical Pharmacologic Techniques in Drug Evaluation," 3rd ed., Vol. 2. Year Book Publ., Chicago, Illinois. 876 pp.
Sjoerdsma, A. (1966). Catecholamine drug interactions in man. *Pharmacol. Rev.* **18,** 673.
Smith, C. M. (1965). Relaxants of skeletal muscle. *In* "Physiological Pharmacology. A Comprehensive Treatise" (W. S. Root and F. G. Hofmann, eds.), Vol. 2, p. 486. Academic Press, New York.
Sokoloff, L. (1959). The action of drugs on the cerebral circulation. *Pharmacol. Rev.* **11,** 1.
Soulairac, A. *et al.* (eds.) (1968). "Pain." Academic Press, New York. 562 pp.
Spinks, A., and Waring, W. S. (1963). Anticonvulsant drugs. *Progr. Med. Chem.* **3,** 261.
Spinks, A., and Young, E. H. P. (1963). The relation between structure and central nervous action of some hydrazine derivatives. *In* "Modern Concepts in the Relationship between Structure and Pharmacological Activity" (B. Üvnas, *et al.,* eds.), Vol. 7, p. 303. Macmillan, New York.
Steinberg, H., and Kumar, R. (1970). Psychopharmacology. *Ann. Rev. Psychol.* **20** (in press).
Steinberg, H. *et al.* (eds.) (1964). "Animal Behavior and Drug Action." Little, Brown, Boston, Massachusetts; Churchill, London. 491 pp.
Stern, J. A., and McDonald, D. C. (1965). Physiological correlates of mental disease. *Ann. Rev. Psychol.* **16,** 225.
Sternbach, L. H. *et al.* (1968). Structure-activity relationships in the 1,4-benzodiazepine series. *In* "Drugs Affecting the Nervous System" (A. Burger, ed.), Medicinal Research: Vol. 2, p. 237. Marcel Dekker, New York.
Stewart, G. A. (1963). Statistics as applied to pharmacological and toxicological screening. *Progr. Med. Chem.* **3,** 187.
Stolman, A. (1965). Thin layer chromatography application in toxicology. *Progr. Chem. Toxicol.* **2,** 321.
Stone, C. A., and Porter, C. C. (1966). Methyldopa and adrenergic nerve function. *Pharmacol. Rev.* **18,** 569.
Stone, G. C. (1966). Prediction of drug-induced changes in rats' avoidance behavior. *In* "Prediction of Response to Pharmacotherapy" (J. R. Wittenborn and P. R. A. May, eds.), p. 156. Thomas, Springfield, Illinois.
Stumpf, C. (1965). Drug action on the electrical activity of the hippocampus. *Intern. Rev. Neurobiol.* **8,** 77.

Tedeschi, D. H., and Tedeschi, R. E. (1968). "Fundamental Principles in Drug Evaluation," Raven Press, Hewlett, New York. 500 pp.

Tislow, R. F. (1968). Evaluation of sedative-hypnotics in the course of psychopharmacological testing. *In* "Selected Pharmacological Testing Methods" (A. Burger, ed.), Medicinal Research: Vol. 3, p. 421. Marcel Dekker, New York.

Toman, J. E. P. (1963). Some aspects of central nervous pharmacology. *Ann. Rev. Pharmacol.* **3,** 153.

Turner, R. A. (1965). "Screening Methods in Pharmacology." Academic Press, New York. 332 pp.

Usdin, E., and Efron, D. H. (1967). "Psychotropic Drugs and Related Compounds," Public Health Publ. No. 1589. U.S. Govt. Printing Office, Washington, D.C. 365 pp.

Üvnas, B. *et al.* (eds.) (1962). "Modern Concepts in the Relationship between Structure and Pharmacological Activity," Mode of Action of Drugs. Vol. 7 (Proc. 1st Intern. Pharmacol. Meeting, Stockholm, Sweden, 1961). Macmillan, New York. 387 pp.

Valdman, A. V. (ed.) (1967). Pharmacology and physiology of the reticular formation. *Progr. Brain Res.* **20,** 1.

Van Praag, H. M. (1967a). Antidepressants, catecholamines and 5-hydroxyindoles. Trends towards a more specific research in the field of antidepressants. *Psychiat. Neurol. Neurochir.* **70,** 219.

Van Praag, H. M. (1967b). The possible significance of cerebral dopamine for neurology and psychiatry. *Psychiat. Neurol. Neurochir.* **70,** 361.

Volle, R. L. (1966). Modification by drugs of synaptic mechanisms in autonomic ganglia. *Pharmacol. Rev.* **18,** 839.

Votava, Z. (1967). Pharmacology of the central cholinergic synapses. *Ann. Rev. Pharmacol.* **7,** 223.

Votava, Z. *et al.* (eds.) (1963). "Psychopharmacological Methods." Macmillan, New York. 360 pp.

Walaszek, E. J. *et al.* (1966). Pharmacology of the central nervous system. *Progr. Neurol. Psychiat.* **21,** 117.

Way, E. L., and Adler, T. K. (1960). The pharmacologic implications of the fate of morphine and its surrogates. *Pharmacol. Rev.* **12,** 383.

Weiss, B., and Laties, V. G. (1964). Drug effects on the temporal patterning of behavior. *In* "Types of Behavior on which Drugs Act" (P. B. Dews, ed.), *Federation Proc.* **23,** 801 (Symp.)

Welsh, J. H. (1955). Neurohormones. *In* "The Hormones. Physiology, Chemistry, and Application" (G. Pincus and K. V. Thimann, eds.), Vol. 3, p. 97. Academic Press, New York.

Wolpe, J. (1967). Parallels between animal and human neuroses. *Proc. Am. Psychopathol. Assoc.* **55,** 305.

Wolstenholme, G. E. W. (ed.) (1952). Hormones, psychology and behavior, and steroid hormone administration. *Ciba Found. Colloq. Endocrinol.* **3,** 380 pp.

Wolstenholme, G. E. W., and O'Connor, C. N. (eds.) (1958). "Neurological Basis of Behavior," Ciba Found. Symp. Little, Brown, Boston, Massachusetts. 400 pp.

Wolstenholme, G. E. W., and O'Connor, M. (eds.) (1960). "Adrenergic Mechanisms," Ciba Found. Symp. jointly with Committee for Symposia on Drug Action. Churchill, London. 632 pp.

Yonkman, F. (ed.) (1954). Reserpine (Serpasil) and other alkaloids of *Rauwolfia serpentinia:* Chemistry, pharmacology and clinical applications. *Ann. N.Y. Acad. Sci.* **59,** 140 pp.

Young, R. D. (1966). Developmental psychopharmacology: A beginning. *Psychol. Bull.* **67,** 73.

Zbindin, G., and Randall, L. O. (1967). Pharmacology of benzodiazepines: Laboratory and clinical correlations. *Advan. Pharmacol.* **5,** 213.

Zimmer, H., and Krusberg, R. J. (1966). "Psychophysiological Components of Human Behavior." Univ. of Georgia Press, Athens, Georgia. 534 pp.

G. Genetic and Environmental Aspects of Drugs, Including Nutritional and Developmental Problems, Inborn Errors of Metabolism, Sensory Function, Etc.

Adansons, K., Jr., and Joelsson, I. (1966). The effects of pharmacologic agents upon the fetus. *Am. J. Obstet. Gynecol.* **96**, 437.

Becker, P. E., ed. (1964–1968). "Humangenetik; ein kurzes Handbuch in fünf Bänden." Thieme, Stuttgart.

Ginsburg, B. E. (1958). Genetics as a tool in the study of behavior. *Perspectives Biol. Med.* **1**, 397.

Herxheimer, A. (ed.) (1968). "Drugs and Sensory Functions." Churchill, London. 338 pp.

Hsia, D. Y. (1966a). "Inborn Errors of Metabolism," Part I. Year Book Publ., Chicago, Illinois. 396 pp.

Hsia, D. Y. (1966b). "Medical Genetics." Year Book Publ., Chicago, Illinois. 200 pp.

Kalow, W. (1967). Pharmacogenetics. *Postgrad. Med.* **42**, 32.

Khanna, J. L. (1968). "Brain Damage and Mental Retardation: A Psychological Evaluation." Thomas, Springfield, Illinois. 224 pp.

Kugelmass, I. N. (1964). "Biochemical Diseases (Chemical Pediatrics)." Thomas, Springfield, Illinois. 1229 pp.

Leuner, H. (1962). Die experimentelle Psychose. Ihre Psychopharmakologie, Phänomenologie und Dynamik in Beziehung zur Person. Versuch einer konditional-genetischen und funktionalen Psychopathiologie der Psychose. *Monograph. Neurol. Psychiat.* **95**, 275.

Lyman, F. L. (1963). "Phenylketonuria." Thomas, Springfield, Illinois. 318 pp.

Meier, H. (1963a). "Experimental Pharmacogenetics. Physiopathology of Hereditary and Pharmacologic Responses." Academic Press, New York. 213 pp.

Meier, H. (1963b). Potentialities for and present status of pharmacological research in genetically controlled mice. *Advan. Pharmacol.* **2**, 161.

Menkes, J. H., and Philippart, M. (1965). Biochemical methods in the detection and diagnosis of metabolic diseases affecting the nervous system. *J. Neurol. Sci.* **2**, 108.

Newton, G., and Levine, S. (1968). "Early Experience and Behavior: The Psychobiology of Development." Thomas, Springfield, Illinois. 800 pp.

Peters, J. H. (1968). Genetic factors in relation to disease. *Pharmacol. Rev.* **8**, 427.

Ruff, G. E. (1966). Isolation and sensory deprivation. *Am. Handbook Psychiat.* **3**, 362.

Stanbury, J. B. *et al.* (1966). "The Metabolic Basis of Inherited Disease," 2nd ed. McGraw-Hill, New York. 1434 pp.

Van Praag, H. M. (ed.) (1968). "Brain Damage by Inborn Errors of Metabolism." DeEven *et al.*, Haarlem, The Netherlands.

Vandenberg, S. G. (ed.) (1965). "Methods and Goals in Human Genetics." Academic Press, New York.

Young, R. D. (1966). Developmental psychopharmacology: A beginning. *Psychol. Bull.* **67**, 73.

VI. Clinical Psychopharmacology and Psychology, Methodology, Drug Study Design, Statistics, Etc.

Anonymous. (1966). Guides to the evaluation of permanent impairment: Mental illness. Committee on rating of mental and physical impairment. *J. Am. Med. Assoc.* **198**, 1284.

Anonymous. (1967). Collaborative Study Group: National Institute of Mental Health, Psychopharmacology Research Branch. Differences in clinical effects of three phenothiazines in "acute" schizophrenia. *Diseases Nervous System* **28**, 369.

Ban, T. A. (1965). Human pharmacology and systematic clinical studies with a new phenothiazine (Propericiazine). *In* "Proceedings of the Symposium on Behavioral Disorders, Leeds, March, 1965" (F. A. Jenner *et al.*, ed.), p. 2. May & Baker, Dangenham, England.

Benor, D., and Ditman, S. (1967). Clinical psychopharmacological research: Problems, questions, and some suggestions in analyzing reports. *J. Clin. Pharmacol.* **7,** 68.

Cattell, R. *et al.* (1962). Recent advances in the measurement of anxiety, neuroticism, and the psychotic syndromes. *Ann. N.Y. Acad. Sci.* **93,** 813.

Cleghorn, R. A. (1957). Steroid hormones in relation to neuropsychiatric disorder. *In* "Hormones, Brain Function and Behavior" (H. Hoagland, ed.), p. 3. Academic Press, New York.

Crane, G. E. (1966). A systematic evaluation of data obtained from studies of psychotropic drugs. *Psychopharmacol. Bull.* **3,** 43 pp.

Craver, B. N. (ed.) (1956). Experimental methods for the evaluation of drugs in various disease states. *Ann. N.Y. Acad. Sci.* **64,** 463.

Eberhard, G. *et al.* (1965). Clinical and experimental approaches to the description of depression and antidepressive therapy. *Acta Psychiat. Scand.* **41,** Suppl. 186, 1.

Eysenck, H. J. (1960). Objective psychological tests and the assessment of drug effects. *Intern. Rev. Neurobiol.* **2,** 333.

Eysenck, H. J. (ed.) (1963). "Experiments with Drugs: Studies in the Relation between Personality, Learning Theory and Drug Action." Pergamon Press, Oxford. 421 pp.

Farrenberg, J., and Prystav, G. (1966). Psychophysiologische Untersuchungen eines Tranquilizers nach kovariananalytischen Plan zur Kontrolle von Ausgangerserten und Personlichkeitsdimensionen. *Arzneimittel-Forsch.* **16,** 175.

Fisher, S. (ed.) (1959). "Child Research in Psychopharmacology." Thomas, Springfield, Illinois. 216 pp.

Forrest, F. M. *et al.* (1964). Drug maintenance problems of rehabilitated mental patients. The current drug dosage "merry-go-round." *Am. J. Psychiat.* **121,** 33.

Forster, F. M. (ed.) (1961). "Evaluation of Drug Therapy." Univ. of Wisconsin Press, Madison, Wisconsin. 167 pp.

Fulkerson, S. C. B., Jr. (1961). Methodology and research on the prognostic use of psychological tests. *Psychol. Bull.* **58,** 177–204.

Glick, B. S. (1968). Attitude toward drug and clinical outcome. *Am. J. Psychiat.* **124,** Suppl., No. 8, 37.

Green, A. (1961). Chimiothérapies et psychothérapies. (Problèmes poses par les comparaisons des techniques chimiotherapiques et psychotherapiques et leur association en thérapeutique psychiatrique.) *Encéphale* **50,** 29.

Haas, H. *et al.* (1959). Das Placeboproblem. *Progr. Drug. Res.* **1,** 279.

Herrick, A. D., and Cattell, M. (eds.) (1965). "Clinical Testing of New Drugs." Revere, New York. 362 pp.

Hoch, P. H., and Zubin, J. (eds.) (1964). "The Evaluation of Psychiatric Treatment." Grune & Stratton, New York. 326 pp.

Hoffer, A. (1962). "Niacin Therapy in Psychiatry." Thomas, Springfield, Illinois. 165 pp.

Hordern, A. (1965). "Depressive States; A Pharmacotherapeutic Study." Thomas, Springfield, Illinois. 166 pp.

"International Encyclopedia of Pharmacology and Therapeutics." Sect. 6, Vol. 1: Clinical Pharmacology; Sect. 7: Biostatistics in Pharmacology. Pergamon Press, Long Island City, New York (in press).

Irwin, S. (1962). Drug screening and evaluation procedures. *Science* **136,** 123.

Irwin, S. (1966). Considerations for the pre-clinical evaluation of new psychiatric drugs. A case study with phenothiazine-like tranquilizers. *Psychopharmacologia* **9,** 259.

Irwin, S. (1968). A rational framework for the development, evaluation, and use of psychoactive drugs. *Am. J. Psychiat.* **124,** Suppl., No. 8, 21.

Jacobsen, E. (1964). Tranquilizers and sedatives. *In* "Evaluation of Drug Activities. Pharmacometrics" (D. R. Laurence and A. L. Bacharach, eds.), Vol. 1, p. 215. Academic Press, New York.

Janke, W. (1964). "Experimentelle Untersuchungen zur Abhängigkeit der Wirkung Psychotroper Substanzen von Personlichkeitsmerkmalen." Akad. Verlag., Frankfurt. 146 pp.

Kissel, P., and Barrucand, D. (eds.) (1964). "Placebos et effet placebo en médecine." Masson, Paris. 240 pp.

Klein, D. F. *et al.* (1968). Prediction of drug effect by diagnostic decision tree. *Diseases Nervous System* **29,** No. 5, Suppl., 159.

Klerman, G. L. (1966). Comments from the viewpoint of a clinical psychiatrists. In "Prediction of Response to Pharmacotherapy" (J. R. Wittenborn and P. R. A. May, eds.), p. 183. Thomas, Springfield, Illinois.

Klerman, G. L., and Cole, J. O. (1965). Clinical pharmacology of imipramine and related antidepressant compounds. *Pharmacol. Rev.* **17,** 101.

Kline, N. S. *et al.* (eds.) (1958). Research in psychiatry with special reference to drug therapy. *Psychiat. Res. Rept.* **9,** 181.

Kornetsky, C., and Mirsky, A. F. (1966). On certain psychopharmacological and physiological differences between schizophrenic and normal persons. *Psychopharmacologia* **8,** 309.

Kranz, H., and Heinrich, K. (eds.) (1967). "Pharmakopsychiatrie und Psychopathologie." Thieme, Stuttgart. 203 pp.

Kranz, H., and Petrilowitsch, N. (1966). "Probleme der Pharmakopsychiatrischen Kombinations und langzeit-Behandlung." Karger, Basel. 212 pp.

Kuhn, E. *et al.* (1963). Multidimensional approach to the psychopharmacological experiment. *In* "The Effects of Psychotropic Drugs in Higher Nervous Activity" (Z. Votava *et al.*, eds.), p. 281. Macmillan, New York.

Lader, M. H., and Wing, L. (1966). "Physiological Measures, Sedative Drugs, and Morbid Anxiety," Maudsley Monographs No. 14. Oxford Univ. Press, London and New York. 179 pp.

Lasagna, L., and Meier, P. (1958). Clinical evaluation of drugs. *Ann. Rev. Med.* **9,** 347.

Laurence, D. R. (ed.) (1959). "Quantitative Methods in Human Pharmacology and Therapeutics." Pergamon Press, Oxford. 253 pp.

Laurence, D. R. (1966). "Clinical Pharmacology," 3rd ed. Churchill, London. 678 pp.

Laurence, D. R., and Bacharach, A. L. (eds.) (1964). "Evaluation of Drug Activities. Pharmacometrics," Vols. 1 and 2. Academic Press, New York. 456 pp. and 444 pp. resp.

Lehmann, H. E. (1966). Pharmacology of Schizophrenia. *Proc. Am. Psychopathol. Assoc.* **54,** 388.

Ling, T. M., and Buckman, J. A. (1963). "Lysergic Acid (LSD-25) and Ritalin in the Treatment of Neurosis." Lambarde Press, London. 172 pp.

Lorr, M. (1967). "Explorations in Typing Psychotics." Pergamon Press, Oxford. 241 pp.

Marks, J. (1965). Placebomania. *In* "Clinical Testing of New Drugs." (A. D. Herrick and M. Cattell, eds.), p. 205. Revere, New York.

Martin, B. (1961). The assessment of anxiety by physiological behavioral measures. *Psychol. Bull.* **58,** 234.

Mendels, J. (1968). Comparative trial of nortriptyline and amitryptycline in 100 depressed patients. *Am. J. Psychiat.* **124,** No. 8, Suppl. 1, 59.

Miller, N. E., and Barry, H., 3rd. (1960). Motivational effects of drugs: Methods which illustrate some general problems in psychopharmacology. *Psychopharmacologia* **1,** 169.

Murphy, C. W., and Parker, J. M. (eds.) (1965). "Conference on Human Pharmacology." McGill Univ. Press, Montreal. 98 pp.

Nodine, J. H., and Siegler, P. E. (eds.) (1964). "Animal and Clinical Pharmacologic Techniques in Drug Evaluation." Year Book Publ., Chicago, Illinois. 659 pp.

Pachter, I. J. *et al.* (1968). Antipsychotic and antianxiety agents. *In* "Annual Reports in Medicinal Chemistry, 1967" (C. K. Cain, ed.), Vol. 3, p. 1. Academic Press, New York.

Parr, D. (1962). Problems in the appraisal and use of tranquilizers, analgesics and hypnotics. *In* "Modern Trends in Neurology" (D. Williams, ed.), p. 336. Butterworth, London and Washington, D.C.

Petrilowitsch, N. (1966). "Psychiatrische Krankheitslehre und psychiatrische Pharmakotherapie." Karger, Basel. 120 pp.

Petrilowitsch, H., and Kranz, H. (1966). "Parmakopsychiatrischen Kombinations—und Langzeitbehandlung." Karger, Basel. 120 pp.
Remmen, E. *et al.* (1962). "Psychochemotherapy. The Physicians Manual." Western Med. Publ., Los Angeles, California. 152 pp.
Richards, R. K. (ed.) (1968). "Clinical Pharmacology." Pergamon Press, Oxford. 113 pp.
Richter, D. (ed.) (1962). "Aspects of Psychiatric Research." Oxford Univ. Press, London and New York. 445 pp.
Rickels, K. *et al.* (1966). Controlled psychopharmacological research in private psychiatric practice. *Psychopharmacologia* **9**, 288.
Rickels, K., ed. (1968). "Non-Specific Factors in Drug Therapy." Thomas, Springfield, Illinois. 149 pp.
Rinkel, M. (ed.) (1963). "Specific and Non-Specific Factors in Psychopharmacology." Philosophical Library, New York. 174 pp.
Russell, R. W. (ed.) (1966). "Frontiers in Physiological Psychology." Academic Press, New York. 261 pp.
Rutschmann, J. *et al.* (1966). Time estimation, knowledge of results and drug effects. *J. Psychiat. Res.* **4**, 107.
Schindel, L. (1967). Placebo und Placebo-Effekte in Klinik und Forschung. *Progr. Drug Res.* **17**, 892.
Schmitt, W. (1965). "Psychiatrische Pharmakotherapie. Experimentelle und Klinische Frundlagen eines Klassifizierungsversuches." A. Kiething, Heidelberg. 240 pp.
Shepherd, M. (1965). Centrally acting drugs. *In* "Evaluation of New Drugs in Man" (E. Zaimis, ed.), Vol. 8, p. 111 (Proc. 2nd Intern. Pharmacol. Meeting Prague, 1963). Pergamon Press, Oxford.
Shepherd, M. *et al.* (1967). "Clinical Psychopharmacology." English Univ. Press, London. 320 pp.
Sherman, L. J. *et al.* (1963). "Prognosis in Schizophrenia. A Follow-up Study of 588 Patients," V. A. Coop. Studies Psychiat. Rept. No. 51. Vet. Admin. Central Neuropsychiat. Res. Lab., Perry Point, Maryland. 17 pp.
Siegler, P. E., and Moyer, J. H. (eds.) (1967). "Animal and Clinical Pharmacologic Techniques in Drug Evaluation," 3rd ed., Vol. 2. Year Book Publ., Chicago, Illinois. 876 pp.
Silverman, C. (1968). The epidemiology of depression. A review. *Am. J. Psychiat.* **124**, 883.
Soulairac, A. *et al.* (eds.) (1968). "Pain." Academic Press, New York. 562 pp.
Symposium on Clinical Drug Evaluation and Human Pharmacology. (1962). *Clin. Pharmacol. Therap.* **3**, 235.
Tanner, J. M. (ed.) (1952). "Prospects in Psychiatric Research." Oxford Univ. Press, London and New York. 197 pp.
Tanner, J. M. (ed.) (1962). "Aspects of Psychiatric Research." Oxford Univ. Press, London and New York. 445 pp.
Tedeschi, D. H., and Tedeschi, R. E. (1968). "Fundamental Principles in Drug Evaluation." Raven Press, Hewlett, New York. 500 pp.
Toman, J. E. P. (1963). Some aspects of central nervous pharmacology. *Ann. Rev. Pharmacol.* **3**, 153.
Tuma, A. (1966). The prediction of response of pharmacotherapy among schizophrenics. *In* "Prediction of Response to Pharmacotherapy" (J. R. Wittenborn and P. R. A. May, eds.), p. 43. Thomas, Springfield, Illinois.
Vance, F. L. (1966). Psychological assessment methods. *Progr. Neurol. Psychiat.* **21**, 567.
Vinar, O. (1963). The possibilities of the use of conditioned reflex methods in clinical psychiatry. *In* "Psychopharmacological Methods" (Z. Votava, *et al.*, eds.), p. 259. Macmillan, New York.
Winder, C. L. (1961). Psychiatry: Psychometrics. *Ann. Rev. Med.* **12**, 335.
Wittenborn, J. R., and May, P. R. A. (eds.) (1966). "Prediction of Response to Pharmacotherapy," Thomas, Springfield, Illinois. 829 pp.
Wolstenholme, G. E. W., and Porter, R. (eds.) (1967). "Drug Responses in Man. A Ciba Foundation Volume." Little, Brown, Boston, Massachusetts. 257 pp.

Zaimis, E. (ed.) (1965). "Evaluation of New Drugs in Man," Vol. 8 (Proc. 2nd Intern. Pharmacol. Meeting, Prague, 1963). Pergamon Press, Oxford.

Zimmer, H., and Krusberg, R. J. (1966). "Psychophysiological Components of Human Behavior. A compendium." Univ. of Georgia Press, Athens, Georgia. 534 pp.

Zubin, J. (1967). Classification of the behavior disorders. *Ann. Rev. Psychol.* **18**, 373.

Zubin, J., and Katz, M. M. (1964). Psychopharmacology and personality. *In* "Personality Change" (P. Worchel and D. Byrne, ed.), 367 pp. Wiley, New York.

VII. Forensic, Legal, Sociological, and Ethical Problems of Drug Use and Abuse, Narcotics, Addiction, Alchohol, Etc.

Abramson, H. A. (ed.) (1967). "The Use of LSD in Psychotherapy and Alcoholism." Bobbs-Merrill, New York. 697 pp.

Anonymous. (1967). "Commission on Narcotic Drugs," United Nations Economic and Social Council, Ann. Repts., 1964, 144 Countries. UNESCO Publ. Center, New York. 63 pp.

Anonymous. (1968). Drug Abuse, National Conference on Public Education in Drug Abuse, Washington, D.C., Jan. 10–11, 1968. Sponsored by Am. Pharm. Assoc. *J. Am. Pharm. Assoc.* **NS8**, 11.

Archer, S., and Harris, L. S. (1965). Narcotic antagonists. *Progr. Drug Res.* **8**, 261.

Beecher, H. K. (1946). Experimentation in man. *J. Am. Med. Assoc.* **132**, 1090.

Berger, F. M. (1967). Drugs and suicide in the United States. *Clin. Pharmacol. Therap.* **8**, 219.

Brazier, M. A. (1963). Effects upon physiological systems: The electrophysiological effects of barbiturates on the brain. *In* "Physiological Pharmacology. A Comprehensive Treatise" (W. S. Root and F. G. Hofmann, eds.), p. 219. Academic Press, New York.

Cain, C. K. (1967). Sedatives, hypnotics, anticonvulsants, muscle relaxants, general anesthetics. *In* Annual Reports in Medicinal Chemistry, 1966" (C. K. Cain, ed.), Vol. 2, p. 24. Academic Press, New York.

Chen, G. (1964). Antidepressives, analeptics and appetite suppressants. *In* "Evaluation of Drug Activities. Pharmacometrics" (D. R. Laurence and A. L. Bacharach, eds.), Vol. 1, p. 239. Academic Press, New York.

Cochin, J. (1968). Methods for the appraisal of analgetic drugs for addiction liability. *In* "Selected Pharmacological Testing Methods" (A. Burger, ed.), Medicinal Research: Vol. 3, p. 121. Marcel Dekker, New York.

Cohen, S. *et al.* (1964). Tranquilizers and suicide in the schizophrenic patient. *Arch. Gen. Psychiat.* **11**, 312.

Compton, W. A. (ed.) (1954). "Symposium on Sedative and Hypnotic Drugs." Williams & Wilkins, Baltimore, Maryland. 111 pp.

Connell, P. H. (1958). "Amphetamine Psychoses." Oxford Univ. Press, London and New York. 133 pp.

Deneau, G. A., and Seevers, M. H. (1964). Pharmacological aspects of drug dependence. *Advan. Pharmacol.* **3**, 267.

Ebin, D. (ed.) (1961). "The Drug Experience." Orion Press, New York. 386 pp.

Eddy, N. B. *et al.* (1966). Dependence: Its significance and characteristics. *Psychopharmacol. Bull.* **3**, 1.

Esplin, D. W., and Zablocka, B. (1966). Central nervous system stimulants. *In* "The Pharmacological Basis of Therapeutics" (L. S. Goodman and A. Gilman, eds.), 3rd ed., p. 345. Macmillan, New York.

Essig, C. F. (1964). Addiction to nonbarbiturate sedative and tranquilizing drugs. *Clin. Pharmacol. Therap.* **5**, 334.

Fraser, H. F., and Harris, L. S. (1967). Narcotic and narcotic antagonist analgesics. *Ann. Rev. Pharmacol.* **7**, 277.

Freedman, L. Z. (1966). Psychiatry and law. *Progr. Neurol. Psychiat.* **21**, 487.

Gates, M. (1966). Analgesic drugs. *Sci. Am.* **215**, 131.

Goldstein, J., and Katz, J. (1965). "The Family and the Law." Free Press, New York. 1,229 pp.

Gunne, L. (1963). Catecholamines and 5-hydroxytryptamine in morphine tolerance and withdrawal. *Acta Physiol. Scand.* **58**, Suppl. 204, 5.

Hahn, F. (1960). Analeptics. *Pharmacol. Rev.* **12**, 447.

Harris, S. *et al.* (1968). Analgetics—strong and weak. *In* "Annual Reports in Medicinal Chemistry, 1967" (C. K. Cain, ed.), Vol. 3, p. 36. Academic Press, New York.

Heath, R. G., and Wells, B. (1967). Drugs for stimulation of mental and physical activity. *In* "Drugs of Choice" (W. Modell, ed.), p. 164. Mosby, St. Louis, Missouri.

Hekimian, L. J., and Gershon, S. (1968). Characteristics of drug abusers admitted to a psychiatric hospital. *J. Am. Med. Assoc.* **205**, 125.

Himwich, H. E. (1959). Stimulants. *Res. Publ., Assoc. Res. Nervous Mental Disease* **37**, 357.

Hirsch, J. B. (1967). "Opportunities and Limitations in the Treatment of Alcoholics." Thomas, Springfield, Illinois. 103 pp.

Hollister, L. E. (1964). Chemical psychoses. *Ann. Rev. Med.* **15**, 203.

"International Encyclopedia and Pharmacology and Therapeutics." Sect. 4, Vol. 1: Drug Abuse and Drug Addiction; Sect. 18, Vol. 1: Hypnotics and Sedatives; Sect. 20, Vol. 1: Alcohols and Derivatives; Sect. 21, Vol. 1: Stimulants and Convulsants; Sect. 22, Vol. 1: Analgesics; Sect. 83, Vol. 1: Drugs Under the Law. Pergamon Press, Long Island City, New York (in press).

Jaffe, J. H. (1966). Narcotic analgesics. Drug addiction and drug abuse. *In* "The Pharmacological Basis of Therapeutics" (L. S. Goodman and A. Gilman, eds.), 3rd ed., pp. 247 and 285. Macmillan, New York.

Janssen. P. A., and Van der Eycken, C. A. M. (1968). The chemical anatomy of potent morphine-like analgesics. *In* "Drugs Affecting the Nervous System" (A. Burger, ed.), Medicinal Research: Vol. 2, p. 25. Marcel Dekker, New York.

Katz, J. *et al.* (1967). "Psychoanalysis, Psychiatry and Law." Macmillan, New York. 845 pp.

Larsen, E. *et al.* (1968). Mechanisms of narcosis. *Med. Res.* **2**, 1.

Leonard, F. (ed.) (1965). The detection and control of abuse of narcotics, barbiturates, and amphetamines. *Psychopharmacol. Bull.* **3**, 21.

Lipscomb, W. R. (1966). Survey measurements on the prevalence of alcoholism. A review of five surveys. *Arch. Gen. Psychiat.* **15**, 455.

Lister, R. E. (1966). The toxicity of some of the newer narcotic analgesics. *J. Pharm. Pharmacol.* **18**, 364.

Lunsford, C. D. *et al.* (1968). Sedatives, hypnotics, anticonvulsants, muscle relaxants, general anesthetics. *In* "Annual Reports in Medicinal Chemistry, 1967" (C. K. Cain, ed.), Vol. 3, p. 28. Academic Press, New York.

McBay, A. J., and Algeri, E. J. (1963). Ataraxics and nonbarbiturate sedatives. *Progr. Chem. Toxicol.* **1**, 157.

Maickel, R. P. (1967). "Biochemical Factors in Alcoholism." Pergamon Press, Oxford. 256 pp.

Margolin, S. (1963). Effects on physiological systems: Non-barbiturates. *In* "Physiological Pharmacology. A Comprehensive Treatise" (W. S. Root and F. G. Hofmann, eds.), Vol. 1, p. 23. Academic Press, New York.

Martin, W. R. (1965). Drug addiction. *In:* "Drill's Pharmacology in Medicine" (J. R. DiPalma, ed.), 3rd ed., p. 274. McGraw-Hill, New York.

Maurer, D. W., and Vogel, V. H. (1967). "Narcotics and Narcotic Addiction," 3rd ed. Thomas, Springfield, Illinois. 411 pp.

Maynert, E. W. (1965). Sedatives and hypnotics. I. Nonbarbiturates. II. Barbiturates. *In* "Drill's Pharmacology in Medicine" (J. R. DiPalma, ed.), 3rd ed., p. 169. McGraw-Hill, New York.

Wikler, A. (ed.) (1968). The addictive states. *Res. Publ. Assoc. Res. Nervous Mental Disease* Printing Office, Washington, D.C. 47 pp.

Mellett, L. B., and Woods, L. A. (1963). Analgesia and Addiction. *Progr. Drug Res.* **5**, 155.

"Mental Illness: Due Process and the Criminal Defendant." (1968). By the Special Committee on the Study of Commitment Procedures and the Law Relating to Incompetents of the Association of the Bar of the City of New York. Fordham Univ. Press, Bronx, New York. 261 pp.

Modell, W., and Reader, G. G. (1967). Anorexiants. *In* "Drugs of Choice" (W. Modell, ed.), p. 276. Mosby, St. Louis, Missouri.

Murphree, H. B. (1965). Narcotic Analgesics. I. Opium alkaloids. II. Synthetic analgesics. *In* "Pharmacology in Medicine" (J. R. DiPalma, ed.), 3rd ed., p. 246. McGraw-Hill, New York.

Palopoli, F. P. (1968). Anorexigenic agents. *In* "Annual Reports in Medicinal Chemistry, 1967" (C. K. Cain, ed.), Vol. 3, p. 47. Academic Press, New York.

Parker, K. D., and Hine, C. H. (1967). Manual for the determination of narcotics and dangerous drugs in the urine. *Bull. Narcotics, U.N., Dept. Social Affairs* **19**, 51.

Petit, W. (1962). "A Manual of Pharmaceutical Law." Macmillan, New York. 284 pp.

Poos, G. I. (1967). Anorexigenic agents. *In* "Annual Reports in Medicinal Chemistry, 1966" (C. K. Cain, ed.), Vol. 2, p. 51. Academic Press, New York; *ibid.* Vol. 1, p. 44 (1966).

Rea, R. B. (1966). The rights of the mentally ill: A proposal for procedural changes in hospital admission and discharge. *Psychiatry* **29**, 213.

Reynolds, A. K., and Randall, L. O. (1957). "Morphine and Allied Drugs." Univ. of Toronto Press, Toronto. 393 pp.

Seevers, M. H., and Deneau, G. A. (1963). Physiological aspects of tolerance and physical dependence. *In* "Physiological Pharmacology. A Comprehensive Treatise" (W. S. Root and F. G. Hofmann, eds.), Vol. 1, p. 565. Academic Press, New York.

Sharpless, S. K. (1966). Hypnotics and sedatives. I. The barbiturates. II. Miscellaneous agents. *In* "The Pharmacological Basis of Therapeutics" (L. S. Goodman and A. Gilman, eds.), 3rd. ed., 2nd Printing, p. 105. Macmillan, New York.

Unwin, J. R. (1968). Illicit drug use among Canadian youth. *Can. Med. Assoc. J.* **98**, 402 and 449.

Way, E. L., and Adler, T. K. (1960). The pharmacologic implications of the fate of morphine and its surrogates. *Pharmacol. Rev.* **12**, 383.

Wikler, A., ed. (1968). The addictive states. *Res. Publ., Assoc. Res. Nervous Mental Disease* **46**, 502 pp.

Yolles, S. F. (1966). The government's stake in psychiatric drugs research. *In* "Psychiatric Drugs" (P. Solomon, ed.), p. 121. Grune & Stratton, New York.

VIII. Hallucinogens (and Related Compounds)

Abood, L. G. (1968). The psychotomimetic glycolate esters. *In* "Drugs Affecting the Nervous System" (A. Burger, ed.), Medicinal Research: Vol. 2, p. 127. Marcel Dekker, New York.

Abramson, H. A. (ed.) (1960). "The Use of LSD in Psychotherapy." Transactions of a Conference on D-lysergic and Diethylamide (LSD-25). Josiah Macy, Jr. Found. Bobbs-Merrill, New York. 304 pp.

Abramson, H. A. (ed.) (1967). "The Use of LSD in Psychotherapy and Alcoholism." Bobbs-Merrill, New York. 697 pp.

Borenstein, P. *et al.* (1965). Epreuve á la diethylamide de l'acide lysergique (LSD-25) et thérapeutiques psychotropes—étude clinique et psychologique. *Ann. Med.-Psychol.* **123**, 223.

Cholden, L. (ed.) (1965). "Lysergic Acid Diethylamide and Mescaline in Experimental Psychiatry." Grune & Stratton, New York. 85 pp.

Cohen, S. (1967). Psychotomimetic drugs. *Ann. Rev. Pharmacol.* **7**, 301.

Downing, D. F. (1964). Psychotomimetic compounds. *In* "Psychopharmacological Agents" (M. Gordon, ed.), Vol. 1, p. 555. Academic Press, New York.

Elkes, J. *et al.* (eds.) (1958). Ataractic and hallucinogenic drugs in psychiatry. Report of a study section. *World Health Organ., Tech. Rept. Ser.* **152**, 1–72.

Fink, M. (1965). Cholinergic mechanisms in mental illness: Anticholinergic hallucinogens. *Recent Advan. Biol. Psychiat.* **8**, 115.

Gershon, S. (1965). Behavioral effects of anticholinergic psychotomimetics and their antagonists in man and animals. *Recent Advan. Biol. Psychiat.* **8**, 141.

Hoffer, A., and Osmond, H. (1967). "The Hallucinogens." Academic Press, New York. 626 pp.

Holman, A. (1968). Psychotomimetic agents. *In* "Drugs Affecting the Nervous System" (A. Burger ed.), Medicinal Research: Vol. 2, p. 169. Marcel Dekker, New York.

Hollister, L. E. (1964). Chemical psychoses. *Ann. Rev. Med.* **15**, 203.

Kety, S. S. (ed.) (1957). The pharmacology of psychotomimetic and psychotherapeutic drugs. *Ann. N.Y. Acad. Sci.* **66**, 417.

Korte, F., and Sieper, H. (1965). Recent results of hashish analysis. *In* "Hashish—Its Chemistry and Pharmacology" (G. E. W. Wolstenholme and J. Knight, eds.), Ciba Found. Study Group No. 21, p. 15. Little, Brown, Boston, Massachusetts.

LaBarre, W. (1964). "The Peyote Cult." Shoe String Press, Hamden, Connecticut. 260 pp.

Lewin, L. (1964). "Phantastica: Narcotic and Stimulating Drugs," 2nd ed. Routledge & Kegan, London. 335 pp.

Ling, T. M., and Buckman, J. A. (1963). "Lysergic Acid (LSD-25) and Ritalin in the Treatment of Neurosis." Lambarde Press, London. 172 pp.

Longo, V. G.. and Scotti de Carolis, A. (1968). Anticholinergic hallucinogens: Laboratory results vs. clinical trials. *Progr. Brain Res.* **28**, 106.

Ludwig, A. M., and Levine, J. (1967). Hypnodelic therapy. *Curent Psychiat. Therap.* **7**, 130.

Masters, R. E. L., and Houston, J. (1966). "The Varieties of Psychedelic Experience." Holt, New York, 326 pp.

Patel, A. R. (1968). Mescaline and related compounds. *Progr. Drug Res.* **11**, 11.

Pfeiffer, C. C., and Murphree, H. B. (1965). Introduction to psychotropic drugs and hallucinogenic drugs. *In* "Drill's Pharmacology in Medicine" (J. R. DiPalma, ed.), 3rd ed., p. 321. McGraw-Hill, New York.

Pollard, J. C. *et al.* (1965). "Drugs and Fantasy: The Effects of LSD, Psilocybin, and Sernyl on College Students." Little, Brown, Boston, Massachusetts. 205 pp.

Schwartz, C. J. (1968). The complications of LSD: A review of the literature. *J. Nervous Mental Disease* **146**, 174.

Smart, R. G., and Bateman, K. (1967). Unfavorable reactions to LSD: A review and analysis of the available case reports. *J. Can. Med. Assoc.* **97**, 1214.

Smythies, J. R. (1962). Hallucinogenic drugs. *In* "Modern Trends in Neurology" (D. Williams ed.), Vol. 3, p. 353. Butterworth, London and Washington, D.C.

Soloman, D. (ed.) (1964). "LSD: The Consciousness-Expanding Drug." Putnam, New York. 273 pp.

Weil, G. M., Metzner, R., and Leary, T. (eds.) (1965). "The Psychedelic Reader." University Books, New Hyde Park, New York. 260 pp.

Whitelock, O. V. St. *et al.* (eds.) (1957). The pharmacology of psychotomimetic and psychotherapeutic drugs. *Ann. N.Y. Acad. Sci.* **66**, 417.

Wolstenholme, G. E. W., and Knight, J. (eds.) (1965). "Hashish—Its Chemistry and Pharmacology," Ciba Found. Study Group No. 21. Little, Brown, Boston, Massachusetts. 96 pp.

Young, W., and Hixson, J. (1966). "LSD on Campus." Dell, New York. 192 pp.

IX. Toxicity, Adverse Reactions, and Side Effects of Drugs

Bignami, G., and Gatti, G. L. (1967). Neurotoxicity of anticholinesterase agents: Antagonistic action of various centrally acting drugs. *In* "Neurotoxicity of Drugs" Vol. 8, p. 93 (Proc. European Soc. Study Drug Toxicity). Excerpta Med. Found., Amsterdam.

Bosissier, J. R., and Simon, P. (1967). Comportement et toxicologie provisionnelle. *In* "Neurotoxicity of Drugs," Vol. 8 (Proc. European Soc. Study Drug Toxicity). Excerpta Med. Found., Amsterdam.

Bordeleau, J. (ed.) (1961). "Extrapyramidal System and Neuroleptics." Editions Psychiatriques, Montreal. 574 pp.

Burns, J. J. (ed.) (1965). Evaluations and mechanisms of drug toxicity. *Ann. N.Y. Acad. Sci.* **123**, 1.

Cornu, F. (1967). Begleitwirkungen, Komplikationen und Unverträglichkeitserscheinungen bei psychiatrischer Pharmakotherapie. *Arch. Psychiat. Z. Ges. Neurol.* **210**, 97.

Costa, E. *et al.* (eds.) (1966). "Biochemistry and Pharmacology of the Basal Ganglia." Raven Press, Hewlett, New York. 238 pp.

Crane, G. E. (1968). Tardive Dyskinesia in patients treated with major neuroleptics. *Am. J. Psychiat.* **124**, 40.

Cremer, J. E. (1967). Biochemical changes associated with neurotoxicity. *In* "Neurotoxicity of Drugs," Vol. 8, p. 169 (Proc. European Soc. Study Drug Toxicity). Excerpta Med. Found., Amsterdam.

Davey, D. G. (ed.) (1967). "Neurotoxicity of Drugs," Vol. 8 (Proc. European Soc. Study Drug Toxicity). Excerpta Med. Found., Amsterdam. 227 pp.

De C. Baker, S. B., and Scott, A. I. (eds.) (1966). "Neurotoxicity of Drugs," Vol. 8 (Proc. European Soc. Study Drug Toxicity). Excerpta Med. Found., Amsterdam.

De C. Baker, S. B. *et al.* (1968). Toxicity and side-effects of psychotropic drugs. *In* "Neurotoxicity of Drugs," Vol. 9, p. 1, Intern. Congr. Series No. 145 (Proc. European Soc. Study Drug Toxicity, Paris, 1967). Excerpta Med. Found., Amsterdam.

Degkwitz, R. *et al.* (1966). Zum Problem des terminalen extrapyramidalen Hyperkinesian an Hand von 1600 lang Freistig mit Neuroleptica behandelten. *Arzneimittel-Forsch.* **16**, 276.

Esplin, D. W. (1966). Centrally acting muscle relaxants; drugs for Parkinson's disease. *In* "The Pharmacological Basis of Therapeutics" (L. S. Goodman and A. Gilman, eds.), 3rd ed., p. 237. Macmillan, New York.

European Society for the Study of Drug Toxicity. Proceedings. (1963–1968). Vol. 1: Effects of Drugs on the Foetus (1963); Vol. 2: Viewpoints on the Study of Drug Toxicity (1964); Vol. 5: Advances in Toxicological Methodology (1965); Vol. 6: Experimental Studies and Clinical Experience. The Assessment of Risk (1965); Vol. 8: Neurotoxicity of Drugs (1967); Vol. 9: The Toxicity and Side Effects of Psychotropic Drugs (1968). Excerpta Med. Found., Amsterdam. 58 pp., 216 pp., 148 pp., 252 pp., 212 pp., and 331 pp. resp.

Faurbye, A. *et al.* (1964). Neurological symptoms in pharmacotherapy of psychoses. *Acta Psychiat. Scand.* **40**, 10.

Friedman, A. H., and Everett, G. M. (1964). Pharmacological aspects of Parkinsonism. *Pharmacol. Rev.* **3**, 83.

Goldbaum, L. R., and Bomanski, T. J. (1965). An approach to the analysis of biological specimens for basic drugs. *Progr. Chem. Toxicol.* **2**, 221.

Grebe, R. M. (ed.) (1959). "Handbook of Toxicology," Vol. 4: Tranquilizers. Saunders, Philadelphia, Pennsylvania. 120 pp.

Haase, H. (1961). Das therapeutische Achsensyndrom neuroleptischer Medikamente und seine Beziehungen zu extrapyramidaler Symptomatik. *Fortsch. Neurol. Psychiat. Grenzgeb.* **29**, 245.

Haase, H. (1962). Intensität und Äquivalenz neuroleptischer Wirkung und ihre Therapeutische Bedeutung. *Nervenarzt* **33**, 213.

Holden, J. M. C., and Itil, T. M. (1968). The application of automated techniques in assessing psychotropic drug-induced side effects. *Am. J. Psychiat.* **125**, 562.

Hornykiewicz, O. (1967). Extrapyramidale Nebenwirkungen der Neuro-(Psycho-) Pharmaka. *In* "Neurotoxicity of Drugs" (S. B. De C. Baker and A. I. Scott, eds.), Vol. 8, p. 107 (Proc. European Soc. Study Drug Toxicity). Excerpta Med. Found., Amsterdam.

Horvath, M. *et al.* (1963). Experimental studies of higher nervous system functions in pharmacology and toxicology. *In* "Psychopharmacological Methods" (Z. Votava *et al.*, eds.), p. 131. Macmillan, New York.

Jacobs, J. (1967). Recherches sur la psychotoxicité des médicaments. Equivalents expérimentaux des effets psychotomimétiques. *In* "Neurotoxicity of Drugs" (S. B. De C. Baker and A. L. Scott, eds.), Vol. 8, p. 30 (Proc. European Soc. Study Drug Toxicity). Excerpta Med. Found., Amsterdam (English transl., p. 59).

Janků, I., and Krsiak, M. (1967). Experimental detection of neurotoxic side-effects. *In* "Neurotoxicity of Drugs" (S. B. De C. Baker and A. L. Scott, eds.), Vol. 8, p. 86 (Proc. European Soc. Study Drug Toxicity). Excerpta Med. Found., Amsterdam.

Kaehler, H. J. (1960). II. Neuroleptica und Antihistaminica. Ihre Erwünschten und Unerwünschten Arzneimittel Wirkungen. *Ergeb. Inn. Med. Kinderheilk.* [N.S.] 13, 44.

Koch, G. (1966). Diseases with a predominating participation of the extra-pyramidal system. *In* "Humangenetik" (P. E. Becker, ed.), Vol. 5, Part 1, p. 130. Springer, Berlin and New York.

Lambert, P. A. (ed.) (1965). "La relation médecin-malade au cours des chimiothérapies psychiatriques." Masson, Paris. 222 pp.

Leestman, J. E., and Koenig, K. L. (1968). Sudden death and phenothiazines. A current controversy. *Arch. Gen. Psychiat.* **18**, 137.

McBay, A. J., and Algeri, E. J. (1963). Ataraxics and nonbarbiturate sedatives. *Progr. Chem. Toxicol.* **1**, 157.

Marlin, R. L. (ed.) (1968). Proceedings of the Symposium on Adverse Drug Reactions. *Drug Inform. Bull.* **2**, 63.

Meyler, L. (ed.) (1957, 1958, 1960, 1964, 1966). "Side Effects of Drugs," Vol. I: Untoward Effects of Drugs as Reported in Medical Literature of the World During the Period 1955–1956; Vol. II (1956–1957); Vol. III (1958–1960); Vol. IV (1960–1962); Vol. V (1963–1965). Excerpta Med. Found., Amsterdam. 128 pp., 194 pp., 239 pp., 356 pp., and 578 pp. resp.

Meyler, L., and Peck, H. M. (eds.) (1962). "Drug-induced Diseases." Thomas, Springfield, Illinois, and Royal Vangorcum Publ. Ltd., Essen, The Netherlands. 237 pp.

Modell, W. (1967). Mass drug catastrophies and the role of science and technology. *Science* **156**, 346.

Nashold, B. S., and Huber, W. V. (eds.) (1966). The Second Symposium on Parkinson's. Suppl. to: *J. Neurosurg.* **24**, No. 1, Part II. 481 pp.

Nijdam, S. J. (1962). Neurological and psychiatric side effects during treatment with modern psychotropic drugs. *In* "Drug Induced Diseases" (L. Meyler and H. M. Peck, eds.), p. 211. Thomas, Springfield, Illinois, and Royal Vangorcum Publ., Ltd., Essen, The Netherlands.

Rǎsková, H. (ed.) (1968). "Mechanisms of Drug Toxicity." Pergamon Press, Oxford. 104 pp.

Refsom, S. *et al.* (eds.) (1963). Report on the Sixteenth Congress of Scandinavian Neurologists, Oslo, 1962. Part I. The so-called extrapyramidal system. *Acta Neurol. Scand.* **39**, Suppl. 4, 17–255.

Sirnes, T. B. (1963). Drug-induced extrapyramidal reactions. *Acta Neurol. Scand.* **39**, Suppl. 4, 209.

Stewart, C. P. (ed.) (1960–1961). "Toxicology. Mechanisms and Analytical Methods," Vols. 1 and 2. Academic Press, New York. 774 pp. and 921 pp. resp.

Stewart, G. A. (1963). Statistics as applied to pharmacological and toxicological screening. *Progr. Med. Chem.* **3**, 187.

Stolman, A. (1965). Thin layer chromatography application in toxicology. *Progr. Chem. Toxicol.* **2**, 321.

Stolman, A. (ed.) (1963, 1965). "Progress in Chemical Toxicology," Vols. 1 and 2. Academic Press, New York. 436 pp. and 416 pp. resp.

Sunshine, I. (1967). Problems of obtaining information on accidental ingestions and poisoning incidents. *J. Clin. Pharmacol.* **7**, 61.

Svenson, S. *et al.* (1966). A critique of overemphasis on side effects with the psychotropic drugs: An analysis of 18,000 chlordiazepoxide-treated cases. *Current Therap. Res.* **8**, 455.

Walaas, E., and Walaas, O. (1963). Biochemical aspects of copper and aromatic amines in relation to the extrapyramidal system. *Acta Neurol. Scand.* **39**, Suppl. 4, 84.

Worden, A. N. *et al.* (1967). Lesions in the brain of the dog induced by prolonged administration of monoamine oxidase inhibitors and isoniazid. *In* "Neurotoxicity of Drugs" (S. B. De C. Baker and A. I. Scott, eds.), Vol. 8, p. 149 (Proc. European Soc. Study Drug Toxicity). Excerpta Med. Found., Amsterdam.

Yahr, M. D., and Purpura, D. P. (eds.) (1967). "Neurophysiological Basis of Normal and Abnormal Motor Activities" (Proc. 3rd Symp. Parkinson's Disease Information and Research Center, Nov., 1966). Raven Press, Hewlett, New York. 500 pp.

Zbindin, G. (1962). Experimental and clinical aspects of drug toxicity. *Advan. Pharmacol.* **2,** 1.

X. Clinical Use of Psychotherapeutic Drugs

A. *General*

Adelson, D. (1960). Are nurses needed in psychopharmacological research? *Am. J. Nursing* **60,** 1278.

Anonymous. (1968). Drug therapy. *Am. J. Psychiat.* **124,** No. 8, Suppl. 2, 1.

Arneson, G. A. (1967). Psychopharmacologic roulette. *Southern Med. J.* **60,** 67.

Blair. D. (1965). "Modern Drugs for the Treatment of Mental Illness." Thomas, Springfield, Illinois. 327 pp.

Bradley, C. (1958). Tranquilizing drugs in pediatrics. *Pediatrics* **21,** 325.

Caffey, E. M. *et al.* (1964). Discontinuation or reduction of chemotherapy in chronic schizophrenics. *J. Chronic Diseases* **17,** 347.

Casey, J. F. (ed.) (1956–1961). "Transactions of Six Research Conferences on Chemotherapy in Psychiatry," Vols. 1–6. Vet. Admin., Washington, D.C. 123 pp., 257 pp., 303 pp., 366 pp., 375 pp., and 410 pp. resp.

Chance, P., and Chance-serve, C. (eds.) "Memento de thérapeutique neuropsychiatrique." Masson, Paris. 253 pp.

Cohen, S. (1966). Thioridazine (Mellaril)—recent developments. *J. Psychopharmacol.* **1,** 1.

Davis, J. M. (1965). Efficacy of tranquilizing and antidepressant drugs. *Acta Gen. Psychiat.* **13,** 552.

Delay, J., and Deniker, P. (1961). "Méthodes chimiothérapiques en psychiatrie." Les Nouveaux Médicaments Psychotropes. Masson, Paris. pp.

DiPalma, J. R. (1965). Drugs in epilepsy and hyperkinetic states. *In* "Drill's Pharmacology in Medicine" (J. R. DiPalma, ed.), 3rd ed., p. 246. McGraw-Hill, New York.

Domino, E. F. (1965). Psychosedative drugs. I. Substituted phenothiazines, reserpine and derivatives. II. Meprobarmate, chlordiazepoxide, and miscellaneous agents. In "Drill's Pharmacology in Medicine" (J. R. DiPalma, ed.), 3rd ed., p. 337. McGraw-Hill, New York.

Engelhardt, D. M. (1967). Drug treatment of chronic ambulatory patients. *Am. J. Psychiat.* **123,** 1329.

Fish, B. (1968). Drug use in psychiatric disorders of children. *Am. J. Psychiat.* **124,** No. 8, Suppl., 31.

Flugel, F., ed. (1961). Neuropsychopharmakologie. (2nd Symposium der Deutschen Arbeitsgemeinschaft. Nürnberg, 1961.) *Med. Exptl.* **5,** 299 pp.

Freeman, H. (1967). The therapeutic value of combinations of psychotropie drugs: A review. *Psychopharmacol. Bull.* **4,** 1.

Frøvig, A. G. (1963). The medical treatment of Parkinsonism. *Acta Neurol. Scand.* **39,** Suppl. 4, 169.

Gittelman-Klein, R., and Klein, D. F. (1969). *In* "Psychopharmacology. A Review of Progress. 1957–1967" (H. Efron *et al.,* eds.), Proc. Am. Coll. Neuropsychopharmacol., Public Health Serv. Publ. No. 1836, p. 1119. U.S. Govt. Printing Office, Washington, D.C.

Haase, H. J. (1966). "Neuroleptika, Tranquilizer, und Anti-depressiva in Klinik und Praxis." Janssen, Düsseldorf. 94 pp.

Hertrich, O. (1965). Differentiallindikationen für psychosenspezifische Drogen nach Zielsymptomen. *Fortschr. Neurol., Psychiat. Grenzgeb.* **33,** 49.

"International Encyclopedia of Pharmacology and Therapeutics." Sect. 25, Vol. 1: Parkinsonian Drugs. Pergamon Press, Long Island City, New York (in press).

Jacobsen, E. (1964). Benactyzine. *In* "Psychopharmacological Agents" (M. Gordon, ed.), Vol. 1, p. 287. Academic Press, New York.

Jenden, D. J. (1968). Testing of drugs for therapeutic potential in Parkinson's Disease. *In* "Selected Pharmacological Testing Methods" (A. Burger, ed.), Medicinal Research: Vol. 3, p. 337. Marcel Dekker, New York.

Kielholz, P. (1965). "Psychiatrische Pharmakotherapie in Klinik und Praxis." Huber, Bern. 293 pp.

Kranz, H., and Heinrich K. (eds.) (1964). "Begleitwirkungen und Misserfölge der psychiatrischen Pharmakotherapie." Thieme, Stuttgart. 202 pp.

Labhardt, F. von (1966). Die Anwendung von Psychopharmaka in der Psychosomatischen Medizin. *Progr. Drug Res.* **10,** 530.

Lutz, V. J. (ed.) (1965). "Psychopharmakologie in Kindesalter. (Series Paedopsychiatrica 1)." Schwabe, Stuttgart. 112 pp.

Millichap, J. G. (1965). Anticonvulsant drugs. *In:* "Physiological Pharmacology. A Comprehensive Treatise" (W. S. Root and F. G. Howmann, eds.), Vol. 2, p. 97. Academic Press, New York.

Nashold, B. S., and Huber, W. V. (eds.) (1966). "The Second Symposium on Parkinson's Disease." Suppl. to: *J. Neurosurg.* **24,** No. 1, Part II, 481 pp.

Ostow, M. (1966). "Psychopharmaka in der Psychotherapie" (Transl. by R. Polaczek). E. Klett, Stuttgart. 442 pp.

Paterson, A. S. (1968). "Electrical and Drug Treatments in Psychiatry." Elsevier, Amsterdam. 248 pp.

Pětrilowitsch, N. (1966). "Psychiatrische Krankheitslehre und Psychiatrische Pharmakotherapie." Karger, Basel. 120 pp.

Pětrilowitsch, N., and Kranz, H. (1966). "Psychiatrischen Kombinations und Langzeitbehandlung." Karger, Basel. 212 pp.

"Psychopharmakologie im Kindesalter." (1965).

Reynolds, A. K., and Randall, L. O. (1957). "Morphine and Allied Drugs." Univ. of Toronto Press, Toronto. 393 pp.

Rickels, K. (1968). Drug use in outpatient treatment. *Am. J. Psychiat.* **124,** No. 8, Suppl., 20.

Root, W. S., and Hofmann, F. G. (eds.) (1963, 1965, 1967). "Physiological Pharmacology. A Comprehensive Treatise," Vols. 1, 2, and 3. Academic Press, New York. 703 pp., 486 pp., and 519 pp. resp.

Sargent, L., and Slater, E. (1963). "Introduction to Physical Methods of Treatment in Psychiatry." 4th ed. Williams & Wilkins, Baltimore, Maryland. 346 pp.

Schmitt, W. (1965). "Psychiatrische Pharmakotherapie. Experimentelle und Klinische Grundlagen eines Klassifizierungsversuches." A. Hüthing, Heidelberg. 240 pp.

Siegfried, J. (1968). "Die Parkinsonische Krankheit und ihre Behandlung." Springer, Vienna. 262 pp.

Spinks, A., and Waring, W. S. (1963). Anticonvulsant drugs. *Progr. Med. Chem.* **3,** 261.

Wandrey, D., and Leutner, V. (1965). "Neuro-Psychopharmaca in Klinik und Praxis." Schattauer, Stuttgart. 317 pp.

B. Antipsychotic Agents

Anonymous. (1966). "Stelazine Brand of Trifluoperazine in Psychiatry." Smith, Kline & French Laboratories, Philadelphia, Pennsylvania. 126 pp.

Anonymous. (1968). "Thorazine Brand of Chlorpromazine Fundamental in Psychiatry." Smith, Kline & French Laboratories, Philadelphia, Pennsylvania. 68 pp.

Bickel, M. H. (1968). Untersuchungen zur Biochemie und Pharmakologie der Thymoleptika. *Progr. Drug Res.* **11,** 121.

Bradley, P. B. (1963). Tranquilizers: Phenothiazine derivatives. *In* "Physiological Pharmacology. A Comprehensive Treatise" (W. S. Root and F. G. Hofmann, eds.), p. 417. Academic Press, New York.

Delay, J. (ed.) (1956). Colloque international sur la chlorpromazine et less medicaments neuroleptiques en thérapeutique psychiatrique, Paris, Oct. 20–22, 1955. *Encéphale* **40,** 301.

Domino, E. F. *et al.* (1968). Substituted phenothiazines: Pharmacology and chemical structure. *In* "Drugs Affecting the Nervous System" (A. Burger, ed.), Medicinal Research: Vol. 2, p. 327. Marcel Dekker, New York.

Gastadli, G. (ed.) (1962). "Symposium Internazionale sull' Haloperidol e Triperidol." Farmaco d'Italia. Milano. 768 pp.

Janssen, P. A. J. (ed.) (1967). The pharmacology of Haloperidol. International Symposium of Pharmacology. *Intern. J. Neuropharmacol.* 3, Suppl. 155 pp.

Kinross-Wright, J. (1967). The current status of phenothiazines. *J. Am. Med. Assoc.* **200,** 461.

Kranz, H., and Heinrich, K. (eds.) (1962). "Neurolepsie and Schizophrenie." Thieme, Stuttgart. 176 pp.

Lewis, J. J. (1963). Tranquilizers: Rauwolfia derivatives. *In* "Physiological Pharmacology. A Comprehensive Treatise" (W. S. Root and F. G. Hoffmann, eds.), p. 479. Academic Press, New York.

Pachter, I. J. *et al.* (1968). Antipsychotic and antianxiety agents. *In* "Annual Reports in Medicinal Chemistry, 1967" (C. K. Cain, ed.), Vol. 3, p. 1. Academic Press, New York.

Petersen, P. V., and Nielsen, I. M. (1964). Thiaxanthene Derivatives. *In* "Psychopharmacological Agents" (M. Gordon, ed.), Vol. 1, p. 301. Academic Press, New York.

Pletscher, A. *et al.* (1960). Monoaminoxydasehemmer. *Progr. Drug Res.* **2,** 417.

Pollitt, J. (1965). "Depression and Its Treatment." Thomas, Springfield, Illinois. 114 pp.

Prien, R. F., and Cole, J. O. (1968). High dose chlorpromazine therapy in chronic schizophrenia. *Arch. Gen. Psychiat.* **18,** 482.

Rokhlin, L. L. (ed.) (1965). [Reserpine in Psychiatric Practice. A Symposium.] Ministry of Public Health of the R.S.F.S.R., U.S.S.R. (in Russian) 246 pp.

Schenker, E. von, and Herbst, H. (1963). Phenothiazine und Azaphenothiazine als Arzneimittel. *Progr. Drug Res.* **5,** 269.

Schlittler, E., and Plummer, A. J. (1964). Tranquilizing drugs from Rauwolfia. *In* "Psychopharmacological Agents" (M. Gordon, ed.), Vol. 1, p. 9. Academic Press, New York.

Wied, D. de (1967). Chlorpromazine and endocrine function. *Pharmacol. Rev.* **19,** 251.

Yonkman, F., ed. (1954). Reserpine (Serpasil) and other alkaloids of *Rauwolfia serpentina:* Chemistry, pharmacology and clinical applications. *Ann. N.Y. Acad. Sci.* **59,** 140 pp.

Yonkman, F. F. (ed.) (1955). Reserpine in the treatment of neuropsychiatric, neurological, and related clinical problems. *Ann. N.Y. Acad. Sci.* **61,** 280 pp.

C. *Antidepressant Agents*

Beck, A. T. (1967). "Depression: Clinical, Experimental and Theoretical Aspects." Harper (Hoeber), New York. 359 pp.

Biel, J. H. (1968). Chemopharmacological approaches to the treatment of mental depression. *In* "Drugs Affecting the Nervous System" (A. Burger, ed.), Medicinal Research: Vol. 2, p. 61. Marcel Dekker, New York.

Bryant, J. M. (1967). Monamines oxidase (MAO) inhibition—a therapeutic adjunct. *Med. Times* **95,** 420.

Cole, J. O., and Wittenborn, J. R. (eds.) (1966). "Pharmacology of Depression." Thomas, Springfield, Illinois. 189 pp.

Di Mascio, A. *et al.* (1968). Effect of Imipramine on individuals varying in level of depression. *Am. J. Psychiat.* **124,** Suppl., 55.

Flügel, F. *et al.* (eds.) (1964). Wirkungsmodalitäten und Qualitäten des Antidepressiven Effecktes. Symposium der Deutschen Arbeitsgemeinschaft für Neuropsychophamakologie. *Arzneimittel-Forsch.* **14.** 125 pp.

Garattini, S., and Dukes, M. N. G. (eds.) (1967). "Antidepressant Drugs. Proceedings of the First International Symposium," Excerpta Med. Found., Intern. Congr. Ser. No. 122. Excerpta Med. Found., Amsterdam. 407 pp.

Giarman, J. J. (1965). Antidepressant drugs. *In* "Drill's Pharmacology in Medicine" (J. R. DiPalma, ed.), 3rd ed., p. 365. McGraw-Hill, New York.

Haider, I. (1967). Drugs in the treatment of depression. *Brit. J. Clin. Pract.* **21,** 215.

Holtz, P., and Westermann, E. (1965). Psychic energizers and antidepressant drugs. *In* "Physiological Pharmacology. A Comprehensive Treatise" (W. S. Root and F. G. Hofmann, eds.), Vol. 2, p. 201. Academic Press, New York.

Jacobsen, E. (1958). The pharmacological classification of central nervous depression. *J. Pharm. Pharmacol.* **10,** 273.

Kranz, H. (1965). Die Moderne Behandlung Depressiver Psychosen. *Anglo-German Med. Rev.* **2,** 715.

Lapine, I. P. (1961). Characteristiques pharmacologiques de l'imipramine. *Therapie* **19,** 1107.

McGill University Conference on Depression and Allied States. (1959). *Can. Psychiat. Assoc. J.* Spec. Suppl. 4. 197 pp.

Malitz, S. (1966). Drug therapy: Antidepressants. *In* "American Handbook of Psychiatry" (S. Arieti, ed.), Vol. 3, p. 477. Basic Books, New York; Neuroleptics and tranquilizers, *ibid.* p. 458.

Mendels, J. (1968). Comparative trial of nortriptyline and amitryptyline in 100 depressed patients. *Am. J. Psychiat.* **124,** No. 8, Suppl. 1, 59.

D. Antianxiety Agents

Berger, F. M. (ed.) (1957). Meprobamate and other agents used in mental disturbances. *Ann. N.Y. Acad. Sci.* **67,** 671.

Berger, F. M., and Ludwig, B. J. (1964). Meprobamate and related compounds. *In* "Psychopharmacological Agents" (M. Gordon, ed.), Vol. 1, p. 103. Academic Press, New York.

Donahue, H. B., and Kimura, K. K. (1968). Synthetic centrally acting skeletal muscle relaxants. *In* "Drugs Affecting the Nervous System" (A. Burger, ed.), Medicinal Research: Vol. 2, p. 265.

"International Encyclopedia of Pharmacology and Therapeutics." Sect. 24: Centrally Acting Skeleton Muscle Relaxants. Pergamon Press, Long Island City, New York (in press).

Pachter, I. J. *et al.*, (1968). Antipsychotic and anti-anxiety agents. *In* "Annual Reports in Medicinal Chemistry, 1967" (C. K. Cain, ed.), Vol. 3, p. 1. Academic Press, New York.

Sherrod, T. R. (1963). Diphenylmethane derivatives. *In* "Physiological Pharmacology. A Comprehensive Treatise" (W. S. Root and F. Hofmann, eds.), Vol. 1, p. 538. Academic Press, New York.

Smith, C. M. (1965). Relaxants of skeletal muscle. *In* "Physiological Pharmacology. A Comprehensive Treatise" (W. S. Root and F. G. Hofmann, eds.), p. 486. Academic Press, New York.

Sternbach, L. H. *et al.* (1968). Structure-activity relationships in the 1,4-benzodiazepine series. *In* "Drugs Affecting the Nervous System" (A. Burger, ed.), Medicinal Research: Vol. 2, p. 237. Marcel Dekker, New York.

Svenson, S. E., and Gordon, L. E. (1965). Diazepam: A progress report. *Current Therap. Res.* **7,** 367.

Zbindin, G., and Randall, L. O. (1967). Pharmacology of benzodiazepines: Laboratory and clinical correlations. *Advan. Pharmacol.* **5,** 213.

E. Anti-Matic Depressant Agents (Lithium, Etc.)

Barratt, E. S. *et al.* (1968). The effects of lithium salts on brain activity in the cat. *Am. J. Psychiat.*, **125,** No. 4, 530.

Bunney, W. E., Jr. *et al.* (1968). A behavioral-biochemical study of lithium treatment. *Am. J. Psychiat.* **125**, 499.
Cole, J. O. (Editorial). (1968). Lithium carbonate: Some recommendations. *Am. J. Psychiat.* **125**, 556.
Dyson, W. L., and Mendelson, M. (1968). Recurrent depressions and the lithium ions. *Am. J. Psychiat.* **125**, 544.
Fieve, R. R., and Platman, S. (1968). Lithium and thyroid function in manic-depressive psychosis. *Am. J. Psychiat.* **125**, 527.
Fieve, R. R. *et al.* (1968). The use of lithium in affective disorders. I. Acute endogenous depression. II. Prophylaxis of depression in chronic recurrent affective disorder. *Am. J. Psychiat.* **125**, 487 and 492.
Greenspan, K. *et al.* (1968). Retention and distribution patterns of lithium, a pharmacological tool in studying the pathophysiology of manic-depressive psychosis. *Am. J. Psychiat.* **125**, 512.
Johnson, G. *et al.* (1968). Controlled evaluation of lithium and chlorpromazine in the treatment of manic states: An interim report. *Compr. Psychiat.* **9**, 563.
Kline, N. S. (Editorial). (1968). Lithium comes into its own. *Am. J. Psychiat.* **125**, 150.
Meyer, H. H. (1968). Fortschritte der Pharmakotherapie der manischdepressiven Erkankungen (der Zyklothymie). *Fortschr. Neurol., Psychiat. Grenzgeb.* **36**, 61.
Schou, M. *et al.* (1968). Lithium poisoning. *Am. J. Psychiat.* **125**, 520.
Tupin, J. P. *et al.* (1968). Lithium effects in electrolyte excretim. *Am. J. Psychiat.* **125**, 536.
Zall, H. *et al.* (1968). Lithium carbonate: A clinical study. *Am. J. Psychiat.* **125**, 549.

XI. Ethnology, Sociology, Epidemiology, Social Psychology, Anthropology, Ethology, Aggression, Etc.

Achelis, J. D. (ed.) (1963). "Anthropologische und naturwissenschaftliche Grundlagen der Pharmako-Psychiatrie," Thieme, Stuttgart. 114 pp.
Andry, R. G., and Sington, D. (1965). "Psychosocial Aspects of Drug-Taking." Pergamon Press, Oxford. 45 pp.
Barber, B. (1967). "Drugs and Society." Russell Sage Found., New York. 212 pp.
Clemente, C. D., and Lindsley, D. B. (eds.) (1967). Brain function: Vol. 5. "Aggression and Defense Neural Mechanisms and Social Patterns." Univ. of California Press, Los Angeles, California. 361 pp.
de Reuck, A. V. S., and Porter, R. J. (eds.) (1965). "Transcultural Psychiatry," Ciba Found. Symp. Little, Brown, Boston, Massachusetts. 396 pp.
Gay, W. I. (ed.) (1965). "Methods of Animal Experimentation," Vols. 1 and 2. Academic Press, New York. 382 pp. and 608 pp. resp.
Hafez, E. S. E. (ed.) (1962). "The Behavior of Domestic Animals." Williams & Wilkins, Baltimore, Maryland. 619 pp.
Henry, J. P. *et al.* (1967). The use of psychosocial stimuli to induce prolonged systolic hypertension in mice. *Psychosomat. Med.* **29**, 408.
Herxheimer, A. (ed.) (1968). "Drugs and Sensory Functions." Churchill, London. 338 pp.
Holmstedt, B. (1967). Historical survey. *In* "Ethnopharmacologic Search for Psychoactive Drugs" (D. H. Efron *et al.*, eds.), p. 3, Public Health Serv. Publ. No. 1645. U.S. Dept. Health, Education and Welfare, Washington, D.C.
Leiderman, P. H., and Shapiro, D., (eds.) (1964). "Psychobiological Approaches to Social Behavior." Stanford Univ. Press, Palo Alto, California. 203 pp.
Opler, M. K. (ed.) (1959). "Culture and Mental Health. Cross-Culture Studies." Macmillan, New York. 533 pp.
Silverman, C. (1968). The Epidemiology of Depression. A review. *Am. J. Psychiat.* **124**, 883.

XII. Comparative Animal and Human Behavior, Learning, Memory, Sleep, Dreams, Etc.

Baruk, H. (1964). "La Psychopathologie Expérimentale." Presses Univ. de France, Paris. 127 pp.

Brion, A., and Ey, H. (eds.) (1964). "Psychiatrie Animale." Desclee de Brouwer, Paris. 605 pp.

Candland, D. K. (1968). "Psychology: The Experimental Approach." McGraw Hill, New York. 711 pp.

Cook, L., and Catania, A. C. (1964). Effects of drugs on avoidance and escape behavior. *In* "Types of Behavior on which Drugs Act" (P. B. Dews, ed.), *Federation Proc.* **23**, 818. (Symp.)

Dews, P. B., ed. (1964). "Types of Behavior on which Drugs Act." *Federation Proc.* 23, 799. (Symp.)

Dews, P. B. (1966). Conditioned behavior as a substrate for behavioral effects of drugs. *In* "Psychiatric Drugs" (P. Solomon, ed.), p. 22. Grune & Stratton, New York.

Hunt, H. F. (1961). Methods for studying the behavioral effects of drugs. *Ann. Rev. Pharmacol.* **1**, 125.

Kelleher, R. T., and Morse, W. H. (1964). Escape behavior and punished behavior. *In* "Types of Behavior in which Drugs Act. Pharmacology Symposium" (P. B. Dews, ed.), *Federation Proc.* **23**, 808. (Symp.)

McGaugh, J. L., and Petrinovich, L. F. (1965). Effects of drugs on learning and memory. *Intern. Rev. Neurobiol.* **8**, 139.

Malmo, R. B. (1957). Anxiety and behavioral arousal. *Psychol. Rev.* **64**, 276.

Mikhelson, M. I. *et al.* (eds.) (1965). "Pharmacology of Conditioning, Learning and Retention," Vol. 1 (Proc. 2nd Intern. Pharmacol. Meeting, Prague, 1963). Pergamon Press, Oxford. 365 pp.

Stone, G. C. (1966). Prediction of drug-induced changes in rats' avoidance behavior. *In* "Prediction of Response to Pharmacotherapy Therapy" (J. R. Wittenborn and P. R. A. May, eds.), p. 156. Thomas, Springfield, Illinois.

Stretch, R. (1966). Operant conditioning in the study of animal behaviour. *In* "New Horizons in Psychology" (B. M. Foss, ed.), p. 287. Penguin Books, Baltimore, Maryland.

Weiss, B., and Laties, V. G. (1964). Drug effects on the temporal patterning of behavior. *In* "Types of Behavior on which Drugs Act. Pharmacology Symposium" (P. B. Dews, ed.), *Federation Proc.* **23**, 801. (Symp.)

Wolstenholme, G. E. W. (ed.) (1952). Hormones, psychology and behavior, and steroid hormone administration. *Ciba Found. Colloq. Endocrinol.* **3**. 380 pp.

XIII. Drug Metabolism: Blood-Brain Barrier, Absorption, Excretion, Transport

Bonnycastle, D. D. (1965). Intimate study of drug action. I. Absorption and distribution. *In* "Drill's Pharmacology in Medicine" (J. R. DiPalma, ed.), 3rd ed., p. 16. McGraw-Hill, New York.

Bush, M. T., and Sander, E. (eds.) (1967). Metabolic fate of drugs: Barbiturates and closely related compounds. *Ann. Rev. Pharmacol.* **7**, 57.

Buyske, D. A., and Dvornik, D. (1967). Fate and redistribution of drugs. *In* "Annual Reports in Medicinal Chemistry, 1966" (C. K. Cain, ed.), Vol. 3, p. 237. Academic Press, New York.

Conney, A. H., and Burns, J. J. (1962). Factors influencing drug metabolism. *Advan. Pharmacol.* **1**, 31.

Euler, U. S. von (1965). Aufnahme, Speicherung und Freisetzung von Katecholaminen in Adrenergischen Neuronen. *Z. Vitamin-, Hormon- Fermentforsch.* **14**, 174.

Gillette, J. R. (1963). Metabolism of drugs and other foreign compounds by enzymatic mechanisms. *Progr. Drug Res.* **6**, 11.

Gillette, J. R. (1965). Reversible binding as a complication in relating the *in vitro* effect of drugs to their *in vivo* activity. *In* "Drugs and Enzymes" (B. B. Brodie and J. R. Gillette, eds.), Vol. 4, p. 9 (Proc. 2nd Intern. Pharmacol. Meeting, Prague, 1963). Pergamon Press, Oxford.

"International Encyclopedia of Pharmacology and Therapeutics." Sect. 3: Distribution and Metabolism of Drugs. Pergamon Press, Long Island City, New York (in press).

Lajtha, A., and Ford, D. H. (eds.) (1968). Brain-barrier systems. *Progr.* Brain Res. **29.** 552 pp.

McIlwain, H. (1963). Metabolic and electrical measurements with isolated cerebral tissues: Their contribution to study of the action of drugs on cortical excitability. *In* "Brain Function" (M. A. B. Brazier, ed.), p. 49. Univ. of California Press, Los Angeles, California.

Mannering, G. J. (1968). Significance of stimulation and inhibition of drug metabolism in pharmacological testing. *In* "Selected Pharmacological Testing Methods" (A. Bruger, ed.), Medicinal Research: Vol. 7, p. 51. Marcel Dekker, New York.

Nodiff, E. A. *et al.* (1967–1968). Syntheses of possible metabolites of chlorpromazine. I and II. *J. Heterocyclic. Chem.* **4,** 239; **5,** 165.

Rall. D. P., and Zubrod, C. G. (1962). Mechanisms of drug absorption and excretion. Passage of drugs in and out of the central nervous system. *Ann. Rev. Pharmacol.* **2,** 109.

Rysanek, K., and Vojtcechovsky, M. (1966). [Current Data on Catecholamine Metabolism and Its Relation to the Central Nervous System.] *Physiol. Bohemoslov.* **15,** 282 (in Czech.)

Schain, R. J. (1960). Neurohumors and other pharmacologically active substances in cerebrospinal fluid: A review of the literature. *Yale J. Biol. Med.* **33,** 15.

Schanker, L. S. (1964). Physiological transport of drugs. *Advan. Drug Res.* **1,** 71.

Schildkraut, J. J. *et al.* (1967). Norepinephrine metabolism and drugs used in the affective disorders: A possible mechanism of action. *Am. J. Psychiat.* **124,** 600.

Shideman, F. E., and Mannering, G. J. (1963). Metabolic fate. *Ann. Rev. Pharmacol.* **3,** 33.

Smith, R. L. (1966). The biliary excretion and enterohepatic circulation of drugs and other organic compounds. *Progr. Drug Res.* **9,** 299.

Spirtes, M. A. (1965). Intimate study of drug action. II. Fate of drugs in the body. *In* "Drill's Pharmacology in Medicine" (J. R. DiPalma, ed.), 3rd ed., p. 26. McGraw-Hill, New York.

Steinecker, G. *et al.* (1968). Répartition et métabolism des phénothiazines. II. Etude expérimentalle sur le rat de la propériciazine et de la fluphénazine à dose toxique. Comparaison avec la chlorpromazine. *Ann. Pharm. Franc.* **26,** 143.

Weiner, I. M. (1967). Mechanisms of drug absorption and excretion. *Ann. Rev. Pharmacol.* **7,** 39.

Williams, R. T. (1959). "Detoxication Mechanisms. The Metabolism and Detoxication of Drugs, Toxic Substances and Other Organic Compounds," 2nd ed. Wiley, New York. 796 pp.

Wurtman, R. J., and Axelrod, J. (1966). The effect of thyroid and estrogen on the fate of catecholamines. *Res. Publ., Assoc. Res. Nervous Mental Disease* **43,** 354.

XIV. Neuroanatomy (Including Ultrastructure), Neuropathology

Bischoff, A., and Lüthy, F. (eds.) (1965). "Neuropathology," Proc. 5th Intern. Cong. Neuropathol., Zurich, 1965. Excerpta Med. Found., Amsterdam. 1000 pp.

Cambell, P. N. (ed.) (1968). "The Interaction of Drugs and Subcelluar Components in Animal Cells." Churchill, London. 355 pp.

Crosby, E. C. *et al.* (eds.) (1962). "Correlative Anatomy of the Nervous system." Macmillan, New York. 731 pp.

Dell, P. (1962). Monoamines et systèmes de projections diffusés. *In* "Monoamines et système nerveux central" (J. de Ajuriaguerra, ed.), p. 133. Masson, Paris.

De Robertis, E. (1963). Ultrastructure and chemical organization of synapses in the central nervous system. *In* "Brain Function" (M. A. B. Brazier, ed.), Vol. 1, p. 15. Univ. of California Press, Los Angeles, California.

Field, J. *et al.* (eds.) (1960). "Handbook of Physiology," Sect. 1: Neurophysiology, 3 vols. Williams & Wilkins, Baltimore, Maryland. 2013 pp.

Hillarp, N. A. *et al.* (1966). Demonstration and mapping of central neurons containing dopamine, noradrenaline, and 5-hydroxytryptamine and their reactions to psychopharmaca. *Pharmacol. Rev.* **18**, 727.

Jasper, H. H. *et al.* (eds.) (1958). "Reticular Formation of the Brain." Little, Brown, Boston, Massachusetts. 766 pp.

Lajtha, A., and Ford, D. H. (eds.) (1968). Brain-barrier systems. *Progr. Brain Res.* **29**. 552 pp.

Robertson, J. D. (1965). The synapse: Morphological and chemical correlates of function. *Neurosci. Res. Program Bull.* **3**, 1.

Sarkisov, S. A. (1966). "The Structure and Function of the Brain." Indiana Univ. Press, Bloomington, Indiana. 291 pp.

Segawa, T. (1967). [The subcellular localization of biogenic amines at synapses.] *J. Japan. Biochem. Soc.* **39**, 67 (in Japanese).

Waelsch, H., ed. (1957). "Ultrastructure and Cellular Chemistry of Neural Tissue." Harper, New York. 620 pp.

Williams, D., ed. (1962). "Modern Trends in Neurology." Butterworth, London and Washington, D.C. 348 pp.

Wolstenholme, C. E. W., and O'Connor, M. (eds.) (1968). "Growth of the Nervous System. A Ciba Foundation Symposium." Churchill, London. 295 pp.

XV. Neurochemistry, Histochemistry, Biochemistry

Barbeau, A. (1967). The "Pink Spot," 3,4-dimethoxyphenylethylamine and dopamine. Relationship to Parkinson's disease and to schizophrenia. *Rev. Can. Biol.* **26**, 55.

Barbeau, A. *et al.* (1962). Les catecholamines dans la maladie de Parkinson. *In* "Monoamine et système nerveux central" (J. de Ajuriaguerra, ed.), p. 247. Masson, Paris.

Bertler, A., and Rosengren, E. (1966). Possible role of brain dopamine. *Pharmacol. Rev.* **18**, 769.

Bonavita, V. (1966). La base neurochimiche della psicofarmacologia. *Sistema Nervoso* **18**, 251.

Brazier, M. A. B. (ed.) (1965). Brain function. Vol. 2. "RNA and Brain Function, Memory, and Learning." Univ. of California Press, Los Angeles, California, 360 pp.

Bremer, F. (1957). Médiateurs chimiques et activités nerveuses centrales chex les vertébrés. *Actualites Pharmacol.* **10**, 25.

Brodie, B. B. *et al.* (1959). Interaction of drugs with norepinephrine in the brain. *Pharmacol. Rev.* **11**, 548.

Brodie, B. B. et al. (eds.) (1963). "Metabolic Factors Controlling Duration of Drug Action," Vol. 6 (Proc. 1st Intern. Pharmacol. Meeting Stockholm, 1961). Macmillan, New York. 330 pp.

Brune, G. G. (1965). Biogenic amines in mental illness. *Intern. Rev. Neurobiol.* **8**, 197.

Bueno, J. R., and Himwich, H. E. (1967). A dualistic approach to some biochemical problems in endogenous depressions. *Psychosomatics* **8**, 82.

Campbell, P. N. (ed.) (1968). "The Interaction of Drugs and Subcellular Components in Animal Cells." Churchill, London. 355 pp.

Carlsson, A. (1966). Pharmacological depletion of catecholamine stores. *Pharmacol. Rev.*

Cerletti, A., von (1960). Über Vorkommen und Bedeutung der Indolstruktur in der Medizin und Biologie. *Progr. Drug Res.* **2**, 227.

18, 541.

Childress, S. J. (1967). Antipsychotic and anti-anxiety agents. *In* "Annual Report in Medicinal Chemistry, 1966" (C. K. Cain, ed.), Vol. 2, p. 1. Academic Press, New York.

Costa, E., and Sandler, M. (eds.) (1968). Biological role of indolealkylamine derivatives *Advan. Pharmacol.* **6A,** 1; **6B,** 1.

Costa, E. *et al* (eds.) (1966). "Biochemistry and Pharmacology of the Basal Ganglia. Raven Press, Hewlett, New York. 238 pp.

Couteoux, R. *et al.* (1965). Données histochimiques sur l'inhibition *in vitro* et *in vivo* des monoamine oxydases. *Actualites Pharmacol.* **18,** 33.

Cremer, J. E. (1967). Biochemical changes associated with neurotoxicity. *In* "Neurotoxicity of Drugs, Vol. 8, p. 169. (Proc. European Soc. Study Drug Toxicity). Excerpta Med. Found., Amsterdam.

Crossland, J. (1967). Psychotropic drugs and neurohumoral substances in the central nervous system. *Progr. Med. Chem.* **5,** 251.

Cumings, J. M., and Kremer, M. (eds.) (1965). "Biochemical Aspects of Neurological Disorders," 2nd Ser. Davis, Philadelphia, Pennsylvania. 326 pp.

de Ajuriaguerra, J. (ed.) (1962). "Monoamines et système nerveux central." Masson, Paris. 293 pp.

Decsi, L. (1965). Biochemical effects of drugs acting on the central nervous system. *Progr. Drug Res.* **8,** 53.

Dell, P. (1962). Monoamines et systèmes de projections diffusés. *In* "Monoamines et système nerveux central" (J. de Ajuriaguerra, ed.), p. 133. Masson, Paris.

De Robertis, E. (1963). Ultrastructure and chemical organization of synapses in the central nervous system. *In* "Brain Function" (M. A. B. Brazier, ed.), Vol. 1, p. 15. Univ. of California Press, Los Angeles, California.

Dewhurst, W. (1965). On the chemical basis of mood. *J. Psychosomat. Med.* **9,** 115.

Elkes, J. F. (1962). Amines in relation to behavior—some problems and approaches. *In* "Monoamines et système nerveux central" (J. de Ajuriaguerra, ed.) Masson, Paris. 153 pp.

Elliott, K. A. C. *et al.* (eds.) (1962). "Neurochemistry: The Chemical Dynamics of Brain and Nerve," 2nd ed. Thomas, Springfield, Illinois. 1035 pp.

Engelhard, N. *et al.* (1967). Acetylcholinesterase. *Angew. Chem.* **6,** 615.

Eränkö, O. (1967). Histochemistry of nervous tissues: Catecholamines and cholinesterases. *Ann. Rev. Pharmacol.* **7,** 203.

Erspamer, V. (1961). Recent research in the field of 5-hydroxytryptamine and related indolealkylamines. *Progr. Drug Res.* **3,** 151.

Euler, U. S., von (1965). Aufnahme, Speichergung und Freisetzung von Katecholaminen in Adrenergischen Neuronen. *Z. Vitamin-, Hormon- Fermentforsch.* **14,** 174.

Euler, U. S., von (1966). Twenty years of noradrenaline. *Pharmacol. Rev.* **18,** 29.

Florey, E. (1967). Neurotransmitters and modulators in the animal kingdom. *Federation Proc.* **26,** 1164. (Symp.)

Foo, J. W. *et al.* (1968). The effects of some β-adrenoreceptor blocking drugs on the uptake and release of noradrenaline by the heart. *Brit. J. Pharmacol.* **34,** 1.

Freedman, D. X. (1966). Aspects of the biochemical pharmacology of psychotropic drugs. *In* "Psychiatric Drugs" (P. Solomon, ed.), p. 32. Grune & Stratton, New York.

Fried, R. (1968). Introduction to neurochemistry. *J. Chem. Educ.* **45,** 181 and 322.

Friede, R. L. (1966). "Topographic Brain Chemistry." Academic Press, New York 510 pp.

Friedman, A. H., and Everett, G. M. Pharmacological aspects of Parkinsonism. *Advan. Pharmacol.* **3,** 83.

Gaito, J. (1966). "Molecular Psychobiology." Thomas, Springfield, Illinois. 259 pp.

Gaito, J. (1967). Neurochemical approaches to learning. *In* "Brain Function" (D. B. Lindsley and A. A. Lumsdaine, eds.), Vol. 4, p. 1. Univ. of California Press, Los Angeles, California.

Hillarp, N. A. *et al.* (1966). Demonstration and mapping of central neurons containing dopamine, noradrenaline, and 5-hydroxytryptamine and their reactions to psychopharmaca. *Pharmacol. Rev.* **18,** 727.

Kety, S. S. (1959). Biochemical theories of schizophrenia (in two parts). *Science* **129,** 1528 and 1590.

Kety, S. S. (1966). Catecholamines in neuropsychiatric states. *Pharmacol. Rev.* **18,** 787.
Kety, S. S. (1967). Current biochemical approaches to schizophrenia. *New Engl. J. Med.* **276,** 325.
Kety, S. S., and Elkes, J. (eds.) (1961). "Regional Neurochemistry." Pergamon Press, Oxford. 540 pp.
Korey, S. R., and Nurnberger, J. I. (eds.) (1956). "Progress in Neurobiology," Vol. I: Neurochemistry. Elsevier, Amsterdam. 244 pp.
Maickel, R. P. (1967). "Biochemical Factors in Alcoholism." Pergamon Press, Oxford. 256 pp.
Mongar, J. L., and de Reuck, A. V. S. (eds.) (1962). "Enzymes and Drug Action," Ciba Found. Symp. jointly with Co-Ordinating Committee for Symposia on Drug Action. Little, Brown. Boston, Massachusetts, 556 pp.
Nakajima, H., and Thullier, J. (1965). Contribution à l'étude des mécanismes d'action biochimique des drogues psychotropes. Correlation avec les effets pharmacologiques. *Encéphale* **54,** 285.
Nashold, B. S., and Huber, W. V. (eds.) (1966). The Second Symposium on Parkinson's. Suppl. to: *J. Neurosurg.* **24,** No. 1, Part II. 481 pp.
Pearse, A. G. (1967). Fundamentals of functional neurochemistry. *Brain Res.* **4,** 125.
Rinkel, M., and Denber, H. C. B. (eds.) (1958). "Chemical Concepts of Psychosis." McDowell & Obolensky, New York. 485 pp.
Roberts, E. *et al.* (eds.) (1960). "Inhibition in the Nervous System and Gamma-Aminobutyric Acid." Pergamon Press, Oxford. 591 pp.
Robertson, J. D. (1965). The synapse: Morphological and chemical correlates of function. *Neurosci. Res. Program. Bull.* **3,** 1.
Schain, R. J. (1960). Neurohumors and other pharmacologically active substances in cerebrospinal fluid: A review of the literature. *Yale J. Biol. Med.* **33,** 15.
Segawa, T. (1967). [The subcellular localization of biogenic amines at synapses.] *J. Japan. Biochem. Soc.* **39,** 67 (in Japanese).
Selbach, H., and Pletscher, A. (1960). Pharmaka mit Wirkung auf den Monoamin Stoffwechsel des Zentralnervensystems. *Psychiat. Neurol.* **140,** 1.
Tower, D. B. (1957). Some neurochemical factors affecting cerebral function and activity. *Southern Med. J.* **50,** 1453.
Triggle, D. J. (1965). "Chemical Aspects of the Autonomic Nervous System." Academic Press, New York. 329 pp.
Udenfriend, S. (1966). Biosynthesis of the sympathetic neurotransmitter, norepinephrine. *Harvey Lectures* **60,** 57.
Van der Schoot, J. B., and Creveling, C. R. (1965). Substrates and inhibitors of dopamine-beta-hydroxylase (DBH). *Advan. Drug Res.* **2,** 47.
Van Praag, H. M. (1967). The possible significance of cerebral dopamine for neurology and psychiatry. *Psychiat. Neurol. Neurochir.* **70,** 361.
Waelsch, H., ed. 1957). "Ultrastructure and Cellular Chemistry of Neural Tissue." Harper, New York. 260 pp.
Walaas, E., and Walaas, O. (1963). Biochemical aspects of copper and aromatic amines in relation to the extrapyramidal system. *Acta Neurol. Scand.* **39,** Suppl. 4, 84.
Wolstenholme, G. E. W., and O'Connor, M., eds. (1960). "Adrenergic Mechanisms," Ciba Found. Symp. jointly with Committee for Symposia on Drug Action. Churchill, London. 632 pp.
Wurtman, R. J., and Axelrod, J. (1966). The effect of thyroid and estrogen on the fate of catecholamines. *Res. Publ., Assoc. Res. Nervous Mental Disease* **43,** 354.

XVI. General

Abrams, A. *et al.,* eds. (1964). "Unfinished Tasks in the Behavioral Sciences." Williams & Wilkins, Baltimore, Maryland. 264 pp.

Achelis, J. D., and Scholibo, T. (1966). "Probleme der Pharmakopsychiatrie." Thieme, Stuttgart. 119 pp.
Acheson, G. H. (ed.) (1966). Second symposium on catecholamines. *Pharmacol. Rev.* **18**, 1.
Anonymous. (1959). McGill University Conference on Depression and Allied States. *Can. Psychiat. Assoc. J.* Spec. Suppl. 4. 197 pp.
Anonymous. (1963). Guides to the evaluation of permanent impairment: Central nervous system. Committee on rating of mental and physical impairments. *J. Am. Med. Assoc.* **185**, 24.
Anonymous. (1968). Toward a definition of schizophrenia. *Diseases Nervous System* **29**, Suppl., 1.
Ariëns, E. J. (1966). Molecular pharmacology, a basis for drug design. *Fortschr. Arzneimittelforsch.* **10**, 429.
Arieta, S. (ed.) (1959, 1966). "American Handbook of Psychiatry," Vols. 1, 2, and 3 Basic Books, New York. 999 pp., 1094 pp., and 778 pp., resp.
Beck, A. T. (1967). "Depression: Clinical, Experimental and Theoretical Aspects." Harper (Hoeber), New York. 359 pp.
Bickel, M. H. (1968). Untersuchungen zur Biochemie und Pharmakologie der Thymoleptika. *Progr. Drug Res.* **11**, 121.
Biel, A. H. (1966). Antidepressants, stimulants, hallucinogens. *In* "Annual Reports in Medicinal Chemistry, 1965" (C. K. Cain, ed.), Vol. 1, p. 12. Also (1967). *In* "Annual Reports in Medicinal Chemistry," Vol. 1, p. 11. Academic Press, New York.
Biel, J. H. (1968). Chemopharmacological approaches to the treatment of mental depression. *In* "Drug Affecting the Nervous System" (A. Burger, ed.), Medicinal Research: Vol. 2, p. 61. Marcel Dekker, New York.
Bovet, D., and Gatti, G. L. (1957). Introduzione farmacologica all'impeigo dei tranquillanti e dei neuroletici in clinica psichiatrica. *Clin. Terap.* **13**, 475.
Brazier, M. A. B. (ed.) (1959, 1959, 1960). "The Central Nervous System and Behavior," Transactions of the Three Conferences. Josiah Macy, Jr. Found., New York. 450 pp., 358 pp., and 475 pp., resp.
Brazier, M. A. B. (ed.) (1961). "Brain and Behavior" (Proc. 1st Am. Inst. Biol. Sci., Washington, D.C.). Stechert-Hafner, New York. p. 434.
Brill, H. (1955). "Chlorpromazine and Mental Health." Lea & Febiger, Philadelphia, Pennsylvania. 198 pp.
Brill, H. (ed) (1958). "Trifluoperazine, Clinical and Pharmacological Aspects." Lea & Febiger, Philadelphia, Pennsylvania. 219 pp.
Brodie, B. B. *et al.* (1958). The action of psychotropic drugs (a biochemical and physiological interpretation). *In* "Chemical Concepts of Psychosis" (M. Rinkel and H. C. B. Denbar, eds.), p. 190. Obolensky, New York.
Brodie, B. B. *et al.* (1961). Psychotherapeutic drugs. *Ann. Rev. Med.* **12**, 349.
Brodie, B. B. (1964). Difficultés de transposer à l'homme les résultats expérimentaux obtenus sur l'animal. *Actualites Pharmacol.* **17**, 1.
Brooks, C. M. *et al.* (1962). "Humors, Hormones and Neurosecretion. The Origins and Development of Man's Present Knowledge of the Humoral Control of Body Function." Comet Press, New York. 313 pp.
Campbell, H. J. (1965). "Correlative Physiology of the Nervous System." Academic Press, New York. 313 pp.
Casey, J. F. (ed.) (1956–1961). "Transactions of Six Research Conferences on Chemotherapy in Psychiatry," Vols. 1–6. Vet. Admin., Washington, D.C. 123 pp., 257 pp., 303 pp., 366 pp., 375 pp., and 410 pp., resp.
Clark, W. G., and Ditman, K. S. (eds.) (1964). "Lectures in Psychopharmacology." Vet. Admin. Hosp., Sepulveda, California. 478 pp.
Clark, W. G., and Ungar, G. (eds.) (1964). Histamine and the nervous system. *Federation Proc.* **23**, 1092. (Symp.)
Cole, J. *et al.* (1966). Drugs in the treatment of psychosis—controlled studies. *In* "Psychiatric Drugs" (P. Solomon, ed.), p. 153. Grune & Stratton, New York.

Cumings, J. M., and Kremer, M. (eds.) (1965). "Biochemical Aspects of Neurological Disorders," 2nd ser., Davis, Philadelphia, Pennsylvania. 326 pp.

David, G. B. (1957). The pathological anatomy of the schizophrenias. *In* "Schizophrenia: Somatic Aspects" (D. Richter, ed.), p. 93. Pergamon Press, Oxford.

Davis, M. A. (1968). Antidepressants, stimulants, hallucinogens. *In* "Annual Reports in Medicinal Chemistry, 1967" (C. K. Cain, ed.), Vol. 3, p. 14. Academic Press, New York.

de Boor, W. (1956). "Pharmakopsychologie und Psychopathologie." Springer, Berlin. 291 pp.

Deghwitz, R. (1967). "Leitfaden der Psychopharmakologie." Wiss. Verlag., Stuttgart. 512 pp.

Delafresnaye, J. F. (ed.) (1961). "Brain Mechanisms and Learning; A Symposium." Blackwell, Oxford. 701 pp.

Delay, J. (ed.) (1956). Colloque international sur la chlorpromazine et les médicaments neuroleptiques en thérapeutique psychiatrique, Paris, Oct. 20–22, 1955. *Encéphale* **40,** 301.

Dell, P. (1962). Monoamines et systèmes de projections diffusés. *In* "Monoamines et système nerveux central" (J. de Ajuriaguerra, ed.), p. 133. Masson, Paris.

Deniker, P. (1966). "La Psychopharmacologie." Presses Univ. de France, Paris. 128 pp.

De Schaepdryvver, A. (1964). La psychopharmacologie. *Ars Medica* **19,** 1.

Dewhurst, W. (1965). On the chemical basis of mood. *J. Psychosomat. Med.* **9,** 115.

Domino, E. F. (1965). Psychosedative drugs. I. Substituted phenothiazines, reserpine and derivatives. II. Meprobamate, chlordiazepoxide, and miscellaneous agents. *In* "Drill's Pharmacology in Medicine" (J. R. DiPalma, ed.), 3rd ed., p. 337. McGraw-Hill, New York.

Eccles, J. C. (ed.) (1966). "Brain and Conscious Experience." Springer, Berlin, 590 pp.

Efron, H. *et al.* (eds.) (1969). "Psychopharmacology. A Review of Progress 1957–1967." Proc. Am. Coll. Neuropsychopharmacol., Public Health Serv. Publ. No. 1836. U.S. Govt. Printing Office, Washington, D.C. 1342 pp.

Ehrhart, G., and Ruschig, H. (1968). "Arzneimittel. Entwicklung, Wirkung, Darstellung," 2 vols. Verlag Chemie, Berlin. 1952 pp.

Eiduson, S. *et al.* (1964). "Biochemistry and Behavior." Van Nostrand, Princeton, New Jersey. 554 pp.

Elkes, J. C. (1962). Amines in relation to behavior—some problems and approaches. *In* "Monoamines et Système nerveux central" (J. de Ajuriaguerra, ed.). Masson, Paris. 153 pp.

Elkes, J. C. (1966). Psychoactive drugs—some problems and approaches. *In* "Psychiatric Drugs" (P. Solomon, ed.), p. 4. Grune & Stratton, New York.

Elkes, J. C. *et al.* (eds.) (1958). Ataractic and hallucinogenic drugs in psychiatry. Report of study section. *World Health Organ., Tech. Rept. Ser.* **152,** 1–72.

Erspamer, V. (1961). Recent research in the field of 5-hydroxytryptamine and related indolealkylamines. *Progr. Drug Res.* **3,** 151.

Euler, U. S. von (1966). Twenty years of noradrenaline. *Pharmacol. Rev.* **18,** 29.

Featherstone, R. M., and Simon, A. (eds.) (1959). "A Pharmacologic Approach to the Study of the Mind." Thomas, Springfield, Illinois. 399 pp.

Feldberg, W., and Fleischhauer, W. (1965). A new experimental approach to the physiology and pharmacology of the brain. *Brit. Med. Bull.* **21,** No. 1, 36.

Field, J. *et al.* (eds.) (1960). "Handbook of Physiology," Sect. I: Neurophysiology, 3 vols. Williams & Wilkins, Baltimore, Maryland. 2013 pp.

Fields, W. S. (ed.) (1957). "Brain Mechanism and Drug Action." Thomas, Springfield, Illinois. 147 pp.

Freedman, A. M., and Kaplan, H. I. (eds.) (1967). "Comprehensive Textbook of Psychiatry." Williams & Wilkins, Baltimore, Maryland. 1666 pp.

Friend, D. G. (1967). Sedatives and tranquilizers in general medical practice. *In* "Drugs of Choice" (W. Modell, ed.), p. 233. Mosby, St. Louis, Missouri.

Garattini, S., and Valzelli, L. (1965). "Serotonin." Elsevier, Amsterdam. 392 pp.

Gastadli, B. (ed.) (1962). "Symposium Internazionale sull' Haloperidol e Triperidol." 1st Luso Farmaco d'Italia. 768 pp.

Gellhorn, E. (1967). "Principles of Autonomic-Somatic Integrations. Physiological Basis and

Psychological and Clinical Implications." Univ. of Minnesota Press, Minneapolis, Minnesota. 318 pp.

Gerard, R. (ed.) (1966). "Information Processing in the Central Nervous System," Vol. 3, Intern. Congr. Ser. No. 49 (Proc. 22nd Intern. Congr. Intern. Union Physiol. Sci., Leiden, 1962). Excerpta Med. Found., Amsterdam. 470 pp.

Gibbs, F. A. (1959). "Molecules and Mental Health." Lippincott, Philadelphia, Pennsylvania. 189 pp.

Gittelman-Klein, R., and Klein, D. F. (1969). *In* "Psychopharmacology. A Review of Progress. 1957–1967" (H. Efron *et al.*, eds.), Proc. Am. Coll. Neuropsychopharmacol., Public Health Serv. Publ. No. 1836, p. 1119. U.S. Govt. Printing Office, Washington, D.C.

Goodman, L. S., and Gilman, A. (eds.) (1966). "The Pharmacological Basis of Therapeutics," 3rd ed. Macmillan, New York. 1785 pp.

Goth, A. (1968). "Medical Pharmacology. Principles and Concepts," 4th ed. Mosby, St. Louis, Missouri. 749 pp.

Gourley, D. R. H. (1964). Basic mechanisms of drug action. *Progr. Drug Res.* **7**, 11.

Grashchenkov, N I. (ed.) (1964). ["Adrenaline and Noradrenaline."] Izd. Stvo Nauka, Moscow. 310 pp. (in Russian.)

Grollman, A., and Grollman, E. F. (1965). "Pharmacology and Therapeutics," 6th ed. Lea & Febiger, Philadelphia, Pennsylvania. 1181 pp.

Heath, R. G., and Wells, B. (1967). Drugs for stimulation of mental and physical activity. *In* "Drugs of Choice" (W. Modell, ed.), p. 164. Mosby, St. Louis, Missouri.

Heinzelman, R. V., and Szmuszkovicz, (1963). Recent studies in the field of indole compounds. *Progr. Drug Res.* **6**, 75.

Himwich, H. E. (1959). Stimulants. *Res. Publ. Assoc. Res. Nervous Mental Disease* **37**, 357.

Himwich, W. A. *et al.* (eds.) (1967). "Amines and Schizophrenia." Pergamon Press, Oxford. 280 pp.

Hoagland, H. (ed.) (1957). "Hormones, Brain Function and Behavior." Academic Press, New York. 257 pp.

Hoffer, A. (1962). "Niacin Therapy in Psychiatry." Thomas, Springfield, Illinois. 165 pp.

Hoffer, A., and Osmond, H. (1960). "The Chemical Basis of Clinical Psychiatry." Thomas, Springfield, Illinois. 277 pp.

Hollister, L. E. (1966). Psychopharmacological drugs. *J. Am. Med. Assoc.* **196**, 411.

Holtz, P., and Westermann, E. (1965). Psychic energizers and antidepressant drugs. *In* "Physiological Pharmacology. A Comprehensive Treatise" (W. S. Root and F. G. Hofmann, eds.), Vol. 2, p. 201. Academic Press, New York.

"International Encyclopedia of Pharmacology and Therapeutics." Vol. 1, Sect. 2: Mechanisms of Drug Action; Sect. 3: Distribution and Metabolism of Drugs; Sect. 5: Structure-Activity Relationships; Sect. 7: Biostatistics in Pharmacology; Sect. 9: Physiology and Pharmacology of Synaptic Transmission; Sect. 10: Parasympathomimetic Agents; Sect. 11: Parasympathetic Blocking Agents; Sect. 12: Anticholinesterase Agents; Sect. 13: Sympathomimetic Agents; Sect. 18: Hypnotics and Sedatives; Sect. 19: Anticonvulsant Agents; Sect. 20: Alcohol and Derivatives; Sect. 21: Stimulants and Convulsants; Sect. 22: Analgesics; Sect. 24: Centrally Acting Skeletal Muscle Relaxants; Sect. 25: Antiparkinsonian Drugs; Sect 28: Effect of Autonomic Drugs on Central Nervous System; Sect. 33: Pharmacology of the Cerebral Circulation. Pergamon Press, Long Island City, New York (in press).

Jacobsen, E. (1958). The pharmacological classification of central nervous depression. *J. Pharm. Pharmacol.* **10**, 273.

Jacobsen, E. (1964a). Tranquilizers and sedatives. *In* "Evaluation of Drug Activities. Pharmacometrics" (D. R. Laurence and A. L. Bacharach, eds.), Vol. 1, p. 215. Academic Press, New York.

Jacobsen, E. (1964b). Benactyzine. *In* "Psychopharmacological Agents" (M. Gordon, ed.), Vol. 1, p. 287. Academic Press, New York.

Jacobsen, E. (1967). An analysis of the gross action of drugs on the central nervous system.

In "Molecular Basis of Some Aspects of Mental Activity" (O. Walaas, ed.), Vol. 2, p. 3. Academic Press, New York.

Janz, H. W. (1963). "Psyche und Pharmakon." Dr. C. J. Hogrefe, Göttingen. 60 pp.

Jarvik, M. E. (1966). Drugs used in the treatment of psychiatric disorders. *In* "The Pharmacological Basis of Therapeutics" (L. S. Goodman and A. Gilman, eds.), 3rd ed, 2nd printing, p. 159. Macmillan, New York.

Jenner, F. A. *et al.* (eds.) (1965). "Proceedings of the Symposium in Behavioral Disorders, Leeds, March, 1965." May & Baker, Dangenham, England. 272 pp.

Joyce, C. R. B. (ed.) (1968). "Psychopharmacology; Dimensions and Perspectives." Tavistock, London; and Lippincott, Philadelphia, Pennsylvania. 430 pp.

Kelleher, R. T., and Morse, W. H. (1968). Determinants of the specificity of behavioral effects of drugs. *Ergeb. Physiol., Biol. Chem. Exptl. Pharmakol.* **60,** 1.

Kety, S. S. (1959). Biochemical theories of schizophrenia (in two parts). *Science* **129,** 1528 and 1590.

Kety, S. S. (1966). Catecholamines in neuropsychiatric states. *Pharmacol. Rev.* **18,** 787

Kety, S. (1967). Current biochemical approaches to schizophrenia. *New Engl. J. Med.* **276,** 325.

Klerman, G. L. (1965). The teaching of psychopharmacology in the psychiatric residency. *Compr. Psychiat.* **6,** 255.

Kline, N. S. (ed.) (1956). "Psychopharmacology," Publ. No. 42. Am. Assoc. Advance. Sci., Washington, D.C. 164 pp.

Kline, N. S. (ed.) (1959). "Psychopharmacology Frontiers." Little, Brown. Boston, Massachusetts. 533 pp.

Kline, N. S. (ed.) (1961). Pavlovian conference on higher nervous activity. *Ann. N.Y. Acad. Sci.* **92,** 813.

Kobayashi, T. (ed.) (1968). ["Recent Aspects of Psychopharmacology—Pharmacological Approach to the Mechanism of Behavior."] Igaku Shoin, Ltd., Tokyo. 667 pp. (in Japanese, with bibliography, appendices and indices also in English).

Koelle, G. B. (ed.) (1963). Cholinesterase and anticholinesterase agents. *Handbuch Exptl. Pharmakol.* **15.** 1220 pp.

Kopin, I. J. (1968). Adrenergic transmitters. *Pharmacol. Rev.* **8,** 377.

Kraines, S. H. (1967). Schizophrenic physiopathology. *Psychosomatics* **9,** 19.

Krakowski, A. J. (1966). Recent advances in psychopharmacology—a review. *Med. Times* **94,** 1209.

Krayer, O. K. (ed.) (1959). Symposium on catecholamines. *Pharmacol. Rev.* **11,** 241.

Kuhn, E. *et al.* (1963). Multidimensional approach to the psychopharmacological experiment. *In* "The Effects of Psychotropic Drugs in Higher Nervous Activity" (Z. Votava *et al.*, eds.), p. 281. Macmillan, New York.

Lattanzi, A. (1961). [The Psychopharmacological Drugs.] *Clin. Terap.* **20,** 345 (in Italian).

Leake, C. D. (1964). Introduction to symposium on anxiety and a decade of tranquilizer therapy. *J. Neuropsychiat.* **386,** 395.

Levi, R., and Green, J. P. (1967). 5-hydroxytryptamine and the central nervous system. *In* Annual Reports in Medicinal Chemistry, 1966 (C. K. Cain, ed.), Vol. 2, p. 273. Academic Press, New York.

Levine, R. (ed.) (1966). Endocrines and the central nervous system. *Res. Publ. Assoc. Nervous Mental Disease* **43.** 475 pp.

Lewis, A. B., Jr. (1966). Effective utilization of the psychiatric hospital. *J. Am. Med. Assoc.* **197,** 871.

Lindsley, D. B., and Lumsdaine, A. A. (eds.) (1967). "Brain Function," Vol. 4. Univ. of California Press, Los Angeles, California. 364 pp.

Lippert, H. (1959). "Einfuhrung in die Pharmakopsychologie." Huber, Bern. 254 pp.

Livingston, S. (1966). "Drug Therapy for Epilepsy. Anticonvulsant Drugs: Usage, Metabolism and Untoward Reaction (Prevention, Detection and Management)." Thomas, Springfield, Illinois. 234 pp.

Lovtrup, S. (1967). On the correlation between psychic action, chemical effects and physical properties of chlorpromazine and imipramine. *In* "Molecular Basis of Some Aspects of Mental Activity" (O. Walaas, ed.), Vol. 2, p. 39. Academic Press, New York.

Luce, G. G., and Segal, J. (eds.) (1965). "Current Research on Sleep and Dreams," Publ. No. 1389. U.S. Public Health Serv., Washington, D.C. 125 pp.

Lunsford, C. D. *et al.* (1968). Sedatives, hypnotics, anticonvulsants, muscle relaxants, general anesthetics. *In* "Annual Reports in Medicinal Chemistry, 1967" (C. K. Cain, ed.), Vol. 3, p. 28. Academic Press, New York.

Marks, J., and Pare, C. M. B. (1965). "The Scientific Basis of Drug Therapy in Psychiatry." Pergamon Press, Oxford. 326 pp.

Nashold, B. S., and Huber, W. V. (eds.) (1966). "The Second Symposium on Parkinson's." Suppl. to: *J. Neurosurg.* **24**, No. 1, Part II. 481 pp.

Nowakowski, H. (ed.) (1958). "Hormone and Psyche." Springer, Berlin. 355 pp.

Ostow, M. (1966). The complementary roles of psychoanalysis and drug therapy. *In* "Psychiatric Drugs" (P. Solomon, ed.), p. 91. Grune & Stratton, New York.

Overholser, W., and Werkman, S. L. (1959). Etiology pathogenesis and pathology. *In* "Schizophrenia: A Review of the Syndrome" (L. Bellak, ed.), p. 82. Logos Press, New York.

Parr, D. (1962). Problems in the appraisal and use of tranquillizers, analgesics and hypnotics. *In* "Modern Trends in Neurology" (D. Williams, ed.), p. 336. Butterworth, London and Washington, D.C.

Paton, W. D. M. (1968). The principles of drug action. *Proc. Roy. Soc. Med.* **33**, 815.

Pennes, H. (ed.) (1958)."Psychopharmacology. Pharmacologic Effects on Behavior." Cassell, London, and Harper (Hoeber), New York. 362 pp.

Pflanz, M. (1961). Psychopharmacology in the psychosomatic fundamentals. *In* "Symposium of the Fourth European Conference on Psychosomatic Research, 1959" (A. Jores and H. Freyberger, eds.), p. 5. Branner, New York; cf. also *Fortschr. Psychosom. Med.* **1**, 5 (1961).

Poldinger, W. (1967). "Compendium of Psychopharmacotherapy," Sci. Serv., F. Hoffmann-LaRoche & Co., Ltd., Basel. 125 pp.

Poos, G. I. (1967). Anorexigenic agents. *In* "Annual Reports in Medicinal Chemistry, 1966" (C. K. Cain, ed.), Vol. 2, p. 51. Academic Press, New York; *ibid.* Vol. 1, p. 44 (1966).

Quarton, G. C. *et al.* (1967). "The Neurosciences: A Study Program." Rockefeller Univ. Press, New York. 962 pp.

Quastel, J. H. (1967). The effects of neurotropic drugs on brain metabolism *in vitro*. *In* "Molecular Basis of Some Aspects of Mental Activity" (O. Walaas, ed.), Vol. 2, p. 19. Academic Press, New York.

Reiss, M. (ed.) (1958). "Psychoendocrinology." Grune & Stratton, New York. 208 pp.

Richter, D. (ed.) (1962). "Aspects of Psychiatric Research." Oxford Univ. Press, London and New York. 445 pp.

Rinkel, M. (ed.) (1966). "Biological Treatment of Mental Illness." Farrar, Straus & Giroux, New York. 1025 pp.

Rinkel, M., and Denber, H. C. B. (eds.) (1958). "Chemical Concepts of Psychosis." Obolensky, New York. 485 pp.

Root, W. S., and Hofmann, F. G. (eds.) (1963, 1965, 1967). "Physiological Pharmacology. A Comprehensive Treatise," Vols. 1, 2, and 3. Academic Press, New York. 703 pp., 486 pp., and 519 pp., resp.

Rosen, A. (1965). [Psychopharmacologic drugs: Mechanism of action.] *Lakartidningen* **62**, Suppl. 2, 27 (in Swedish).

Ross, S., and Cole, J. O. (1960). Psychopharmacology. *Ann. Rev. Psychol.* **11**, 415.

Rothlin, E. (ed.) (1959). "Neuropsychopharmacology," Vol. 2, Elsevier, Amsterdam. 521 pp.

Russell, R. W. (1964). Psychopharmacology. *Ann. Rev. Psychol.* **15**, 87.

Russell, R. W. (ed.) (1966). "Frontiers in Physiological Psychology." Academic Press, New York. 261 pp.

Rysanek, K., and Vojtcechovsky, M. (1966). ["Current Data on Catecholamine Metabolism and Its Relation to the Central Nervous System."] *Physiol. Bohemoslov.* **15,** 282 (in Czech.).

Sankar, D. V. S. (eds.) (1962). Some biological aspects of schizophrenic behavior. *Ann. N.Y. Acad. Sci.* **96.** 490 pp.

Sarwer-Foner, G. J. (ed.) (1960). "The Dynamics of Psychiatric Drug Therapy." Thomas, Springfield, Illinois. 642 pp.

Schildkraut, J. J., and Kety, S. S. (1967). Biogenic amines and emotions. *Science* **156,** 21.

Schildkraut, J. J. *et al.* (1967). Norepinephrine metabolism and drugs used in the affective disorders: A possible mechanism of action. *Am. J. Psychiat.* **124,** 600.

Sedman, G. (1967). Experimental and phenomenological approaches to the problem of hallucinations in organic psychodromes. *Brit. J. Psychiat.* **113,** 1115.

Shepherd, M., and Wing, L. (1962). Pharmacological aspects of psychiatry. *Advan. Pharmacol.* **1,** 227.

Silverman, C. (1968). The epidemiology of depression. A review. *Am. J. Psychiat.* **124,** 883.

Smythies, J. R. (1963). "Schizophrenia. Chemistry, Metabolism and Treatment," Thomas, Springfield, Illinois. 86 pp.

Smythies, J. R. (ed.) (1966). "The Neurological Foundations of Psychiatry. An Outline of the Mechanisms of Emotion, Memory, Learning and the Organization of Behavior, with Particular Regard to the Limbic System." Academic Press, New York. 160 pp.

Solomon, P. (ed.) (1966). "Psychiatric Drugs: Proceedings of a Research Conference held in Boston." Grune & Stratton, New York. 689 pp.

Soulairac, A. *et al.* (eds.) (1968). "Pain." Academic Press, New York. 562 pp.

Sourkes, T. L. (1962). "Biochemistry of Mental Diseases." Harper (Hoeber), New York. 402 pp.

Steinberg, H., and Kumar, R. (1970). Psychopharmacology. *Ann. Rev. Psychol.* **20,** (in press).

Steinberg, H. *et al.* (eds.) (1964). "Animal Behavior and Drug Action." Little, Brown. Boston, Massachusetts, and Churchill, London. 491 pp.

Stern, J. A., and McDonald, D. C. (1965). Physiological correlates of mental disease. *Ann. Rev. Psychol.* **16,** 225.

Stur, O., ed. (1963). "Imbecility Drug Treatment. Proc. 2nd International Congress on Mental Retardation," 2 vols., Parts I and II. Karger, Basel. 416 pp. and 216 pp., resp.

Summerfield, A. (1964). Drugs and human behavior. *Brit. Med. Bull.* **20,** 70.

Syndicat des médicins du Rhone. (1965). Les tranquilliseurs les neuroléptiques et les antidepresseurs. *Lyon Med.* **213,** 135.

Talalay, P. (ed.) (1964). "Drugs in Our Society." Johns Hopkins Press, Baltimore, Maryland. 311 pp.

Tanner, J. M. (ed.) (1952). "Prospects in Psychiatric Research." Oxford Univ. Press, London and New York. 197 pp.

Tedeschi, D. H., and Tedeschi, R. E. (1968). "Fundamental Principles in Drug Evaluation." Raven Press, Hewlett, New York. 500 pp.

Thompson, T., and Schuster, C. R. (1968). "Behavioral Pharmacology." Prentice-Hall, Englewood Cliffs, New Jersey. 297 pp.

Timeofeev, N. N. (1958). ["Psychopharmacology and Its Relation to Other Methods of Therapy of Psychoses."] *Zh. Nevropatol. i Psikhiat.* **58,** 129 (in Russian).

Toman, J. E. (1963). Some aspects of central nervous pharmacology. *Ann. Rev. Pharmacol.* **3,** 153.

Turner, W. J. *et al.* (1967). Diphenylhydantoin. Its usefulness in clinical disorders of a non-epileptic nature. *Intern. J. Neuropsychiat.* **3,** Suppl. 2, S-1.

Uhr, L., and Miller, J. G. (eds.) (1960). "Drugs and Behavior." Wiley, New York. 676 pp.

Van Praag, H. M. (1967). Antidepressants, catecholamines and 5-hydroxyindoles. Trends towards a more specific research in the field of antidepressants. *Psychiat. Neurol. Neurochir.* **70,** 219.

Walaas, O. (ed.) (1967). "Molecular Basis of Some Aspects of Mental Activity," Vol. 2. Academic Press, New York. 515 pp.

Walaszek, E. J. *et al.* (1966). Pharmacology of the central nervous system. *Progr. Neurol. Psychiat.* **21**, 117.

Welsh, J. H. (1955). Neurohormones. *In* "The Hormones: Physiology, Chemistry, and Applications" (G. Pincus and K. V. Thimann, eds.), Vol. 3, p. 97. Academic Press, New York.

Whalen, R. E. (1967). "Hormones and Behavior: An Enduring Problem in Psychology." Van Nostrand, Princeton, New Jersey. 266 pp.

Wikler, A. (1957). "The Relation of Psychiatry to Pharmacology." Williams & Wilkins, Baltimore, Maryland. 322 pp.

Wolpe, J. (1967). Parrallels between animal and human neuroses. *Proc. Am. Psychopathol. Assoc.* **55**, 305.

Wolstenholme, G. E. W. (ed.) (1952). "Hormones, psychology and behavior, and steroid hormone administration." Ciba Found. Colloq. Endocrinol. Vol. 3. Blakiston, Philadelphia. 380 pp.

Wolstenholme, G. E. W., and O'Conner, M. (eds.) (1960). "Adrenergic Mechanisms," Ciba Found. Symp. jointly with Committee for Symposia on Drug Action, Churchill, London. 632 pp.

Wolstenholme, G. E. W., and O'Conner, M. (eds.) (1968). "Growth of the Nervous System," A Ciba Foundation Symposium. Churchill, London. 295 pp.

Wolstenholme, G. E. W., and Porter, R. (1966). "Drug Responses in Man," Ciba Found. Symp. Churchill, London. 146 pp.

Wolstenholme, G. E. W., and Porter, R. (eds.) (1967). "Drug Responses in Man." A Ciba Foundation Volume. Churchill, London, and Little, Brown. Boston, Massachusetts. 257 pp.

Wurtman, R. J. (1966). "Catecholamines," *New England J.* Med. Progr. Ser. Little, Brown. Boston, Massachusetts. 111 pp.

Yahr, M. D., and Purpura, D. P. (eds.) (1967). "Neurophysiological Basis of Normal and Abnormal Motor Activities" (Proc. 3rd Symp. Parkinson's Disease Information and Research Center, Nov., 1966). Raven Press, Hewlett, New York. 500 pp.

Yolles, S. F. (1966). The government's stake in psychiatric drug research. *In* Psychiatric Drugs" (P. Solomon, ed.), p. 121. Grune & Stratton, New York.

Zimmer, H., and Krusberg, R. J. (1966). "Psychophysiological Components of Human Behavior. A Compendium." Univ. of Georgia Press, Athens, Georgia. 534 pp.

Zubin, J. (1967). Classification of the behavior disorders. *Ann. Rev. Psychol.* **18**, 373.

Zubin, J., and Katz, M. M. (1964). Psychopharmacology and personality. *In* "Personality Change" (P. Worchel and D. Byrne, eds.), p. 367. Wiley, New York.

APPENDIX

3

ANNUALS AND SERIALS

Acta Pharmaceutica Suecica, Supplementum. (Apotekarsocieten, Stockholm)
Acta Pharmaciae Historica. (Gravenhage, Netherlands)
Acta Pharmacologica et Toxicologica, Supplementum. (Nordisk Selskab for Farmakologi, Copenhagen)
Actualites Pharmacologiques. Conférences sur des Sujets d'Actualité. (Masson, Paris)
Advances in Biological and Medical Physics. (Academic Press, New York & London)
Advances in Child Development and Behavior. (Academic Press)
Advances in Clinical Chemistry. (Academic Press)
Advances in Comparative Physiology and Biochemistry. (Academic Press)
Advances in Drug Research. (Academic Press)
Advances in Neurological Sciences. (Shinkei Kenkyu no Shimpo.) (Tokyo) (In Japanese)
Advances in Pharmaceutical Sciences. (Academic Press)
Advances in Pharmacology. (Academic Press)
Advances in Psychosomatic Medicine. (Fortschritte der Psychosomatischen Medizin; Progrès en Médecine Psychosomatique.) (Karger, Basel)
Advances in the Study of Behavior. (Academic Press)
American Behavioral Scientist. ABS Guide Supplement. (American Behavioral Scientists, a division of Saga Publishers, Inc., New York)
American Drug Index. (Lippincott, Philadelphia and Montreal)
American Druggist Blue Book. (Hearst Magazine, New York)
American Psychological Association. Psychological Monographs: General and Applied. (Am. Psychol. Assoc., Washington, D.C.)
American Psychopathological Association. Proceedings of Annual Meetings. (St. Elizabeth's Hospital, Washington, D.C.)
American Psychopathological Association. Publications. (Grune & Stratton, New York)
Annales Moreau de Tours. (Presses Univ. France, Paris)

Annales Pharmaceuticae. (Panetwowe, Wydawnictwo Naukowe, Warsaw)
Annals of Psychotherapy. (Am. Acad. Psychotherap., New York)
Année Thérapeutique. Médications et Procèdes Nouveaux. (Masson, Paris)
Annuaire des Produits Chemiques et de la Droguerie. (Paris)
Annual Reports in Medicinal Chemistry. (Academic Press)
Annual Review of Medicine. (Annual Reviews, Inc., Palo Alto, California)
Annual Review of Pharmacology. (Annual Reviews, Inc., Palo Alto, California)
Annual Review of Physiology. (Annual Reviews, Inc., Palo Alto, California)
Annual Review of Psychology. (Annual Reviews, Inc., Palo Alto, California)
Apotheker-Jahrbuch. (Wissenschaftliche, Verlagsgesellschaft GMBH, Stuttgart)
Arzneimittel Standardisierung. (Staatliches Institut fuer Arzneimittelprüfung, Berlin)
Association for Research in Nervous and Mental Disease. Proceedings of the Association. (Williams & Wilkins, Baltimore)
Atualizacao Terapeutica. (Livraria Luso-Espanhola, e Brasileia, Ltd., Rio de Janeiro)
Behavior Science Field Guides. (Human Relations Area Files Press, New Haven)
Behavior Science Monographs. (Human Relations Area Files Press, New Haven)
Behavior Science Outlines. (Human Relations Area Files Press, New Haven)
Beiträge zur Geschichte der Pharmazie und Ihrer Nachbargebiete. (Verlag Volk und Gesundheit, Berlin)
Biological Council's Coordinating Committee for Symposia on Drug Action Series. (Pergamon Press, Long Island City, New York, London)
Biological Psychiatry, The Proceedings of the Scientific Sessions of the Society of. (Grune & Stratton, New York, Vol. 1959; Academic Press, Vol. 2, 1962, to date)
British Journal of Psychology. Monograph Supplements. (Cambridge Univ. Press, London)
British National Formulary. (Pharmaceutical Press, London)
British Pharmaceutical Codex. (Pharmaceutical Press, London)
Ciba Foundation Study Groups. (Little, Brown, Boston)
Clinical Excerpts. A Journal of Modern Therapeutics. (Bayer Products Ltd., England)
Collana di Farmacoterapia. (Ed. Sci. Ital., Naples)
Collegium International Neuro-Psycho-Pharmacology, Proceedings of International Congresses. (Sometimes called "Neuro-Psycho-Pharmacology") (Excerpta Med. Found., Amsterdam)
Compendium of Pharmaceutical Specialties." (Can. Pharm. Assoc., Toronto)
Conference on Engineering in Medicine and Biology. Proceedings. (Institute of Electrical and Electronics Engineers, New York)
Conferences, Seminars, Symposia and Other Post-Graduate Activities in Medicine and Allied Fields. (Science Information Bureau, New York)
Contributions to Sensory Physiology. (Academic Press)
COPNIP List. (Committee on Pharmacomedical Nonserial Industrial Publications of the Pharmaceutical Section, Science-Technology Div., Special Libraries Assoc., Wyeth Laboratories, Philadelphia) (Quarterly. 300 refs. a year to nonserial industrial publications on pharmaceuticals)
Cross-Cultural Studies in Mental Health. (Tavistock, London)
Curitiba. Universidade do Parana. Departmento de Botanica e Farmacognosia. (Parana, Brazil)
Current Psychiatric Therapies. (Grune & Stratton, Vol. 1, 1961, to date)
Deutsche Arbeitgemeinschaft für Neuropsycho-Pharmakologie. Symposium. Vorträge. (Karger, Basel)
Dictionaire Vidal. (Louis Vidal, Paris) (Biannual Equiv. to U.S. Physicians Desk Ref. French Drugs)
The Dispensatory of the United States of America. (Lippincott)
Drug Directories of Canada, Mexico and South American Countries. (J. P. Morgan, Islamorada, Florida); Drug Information Sources; A World List. (Special Library Assoc., Librarian, Philadelphia College of Pharmacy and Science)
Drug Information Sources; A World List. *Am. J. Pharm.* 1964–5. App. IV.
Drugs Most Frequently Used. (Mosby, St. Louis)

Drugs of Choice. (Mosby, St. Louis)
Drug Topics Red Book. (Topics Publ. Co., New York)
Ergebnisse der Physiologie, Biologischen Chemie und Experimentellen Pharmakologie. (Reviews of Physiology, Biochemistry and Experimental Pharmacology). (Springer, Berlin, New York) (Multilingual)
European Society for the Study of Drug Toxicity. Proceedings of 9 International Congresses (1963–1967), Vols. 1–9, pp. 58, 94, 112, 117, 145, 251, 240, 227, and 375 resp. (Excerpta Med. Found., multilingual)
Evaluation of Drug Activities. Pharmacometrics. (Academic Press)
Excerpta Medica. International Congress Series. (Excerpta Med. Found., multilingual)
Extra-Pharmacoepia Marlindale. (Pharmaceutical Press, London) (Equiv. to U.S. Pharmacoepia, plus English drug directory)
Folia Psychiatrica et Neurologica Japonica, Supplementum. (Japan. Soc. Psychiat. Neurol., Niigata Univ., Japan) (In Japanese)
Fortschritte der Arzneimittelforschung (see Progress in Drug Research)
Gendai Igaku. (Current Medicine) (Aichi Med. Assoc., Nagoya, Japan) (In Japanese)
Group for the Advancement of Psychiatry. (Group Advan. Psychiat., New York)
Handbook of Physiology. (Am. Physiol. Soc., Washington, D.C.)
Handbuch der Experimentellen Pharmakologie. (Springer) (Multilingual)
History of the Behavioral Sciences Newsletter. (Payne Whitney Psychiatric Clinic, New York)
Index Medicamentorum. (Calle Medico Rodriguez II, La Coruna, Spain)
Index of Modern Remedies. (Scottish Chemist, Glasgow)
Indian Pharmaceutical Guide. (Pampish Publications, New Delhi)
Institute for the Study of Analgesic and Sedative Drugs. Monographs. (Elkhart, Ind.)
International Congress for Child Psychiatry. Proceedings. (Intern. Assoc. Child Psychiat., Glasgow)
International Congress of Electroencephalography and Clinical Neurophysiology. Proceedings. (Wiener Medizinische Akademie, Vienna) (Multilingual)
International Congress of Neurology. Proceedings. (Multilingual)
International Congress of Neuro-Pharmacology. Proc. (Elsevier) (Multilingual)
International Congress of Pharmaceutical Sciences. Proceedings. (Butterworth, London) (Multilingual)
International Congress of Psychotherapy. Proceedings. (Karger) (Multilingual)
International Congress of Scientific Psychology. Proceedings. (North-Holland, Amsterdam) (Multilingual)
International Congress on Mental Retardation. Proceedings. (Karger) (Multilingual)
International Encyclopedia of Pharmacology and Therapeutics. (See Appendix 2.) (Pergamon, Long Island City, New York)
International Meetings of Neurobiologists. Proceedings. (Elsevier) (Multilingual)
International Neurochemical Symposium. Proceedings. (Pergamon) (Multilingual)
International Pharmacological Meeting. Proceedings. (Pergamon)
International Psychiatry Clinics. (Little, Brown)
International Review of Neurobiology. (Academic Press)
International Review of Research in Mental Retardation. (Academic Press)
International Series of Monographs in Cerebrovisceral and Behavioral Psychology and Conditioned Reflexes. (Pergamon) (Multilingual)
International Series of Monographs on Experimental Psychology. (Pergamon)
Irregular Serials and Annuals: An International Directory. A Classified Guide to Current Foreign and Domestic Serials, excepting Periodicals issued more frequently than once a year. (Bowker, New York and London, 1967)
Jahrbuch für Psychologie, Psychotherapie und medizinische Anthropologie. (Title varies) (Karl Alber Verlag, Munich) (Multilingual)
Japanese Drug Directory. (Japan Pharm. Traders' Assoc., Japan) (In English)
Japan Medical Society. Transactions of Congress. (Nippon Igakki, Tokyo, Japan) (In Japanese)
L'Informatore Farmeceutico. (Organizzazione Editoriale. Medico-Farmaceutica. Milan) (Italian Drug Directory)

Medicinal Chemistry. (Am. Chem. Soc.; Wiley, New York)
Medicinal Research. A Series of Monographs. (Dekker, New York)
Merck Index (eighth ed., 1968). (Merck & Co., Rahway, New Jersey)
Methods in Medical Research. (Yearbook Med. Publ., Chicago)
Mind and Medicine Monographs. (Tavistock)
Modern Drug Encyclopedia and Therapeutic Index. (R. H. Donnelly Corp., New York)
Modern Problems in Psychiatry and Neurology. (Karger)
Modern Tedavi Mecmuaoi. Revue de Therapeutique Moderne. (Societé parisienne d'expansion chimique, Istanbul)
Modern Treatment Yearbook. (Ballière, London)
Monograph Series on Schizophrenia. (Intern. Univ. Press, New York)
Monographien aus der Gesamptgebiete der Neurologie und Psychiatrie. (Springer) (Multilingual)
Monographs in Soviet Medical Sciences. (Fordham Univ., Bronx, New York)
Monthly Index of Medical Specialties ("MIMS"). (Med. Publ. London) (Lists names of marketed drug products)
The National Formulary. (Am. Pharm. Assoc., Washington, D.C.)
Neuro-Psycho-Pharmacology. (See Collegium International . . .)
New and Non-Official Drugs. (Lippincott)
New Drugs. (AMA, Chicago)
Pan American Symposia on Pharmacology and Therapy, Proceedings of. (Actas del Simposio Panamericano de Farmacologia y Terapeutica) (Excerpta Med. Found.) (In Spanish)
Perspectives in Psychology. (Wiley)
Pharmaceutical Directory. (Star Publ., Bombay)
Pharmacopeia of the United States of America. (U.S. Pharmacopeial Convention, New York)
Pharmakotherapia. (J. F. Lehmanns Verlag, Munich)
Pharmazeutisches Jahrbuch. (Verlag für Medicin und Naturwissenschaften, Frankfurt)
Physician's Desk Reference to Pharmaceutical Specialties and Biologicals. (Medical Economics Inc., Ordell, New Jersey)
Physician's Index of Drugs in New England and Australia. (Butterworth, Wellington, New Zealand, London, Toronto)
Progrès des Recherches. (See Progress in Drug Research)
Progress in Biochemical Pharmacology. (Karger)
Progress in Brain Research. (Elsevier)
Progress in Chemical Toxicology. (Academic Press)
Progress in Clinical Psychology. (Grune & Stratton)
Progress in Drug Research. (Fortschritte der Arzneimittelforschung; Progrès des recherches pharmaceutiques.) (Birkhäuser, Basel & Stuttgart) (Multilingual)
Progress in Medicinal Chemistry. (Butterworth; Plenum, New York)
Progress in Medical Genetics. (Butterworth)
Progress in Neurobiology. (Elsevier)
Progress in Neurology and Psychiatry. (Grune & Stratton)
Progress in Physiological Psychology. (Academic Press)
Recent Advances in Biological Psychiatry. (Plenum)
Recent Advances in Pharmacology. (Grune & Stratton)
Recent Progress in Hormone Research. (Academic Press)
Research Publications, Association for Research in Nervous and Mental Disease. Proceedings. (Williams & Wilkins)
Rote Liste. (Cantor, Aulendorf i. Württ, Germany) (Biannual Equiv. to U.S. "Physician's Desk Reference.") (Covers W. Germany)
Schweizerisches medizinisches Jahrbuch. (Schwabe, Basel)
Scientiä Pharmaceuticä. Proceedings of the Congress of Pharmaceutical Sciences. (Butterworth)
Societa Italiana Discienze Farmaceutiche. Atti Convegno. (Societa Italiana di Scienze Farmaceutiche, Milan)

Society of Biological Psychiatry. Proceedings of the Annual Meetings and Scientific Programs. (Also called Recent Advances in Biological Psychiatry) (Plenum)

The Society for the Study of Inborn Errors of Metabolism. Proceedings of Symposia. (Livingstone, Edinburgh)

Topical Problems in Psychiatry and Neurology. (Aktuelle Fragen der Psychiatrie und Neurologie. Problėms Actuels de Psychiatrie et Neurologie.) (Karger)

World Congress of Psychiatry. Abstracts (Résumés; Vortragsauszüge; Temas) (Excerpta Med. Found.)

World Federation for Mental Health. Annual Reports of Meetings. (Mental Health Assoc., Bangkok, Thailand)

World Federation for Mental Health. Proceedings of Conferences. (The Federation, Geneva)

Year Book of Medicine. (Year Book Med. Publ., Chicago)

Year Book of Neurology, Psychiatry, and Neurosurgery. (Titles vary) (Year Book Med. Publ.)

APPENDIX

4

CORE JOURNALS*

Acta Neurologia et Psychiatrica Belgica
Acta Pharmacologica et Toxicologica
Acta Psychiatrica Scandinavica
Activitas Nervosa Superior
Adverse Reaction Titles
Agressologie
American Journal of Pharmacology and Experimental Therapeutics
American Journal of Pharmacy
American Journal of Psychiatry
Annales Medico-Psychologiques
Annales Moreau de Tours
Archives Internationales de Pharmacodynamie et de Therapie
Archivos del Instituto de Farmacologia Experimental (Medicina) (Madrid)
Arzneimittel-Forschung
British Journal of Addiction
British Journal of Pharmacology and Chemotherapy
British Journal of Psychiatry
Bulletin on Narcotics, United Nations, Department of Social Affairs
Canadian Psychiatric Association Journal
Chemotherapy Review (London)
Clinical Pharmacology and Therapeutics
Communications in Behavioral Biology: Part A. Original Communications

* 15% of average issue contain sound articles on psychopharmacology. Hormones are classified as drugs in some instances. Key reviews in "noncore" journals are in Appendix 2.

Comprehensive Psychiatry
Current Psychiatric Therapies
Current Therapeutic Research, Clinical and Experimental, Supplement
Diseases of the Nervous System
Drug Intelligence, An Interdisciplinary Journal for Health Professions
(College of Pharmacy, Univ. Cincinnati Med. Center, Cincinnati, Ohio 45221)
European Journal of Pharmacology
Farmakologiya i Toksikologiya
Farmakoterapi (Oslo)
FDA Clinical Experience Abstracts (Food & Drug Admin., Washington, D.C.)
Fortschritte der Arzneimittelforschung
Giornale di psichiatria e di neuropatologia
Hormones and Behavior
International Drug Therapy Newsletter
International Journal of Neuropharmacology
International Journal of Neuropsychiatry
International Journal of Psychiatry
Japanese Journal of Pharmacology
Journal of American Pharmaceutical Association
Journal of Clinical Pharmacology and Journal of New Drugs
Journal of Medicinal Chemistry
Journal of Pharmacology and Experimental Therapeutics
Journal of Pharmacy and Pharmacology
Journal of Psychiatric Research
Journal of Psycho-pharmacology
Medicina et Pharmacologia Experimentalis
Mental Health Digest
Nervenarzt
Neurologia i Neurochirurgia Polska (formerly Neurologia, Neurochirurgia i Psychiatria Polska)
Pharmakopsychiatrie-Neuro-Psychopharmakologie
Pharmalogical Reviews
Psychopharmacologia
Psychopharmacology Bulletin
Quarterly Journal of Studies on Alcohol
Side Effects of Drugs
Unlisted Drugs
World Periodicals Related to Psychopharmacology (Publ.: Yoshitomi Pharm. Ind. Ltd., Osaka)

APPENDIX

5

BIBLIOGRAPHIC AND LITERATURE SEARCH AIDS

Abstracts of Human Developmental Biology (Excerpta Medica Found., Amsterdam).
Abstracts of world's literature. In English.

Abstracts of World Medicine (Brit. Med. Assoc., London).

Activitas Nervosa Superior (Československé lékařské společnosti J. Ev. Purkyňe, Prague).
Annual Psychopharmalogical meetings supplements. Multilingual.

Adverse Reaction Titles (Vol. 1, 1966 to date) (Excerpta Medica Found., Amsterdam).
A monthly bibliography of titles from approximately 3000 international biomedical journals.

Animal Research in Psychopharmacology (1954–1963).
Handbook Series, National Clearinghouse for Mental Health Information, National Institute for Mental Health. (Chevy Chase, Maryland). Vols. 1–4 covering 1954–1963.

Annual Reviews of Progress in Science and Technology (UNESCO, Paris).

Automatic Subject Citation Alert (ASCA) (Inst. Scientific Information, Philadelphia).
Weekly printouts of papers in fields of interest of subscribers.

Behavior Science Bibliographies (Yale Station, New Haven, Conn.).

Behavior Science Reprints (Yale Station, New Haven, Conn.).

Behavior Science Translations (Yale Station, New Haven, Conn.).

Berichte über die Gesampte Physiologie und Experimentelle Pharmacologie (Springer, Berlin).
Comprehensive abstracting journal of world literature in physiology and pharmacology. In German.

Berichte über die Wissenschaftliche Biologie (Springer, Berlin).
Comprehensive abstracting journal of world literature in general biological science. In German.

Bibliographia Medica Cechslovaca (State Inst. Med. Doc. Prague).

Text in Czech and Latin. Annual. 8000+ references a year from 50 journals, many Slavic, especially Czech.

Bibliographia Medica Helvetica (Schwabe, Basel).

Complete catalog of Swiss medical literature. Text in French and German. 1943 to date

Bibliographia Neuroendocrinologia (Comp. by M. Weitzman, Dept. Anatomy, Albert Einstein College of Medicine, Bronx, New York).

Bibliography of Chemical Reviews (Am. Chem. Soc., Washington, D.C.).

Bibliography on Clinical Psychopharmacology 1958–1960 (U.S. Health Publ. No. 1293. Public Health Service Bibliography Series No. 60, Jan. 1965).

3791 references. 1960 to date is covered by "Psychopharmacology Abstracts."

Bibliography Documentation, Terminology (UNESCO, Paris).

Bibliography of Medical Reviews (Nat. Library Med., Bethesda, Maryland).

Annual. Med. reviews listed in Index Medicus.

Bibliography of Translations in the Neural Sciences. July–Dec. 1964, Quart. Supps. 9 and 10. 205 pp. (Listing of transl. by broad subject areas. Selected from Technical Translations: Semimonthly compilation published by Clearinghouse for Fed. Sci. and Tech. Information, Dept. Commerce, Springfield, Virginia). (Listed in monthly catalog, Natl. Library Med., Bethesda, Maryland). Clearinghouse for Government Research Information, Natl. Sci. Found., Washington, D.C.).

Information on all U.S government supported research.

Biblioteca Psicologias del Siglo XX (Editorial Paidos, Buenos Aires). In Spanish.

Bibliotheca Psychiatrica et Neurologica (S. Karger, Basel).

Text in English, French, German. 1917, prior *et seq.*

Biochemical Title Index (Biological Abstracts, Inc., Philadelphia).

Monthly. 25,000 references a year to over 500 journals of the world.

Biological Abstracts (Biol. Abstracts, Inc., Philadelphia).

Extremely comprehensive abstracting journal of world biology and ancillary literature Cf. also Vol. 48 [1967]. List of journals covered, 199 pp., 10,000+ entries.

Biomedical Serials 1950–1960. National Laboratory of Medicine. Public Health Service. Publ. No. 110, Sup. Doc., Govt. Printing Office.

Birth Defects. Abstracts of selected articles (National Foundation—March of Dimes, New York).

Gratis monthly. Covers over 2600 journals.

Books in Print, U.S.A. (Bowker, New York and London).

Brain Information Center (Brain Res. Inst., Univ. California, Los Angeles).

Literature Searches, including *Medlars.*

Brion, A., and Ey, H. (1964). Psychiatric animale. Bibliothetique neuro-psychiatrique de langue francaise (Brouwer, Paris) (605 pp.) In French.

British Abstracts A. III. Physiology Biochemistry, Anatomy, Pharmacology and Experimental Medicine (Med. Publ., Ltd., London).

British Medical Abstracts (London).

Abstracts of world's medical literature.

Bry, I. and Afflerbach, L. (eds.), Mental Health Book Review Index, Vol. 1, 1955 to date annually. (Paul Klappen Library, Queens College, Flushing, N.Y.).

Sponsored by World Fed. Mental Health, Intern. Council of Psychologists and Res. for Mental Health, New York Univ. Each issue lists about 300 books with references to three or more reviews, which are also listed. Since No. 1, 3582 books have been listed with a total of 20,000 references. The books are listed alphabetically by first author or editor. Each member is prefaced with an editorial.

Bulletin de l'Institut Pasteur (Paris).

Medical literature abstracting agency.

Bulletin of Narcotics. Section: Bibliography (United Nations, Geneva).

Quarterly. References to world literature on narcotics, addictions, etc).

Bulletin Signalétique. Section 7: Chimie I. Chimie général. Chimie physique. Chimie minéral. Chimie analytique. Chimie organique (Paris) In French.
Monthly. Since 1940. 25,000+ abstracts a year from world literature on chemistry.
Bulletin Signalétique. Section 12: Biophysique biochimie. Chimie analytique biologique.
Monthly. Over 15,000 abstracts a year from world literature on biochemistry and biophysics.
Bulletin Signalétique. Section 13: Sciences pharmacologiques, toxicologie.
Monthly. Over 10,000 abstracts a year in pharmacology and toxicology.
Bulletin Signalétique. Section 15: Pathologie générale et expérimentale.
Monthly. Over 15,000 abstracts a year from world literature on pathology.
Bulletin Signalétique. Section 16: Biologie et physiologie animales.
Monthly. Over 40,000 abstracts a year from world literature on zoology, biology, and animal physiology.
Caldwell, A. (1970). Origins of Psychopharmacology from CPZ to LSD (Thomas, Springfield, Illinois). (In press.)
Center for Research Libraries (Formerly Midwest Library Center, 5721 Cottage Grove Ave., Chicago, Illinois 60632).
Has subscriptions of all journals abstracted in Chemical Abstracts. Loan and photoduplicating services.
Chartotheca Translationum Alphabetica (H. W. Benz Verlag, Frankfurt).
Monthly since 1954. 18,000 card references a year of translations from world literature, with annual bound catalog. Listed by author.
Chemical Abstracts (Am. Chem. Soc., Washington, D.C.).
Biweekly since 1907. Weekly since 1968. 165,000 abstracts a year from world literature including patents from ca. 8150 periodicals, with a key to 344 library files. List of periodicals covered separately available as supplements since 1957. Collective and Decennial Indices available. Each issue has a Keyword Study Index. Even numbered issues contain subject and author indices.
Chemical-Biological Activities (CBAC) (Am. Chem. Soc., Washington, D.C.).
Bimonthly. Index to Current Literature on the Biological Activity of Organic Compounds.
Chemical Titles (Am. Chem. Soc., Washington, D.C.).
Semimonthly since 1961; 75,000 references a year to world journal literature. Keyword Indices; bibliography of journal contents by journals; author indices.
Chemische Berichte (Chemie GMBH, Weinheim).
Comprehensive abstracting journal of world literature in chemistry.
Chemisches Zentralblatt (Akad.-Verlag, GMBH, Berlin).
Abstracts of world chemical literature.
Chemotherapy Research Bulletin: International Information Bulletin. Describing New Drug Developments in Pharmacology and Chemotherapy (Chemotherapy Res. Inst., New York).
Child Development Abstracts and Bibliography (Purdue Univ., Lafayette, Indiana).
Quarterly. Abstracts from world literature.
Classified Abstract Archives of the Alcohol Literature (Rutgers Center of Alcohol Studies, Rutgers—The State University, New Brunswick, New Jersey).
Annual since 1954; 450 abstracts of world literature a year on 7-by-7 edge-slotted cards; subject classified.
Clearinghouse for Federal Scientific and Technical Information (CFSTI) (Springfield, Virginia).
Central Nervous System and Behavior: Collection of Articles, Saltpetriere, Hospital, Paris, 1959. 1060 pp. Order from CFSTI. 61-28383.
Central Nervous System Mechanisms and Models: Bibliography, English transl.: 1962. 12 pp. Order from CFSTI. 63-13050.
Collection of Theses on Achievements in Medical Sciences in Commemoration of the 10th National Foundation Day in China, Peiping, 1959, Vol. II, Articles on Neurology. English transl.: 1962. 127 pp. Order from CFSTI. 62-32849.
Current Problems of Electrophysiological Investigations of the Nervous System. Original Russian publ., 1965. English transl. 116 pp. Order from CFSTI. TT65-30303.

Experimental Study of the Rules and Regulations of Work of the Cerebral Cortex; Selected Articles, Original Russian publ., 1960. English transl.: 1962. 148 pp. Order from CFSTI. 62-23455.

Clinical Literature Untoward Effects (CLUE) (Intern. Inform. Inst., Philadelphia).
Drug information from foreign literature.

Communications in Behavioral Biology. Part B—Abstracts (Academic Press, New York).

Consolidated Translation Survey (including mainly Russian translated articles Tables of Contents of Foreign Journals) Central Intelligence Agency, Washington, D.C.

John Crerar Library (Chicago, Illinois).
Lit. searches, xeroxes, book loans. Information on sources of translations, etc. Holds 100,000 translations and provides photoduplication services.

Cumulated Index Medicus (A.M.A., Chicago, Illinois).
Annual for 1960, 1961, 1962 from Index Medicus.

Current Contents of Chemical, Pharmaco-Medical and Life Sciences. (Inst. Scientific Information, Philadelphia).
Weekly tables of contents of 900 world journals, 155,000+ articles. Alphabetical Journal Index, author address directory in each issue.

Current List of Medical Literature (Nat. Library of Med., Bethesda, Maryland. Succeeded by Index Medicus in 1960).

Current Medical Abstracts for Practitioners (Edinburgh).

De Haen Drugs in Use. (Paul de Haen, Inc., New York). De Haen Drugs in Prospect. (Paul de Haen, Inc., New York). De Haen Drugs in Research. (Paul de Haen, Inc., New York).

Deutsche Zeitschrift für die Gesampte Gerichtliche Medizin (Section: Referate) Springer, Berlin). In German.
Irregular, ca. 6 times a year since 1922. Several thousand abstracts a year from world literature. In German.

Developmental Biology and Teratology.
(Formerly Abstracts of Human Developmental Biology) (Excerpta Med. Found., Amsterdam).

Directory of Free-lance Writers. Editors and Researchers (American Medical Writer's Assoc., New York).
Editing, technical rewriting, transl., and medical illustration.

Dissertation Abstracts (Univ. Microfilms, Inc. subsidiary of Xerox Corporation, Ann Arbor, Michigan).
Microfilm, microfiche, and zerograph prints of dissertations and their abstracts from 160 cooperating institutes. Also prints a monthly "Dissertation Abstracts" listing current ones available. Science and Technol. in general.

Drug Dependence and Abuse Notes (Natl. Clearinghouse for Mental Health Information, Natl. Inst. Mental Health, Chevy Chase, Maryland).

Drug Digests from the Foreign Literature (Natl. Sci. Found., Washington, D.C.).
Three volumes to date, Vol. 3, No. 10 from 50 non-english journals, 1967–1968.

Farmaceutický Obzor. (Ex Farmacia, Trencín, Bratislava, Czehoslovakia).
Monthly. Tables of Contents of world's pharmaceutical and pharmacological literature. In Czech.

Fenz, E., Bibliographia Neurovegetativa 1900–1950, Acta Neurovegetativa Supplementum II, Springer, Vienna, 1953. 343 pp.

Food and Drug Administration (F.D.A.) Clinical Experience Abstracts (formerly M.L.B.J. of Lit. Abstracts) (Food and Drug Admin., U.S. Dept. Health, Education and Welfare, Washington, D.C.).

FDA Reports of Suspected Adverse Reactions to Drugs and Therapeutic Devices (Food and Drug Admin., Washington, D.C.).

Grebe, R. M., ed. (1959). Handbook of Toxicology. Vol. 4. Tranquilizers. Saunders, Philadelphia. 120 pp.

Excerpta Medica (monthlies) (Excerpta Med. Found., Amsterdam).
Section
1. Anat., Anthropol., Embryol., Histol.
2A. Physiol.
2B. Biochem.
2C. Pharmacol., Toxicol.
3. Endocrinol.
5. Gen. Pathol. and Pathol. Anat.
6. Internal Med.
7. Pediatrics
8A. Neurol.
8B. Psychiat.
17. Public Health, Soc. Med., Hyg.
19. Rehab. and Phys. Med.
20. Gerentol. and Geriatrics
22. Human Genetics
24. Anesthesiol.
27. Med. Instru.

Excerpta Criminologica (bimonthly).
Abstracts of world literature in English.

Fink, M. (1964. A Selected Bibliography of Electroencephalography in Human Pharmacology. *EEG Clin. Neurophysiol. Supplement* 23. 68 pp.

Fleurent, C. H. A. (Comp.) (1961). World Medical Periodicals," 3rd ed. (World Medical Assoc., New York).
407 pp. More recent edition upcoming.

Guide to World's Abstracting and Indexing Services in Science and Technology (1963) (Report No. 102) (Natl. Fed. Sci. Abstr. and Indexing Serv., Washington, D.C.).
183 pp. and 1855 annotated entrees.

Himwich, W. A., *et. al.,* Survey of World Medical Serials and Coverage by Indexing and Abstracting Services (Welch Medical Library Indexing Project, Johns Hopkins Univ., Baltimore, Maryland).
79 pp. plus appendices and tables. Older but, together with a Guide to World's Abstracting, etc., is very complete and highly critical and analytical.

Houck, L. D. (1962). Bibliography on Anxiety States (Hoffmann-La Roche Laboratories, Nutley, New Jersey) (121 pp.).

Human Engineering Bibliography (Inst. Applied Psychol., Dept. Navy. Office of Tech. Serv., Dept. Commerce).
Abstracts from journals and government, industrial, and academic laboratories.

Igaku Chūo Zassshi. Japana Centra Revuo Medicina (Tokyo).
Weekly. 20,000+ abstracts a year from Japanese medical literature. In Japanese.

Index Catalogue of the Library of the Surgeon-General's Office (U.S. Army Med. Library, Washington, D.C. and Natl Library Med., Bethesda, Maryland. U.S. Govt. Printing Office, Washington, D.C).
Succeeded by Index Medicus in 1960. Was an annual multivolume series of world medical literature from 1879. In original languages, except Slavic and oriental languages, which are transliterated or translated. Items in fifth and last series (1959) monographic (non-serial). Indexed by author and subjects. Prior to fifth series, it also covered journal articles.

Index Chemicus (Inst. Sci. Inform., Philadelphia.)
Weekly abstracts, including structures, on syntheses, isolation and/or identification of new chemical compounds. Includes annual cumulative index. Also available: Index Chemicus Registry System and Computerized Chemical Data Retrieval.

Index Clinicus Sandoz: International Literature Survey in Neurology and Psychiatry (Sandoz, Ltd., Basel) (quarterly).

Index to Indian Medical Periodicals (Natl. Med. Library, New Delhi, India).

Index Medicus (Natl. Library Med., Bethesda, Maryland) .

Monthly lists of titles from world literature. Formerly, before 1960, Current List of Medical Literature.

(See also Index Medicus Lists of Journals covered).

Index Medicus Danicus (Danish Med. Assoc., Copenhagen).

Supplement of Dan. Med. Bull. Biannual. Abstracts of Danish medical literature.

International Brain Research Organization (Nat. Acad. Sciences, Washington, D.C.).

(Survey on Research Facilities and Manpower in Brain Sciences in the United States. IBRO. [1968]). (314 pp.)

International Journal of Abstracts: Statistical Theory and Method (Intern. Statistical Inst., London).

Quarterly. Ca. 1000 abstracts a year from world literature on statistics.

International Pharmaceutical Abstracts (Am. Soc. Hosp. Pharmacists, Wash., D.C.).

International Reference Center for Information on Psychotropic Drugs (Psychopharmacology Research Service Branch, National Inst. Mental Health, Chevy Chase, Maryland).

Japan Science Review; Medical Sciences (Gihodo Co., Ltd., Tokyo).

Annual. Since 1954. Ca. 12,000–15,000 bibliographic references and 4000+ abstracts in English from Japanese publications on medicine.

Japan Science Review; Biological Sciences (Gihodo Co., Ltd., Tokyo).

Irregular abstracts and references in English from Japanese literature.

Khimiya i meditsina (Vsesoyznyĭ nauchnessledovatel'skii khimikofarmatsevticheskii institut, (Moscow).

Thousands of references a year to world chemical literature. In Russian.

Kobayashi, T., ed. (1968). [Recent Aspects of Psychopharmacology. Pharmacologic Approach to the Mechanism of Behavior] (Igaku Shoin, Tokyo).

In Japanese. Appendices in English, including references cited by authors, key reviews and texts, bibliographic aids, symposia, etc. 677 pp.

Kobayashi, T., ed. (1968). World Periodicals Related to Psychopharmacology (Yoshitomi Pharmaceutical Industries, Ltd., Osaka, Japan). In English.

16 pp.. 192 journals. 73 of which are "core" journals [but cf. Appendix 4, this text].

Kolfay, E. (1967). Irregular Serials and Annuals: An International Directory. A classified guide to current foreign and domestic serials, excepting periodicals issued more frequently than once a year. 1st ed. R. R. Bowker Co., New York and London.

Kongresszentralblatt für die Gesampte Innere Medizin und Ihre Genzebiete (Springer, Berlin). In German.

Kwan, V. H. Y., and Rajeswaren, P. M. C. (1968). Recent Additions to a Bibliography on Cannabis. *J. Forensic Sci.* **13**, 279.

Library Research in Progress (Office of Education, U.S. Dept. of Health, Education and Welfare, Washington, D.C.).

For information on library reference sources in the United States, including industrial.

List of Science Serials Covered by Members of the National Federation of Science Abstracting and Indexing Services (Nat. Sci. Found., Washington, D.C.).

Two volumes, 1962. 1340 pp. 20,017 entries.

Louttit, R. T. (1966). A Bibliography in Neuropsychology: Reviews and Books, 1960–1965 (U.S. Public Health Serv. Publ. No. 1473. 15 pp.).

Louttit, R. T., and Hanik, M. J. (1967). Bibliography of Translations in the Neural Sciences. 1950–1960 (U.S. Public Health Serv. Publ. No. 1635).

111 pp., plus list of translated books and other sources of information on translations.

Meditsinskiĭ Referativnyĭ Zhurnal. Razdel IX: Nervopatologiya I Psikhiatriya (Gosudarstvennoe izdatel'stvo meditsinskoĭ literatury, Moscow).

Monthly. Abstracts of world literature in psychiatry and neuropathology.

Medizin der Sowjetunion und der Volksdemokratien im Referat (VEB Verlag Volk und Gesundheit East Berlin).

Monthly. Abstracts from German and Slavic medical literature with titles in German.

Medlars (literature searches) (National Library Med., Bethesda, Maryland; Brain Res. Inst., Univ. of California, Los Angeles).

Computerized literature retrieval service.

Mental Health Book Review Index (Paul Klapper Library, Queens College, Flushing, N.Y.).

Miltown® (Meprobamate).
1. Bibliography. 1955 to Jan. 31, 1968.
2. Abstracts of Literature from Feb. 1, 1967 to Jan. 31, 1968.
3. Current Product Abstracts.
(Wallace Laboratories Library, Cranbury, New Jersey).

Minerva Medicobiliografica; Indici trimestrali della letteratura medica chiurgica e specilistica mondiale (Edizioni Minerva Medica, Turin, Italy).
50,000 references a year from worlds' medical literature. In Italian.

Naranjo, P. (1965). Manual de Farmacosologia (reacciones indeseables por drogas). (Editorial Universitaria, Quito, Ecuador). In Spanish. (300 pp.)

National Clearinghouse for Mental Health Information (National Institute of Mental Health, Chevy Chase, Maryland).
Abstracting and literature search services. (See Intern. Ref. Center, NIMH).

National Institute of Health Library Translations Index (Transl. Unit, Natl. Inst. Health Library, Bethesda, Maryland).
Irregular supplements. Supplement 3 [1966] was 65 pp.

National Library of Medicine. Lister Hill National Center for Biomedical Communications. (Natl. Library Med., Bethesda, Maryland).
Provides Bibliographic Citations, access to literature, interlibrary loans, xeroxes, Medlars (see Medlars, this appendix).

National Library of Medicine Current Catalogue. (Weekly, quarterly, and annual cumulative listings of Index Medicus). (U.S. Dept. of Health, Education and Welfare, Public Health Serv. Sup. of Doc., Govt. Printing Office, Washington, D.C.).
Keeps all world's literature current.

National Library of Medicine (NLM) Literature Search, L.S. No. 24–68, "Adverse Effects of LSD" Jan. 1964 to Aug. 1968. (Natl. Library Med,, Bethesda, Maryland).
Available on request.

NLM L.S. No. 5-66. Effects on Conditioning and Avoidance-Escape Learning.
From mid-1963 to Dec. 1965. 150 citations.

National Referral Center for Science and Technology. (Library of Congress, Washington, D.C.). Literature searches. Photocopy and Loan Services.

The Nature of Magnitude of the Drug Literature (1963) (Natl. Library Med., Bethesda, Maryland).
62 pp. with 83 entrees. 8 appendices. World lists.

Neurological Studies Involving Sight and Touch Analysis. Doklady Akademiya Pedagogicheskikh Nauk RSFSR, 1960. (4), pp. 73–76, 87–91, 93–100. English transl. Order from CFSTI. 61-28560.

Neuropsychiatric Literature (Brain Information Center, Biomedical Library, Univ. of California, Los Angeles).
Monthly listings.

Nihon Kagaku Sôran (Japanese Chemical Research Assoc., Sendai-Shi, Japan. Tokyo).
Complete Chemical Abstracts of Japan. In Japanese.

Oatfield, H., and Emilio, B. R. (1958). Some Aspects of Searching in the Pharmaceutical Sciences. Am. Doc. **9**, 238.

Otis, L. S. *et al.*, Eds. (1966). Decennial Index of Psychopharmacology Handbooks, Vols. 1–4 (1954–1963). (Publ. Health Serv. Publ. No. 1576. 457 pp.).
For 1963, see Psychopharmacol. Abstracts.

Parkinson's Disease and Related Disorders. Citations from the Literature (Parkinson's Information Center, Columbia Univ., New York).
Cratis weekly coverage of neurosciences journals, with authors' addresses.

Pasztor, M., and Hopkins, B. (Comps.) (1968). Bibliography of Pharmaceutical References Literature (Pharmaceutical Press, London).

Material published from 1960 to March 1968, with a few earlier items included. Authors, titles, directory of associations, and learned societies; directory of British Schools of Pharmacy. (167 pp.).

Pharmazeutisches Jahrbuch; Referatesammlung der Internationalen Pharmazeutisches Schrifftums (Govi-Verlag. G.M.B.H., Pharmazeutischer Verlag, Frankfurt). In German.
Abstracts of world literature in pharmacy and pharmacology.

Poldinger, W., and Schmidlin, P. Index Psychopharmacorum 1966, 2nd ed. H. Huber, Bern (88 pp.).

Prehled Světove Zdravotnické Literatury (Ustav. prozdravotnickou dokumentaci, Prague).
Monthly. 35,000–50,000 references a year to world literature in biology, drugs, medicine, psychiatry, psychology, public health.

Principles of Methodical Approach to the Study of Human Types of Higher Nervous Activity, Original Russian publ., 1962. p. 22–23. English transl.: 1963. 3 pp. Order from CFSTI, TT64-13546.

Problems of Physiology of Higher Nervous Activity and of the Nervous System. Akademiya Nauk SSSR. Institut Fiziologii Trudy, 1962. 10 pp. English transl.: 1963. 432 pp. Order from CFSTI. 63-11173.

Psychological Abstracts (Am. Psychol. Assoc., Inc., Washington, D C.).
Comprehensive abstracts of world psychological literature.

Psychopharmaca. A Bibliography of Psychopharmacology. 1952–1957. (1958). Comp. by Anne E. Caldwell. Public Health Publ. No. 581. Publ. Health Biblio. Ser. No. 19). (258 pp.).

Psychopharmacology Abstracts (U.S. Dept. Health, Education, and Welfare, Washington, D.C.).

Psychopharmacology Bulletin, U.S. Dept. Health, Education, and Welfare, Washington, D.C.

Psychophysiological Research Association. Proceedings of Annual Meeting (Am. Psychiatric Assoc. Washington, D.C.).

Psychophysiological Society for the Study of Sleep. Proceedings of Annual Meetings (Am. Psychiatric Assoc.).

Quarterly Check-List of Psychology (Am. Bibliographic Serv., Darien, Conn.).
Intern. Index of Current Books, Monographs, Brochures, and Separates. Text in all Western European languages.

Quarterly Cumulative Index Medicus (A.M.A., Chicago, Illinois).
References to worlds' literature. Succeeded by Index Medicus in 1956.

Recent Translations. Selected List (Transl. Unit, Natl., Inst. Health Libr., Bethesda, Maryland).
Translations available on loan.

Referativnyĭ Zhurnal: Biologiya (Akademiy Nauk SSSR, Institut nauchnoĭ informat͡sii Moscow). In Russian.
Biweekly. More than 150,000 abstracts a year of world's biological literature. In Russian.

Referativnyĭ Zhurnal: Khimiya (Same as above).
Chemical abstracts of Russia. In Russian.

Research Grants Index (Natl. Inst. Health, Bethesda, Maryland).
Current lists of all NIH-supported grants.

Research Relating to Emotionally Disturbed Children (1968). (Clearinghouse for Research In Child Life, Children's Bureau, Social and Rehabilitation Serv. U.S. Dept. of Health, Education and Welfare, Washington, D.C.).
842 projects, including resultant publications. 1956–1968. (182 pp.)

Schilling, C. W., and Benton, M. (1966). Pharmacology, Toxicology and Cosmetic Serials. Their Identification and an Analysis of Their Characteristics (Clearinghouse for Federal Scientific and Technical Information. Natl. Bureau of Standards, U.S. Dept. of Commerce, Springfield, Va.).
Lists 1693 periodicals and abstracting and indexing journals which cover them.

Science Citation Index (Inst. Scientific Information, Philadelphia).
Rapid Computer Retrieval System for literature searches .

Science Information Exchange (Smithsonian Institution, Washington, D.C.).
Abstracts of grant-supported research.
Semaine des Hôpitaux (Expansion scientifique française, Paris).
Med. Lit. Abstracting Agency. In French.
Solacen® (Tybamate) Biolography through Dec. 31, 1967 (Wallace Laboratories Library, Cranbury, New Jersey).
Studies of the Brain. Doklady Akademia Nauk SSSR, 1961. pp. 141, 461–463, 505–508. English transl.: 1962. 14 pp. Order from CFSTI 62-23576.
See: Medical Bibliography Annual Indices. (1965 was published in 1967, 321 pp.) Listings selected from Tech. Transl. available from CFSTI. English translations.
Technical Abstract Bulletin (Defense Documentation Center, Alexandria, Virginia).
Abstracts of research supported by U.S. Defense Dept.
Technical Literature Searching Service (Office of Technical Services, Library of Congress, Dept. of Commerce, Washington, D.C.).
Toxicity Bibliography (Natl. Library of Med., Bethesda, Maryland).
Translators and Translations: Services and Sources in Science Technology (Special Libraries Assoc., New York).
Lists nearly 500 freelance translators and 87 commercial translating firms.
The Treatment of Psychiatric Disorders with Insulin, 1936–1960; A Selected Annotated Bibliography (U.S. Public Health Serv. Bibliography Ser. No. 37, 1962) (33 pp.).
The Treatment of Psychiatric Disorders with Metrazol, 1935–1960; A Selected Annotated Bibliography (U.S. Public Health Serv. Bibliography Ser. No. 39, 1963) (22 pp.).
Trumball, R. (1958). An Annotated Bibliography and Critical Review of Drugs and Performance (Office of Naval Research, Washington, D.C.) (85 pp.).
Ulrich's International Periodicals Directory (1967). Vol. 1. Scientific, Technical and Medical Periodicals. A Classified Guide to a Selected List of Current Periodicals, Foreign and Domestic (E. C. Graves, ed.) (Bowker, Co., New York).
Unger, S. M. (1964). LSD and Psychotherapy: A Bibliography of the English Language Literature. *Psychedelic Rev.* **1**, 442.
United States Government Research and Development Reports (Clearinghouse for Tech. Inform. and Fed. Sci., Springfield, Va.).
Semimonthly abstracts of reports by contractees and grant recipients supported by U.S. Federal agencies.
University Microfilms Library Services (Ann Arbor, Michigan).
Xeroxes, microfiches, or microfilms of articles, dissertations, and books printed anywhere.
Vernior, C. M. (1961). Annotated Bibliography of Data Processing Applications in the Fields of Neurology, Psychiatry and Pharmacology. *In* Transactions of the Sixth Research Conference in Cooperative Chemotherapy Studies in Psychiatry and Broad Research Approaches to Mental Illness (J. F. Casey, ed.) (Vet. Admin., Washington, D.C.). (p. 388).
Was Gibt es Neues In Der Medizin? (Schlütersche Verlagsanstalt und Buchdruckerei, Hannover).
Annual. Abstracts from European medical journals.
World-wide Abstracts of General Medicine (Excerpta Med. Found., Amsterdam).
Monthly. Abstracts from world medical journals. Gratis to U.S. physicians.
Williams, R. L., and Webb, W. B. (1966). Sleep Therapy. A Bibliography and Commentary (Thomas, Springfield, Illinois) (112 pp.).
World Information Sources (Special Libraries Assoc., New York).
World Drug Directory. 60 pp.
Zentralblatt für die Gesampte Neurologie und Psychiatrie (Springer, Berlin-Wilmersdorf).
Irregular. About four volumes a year since 1910. Ca. 2000–3000 abstracts each volume from world literature in neurology and psychiatry. In German.

Subject Index

A

C

E

F

G

I

N

O

P

Q

R

U

V